COMPREHENSIVE RENEWABLE ENERGY

COMPREHENSIVE RENEWABLE ENERGY

EDITOR-IN-CHIEF
Ali Sayigh
Chairman of WREC, Director General of WREN, and Chairman of IEI, Brighton, UK

VOLUME 5
BIOMASS AND BIOFUEL PRODUCTION

VOLUME EDITOR
Dermot J. Roddy
Newcastle University, Newcastle upon Tyne, U.K.

ELSEVIER

AMSTERDAM BOSTON HEIDELBERG LONDON NEW YORK OXFORD
PARIS SAN DIEGO SAN FRANCISCO SINGAPORE SYDNEY TOKYO

Elsevier
Radarweg 29, PO Box 211, 1000 AE Amsterdam, The Netherlands
The Boulevard, Langford Lane, Kidlington, Oxford OX5 1GB, UK
225 Wyman Street, Waltham, MA 02451, USA

Copyright © 2012 Elsevier Ltd. All rights reserved.

4.04   Hydrogen Safety Engineering: The State-of-the-Art and Future Progress
Copyright © 2012 V Molkov

5.16   Renewable Fuels: An Automotive Perspective
Copyright © 2012 Lotus Cars Limited

The following articles are US Government works in the public domain and not subject to copyright:
1.19   Cadmium Telluride Photovoltaic Thin Film: CdTe
1.37   Solar Power Satellites
4.02   Current Perspective on Hydrogen and Fuel Cells
5.02   Historical Perspectives on Biofuels

No part of this publication may be reproduced, stored in a retrieval system or transmitted in any form or by any means electronic, mechanical, photocopying, recording or otherwise without the prior written permission of the publisher

Permissions may be sought directly from Elsevier's Science & Technology Rights Department in Oxford, UK: phone (+44) (0) 1865 843830; fax (+44) (0) 1865 853333; email: permissions@elsevier.com. Alternatively you can submit your request online by visiting the Elsevier web site at http://elsevier.com/locate/permissions, and selecting *Obtaining permission to use Elsevier material*

Notice
No responsibility is assumed by the publisher for any injury and/or damage to persons or property as a matter of products liability, negligence or otherwise, or from any use or operation of any methods, products, instructions or ideas contained in the material herein. Because of rapid advances in the medical sciences, in particular, independent verfication of diagnoses and drug dosages should be made.

British Library Cataloguing in Publication Data
A catalogue record for this book is available from the British Library

The Library of Congress Control Number: 2012934547

ISBN: 978-0-08-087872-0

For information on all Elsevier publications
visit our website at books.elsevier.com

Printed and bound in Italy

11 12 13 14   10 9 8 7 6 5 4 3 2 1

Editorial: Gemma Mattingley, Joanne Williams
Production: Edward Taylor, Maggie Johnson

EDITOR-IN-CHIEF

Professor Ali Sayigh, BSc, DIC, PhD, CEng, a British citizen, graduated from Imperial College London and the University of London in 1966. He is a fellow of the Institute of Energy, a fellow of the Institution of Electrical Engineers, and is a chartered engineer.

From 1966 to 1985, Prof. Sayigh taught in the College of Engineering at the University of Baghdad and at King Saud University, Saudi Arabia, as a full-time professor, and also at Kuwait University as a part-time professor. From 1981 to 1985, he was Head of the Energy Department at the Kuwait Institute for Scientific Research (KISR) and expert in renewable energy at the Arab Organization of Petroleum Exporting Countries (AOPEC), Kuwait.

He started working in solar energy in September 1969. In 1984, he established links with Pergamon Press and became Editor-in-Chief of his first international journal, *Solar & Wind Technology*. Since 1990 he has been Editor-in-Chief of *Comprehensive Renewable Energy* incorporating *Solar & Wind Technology*, published by Elsevier Science Ltd., Oxford, UK. He is the editor of several international journals published in Morocco, Iran, Bangladesh, and Nigeria.

He has been a member of the International Society for Equitation Science (ISES) since 1973, founder and chairman of the ARAB Section of ISES since 1979, chairman of the UK Solar Energy Society for 3 years, and consultant to many national and international organizations, among them, the British Council, the Islamic Educational, Scientific and Cultural Organization (ISESCO), the United Nations Educational, Scientific and Cultural Organization (UNESCO), the United Nations Development Programme (UNDP), the Economic and Social Commission for Western Asia (ESCWA), and the United Nations Industrial Development Organization (UNIDO).

Since 1977 Prof. Sayigh has founded and directed several renewable energy conferences and workshops in the International Centre for Theoretical Physics (ICTP) – Trieste, Italy, Canada, Colombia, Algeria, Kuwait, Bahrain, Malaysia, Zambia, Malawi, India, the West Indies, Tunisia, Indonesia, Libya, Taiwan, UAE, Oman, the Czech Republic, Germany, Australia, Poland, the Netherlands, Thailand, Korea, Iran, Syria, Saudi Arabia, Singapore, China, the United States, and the United Kingdom.

In 1990 he established the World Renewable Energy Congress (WREC) and, in 1992, the World Renewable Energy Network (WREN), which hold their Congresses every 2 years, attracting more than 100 countries each time. In 2000, he and others in UAE, Sharjah, founded the Arab Science and Technology Foundation (ASTF) and regional conferences have been held in Sweden, Malaysia, Korea, Indonesia, Australia, UAE, and Libya, to name but a few. Prof. Sayigh has been running an annual international seminar on all aspects of renewable energy since 1990 in the United Kingdom and abroad. In total, 85 seminars have been held.

Prof. Sayigh supervised and graduated more than 34 PhD students and 64 MSc students at Reading University and the University of Hertfordshire when he was a professor from 1986 to 2004.

He has edited, contributed, and written more than 32 books and published more than 500 papers in various international journals and conferences.

In 2000–09, he initiated and worked closely with Sovereign Publication Company to produce the most popular magazine at annual bases called *Renewable Energy*, which was distributed freely to more than 6000 readers around the world. Presently, he is the editor-in-chief of *Comprehensive Renewable Energy*, coordinating 154 top scientists', engineers', and researchers' contributions in eight volumes published by Elsevier Publishing Company, Oxford, UK.

VOLUME EDITORS

Dr. Wilfried G. J. H. M. van Sark graduated from Utrecht University, the Netherlands, with an MSc in experimental physics in 1985, and with an MSc thesis on measurement and analysis of *I–V* characteristics of c-Si cells. He received his PhD from Nijmegen University, the Netherlands; the topic of his PhD thesis was III–V solar cell development, modeling, and processing. He then spent 7 years as a postdoc/senior researcher at Utrecht University and specialized in a-Si:H cell deposition and analysis. He is an expert in plasma chemical vapor deposition, both radio frequency and very high frequency. After an assistant professor position at Nijmegen University, where he worked on III–V solar cells, he returned to Utrecht University, with a focus on (single-molecule) confocal fluorescence microscopy of nanocrystals. In 2002, he moved to his present position as assistant professor at the research group Science, Technology and Society of the Copernicus Institute at Utrecht University, the Netherlands, where he performed and coordinated research on next-generation photovoltaic devices incorporating nanocrystals; for example, luminescent solar concentrators, as well as photovoltaic performance, life cycle analysis, socioeconomics, and policy development. He is member of the editorial board of Elsevier's scientific journal *Renewable Energy*, and member of various organizing committees of the European Union, the Institute of Electrical and Electronics Engineers (IEEE), and the SPIE PV conferences. He is author or coauthor of over 200 peer-reviewed journal and conference paper publications and book chapters. He has (co-)edited three books, including the present one.

Professor John K. Kaldellis holds a mechanical engineering degree from the National Technical University of Athens (NTUA) and a business administration diploma from the University of Piraeus. He obtained his PhD from NTUA (Fluid Sector) sponsored by Snecma–Dassault, France, and Bodossakis Foundation, Greece. He is currently the head of the Mechanical Engineering Department and since 1991 the director of the Soft Energy Applications and Environmental Protection Laboratory of the Technological Education Institute (TEI) of Piraeus. Prof. Kaldellis is also the scientific director (for TEI of Piraeus) of the MSc in Energy program organized by Heriot-Watt University and TEI of Piraeus. His scientific expertise is in the fields of energy and the environment. His research interests include feasibility analysis of energy sector applications; technological progress in wind, hydro, and solar energy markets; hybrid energy systems; energy storage issues; social attitudes toward renewable energy applications; and environmental technology–atmospheric pollution. He has participated in numerous research projects, funded by the European Union, European/Greek Industries, and the Greek State. Prof. Kaldellis has published six books concerning renewable energy applications and environmental protection. He is also the author of more than 100 scientific/research papers in international peer-reviewed journals and more than 300 papers for international scientific conferences. During the last decade, he was also a member of the Scientific Committee of the Hellenic Society of Mechanical–Electrical Engineers as well as a member of the organizing and scientific committee of several national and international conferences. He is currently a member of the editorial board of the *Renewable Energy International* journal and reviewer in more than 40 international journals in the energy and environment sector. He is the editor of the book *Stand-Alone and Hybrid Wind Energy Systems: Technology, Energy Storage and Applications* that has recently been published.

Dr. Soteris A. Kalogirou is a senior lecturer at the Department of Mechanical Engineering and Materials Science and Engineering at the Cyprus University of Technology, Limassol, Cyprus. He received his Higher Technical Institute (HTI) degree in mechanical engineering in 1982, his MPhil in mechanical engineering from the Polytechnic of Wales in 1991, and his PhD in mechanical engineering from the University of Glamorgan in 1995. In June 2011, he received the title of DSc from the University of Glamorgan.

For more than 25 years, he has been actively involved in research in the area of solar energy and particularly in flat-plate and concentrating collectors, solar water heating, solar steam generating systems, desalination, and absorption cooling. Additionally, since 1995, he has been involved in pioneering research dealing with the use of artificial intelligence methods, such as artificial neural networks, genetic algorithms, and fuzzy logic, for the modeling and performance prediction of energy and solar energy systems.

He has 29 books and book contributions and published 225 papers, 97 in international scientific journals and 128 in refereed conference proceedings. To date he has received more than 2550 citations on this work. He is Executive Editor of *Energy*, Associate Editor of *Renewable Energy*, and Editorial Board Member of another 11 journals. He is the editor of the book *Artificial Intelligence in Energy and Renewable Energy Systems*, published by Nova Science Inc.; coeditor of the book *Soft Computing in Green and Renewable Energy Systems*, published by Springer; and author of the book *Solar Energy Engineering: Processes and Systems*, published by Academic Press of Elsevier.

He has been a member of the World Renewable Energy Network (WREN) since 1992 and is a member of the Chartered Institution of Building Services Engineers (CIBSE), the American Society of Heating Refrigeration and Air-Conditioning Engineers (ASHRAE), the Institute of Refrigeration (IoR), and the International Solar Energy Society (ISES).

Dr. Andrew Cruden, a British citizen, was born in 1968. He obtained his BEng, MSc, and PhD in electrical engineering from the University of Strathclyde and CEng, MIEE Dr. Cruden is a past member of BSI GEL/105 Committee on Fuel Cells and Committee member of the IET Scotland Power Section. He is Director of the Scottish Hydrogen and Fuel Cell Association (SHFCA; www.shfca.org.uk) and Director of Argyll, Lomond and the Islands Energy Agency (www.alienergy.org.uk).

Dr. Cruden has been active in the field of hydrogen and fuel cells since 1995, when he acted as a consultant for Zevco Ltd., providing assistance with power electronic interfaces for early fuel cell systems. Later in 1998, he helped found the Scottish Fuel Cell Consortium (SFCC), supported by the Scottish Enterprise Energy Team, which ultimately developed a battery/fuel cell hybrid electric vehicle based on an AC Cobra kit car. The experience and contacts from the SFCC eventually gave rise to the formation of the Scottish Hydrogen and Fuel Cell Association (SHFCA), a trade body for the industry to promote and commercialize Scottish expertise in this field. Dr. Cruden was the founding chairman of the SHFCA.

Dr. Cruden is currently investigating alkaline electrolyzers in terms of improving their part load efficiency and lifetime when powered by variable renewable power sources, for example, wind turbines, as part of a £5 million EPSRC Supergen project on the 'Delivery of Sustainable Hydrogen' (EP/G01244X/1). He is also working with a colleague within Electronic and Electrical Engineering (EEE) at Strathclyde, studying the concept of vehicle-to-grid energy storage, as a mechanism not only to allow controlled load leveling on the power system, but also to potentially 'firm' up renewable energy generation. This work is supported by two research grants, an international E.On Research Initiative 2007 award and an ESPRC grant (EP/F062133/1).

Dr. Cruden is a senior lecturer within the Department of Electronic and Electrical Engineering at the University of Strathclyde. His current fields of research are modeling fuel cell and electrolyzer systems, fuel cell combined heat and power (CHP) systems, power electronic devices for interfacing both vehicular and stationary fuel cell systems, condition monitoring systems for renewable energy sources (i.e., wind turbines as part of EPSRC Supergen on Wind Energy Technologies, EP/D034566/1), and energy management systems for hybrid electric vehicles.

His areas of expertise include hydrogen-powered fuel cells and electrolyzers, energy storage for electric vehicles, and renewable energy generation.

Professor Dermot J. Roddy, BSc, PhD, CEng, FIET, joined Newcastle University as Science City Professor of Energy in 2008 after a period of some 20 years in the energy industry and petrochemical sectors. He is also Director of the Sir Joseph Swan Centre for Energy Research, which integrates energy research across Newcastle University and links with a powerful external industrial base in the energy sector. Outside of the university he is Chairman of Northeast Biofuels, Finance Director of the UK Hydrogen Association, and Vice-President of the Northern England Electricity Supply Companies Association. Prior to coming to Newcastle University, he was Chief Executive of Renew Tees Valley Ltd. – a company which he set up in 2003 to create a viable and vibrant economy in the Tees Valley based on renewable energy and recycling – where he was instrumental in a wide range of major renewable energy and low-carbon projects relating to biomass, biofuels, hydrogen, carbon capture and storage, wind, and advanced waste processing technologies. From 1998 to 2002, he ran the crude oil refinery on Teesside as a site director for a $5 billion turnover facility before moving to the Netherlands to work on Petroplus' international growth plans. Roddy's experience in the petrochemical industry began in 1985, involving a variety of UK and international roles in operations, engineering, and technology with ICI and others. Prior to that he developed leading-edge technology at Queen's University, Belfast, for optimization and control in aerospace applications.

André G. H. Lejeune was born on 2 August 1942 in Belgium. He was graduated in 1967 as a civil engineer, in 1972 as doctor in applied sciences (PhD), and in 1973 as master in oceanography in the University of Liège in Belgium. He was appointed full-time professor in the same university in 1976, and was visitor professor at the UNESCO–IHE Institute for Water Education in the Netherlands and Ecole Polytechnique Fédérale de Lausanne (EPFL) in Switzerland. Within the framework of his activities of professor, director of the Hydraulic Constructions and Hydraulic Research Laboratory, and expert, he took part in studies of dams and hydraulic structures and went on site in more than 90 countries of the world. In particular, he was for the last 6 years the chairman of the Technical Committee on Hydraulics for Dams in ICOLD (International Commission of Large Dams). He is a member of the Belgian Royal Academy of Sciences. He made his PhD thesis in hydraulic numerical modelization. This thesis received the Lorenz G. Straub Award in Minneapolis, USA (H. Einstein Jr. was a member of the Jury), and was used in particular by Chinese colleagues in the Three Gorges Project. Due to his practice and experience, he has a very complete knowledge of the hydraulic phenomena modelizations through both numerical and physical means.

With his wife, he has 3 children and 11 grandchildren. He likes books, tennis, and diving.

Thorsteinn I. Sigfusson is an internationally recognised physicist, educated in Copenhagen, Denmark, and Cambridge, UK. He is Director-General of the Innovation Center, Iceland and Professor of physics at the University of Iceland. He has been a visiting professor at Columbia University, New York, and he is currently the lead scientist in a prize-winning energy technology project performed at Tomsk Polytechnic University in Tomsk, Russia.

He has been a key figure in the introduction of new ideas and opportunities in the further greening of Icelandic society through the energy industry, and instrumental in the challenge of saving imported hydrocarbons by focusing on hydrogen from renewable energy.

He has started over a dozen start-up companies from research in Iceland and chaired various international societies in alternative energy. Among his achievements in geothermal energy is the construction of the world's largest solid-state thermoelectric generator powered with geothermal steam in southern Iceland. At the Innovation Center, Iceland, efforts are made to develop materials to withstand erosion in geothermal environments.

AbuBakr S. Bahaj is Professor of Sustainable Energy at the University of Southampton. After completing his PhD, he was employed by the University, progressing from a researcher to a personnel chair of Sustainable Energy. Over the past 20 years, Prof. Bahaj has established the energy theme within the University and directed his Sustainable Energy Research Group (SERG, www.energy.soton.ac.uk), which is now considered to be one of the United Kingdoms's leading university-based research groups in renewable energy and energy in buildings. He initiated and managed research in ocean energy conversion (resources, technologies, and impacts), photovoltaics, energy in buildings, and impacts of climate change on the built environment in the University. This work has resulted in over 230 articles published in academic refereed journals and conference series of international standing (see www.energy.soton.ac.uk).

Prof. Bahaj is the head of the Energy and Climate Change Division (ECCD) within the highly rated Faculty of Engineering and the Environment – Civil Engineering and the Environment – (www.civil.soton.ac.uk/research/divisions/divlist.asp?ResearchGroupID=1) (second in the United Kingdom, Research Assessment Exercise in 2008, with 80% of research judged to be either 'World Leading' or 'Internationally Excellent'). The aims of the Division and SERG are to promote and execute fundamental and applied research and preindustrial development in the areas of energy resources, technologies, energy efficiency, and the impact of climate change.

Prof. Bahaj is an experienced research team director and has many internationally focused research projects including collaborative projects in China, the European Union, the Middle East, and Africa. He also coordinated (2006–10) the United Kingdom's Engineering and Physical Sciences Research Council (EPSRC), Ecoregion Research Networks that aim to develop research themes and projects to study eco-city development encompassing resource assessment, technology pathways for the production and conservation of energy, planning, and social and economic studies required in establishing eco-regions in China and elsewhere (http://www.eco-networks.org). He is a founding member of the Sino-UK Low Carbon City Development Cooperation (LCCD) which aims to promote and undertake research into pathways for low-carbon development in Chinese cities. His work also encompasses an ongoing multimillion pound program in Africa, 'Energy for Development' for promoting and implementing village electrification systems, addressing villager's needs, and establishing coherent approaches to the commercial sustainability of the projects. This program is funded by the Research Councils and the UK Department for International Development (DFID; www.energyfordevelopment.net).

Prof. Bahaj is the editor-in-chief of the *International Journal of Sustainable Energy* and associate Editor of the *Renewable & Sustainable Energy Review*. He was on the editorial boards of the journals *Sustainable Cities and Society* and *Renewable Energy* (2005–11), and the United Kingdom's Institute of Civil Engineering journal *Energy* (2006–09). He was a member of the Tyndall Centre for Climate Change Research Supervisory Board (2005–10), and from 2001 to 2007 he was a member of the UK Government Department of Business, Enterprise and Regulatory Reform (now Department for Business Innovations and Skills, BIS), Technology Programmes Panels on Water (including ocean energy) and Solar Energy, now being administered by the Technology Strategy Board (TSB). Prof. Bahaj was the chair of the Technical Committees of the World Renewable Energy Congress – held in Glasgow (July 2008) and in Abu Dhabi (September 2010). He was a member of the Technical Committee of the 27th International Conference on Offshore Mechanics and Arctic Engineering (OMAE, 2008), a member of the management and technical committees of the European Wave and Tidal Energy Conferences (EWTEC, Porto, Portugal, September 2007; and Uppsala, Sweden, September 2009). He is also a member of the British Standards Institution (BSI) Committee GEL/82 on PV Energy Systems. Recently, at the invitation of the International Energy Agency, he has completed the 2008 status report on tidal stream energy conversion and in September 2009 was elected to chair the next EWTEC conference in the series – EWTEC2011 which was held in Southampton, 5–9 September 2011, and attended by around 500 participants.

To address training in the areas of energy and climate change Prof. Bahaj has coordinated and developed a set of MSc programs under the banner 'Energy and Sustainability' that address Energy Resources and Climate Change and Energy, Environment and Buildings.

CONTRIBUTORS FOR ALL VOLUMES

P Agnolucci
Imperial College London, London, UK

EO Ahlgren
Chalmers University of Technology, Gothenburg, Sweden

D Aklil
Pure Energy Center, Unst, Shetland Isles, UK

D-C Alarcón Padilla
Centro de Investigaciones Energéticas Medioambientales y Tecnológicas (CIEMAT), Plataforma Solar de Almeria, Almeria, Spain

K Alexander
University of Canterbury, Christchurch, New Zealand

S Alexopoulos
Aachen University of Applied Sciences, Jülich, Germany

A Altieri
UNICA – Brazilian Sugarcane Industry Association, São Paulo, Brazil

A Anthrakidis
Aachen University of Applied Sciences, Jülich, Germany

E Antolín
Universidad Politécnica de Madrid, Madrid, Spain

P Archambeau
University of Liège, Liège, Belgium

H Ármannsson
Iceland GeoSurvey (ISOR), Reykjavík, Iceland

MF Askew
Wolverhampton, UK

A Athienitis
Concordia University, Montreal, QC, Canada

G Axelsson
University of Iceland, Reykjavik, Iceland

V Badescu
Polytechnic University of Bucharest, Bucharest, Romania

AS Bahaj
The University of Southampton, Southampton, UK

P Banda
Instituto de Sistema Fotovoltaicos de Concentración (ISFOC), Puertollano, Spain

VG Belessiotis
'DEMOKRITOS' National Center for Scientific Research, Athens, Greece

P Berry
ADAS High Mowthorpe, Malton, UK

F Bidault
Imperial College London, London, UK

D Biro
Fraunhofer Institute for Solar Energy Systems, Freiburg, Germany

G Boschloo
Uppsala University, Uppsala, Sweden

C Boura
Aachen University of Applied Sciences, Jülich, Germany

E Bozorgzadeh
Iran Water and Power Resources Development Company (IWPCO), Tehran, Iran

CE Brewer
Iowa State University, Ames, IA, USA

M Börjesson
Chalmers University of Technology, Gothenburg, Sweden

RC Brown
Iowa State University, Ames, IA, USA

F Bueno
University of Burgos, Burgos, Spain

K Burke
NASA Glenn Research Center, Cleveland, OH, USA

LF Cabeza
GREA Innovació Concurrent, Universitat de Lleida, Lleida, Spain

L Candanedo
Dublin Institute of Technology, Dublin, Ireland

YG Caouris
University of Patras, Patras, Greece

UB Cappel
Uppsala University, Uppsala, Sweden

JA Carta
Universidad de Las Palmas de Gran Canaria, Las Palmas de Gran Canaria, Spain

P Chen
Dalian Institute of Chemical Physics, Dalian, China

DG Christakis
Wind Energy Laboratory, Technological Educational Institute of Crete, Crete, Greece

DA Chwieduk
Warsaw University of Technology, Warsaw, Poland

J Clark
University of York, York, UK

G Conibeer
University of New South Wales, Sydney, NSW, Australia

AJ Cruden
University of Strathclyde, Glasgow, UK

MC da Silva

B Davidsdottir
University of Iceland, Reykjavík, Iceland

O de la Rubia
Instituto de Sistema Fotovoltaicos de Concentración (ISFOC), Puertollano, Spain

E Despotou
Formerly of the European Photovoltaic Industry Association, Brussels, Belgium

BJ Dewals
University of Liège, Liège, Belgium

AL Dicks
The University of Queensland, Brisbane, QLD, Australia

R DiPippo
University of Massachusetts Dartmouth, Dartmouth, MA, USA

E Dunlop
European Commission DG Joint Research Centre, Ispra, Italy

NM Duteanu
Newcastle University, Newcastle upon Tyne, UK;
University 'POLITEHNICA' Timisoara, Timisoara, Romania

LM Eaton
Oak Ridge National Laboratory, Oak Ridge, TN, USA

H-J Egelhaaf
Konarka Technologies GmbH, Nürnberg, Germany

T Ehara
Mizuho Information & Research Institute, Tokyo, Japan

B Erable
Newcastle University, Newcastle upon Tyne, UK;
CNRS-Université de Toulouse, Toulouse, France

S Erpicum
University of Liège, Liège, Belgium

G Evans
NNFCC, Biocentre, Innovation Way, Heslington, York, UK

AFO Falcão
Instituto Superior Técnico, Technical University of Lisbon, Lisbon, Portugal

G Faninger
University of Klagenfurt, Klagenfurt, Austria; Vienna University of Technology, Vienna, Austria

GA Florides
Cyprus University of Technology, Limassol, Cyprus

ÓG Flóvenz
Iceland GeoSurvey (ISOR), Reykjavík, Iceland

RN Frese
VU University Amsterdam, Amsterdam, The Netherlands

Þ Friðriksson
Iceland GeoSurvey (ISOR), Reykjavík, Iceland

VM Fthenakis
Columbia University, New York, NY, USA; Brookhaven National Laboratory, Upton, NY, USA

M Fuamba
École Polytechnique de Montréal, Montreal, QC, Canada

A Fuller
University of Canterbury, Christchurch, New Zealand

LMC Gato
Instituto Superior Técnico, Technical University of Lisbon, Lisbon, Portugal

R Gazey
Pure Energy Center, Unst, Shetland Isles, UK

TA Gessert
National Renewable Energy Laboratory (NREL), Golden, CO, USA

MM Ghangrekar
Newcastle University, Newcastle upon Tyne, UK; Indian Institute of Technology, Kharagpur, India

M Giannouli
University of Patras, Patras, Greece

EA Gibson
University of Nottingham, Nottingham UK

A Gil
Hydropower Generation Division of Iberdrola, Salamanca, Spain

SW Glunz
Fraunhofer Institute for Solar Energy Systems, Freiburg, Germany

JC Goldschmidt
Fraunhofer Institute for Solar Energy Systems ISE, Freiburg, Germany

R Gottschalg
Loughborough University, Leicestershire, UK

MA Green
The University of New South Wales, Sydney, NSW, Australia

J Göttsche
Aachen University of Applied Sciences, Jülich, Germany

J Guo
China Institute of Water Resources and Hydropower Research (IWHR), Beijing, China

A Hagfeldt
Uppsala University, Uppsala, Sweden

B Hagin
Ingénieur-Conseil, Lutry, Switzerland

K Hall
Technology Transition Corporation, Ltd., Tyne and Wear, UK

O Hamandjoda
University of Yaounde, Yaounde, Republic of Cameroon

AP Harvey
Newcastle University, Newcastle upon Tyne, UK

JA Hauch
Konarka Technologies GmbH, Nürnberg, Germany

D Heinemann
University of Oldenburg, Oldenburg, Germany

V Heller
Imperial College London, London, UK

GP Hersir
Iceland GeoSurvey (ISOR), Reykjavík, Iceland

T Heyer
Technical University of Dresden, Dresden, Germany

P Hilger
Aachen University of Applied Sciences, Jülich, Germany

B Hillring
Swedish University of Agricultural Sciences, Skinnskatteberg, Sweden

T Hino
CTI Engineering International Co., Ltd., Chu-o-Ku, Japan

LC Hirst
Imperial College London, London, UK

B Hoffschmidt
Aachen University of Applied Sciences, Jülich, Germany

H Horlacher
Technical University of Dresden, Dresden, Germany

N Hughes
Imperial College London, London, UK

SL Hui
Bechtel Civil Company, San Francisco, CA, USA

D Husmann
University of Wisconsin–Madison, Madison, WI, USA

JTS Irvine
University of St Andrews, St Andrews, UK

D Jacobs
Freie Universität Berlin, Berlin, Germany

Y Jestin
Advanced Photonics and Photovoltaics Group, Bruno Kessler Foundation, Trento, Italy

A Jäger-Waldau
Institution for Energy Transport, Ispra, Italy

S Jianxia
Design and Research Institute, Yangzhou City, Jiangsu Province, China

E Johnson
Pure Energy Center, Unst, Shetland Isles, UK

HF Kaan
TNO Energy, Comfort and Indoor Quality, Delft, The Netherlands

JK Kaldellis
Technological Education Institute of Piraeus, Athens, Greece

SA Kalogirou
Cyprus University of Technology, Limassol, Cyprus

HD Kambezidis
Institute of Environmental Research and Sustainable Development, Athens, Greece

M Kapsali
Technological Education Institute of Piraeus, Athens, Greece

M Karimirad
Norwegian University of Science and Technology, Trondheim, Norway

T Karlessi
National and Kapodistrian University of Athens, Athens, Greece

SN Karlsdóttir
Innovation Center Iceland, Iceland

D Al Katsaprakakis
Wind Energy Laboratory, Technological Educational Institute of Crete, Crete, Greece

O Kaufhold
Aachen University of Applied Sciences, Jülich, Germany

CA Kaufmann
Helmholtz Zentrum für Materialien und Energie GmbH, Berlin, Germany

KA Kavadias
Technological Education Institute of Piraeus, Athens, Greece

LL Kazmerski
National Renewable Energy Laboratory, Golden, CO, USA

A Kazmi
University of York, York, UK

K Kendall
University of Birmingham, Birmingham, UK

J Kenfack
University of Yaounde, Yaounde, Republic of Cameroon

R Kenny
European Commission DG Joint Research Centre, Ispra, Italy

HC Kim
Brookhaven National Laboratory, Upton, NY, USA

L Kloo
KTH—Royal Institute of Technology, Stockholm, Sweden

G Knothe
USDA Agricultural Research Service, Peoria, IL, USA

FR Kogler
Konarka Technologies GmbH, Nürnberg, Germany

D Kolokotsa
Technical University of Crete, Crete, Greece

K Komoto
Mizuho Information & Research Institute, Tokyo, Japan

E Kondili
Technological Education Institute of Piraeus, Athens, Greece

H Kristjánsdóttir
University of Iceland, Reykjavík, Iceland

LA Lamont
Petroleum Institute, Abu Dhabi, UAE

GA Landis
NASA Glenn Research Center, Cleveland, OH, USA

JGM Lee
Newcastle University, Newcastle upon Tyne, UK

G Leftheriotis
University of Patras, Patras, Greece

A Lejeune
University of Liège, Liège, Belgium

T Leo
FuelCell Energy Inc., Danbury, CT, USA

E Lester
The University of Nottingham, Nottingham, UK

E Lorenz
University of Oldenburg, Oldenburg, Germany

JW Lund
Geo-Heat Center, Oregon Institute of Technology, Klamath Falls, OR, USA

A Luque
Universidad Politécnica de Madrid, Madrid, Spain

BP Machado
Intertechne, Curitiba, PR, Brazil

EBL Mackay
GL Garrad Hassan, Bristol, UK

T-F Mahdi
École Polytechnique de Montréal, Montreal, QC, Canada

GG Maidment
London South Bank University, London, UK

A Malmgren
BioC Ltd, Cirencester, UK

C Manson-Whitton
Progressive Energy Ltd., Stonehouse, UK

Á Margeirsson
Magma Energy Iceland, Reykjanesbaer, Iceland

A Martí
Universidad Politécnica de Madrid, Madrid, Spain

M Martinez
Instituto de Sistema Fotovoltaicos de Concentración (ISFOC), Puertollano, Spain

S Mathew
University of Brunei Darussalam, Gadong, Brunei Darussalam

PH Middleton
University of Agder, Grimstad, Norway

R Mikalsen
Newcastle University, Newcastle upon Tyne, UK

D Milborrow
Lewes, East Sussex, UK

H Müllejans
European Commission DG Joint Research Centre, Ispra, Italy

V Molkov
University of Ulster, Newtownabbey, Northern Ireland, UK

M Moner-Girona
Joint Research Centre, European Commission, Institute for Energy and Transport, Ispra, Italy

PE Morthorst
Technical University of Denmark, Roskilde, Denmark

N Mortimer
North Energy Associates Ltd, Sheffield, UK

E Mullins
Teagasc, Oak Park Crops Research Centre, Carlow, Republic of Ireland

P Mulvihill
Pioneer Generation Ltd., Alexandra, New Zealand

DR Myers
National Renewable Energy Laboratory, USA

D Nash
University of Strathclyde, Glasgow, UK

GF Nemet
University of Wisconsin–Madison, Madison, WI, USA

H Nfaoui
Mohammed V University, Rabat, Morocco

T Nikolakakis
Columbia University, New York, NY, USA

X Niu
Changjiang Institute of Survey, Planning, Design and Research, Wuhan, China

B Norton
Dublin Institute of Technology, Dublin, Ireland

A Nuamah
The University of Nottingham, Nottingham, UK; RWE npower, Swindon, UK

B O'Connor
Aachen University of Applied Sciences, Jülich, Germany

O Olsson
Swedish University of Agricultural Sciences, Skinnskatteberg, Sweden

V Ortisi
Pure Energy Center, Unst, Shetland Isles, UK

H Ossenbrink
European Commission DG Joint Research Centre, Ispra, Italy

AG Paliatsos
Technological Education Institute of Piraeus, Athens, Greece

A Pandit
VU University Amsterdam, Amsterdam, The Netherlands

E Papanicolaou
'DEMOKRITOS' National Center for Scientific Research, Athens, Greece

A Paurine
London South Bank University, London, UK

N Pearsall
Northumbria University, Newcastle, UK

RJ Pearson
Lotus Engineering, Norwich, UK

RD Perlack
Oak Ridge National Laboratory, Oak Ridge, TN, USA

H Pettersson
Swerea IVF AB, Mölndal, Sweden

GS Philip
KCAET, Malapuram, Kerala, India

S Pillai
The University of New South Wales, Sydney, NSW, Australia

M Pirotton
University of Liège, Liège, Belgium

BG Pollet
University of Birmingham, Birmingham, UK

D Porter
Association of Electricity Producers, London, UK

A Pouliezos
Technical University of Crete, Hania, Greece

R Preu
Fraunhofer Institute for Solar Energy Systems, Freiburg, Germany

CM Ramos

C Rau
Aachen University of Applied Sciences, Jülich, Germany

AA Refaat
Cairo University, Giza, Egypt

TH Reijenga
BEARiD Architecten, Rotterdam, The Netherlands

AHME Reinders
Delft University of Technology, Delft, The Netherlands;
University of Twente, Enschede, The Netherlands

G Riley
RWE npower, Swindon, UK

DJ Roddy
Newcastle University, Newcastle upon Tyne, UK

S Rolland
Alliance for Rural Electrification, Brussels, Belgium

A Roskilly
Newcastle University, Newcastle upon Tyne, UK

F Rubio
Instituto de Sistema Fotovoltaicos de Concentración (ISFOC), Puertollano, Spain

F Rulot
University of Liège, Liège, Belgium

L Rybach
GEOWATT AG, Zurich, Switzerland

M Santamouris
National and Kapodistrian University of Athens, Athens, Greece

J Sattler
Aachen University of Applied Sciences, Jülich, Germany

M Sauerborn
Aachen University of Applied Sciences, Jülich, Germany

TW Schmidt
The University of Sydney, Sydney, NSW, Australia

N Schofield
University of Manchester, Manchester, UK

REI Schropp
Utrecht University, Utrecht, The Netherlands

K Scott
Newcastle University, Newcastle upon Tyne, UK

SP Sen
NHPC Ltd., New Delhi, India

TI Sigfusson
Innovation Center, Reykjavik, Iceland

L Sims
Konarka Technologies GmbH, Nürnberg, Germany;
Universität Augsburg, Augsburg, Germany

C Smith
NNFCC, Biocentre, Innovation Way, Heslington, York, UK

K Sæmundsson
Iceland GeoSurvey (ISOR), Reykjavík, Iceland

BK Sovacool
Vermont Law School, South Royalton, VT, USA

J Spink
Teagasc, Oak Park Crops Research Centre, Carlow, Republic of Ireland

JN Sørensen
Technical University of Denmark, Lyngby, Denmark

T Stallard
The University of Manchester, Manchester, UK

GS Stavrakakis
Technical University of Crete, Chania, Greece

R Steim
Konarka Technologies GmbH, Nürnberg, Germany

BJ Stokes
CNJV LLC, Washington, DC, USA

L Sun
KTH—Royal Institute of Technology, Stockholm, Sweden;
Dalian University of Technology (DUT), Dalian, China

L Suo
Science and Technology Committee of the Ministry of Water Resources, Beijing, China

DT Swift-Hook
Kingston University, London, UK;
World Renewable Energy Network, Brighton, UK

A Synnefa
National and Kapodistrian University of Athens, Athens, Greece

S Szabo
Joint Research Centre, European Commission, Institute for Energy and Transport, Ispra, Italy

MJY Tayebjee
The University of Sydney, Sydney, NSW, Australia

A Tesfai
University of St Andrews, St Andrews, UK

P Thornley
The University of Manchester, Manchester, UK

Y Tripanagnostopoulos
University of Patras, Patras, Greece

L Tsakalakos
General Electric – Global Research Center, New York, NY, USA

JWG Turner
Lotus Engineering, Norwich, UK

E Tzen
Centre for Renewable Energy Sources and Saving (CRES), Pikermi, Attica, Greece

T Unold
Helmholtz Zentrum für Materialien und Energie GmbH, Berlin, Germany

J van der Heide
imec vzw, Leuven, Belgium

P van der Vleuten
Free Energy Consulting, Eindhoven, The Netherlands

F Van Hulle
XP Wind Consultancy, Leuven, Belgium

GC van Kooten
University of Victoria, Victoria, BC, Canada

WGJHM van Sark
Utrecht University, Utrecht, The Netherlands

I Waller
FiveBarGate Consultants Ltd, Cleveland, UK

I Walsh
Opus International Consultants Ltd., New Zealand

Y Wang
Newcastle University, Newcastle upon Tyne, UK

T Wizelius
Gotland University, Visby, Sweden; Lund University, Lund, Sweden

LL Wright
University of Tennessee, Knoxville, TN, USA

H Xie
Changjiang Institute of Survey, Planning, Design and Research, Wuhan, China

M Yamaguchi
Toyota Technological Institute, Tempaku, Nagoya, Japan

P Yianoulis
University of Patras, Patras, Greece

EH Yu
Newcastle University, Newcastle upon Tyne, UK

H Yu
Newcastle University, Newcastle upon Tyne, UK

DP Zafirakis
Technological Education Institute of Piraeus, Athens, Greece

G Zaragoza
Centro de Investigaciones Energéticas Medioambientales y Tecnológicas (CIEMAT), Plataforma Solar de Almeria, Almeria, Spain

M Zeman
Delft University of Technology, Delft, The Netherlands

PREFACE

Comprehensive Renewable Energy is the only multivolume reference work of its type at a time when renewable energy sources are increasingly in demand and realistically sustainable, clean, and helping to combat climate change and global warming. Renewable energy investment has exceeded US$10 billion per year during the past 5 years. The World Renewable Energy Network (WREN) predicts that this figure is set to increase to US$20 billion per year by 2015.

As Editor-in-Chief, I have assembled an impressive world-class team of 154 volume editors and contributing authors for the eight volumes. They represent policy makers, researchers, industrialists, financiers, and heads of organizations from more than 80 countries to produce this definitive complete work in renewable energy covering the past, explaining the present, and giving the ideas and prospects of development for the future. There are more than 1000 references from books, journals, and the Internet within the eight volumes. *Comprehensive Renewable Energy* is full of color charts, illustrations, and photographs of real projects and research results from around the world. Each chapter has been painstakingly reviewed and checked for consistent high quality. The result is an authoritative overview that ties the literature together and provides the user with reliable background information and a citation resource.

The field of renewable energy research and development is represented by many journals that are directly and indirectly concerned with the field. But no reference work encompasses the entire field and unites the different areas of research through in-depth foundational reviews. *Comprehensive Renewable Energy* fills this vacuum, and is the definitive work for this subject area. It will help users apply context to diverse journal literature, aiding them in identifying areas for further research and development.

Research into renewable energy is spread across a number of different disciplines and subject areas. These areas do not always share a unique identifying factor or subject themselves to clear and concise definitions. This work unites the different areas of research and allows users, regardless of their background, to navigate through the most essential concepts with ease, saving them time and vastly improving their understanding so that they can move forward, whether in their research, development, manufacturing, or purchase of renewable energy.

The first volume is devoted to Photovoltaic Technology and is edited by Mr. Wilfried G. J. H. M. van Sark from the Netherlands. It consists of 38 chapters, written by 41 authors from Europe, the United States, Japan, China, India, Africa, and the Middle East. The topics covered range from the smallest applications to MW projects. A brief introduction and history is followed by chapters on finance and economics, solar resources, up- and downconversion, crystalline photovoltaic (PV) cells, luminescent concentrators, thin-film and multiple-junction plastic solar cells, dye-sensitized solar cells, bio-inspired converters, application of micro- and nanotechnology, building integrated photovoltaics (BIPV) application in architecture, and very large-scale PV systems. Without doubt, this is an impressive tour of an immense field.

Volume 2 is devoted to Wind Energy and is edited by Professor John K. Kaldellis from Greece. It consists of 22 chapters written by 22 authors, again from various parts of the world, covering all aspects of wind energy from small wind mills to very large wind farms. The volume includes chapters on the history of wind power, the potential of wind power, wind turbine development, aerodynamic analysis, mechanical and electrical loads, control systems, noise and testing, onshore and offshore wind systems, policy, industry, and special wind power applications.

Volume 3 is devoted to Solar Thermal Applications and the editor is Professor Soteris A. Kalogirou from Cyprus. It consists of 19 chapters written by 17 authors. All aspects of solar thermal energy and its applications are covered. The volume begins with solar energy as a source of heat and goes on to describe the history of thermal applications, low-temperature and high-temperature storage systems, selective coating, glazing, modeling and simulation, hot water systems, space heating and cooling, water desalination, industrial and agricultural applications, concentration power, heat pumps, and passive solar architecture. The authors have looked at the Sun from the thermal energy aspect and put together a very informative and up-to-date volume from which every interested person, no matter what their level of knowledge, can benefit.

Volume 4 is on Fuel Cells and Hydrogen Technology and is edited by Dr. Andrew Cruden from the United Kingdom. It consists of 14 chapters covering the following topics: introduction and perspectives on hydrogen and fuel cells; theory and application of alkaline fuel cells; application of proton exchange membrane (PEM) fuel cells; molten carbonate fuel cells; solid oxide fuel cells; microbial and biological fuel cells; storage of compressed gas and hydrogen; the economy and policy of hydrogen technology; hydrogen safety engineering and future progress; the use of hydrogen for transport; and hydrogen and fuel cell power electronics. The 14 chapters were written by 16 authors. All aspects of practice, innovative technology, and future guidelines for researchers and industry have been addressed in this definitive volume.

Volume 5 deals with the huge field of Biomass and Biofuels and is edited by Professor Dermot J. Roddy from the United Kingdom. This work consists of 21 chapters written by 23 authors, again covering all aspects of biomass and biofuels, including their past, present, and future. The volume explains the history and prospective future of biofuels; bioethanol development in Brazil; power generation from biomass; biomass co-firing stations; biomass world market; a critical assessment of biomass – combined heat and power (CHP) energy systems; the ethics of biofuel production – issues, constraints, and limitations; greenhouse gases life cycle analysis; six different solutions from gasification and pyrolysis; new processes in biomass-to-liquid technology; new processes in biofuel production; biofuels from waste materials; novel feedstocks and woody biomass; feedstocks with the potential of yield improvement; renewable fuels – an automotive prospective; and novel use of biofuels in a range of engine configurations. Under Expanding the Envelope, there are chapters on biochar, extracting additional value from biomass, and biomass to chemicals. Finally, the chapter on bioenergy policy development concludes the volume.

Volume 6 is concerned with Hydro Power and is edited by Professor André G. H. Lejeune from Belgium. This is the oldest of all the renewable energy applications and has progressed over the ages from pico-hydro of a few hundred watts to large- and mega-scale dams generating more than 3000 MW with innovative civil engineering capability. This volume consists of 18 chapters prepared by 21 authors. It contains introduction – benefits and constraints of hydropower, recent developments and achievements in hydraulic research in China, and the management of hydropower and its impacts through construction and operation. The volume then assesses nine hydropower schemes around the world: the Three Gorges Project in China; large hydropower plants of Brazil; hydropower in Iran – vision and strategy; the recent trend in developing hydropower in India; the evolution of hydropower in Spain; hydropower in Japan; hydropower in Canada; an overview of institutional structure reform of the Cameroon power sector and assessment; and hydropower reliability in Switzerland. Other important issues are covered: pumped storage power plants; simplified generic axial-flow microhydro turbines; the development of a small hydroelectric scheme at Horseshoe Bend, Teviot River, New Zealand; concrete durability in dam design structure; and long-term sediment management for sustainable hydropower.

Volume 7 deals with Geothermal Energy. The editor of this volume is Professor Thorsteinn I. Sigfusson from Iceland. The volume consists of 10 chapters, which are written by 15 different authors. It covers the following areas: introduction and the physics of geothermal resources and management during utilization; geothermal shallow systems – heat pumps; geothermal exploration techniques; corrosion, scaling, and material selection in geothermal power production; direct heat utilization of geothermal energy; geothermal power plants; geochemical aspects of geothermal utilization; geothermal cost and investment factors; and the role of sustainable geothermal development.

Volume 8 is devoted to Generating Electricity from the Oceans, edited by Professor AbuBakr S. Bahaj from the United Kingdom. It consists of six chapters written by five authors. The volume covers the historical aspects of wave energy conversion, resource assessment for wave energy, development of wave devices from initial conception to commercial demonstration, air turbines, and the economics of ocean energy.

One chapter is totally devoted to Renewable Energy Policy and Incentives. It is included in the first volume only. The author of this chapter is Mr. David Porter, Chief Executive of the Association of Electricity Producers in the United Kingdom, an author who has had vast experience of dealing with electricity generation in the United Kingdom over many years. He has advised the British Government on how to meet supply and demand of electricity and coordinate with all electricity producers regarding their sources and supply. The chapter outlines the types of mechanisms used to promote renewable energy and their use, the impact on their deployment, ensuring investor certainty, the potential for harmonizing support schemes, and the conclusion.

In short, my advice to anyone who wants to acquire comprehensive knowledge concerning renewable energy, no matter which subject or application, is that they should acquire this invaluable resource for their home, research center and laboratory, company, or library.

Professor Ali Sayigh BSc, DIC, PhD, FIE, FIEE, CEng
Chairman of WREC (World Renewable Energy Congress)
Director General of WREN (World Renewable Energy Network)
Chairman of IEI (The Institution of Engineers (India))
Editor-in-Chief of *Renewable Energy*
Editor-in-Chief of *Renewable Energy Magazine*

CONTENTS

Editor-in-Chief	v
Volume Editors	vii
Contributors for All Volumes	xi
Preface	xix

Volume 1   Photovoltaic Solar Energy

Renewable Energy

1.01	Renewable Energy Policy and Incentives *D Porter*	1

Photovoltaic Solar Energy

1.02	Introduction to Photovoltaic Technology *WGJHM van Sark*	5
1.03	Solar Photovoltaics Technology: No Longer an Outlier *LL Kazmerski*	13
1.04	History of Photovoltaics *LA Lamont*	31

Economics and Environment

1.05	Historical and Future Cost Dynamics of Photovoltaic Technology *GF Nemet and D Husmann*	47
1.06	Feed-In Tariffs and Other Support Mechanisms for Solar PV Promotion *D Jacobs and BK Sovacool*	73
1.07	Finance Mechanisms and Incentives for Photovoltaic Technologies in Developing Countries *M Moner-Girona, S Szabo, and S Rolland*	111
1.08	Environmental Impacts of Photovoltaic Life Cycles *VM Fthenakis and HC Kim*	143
1.09	Overview of the Global PV Industry *A Jäger-Waldau*	161
1.10	Vision for Photovoltaics in the Future *E Despotou*	179

| 1.11 | Storage Options for Photovoltaics
VM Fthenakis and T Nikolakakis | 199 |

Resource and Potential

| 1.12 | Solar Radiation Resource Assessment for Renewable Energy Conversion
DR Myers | 213 |
| 1.13 | Prediction of Solar Irradiance and Photovoltaic Power
E Lorenz and D Heinemann | 239 |

Basics

| 1.14 | Principles of Solar Energy Conversion
LC Hirst | 293 |
| 1.15 | Thermodynamics of Photovoltaics
V Badescu | 315 |

Technology

1.16	Crystalline Silicon Solar Cells: State-of-the-Art and Future Developments SW Glunz, R Preu, and D Biro	353
1.17	Thin-Film Silicon PV Technology M Zeman and REI Schropp	389
1.18	Chalcopyrite Thin-Film Materials and Solar Cells T Unold and CA Kaufmann	399
1.19	Cadmium Telluride Photovoltaic Thin Film: CdTe TA Gessert	423
1.20	Plastic Solar Cells L Sims, H-J Egelhaaf, JA Hauch, FR Kogler, and R Steim	439
1.21	Mesoporous Dye-Sensitized Solar Cells A Hagfeldt, UB Cappel, G Boschloo, L Sun, L Kloo, H Pettersson, and EA Gibson	481
1.22	Multiple Junction Solar Cells M Yamaguchi	497
1.23	Application of Micro- and Nanotechnology in Photovoltaics L Tsakalakos	515
1.24	Upconversion TW Schmidt and MJY Tayebjee	533
1.25	Downconversion MJY Tayebjee, TW Schmidt, and G Conibeer	549
1.26	Down-Shifting of the Incident Light for Photovoltaic Applications Y Jestin	563
1.27	Luminescent Solar Concentrators JC Goldschmidt	587
1.28	Thermophotovoltaics J van der Heide	603
1.29	Intermediate Band Solar Cells E Antolín, A Martí, and A Luque	619
1.30	Plasmonics for Photovoltaics S Pillai and MA Green	641
1.31	Artificial Leaves: Towards Bio-Inspired Solar Energy Converters A Pandit and RN Frese	657

Applications

1.32	Design and Components of Photovoltaic Systems *WGJHM van Sark*	679
1.33	BIPV in Architecture and Urban Planning *TH Reijenga and HF Kaan*	697
1.34	Product-Integrated Photovoltaics *AHME Reinders and WGJHM van Sark*	709
1.35	Very Large-Scale Photovoltaic Systems *T Ehara, K Komoto, and P van der Vleuten*	733
1.36	Concentration Photovoltaics *M Martinez, O de la Rubia, F Rubio, and P Banda*	745
1.37	Solar Power Satellites *GA Landis*	767
1.38	Performance Monitoring *N Pearsall and R Gottschalg*	775
1.39	Standards in Photovoltaic Technology *H Ossenbrink, H Müllejans, R Kenny, and E Dunlop*	787

Volume 2   Wind Energy

2.01	Wind Energy – Introduction *JK Kaldellis*	1
2.02	Wind Energy Contribution in the Planet Energy Balance and Future Prospects *JK Kaldellis and M Kapsali*	11
2.03	History of Wind Power *DT Swift-Hook*	41
2.04	Wind Energy Potential *H Nfaoui*	73
2.05	Wind Turbines: Evolution, Basic Principles, and Classifications *S Mathew and GS Philip*	93
2.06	Energy Yield of Contemporary Wind Turbines *DP Zafirakis, AG Paliatsos, and JK Kaldellis*	113
2.07	Wind Parks Design, Including Representative Case Studies *D Al Katsaprakakis and DG Christakis*	169
2.08	Aerodynamic Analysis of Wind Turbines *JN Sørensen*	225
2.09	Mechanical-Dynamic Loads *M Karimirad*	243
2.10	Electrical Parts of Wind Turbines *GS Stavrakakis*	269
2.11	Wind Turbine Control Systems and Power Electronics *A Pouliezos*	329
2.12	Testing, Standardization, Certification in Wind Energy *F Van Hulle*	371
2.13	Design and Implementation of a Wind Power Project *T Wizelius*	391
2.14	Offshore Wind Power Basics *M Kapsali and JK Kaldellis*	431

2.15	Wind Energy Economics *D Milborrow*	469
2.16	Environmental-Social Benefits/Impacts of Wind Power *E Kondili and JK Kaldellis*	503
2.17	Wind Energy Policy *GC van Kooten*	541
2.18	Wind Power Integration *JA Carta*	569
2.19	Stand-Alone, Hybrid Systems *KA Kavadias*	623
2.20	Wind Power Industry and Markets *PE Morthorst*	657
2.21	Trends, Prospects, and R&D Directions in Wind Turbine Technology *JK Kaldellis and DP Zafirakis*	671
2.22	Special Wind Power Applications *E Kondili*	725

Volume 3 Solar Thermal Systems: Components and Applications

Solar Thermal Systems

3.01	Solar Thermal Systems: Components and Applications – Introduction *SA Kalogirou*	1
3.02	Solar Resource *HD Kambezidis*	27
3.03	History of Solar Energy *VG Belessiotis and E Papanicolaou*	85

Components

3.04	Low Temperature Stationary Collectors *YG Caouris*	103
3.05	Low Concentration Ratio Solar Collectors *SA Kalogirou*	149
3.06	High Concentration Solar Collectors *B Hoffschmidt, S Alexopoulos, J Göttsche, M Sauerborn, and O Kaufhold*	165
3.07	Thermal Energy Storage *LF Cabeza*	211
3.08	Photovoltaic/Thermal Solar Collectors *Y Tripanagnostopoulos*	255
3.09	Solar Selective Coatings *P Yianoulis, M Giannouli, and SA Kalogirou*	301
3.10	Glazings and Coatings *G Leftheriotis and P Yianoulis*	313
3.11	Modeling and Simulation of Passive and Active Solar Thermal Systems *A Athienitis, SA Kalogirou, and L Candanedo*	357

Applications

3.12	Solar Hot Water Heating Systems G Faninger	419
3.13	Solar Space Heating and Cooling Systems SA Kalogirou and GA Florides	449
3.14	Solar Cooling and Refrigeration Systems GG Maidment and A Paurine	481
3.15	Solar-Assisted Heat Pumps DA Chwieduk	495
3.16	Solar Desalination E Tzen, G Zaragoza, and D-C Alarcón Padilla	529
3.17	Industrial and Agricultural Applications of Solar Heat B Norton	567
3.18	Concentrating Solar Power B Hoffschmidt, S Alexopoulos, C Rau, J Sattler, A Anthrakidis, C Boura, B O'Connor, and P Hilger	595
3.19	Passive Solar Architecture D Kolokotsa, M Santamouris, A Synnefa, and T Karlessi	637

Volume 4 Fuel Cells and Hydrogen Technology

4.01	Fuel Cells and Hydrogen Technology – Introduction AJ Cruden	1
4.02	Current Perspective on Hydrogen and Fuel Cells K Burke	13
4.03	Hydrogen Economics and Policy N Hughes and P Agnolucci	45
4.04	Hydrogen Safety Engineering: The State-of-the-Art and Future Progress V Molkov	77
4.05	Hydrogen Storage: Compressed Gas D Nash, D Aklil, E Johnson, R Gazey, and V Ortisi	111
4.06	Hydrogen Storage: Liquid and Chemical P Chen	137
4.07	Alkaline Fuel Cells: Theory and Application F Bidault and PH Middleton	159
4.08	PEM Fuel Cells: Applications AL Dicks	183
4.09	Molten Carbonate Fuel Cells: Theory and Application T Leo	227
4.10	Solid Oxide Fuel Cells: Theory and Materials A Tesfai and JTS Irvine	241
4.11	Biological and Microbial Fuel Cells K Scott, EH Yu, MM Ghangrekar, B Erable, and NM Duteanu	257
4.12	Hydrogen and Fuel Cells in Transport K Kendall and BG Pollet	281
4.13	H_2 and Fuel Cells as Controlled Renewables: FC Power Electronics N Schofield	295
4.14	Future Perspective on Hydrogen and Fuel Cells K Hall	331

Volume 5 Biomass and Biofuel Production

Biomass and Biofuels

5.01	Biomass and Biofuels – Introduction *DJ Roddy*	1
5.02	Historical Perspectives on Biofuels *G Knothe*	11

Case Studies

5.03	Bioethanol Development in Brazil *A Altieri*	15
5.04	Biomass Power Generation *A Malmgren and G Riley*	27
5.05	Biomass Co-Firing *A Nuamah, A Malmgren, G Riley, and E Lester*	55

Issues, Constraints & Limitations

5.06	A Global Bioenergy Market *O Olsson and B Hillring*	75
5.07	Biomass CHP Energy Systems: A Critical Assessment *M Börjesson and EO Ahlgren*	87
5.08	Ethics of Biofuel Production *I Waller*	99
5.09	Life Cycle Analysis Perspective on Greenhouse Gas Savings *N Mortimer*	109

Technology Solutions – New Processes

5.10	Biomass Gasification and Pyrolysis *DJ Roddy and C Manson-Whitton*	133
5.11	Biomass to Liquids Technology *G Evans and C Smith*	155
5.12	Intensification of Biofuel Production *AP Harvey and JGM Lee*	205
5.13	Biofuels from Waste Materials *AA Refaat*	217

Technology Solutions – Novel Feedstocks

5.14	Woody Biomass *LL Wright, LM Eaton, RD Perlack, and BJ Stokes*	263
5.15	Potential for Yield Improvement *J Spink, E Mullins, and P Berry*	293

Technology Solutions – Novel End Uses

5.16	Renewable Fuels: An Automotive Perspective *RJ Pearson and JWG Turner*	305
5.17	Use of Biofuels in a Range of Engine Configurations *A Roskilly, Y Wang, R Mikalsen, and H Yu*	343

Expanding the Envelope

5.18	Biochar *CE Brewer and RC Brown*	357
5.19	Extracting Additional Value from Biomass *MF Askew*	385
5.20	Biomass to Chemicals *A Kazmi and J Clark*	395
5.21	Bioenergy Policy Development *P Thornley*	411

Volume 6 Hydro Power

Hydro Power

6.01	Hydro Power – Introduction *A Lejeune*	1

Constraints of Hydropower Development

6.02	Hydro Power: A Multi Benefit Solution for Renewable Energy *A Lejeune and SL Hui*	15
6.03	Management of Hydropower Impacts through Construction and Operation *H Horlacher, T Heyer, CM Ramos, and MC da Silva*	49

Hydropower Schemes Around the World

6.04	Large Hydropower Plants of Brazil *BP Machado*	93
6.05	Overview of Institutional Structure Reform of the Cameroon Power Sector and Assessments *J Kenfack and O Hamandjoda*	129
6.06	Recent Hydropower Solutions in Canada *M Fuamba and TF Mahdi*	153
6.07	The Three Gorges Project in China *L Suo, X Niu, and H Xie*	179
6.08	The Recent Trend in Development of Hydro Plants in India *SP Sen*	227
6.09	Hydropower Development in Iran: Vision and Strategy *E Bozorgzadeh*	253
6.10	Hydropower Development in Japan *T Hino*	265
6.11	Evolution of Hydropower in Spain *A Gil and F Bueno*	309
6.12	Hydropower in Switzerland *B Hagin*	343

Design Concepts

6.13	Long-Term Sediment Management for Sustainable Hydropower *F Rulot, BJ Dewals, S Erpicum, P Archambeau, and M Pirotton*	355
6.14	Durability Design of Concrete Hydropower Structures *S Jianxia*	377
6.15	Pumped Storage Hydropower Developments *T Hino and A Lejeune*	405

6.16	Simplified Generic Axial-Flow Microhydro Turbines A Fuller and K Alexander	435
6.17	Development of a Small Hydroelectric Scheme at Horseshoe Bend, Teviot River, Central Otago, New Zealand P Mulvihill and I Walsh	467
6.18	Recent Achievements in Hydraulic Research in China J Guo	485

Volume 7 Geothermal Energy

7.01	Geothermal Energy – Introduction TI Sigfusson	1
7.02	The Physics of Geothermal Energy G Axelsson	3
7.03	Geothermal Energy Exploration Techniques ÓG Flóvenz, GP Hersir, K Sæmundsson, H Ármannsson, and Þ Friðriksson	51
7.04	Geochemical Aspects of Geothermal Utilization H Ármannsson	95
7.05	Direct Heat Utilization of Geothermal Energy JW Lund	169
7.06	Shallow Systems: Geothermal Heat Pumps L Rybach	187
7.07	Geothermal Power Plants R DiPippo	207
7.08	Corrosion, Scaling, and Material Selection in Geothermal Power Production SN Karlsdóttir	239
7.09	Geothermal Cost and Investment Factors H Kristjánsdóttir and Á Margeirsson	259
7.10	Sustainable Energy Development: The Role of Geothermal Power B Davidsdottir	271

Volume 8 Ocean Energy

8.01	Generating Electrical Power from Ocean Resources AS Bahaj	1
8.02	Historical Aspects of Wave Energy Conversion AFO Falcão	7
8.03	Resource Assessment for Wave Energy EBL Mackay	11
8.04	Development of Wave Devices from Initial Conception to Commercial Demonstration V Heller	79
8.05	Air Turbines AFO Falcão and LMC Gato	111
8.06	Economics of Ocean Energy T Stallard	151
Index		171

5.01 Biomass and Biofuels – Introduction

DJ Roddy, Newcastle University, Newcastle upon Tyne, UK

© 2012 Elsevier Ltd. All rights reserved.

5.01.1	Background	1
5.01.2	Basic Technology	2
5.01.3	Widespread Deployment of Biomass and Biofuels	3
5.01.3.1	Biodiesel	3
5.01.3.2	Other Biofuels	4
5.01.4	Issues, Constraints, and Limitations	4
5.01.5	Technology Solutions – New Processes	5
5.01.5.1	Anaerobic Digestion	5
5.01.5.2	Advanced Biofuel Processes	6
5.01.6	Technology Solutions – New Feedstocks	6
5.01.6.1	Algae	6
5.01.6.2	Other Options for Increasing Feedstock Availability	7
5.01.7	Expanding the Envelope	7
5.01.8	Recent Developments	8
5.01.9	The Way Forward for Biomass and Biofuels	9
References		9

5.01.1 Background

The largest source of renewable energy in use in the world today is biomass [1]. This assertion surprises people who expect the crown to be worn by wind, solar photovoltaic, or one of the other high-profile technologies. However, when you consider that large parts of the world's population are still dependent on firewood for cooking and heating, perhaps it is not so surprising. Recent estimates place the number of people relying on traditional biomass for their energy needs at 2.5 billion [2]. In many countries, there is the unfortunate associated problem of household air pollution, leading to 1.3 million premature deaths per year [2].

Biomass is also the most versatile of the renewable resources. This is due in part to the sheer breadth of materials that can be classified as biomass. Basically, anything that grows and is available in non-fossilized form can be classified as biomass. (Today's fossil fuels used to be biomass several tens of millions of years ago, but they are obviously not 'renewable' on any relevant timescale, so it is not helpful to include them.) However, arable crops, trees, bushes, animals, human and animal waste, waste food, and any other waste stream that rots quickly are all biomass materials. The United Kingdom alone produces around 25 million tonnes of segregated organic waste per year, equivalent to around 7.5 TWh of energy [3]. The volume and variety of biomass materials available are truly remarkable.

The other reason for biomass' ubiquity is that it can be used to displace all forms of energy: electricity, heating, and transport fuels. Biomass has been used for heating and cooking since mankind first discovered fire, and technology has evolved ever since through various high-efficiency combustion technologies on to the gasification and pyrolysis technologies described by Roddy to offer very high-efficiency heating processes. Using a wood-fired boiler to raise steam for power generation is a very basic idea which has been refined and scaled up over time to the 800 MW$_e$ scale described by Malmgren (Chapter 5.04). The history of converting biomass into liquid transport fuels is charted in a fascinating fashion by Knothe (Chapter 5.02), going all the way back to Nikolaus August Otto's work on spark-ignition engines running on ethanol from fermented biomass and early compression-ignition engines running on vegetable oils, especially in parts of Africa where oil-bearing crops were abundant and used as a wartime fuel. It is interesting to note that in the early days of the petroleum industry, ethanol was heavily taxed in the United States while the new gasoline fuel was untaxed.

The very versatility of biomass is arguably also the 'Achilles heel' of the technology, because biomass (in some forms) also supplies mankind's food needs – both directly via food crops and indirectly via animal feed. One could argue that other forms of biomass provide shelter in the form of wooden construction materials, various types of roofing material, and so on. Inevitably, as populations expand and renewable resources whose annual availability is ultimately finite start to come under pressure, questions are asked about what the priorities ought to be for biomass utilization. That very debate is currently slowing the pace of biomass development activity.

The prime drivers for biomass development vary from country to country. In very, very broad terms, the drivers tend to be climate change in Europe, national energy security in the United States, and economic development in Asia Pacific. While this assertion is doubtless an oversimplification, it highlights a number of important features of biomass. In a climate change context, there is particular interest in growing biomass feedstocks with minimum reliance on chemical fertilizers (whose manufacture can be energy-intensive), with short distances between feedstock production and use (so that fossil fuels are not consumed in transporting materials), and processing them in a manner that minimizes fossil energy use. In this way, one can aspire to reach the ideal position in which every tonne of CO_2 emitted when a biomass crop is combusted is canceled out by the tonnes of CO_2 that are extracted from the atmosphere during photosynthesis in growing the next season's biomass crop. The subtleties of the argument are explored in detail by Mortimer (Chapter 5.09). In a national energy security context, countries whose energy 'needs' exceed their forecast ability to supply from indigenous coal, oil, and gas are interested in exploring the limits of their ability to cultivate biomass on a large scale. Developing countries whose agriculture has not yet been developed to the limit of its potential are interested in new biomass and biofuel markets (which they hope will be predictable, steadily growing, high-value markets) to provide the stimulus for economic development.

Of course, in practice, there is often an interplay between these various drivers. As Altieri (Chapter 5.03) explains, the story of bioethanol development in Brazil grew out of necessity at the time of the 1970s' oil price shock when crude oil imports became unaffordable; then it became a huge engine for development of the agricultural economy; and now it is being taken forward in a way that enables all products and by-products of the sugarcane crop to be used productively without impinging on the rain forest areas that are so critical to maintaining the world's CO_2 balance.

Before going any further, it is appropriate to say something about terminology. In a field that is as wide as the one outlined above, it is inevitable that people around the world will use terminology in slightly different ways. Insofar as it has been possible in a volume that draws upon expertise from all over the world, an attempt has been made to standardize terminology such that the term 'biomass' refers to solid material while the term 'biofuel' refers to liquid fuels (refined or unrefined) used primarily for transport.

The biomass/biofuels opportunity impinges on the activities of a great many existing interests. People often speculate as to whether those parties are supportive or unsupportive. Take farming for example. In some countries, the clear priority of small farmers is first to grow subsistence crops to meet their food needs, and then to grow a crop that they can sell – ideally for a reliable price. For them, the opportunity to supply into growing biofuels markets is potentially attractive provided they can afford to reinvest in improved agricultural techniques which will secure their food production capability. That is one of several different perspectives on the so-called 'food versus fuel' debate. Other aspects are explored by Waller (Chapter 5.08). Larger farmers in the developed world see an opportunity to sell some of their arable crops under long-term contracts while continuing to sell the remainder on the spot market. Preferences vary. However, there is a noticeable reluctance among landowners to commit to short rotation willow coppicing (for example) where in order to maximize profit (in theory) you need to commit your land to one end use for (say) 30 years. The general farmer reaction to biomass and biofuels as a whole is therefore guardedly supportive rather than enthusiastic.

The oil industry's reaction to biofuels has been the subject of speculation for a long time. In some ways, the early biofuels industry was too small to fit comfortably with oil industry's aspirations and practices. However, in countries like Brazil, the scale of the biofuels industry has reached a point where the oil industry embraces it. In other countries, it is interesting to note that when exploring questions about whether there is an impending 'peak oil' issue [4] or whether the future will look more like a plateau, future supply-side forecasts are now tending to factor in liquid biofuels and synthetic fuels derived from biomass as part of the industry's ability to meet forecast demand. More controversial for oil companies is any scheme whereby governments incentivize biofuel production over fossil fuels. UKPIA (United Kingdom Petroleum Industry Association) offers an interesting petroleum industry perspective on the future of the sector [5].

This volume sets out to provide an up-to-date assessment of the current state of development of an energy technology whose complexities are many and diverse, as the broad outline above has begun to suggest. In order to provide a structure for those thinking of delving into the detail, the remainder of this chapter provides a general road map of the main topics covered.

5.01.2 Basic Technology

Fermentation is the basic technology behind bioethanol production. It could be argued that even primitive tribes mastered that technology a long time ago, brewing up whatever sugar-rich crops were available locally, adding yeast, and allowing the sugar to then turn to alcohol.

The basic reaction for converting the simple sugar glucose into alcohol is

$$C_6H_{12}O_6 \rightarrow 2C_2H_5OH + 2CO_2$$

To make a strong alcohol, it is then necessary to distill the mixture to separate alcohol from water. Whether this is done in a small, rural (often illegal) still or in a large-scale whiskey/gin/vodka distillery, distillation reaches an azeotropic limit of 96% (by mass) – which is not pure enough for a transport fuel (where the water content must be less than 1%). A different process is therefore needed for removing the residual water (Harvey, Chapter 5.12).

With more 'difficult' feedstocks it may be necessary first to separate the biomass into different fractions – lignin, cellulose, and hemicelluloses – and then process some of those fractions (sometimes via acid hydrolysis) into fermentable sugars before the simple process described above can work. Refaat (Chapter 5.13) provides detail on how this can be done for a range of feedstocks including various waste streams. There is also a question as to whether everything should be converted into alcohol or whether some streams are better used for some other energy-related purpose. Altieri (Chapter 5.03) provides a very practical exposition of this subject based on experience on a large scale in Brazil.

For biodiesel production, the basic starting technology is transesterification, which involves reaction with an alcohol and an alkaline catalyst. A typical vegetable oil differs from conventional petroleum-based diesel by being more viscous, less flammable, and more difficult to atomize reliably [6]. At a molecular level, a vegetable oil contains three so-called 'fatty acids' linked together on a glycerol 'backbone'. In transesterification, the three fatty acid chains are stripped off and converted into a fatty acid methyl ester – which is the generic biodiesel. The reaction is

$$\text{triglyceride} + \text{methanol} \leftrightarrow \text{methyl ester} + \text{glycerol}$$

Harvey (Chapter 5.12) explains the process in more detail before going on to highlight the shortcomings of the process and then develop ideas for addressing them. Meanwhile, the basic process has been used around the world to manufacture biodiesel successfully as described in the next section. The choice of feedstock varies from country to country. In Europe, for example, the principal feedstock is oilseed rape. This has moved oilseed rape from being a largely neglected break crop within a crop rotation cycle to a new status as a significant crop in its own right. Much work has therefore been done to find ways of improving plant yields from 3 to 6 te yr^{-1} ha^{-1} and possibly more – notably in Austria and Germany. In other climates, different feedstocks predominate, for example, palm oil and sunflower oil. There is increasing interest in *Jatropha* – an oil-bearing bush that grows in semiarid conditions.

5.01.3 Widespread Deployment of Biomass and Biofuels

In broad terms, Europe leads the world in deployment of biodiesel technology; the deployment of bioethanol technology is dominated by Brazil and the United States; and a number of countries (particularly those with a large tree cover) are achieving significant levels of biomass use for other purposes such as heating, power generation, and combined heat and power (CHP). Table 1 shows steady growth in liquid biofuels year-on-year, with bioethanol dominating. World biofuel production increased by 7.4% in 2009 and by 12.9% in 2010. In 2010, it reached around 114 billion liters, representing about 2% of all road transport fuels consumed. Europe's share of biodiesel production was 49.8% in 2009, followed by the Americas with 32.8%. The top five biodiesel producing countries in the world are Germany, the United States, France, Argentina, and Brazil, producing 68.4% of the world's biodiesel. Australia is the largest producer of biodiesel in Asia Pacific, followed by China and India [7]. On the bioethanol side, the United States and Brazil accounted for 86% of world production in 2009.

5.01.3.1 Biodiesel

Biodiesel has been produced on an industrial scale in the European Union since 1992, largely in response to positive signals from the EU institutions. Today, there are more than 120 plants in the European Union. Whereas plant capacities of around 100 000 te yr^{-1} were once considered to be the state of the art, there are now some plants with capacities of 250 000 te yr^{-1} (e.g., in Sluiskil in the Netherlands and in North East England). Germany (where for many years the government provided a very generous incentive for biodiesel both as a straight fuel and as a blend) has dominated the European biodiesel picture for many years, but Spain, France, Italy, and the Netherlands are now catching up. Of the 9 million tonnes of biodiesel produced in the European Union in 2009, 28% came from Germany and 22% from France (source: European Biodiesel Board, http://www.ebb-eu.org). In terms of installed biodiesel production capacity, the 2010 figures are summarized in Table 2.

Table 1 World biofuel production (in billion liters)

Biofuel	2005	2006	2007	2008	2009	2010
Ethanol	40	49	64	77	82	93
Biodiesel	5	8	12	16	18	21
Total biofuels	45	57	75	94	101	114

Source: Database – OECD/FAO Agricultural Outlook 2011–2020.

Table 2 EU biodiesel production capacity broken down by country

Country	Capacity (kte yr^{-1})	Capacity (%)
Germany	4 933	22.5
Spain	4 100	18.7
France	2 505	11.4
Italy	2 375	10.9
Netherlands	1 328	6.1
Other EU countries	6 663	30.4
Total	21 904	100

Source: UFOP (2010) Biodiesel 2009/1010 – Report on the current situation and prospects. http://www.ufop.de (accessed 7 March 2011) [8].

In recent years, the European Union has moved away from incentives for biodiesel production toward targets and mandates for biodiesel inclusion in blended fuels. As a result, the European Union has now got an excess of production capacity. From the 22 million tonnes of annual production capacity given in **Table 2**, only about 10 million tonnes of biodiesel was actually produced in 2010 [8].

The EU target for biofuels inclusion was raised from 5% to 7% (by volume) in February 2009. Seven percent of EU diesel consumption equates to around 14 million tonnes per year of biodiesel. The adoption of the new target across the European Union is proceeding slowly. Prospects for raising the target beyond 7% are impacted by societal reactions to debates about biofuel sustainability (Waller, Chapter 5.08), although there remains an EU biofuels target for 2020 of 10% (by energy, which is significantly higher than 10% by volume). There is also an issue with subsidized biodiesel from overseas countries being imported into the European Union, depressing demand for EU-produced biodiesel.

5.01.3.2 Other Biofuels

Turning to bioethanol, the Brazilian success story is well known. Given the country's capacity for growing sugarcane, the response to the oil price shocks of the 1970s was to promote indigenous production of bioethanol from sugarcane. A mandate for blending bioethanol into gasoline was enacted in 1976, with the current target now standing at 25%. The ability of the Brazilians to find profitable uses for the various by-product streams led to a very attractive production cost for bioethanol. The combination of government policy and targets alongside low production costs has encouraged the manufacturers of so-called 'flex fuel vehicles' to focus on the Brazilian market, with more than 12 million such vehicles now on Brazilian roads. A flex fuel vehicle can run on bioethanol or conventional gasoline or any blend of the two. The Brazilian success story in the area of bioethanol is told in more detail by Altieri (Chapter 5.03). The United States has also seen significant levels of bioethanol promotion and bioethanol investment. There the drivers appear to be a combination of reducing dependence on imported oil for gasoline and support for the corn production agricultural sector.

There is a long-term desire to extend the deployment of so-called 'first-generation' biofuel technologies by developing processes that can use more difficult feedstocks such as agricultural straws, fast-growing woody biomass, waste wood, and various refuse-derived fuels. Some of these materials are already used for producing heating fuels on a small scale. Larger plants have been developed in recent years for the purposes of power generation and also for CHP. Initially, the biomass power plants tended to be on a fairly modest scale, for example, 150 000 dry tonnes per year to generate 30 MW. Projects are now being developed that are 20 times bigger than that as described by Malmgren (Chapter 5.04). The other route to large-scale use of biomass for power generation is by using it to displace a proportion (say 10%) of the feedstock supplying a large coal-fired power station (known as 'biomass cofiring'). The development of cofiring technology is covered by Lester (Chapter 5.05). It is presently unclear whether such demands for millions of tonnes per year of biomass will encourage developments in biomass supply to the advantage of 'next-generation' transport biofuels, or whether they will compete directly for limited supplies.

5.01.4 Issues, Constraints, and Limitations

Up until 2006, there was a widespread view that biofuels could provide solutions to many issues associated with climate change. Levels of investment activity were high, and many countries offered support mechanisms to encourage further investment and uptake of the products. The constraints and limitations at that time tended to be of a technical nature: how to scale up the technology; how to widen the feedstock slate; how to develop engines that could handle larger proportions of biofuel in the fuel blend; how to improve agricultural feedstock yields, and so on. Then serious questions were asked about the sustainability of biofuels, with some authors reaching broadly negative conclusions and others broadly positive conclusions [9, 10]. The debate has unfortunately tended to continue more in the popular press than in the scientific literature, and has had the effect of causing governments to review their levels of support. This, in turn, has had an adverse impact on investor confidence levels. Given that a typical biofuels project can take up to 10 years to design, build, start up, and then run for long enough to deliver a return on investment, and given that incentive and regulatory regimes can change very markedly over such a time period, this latter point about investor confidence becomes very important. Consequently, any list of biofuels issues and constraints today looks quite different from those of 2006.

One of the most serious challenges is to the carbon-saving claims of biofuels. Governments that are promoting biofuels as a counter to climate change react strongly to such challenges. There is a lot of interest now in calculating the CO_2 impact of biofuels, looking at CO_2 absorption during crop growth, the CO_2 impact of harvesting, transporting, and processing a crop, and the CO_2 footprint associated with fertilizer use and with supplying heat and electricity into the fuel production process. Processes for calculating the full life-cycle impact of biofuels from a greenhouse gas perspective are described in detail by Mortimer (Chapter 5.09), drawing a distinction between the type of approach that is appropriate in exploring possible new policies and the type of approach that is appropriate for regulation once policy has been decided.

Beyond greenhouse gas savings there are additional dimensions to the sustainability claim of biofuels. People now ask about alternative land uses, water usage rates, impact on biodiversity, and so on. There are also ethical questions relating to land rights, workers' rights, and so on. When public money is used to incentivize adoption of a new technology, it is not surprising to find people testing the ethics of that technology. The general approach being taken in Europe is to say that only those biofuels that can provide verifiable evidence of their provenance with respect to carbon and sustainability criteria in a very broad sense will be allowed to count toward a county's (or a company's) mandated quota. The development of practicable processes for enacting such requirements is a complex task, which is explored in detail by Waller (Chapter 5.08).

Broad principles concerning carbon and sustainability ultimately translate into hard, physical constraints in a particular country where land availability is finite, water availability is finite, and so on. To some extent, limitations in one country can be addressed by importing additional bioresources from countries that have an abundance. Hillring (Chapter 5.06) makes the point that while traditionally bioenergy markets have been local or regional, in recent years international as well as intercontinental trade in solid and liquid biofuels has developed. At present, the markets for both liquid and solid biofuels are still a long way from being globalized to the same extent as the markets for crude oil, but the implications are potentially far-reaching since they extend into forestry, agriculture, waste management, food, and animal feed markets. Hillring (Chapter 5.06) also examines the current status in respect of formal and informal barriers to trade.

Meanwhile, the more technical constraints that were being addressed before the upsurge in interest in sustainability issues continue to receive attention: improving the efficiency and cost effectiveness of the production processes, and broadening the prospective feedstock slate to facilitate market expansion.

5.01.5 Technology Solutions – New Processes

5.01.5.1 Anaerobic Digestion

Anaerobic digestion (AD) is arguably not a new process: it has been used for many years for animal manure management. Increasingly, however, it is now being used as a means of converting waste materials – usually wet materials with a high organic content – into a biogas that can be used directly as a heating fuel or upgraded to serve as a replacement for natural gas. At one end of the technology spectrum, it can be found in the form of a small on-farm unit in (say) China where it is used to convert animal wastes and vegetable wastes into a cooking fuel. At the other end of the spectrum, there are people in Germany (where there are more than 6000 sizable plants in operation) working on technology for upgrading the gas to be compatible with the standard of their national gas grids [11], and others working on the efficiency of the AD process itself.

AD is a microbial process in which complex organic materials are broken down into their simpler chemical components by various enzymes [12]. This occurs in the absence of oxygen and results in the production of biogas and a digestate. Biogas composition is approximately 60% methane and 40% carbon dioxide. Typical feedstocks for AD reactors often consist of animal slurries, energy crops, and other agricultural, retail, and industrial wastes. The process can be summarized in four main stages:

1. *Hydrolysis*. The complex organic materials (e.g., proteins, lipids, and carbohydrates) are broken down into low-molecular-weight compounds such as amino acids, fatty acids, and simple sugars.
2. *Acidogenesis*. Acid bacteria promote a process of fermentation, producing volatile fatty acids (VFAs), alcohols, hydrogen, and carbon dioxide.
3. *Acetogenesis*. Acetic acid, carbon dioxide, and hydrogen are formed from the VFAs by acid-forming bacteria or acetogens.
4. *Methanogenesis*. Methanogenic bacteria continue the consumption of the VFAs and produce methane gas [13].

The biogas produced can be used as a renewable fuel for various purposes, for instance in the production of heat and/or power by direct combustion. The digestate produced can be used as a fertilizer, subject to appropriate storage and application methods to prevent nitrate leaching [14]. Feedstocks with a high lipid content tend to produce higher methane yields, while feedstocks with a high carbohydrate content tend to produce more CO_2.

Three different forms of bacteria are active during the AD process: fermentative bacteria, acetogens, and methanogens. The efficiency of these different bacteria, and ultimately therefore the gas yield of the digester, is directly affected by temperature and pH. It is therefore important to find the right balance to provide a dynamic equilibrium among the three bacterial groups. AD systems usually operate in one of two main temperature ranges: mesophilic (20–40 °C) and thermophilic (>40 °C). Thermophilic temperatures have the benefit of providing sanitation by killing more pathogens. The optimum temperature for thermophilic digestion is around 60 °C, although a temperature between 52 and 56 °C may be used in practice to allow for variations in temperature without threatening some of the active microbes [15]. Because the microorganisms active during the different phases of AD have different requirements, the process is often carried out in two stages, with thermophilic conditions in the first stage and mesophilic conditions in the second stage [16].

Thermophilic processes require a shorter retention time of up to 20 days compared to mesophilic digestion, which may take over a month. An increase in process temperature generally increases the metabolic rate of the bacteria. However, this also results in a higher concentration of free ammonia, which itself inhibits the AD process. Some studies have found that wastes with high ammonia content (e.g., cow manure) were inhibited at higher temperatures [17]. Fluctuations in temperature can cause instability in the digestion process, affecting the gas yield. This can result from large variations in outdoor temperature, especially in highland and northern climates [15, 18].

The United Kingdom is an example of a country where AD technology is currently underexploited but may be about to attract significant interest under new incentive regimes. The United Kingdom has substantial biomass resources, which could be processed via AD: about 150 million wet tonnes of livestock slurry (pig and cattle), 3.4 million wet tonnes of used poultry litter and excreta, together with 1 million tonnes of food production residues (vegetable and dairy processing residues). In addition to this, there is about 90 million tonnes of waste produced in the United Kingdom each year with a high biodegradable fraction of 62%. This biodegradable waste will produce about 150 m^3 tonne^{-1} of biogas at 60% methane concentration. Using a process efficiency of 70%, a 70% load factor, and the known 37 GJ tonne^{-1} energy content for methane, after accounting for the 20–40% of energy needed to maintain the temperature of the processor, AD could provide the United Kingdom with about 1.4 GW of electricity, representing about 2% of the UK's installed capacity.

UK agriculture contributes 7% of all UK greenhouse gas emissions, including 67% of nitrous oxide and 37% of methane. Main sources of greenhouse gas emissions are from animals (32%), manure management (20%), and soil breakdown (48%). During storage of animal manure, significant greenhouse gas emissions occur, particularly of N$_2$O and CH$_4$, as a result of uncontrolled AD processes. AD exploits this process so that methane can be used as a fuel resulting in reduced emissions of approximately 90%. A well-managed AD scheme aims to maximize methane generation, but not to release any gas to the atmosphere, thereby reducing overall emissions. In addition, it provides an energy source with no net release of carbon. AD has considerable potential to contribute to the production of renewable energy on farms in addition to reducing the overall contribution of agriculture to global warming.

In order to upgrade biogas to make it compatible with natural gas (which is mainly methane with small amounts of higher hydrocarbons), there is a requirement to remove CO$_2$, hydrogen sulfide, and siloxanes. Hydrogen sulfide levels can be reduced using biological scrubbing (with alkaline water) or chemical desulfurization (using iron oxides and other iron salts). This would usually be followed by fine desulfurization in an adsorptive process using activated carbon or possibly zinc oxide [11]. Siloxanes are usually removed using activated carbon [19]. There are a number of options for CO$_2$ removal, ranging from mature technologies using chemical solvents (e.g., amine solutions) or physical solvents (e.g., Selexol) to the latest developments in membrane separation technology [20]. For further information on the upgrading of biogas to make it compatible with natural gas, the reader is referred to Reference 11.

5.01.5.2 Advanced Biofuel Processes

Much of the interest in advanced bioethanol production processes centers on ways of enabling a wider range of feedstocks to be used, particularly nonfood feedstocks. A biomass feedstock will consist mainly of cellulose, hemicellulose, and lignin. Of the three, cellulose is the easiest to convert via fermentation into alcohol. The first step in a biochemical route to ethanol production is to separate the cellulose, hemicellulose, and lignin [21]. Once these constituents are separated, the cellulose and hemicellulose can be hydrolyzed to sugars, which are subsequently fermented into alcohols and distilled. Biochemical processes typically employ a pretreatment process to accelerate the hydrolysis process. Common pretreatment processes include dilute acid treatment, steam explosion, and ammonia fiber explosion. Following pretreatment, the cellulose and hemicellulose are hydrolyzed into fermentable sugars using acid hydrolysis or enzyme hydrolysis. The fermentation and purification processes then follow as in a conventional bioethanol plant. There are several companies working on versions of this technology, including Abengoa, BlueFire Ethanol, Iogen, Mascoma, and POET. This topic is explored in detail by Refaat (Chapter 5.13), looking in detail at a range of pretreatment options and at the overall energy balance.

An alternative to the biochemical treatment routes described above is a set of thermochemical routes. Here the first step is to gasify the biomass to produce synthesis gas: a mixture of hydrogen and carbon monoxide. A range of technologies for achieving the gasification step and the sometimes associated pyrolysis step are presented by Roddy (Chapter 5.10). Starting with synthesis gas (or syngas), there are several different routes to synthesizing fuels. One option is the catalytic conversion of syngas into alcohols. This represents a major alternative route to the biochemical production of bioethanol as described above. Alternatively, it can be used to produce a simpler alcohol, methanol, which is favored by some automotive companies (Pearson, Chapter 5.16). Another option is to use a methanation process to convert the syngas into methane. Such a process can be seen as an alternative to the AD route described in the previous section. However, perhaps the best known option for converting syngas into fuels is the Fischer–Tropsch process for synthesizing long-chain alkanes, typically used to produce an equivalent fuel to diesel. The term 'advanced biodiesel processes' usually refers to this route – also often labeled as BtL or biomass-to-liquids. Evans (Chapter 5.11) provides a detailed treatment of this subject.

It is difficult to predict at this stage which advanced biofuels routes will be commercially successful long-term in converting particular types of biomass into particular biofuels. Much will depend on how the pilot-scale projects and demonstration projects described in this volume perform in practice. However, a design approach that cuts across all of these processes is process intensification. This approach can be applied to individual unit operations in a process or it can be applied to the whole process. Harvey (Chapter 5.12) explores the process intensification approach for some bioethanol and biodiesel processes.

5.01.6 Technology Solutions – New Feedstocks

5.01.6.1 Algae

The quest for alternative feedstocks has led many people to algae. For those who consider that land availability may at some point in the future become the limiting factor, looking at feedstocks that grow in water holds some attractions – especially since the Earth's water surface is significantly greater than its land surface. There are two broad areas of interest: macroalgae (usually known as seaweed) and microalgae (often found in the form of pond scum).

Since they are autotrophs, algae do not generally need complex nutritional elements such as proteins, lipids, or carbohydrates. They feed on inorganic salts, water, and carbon dioxide, using the sun's energy to synthesize biomolecules from these simple substrates. In fact, their rapid growth rate can sometimes be a problem as has been found on occasions when water has become contaminated with excess phosphorus and nitrogen input from sewerage or farmland runoff.

Algae synthesize a variety of complex carbon compounds, which are used as food storage materials. These compounds include fatty acid esters of glycerol and other lipids and a number of glucose oligomers. Many algal strains have more than 50% lipid in their body mass. Where this is predominantly triacylglycerides, they provide a good feedstock for transesterification into biodiesel (e.g., *Chlorella*, *Dunaliella salina*, and *Spirulina*). One form of algae (*Botryococcus braunii*) produces a hydrocarbon oil that is similar to crude oil, so in principle it could serve as a replacement feedstock for the whole petrochemicals chain except that it grows very, very slowly.

With microalgae there are two broad strands of activity. The first is based on open-pond technology, where water is circulated in pond races and the algae skimmed off the surface. For rapid algal growth, the water needs to be reasonably warm – so this version is favored in tropical climates and also in locations where there is waste industrial heat available. The other is based on photobioreactor technology, with the algae growing in glass tubes which trap the sun's heat. Some have likened these two strands of activity to growing crops outdoors in a large field compared with growing crops indoors in a small greenhouse, with both approaches having their place.

Another possibility is to grow algae as a source of carbohydrate, harvest their carbohydrate reserves, and hydrolyze them to glucose, which when fermented would produce ethanol for use as fuel. Algal biomass waste from fermentation could then be processed thermochemically as outlined above.

Yet another line of research involves those who cultivate whatever algae that grow naturally in a location, and concentrate on finding uses for those algae. This contrasts with an alternative line of research that is based on identifying the specific algae that will exhibit the desired properties for a particular application, and then concentrating on finding ways of making such algae grow.

One of the attractions of algae is that it can grow very fast. It is not unusual for a whole crop to grow in a matter of weeks (compared with a summer for land-based materials). Some extrapolations from experimental work suggest that production rates of $60\,000\,l\,ha^{-1}\,yr^{-1}$ should be possible – significantly higher than that from land-based oil-bearing crops. One of the drawbacks is that algal research is at a relatively early stage of development, and total annual production of algal biomass stands at only 9000 tonnes. While today's agricultural crops and practices have developed over a period of 3000 years, algal development originated about 50 years ago. Much remains to be done in areas such as microalgal chemical ecology, culture, and growth physiology; finding or developing improved strains of algae; maintaining culture stability; effective harvesting of algae; acceptable provision of nutrients for macroalgae in the open sea; developing systems that combine water purification with algal production; developing ways of enabling light to penetrate beyond the surface layer where algae grow; supplying CO_2 from industrial processes including bioethanol production; establishing high levels of thermodynamic efficiency; examining the overall water usage from a life-cycle perspective; regulating algal biochemical pathways; and aiming for practical productivity rates of more than $100\,tonnes\,ha^{-1}\,yr^{-1}$.

For further information on the subject of algal biofuels, the reader is referred to a seminal report on the subject by Benemann *et al.* [22] and a more recent report by Darzins *et al.* [23].

5.01.6.2 Other Options for Increasing Feedstock Availability

A more conventional place to look for additional feedstocks is on land that can support the growth of woody biomass, especially land that is too uneven to support modern arable crop farming with its combine harvester technology. Quite often the upland areas that are otherwise used for sheep farming could be suitable for growing woody biomass. One approach is to plant woody crops that can be coppiced – effectively providing a harvest every few years. Another approach is to let the trees grow to an optimum age as single-stem trees, and then harvest them sustainably. Perlack (Chapter 5.14) provides an in-depth treatment of this subject, providing a rich source of data on achievable yields under various planting strategies and looking in particular at willow, poplar, eucalyptus, and pine. He also comments on the extent of feasible planting in the United States, and calculates the contribution that woody biomass could make to reaching renewable fuel targets under various incentive regimes.

Another obvious option to consider is the use of various types of waste stream as feedstock. While there are many possible feedstocks, this volume pays particular attention to bioethanol production from lignocellulosic waste and biodiesel production from waste vegetable oil, looking at the level of pretreatment required in each case (Refaat, Chapter 5.13). The topic of biogas production from agricultural waste streams has been addressed above.

The other obvious approach is to improve crop yields. Spink (Chapter 5.15) provides data to show how the annual yields of oilseed rape across the United Kingdom can be increased from 3 to $6.5\,tonnes\,ha^{-1}$, with the potential possibly to reach $9.2\,tonnes\,ha^{-1}$. Generalizing his approach, he draws some interesting conclusions about the potential for improving other crop yields in a similar manner via changes to agronomy and husbandry and improving genetics via plant breeding. The prospects look particularly promising where the limiting factor is light availability as opposed to water availability.

5.01.7 Expanding the Envelope

In order to improve the overall commercial viability of biomass and biofuel developments, it is informative to examine them in their broader context, see whether they are overspecified for their intended purpose, whether they can be used for additional purposes in such a way as to accrue benefits of scale during production, and whether the production processes involved can yield additional high-value products in a way that benefits the overall economics.

It is interesting to see what players from the auto industry ask for in a fuel, and to consider how planned long-term developments in transport fuels align with planned long-term developments in vehicle technology. Pearson (Chapter 5.16) provides an interesting perspective in suggesting that targets for vehicle manufacturers should be specified in terms of fuel energy requirements per kilometer traveled, while targets for fuel suppliers should be specified in terms of grams of fossil-derived CO_2 per unit of fuel energy delivered. This is quite different from the current practice of setting CO_2 emission targets for vehicle manufacturers irrespective of the source of the CO_2. His analysis points to methanol as a particularly attractive fuel, especially if used within a multi-flex-fuel vehicle.

Conventional thinking tends to assign liquid biofuels to transport applications, solid biomass to power generation, and biogas to heating applications. It is therefore interesting to note how liquid biofuels (in pure form, in blends, and in emulsions) and even some of their unprocessed feedstocks can be used effectively for CHP applications and for transport (Roskilly, Chapter 5.17). Taken together with options for dual-fueling bioliquids and biogases, this opens up some new avenues for optimizing the process of matching feedstocks to end uses.

It is sometimes said that biomass is too good to burn. The same may soon be said of natural gas (which is an important petrochemicals feedstock) if the world's population wants a steady supply of fossil fuel-derived plastics and polymers. Considering the range of very high-value components that are present in various types of biomass, there is a case to be made for extracting some of them before going through a thermochemical or biochemical biofuels production process that would destroy them. Moreover, just as a crude oil refining process linked to a downstream petrochemicals industry leads to a wide variety of carbon-containing products and materials, so too can a biorefining process lead to a wide range of carbon-containing products. The difference is that in the latter case the carbon is not of fossil origin (derived as it is from a short carbon cycle) and so the fossil carbon content of the final products is very low. Given that the main drivers behind biomass and biofuel developments are usually linked to climate change and dwindling oil and gas supplies, the broader biorefining agenda is highly pertinent. This thinking is developed further in a chapter by Askew which looks at small-volume, high-added-value products and in a chapter by Clark (Chapter 5.20) which looks at high-volume opportunities.

As a specific example of extracting maximum value from biomass and locking in every benefit, a chapter on biochar has been included (Chapter 5.20). Biochar is formed in pyrolysis processes and gasification processes. Whether it is labeled as a product, a coproduct, or a by-product, it has some fascinating properties. Initial interest stemmed from its benefits as a soil improver, leading to higher yields, displacing fertilizer use, and improving moisture retention in arid areas. More recently, it has been found to trap or sequester carbon in soils over a timescale of centuries to millennia. If biochar produced in a thermochemical process is used in this way, it opens up the prospect of a carbon-negative energy supply chain. Brown (Chapter 5.18) provides a review of the current state of the art in biochar research.

The volume would not be complete without a chapter that explores the societal impact of biomass and biofuels and the challenge of developing policies to incentivize the intended responses and behaviors. The fact that the point of carbon absorption and the point of carbon release lie in different locations – sometimes different countries and even different continents – introduces a level of complication. This is compounded by the manner in which biomass pervades so many aspects of life. Thornley (Chapter 5.21) reviews the issues involved and suggests some new frameworks that may work better.

5.01.8 Recent Developments

In the time since work began on this volume, one of the biggest changes in the bioenergy environment is that interest in the alternative of electric vehicles (EVs) has accelerated rapidly. The EU target of 10% biofuels (on an energy basis) by 2020 has been translated into a requirement for 10% renewable energy content in transport fuels – specifically to include EVs powered by renewable electricity. A number of vehicle manufacturers are bringing EVs to market. Unlike the 'kit cars' of old, these are designed as production cars for the mass market. In order to address the phenomenon of so-called 'range anxiety', the vehicles are fitted with sophisticated communication equipment for locating the nearest charging point, and those same technology platforms are offering attractive new features such as remote communication facilities and sophisticated navigation systems. Priced at the luxury car end of the spectrum, they will not displace sales of internal combustion engine vehicles overnight, but they have to be seen as serious competition by proponents of biofueled vehicles.

As for how long it will be until sales of EVs outstrip sales of internal combustion engine vehicles, the year 2050 is often cited – with some saying earlier and others later. The prevalent view is that EVs will penetrate the market for city center 'runabout' vehicles quite early, with slower progress in the long-distance driving market, and there are serious doubts about whether road freight or air transport will ever switch to electric propulsion.

There is a related strand of emerging thought which is perhaps best summed up as a move to an all-electric society. With an expanding array of low-carbon electricity solutions under active development (including nuclear power and coal-fired generation with carbon capture and storage alongside a maturing set of renewable electricity technologies), and seemingly fewer options for low-carbon heating and low-carbon transport, governments are starting to speculate about the desired future balance between electricity, heat, and transport fuels in the overall energy mix.

Interestingly, biomass can supply all three. However, the technologies required to do this cost-effectively are still under development. There is a short-term challenge for those working in the biomass sector to influence the funders of research and development activity to continue funding broad-based biomass R&D.

5.01.9 The Way Forward for Biomass and Biofuels

Specific plans for the various biomass technologies are mapped out in the relevant chapters of this volume. Different countries are progressing at different rates. This is due in part to different starting points in respect of natural resource availability, with countries tending to play to their strengths. However, it is also due in part to some countries waiting for others to go first in the hope of benefiting from their experience. As in other parts of the energy sector, there is an increasing reliance on the development of road maps as a process for building consensus, differentiating between short-term, medium-term, and long-term requirements.

The field of biomass and biofuels has moved in recent years from one of almost unstinting praise through a period of intense (often ill-informed) criticism, emerging now into an environment where developments are viewed with healthy skepticism. The chapters of this volume provide some of the science behind the increasingly important sustainability challenge alongside the signposts for future technology development.

References

[1] Knoef HAM (2005) *Handbook of Biomass Gasification*. Enschede, The Netherlands: BTG.
[2] International Energy Agency (IEA), Paris (2008) World energy outlook, 2008. http://www.worldenergyoutlook.org/docs/weo2008/WEO2008_es_english.pdf (accessed 25 March 2011).
[3] WRAP (2008) Realising the value of organic waste. http://www.wrap.org.uk/downloads/Organics_MSR_Final_v2.ef333495.5238.pdf (accessed 25 March 2011).
[4] ITPOES (2010) The oil crunch – A wake-up call for the UK economy. International Task Force on Peak Oil & Energy Security. http://peakoiltaskforce.net (accessed 25 March 2011).
[5] Florio N and Vanderwell N (2009) Biofuels in the UK. UK Petrochemical Industries Association (UKPIA), London. http://www.ukpia.com/files/pdf/ukpia-briefing-biofuels-april-2009.pdf (accessed 25 March 2011).
[6] Mittelbach M and Remschmidt C (2004) *Biodiesel, the Comprehensive Handbook*. Graz, Austria: Martin Mittelbach.
[7] GlobalData (2010) Global biodiesel market analysis & forecasts to 2020. Report code GDAE0112ICR. http://www.globalmarketsdirect.com.
[8] UFOP (2010) Biodiesel 2009/2010 – Report on the current situation and prospects. http://www.ufop.de (accessed 7 March 2011).
[9] Roddy DJ (2009) Biofuels – Environmental friend or foe? *Proceedings of the Institution of Civil Engineers: Energy* 162(3): 121–130.
[10] Searchinger T, Heimlich R, Houghton RA, *et al.* (2008) Use of US croplands for biofuels increases greenhouse gases through emissions from land-use change. *Science* 319(5867): 1238–1240.
[11] Graf F and Klaas U (2009) State of biogas injection to the gas grid in Germany. *24th World Gas Conference*, Buenos Aires, Argentina. http://www.igu.org/html/wgc2009/papers/docs/wgcFinal00259.pdf (accessed 10 March 2011).
[12] Boyle G (2004) *Renewable Energy*. Oxford, UK: Oxford University Press in association with the Open University.
[13] Macias-Corral M, Samani Z, Hanson A, *et al.* (2008) Anaerobic digestion of municipal solid waste and agricultural waste and the effect of co-digestion with dairy cow manure. *Bioresource Technology* 99: 8288–8293.
[14] Holm-Nielsen JB, Al Seadi T, and Oleskowicz-Popiel P (2009) The future of anaerobic digestion and biogas utilization. *Bioresource Technology* 100: 5478–5484.
[15] Cavinato C, Fatone F, Bolzonella D, and Pavan P (2010) Thermophilic anaerobic co-digestion of cattle manure with agro-wastes and energy crops: Comparison of pilot and full scale experiences. *Bioresource Technology* 101: 545–550.
[16] Deublein D and Steinhauser A (2008) *Biogas from Waste and Renewable Resources: An Introduction*. Weinheim, Germany: Wiley-VCH.
[17] Chen Y, Cheng JJ, and Creamer KS (2008) Inhibition of anaerobic digestion process: A review. *Bioresource Technology* 99(10): 4044–4064.
[18] Alvarez R and Liden G (2008) The effect of temperature variation on biomethanation at high altitude. *Bioresource Technology* 99: 7278–7284.
[19] Accettola F, Guebitz GM, and Schoeftner R (2008) Siloxane removal from biogas by biofiltration: Biodegradation studies. *Clean Technologies and Environmental Policy* 10: 211–218.
[20] Zhu Y and Frey HC (2010) Integrated gasification combined cycle (IGCC) power plant design and technology. In: Roddy D (ed.) *Advanced Power Plant Materials, Design and Technology*. Cambridge: Woodhead Publishing.
[21] Black & Veatch (2008) Lignocellulosic ethanol plant in the UK – Feasibility study. NNFCC 08-007. http://nnfcc.co.uk (accessed 8 September 2011).
[22] Benemann JR, Goebel RP, Weissman JC, and Augenstein DC (1982) Microalgae as a source of liquid fuels. Final Technical Report to U.S.DOE BER. http://www.osti.gov/bridge/ (accessed 7 March 2011).
[23] Darzins A, Pienkos P, and Edye L (2010) Current status and potential for algal biofuels production. Report T39-T2, IEA Bioenergy Task 39. http://www.task39.org (accessed 7 March 2011).

5.02 Historical Perspectives on Biofuels

G Knothe, USDA Agricultural Research Service, Peoria, IL, USA

Published by Elsevier Ltd.

5.02.1	Introduction	11
5.02.2	Early Engine Developments	11
5.02.3	Ethanol	11
5.02.4	Vegetable Oil-Based Fuels	12
Conclusion		13
References		14

5.02.1 Introduction

The Industrial Revolution of the nineteenth century was to a significant degree enabled by the development of mechanized energy, that is, the development of engines that could perform work previously performed by human or animal labor, or, in some cases, replace a natural resource, for example, wind, to power ships. A major use of these engines was in transportation, for the more efficient, that is, time- and labor-saving, overcoming of great distances. While originally the steam engine was practically the only choice for the various applications, within a few decades other engines were developed. The most salient was the internal-combustion engine, of which two major versions came to exist.

This chapter summarizes research results and commercial development of fuels derived from agricultural sources used to power these engines in 'historical' times up to around World War II. It relies heavily on previously published accounts on the history of ethanol [1] and vegetable oil-based diesel fuels and biodiesel [2, 3]. Many additional references and details are available by referring to these chapters. A list of relevant technical chapters has also been compiled [4]. Another account of ethanol and vegetable oil fuels is also available [5].

5.02.2 Early Engine Developments

While experiments with what could be considered forerunners of the internal-combustion engine were already conducted in the sixteenth and seventeenth centuries, the first version of an internal-combustion engine was apparently developed by the American inventor Samuel Morey (1762–1843) and was discussed in several articles in the *American Journal of Science* [1]. A few decades later, in the early 1860s, the four-stroke version of the internal-combustion engine was developed by the German inventor Nikolaus August Otto (1832–91) in collaboration with the mechanic Michael Joseph Zons [6, 7], giving rise to what is now termed the spark-ignition (or gasoline) engine (also called the Otto engine). The Otto engine was apparently the first practical four-stroke engine, while, for example, the internal-combustion engine developed in 1859 by the Belgian inventor Étienne Lenoir (1822–1900) was a two-stroke engine. Another few decades later, another version of the internal-combustion engine, the compression-ignition engine, usually called the diesel engine after its inventor Rudolf Diesel (1858–1913), was developed.

Both the internal-combustion engines commonly utilize products derived from petroleum: the spark-ignition engine using gasoline (petrol) and the diesel engine using diesel fuel. These are hydrocarbon fuels with the main differences to be found in the structure of the compounds comprising them. Gasoline (petrol) preferably contains lighter branched compounds, exemplified by isooctane, the compound which gives the octane scale its name and is actually 2,2,4-trimethylpentane. Diesel fuel, on the other hand, preferably consists of long, straight-chain hydrocarbons, exemplified by hexadecane, the trivial name of which is cetane, providing the name to the cetane scale used for rating the ignition quality of diesel fuel. However, as discussed here, other fuels derived from a variety of biomass feedstocks are also suitable.

5.02.3 Ethanol

Thus, within a few years of their development, different kinds of fuels were being tested for both kinds of internal-combustion engines. One of the fuels of prime interest from the early days of the spark-ignition engine was ethanol, derived from fermentation of various biomass materials. This observation has an additional interesting aspect as Eugen Langen (1833–95), a German inventor and entrepreneur who partnered with Otto to find the first company commercializing the internal-combustion engine, also was involved with a sugar refinery owned by his family [8, 9]. Otto apparently used alcohol as a fuel when first developing the engine [1]. In the case of the diesel engine, Diesel himself discusses the variety of fuels tested in 'his' engine [10–12]. The finite nature of petroleum-based fuels was already noted at that time and agriculturally derived fuels were recognized as renewable alternatives. This observation served as an incentive to promote renewable fuels from agricultural feedstocks. Accordingly, significant research efforts were devoted to alcohol fuels for spark-ignition engines and vegetable oil-based fuels for diesel engines in the years through World

War II. In the years after World War II, with petroleum available abundantly and cheaply, research on alternative fuels was largely dormant until the fuel crises of the 1970s and early 1980s rekindled interest in renewable fuels.

As mentioned above, Otto reportedly used ethanol as fuel to power 'his' engine. This was probably straightforward as it appears that ethanol could not be considered an 'alternative' fuel [1] at that time. Petroleum, which would become a major source of energy powering world economies in the decades to come, especially after the discovery in Pennsylvania in 1859 (although petroleum was known prior to this event) by Edwin Drake (1819–80), was emerging as an energy source, while ethanol as fuel, for example, for lighting purposes, was already well known, especially a mixture called 'camphene' consisting of ethanol with turpentine and a small amount of camphor oil [1]. Such mixtures with ethanol had gradually replaced whale oil as lamp fluid. In the United States, a heavy tax of $2.08 per gallon gradually imposed on ethanol during the American Civil War (1861–65) was apparently a major contributing factor to the rise of the petroleum industry, as the latter benefited from not being subject to this tax [1]. This tax was abolished in 1906.

In European countries, concerns about the security of the petroleum supply existed from the very beginning, which is why countries such as France, Germany, and Great Britain promoted the utilization of ethanol. Engines were designed to run on both gasoline and ethanol and some engines were even designed to run on pure ethanol. In Germany, tariffs were imposed on petroleum imports and a 'Centrale für Spiritus-Verwerthung' was in charge of regulating the ethanol market. It has been stated that the adaptation of vehicles in Germany to run on ethanol may even have prolonged World War I [1].

Most research regarding ethanol showed that it was a satisfactory fuel, often even stated to be superior to gasoline [1], and most certainly played a role in promoting its use. Engine knock did not occur with ethanol or ethanol–gasoline blends as fuel. Fuel economy could be improved by adjusting the compression ratio of the engine, largely overcoming the lower energy content of ethanol versus gasoline. Overall, efficiency was stated to be equal or superior to gasoline. It was also stated that the use of ethanol was cleaner than that of gasoline, with specific notice that the exhaust was clearer when operating an engine on ethanol instead of gasoline. Some problems such as separation of ethanol and gasoline or cold start could be overcome by the use of 'binders' or starting assist agents such as ether. Stability of alcohol–gasoline blends in the presence of water was noted but not seen as a major problem if tank cleanliness, and so on, was ensured. The competition with petroleum, however, led interests related to this energy source to continuously state that ethanol was an inferior fuel [1].

In the United States, however, the lifting of the aforementioned heavy tax on ethanol did not cause the expected revival of the fuel ethanol market. Ethanol derived from feedstocks such as potatoes or grain was more expensive than gasoline as more petroleum fields were coming online in locations such as Texas. On the other hand, alcohol from molasses was less expensive, with collusion between petroleum companies and the Caribbean alcohol market suspected by some contemporaries [1].

The competition between alcohol and petroleum manifested itself in the following years in other respects. While it was well known at the time that blending ethanol with gasoline alleviated engine knock, eventually the additive tetraethyl lead was used for this purpose in gasoline, largely due to a switching of positions around 1923 or 1924 of two researchers in industry, Thomas Midgley (1889–1944) and Charles Kettering (1876–1958) [1]. The background for this was originally to provide a 'bridge' across the perceived gap between petroleum-based fuels becoming exhausted and renewable fuels becoming available in sufficient quantities. Studies on the health effects of leaded gasoline were not discussed or were suppressed. However, eventually due to health concerns, leaded gasoline was banned in the United States in 1986.

With the exception of the United States, in the 1920s and 1930s ethanol was blended with gasoline in every industrialized nation [1]. In European countries, ethanol was obtained from potatoes, grapes, and other crops, while elsewhere sugarcane and molasses served among the primary feedstocks. The use of ethanol was promoted through mandatory blending or tax incentives in many countries. In some locations, ethanol was less expensive than imported gasoline. The aspect of energy security played a major role in these actions promoting the use of ethanol as did the issue of providing income to the agricultural sector by utilizing surplus crops. However, in the years shortly before and during World War II, ethanol production decreased due to production changing to ammunition and vanishing crop surpluses.

Despite this development, some isolated efforts to commercialize ethanol–gasoline blends occurred in the United States in the 1930s, mainly in the Midwest [1]. Legislative proposals to promote the cause of ethanol were unsuccessful. This eventually merged in the farm chemurgy movement of the 1930s, the goal of which was to lead to industrial products from agricultural feedstocks and was supported by Henry Ford (1863–1947). This reemergence of ethanol–gasoline blends was met by opposition from the petroleum industry.

5.02.4 Vegetable Oil-Based Fuels

The competition mentioned above between a petroleum-derived fuel and a fuel derived from biomass appears to be less noticeable in the literature regarding diesel engines and diesel fuel. It may be surmised that a major reason for this is the supply issue as considerably less vegetable oil was available for petrodiesel replacement and often vegetable oils were considered for more remote locations. It may also be interesting to note that while Otto was inspired to work on what was to become the four-stroke internal-combustion engine by hearing about the work of Lenoir, Diesel was inspired to develop his engine as an efficient alternative to the steam engine originally through lectures in thermodynamics at what is now the Technical University of Munich.

In his book *Die Entstehung des Dieselmotors* [11], Diesel describes experiments with various liquid fuels, most of them petroleum-type or petroleum-derived fuels. Interestingly, he also describes experiments conducted with alcohol. Due to water content and lower energy content, several adjustments were needed to have the engine run on 90% alcohol for an extended period of time with energy output identical to that of petroleum. On the other hand, vegetable oils, the alkyl esters of which are now alternative fuels as biodiesel, were not originally investigated by Diesel. Rather, on page 115 of his book [11], Diesel addresses the use of vegetable oils as a fuel (translated):

> For sake of completeness it needs to be mentioned that already in the year 1900 plant oils were used successfully in a diesel engine. During the Paris Exposition in 1900, a small diesel engine was operated on a rachide (peanut) oil by the French Otto company. It worked so well that only a few insiders knew about this inconspicuous circumstance. The engine was built for petroleum and was used for the plant oil without any change. In this case also, the consumption experiments resulted in heat utilization identical to petroleum.

Similar to the background for promoting the use of ethanol, the background in the papers by Diesel [10, 12] on using vegetable oils was to provide European tropical colonies, especially those in Africa, with a certain degree of energy self-sufficiency. This pattern of energy independence can be found in the related literature throughout the 1940s. Palm oil was often considered as a feedstock in historic times, although feedstock diversity was reflected in other historic investigations. Vegetable oils were also used as emergency fuels and for other purposes during World War II in countries such as Argentina, Brazil, China, and India. In the United States, some post-World War II research programs dealt with vegetable oil fuels, also inspired by concerns over the rising use of petroleum fuels and the possible resulting shortages.

Many different feedstocks were used in historic times as vegetable oil fuels. Besides palm oil, these included soybean, cottonseed, castor, babassu, groundnut, and raisinseed oil, and many others as well as non-vegetable sources such as industrial tallow and even fish oils. In modern times, biodiesel is derived or has been reported to be producible from many different sources including vegetable oils, animal fats, used frying oils, and even soapstock. Generally, factors such as geography, climate, and economics determine which vegetable oil is of most interest for potential use in biodiesel fuels. Thus, presently in the United States, soybean oil is considered as a prime feedstock; in Europe, it is rapeseed (canola) oil; and in tropical countries, it is palm oil. In parallel to the present, many historic publications discuss the satisfactory performance of vegetable oils as fuels or fuel sources although it is often noted that their higher costs relative to petroleum-derived fuel would prevent widespread use.

The high viscosity of vegetable oils in comparison with petrodiesel was noted and the formation of engine deposits ascribed to this property. Reducing the high viscosity of vegetable oils was usually achieved by heating the vegetable oil fuel. Often the engine was started on petrodiesel and after a few minutes of operation switched to the vegetable oil fuel. The performance of the vegetable oil fuels was generally satisfactory, but power output was reportedly slightly lower than with petroleum-based diesel fuel and fuel consumption was slightly higher, although engine load-dependent or opposite effects were reported. It is mentioned in many publications that the diesel engines used operated more smoothly on vegetable oils than on petroleum-based diesel fuel. Fuel quality issues were also addressed; for example, it was suggested to keep the acid content at a minimum and the effects of different kinds of vegetable oils on metal corrosion and lube oil dilution were studied. Similar to the observations when running engines on ethanol, it was observed that the exhaust appeared cleaner when running an engine on vegetable oil instead of petrodiesel.

Pyrolysis, cracking, or other methods of decomposition of vegetable oils to yield fuels of varying nature account for a significant amount of the literature in historic times with artificial 'gasoline', 'kerosene', and 'diesel' being obtained from various oils such as tung oil, fish oils, and linseed, castor, palm, cottonseed, and olive oils. The other approaches to reducing the high viscosity of vegetable oils [13] – dilution with petrodiesel and, especially, microemulsification – appear to have received little attention during the historic times. In one case, ethanol was used for improving the atomization and combustion of highly viscous castor oil.

Besides powering vehicles, the use of vegetable oils for other related purposes found some attention. These uses included lubricating oils and greases as well as heating and power purposes.

In 1938, it was recommended [14] that to obtain the best value from vegetable oil fuels it would be necessary to cleave the triglycerides and use residual fatty acid, but problems with free fatty acids as fuel were anticipated. On the other hand, the glycerides were seen as not possessing fuel value, but rather causing excess deposits. A step beyond Walton's statement is the first reports on what is now termed biodiesel. A Belgian patent, No. 422,877, was granted on 31 August 1937 to C. G. Chavanne [15] and probably constitutes the first report on what is today known as biodiesel. It describes the use of ethyl esters of palm oil (although other oils and methyl esters are mentioned) as diesel fuel. These esters were produced by acid-catalyzed transesterification of the oil (base catalysis is now more common). The work conducted in Belgium and the Belgian Congo has been described in more detail [16, 17]. It was mentioned that a bus fueled with palm oil ethyl ester served the commercial passenger line between Brussels and Louvain (Leuven) in the summer of 1938. It was noted that the viscosity difference between the esters and conventional diesel fuel was considerably less than that between the parent oil and conventional diesel fuel. It was also pointed out that the esters are miscible with other fuels and probably the first cetane number testing of a biodiesel fuel was discussed.

Conclusion

This chapter summarizes the history through the 1940s of biomass-derived fuels, particularly ethanol as replacement for gasoline and vegetable oil-derived diesel fuels, including biodiesel, as replacement for petroleum-derived diesel fuels. In summary, 'alternative' fuels are not a new concept. Many technical insights obtained in historic times on the properties of these fuels have been proven to be correct. The background issues for using these fuels, namely, obtaining them from renewable, domestic feedstocks to provide energy security as well as supporting the agricultural economy, are also more current than ever.

Disclaimer: Mention of trade names or commercial products in this publication is solely for the purpose of providing specific information and does not imply recommendation or endorsement by the US Department of Agriculture (USDA). USDA is an equal opportunity provider and employer.

References

[1] Kovarik W (1998) Henry Ford, Charles Kettering and the "Fuel of the Future". *Automotive History Review* 32: 7–27.
[2] Knothe G (2001) Historical perspectives on vegetable oil-based diesel fuels. *Inform* 12: 1103–1107.
[3] Knothe G (2010) The history of vegetable oil-based diesel fuels. In: Knothe G, Van Gerpen J, Krahl J (eds.) *The Biodiesel Handbook*, 2nd edn. Urbana, IL: AOCS Press.
[4] Wiebe R and Nowakowska J (1949) The technical literature of agricultural motor fuels. *USDA Bibliographic Bulletin No. 10.* pp. 183–195. Washington, DC: US Department of Agriculture.
[5] Songstad DD, Lakshmanan P, Chen J, *et al.* (2009) Historical perspective of biofuels: Learning from the past to rediscover the future. *In Vitro Cellular and Developmental Biology Plant* 45: 189–192.
[6] Feldhaus FM (1906) Otto, Nicolaus August. *Allgemeine Deutsche Biographie* 52: 734–735.
[7] Graf von Seherr-Thoß HC (1998) Otto, Nicolaus August. *Neue Deutsche Biographie* 19: S700–S702.
[8] Feldhaus FM (1907) Langen, Eugen. *Allgemeine Deutsche Biographie* 53: S769–S770.
[9] Goldbeck G and Reuß H-J (1982) Langen, Eugen. *Neue Deutsche Biographie* 13: 571–573.
[10] Diesel R (1912) The diesel oil-engine. *Engineering* 93: 395–406. *Chemical Abstracts* 6: 1984, 1912.
[11] Diesel R (1913) *Die Entstehung des Dieselmotors*. Berlin, Germany: Verlag von Julius Springer.
[12] Diesel R (1912) The diesel oil-engine and its industrial importance particularly for Great Britain. *Proceedings of the Institution of Mechanical Engineers* 179–280. *Chemical Abstracts* 7: 1605, 1913.
[13] Schwab AW, Bagby MO, and Freedman B (1987) Preparation and properties of diesel fuels from vegetable oils. *Fuel* 66: 1372–1378.
[14] Walton J (1938) The fuel possibilities of vegetable oils. *Gas Oil Power* 33: 167–168. *Chemical Abstracts* 33: 8336, 1939.
[15] Chavanne CG Procédé de transformation d'huiles végétales en vue de leur utilisation comme carburants (Procedure for the transformation of vegetable oils for their uses as fuels). Belgian Patent 422,877, 31 August 1937. *Chemical Abstracts* 32: 43132, 1938.
[16] Chavanne G (1943) Sur un mode d'utilization possible de l'huile de palme à la fabrication d'un carburant lourd (A method of possible utilization of palm oil for the manufacture of a heavy fuel). *Bulletin des Sociétés Chimiques* 10(52): 58. *Chemical Abstracts* 38: 21839, 1944.
[17] van den Abeele M (1942) L'huile de palme: Matière première pour la préparation d'un carburant lourd utilisable dans les moteurs à combustion interne (Palm oil as raw material for the production of a heavy motor fuel). *Bulletin of Agriculture Congo Belge* 33(3): 90. *Chemical Abstracts* 38: 28051, 1944.

5.03 Bioethanol Development in Brazil

A Altieri, UNICA – Brazilian Sugarcane Industry Association, São Paulo, Brazil

© 2012 Elsevier Ltd. All rights reserved.

5.03.1	Background	15
5.03.1.1	Ethanol from Sugarcane: A Brief History	15
5.03.1.2	The Brazilian Sugarcane Industry: An Overview	16
5.03.1.3	Sugarcane Ethanol in Brazil	16
5.03.1.4	Foreign Presence	17
5.03.2	Continuing Industry Growth	17
5.03.2.1	Key Drivers: Flex-Fuel Vehicles and Mandatory Blending	17
5.03.2.2	Best Agricultural and Environmental Practices	18
5.03.2.3	Additional Uses of Bioethanol	18
5.03.2.4	Brazilian Ethanol: A Low-Carbon Solution	19
5.03.2.5	Sugar Production and Sugar Trade	19
5.03.2.6	Bioelectricity: From Self-Sufficiency to New Product	20
5.03.2.7	A Clean Energy Matrix	20
5.03.3	Social and Environmental Responsibility	21
5.03.3.1	Competitive Advantages	21
5.03.3.2	Sugarcane in the Amazon and Other Myths	21
5.03.3.3	'Food versus Fuel' in Brazil	22
5.03.3.4	The 'Green Protocol' to End Sugarcane Burning	22
5.03.3.5	Ensuring Employability of Displaced Workers	22
5.03.3.6	Work Conditions and Social Responsibility	23
5.03.3.7	The 'National Commitment' on Labor Practices	23
5.03.4	Looking to the Future	24
5.03.4.1	About UNICA	25
5.03.4.2	Mission	25
5.03.4.3	Priorities	25
5.03.4.4	Strategies	26
References		26

5.03.1 Background

5.03.1.1 Ethanol from Sugarcane: A Brief History

Portuguese seafarers discovered present-day Brazil in the year 1500, and it was not long before the new settlers began to plant sugarcane. Sugar production and the early stages of a sugarcane industry, recognized today among Brazil's earliest documented economic activities, have been an integral part of the country's social, political, and economic history ever since.

More than five centuries later, sugarcane is in the midst of another quantum leap, this time to offer the world a multiple source of clean, renewable energy that produces both a biofuel and bioelectricity at a time when both are urgently needed. More than that, new uses for sugarcane are rapidly making headway, including the production of bioplastics and green hydrocarbons like renewable diesel, jet fuel, and gasoline.

Since 2008, pure ethanol produced from sugarcane has been replacing more than half of Brazil's gasoline needs in volumetric terms. Its production and use help reduce greenhouse gas (GHG) emissions by up to 90% compared to gasoline, according to a study by the United Nations Environment Program (UNEP) published in 2009.

In 2010, the United States Environmental Protection Agency (EPA) recognized sugarcane ethanol as an advanced biofuel, capable of cutting GHG emissions by 61–91% compared to gasoline, depending on how it is made. The difference between the EPA's findings and the earlier UNEP study is due to emissions that would be required in order to transport Brazilian ethanol to the United States, as well as other specific data considered by the EPA such as emissions resulting from indirect land use change (ILUC).

Unlike other countries that have begun to use biofuels or are still considering expanding their use, drivers in Brazil can fill up with ethanol at any of the country's more than 37 000 service stations. This has been the reality in Brazil for decades, considering that the country launched its ethanol program, initially known as Proálcool, in the mid-1970s.

Although the original program officially ended in the late 1990s, its main aspects remained a part of the Brazilian energy scenario and were eventually upgraded by market changes and consumer demands. That combination produced what is now considered to be the most successful national effort to replace fossil fuels with renewable fuels anywhere in the world.

Ethanol use gained renewed momentum in Brazil as of 2003, when flex-fuel cars were introduced by the auto industry. Their ability to utilize gasoline and ethanol at the same time and in any proportion gave Brazilian consumers the power to decide at the pump which fuel to purchase, a trait that has contributed to making flex-fuel vehicles (FFVs) a resounding success in Brazil. They accounted for 91% of all new light vehicle sales in Brazil in 2010, and are expected to surpass 50% of all cars on the road in Brazil by the end of 2011.

Most importantly, sugarcane expansion to supply the growing demand for ethanol has not brought with it the adverse effects often associated with biofuels in other parts of the world: sugarcane production in Brazil has not caused deforestation or adverse effects on food prices or supplies. On the contrary, over more than three decades, sugarcane ethanol has proven to be the most efficient feedstock for ethanol production using existing technologies in terms of energy and environmental balances, productivity, and cost-effectiveness. This status is now recognized in independent analyses by major institutions like the EPA and the US State of California's Air Resources Board (CARB).

As the global pioneer and leader in the successful large-scale production and use of ethanol and bioelectricity, Brazil's sugarcane industry is now actively pushing to expand global production and use of ethanol, as well as ensuring its free flow throughout the globe, unobstructed by tariffs and other barriers. Sugarcane is poised to make significant new contributions to global development, by turning many emerging economies into producers and exporters of ethanol for the world.

The industry in Brazil supports the idea that sustainably produced biofuels can and should be part of a broad solution to challenges like energy security and global warming; and sugarcane ethanol, produced with all due environmental and social care, has all the prerequisites to become a global energy commodity.

The following pages will examine the next steps in what should become a global energy revolution, with the enormous potential contribution from sugarcane and its derivatives becoming ever more evident. Its already significant achievements have barely scratched the surface, as it becomes an increasingly decisive ingredient in efforts to preserve and ensure the planet's future.

5.03.1.2 The Brazilian Sugarcane Industry: An Overview

Although it is recognized as one of Brazil's longest-established activities, with numerous peaks of influence and vital importance through five centuries of the country's economic and political history, it is over the last 35 years that the sugarcane industry has experienced the sharpest increase in its presence, coupled with continuous technological advancement.

Today, Brazilian sugarcane is the basic input for a diverse and growing range of value-added products including food, animal feed, biofuel, and electricity coming from modern, integrated biorefineries that produce sugar, ethanol, bioelectricity, and bioplastics, with second-generation or cellulosic ethanol as well as biohydrocarbons looming in the future.

Brazil is the world's leading sugarcane producer. The 2009/2010 harvest year saw a record crop of about 550 million tons of sugarcane, or almost a third of world production, which totals nearly 1.4 billion tons and is concentrated primarily in tropical regions, particularly the developing nations of Latin America, Africa, and South and Southeast Asia. (US metric tons are used throughout this chapter.) About 100 countries around the world produce sugarcane, but most direct their crop essentially to sugar production alone.

The Brazilian cane crop is processed at more than 430 mills, of which more than 300 were combined mills and distilleries at the time of the 2010/2011 harvest, producing both sugar and ethanol, while around 100 produced strictly ethanol. All mills are self-sufficient in producing their own electricity and seldom purchase electricity from the grid, while more than 20% of all mills in Brazil already export surplus electricity for local and regional distribution.

In the 2009/2010 harvest, Brazilian sugarcane cultivation occupied just over 8 million hectares, or about 2.4% of the country's total arable land. Sugarcane is grown mainly in south-central and northeastern Brazil, with two different harvest periods: from April to December in south-central Brazil and from September to March in the northeast. The south-central region accounts for almost 90% of the country's total cane production. São Paulo state alone produces more than 60% of Brazil's sugarcane crop.

Annual gross earnings from the sugar and ethanol sectors totaled around US$28 billion in 2009, the most recent year for which total figures are available. About 44% of this came from sugar sales and 54% from ethanol sales, with the remaining 2% from bioelectricity supplied to the domestic market. Most sugar production is exported, as the numbers from 2009 clearly demonstrate: 34% of total production remained in Brazil, while 66% was shipped to dozens of countries in all continents. Ethanol sales on the other hand were primarily aimed at the domestic market, which generated 90% of revenues against only 10% from exports.

5.03.1.3 Sugarcane Ethanol in Brazil

Ethanol, also known as ethyl alcohol, can be produced by the fermentation of sugarcane juice and molasses. It has been used in various forms for thousands of years, and emerged in recent years as a leading clean and renewable fuel for internal combustion engines.

Brazil is a pioneer in the large-scale production and use of ethanol as a motor vehicle fuel. The country first began using ethanol in automobiles as early as the 1920s, but the industry gained significant momentum in the 1970s with the introduction of Proálcool, a trailblazing federal program created in response to global oil crises that forced sharp increases in oil prices.

In the mid-1970s, Brazil imported most of the oil it used, amid a difficult economic situation that featured a multifigure foreign debt and galloping inflation. Ethanol was a solution the country could reach for, to face a challenge that did not have a specific title at the time, but is now known to the world as 'energy security'. In dire economic straits, Brazil did not have the option to continue to import oil, so it chose to expand the production and use of a homegrown fuel it knew well.

From a strictly economic perspective, Proálcool certainly accomplished what its creators intended at the time. Thanks to the large-scale production and use of ethanol, Brazil has saved an estimated US$85.8 billion in oil imports that were not needed over the last three decades because of the expanded use of ethanol.

Proálcool made ethanol an integral part of Brazil's energy matrix. The program has faced numerous setbacks over the years, particularly in the late 1980s when oil prices fell sharply and sugar prices were high. But it blossomed in the first decade of the new millennium, again because of sky-high oil and gasoline prices, environmental concerns, and the introduction of FFVs.

In 2010, ethanol represented about 48% of all fuel consumed by Brazilian automobiles and more than half of the country's total gasoline needs. Brazil produces two types of ethanol: 'hydrous', which contains about 5.6% water content in volume; and 'anhydrous', which is virtually water-free. Hydrous ethanol is used to power vehicles equipped with Flex-Fuel engines that can run on pure ethanol, gasoline or any mix of the two, while anhydrous ethanol is mixed with gasoline by fuel distributors prior to delivery to service stations.

Brazilian ethanol production is expected (at the time of writing) to reach 27 billion liters in the 2010/2011 sugarcane harvest, about the same as in the previous year. As in the past, the domestic market will absorb most of this – close to 90% – with approximately 2 billion liters destined for export.

Eight new sugarcane processing mills came on stream during the 2010/2011 harvest season and investment in the sector is expected to total US$33 billion through 2012. In early 2011, foreign capital controlled 22% of all cane processed in Brazil, up from 7% in 2006. At the same time, more and more countries are adopting anhydrous ethanol blended with gasoline at varying percentages to reduce petroleum use, cut down oil imports, boost the octane rating, and provide motorists with a less-polluting fuel blend.

5.03.1.4 Foreign Presence

Much of the increase in the presence of foreign companies in the Brazilian sugarcane industry is connected to mergers and acquisitions. These deals have gained momentum in recent years, in great measure because of the 2008/2009 global credit crisis, which caught numerous Brazilian companies in a highly leveraged position following years of investing to expand capacity. Consolidation is a trend expected to continue, considering the fragmented nature of the industry, with some 200 economic groups still controlling about 430 mills, even after several major transactions in recent years.

The expanding presence of global corporations in the Brazilian sugarcane industry has created unique situations. For example, Brazil is the only country where major oil companies are involved in large-scale ethanol production. In early 2010, Royal Dutch Shell and Brazil's Cosan Group announced the largest transaction in the history of the industry – a US$12 billion joint venture, finalized in mid-2011.

Brazil's state-controlled oil giant Petrobras is also becoming a major player, with growing involvement in ethanol production through the acquisition of noncontrolling stakes in existing companies. Petrobras is also a significant player in major infrastructure projects, including the country's first ethanol pipeline and a system of river barges to transport ethanol. And in 2008, BP became the first oil company in the world to produce ethanol, when it purchased a stake in a Brazilian mill. BP has since expanded its presence through additional acquisitions.

Other major corporations with a presence in the Brazilian sugarcane industry include France-based commodity giants Louis Dreyfus and Tereos and US-based Bunge, ADM, and Cargill; major Brazilian construction concern Odebrecht; Hong Kong-based Noble Group; and Abengoa.

5.03.2 Continuing Industry Growth

5.03.2.1 Key Drivers: Flex-Fuel Vehicles and Mandatory Blending

The positive performance of Brazil's ethanol program is currently driven by two main factors: mandatory blending and the expansion of the FFV market. All gasoline sold in the country is blended with 18% to 25% anhydrous ethanol, and roughly 9 out of every 10 new cars sold in the Brazilian market are FFVs. In March of 2010, the Brazilian National Association of Automotive Vehicle Producers (Anfavea) celebrated the assembly of the 10 millionth FFV. By 2015, 65% of all light vehicles on the road in Brazil are projected to be FFVs.

The auto industry has invested heavily in flex-fuel technology and is responsible, along with its Brazilian auto parts suppliers and developers, for advancing an existing technology that saw large-scale use only when adopted in Brazil. The country's auto industry currently ranks fifth in the world in terms of vehicles produced, with more than 3.6 million units sent to markets in Brazil and abroad in 2010.

As of January 2011, 12 major automakers were offering over 90 flex-fuel models in the Brazilian market, the vast majority of them manufactured in Brazil. FFVs are offered at the same price as gasoline-powered cars, although most automakers established in Brazil no longer manufacture gasoline-only vehicles. Most have converted their entire production to flex models.

The adoption of flex-fuel technology in 2003 was possible only in Brazil because of measures introduced with the Proálcool program, launched in the mid-1970s. As part of the Brazilian government's decision to expand ethanol use, dedicated ethanol pumps began to appear in service stations in 1976. Today, all 37 000 stations in the country feature at least one dedicated pump offering pure hydrous ethanol (E-100).

When Proálcool was in place, car engines were designed to run exclusively on either gasoline or ethanol, but not both. This meant consumers had to choose their fuel when purchasing the vehicle. With the introduction in 2003 of FFVs, which accept ethanol, gasoline, or any combination of the two, consumers gained the freedom to choose between fuels at the pump, not the showroom. In addition to the E-100 pumps, all gasoline sold in Brazil since the mid-1970s contains between 18% and 25% of anhydrous ethanol as a mandated blend.

In 2010, FFVs represented approximately 91% of all new light commercial vehicles sold in the country, a remarkable jump from a 4% share in 2003, when they were introduced. Market projections suggest that FFV sales will tend to stabilize at around 90%, with the remainder being diesel-powered light vehicles and gasoline-powered imported models that do not offer flex-fuel technology.

According to Brazil's National Association of Automotive Vehicle Producers (Anfavea), by December of 2007 there were 4.5 million FFVs on Brazilian roads, some 20% of all light vehicles. In March of 2010, Anfavea marked the assembly of the 10 millionth FFV with a special celebration involving 10 automakers that offered flex vehicles in Brazil at the time: Citroen, Fiat, Ford, General Motors, Honda, Mitsubishi, Peugeot, Renault, Toyota, and Volkswagen. They have since been joined by two automakers, raising the total to 12: Nissan and KIA.

Steady progress in ethanol engine technology has brought additional gains in mileage and emission standards. Some automakers are now planning to introduce flex engines optimized to run on ethanol, a move that will bring additional efficiency gains.

5.03.2.2 Best Agricultural and Environmental Practices

High productivity is a major feature of ethanol production in Brazil. In terms of liters of biofuel per harvested hectare, sugarcane ethanol has no rivals. New varieties of cane developed in Brazil, combined with the future introduction of hydrolysis and other technologies, have the potential to push yields as high as 13 000 l per hectare from the current 7000–8000 average.

Current productivity levels already represent a sharp improvement over the 3000 l per hectare that prevailed when the Proálcool program was introduced. Beyond the direct implications for production costs, increased productivity is vital because it will allow for higher volumes without a need for further expansion of cultivated areas.

Best practices, both agricultural and environmental, which have become widespread in the sugarcane industry, help to explain the impressive performance of the industry and its potential to achieve even better results. These practices are often the end result of years, often decades, of independent research and development as well as efforts at individual mills that have become benchmarks for the industry as a whole.

Some key advances involving agricultural and environmental aspects include the following:

- The use of pesticides in Brazilian sugarcane fields is low, and in addition the use of fungicides is practically nonexistent. Major diseases that threaten sugarcane are fought through biological control and advanced genetic enhancement programs that help identify the most resistant varieties of sugarcane. Thanks to the innovative use of recycled production residues such as vinasse and filter cake as organic fertilizers, Brazilian sugarcane plantations use lower amounts of industrialized fertilizers than is the case with most other major crops. Vinasse is the water-based liquid residue and filter cake is the solid residue of sugarcane processing. Both are rich in organic nutrients.
- Sugarcane fields have relatively low levels of soil loss, thanks to the semiperennial nature of the sugarcane, which only needs to be replanted every 5–7 years, depending on the variety being used. Current trends indicate that losses, however limited, will decrease significantly in coming years through the use of sugarcane straw, some of which is left on the fields as organic matter after mechanical harvesting.
- Practically no irrigation is required in sugarcane fields because rainfall is abundant and reliable, particularly in the country's main production region, south-central Brazil. Rainfall is complemented by what is known as 'fertirrigation', a process that involves applying vinasse to cane fields. Water use during industrial processing has decreased significantly over the years, from around 5 m^3 per ton to approximately 1.5 m^3 per ton of sugarcane processed. With improved technologies such as dry washing of cane as it is delivered to the mill, the industry projects further reductions in water use.

5.03.2.3 Additional Uses of Bioethanol

Increasingly, the use of fuel ethanol is not limited to light vehicles. In May 2011, São Paulo, Brazil's largest and the world's third-largest city, introduced the first 50 ethanol-powered buses to the city fleet as part of a pilot project cosponsored by the Brazilian Sugarcane Industry Association (UNICA) to use biofuels in public transportation, with significant potential benefits for public health and the environment. It is estimated that replacing 1000 (mineral) diesel buses with ethanol-powered models will reduce CO_2 emissions by 96 000 tons per year, or the equivalent of emissions from 18 000 gasoline-powered automobiles.

Ethanol buses are an established feature of public transport in Europe, where more than 600 such vehicles have been in use in Stockholm since 2005, with a less numerous presence in six other European countries. The buses, which run on a mixture of 95% ethanol and 5% of a special additive that allows the diesel engine to function with ethanol, are manufactured by Swedish multinational Scania, which is now producing the vehicles at its main plant in Brazil. The company is also marketing trucks that utilize the same platform and technology as the buses and are already in operation in four countries.

In 2009, the launch of the first flex-fuel motorcycle in the world by Honda, a major global manufacturer, was a resounding success in Brazil, with sales rising steadily and other makers promising to introduce their own flex models by 2011. Honda has since launched four additional flex models and expects flex motorcycles to account for more than 50% of its overall production in Brazil in 2011. The company controls close to 80% of Brazil's motorcycle market.

Small single-engine crop dusting airplanes manufactured in Brazil have also been available since 2003. The ethanol-powered plane, known as the Ipanema, is produced by Brazilian aircraft manufacturer Embraer. Close to 1100 models have been sold.

The use of ethanol to produce bioplastics is rapidly expanding, with accelerated growth expected in coming years. Perhaps the most visible example is what is known as the PlantBottle, introduced in several markets around the world by the Coca-Cola Company. At a glance, the bottle appears to be no different from any other PET plastic bottle, but 30% of the resins utilized to produce the PlantBottle are extracted from sugarcane ethanol and it is fully recyclable.

Initially, the company launched the new bottle at the COP-15 meetings in Copenhagen and at the 2010 Winter Olympics in Vancouver. Coca-Cola is working to make the PlantBottle 100% sugarcane ethanol based, and intends to gradually replace plastic containers for all its products worldwide with the new technology. The move away from petroleum-based resins results in significant reductions in GHG emissions.

Future perspectives for both sugarcane and ethanol include the development of hydrocarbons directly from sugarcane through biotechnology. A number of companies, primarily US-based Amyris and LS9, are advancing rapidly in the development of customized bacteria that transform sugarcane into renewable versions of hydrocarbons like diesel, jet fuel, gasoline, and fine chemicals. To exemplify, green diesel produced in this way is sulfur-free and does not emit particulates contained in petroleum-based diesel, which are said to be hazardous to human health.

5.03.2.4 Brazilian Ethanol: A Low-Carbon Solution

The success of the Brazilian ethanol program is rooted in the proven economic and environmental advantages of sugarcane ethanol, which offers an unrivaled fossil energy balance compared with other alternative fuels. Under current Brazilian conditions, the production of a given quantity of sugarcane ethanol yields nine times more energy than the energy consumed during its production.

This in turn contributes to a significant reduction in GHG emissions. Specifically, for each unit of fossil energy used to produce Brazilian sugarcane ethanol, 9.4 units of renewable energy are generated, an energy balance that is over 4 times better than that of ethanol from sugar beet and wheat and 7 times that of corn ethanol.

This ratio can further improve as technical advances and efficiency gains are introduced in coming years. The energy balance of other ethanol feedstocks such as corn, grains, and sugar beets rarely exceeds 2–3 units per unit of fossil energy consumed in the production process.

When it comes to climate change mitigation, the performance of sugarcane ethanol is even more impressive. Based on a complete life-cycle analysis, up to 90% of CO_2-equivalent GHG emissions can be avoided when sugarcane ethanol is used instead of gasoline. In 2007, it was estimated that ethanol production and use in Brazil reduced GHG emissions by about 25.8 million tons of CO_2 equivalent.

Another yardstick that serves as an indicator of the environmental impact of ethanol use is the 'carbonometer', a tool developed by UNICA and updated monthly that considers GHG emission reductions strictly from the use of ethanol in FFVs since their introduction in 2003. In January of 2011, the carbonometer showed more than 103 million tons of CO_2 avoided in Brazil so far. Ironically, under the Kyoto Protocol, the use of sugarcane ethanol does not generate emission abatement credits.

According to the US Department of Energy, the production of gasoline and diesel from crude oil does not yield renewable energy and results in negative energy efficiency. For each unit of fossil energy consumed during the production process, only about 0.8 unit of fossil energy is generated.

UNICA considers that many developed countries protect their domestic ethanol industries with steep trade-distorting tariffs as well as nontariff barriers, a position that is in direct conflict with the support by many of these same countries for the need to reduce GHG emissions. Instead, they are in fact encouraging the free trade of environmentally aggressive fossil fuels, while holding back the global expansion of clean, renewable biofuels.

5.03.2.5 Sugar Production and Sugar Trade

Brazil is the world's leading sugar producer and exporter, accounting for approximately 20% of global production and 40% of world exports. National output reached an estimated 32.9 million tons in 2009/2010. Roughly two-thirds of the sugar produced in Brazil, or about 24.1 million tons, is exported, with raw sugar accounting for over 48% of international sales.

In all, Brazilian sugar is exported to more than 125 countries around the globe. Major importers in recent years include the Russian Federation, Nigeria, the United Arab Emirates, and Canada. Virtually all Brazilian sugar exports are traded in the free market and preferential import quotas devoted to Brazil by developed countries are extremely small compared to the total volume of Brazilian sugar sales. The United States and the European Union import less than 1 000 000 tons of Brazilian sugar under preferential conditions, which represents just 4.1% of the country's international sales.

Brazil is a member of the Global Alliance for Sugar Trade Reform and Liberalisation, an organization that defends fair and free trade in sugar. In 2003, after years of protracted negotiations, Brazil, Australia, and Thailand filed a World Trade Organization (WTO) complaint against the European Union's sugar subsidies alleging violation of international trade agreements. In 2005 the WTO ruled in favor of Brazil and the other complainants.

As a result, the EU had to restrain its exports of sugar, directly subsidized or not, according to its WTO schedule of commitments (1.27 million tons). In order to comply with the WTO ruling, the EU revised its sugar program, reducing production quotas and reference prices.

5.03.2.6 Bioelectricity: From Self-Sufficiency to New Product

Bioelectricity is one of the most significant new areas of activity for Brazil's sugarcane industry and one that can spark another revolution on the same scale as that of ethanol. Brazil's sugar and ethanol plants generate their own electrical energy by burning bagasse (see below). This process, known as cogeneration, not only supplies the processing unit's energy requirements but also produces surplus electricity that can be sold in the commercial power market.

Sugarcane bagasse is the dry, fibrous waste that is left after sugarcane has been processed to make sugar and ethanol. Bioelectricity production already happens in all sugarcane mills and ethanol distilleries in Brazil, but much more energy could be produced if the bagasse, as well as the sugarcane straw – the tops and leaves of cane stalks – is burned in high-efficiency boilers. In early 2011, it was estimated that approximately two-thirds of the sugarcane's theoretical total energy potential, contained in the bagasse and straw, remains for the most part unharnessed.

The energy makeup of sugarcane is composed of roughly one-third juice, one-third bagasse, and one-third straw. The juice has always been used to produce sugar and ethanol, while most of the bagasse is burned inefficiently to produce steam and generate bioelectricity to cover the plant's individual needs.

With mechanized harvesting advancing, the straw, which used to be burned to facilitate the manual cutting of the cane, is now separated by harvesting machines and can eventually be recovered and used as additional biomass to produce bioelectricity. The growing use of high-performance boilers is allowing more and more mills to produce surplus electricity, which is then sold to distribution grids.

With hydrolysis technologies being developed, it will also be possible to produce additional ethanol from both the bagasse and the straw, while the lignin – the residual material from producing bioelectricity from bagasse and straw – can be used as additional biomass to generate more bioelectricity.

In an effort to accelerate the phasing out of sugarcane burning, 168 sugar and ethanol mills that operate in São Paulo state have subscribed to a 'Green Protocol' sponsored by UNICA and the São Paulo state government. The document calls for the eradication of preharvest burning by 2014 in areas where mechanized harvesting can be introduced, where inclinations do not exceed 12°. Areas with steeper slopes, where mechanization is currently not technically feasible, will have to be mechanized by 2017.

Once the harvest is fully mechanized, the straw will no longer be wasted. Instead, most of it will be collected and burned, along with the bagasse, in high-efficiency boilers (more than 60 bar pressure), allowing a growing number of sugarcane processing mills to sell surplus bioelectricity to the national electricity distribution grid. In January of 2011, mechanization had already reached about 60% of the sugarcane harvest in São Paulo state, with other key cane producing states gradually following suit.

Official government data show that Brazil's sugarcane processing mills generated more than 1600 average megawatts (MWa) of electricity in 2009. With increased use of biomass from sugarcane and the implementation of high-pressure boilers at older mills, projections indicate that bioelectricity from sugarcane will expand from 3% to about 15% of Brazil's electricity demand by 2020.

With industry estimates for 2020/2021 calling for a sugarcane harvest of 1 billion ton, the bioelectricity potential from bagasse would then reach 7600 MWa, rising to 14 400 MWa when additional bagasse and straw become available as mechanical harvesting expands.

Generating bioelectricity offers numerous benefits: the environmental impact is low and producers can obtain carbon credits, while projects are relatively small and usually involve a broad range of investors. This means reduced risks, in particular of the kind that frequently cause construction delays in large-scale hydroelectric projects.

Moreover, bagasse and straw cogeneration represents a boost for the Brazilian equipment industry and creates numerous jobs, while drawing on know-how developed over many years of cogeneration for internal consumption at sugar and ethanol production facilities.

Bioelectricity from sugarcane is a particularly interesting option for Brazil because much of the country's electricity comes from large hydro dams. The sugarcane harvesting period, when most biomass is available, coincides with the dry season when hydro stations sometimes have to reduce output because of low water levels in their reservoirs. This makes the two sources of electricity complementary. In addition, the majority of sugar and ethanol plants are located fairly close to the more populous regions of Brazil, where electricity demand is highest.

Moving beyond Brazil, bioelectricity represents an economically and environmentally sound energy solution for sugarcane producing countries, especially those with high oil import bills and a dependence on fossil fuels for electricity. While domestic ethanol production would reduce the need for oil imports, bioelectricity generated from sugarcane bagasse can in many cases allow rural populations to turn on a light for the first time.

5.03.2.7 A Clean Energy Matrix

Taken together, ethanol and sugarcane bagasse represent over 18.2% of all of Brazil's energy requirements. Sugarcane-based energy surpassed hydroelectricity in 2008 to take over second spot among all sources of energy in the country. Petroleum remains number one, accounting for almost 38% of the total.

The growing importance of sugarcane in Brazil's matrix makes it a vital ingredient in the country's uniquely clean energy picture, in which 47.3% of all the energy produced comes from renewable sources. That share is significantly higher than the world average of 18.6% and sharply higher than the 7% average among member countries of the Organization for Economic Cooperation and Development (OECD).

5.03.3 Social and Environmental Responsibility

5.03.3.1 Competitive Advantages

Brazil's sugarcane industry offers an outstanding example of how social, economic, and environmental concerns can be addressed within the framework of sustainable development. With existing technology, ethanol production from sugarcane represents the best option for large-scale, sustainable biofuel production, combined with unmatched GHG reduction.

Estimates known as 'well-to-wheel' analyses confirm a significant advantage for Brazilian sugarcane ethanol in terms of cutting GHG emissions over all other types of ethanol produced from different feedstocks. These estimates consider the entire production cycle and calculate when the process is generating emissions or removing CO_2 from the atmosphere, to arrive at a net figure.

For example, when diesel-powered harvesting machines and tractors are utilized, or when sugarcane is being transported in gasoline- or diesel-powered trucks to a mill, the process is generating emissions. But when sugarcane is growing in the fields, it is removing CO_2 from the atmosphere at an accelerated pace – a characteristic of fast-growing plants such as sugarcane, a semiperennial that can be harvested once a year and only needs to be replanted every 5–7 years, depending on the variety.

These calculations show that Brazilian sugarcane ethanol reduces GHG emissions by 90% on average when used instead of gasoline, as confirmed by UNEP. The International Energy Agency (IEA) also confirm a superior energy balance for cane ethanol, 4.5 times better than that of ethanol produced from sugar beets or wheat and almost 7 times better than ethanol produced from corn.

The energy balance for ethanol is the ratio between units of fossil fuel consumed and units of renewable energy produced. The IEA found that in the case of sugarcane ethanol produced in Brazil, that ratio can be superior to 9 units of renewable energy per unit of fossil fuel. The ratio falls to 4 to 1 for ethanol produced from beets or wheat, most common in Europe, and 1.4 to 1 for ethanol made from corn, which prevails in the United States.

5.03.3.2 Sugarcane in the Amazon and Other Myths

Members of the Brazilian sugarcane industry are frequently asked by foreign visitors about deforestation in the Amazon Rainforest and the extent to which sugarcane harvesting and its expansion in recent years are responsible for the damage. But while deforestation in the Amazon does exist, there is no established connection with the activities of the sugarcane industry.

First, sugarcane expansion in the last 25 years has occurred primarily in south-central Brazil, in areas that are significantly distant from the Rainforest and other important ecological areas such as the Pantanal wetlands in central Brazil. In fact, most of this expansion, or the equivalent of 60% of the national output, has occurred in the populous state of São Paulo in traditional agricultural lands, close to established sugar and ethanol processing plants.

This is directly related to the perishable nature of the sugarcane itself. Unlike grains and other crops, sugarcane, once harvested, must be processed within a few hours in order to retain its value (sugar content) by avoiding natural fermentation. Consequently, all sugarcane fields must be relatively close to processing mills.

Second, the Amazon Rainforest does not offer favorable economic and agronomic conditions for sugarcane production, namely alternating dry and wet seasons, which are essential to grow the plant and build up sucrose levels in the cane. Moreover, the absence of a reliable transportation infrastructure to move the final product – sugar or ethanol – out of the processing areas is a major inhibiting factor that discourages sugarcane production in the region.

Third, future expansion is anticipated to continue taking place in south-central Brazil, particularly in degraded pastures. The most promising areas for expansion are in western São Paulo state, western Minas Gerais state, and the southern regions of Mato Grosso do Sul and Goiás states.

Finally, while the Brazilian Amazon Rainforest occupies more than 350 million hectares of land, or about 40% of Brazil's total landmass of 846 million hectares, sugarcane fields for the production of sugar and ethanol occupied just over 8 million hectares in January of 2011, or less than 1% of all land in Brazil.

Looking at it another way, Brazil's total arable land, a calculation that excludes the Amazon and other sensitive areas, totals about 340 million hectares. This means that sugarcane harvested for all purposes occupies about 2.4% of the country's arable lands. Since only about half the sugarcane crop goes to ethanol, it can be said that Brazil has replaced more than half its gasoline needs with a little over 1% of its arable land.

Another recurring question has to do with whether the expansion of sugarcane harvesting in Brazil will somehow 'push' other agricultural activities, such as cattle and soybeans, into the Amazon Rainforest. Again, the hard facts defy and dismiss the myth.

The dynamics of the cattle industry, which has been present in the Amazon region for the past 30 years, are unrelated to sugarcane production. Cattle raising activities in the greater Amazon are linked to the logging industry, which unfortunately has been the 'cash crop' of the Rainforest.

Reliable estimates show that about 80% of all illegal clearings in the Amazon eventually are converted into cattle raising pasture. These tend to survive until the land loses its inherent value for most agricultural activity.

As for soybeans or other grains, there is very limited expansion of total arable land in Brazil. What has occurred, to a small extent, is the replacement of soybean fields in traditional growing areas by sugarcane production, without a related expansion of the overall soybean area. In fact, in the years leading up to 2008, when cane harvesting was expanding, the total area planted with soybeans in Brazil decreased, from 23.3 million hectares, or 7% of the country's total arable land, to 20.6 million hectares, or about 6.1% of all arable land. Soybean fields have expanded to 21.57 million hectares since 2008, a period of much slower sugarcane expansion.

5.03.3.3 'Food versus Fuel' in Brazil

An issue that is often a topic of debate elsewhere in the world and is frequently and erroneously applied to Brazil has to do with whether the expansion of sugarcane growing will somehow affect food production or prices. Again, there are abundant data showing that this is yet another biofuel-related discussion that has no connection to what goes on in Brazil.

While sugarcane production has increased steadily in recent years, there has been no drop in food production. On the contrary, overall production has grown dramatically, from 100 million tons in 1976 to almost 500 million tons in 2009. The grain and oilseed harvests set a new record in 2007 when they reached 135 million tons, a doubling of production over the previous 10 years.

The fact is that Brazil is not just feeding itself better, but also much of the world with its high-productivity agriculture and growing commodity exports. Brazilian agriculture has been transformed into a high-productivity, sustainable agribusiness, particularly in the more developed south-central region. Brazil is currently the world's third-largest agricultural producer.

All of this has improved Brazil's ability to promote the increase of the sugarcane harvest by focusing the expansion on degraded lands and consequently not disturbing other crops or the country's biodiversity.

The Brazilian government estimates there are some 30 million hectares throughout the country of degraded, low-productivity pastures, ready to be improved with sustainable, modern agricultural practices. In the state of São Paulo, thanks to the industry's technology-based agribusiness practices, the expansion of sugarcane growing areas has been met by an increase in the yields of livestock. Growth has been driven by productivity, not mobility or deforestation.

Finally, agricultural technologies continue to improve. Similar to other food crops, enhanced varieties of conventional sugarcane show a 20% increase in the level of sucrose, resulting in many more liters of ethanol per hectare. Looking ahead, cellulosic hydrolysis technology is likely to be commercially viable by 2020 and will allow for the production of additional ethanol from sugarcane straw and bagasse.

The combination of these new technologies will boost ethanol production per hectare, from the current 7000 l to as much as 13 000 l per hectare. Consequently, demand pressure for new cultivated areas will be reduced, even as the industry expands.

5.03.3.4 The 'Green Protocol' to End Sugarcane Burning

One of the most important initiatives launched in recent years by the sugarcane industry is known as the 'Green Protocol', also referred to as the 'Agro-Environmental Protocol'. This set of commitments developed between the state government of São Paulo and the sugarcane industry and signed in 2007 calls for the industry to speed up the elimination of sugarcane burning, an age-old practice that facilitates manual cane harvesting, and is called for in collective agreements between workers and mills.

With the 'Green Protocol', the deadline to end sugarcane burning has been moved from 2021 to 2014 for areas where mechanized harvesting is currently possible, and from 2031 to 2017 for other areas, for example, those with steeper slopes, where harvesters cannot operate with existing technology. Since its introduction in November of 2007, the Protocol also calls for all new sugarcane fields in the state to be harvested mechanically, not manually, in other words without the use of fire to clear the foliage. This means no new sugarcane fields can be implemented unless they are to be harvested mechanically, without burning.

5.03.3.5 Ensuring Employability of Displaced Workers

The Green Protocol and its stated goal of doing away with sugarcane burning, while a highly desirable objective from a strictly environmental perspective because of the emissions that will be eliminated, has also brought a separate challenge to the spotlight: what to do with an estimated 140 thousand sugarcane cutters still active in São Paulo state, whose livelihood depends on an activity that is about to be eradicated.

While many companies in the sugarcane industry have introduced programs to retrain cutters for new positions that demand more training, these were insufficient to deal with the looming situation. A broader effort was needed, in order to avoid a major social problem once the environmental goal of ending the burn is fully accomplished in 2017.

The answer came in 2009, with the launch of the RenovAção (RenovAction) Project, a partnership between UNICA and FERAESP (Federation of Registered Rural Workers in the State of São Paulo), the largest labor union representing the workers directly affected by the end of the burn and the advance of mechanized harvesting. RenovAção is widely considered the largest requalification project ever introduced in the sugarcane industry on a world level, and its objectives are impressive: to retrain up to 3000 sugarcane cutters and others in affected communities per year for new positions, both within the industry and in other areas of activity where there is unfilled demand.

Together, UNICA and Feraesp determine what type of training will be offered, based on positions that need to be filled in the sugarcane industry and other areas that need workers in each affected community. The idea is to retrain cane cutters so that they are able to find work without having to leave their communities.

The RenovAção Project is supported by the Inter-American Development Bank (IDB), and sponsored by major companies directly involved in the mechanization process: John Deere, Case New Holland, Syngenta, and Iveco. In late 2010, Netherlands-based Solidaridad Foundation joined forces with the organizers and sponsors and became a supporting partner of RenovAção.

5.03.3.6 Work Conditions and Social Responsibility

The sugarcane industry is one of Brazil's most important activities in terms of job creation, with more than a million people employed nationwide according to data from 2009. In south-central Brazil, the heart of the industry, sugarcane provides employment for tens of thousands of low-skilled workers. The average wage paid by UNICA member companies is roughly double the current federal minimum wage, which places them among the best paid in Brazilian agriculture, second only to soybean workers – a fully mechanized harvest.

Brazilian legislation, in compliance with International Labor Organization standards, covers all aspects of work conditions and must be observed by employers, whose companies are subject to frequent and detailed government inspections. Cane cutters are covered by a collective labor contract but it is common for employers to offer conditions that go beyond the parameters negotiated with labor unions.

For as long as it exists, manual sugarcane harvesting will be heavy, physically demanding work, as is the case with numerous other primary activities, in agriculture and other sectors. UNICA and its member companies have taken a leading role in developing innovative programs to enhance labor conditions, working with local and global organizations ranging from the largest labor union representing cane cutters in São Paulo state, Feraesp, to the World Bank Institute. UNICA is open to considering new initiatives to further advance labor standards in order to establish national benchmarks.

Major examples include the following:

- In partnership with Feraesp, UNICA is implementing recommendations for enhanced working conditions for rural laborers in the sugarcane industry. Key aims of the labor protocol include the elimination of outsourcing for manual sugarcane cutters, better standards for transportation of rural workers to and from fields, and increased transparency in performance measurements and employee compensations.
- With support from the World Bank Institute, UNICA set up a Socio-Environmental and Responsibility Unit, to implement various programs within the industry and build on best practices for corporate, social, and sustainable competitiveness among current and future workers in the industry. The Unit also works with industry suppliers, media, NGOs (nongovernmental organizations), and executives to encourage sustainable practices.
- In cooperation with the São Paulo-based Ethos Institute, UNICA developed a Socio-Environmental Responsibility Indicator that tracks corporate responsibility performance in the sugarcane industry, with the aim of encouraging best environmental and sustainable practices.
- In 2009, UNICA became the first organization in the world representing an agribusiness sector to produce a sustainability report in accordance with globally recognized standards developed by the Netherlands-based Global Reporting Initiative (GRI). The updated and expanded second edition of the report was published in June 2011.

UNICA maintains a variety of additional partnerships with NGOs, both Brazilian and global, including the IDB. As the largest organization representing the Brazilian sugarcane industry, UNICA is always open to new initiatives to further enhance labor standards and conditions as well as industry performance.

The cane industry's expansion is rapidly generating new job opportunities and employers are increasingly demanding more skills and offering better salaries.

5.03.3.7 The 'National Commitment' on Labor Practices

Change and diversity are two key words when it comes to labor relations in the sugarcane industry. Change has been brought by the fast paced mechanization process in the south-central region of Brazil, which will lead to the virtual vanishing of manual operations in planting and harvesting in sugarcane fields within a decade.

Diversity is the result of the industry's fragmented nature, with some 430 processing mills, over 1000 suppliers and support industries, more than 70 000 independent sugarcane growers, and more than a million workers.

If on the one hand there are still labor-related problems due to the huge workforce spread over 20 Brazilian states, on the other hand the progress that has been made is recognized by all players involved in the cane industry. While there are still difficulties, they are mostly isolated examples, fewer and further apart, that do not represent trends or general practices.

It is within that framework that the industry has been actively promoting the development and broad adoption of best labor practices. Educating, requalifying, and contributing to the placement of workers that lose their jobs because of the mechanization process are the major aspects of this effort.

Highlighting best labor practices, by creating market tools that recognize them as examples to be followed by an expanding number of employers, raises the bar for average standards through proactive and transparent policies. It also refocuses efforts on concrete gains and improvements, rather than concentrating on exceptions, which, at some level, will probably always exist in an industry of this magnitude.

Perhaps the best example of how to push forward with this type of strategy is the 'National Commitment to Enhance Labor Practices in the Sugarcane Industry', officially introduced on 25 June 2009. The document, made possible after a year of intense negotiations led by the experienced Secretary-General for the Presidency, Luiz Dulci, is a unique three-party agreement structured like no labor agreement before it, involving the federal government, industry leaders, and labor unions representing workers in the sugarcane industry.

Mills that subscribe to this voluntary commitment will have to abide by a set of 30 business practices that, in many cases, extend beyond legal obligations. They will receive a 'conformity certificate' from a national commission formed by UNICA, Feraesp, the National Confederation of Workers in Agriculture (CONTAG), and the National Sugar-Energy Forum. At the time of writing, more than 300 sugarcane processing mills have endorsed the agreement.

Recognized best practices included in the Commitment call for the direct hiring of workers for manual planting and harvesting of sugarcane, eliminating middlemen who were often accused of taking a cut of workers' incomes. Other key points include worker transportation improvements, added transparency in measuring and paying for worker production, support for migrants hired from other regions, enhanced practices for health and safety, and strengthening of labor unions and collective bargaining processes.

For its part, the government has introduced a package of specific public policies for education, requalification, and job placement. This is a gradual process of evolving standard practices, inspired on the simple and groundbreaking idea that the market itself should recognize the value of this Commitment, fostering effective changes in the industry through the recognition of best practices already in place.

Between early 2007 and mid-2009, UNICA member companies had already retrained more than 5000 workers impacted by the mechanization process in São Paulo state. This number is now growing at a much quicker pace, following the introduction in 2009 of the RenovAction Project – the largest training and requalification plan for the sugar-energy industry in the world, which aims to benefit some 3500 workers and members of affected communities per year.

The National Commitment and the RenovAction Project are examples of gradual but effective measures that will improve labor conditions and the quality of life of manual workers in the sugarcane industry, while offering new opportunities for those who will move on to other activities as mechanization becomes the norm. These are groundbreaking advances with far-reaching effects, which should be recognized as historic steps in the direction of a better future.

5.03.4 Looking to the Future

Brazil's sugarcane production for all purposes – production of sugar, ethanol, and bioelectricity and a growing array of new uses – is projected to reach one billion tons by 2020. This is more than double the estimated 487 million tons harvested in 2007/2008. In the same period, the total planted area is expected to expand from just over 8 million hectares in early 2011 to 14 million hectares. Output is expected to grow faster than the total cultivated area, thanks to ongoing improvement in crop productivity and other efficiency gains.

Considering investments in new ethanol, sugar, and bioelectricity plants made since 2005, the total is projected to reach US$33 billion through 2012. The majority of new projects involve Brazilian investors, but foreign capital is making gains, having reached a 22% share of all cane produced in the country, up from 7% in 2005.

Current technology for production of ethanol from biomass relies on fermentation and distillation processes, requiring feedstocks that contain sucrose, such as sugarcane and sugar beet, or starch, as is the case with corn, wheat, cassava, and potato. Global demand for alternative, sustainable fuel sources has created the need to experiment with new feedstocks and develop innovative processes for the production of ethanol.

'Second-generation' biofuels are, generally speaking, those produced from cellulose and hemicelluloses, which can be found in agricultural and forestry residues as well as organic wastes. There are other emerging processes, like gasification, that may be able to produce hydrocarbons from biomass feedstocks such as sugarcane bagasse.

Research into hydrolysis technology is advancing quite rapidly in many countries, and the prevailing opinion in technical and academic circles is that second-generation or 'cellulosic' ethanol will become commercially viable within this decade. In Brazil, sugarcane straw and bagasse are particularly attractive as feedstocks for the production of second-generation ethanol, because they would allow an increase in fuel production without the need to expand cultivated areas.

Conservative estimates indicate that hydrolysis has the potential to increase ethanol production by around 40 l per ton of sugarcane, raising the total yield from the 2007 average of 85 l per ton of sugarcane in south-central Brazil to around 125 l per ton by 2020. The introduction of second-generation ethanol, together with new varieties of sugarcane, should allow for continued growth of production without further expansion of the planted area.

Ethanol will be consolidated as a global energy commodity only when it is produced, used, and traded by many more countries. Other essential steps include developing and implementing universal product standards and mechanisms for mandatory blending of gasoline and ethanol.

An important step in this direction came with the Memorandum of Understanding (MoU) signed in 2007 between Brazil and the United States, the world's two leading ethanol producers. Together, the two countries accounted for close to 75% of global production in 2009. The MoU includes provisions to work together toward the harmonization of international specifications for fuel ethanol as well as fomenting the production and use of ethanol in third countries, particularly in the Americas.

Sustainably produced biofuels are a key element in any global solution to the growing challenges of energy security, environmental degradation, and global warming. However, while ethanol enjoys all the qualities necessary to become an established global energy commodity, UNICA believes this can happen only with the reduction of commercial barriers imposed by developed countries.

Until then, one of today's great global contradictions will continue: fossil fuels are traded freely but renewable fuels, which represent progress toward energy security and a safer future, face highly protected markets. In the world of fossil fuels, some 20 countries, often located in politically troubled regions, supply about 200 countries. In the world of renewable fuels, more than 100 countries will be potential suppliers.

Many countries have demonstrated a firm interest in biofuels. Policies to promote their production and use have been adopted not just by Brazil – the world pioneer in successful ethanol production – but also in the United States, the European Union, China, India, Thailand, and various Central American countries. Enthusiasm for biofuels is driven by the urgent need to mitigate the effects of global warming, stem the dramatic rise in energy prices, and increase energy security by reducing the reliance on politically troubled producing regions. In developed countries, biofuels are also seen as a way to enhance farm income by providing new outlets for agricultural products.

Ethanol is the renewable fuel most produced and consumed around the world. Between 2000 and 2007, global production more than doubled and is expected to reach 116 billion liters a year by 2012, with the United States and Brazil as the largest producers. But despite growing interest in renewable fuels, international trade in ethanol remains small, at around 5 billion liters per year, because of high tariff and nontariff barriers imposed by many developed countries.

Certification will play a major role as of 2011, particularly in Europe, where EU rules call for certification of all biofuels marketed in member states. UNICA favors a transparent and voluntary biofuel certification scheme that includes all feedstocks, processes, and producers. The certification process should aim at enhancing product reliability and sustainability, while promoting free and fair international trade.

Certification is a growing global trend in many sectors as manufacturers seek to show customers that their products have been produced in a sustainable manner, respecting clearly defined environmental, social, and economic criteria. UNICA understands that only a global multistakeholder initiative can prevent the proliferation of unilateral certification processes, a possibility that may well turn out to be counterproductive if some certification systems become vehicles for overt or covert commercial protection.

Beyond consolidating production and continuous enhancement of a viable, clean, and renewable biofuel, the Brazilian sugarcane industry is increasingly finding itself involved in a future of numerous, significant new uses for both sugarcane and ethanol, which bring with them new technologies, major investments, and additional global repercussions and expansion.

5.03.4.1 About UNICA

UNICA is the largest organization representing the country's sugarcane industry. It speaks and acts in Brazil and around the world on behalf of the country's leading sugar, ethanol, and bioelectricity producers. UNICA's more than 140 member companies answer for over 50% of the ethanol and 60% of the sugar produced in Brazil.

UNICA is governed by a board of directors comprising representatives of its member companies and has a full-time staff of experienced executives, specialists, and technical advisors. UNICA's expertise covers key areas including the environment, energy, technology, international trade, corporate social responsibility, sustainability, regulatory issues, economics, and communications.

In late 2007, UNICA opened its first international office in the United States (Washington, DC), followed by an office in Europe (Brussels) in early 2008. A third office abroad is being considered in Asia, as part of the organization's policy to provide consumers, governments, NGOs, industry, and the media with objective, detailed, and up-to-date information on the significant socioeconomic and environmental contributions of sugar, sugarcane ethanol, and bioelectricity, as well as the rapidly expanding array of new and innovative uses of ethanol and sugarcane, as the global search for solutions that lead to a low-carbon economy intensifies.

5.03.4.2 Mission

UNICA's mission is to spearhead and help consolidate the transition of the traditional sugarcane industry into a modern agribusiness sector, capable of competing sustainably in Brazil and around the world in the areas of ethanol, sugar, and bioelectricity, as well as contribute to new trends that will generate additional demand, including the production of green plastics (bioplastics) and biohydrocarbons obtained from sugarcane through biotechnology. These include diesel, jet fuel, gasoline, and fine chemicals.

5.03.4.3 Priorities

- Consolidate ethanol as a global commodity in the fuel sector;
- promote demand for ethanol as a clean, low-carbon motor vehicle fuel and expand its use in other sectors;
- foster large-scale production, for the Brazilian market, of bioelectricity obtained from the burning of sugarcane bagasse in high-performance boilers;
- help member companies become benchmarks for socioenvironmental sustainability; and
- disseminate credible scientific data relating to the competitive advantages of sugarcane ethanol.

5.03.4.4 Strategies

- Support best practices in sugarcane agribusiness within a competitive, free-market economy;
- promote the global expansion of ethanol production and consumption and its unrestricted international trade;
- continuously improve the socioenvironmental sustainability of the sugarcane supply chain;
- lead negotiations to reduce and/or eliminate barriers that distort trade in sugar and ethanol;
- promote bioelectricity generation as a reliable alternative to fossil energy;
- encourage research into new technologies for ethanol, including biorefineries; and
- become a global reference for credible information and analysis on the sugarcane industry.

References

[1] Brazilian Energy Balance (2011) Year 2010. Empresa de Pesquisa Energética. Rio de Janeiro, Brazil: EPE.
[2] Earley J and McKeown A (2009) *Smart Choices for Biofuels*. Washington, DC: World Watch Institute.
[3] Instituto Brasileiro de Geografia e Estatística. www.sidra.ibge.gov.br.
[4] Macedo IC and Seabra JEA (2008) Mitigation of GHG emissions using sugarcane bioethanol. In: Zuurbier P and Van de Vooren J (eds.) *Sugarcane Ethanol: Contributions to Climate Change Mitigation and the Environment*, pp. 95–111. Wageningen, The Netherlands: Wageningen Academic Publishers.
[5] Sugarcane Industry Association. http://english.unica.com.br/.
[6] Sugarcane Technology Center. http://www.ctcanavieira.com.br/index.php?option=com_content&view=article&id=171&Itemid=1268.
[7] UNEP (2009) United Nations Environment Programme – 'Towards Sustainable Production and the Use of Resources: Assessing Biofuels'.

5.04 Biomass Power Generation

A Malmgren, BioC Ltd, Cirencester, UK
G Riley, RWE npower, Swindon, UK

© 2012 Elsevier Ltd. All rights reserved.

5.04.1	Why Is There a Trend to Build Stand-Alone Biomass Power Plants?	28
5.04.2	Is Biomass Power Generation Sustainable?	28
5.04.3	Life-Cycle Analysis	29
5.04.4	How Does Biomass Power Generation Pay?	29
5.04.5	Legislation and Regulation	31
5.04.5.1	Emission Limits	31
5.04.5.1.1	Renewable Obligation	32
5.04.6	What Technology Choices Are Available?	32
5.04.6.1	Technology Development	32
5.04.6.2	Fixed and Moving Grates	33
5.04.6.3	Suspension Firing	33
5.04.6.4	Fluidized Beds	34
5.04.6.5	Gasification	37
5.04.7	Potential Biofuels	37
5.04.7.1	Solid Biofuels	37
5.04.7.1.1	Globally sourced biomass	38
5.04.7.2	Liquid Biofuels for Power Generation/Combined Heat and Power	39
5.04.8	Health and Safety	40
5.04.8.1	Personnel Issues	40
5.04.8.1.1	Oxygen depletion and poisoning	40
5.04.8.1.2	Allergies (nuts)	40
5.04.8.1.3	Mold	40
5.04.8.1.4	Dust exposure	41
5.04.8.1.5	Nuisance issues: Odor	41
5.04.8.2	Process Safety	41
5.04.8.2.1	Fire and explosions	41
5.04.8.2.2	Biomass fires	41
5.04.8.2.3	Self-heating	42
5.04.8.2.4	Explosions	42
5.04.8.2.5	Biomass characteristics	42
5.04.8.2.6	DSEAR	43
5.04.9	Material Handling and Fuel Processing	43
5.04.9.1	Bulk Density	43
5.04.9.2	Storing Biomass	43
5.04.9.3	Fuel Preparation	44
5.04.9.3.1	Hammer mills	44
5.04.9.3.2	Vertical spindle mills	45
5.04.9.3.3	Tube-ball mills	45
5.04.9.3.4	Fan beater mills	46
5.04.10	Combustion	47
5.04.10.1	Principles of Combustion	47
5.04.10.2	Practicalities	47
5.04.10.2.1	Flame stability	47
5.04.10.2.2	Conversion efficiency	48
5.04.10.3	Unburnt Carbon and Carbon Monoxide	49
5.04.10.4	Impact of Biomass Combustion	49
5.04.10.4.1	Ash-related problems	49
5.04.10.4.2	Corrosion	50
5.04.11	Environmental Impact	51
5.04.11.1	Gaseous Emissions	51
5.04.11.1.1	Oxides of sulfur (SO_x)	51
5.04.11.1.2	Oxides of nitrogen (NO_x)	51
5.04.11.1.3	Carbon monoxide	51

5.04.11.1.4	Volatile organic compounds	51
5.04.11.1.5	Hydrochloric acid	51
5.04.11.1.6	Dioxins and furans	51
5.04.11.2	Solid Residuals	51
5.04.11.2.1	Particulates	51
5.04.11.2.2	Heavy metals	52
5.04.11.2.3	Ash	52
5.04.12	**Conclusions**	52
References		52

5.04.1 Why Is There a Trend to Build Stand-Alone Biomass Power Plants?

The burning of biomass can make a significant contribution to international objectives of CO_2 reduction. It will provide a dispatchable source of renewable energy at a time when the power grid is becoming increasingly reliant on intermittent wind energy. Biomass is seen as a renewable and carbon-neutral energy source as new plants or trees grow in the place of the ones that are harvested, absorbing the same amount of CO_2 as is released when the harvested plants are burned. The cycle time for this is a few years as opposed to fossil fuels, which take many millions of years to form.

There will be some fossil fuel consumed in connection with planting, producing and applying fertilizer, harvesting, transport, etc., but on the other hand, if the plant was left to decompose in nature, it would be likely to produce methane, which is a more powerful greenhouse gas (GHG) than CO_2. This results in a negative methane emission of $41\,g\,kWh^{-1}$ in a direct-fired biomass power plant burning biomass residue [1].

The fossil fuel used in transport can be replaced with biodiesel and the amount of transport can be limited by using locally sourced biofuels as far as possible, thus reducing the carbon footprint of production and transport. Solid biomass fuels are generally of significantly lower bulk density and have lower energy content per kilogram than fossil fuels, which makes transport more costly. So the preference will be for locally sourced fuels when they are available.

So in short, biomass fuels are renewable, sustainable, and environmentally friendly if they are produced and used in a sensible and responsible way, but can also cause irreversible damage to the environment if produced or used in other ways. They can benefit local communities and in some cases can even be beneficial to biodiversity. They can be used to compensate for one of the major weaknesses of wind power, its intermittent and unpredictable availability, as biomass can be stored and dispatched when needed. There are many technical and logistical challenges to fit biomass into the current power infrastructure, but this is likely to change when the generation mix changes as older fossil-fueled power stations are decommissioned.

5.04.2 Is Biomass Power Generation Sustainable?

The ability to generate electricity in a sustainable way without long-term detrimental impact on the environment has become a very topical issue over recent years. This debate concerns aspects like climate change, biodiversity, deforestation, impact on indigenous populations and wildlife, groundwater levels, use of farmland to grow fuels instead of food, and many more.

The increase in the use of biomass from agriculture and forestry for power production as well as for transport fuels has added to pressure on farmland and forest. Large-scale production of biofuels will have consequences for biodiversity and water resources. It is important that these questions are handled in a sensible and responsible way so that no irreversible detrimental impact is caused.

The sustainability of energy crops has been extensively researched. The results of this work in the United Kingdom are summarized in good practice guidelines for the production of energy crops and extraction of forestry residues [2, 3]. UK grants for the production of energy crops are conditional on implementing the recommendations in the guidelines, including recommendations on transport distances to the end user.

Some early studies into the effect of energy crop plantations on biodiversity indicate that there can even be some positive effects [4] compared to traditional cereal production.

The potential for production of biofuels is large enough (see **Figure 1**), as biofuel production can support even ambitious renewable energy targets and still adhere to strict environmental standards. The European potential for environmentally compatible primary biomass production from agriculture and forestry, for example, has been predicted to increase from around 3.8 EJ in 2010 to around 8.3 EJ in 2030 [5]. This does not include residual biomass materials. It is estimated that a further 4.2 EJ could be available from sources like agricultural residues, wet manures, wood processing residues, the biodegradable fraction of municipal solid waste, and black liquor from the pulp and paper industry. To put this in perspective, the total electricity consumption in the European Union was around 10 EJ in 2007.

Creating a sustainable supply chain for biomass supporting biodiversity and adhering to high environmental and ethical standards is a substantial challenge. A separate chapter in this volume addresses biomass sustainability in detail. The large scale required to fit into the infrastructure of existing power generation plants and the existing cost structure created by the current electricity prices and support mechanisms for renewable energy will require new logistical solutions. Biomass-based power generation lends itself well to

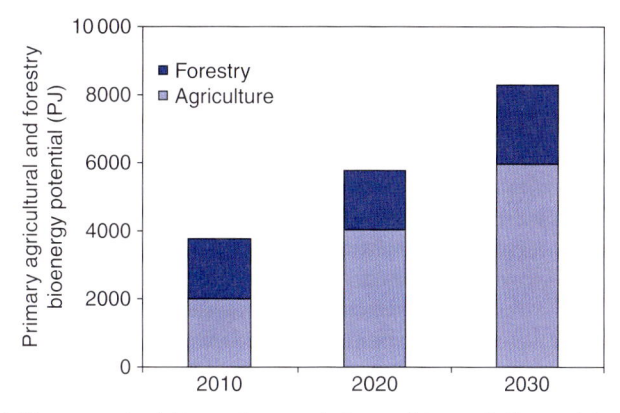

Figure 1 Environmentally compatible bioenergy potential from primary agriculture and forestry in Europe. Adapted from [5].

the combined heat and power (CHP) concept where smaller distributed plants are providing heat for district heating to their local communities as well as electricity and are burning locally produced biomass fuels. This type of installation can deliver overall conversion efficiencies twice that of a dedicated electricity generation plant although the conversion efficiency for electricity generation is lower than for a dedicated generation plant. This type of installation is obviously easier to implement in colder climates where the need for district heating is higher. It can be difficult to install district heating in existing buildings.

5.04.3 Life-Cycle Analysis

While power generation from biomass has been promoted as a mechanism for reducing the net emissions of CO_2 and other GHGs, there have been concerns over the fossil fuel used for planting, harvesting and transporting the material as well as the manufacture, transport, and application of fertilizers and pesticides. Life-cycle analysis (LCA) is a method used to provide information on the cumulative environmental impacts over the life cycle of a process and can be used to assess the overall impact of different alternative fuels. The carbon balance for biomass compared to other fuels used in power generation is shown in **Figure 2** and a selection of biomass fuels are compared in **Figure 3**.

A fuller treatment of the various ways of computing the LCA of a biomass fuel is the subject of a separate chapter in this volume.

5.04.4 How Does Biomass Power Generation Pay?

The decision to invest in a biomass combustion plant will normally be based on commercial considerations. This decision will be governed by current and expected future power price, legislation, expected investment and price levels for the fuel, and also the expectations for future government support for biomass combustion. Biomass is typically not available at a cost comparable to coal

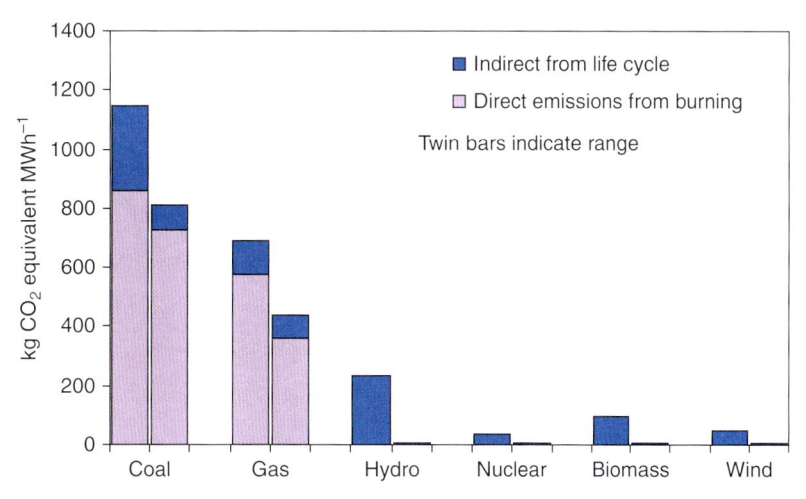

Figure 2 Comparison of life-cycle CO_2 equivalent emissions from different power generation technologies. Adapted from [6].

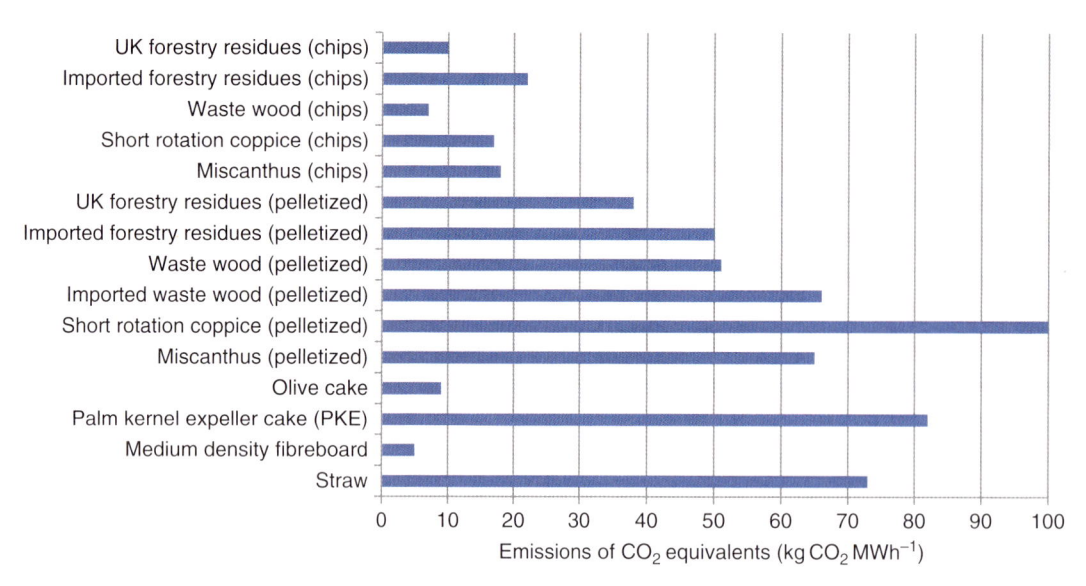

Figure 3 Emissions of greenhouse gas from production and delivery of different biomass fuels to power stations in the United Kingdom, expressed as CO_2 equivalents. Adapted from [7]. PKE, Palm Kernel Expeller cake; SRC, short rotation coppice.

or natural gas, so some additional incentive is required to make biomass-firing happen. Currently, this incentive is, in most countries, in the form of feed-in tariffs or some sort of obligation/quotas.

Many biofuels are internationally traded commodities with highly variable prices over seasons and years. **Figure** 4 shows the level of variation that was seen in the prices of sunflower meal, citrus pulp, wheat feed pellets, rape meal, sunflower husk pellets, and palm kernel expeller cake (PKE) over the period from 2000 to 2007. A high level of covariation between the different commodities is obvious. Examples of factors influencing the prices are weather, crop success, freight costs, supply and demand, political stability in the region of origin, relative prices of alternative products and market dynamics of its core market such as paper and pulp, animal feed, board manufacturers, and road transport fuels.

The 2003 peak was caused by a combination of factors: very hot weather in southern Europe and Ukraine, reduced crop yield, high freight demand to China, and reduced vessel availability due to port bottlenecks. The year 2006/07 saw an even higher price increase driven by poor weather conditions in key areas, high freight costs, low stocks from 2006, increasing proportion of corn going into fuel, changes in attitude to animal feed in Asia, etc. It does not help that the market is characterized by a lack of price

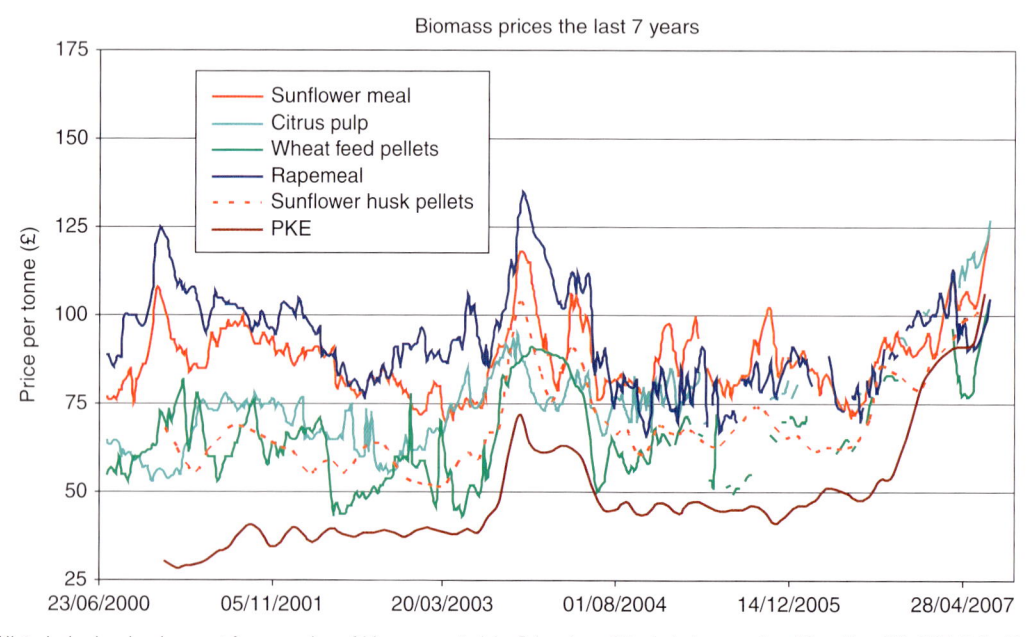

Figure 4 Historical price development for a number of biomass materials. Price doesn't include transport and handling [8]. PKE, Palm Kernel Expeller cake.

transparency, high volatility, and poor credit rating of some players. This is clearly a high-risk environment to make long-term capital investments and the traditional strategy for generators is to avoid high-risk projects.

The two most fundamental factors in the commercial evaluation of a potential fuel for a power station are the available volume and price. A power generating unit producing 100 MW of electricity at a thermal efficiency of 35% will require in the order of 500 kilotonnes of high-quality biomass fuel per year if it is operating around the clock. This is the equivalent of 6 lorries per hour if deliveries take place 8 h a day and the required store to provide a buffer for a long weekend of 4 days would have to hold 5500 tonnes or 8000 m^3 if the fuel is wood pellets or PKE but 30 000 m^3 if it is dry sawdust. This is obviously a situation that requires a high level of logistic control.

The traditional commercial model used by many power generators is based on a few large contracts with a few suppliers and large traded units. This model is not suitable for domestic biomass fuels as many production units are relatively small farms. Exceptions to this are fuels like PKE and olive residue where the fuel is the residual product of a large-scale manufacturing operation. The significant extra administration that is required to manage a large number of contracts with smaller suppliers will add to the cost and risk of the use of biomass fuels or create a business opportunity for organizations that are already operating in this type of market, for example, the cereal and grain market.

5.04.5 Legislation and Regulation

In 1997, many governments signed up to the Kyoto Protocol and made commitments to reduce their CO_2 emissions and help tackle climate change. The methods used in different countries to promote this development vary widely. By early 2010, at least 83 countries had some mechanism or policy for the promotion of renewable generation. Most common is a feed-in tariff, which is used in at least 50 countries. Renewable obligations or quotas are used in 10 countries [9]. The legislation promoting renewable technologies is different in each country and is therefore a complex issue and difficult to discuss in general terms in a way that covers the situation everywhere. Below are a few comments on EU legislation from a British perspective.

In the European Union, there are a number of directives directly regulating the power industry. The EU Integrated Pollution Prevention and Control (IPPC) Directive specifies that best available techniques (BATs) for minimizing the environmental impact of a process should be applied. Environmental emissions from power plants are regulated by either the Large Combustion Plant Directive (LCPD) or the Waste Incineration Directive (WID) via the IPPC process, depending on the fuel. The LCPD limits emissions of nitrogen oxides (NO_x), SO_2, and particulate material from power plants with a thermal input at least 50 MW. The WID comes into play when the plant incinerates or coincinerates wastes. WID imposes stricter limits on emissions into the air, soil, surface water, and groundwater than LCPD. Member states are obliged to report national emissions of listed pollutants to the European Pollution Emission Register (EPER), operating under the umbrella of the IPPC Directive.

The LCPD is a European directive and is therefore applicable to all large combustion plants in the European Union. It introduces stringent emission limit values (ELVs) for all combustion plants over 50 MW$_{th}$. By 1 January 2008, all 'new' combustion plants (those in operation after 1987) had to comply with LCPD or opt out and operate no more than 20 000 h before closing by 2015 at the latest. Most plants have been forced to fit flue gas desulfurization (FGD) equipment and make combustion modifications to reduce NO_x to meet the LCPD requirements.

The Industrial Emissions Directive (IED) was approved by the European Parliament in July 2010. The intention of this directive is to combine a number of pieces of EU legislation into one single directive and also tighten the emission limits further from those in the LCPD (see Section 5.04.5.1). The IED is planned to come into force in 2016 and plants that are opted out will be allowed to operate under their current emission limits for 17 500 h between 2016 and 2023 [10].

5.04.5.1 Emission Limits

In the United Kingdom, the EU IPPC Directive has been transposed into the pollution prevention and control (PPC) regime. Under PPC, power stations are regulated by the Environment Agency (EA). Permits issued under PPC must be based on the BATs, taking into account the local environmental conditions, geographical location, and technical characteristics of the specific installation.

This emphasis on the application of BAT has replaced the best available technology not entailing excessive cost (BATNEEC) to reduce the environmental impact of the process. BAT does still include an economic assessment but this is of less weight than previously (Table 1).

The WID is an EU directive with the purpose to limit, as far as practicable, negative effects on the environment, in particular pollution by emissions into the air, soil, surface water, and groundwater, and minimize the risks to the environment and human health from the incineration and coincineration of waste. The Directive defines stringent operational and technical conditions and emission limits for plants incinerating and coincinerating waste to safeguard a high level of environmental and health protection. Despite being an EU-wide regulation, its interpretation has varied between countries. One example is tallow, which can be cofired in non-WID-compliant plants in some European countries, while it has been classified as a WID substance in other countries and therefore it is legal to burn it in only WID-compliant plants.

Table 1 Emission limits for a large combustion plant under the current LCPD and suggested IED [11]

	LCPD (existing plant)	IED (existing plant)
SO_2, coal plant > 500 MW_{th} (mg Nm^{-3})	400	200
NO_x, coal plant > 300 MW_{th} (mg Nm^{-3})	500	200
Particulates, coal plant > 300 MW_{th} (mg Nm^{-3})	50	20

IED, Industrial Emissions Directive; LCPD, Large Combustion Plant Directive.

5.04.5.1.1 *Renewable Obligation*

The Renewable Obligation (RO) is the UK Government's primary mechanism to support the production of renewable electricity. It was introduced in April 2002 and obliges electricity suppliers to source an increasing percentage of electricity from renewable sources. The obligation rises each year, starting at 3% in 2002/03 in England and Wales and rising to 15.4% by 2015/16.

Electricity generators using renewable sources are awarded Renewable Obligation Certificates (ROCs) in proportion to their renewable generation. Suppliers demonstrate compliance by redeeming these certificates that they have acquired from the generators via a market mechanism. The alternatives are to pay a buyout penalty for each ROC certificate they cannot provide or to purchase ROCs from a supplier who has a surplus. The buyout payments are recycled to those suppliers that redeem ROCs (often referred to as the 'green smear' or 'recycle'). A banded structure was introduced in 2009 where 1 MWh of electricity generated from renewable sources earns a number of ROC certificates ranging from 0.25 to 2 depending on the type of renewable generation used. Cofiring of regular biomass earns 0.5 ROC while stand-alone biomass generation earns 1.5 ROC for the same fuel and if it is using energy crops or is a CHP plant, it earns 2 ROC.

A further support mechanism for renewable generation in the United Kingdom is the 'Levy Exemption Certificate' (LEC), which is awarded to generators for generation of electricity from nonfossil sources and relieves them from paying the climate change levy [12], which is an environmental tax levied on electricity, natural gas, coal, petroleum, and hydrocarbon gas. One LEC is awarded for each MWh of electricity that is generated from renewable sources.

5.04.6 What Technology Choices Are Available?

5.04.6.1 Technology Development

Boilers have been a major part of industrial applications since the industrial revolution in the 1700s and still are. Power and heat can nowadays be distributed more efficiently, and larger and more efficient units can be constructed feeding many end users through distribution networks for both electricity and heat.

Fire-tube boilers were developed early on, with the hot combustion gases passing through tubes submerged in water that is brought to the boil, producing steam. The heat losses in such a system are low as both the fire and the flue gas are kept within the shell containing the water, and thus most heat losses are absorbed by the water. The size and steam pressure are, however, limited by the containment capacity of the shell. These units are still in use in many places but not for modern power generation.

The next development was the water-tube boiler developed in the second half of the 1800s. Here, the steam production takes place in tubes with the water flowing through them. This has the advantage that the production capacity can be increased by simply adding more tubes and the smaller diameter tubes can contain a much higher pressure than the larger shell. On the other hand, the combustion chamber has to be insulated much more heavily as the heat loss through walls is not recovered by the water as in the shell boiler.

The insulation problem was later solved by making the furnace walls out of the water tubes, and thus allowing wall losses to be recovered by the water again. This is the prevailing technology used in all large- and most medium-sized boilers today.

The combustion in a boiler is controlled by four factors:

1. air supply
2. mixing of fuel and air
3. temperature
4. combustion time

Sufficient air for complete combustion has to be provided and it has to be mixed efficiently with the fuel to ensure that fuel is burned completely. If mixing is poor, excess air has to be provided to ensure that the fuel has sufficient oxygen available to it for complete combustion. This extra oxygen comes with 79% nitrogen in the air and has to be heated to the combustion temperature, which increases the gas volume per unit of fuel. This results in lower efficiency and also a requirement for fans, ducts, etc., with a higher flow capacity making the plant more expensive to build. Poor mixing also leads to high emissions of CO and other products from incomplete combustion, causing environmental problems.

The temperature has to be high enough for the combustion reactions to take place at a rate that allows complete combustion in the particular plant. Combustion time is the final factor and will together with the temperature define the size of the fuel particles that can be used. Smaller particles burn faster but need more investment in milling plant as well as more energy for the milling. Unburned carbon in the ash is a loss of efficiency, leading to higher fuel costs as well as increasing the problem with deposition of the ash and can make it impossible to use the ash in cement manufacture or construction projects.

Increasingly sophisticated methods to control and reduce the emissions of harmful substances in the flue gases have been introduced over the years. Textile filters for dust collection have been developed and are no longer only particle collectors. Today, they use limestone, sodium carbonate, and active carbon to capture sulfur oxides, heavy metals, and hydrochloric acid. Injection of ammonia or urea (SNCR – selective noncatalytic reduction) can be used to reduce the emission of NO_x, and if even higher NO_x reduction is required, a catalytic converter (SCR – selective catalytic reduction) can be used.

CHP is the simultaneous production of heat and power (i.e., electricity). At a large scale, a CHP unit is part of a power station. This is an effective way to improve the efficiency of fuel utilization from below 50% in a conventional power-only generation plant to 80–90% or even higher in a CHP plant. This is done by using the power station waste heat as a heat source for district heating or for some industrial process that does not require high-quality steam. The conversion efficiency from fuel to electricity is usually somewhat lower than for a dedicated electricity generator, but the overall efficiency (from fuel to electricity plus usable heat) is much higher. If the heat customer does not require constant heat, then the cost of generating electricity during periods of low or no heat demand will be higher. This concept is most efficient in countries with a climate that requires buildings to be heated to some degree all year-round or in the vicinity of an industry with a constant need for low-quality heat. The CHP concept fits nicely with smaller biomass-fired power stations positioned close to a local fuel source and a district heating network or an industrial heat customer. A separate chapter in this volume looks at biomass CHP in more detail.

5.04.6.2 Fixed and Moving Grates

The simplest combustion configuration is to build a bonfire on the ground. It is a small step to put the fuel on a grate allowing air to pass up through the fuel. This is the grate-fired configuration and is the oldest solution used in boilers. This configuration can be improved by using a fan to force more air through the grate or by using a more sophisticated grate design like a moving grate, vibrating grate, or a chain grate for better control of the combustion process and higher capacity per square meter of grate. The fuel will go through drying, pyrolysis, and char burnout while on the grate, and after complete burnout, the ash will fall off the edge of the grate into the ash pit.

The grate does not permit accurate control of the combustion conditions for individual fuel particles as the airflow through the grate varies with the thickness of the fuel bed. A thinner area of the bed will allow more air through and this will result in more intense combustion, which will make the bed even thinner. The segregated flow of oxygen-rich and lean gas leaving the bed tends to be difficult to mix well. Secondary air jets and a contracting cross section in the furnace exit are used to improve mixing.

The fixed grate consists of a perforated grate that is stationary. It is often water cooled and can be sloping, thus allowing the fuel to slide down the grate when new fuel is pushed onto the feed end. This is a mechanically robust construction with lower cost than grates with moving parts.

The chain grate consists of a moving belt that the fuel can rest on while it is burning. This gives good control of the residence time of the fuel. It looks similar to the traction belt used on tanks and takes the fuel on a journey traveling from one end of the combustion chamber to the other, where it falls over the edge and ends up in the ash pit. The belt is made out of metal to resist the combustion heat and is perforated to allow combustion air to pass through it. The combustion process is controlled by the airflow through the grate and the speed of the grate.

The vibrating grate is based on the same concept as the traveling grate but instead of moving the grate, which is sloping, it is shaken at regular intervals. The shaking makes the fuel bed resting on the grate move toward the ash pit. This is a much simpler construction than the traveling grate and most moving parts can be kept outside the hot section, but the vibrations cause strain on the mechanical parts of the boiler. Burmeister & Wain has built a number of biomass boilers and converted existing boilers to biomass boilers based on a vibrating grate technology. They use a water-cooled grate with a low degree of slope and a vibrator that shakes the bed at regular intervals, typically something like 20 s of shaking every 5 min. It has, according to the manufacturer, "very high availability, low maintenance and low consumption of spare parts" [13].

The spreader stoker system is a hybrid between suspension firing and grate firing. A spreader throws the fuel onto the grate. It is often used together with traveling grates or vibrating grates. Smaller fuel particles will ignite and burn while still suspended in the air and the larger particles are given sufficient time to burn out after landing on the grate. This means that the output from the boiler can be increased without increasing the load on the grate.

The underfeed stoker uses a screw feeder to push fuel up through an opening in the center of the grate. This creates a pile of unburned fuel above the screw. The fuel will then travel toward the edge of the grate while it is burning. This technique is often used in smaller biomass installations for heating applications but not in power generation.

5.04.6.3 Suspension Firing

Suspension firing takes place when small fuel particles are burning while suspended in the combustion chamber. This is common in large utility boilers. It requires that the fuel particles are small enough to burn before falling to the floor or are carried out of the combustion chamber by the combustion gases.

The suspension firing concept allows the load of the boiler to increase in proportion to the volume of the boiler rather than to the area of the bottom surface as is the case for grate combustion. The size of a suspension-fired boiler grows much more slowly than a grate boiler when the output increases. Other advantages with this concept are quick response to load changes, low excess air levels, high efficiency, wide fuel diet, a system that is straightforward for automatic control, and a potential for significant upscaling.

A modern suspension-fired power station boiler usually allows about 2 s for complete burnout of the fuel particle, which is why coal has to be milled to such a fine powder (< 75 µm) before it is burned. It is commonly held that biomass particles that are less dense, more porous, and have a much higher volatile content can be up to 1–2 mm and still burn satisfactorily in such a boiler if the temperature and the oxygen concentration are high enough.

Compared with a grate-based system, this means that a costly and energy-demanding milling plant will be required unless the fuel is supplied as a powder of sufficient fineness. The suspension-fired boiler will also need burners that introduce the fuel and air into the combustion chamber in a way that creates favorable conditions for mixing and ignition of the fuel and air to create stable combustion. A more sophisticated control system is required than for simpler systems like grate firing. Another disadvantage with this concept is that peak temperatures can be high, leading to thermal NO_x formation.

The principal variations to the introduction of fuel and air are wall-fired, corner-fired, and downshot boilers (see **Figure 5**). The wall-fired boiler has a number of burners, each capable of producing a stable flame, mounted on one or two opposing walls. The corner-fired or tangentially fired concept is that the burners are placed in the corners of the furnace and send air and fuel into a fireball in the center of the combustion chamber. This means that rather than having individual discrete flames from each burner as in the wall-fired concept, there is only one flame with lower peak temperatures and longer residence times for the fuel particles. The downshot concept is, finally, a variation on the wall-fired theme where the flames are directed downward giving the fuel particles longer residence time, as they move down and turn to leave the combustion chamber through an opening in the top (see **Figure 5**, left figure). This configuration is mainly used for low-volatile and slow-burning coals such as anthracite.

A number of fossil fuel suspension-fired plants have been converted to burn biomass, wood pellets in particular. One of the earliest conversions was Hässelbyverket power plant just north of Stockholm in Sweden. The plant converted their three boilers of 110 MW_{th} each from coal and oil type to wood pellet firing. The pellets are milled in the original Babcock vertical spindle mills and burned in the original burners, both with small modifications. Other examples of large plants converted from fossil fuel plants to wood pellet plants are Helsingborg in Sweden and Les Awirs in Belgium. There are many examples of smaller oil-fired boilers in the size range from 20 MW_{th} and upward that have been converted to suspension-fire milled wood pellets.

5.04.6.4 Fluidized Beds

The fluidized bed boiler is gaining in popularity and has overtaken the grate-fired boiler in biofuel power generation applications. The principle is very simple: air is blown through a bed of sand and fuel particles at a velocity that is sufficient to suspend the particles on the airstream but not able to lift them permanently out of the bed, that is, 1–3 m s^{-1} at 800–900 °C. This makes the particle bed behave very much like a bubbling fluid and it is called a bubbling fluidized bed (BFB). This bed of constantly moving sand and fuel particles gives very good contact between fuel particles and the air and also very homogeneous conditions, which make it possible to keep peak temperatures low, resulting in low emissions of NO_x. The residence time in the bed is long compared to the conditions in a suspension-fired system. The sand particles give the bed well-defined fluidization properties and maintain the function of the bed even during fluctuations of disturbances in fuel feed. The good contact and long residence time allow combustion with good burnout of relatively large fuel particles. This makes fuel preparation cheaper and less energy demanding. This boiler is also more flexible than a conventional boiler with a wider turndown ratio and very good environmental performance. The capital cost, finally, is low.

A BFB boiler (see **Figure 6**) has a dense bed where the biomass fuel is dried and pyrolyzed. Around 30–40% of the combustion air is introduced through the nozzles at the bottom of the bed (see **Figure 7**) and the rest in the freeboard above the bed where gases and fine particles burn. This type of boiler can handle fuel with a wide range of particle sizes and fuel blends. The best performance is achieved if the majority of the fuel particles are in the size range 5–50 mm. Finer particles tend to blow out of the bed and burn in

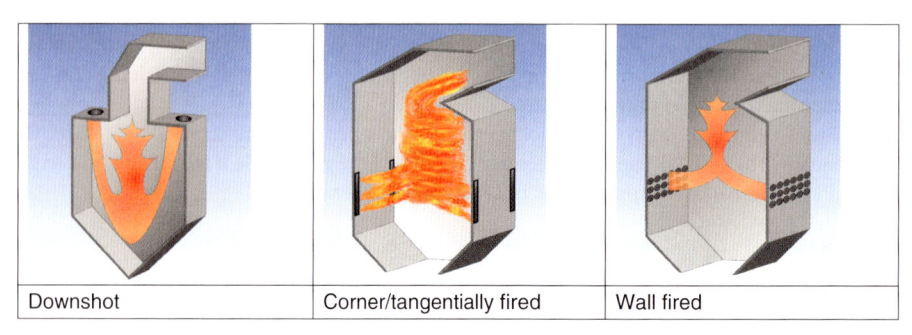

Figure 5 Principal configuration of suspension-fired boilers (courtesy of RWE npower).

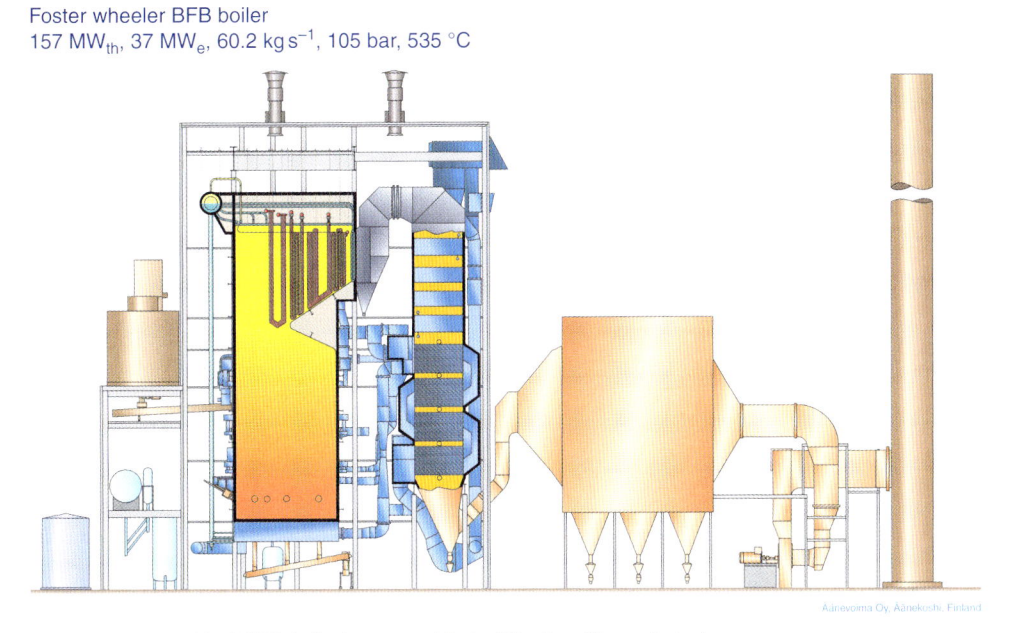

Figure 6 Modern bubbling fluidized bed (BFB) boiler (courtesy of Foster Wheeler with permission).

Figure 7 Primary air nozzles in fluidized bed boiler (courtesy of Foster Wheeler with permission).

the freeboard causing hot zones, which increases NO_x production as well as slagging tendencies. Too large particles will not fluidize properly and can cause the bed to collapse.

Common sizes for BFB boilers are 10–300 MW$_{th}$. Currently, the largest BFB power boiler for biomass fuels in the United Kingdom is the 44 MW$_e$ boiler at Stevens Croft in Scotland.

The circulating fluidized bed (CFB) boiler (see **Figure 8**) takes the principle of the bubbling bed one step further and with increased fluidization velocity the particles are lifted out of the bed and follow the gas out of the combustion chamber. They are then separated from the gas in a cyclone or beam separator and returned to the bed. This usually takes place at velocities of 5–10 m s^{-1} and allows higher turbulence levels and a higher combustion density resulting in more compact boilers. The size of a CFB increases more slowly than a BFB when the steam capacity is scaled up (see **Figure 9**). A modern biomass CFB boiler can be operated with NO_x emissions of less than 150 mg Nm^{-3}, less than 200 mg SO_x and CO Nm^{-3}, and less than 20 mg dust Nm^{-3}.

A weak point in the CFB boiler design is the particle separator, which is large and has traditionally been lined with thick refractory that is exposed to heavy erosion from the fuel particles. Recent advances in design have made it possible to reduce the amount of refractory by using steam-cooled cyclones and thinner refractory.

Another important development in CFB design has been to move the final superheater to the return leg of the particle separator. It is covered by the hot recirculating particles, which are gently fluidized to control the recirculation rate. This creates an

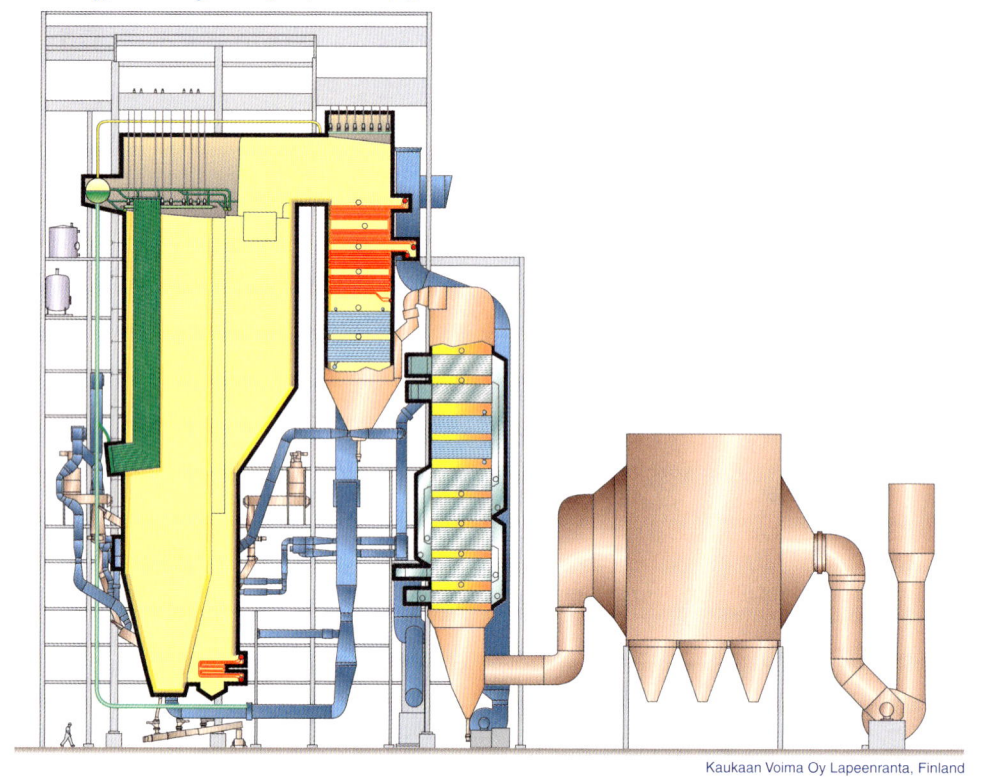

Figure 8 Modern circulating fluidized bed (CFB) boiler (courtesy of Foster Wheeler with permission).

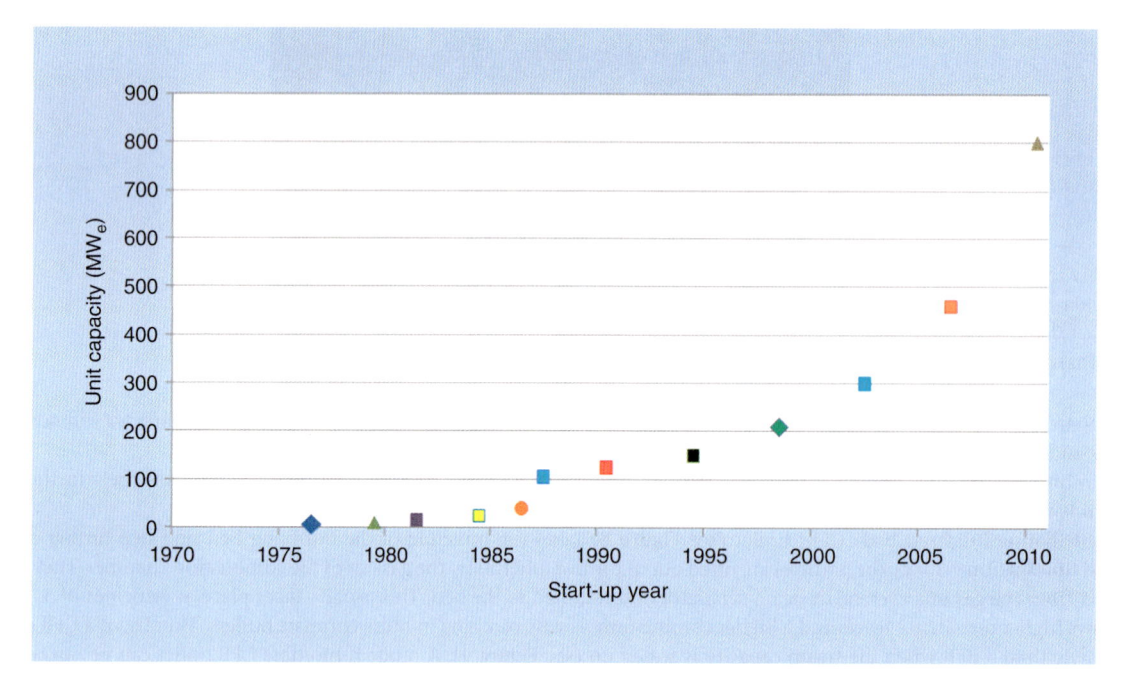

Figure 9 Historical sizes of installed circulating fluidized bed boilers (courtesy of Foster Wheeler with permission).

environment with high heat transfer, low concentrations of corrosive gases, lower peak temperature, and a constant cleaning of the superheater tubes by the fluidized particles. This design can operate at higher steam temperatures and with more corrosive fuels than the traditional design, and use cheaper steel qualities in the superheater.

The most common cause of corrosion in a CFB boiler is the chlorine-induced corrosion. This occurs mostly in the convective heat exchangers. It tends to appear together with high fouling rates due to the presence of alkali and chlorine in fuels that are high in calcium and potassium but low in silica. The mechanisms of this corrosion are currently not well understood but it can be aggravated by the presence of Zn, Pb, and metallic aluminum. This is particularly important if the fuel contains recycled biomass materials that often contain significant amounts of chlorine (from PVC and wood preservatives) and lead and zinc (from paints and wood preservatives).

Alkali chloride corrosion takes place at metal temperatures above 450 °C in carbon steels, and lead/zinc/tin chlorides are corrosive at metal temperatures between 360 and 440 °C. It is therefore important to choose the steam and gas temperatures in a plant intended to burn recycled material so that these temperature windows are avoided as far as possible.

The bed sand has to be chosen carefully to reduce the agglomeration risks with the chosen fuel. No sand works well with all biomass fuels, so a matching procedure is required. Wood ash can react with SiO_2 from the bed sand at temperatures as low as 700–900 °C, forming a layer of calcium or potassium silicate on the bed particles and causing agglomeration. Herbaceous and agricultural fuels like straw, cereals, and grass do not have the same problem with quartz sand as wood does.

One way to reduce the problem of bed agglomeration is to increase the removal rate of bed material and the addition rate of makeup material. This reduces the amount of alkali material available in the bed for the formation of a sticky coat on the bed particles. A better way is to change the bed material to a less troublesome one if such a material can be identified.

The main trend these days seems to be that fluid bed technology is used in most biomass boilers, with the simpler BFB for smaller installations and CFB for anything over 50 MW_e. Leading suppliers [14] are offering commercial solutions for 300 MW_e plant fired on 100% biomass and supercritical plant up to 800 MW_e for cofiring biomass with coal. The main reason for not offering supercritical biomass plant is lack of steels that can resist the corrosion at the metal temperatures reached in such a plant.

5.04.6.5 Gasification

Power generation by gasification takes place in two steps. The first is the actual gasification, which is a pyrolysis process where the solid fuel is heated with insufficient oxygen for combustion. The result is a gas that can be burned, which is the second step. The combustion takes place as a separate process physically removed from the gasification process. The combustion can take place in a gas turbine, a combustion engine, or a boiler. This technology is still in the development phase and has been fraught with technical difficulties. Essent is now operating a gasifier commercially at its Amercentrale power station in Holland. This gasifier uses waste wood and feeds the resulting gas to the 600 MW_e CHP boiler, Amer 9. Gasification is covered in detail in a separate chapter in this volume (*see* Chapter 5.10).

5.04.7 Potential Biofuels

5.04.7.1 Solid Biofuels

Biofuels are completely different from fossil fuels in almost every possible way. As a generalization, solid biomass fuels as a group are soft and fibrous products from plants that have been harvested recently as opposed to hard and brittle coal, which has been geologically deposited deep underground for over 50 million years. Biomass tend to be produced on a much smaller scale than the large mining operations used to extract coal and both the bulk density and the heat content per weight of biomass are considerably lower than for coal while the moisture content of fresh biomass is higher. All this means that transport and handling costs are a much larger part of the total cost of the fuel.

The fact that the properties are so different means that equipment developed for the agricultural sector can sometimes be more suitable than power station equipment that is designed for coal. Although the biomass tends to generate a dust that stays airborne longer than coal, it is not experienced as dirty in the same way as coal dust. Most dry biomass needs to be stored under cover to avoid self-heating, decomposition, and growth of spores and fungi, although product development is changing this situation. Thermally treated wood pellets that are much more hydrophobic are starting to enter the market. While they are more expensive to produce, they can be stored in the open, saving the investment in undercover stores.

Both the lower bulk density (200–800 kg m^{-3}) and the lower calorific value (typically 15–20 MJ kg^{-1} on a dry basis) compared to coal means that the volume to store as well as required transport capacity for biomass is significantly larger per gigajoule. One method to increase the bulk density is pelleting or briquetting, which also improves the bulk handling properties of the fuel, and the drier pellet/briquette will have a higher calorific value, thus reducing the costs for transport, but it is also more expensive to make (**Figure 10**).

The ash content of many biomasses is lower than that of coal, that is, less than 5%, with the ash content of clean stem wood often well below 0.5%. There are also biomass types with very high ash content like rice husks that can have more than 15% ash. The composition of the ash in most biomass is more troublesome than coal ash from a slagging/fouling/bed agglomeration point of view with a high content of alkali like calcium (Ca) and potassium (K). Calcium- and potassium-containing ash deposits very easily on surfaces forming fouling in the form of CaO, $CaSO_4$, and K_2SO_4. These deposits harden on superheaters if not removed frequently by soot blowing. Some biomass fuels can have high concentrations of chlorine, which increases the risk of fouling and particularly high-temperature corrosion in the superheaters, but most of them contain significantly less sulfur than the average coal.

Figure 10 Wood pellets (courtesy of RWE npower).

The format of delivery for biomass fuels is different than for coal as well and requires different systems for reception and handling. The fuel handling system on a power station has to be designed for particular types of fuel as the handling characteristics vary widely. Take straw and coconut shell as two extreme examples: it is easy to see that the requirements and volumetric capacity for a plant delivering the same power output would be completely different for these two fuels.

The chemical characteristics of the fuel in question have a strong impact on its combustion (carbon burnout, slagging, fouling) and environmental (NO_x, SO_x, dust) performance as well as fly ash salability, load capability, and overall plant efficiency. Some of the key factors here are calorific value, moisture, ash content, ash composition, trace element content, and ash fusion temperature.

The most important domestic biomass fuel in the United Kingdom is currently wood. It comes in many forms like virgin wood from the forest, recycled wood from packaging and other sources, demolition wood, forestry residue, and energy crops like willow and poplar. Wood is usually delivered as sawdust, wood chips, or pellets. Dry wood has a calorific value in the order of 19–20 MJ kg^{-1} and typically well below 1% ash. The moisture content varies, with wood pellets typically containing less than 8% and recently felled wood up to 60%.

Energy crop is anything that is grown specifically for the purpose of using it as a fuel. Some of the most popular energy crops are *Miscanthus giganteus* (also known as elephant grass), *Salix* (also known as SRC willow), *Populus* (also known as SRC poplar), switchgrass, and reed canary grass (**Figures 11** and **12**).

5.04.7.1.1 Globally sourced biomass

Olive residues, PKE (see **Figure 13**), shea meal, and other residues such as sunflower husks and citrus pulp pellets are currently produced in the Mediterranean, South East Asia, Indonesia, South America, and Africa and exported to Western countries for use as fuel in power stations. Other examples of biomass fuels on the market are peanut husks, cocoa meal, coconut fiber, and soy residue. They are all by-products from other primary products like olive oil and palm oil. Many are traditionally used for animal feed but have in recent years found an alternative market as fuels for power generation.

Figure 11 *Miscanthus* (furthest away), switchgrass, and reed canary grass (nearest) (courtesy of Rothamsted Research, UK with permission).

Figure 12 A field of *Miscanthus* crop in southern England (courtesy of RWE npower).

Figure 13 Palm oil fruit (~40 mm long). The central kernel can be seen in the left picture. Palm kernel expeller cake is the residue from extraction of the oil content of the kernel (courtesy of RWE npower).

5.04.7.1.1(i) Delivery format

Biomass fuels are available in a number of different formats, varying from a fine dust and sawdust to chips, pellets, briquettes, and bales and as liquids.

Chips and dust are the formats requiring least postharvest processing and are often the cheapest fuel if local production is available. Chipping can be done directly in the forest using a mobile plant. The chips are typically between 10 and 50 mm. They can be milled to form wood dust (sawdust). They have the advantage that they can be stored in the open as long as they are carefully monitored for self-heating and spontaneous ignition. But their bulk density is substantially lower than that of pellets, so transport will be more expensive per unit of energy.

Pellets and briquettes are generally more cost effective to transport due to their higher bulk density of typically 600–700 kg m^{-3} and are less prone to 'hang-up' in the bunkers and conveyors. They are, though, considerably more expensive to produce. Pellets are biofuel compressed into small cylinders with a typical diameter of 5–15 mm and a length of 10–50 mm (**Figure 10**). They have a higher and more standard bulk density than the raw materials and being clean and dry (< 10% moisture) they are easier to transport and handle. They can be stored much longer than other wood sources but they can be very dusty and have to be stored under cover and dry.

Biomass can also be delivered to the power station in bales. This format is mostly used for straw and requires special equipment to remove strings and break up the bales or a plant designed specially to burn bales. Bales are relatively easy to transport and have a good bulk density. They can also be stored in the open for shorter periods of time. A modern large bale can weigh 300–500 kg.

Forestry residues are any part of the tree remaining when the primary product (logs) has been removed. These residues are collected and either chipped in the forest or compressed into bales and transported from the forest by lorry for chipping by the end user, which again requires specialized equipment, that is, a chipping plant.

5.04.7.2 Liquid Biofuels for Power Generation/Combined Heat and Power

Diesel and heavy fuel oil can be replaced with liquid biomass fuels like rapeseed oil, palm oil, tallow, and tall oil. Palm oil has become very sensitive from a public relations point of view due to all the media coverage around palm plantations and their negative impact on biodiversity, orangutans, etc. Biodiesel is an excellent fuel but currently almost twice as expensive as other less refined bio-oils. Tall oil is used in many European plants, but has the disadvantage that some qualities are highly corrosive and supplied quality is highly variable.

Oil burners and systems for power stations have been developed over many years. A conversion of existing systems to burn bio-oil is usually fairly straightforward provided that the fuel can be conditioned to a viscosity that is suitable for the burner in question. Where problems are encountered these are usually associated with fuel handling equipment and burner/flame monitoring systems rather than the burner itself. The flame from liquid biofuels has different characteristics than traditional oil flames and requires intelligent flame detectors programmed to deal with biofuel flames.

Many high calorific value liquid biofuels are good fuels and suitable for use in boiler applications with minor modifications. Potential liquid biofuels that could be used in power stations include crude vegetable oils (palm oil, soybean oil, coconut oil, olive oil, and rapeseed oil), waste vegetable oils (e.g., from potato crisp factories), and nonedible oils (e.g., tall oil).

5.04.8 Health and Safety

There are significant safety hazards associated with the introduction of biomass into power stations. Most safety hazards are however of a similar nature to those already present with coal, for example, fire and explosion risk. Established hazard prevention and control systems can therefore be adapted as necessary.

While this is adequate in many respects, biomass does present some new challenges. The biological nature makes them interesting to various types of vermin and pests, which can cause health hazards and have to be managed properly. There are also some potential health risks related to exposure to dust, mold, and nuts. The supplier of biomass materials is obliged by law (in the United Kingdom) to provide a health and safety data sheet where all health- and safety-related relevant information is stated. It should be part of the procedure to collect and use this information.

5.04.8.1 Personnel Issues

5.04.8.1.1 Oxygen depletion and poisoning

Wood pellets can release significant amounts of CO, CO_2, and CH_4, which can lead to oxygen depletion. An investigation into oxygen depletion and release of CO during ocean transport of wood pellets found that an oxygen-deficient atmosphere and lethal levels of CO can be reached after a week in a confined space [15]. Similar findings for wood chips and logs are presented [16]. It is therefore necessary to monitor these gaseous components and oxygen carefully in closed stores for wood pellets, chips, and logs and during offloading of vessels.

5.04.8.1.2 Allergies (nuts)

An anaphylactic shock in an individual with nut allergy can be fatal. There are several different types of nut-related biomass materials on offer to generators including shell of peanut, groundnut, and cashew nut. To protect staff, all personnel who could possibly come into physical contact with these materials must be screened for nut allergies. Safeguards must also be put in place to ensure that nobody with an allergy is exposed.

5.04.8.1.3 Mold

The assessment of any health risk arising from mold growth (from decomposing biomass) is more difficult than for dust. There are many factors at work, including

- amount of material spilt from process,
- the conditions that any spilt material is exposed to dampness/warmth,
- storage time in any area,
- presence of visible mold,
- rate of mold growth on spilt or compacted biomass, and
- airborne spore level in the breathing zone.

There are no current occupational exposure limits for fungal spores. Information is available from specialist occupational hygiene sources on typical airborne levels found in different occupations and measurements have been made at some power stations. Levels are extremely variable. Increased levels of airborne mold are linked to increased rates of organic dust toxic syndrome (ODTS) and allergic alveolitis. Generally, fungal infections are unlikely to occur because organisms able to grow in decomposed vegetable protein do not usually cause harm to healthy people. Health surveillance should be conducted more regularly for those likely to be susceptible.

5.04.8.1.4 Dust exposure

The main concern with dust exposure is that it can sensitize the respiratory tract causing rhinitis or occupational asthma. Vegetable proteins are present in all biomass, meaning that they are prone to decomposition, especially if subject to warmth and dampness. In this instance, spores from fungi, by-products of mold growth, mycotoxins, and endotoxins from bacterial breakdown can be released. The possible health effects of these substances are occupational asthma, infection, ODTS (toxic febrile reaction), and extrinsic allergic alveolitis. Hardwood dusts are classed as carcinogenic. The type of health problems that different substances can cause are summarized in **Table 2**.

There are strict exposure limits for various materials. Exposure limits that are relevant for biomass handling in power stations are shown in **Table 3**.

5.04.8.1.5 Nuisance issues: Odor

Unlike coal, each biomass has a distinctive smell. This is a result of organic ester compounds contained within the biomass. This odor can be pungent and personnel may not enjoy working with certain biomass types. Organic ester compounds are not listed as dangerous substances and therefore do not have occupational exposure limits.

5.04.8.2 Process Safety

5.04.8.2.1 Fire and explosions

Biomass by its nature is a very reactive material. This means that the risk of fires and explosions is greater than with most other solid fuels processed at a power station. Even minor fires can lead to plant damage and loss of generation. If biomass fuels also act as a source of ignition for other flammable materials, they can lead to catastrophic explosions that can result in loss of life. Some examples of grain silo explosions are Blaye in France where 11 people were killed, an explosion in Kansas in 1998 killing 2 people, and the recent (30 November 2010) silo explosion in Ohio, USA, knocking a house off its foundations.

5.04.8.2.2 Biomass fires

Fire can happen for several reasons, and the most common reasons are

Table 2 Types of health problems that can be caused by exposure to different substances

Eye irritation	Can be caused by exposure to any type of dust
Skin irritation (contact irritant dermatitis)	Can be caused by exposure to any type of dust. Friction and defatting of skin can occur with repeated/prolonged contact
Contact allergic dermatitis	Some wood dusts can sensitize the skin and subsequently cause inflammation of the skin
Allergic rhinitis and conjunctivitis	Can be caused by wood dust and the storage mite found in grain dust. Other solid biomass materials containing vegetable proteins could be potential sensitizers of the nose and eyes. Allergic rhinitis is associated with an increased risk of occupational asthma
Occupational asthma	Caused by sensitization of an employee's airways to an allergen inhaled at work after a period of exposure. This will typically occur within 2 years. Wood and grain dust are among the worst allergens but all biomass should be seen as a possible cause of occupational asthma
Nut allergy	There is a risk that anyone with a nut allergy could experience anaphylactic shock if they ingested dust particles. For this reason, it is recommended that no one with a nut allergy should work with or in proximity to a biomass containing nut extract
Carcinogenicity	Hard wood dust is classified as a group 1 carcinogen (i.e., known to cause cancer in humans) and the Health and Safety Executive have given it a carc rating (carcinogenic)

Table 3 Dust workplace exposure limits according to EH40 [17]

Material	Long-term exposure limit (8 h TWA), (mg m^{-3})	Short-term exposure limit (8 h TWA), (mg m^{-3})	Comment
Flour dust (applies to ground cereals)[a]	10	30	Sen
Grain dust	10		
Hardwood dust[a]	5		Sen, Carc
Softwood dust[a]	5		Sen
Pulverized fuel ash	4 (respirable dust) 10 (inhalable dust)		

[a] Note that the limits for flour, hardwood, and softwood dusts are currently under review.
Carc, carcinogenic; Sen, sensitizer; TWA, time weighted average.

- hot working, such as welding, which is a common cause of fires,
- plant failure, that is, hot surface or energetic sparks, and
- self-heating.

High-risk activities are controlled by procedures, and on a power station site there is normally a permit to work system in place. All high-risk activities would come under this system and therefore be tightly controlled.

Plant failures continue to occur despite best endeavors at prevention. However, as control and instrumentation improve, it is becoming more common to find that the system has a diagnosis or monitoring process built into it. This may be as simple as measuring the bearing temperature of a gearbox. If this exceeds the permitted range, the control system will shut down the process. A serious silo fire was caused by the overheating of the gearbox on the reclaim screw.

5.04.8.2.3 Self-heating

Self-heating occurs when a reactive material generates heat that cannot be dissipated. The heat generated increases the temperature of the material (and hence reaction rates) until it reaches the autoignition temperature at which point the material starts to burn. There are many factors that can influence this process. With coal the risk of self-heating could be reduced by compacting to reduce the supply of oxygen. This works as the self-heating process is based on the oxidation of the coal, but with biomass it is not as simple because a heating process also occurs with biomass based on biological activity.

Aerobic decomposition (composting) occurs in the presence of oxygen and produces CO_2 as well as heat. Nitrogen within the biomass is used for energy by the active bacteria. This means that a specific carbon/nitrogen ratio within the fuel will promote aerobic decomposition. Aerobic decomposition is undesirable not only because it uses up potential fuel, but also because of the CO_2 production. In a large stockpile, this may increase the stockpile temperature to 80 °C. Within the stockpile, where no oxygen is present, anaerobic decomposition may occur. This produces methane, a small proportion of CO_2, and heat. In terms of fire risk, this is much worse, as methane is a highly combustible gas, especially if it is trapped within the stockpile and pressurized as a result. For both processes, higher moisture contents will exacerbate the heating effect. This is the opposite of coal, where drier stockpiles present more risk.

5.04.8.2.4 Explosions

Fine dust from any combustible fuel may present an explosion risk. Explosion can occur where there is a combustible dust that is dispersed in sufficient concentration, enough oxidant in intimate contact with the dust, and a source of ignition. If this event occurs in a confined space, the sudden release of stored energy in a confined space will produce a rapid pressure increase or explosion. If this event occurs and is not constrained, it will produce a flash fire, which would cause injury but not a serious overpressurization.

Accidentally released dust within the plant satisfies all these necessary criteria, so it is a significant safety risk. Other areas at risk of explosion are the pulverized fuel pipework and the mills. The explosion pentagon (**Figure 14**) describes the required conditions for an explosion to occur.

With biomass there are several areas where there is potential for an explosion to occur:

- unloading and handling
- storage
- bunkers
- milling plant

5.04.8.2.5 Biomass characteristics

Information that is important for the risk assessment and design of operating conditions in biomass equipment is the minimum ignition temperature (layer) (MIT_{layer}), minimum ignition temperature for a dust cloud (MIT_{cloud}), minimum ignition energy

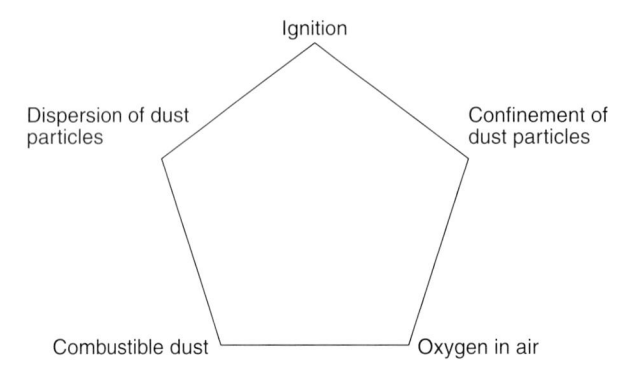

Figure 14 The explosion pentagon.

Table 4 Characteristics of some common biomass fuels

	Coal	Sawdust	Wood pellets	Palm kernel expeller cake	Olive residue	Miscanthus dust
Volatiles (% as rec.)		55–80	70–80	70	60–80	65–75
Ash (% as rec.)		0.1–2	0.5–1.5	1.5–5	2.5–10	2–4
Moisture (% as rec.)		15–40	3–10	5–15	5–20	10–20
NCV (MJ kg^{-1} as rec.)			17–19	16–18	16–18	15.5–17
P_{max} (barg)	7.5–10	6.8	7.2	8.2	8	8.5
Kst (bar, m s^{-1})	85–165	81	70	73	80	123
MIT$_{5\,mm\,layer}$ (°C)	170	355	370		280	31
MIT$_{cloud}$ (°C)	610	465	495	460–470	445	415
MIE (mJ)	60			30–100		
Median particle size (μm)		380	650		80	68.51

Courtesy of RWE npower. NCV, Net calorific value.

(MIE), maximum pressure (P_{max}), and rate of pressure increase (Kst). MIT$_{layer}$ is the lowest temperature of a surface at which a dust layer resting on the surface can self-ignite. This is usually given for a 5 mm layer but it will decrease for thicker layers. MIT$_{cloud}$ and MIE (the lowest energy spark that can ignite an explosive cloud) are crucial in determining the risk of ignition of a dust cloud; Table 4 gives some examples.

If the cloud ignites, the maximum pressure that can develop (P_{max}) and a measure of the rate of pressure increase (Kst) help determine the required strength of a vessel to contain the overpressurization event and how fast an explosion suppression system must be able to act. The particle size and moisture content in the dust cloud are also important factors in that smaller particles have larger specific surface and generally are more reactive, so the exothermic oxidation process taking place between the fuel surface and the oxygen in the atmosphere will be faster. There is therefore a connection between particle size and explosion severity.

5.04.8.2.6 DSEAR

The DSEAR (Dangerous Substances and Explosive Atmosphere Regulations; The UK Health and Safety Executive 2002) legislation sets out the minimum requirements for the protection of workers from fire and explosion risks arising from dangerous substances and potentially explosive atmospheres. DSEAR complements the requirement to manage risks under the Management of Health and Safety at Work Regulations. Following a 3-year transitional period, DSEAR became mandatory for all workplaces on 1 July 2006.

DSEAR separates the workplace into classified zones where there is a risk of fire or explosion. This will include the biomass bulk handling systems on all sites. Furthermore, the use of a different biomass on any plant and the associated change in properties and also occurrences of accidental release may change the zone classification of some areas. This must be investigated and taken into account as it may require a change of control measures on-site.

The current industry guidelines [18] for DSEAR legislation recommend a maximum dust accumulation of 2 mm over small areas and 0.5 mm over wide areas. The ability to maintain dust levels within these limits may therefore limit the blend proportion and identify which fuel is preferred for continued use.

5.04.9 Material Handling and Fuel Processing

5.04.9.1 Bulk Density

The bulk density of biomass materials is highly variable. The denser common materials are PKE and pellets of olive and wood. These materials have a bulk density of 600–700 kg m^{-3}, which can be compared to a typical bulk density of hard coals in the region of 1000 kg m^{-3}. Fluffy and dry materials like dry sawdust, straw, grass, and shredded paper will often be lighter than 200 kg m^{-3}. This is an important consideration in that it affects the required volume of storage and volumetric flow through the fuel supply system. Particularly for fuel with a low calorific value, it is important to ensure that the volumetric capacity of the used system is capable of supporting the required firing rate.

5.04.9.2 Storing Biomass

Any plant burning biomass will require some level of on-site storage. There are several issues associated with storage of biomass materials. The moisture content, the calorific value, and the flow properties can be affected by degradation due to microbiological activity. The temperature in a stockpile of biomass rises from the heat generated by decomposition processes, which, in extreme cases, can lead to self-ignition and even fire. The decomposition also results in loss of both mass and energy content of the material. The heat generation in a biomass pile is controlled by the moisture content and particle size.

Another problem related to storage of biomass materials is that rodents and birds show interest in some materials. PKE in particular seems to be attractive.

Wood pellets have some additional safety-related issues. Maybe the most important aspect of storage of wood pellets is that they can release significant amounts of CO and CH_4. This can constitute a serious health hazard if the pellets are stored in a confined space like a silo or a closed shed. Any such store must be equipped with effective monitoring and rigorous procedures to safeguard the well-being of anybody entering the store.

The amount of installed on-site storage depends on available space but is very much an economical decision as many biomass materials need undercover storage, which is expensive. The most common situation is to have a minimum of 1 day's on-site storage capacity but between 1 and 2 weeks' worth of store is not uncommon. On-site stockpiles of material that can be stored in the open, like wood chips and logs, are generally significantly larger. Some on-site storage is needed to ensure uninterrupted operation in case of supply irregularities but also to be able to accept deliveries already on-route in the case of operational problems. Most common store types are of the shed type or silos. The shed has a smaller footprint than a multisilo solution while the silo can be made completely enclosed and automated, which is more difficult to achieve in a shed.

5.04.9.3 Fuel Preparation

In the United Kingdom, a biomass-fired plant will mostly have a purpose-built milling plant usually based on hammer mills. In the case of a converted coal-fired plant, older existing mills (like vertical spindle mills traditionally used for the milling of hard coal) could be reused.

There are also safety issues when milling biomass due to its high volatile matter content and the fact that combustible volatiles are released in significant quantities at temperatures above about 180 °C, that is, at much lower temperatures than for bituminous coals. The mill atmosphere is normally kept well past the fuel-rich limit of the explosive range to control the risk of explosions. Each time the mill is started or stopped, it will have to pass through the explosive range; this will also take place during loss of feed incidents and intermittent fuel feed. When this takes place, it is extra important to make sure that the temperature in the mill is well below the MIT. It is also important to minimize the risk of tramp material causing sparks in the mill as the minimum ignition energy for biomass can be an order of magnitude lower than for coal. It is necessary to reassess and modify the mill operating procedures on a plant conversion before starting to fire biomass.

5.04.9.3.1 Hammer mills

Hammer mills are suitable for most types of biomass fuels and can be used to produce particle sizes appropriate for pulverized fuel-fired boilers. It is generally not necessary to reduce biomass to the same size or shape as coal (typically 70% < 70 μm). In many suspension-fired plants, biomass firing occurs with particles predominantly less than 2 mm.

Hammer mills are used on many biomass-fired power stations. Some European examples are Amer 8 in the Netherlands and the combined heat and power plants in Hässelby and Helsingborg in Sweden.

A hammer mill is essentially a steel drum containing a vertical or horizontal rotor on which pivoting hammers are mounted. The rotor spins at a high speed inside the drum while biomass is fed into the mill via a feed hopper. The biomass is impacted by the hammers that are free to swing and is reduced in size before being expelled through screens in the drum wall. The particle size distribution can be controlled by the use of different screens in the hammer mills (**Figure 15**).

Hammer mills work better with dry wood than with wet wood. Both throughput and mill current are affected by high moisture content. Aberthaw power station in Wales uses hammer mills to mill fresh wood chips with a moisture content of over 50%. The

Figure 15 Hammer mill; the combined heat and power plants in Hässelby and Helsingborg in Sweden (courtesy of CPM Europe).

experience is that it can be done but it is not easy and limits the capacity of the mill significantly compared to drier wood. The other extreme is to mill wood pellets in hammer mills. Wood pellets are very dry (typically well below 10% moisture) and hard. Amer 8 in the Netherlands uses hammer mills to mill wood pellets. It is reported that all hammers need to be replaced after every 2 weeks of operation due to high wear of the hammer edges.

5.04.9.3.2 Vertical spindle mills

Vertical spindle mills are widely used on UK coal-fired power stations. A number of ongoing and past conversion projects, where coal-fired boilers are converted to neat biomass firing, are based on the use of slightly modified vertical spindle mills to prepare wood pellets to be burned in modified coal burners.

The fuel is, in a vertical spindle mill, pulverized by attrition (brittle particle breakup by friction) between large rollers and a rotating mill table (see **Figure 16**). Most biomass materials are fibrous and ductile and, thus, fundamentally not well suited for milling in vertical spindle mills. The mill product is carried by the air toward the classifier. The classifier works similar to a dust cyclone that allows small particles to carry on toward the burners, and larger particles are recirculated to the mill table. Rejected material that cannot be pulverized falls down into 'reject boxes', which can be emptied while the mill is in service. Examples of vertical spindle mills include the Babcock 'E' series and the NEI/International Combustion LM type. The more recent LM and Babcock mills operate under pressure, whereas earlier LM mills ran under suction.

If the mill function and classification is poor, the consequence is suffering flame stabilization and burnout. However, biomass particles are inherently more reactive than coal, and larger particles can burn completely before leaving the combustion chamber to a greater extent than is the case for coal. The trick is therefore to set the classifier to allow larger biomass particles to pass. This is normally the case for static classifiers without significant modifications, but more modern dynamic classifiers are much more efficient in rejecting larger particles. This can be a problem, and dynamic classifiers will need modifications to operate on neat biomass.

A limiting factor for vertical spindle mills milling biomass is that they have a tendency for the mill differential pressure and the mill power consumption to increase with increasing throughput of biomass and this can often limit throughput. The capacity to mill biomass will be significantly lower in terms of thermal throughput than for coal, and modifications to the mill will be required but they are usually not far reaching. The Amer 9 power station in the Netherlands and Ontario Power Generation (OPG) in Canada have operated vertical spindle mills on 100% wood pellets with encouraging results [19].

5.04.9.3.3 Tube-ball mills

Tube-ball type mills (**Figure 17**) are used on several UK coal-fired power stations but the authors do not know of any cases where this mill type has been converted for neat biomass. A successful trial milling briquettes made from 50% wood and 50% coal was

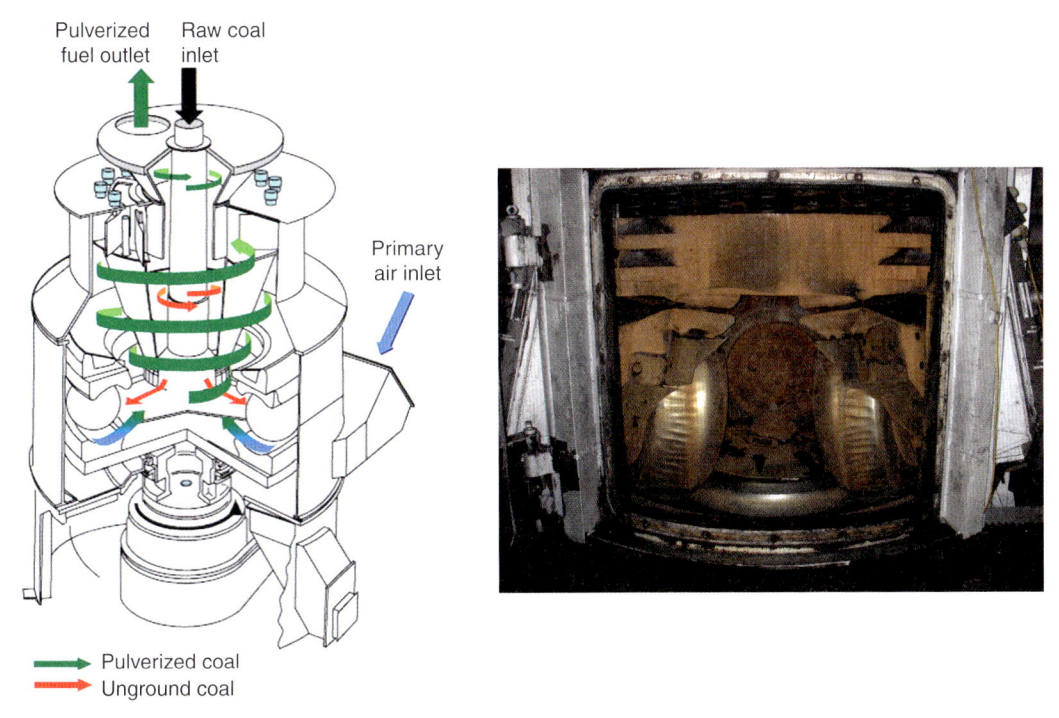

Figure 16 Vertical spindle mill. To the left is a sketch of a Babcock 10E mill used at Didcot A, Ratcliffe-on-Soar, Drax, and Ferrybridge in the United Kingdom and to the right an internal view of an MPS Bertz mill used at the UK stations Tilbury, Rugeley, and Longannet (courtesy of RWE npower).

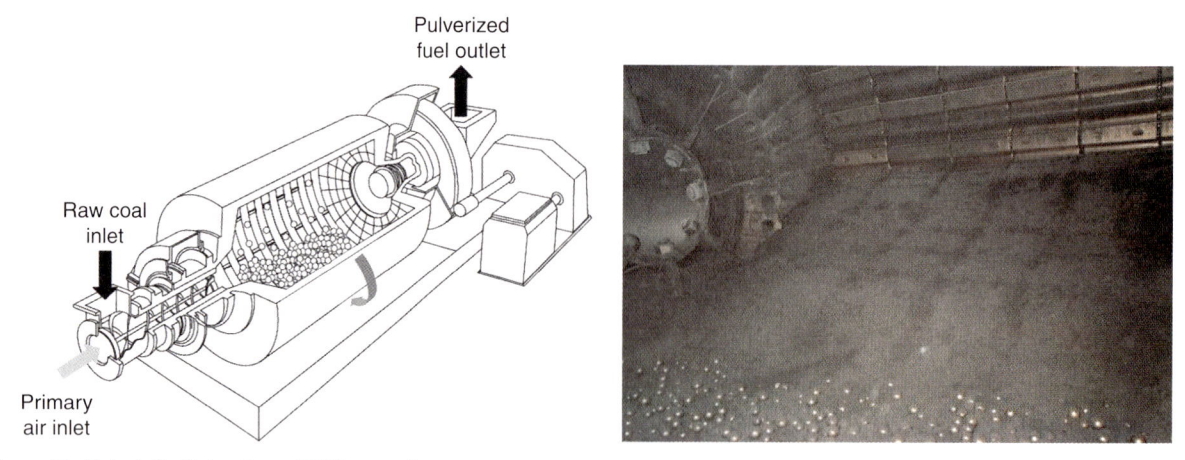

Figure 17 Tube-ball mill (courtesy of RWE npower).

carried out at RWE npower's Aberthaw power station. This did not lead to further work due to the regulatory situation. At the same time, there is no reason why it would not be possible to mill some types of biomass in this mill type. Fibrous fuels like wood will not be suitable but PKE should be possible.

The mill consists of a rotating horizontal cylinder partially filled with steel balls. Coarse fuel is fed in and pulverized fuel extracted at one end ('single-end' type) or both ends ('double-end' type). Particle size reduction is achieved through a combination of impact (larger pieces) and attrition and crushing (finer grinding). As for the vertical spindle mills, pulverized fuel from the mill is graded in a classifier. Fuel particles above a certain size are separated from the airstream and returned to the mill for further pulverizing. The resulting product is blown into the furnace and burnt.

5.04.9.3.4 Fan beater mills

The fan beater mill (**Figure 18**) consists of a large wheel (**Figure 19**) which is up to 4 m diameter and spinning fast, crushing the fuel between the edges of the wheel and fixed impact surfaces in the housing. This type of mill is often used in lignite-fired power stations where hot combustion gases are extracted from the furnace and used to dry the wet fuel while milling it at the same time as making the atmosphere inert. The mill is also acting as a fan sucking the gas from the furnace and blowing it to the burners. These mills are produced with capacities up to 100 tonnes h^{-1} and wheels with a diameter of 4 m. They are mostly used for high-moisture coals, lignite (brown coal), limestone, and other soft materials. The authors are not aware of any case where this type of mill has successfully been used to fire neat biomass. Cofiring of various biomass types with coal has been done at low blending ratios.

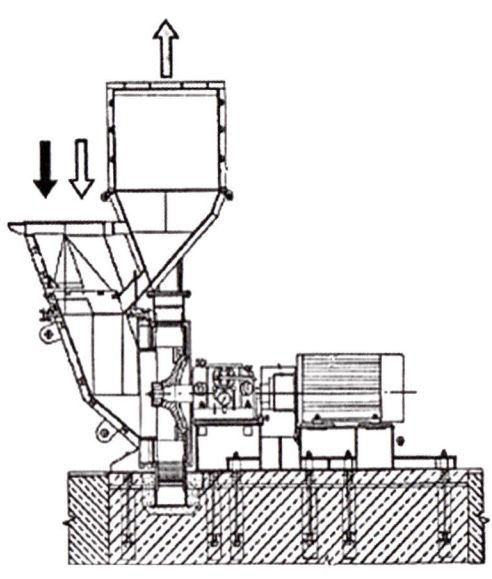

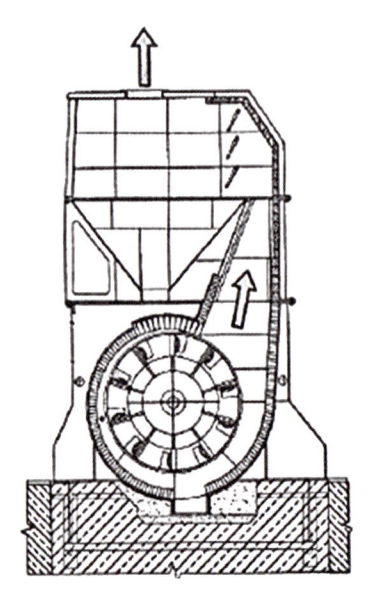

Figure 18 Fan beater mill (courtesy of RWE npower).

Figure 19 Beater wheels from a lignite-fired power station (courtesy of RWE npower).

5.04.10 Combustion

5.04.10.1 Principles of Combustion

Combustion, in essence, is a series of chemical reactions that generate heat. For these reactions to occur, the fuel needs to be above its ignition temperature.

$$\text{carbon} + \text{oxygen} \rightarrow \text{carbon dioxide and heat}$$
$$\text{hydrogen} + \text{oxygen} \rightarrow \text{water and heat}$$

The processes involved are the initial heating of the particles and release of moisture, further heating and release of volatile species and their combustion, and finally the combustion of the char (solid residual).

The nature of biomass can greatly enhance solid combustion as it is generally very reactive and has a much higher volatile content when compared to coal. However, it can also provide some big challenges: many biofuels are extremely wet, and as stated it is important that the solid particles are heated up to their ignition temperature. Green wood can have a moisture content up to 70%, so the amount of useful heat is low and the drying process before combustion can commence can be quite long. For this reason, the traditional pulverized combustion system is not ideal for the burning of this very wet material and the preferred technology is a longer combustion process such as the grate or fluid bed.

Good combustion relies on the oxidation of the organic material in the biomass. It is important to have a combination of high temperature (> 800 °C), oxygen availability, and reactive organic material of the correct size. Problems occur when this is scaled up to industrial scale as the fuel has to be at the correct size for complete combustion (dependent on combustor design), oxygen has to be available to the fuel at each burner/injector, and the rate of combustion has to be controlled to minimize the emissions of NO_x and minimize ash sintering problems. The properties of biomass materials considered for power generation are significantly different from those of coal. Biomass shows greater variation as a class and can impact adversely on the performance of the combustion system.

There are numerous texts available that can give a more detailed discussion of biomass combustion (see, e.g., Reference 20).

5.04.10.2 Practicalities

While the theory appears to be simple, controlling the combustion on a multiburner firing system is complex as a correct amount of fuel and air is needed at each burner and the fuel must be of the correct size to ensure stable and complete combustion. For emissions control, the temperature of the combustion must be closely controlled; otherwise the formation of thermal NO_x will be unacceptable. This must all be achieved in a safe manner while allowing flexible operation.

5.04.10.2.1 Flame stability

Flame stability is fundamental to good combustion in flames. In the past, the loss of a flame followed by reignition has been responsible for boiler explosions. Today, sophisticated burner management systems are in place to ensure that this does not happen.

Good flame stability depends of fuel particles being rapidly heated by hot gases recirculated from the flame to release volatile species, which combust readily in the near-burner region. This feedback system is the key to good combustion. Modern low NO_x burners mix fuel and air in a controlled manner and are sensitive to poor heat release in the near-burner region. Fuel properties important for good flame stability are volatile release and the quality of volatile matter. The physical size of the fuel is important as is the steadiness of the feed system. Biomass fuels containing high levels of moisture are likely to hinder the generation of heat in the flame, delay combustion, and can have a negative impact on flame stability. Wood dust can be burned in a coal burner with no or moderate modifications if the particle size is fine enough and the moisture content is low (see **Figures 20–22**).

Flame stability is not an issue in fluidized bed boilers or grate-fired boilers as the residence time in the combustion zone is magnitudes larger. Tangentially fired boilers are also less susceptible to flame stability issues as the fireball is inherently more stable than individual flames.

5.04.10.2.2 Conversion efficiency

The losses from the biomass combustion are mainly the wet stack loss and the unburnt fuel. As biomass is generally a reactive fuel, the combustion efficiency will be high with unburnt carbon loss typically less than 1% compared to coal combustion, for which unburnt carbon can be up to 3%.

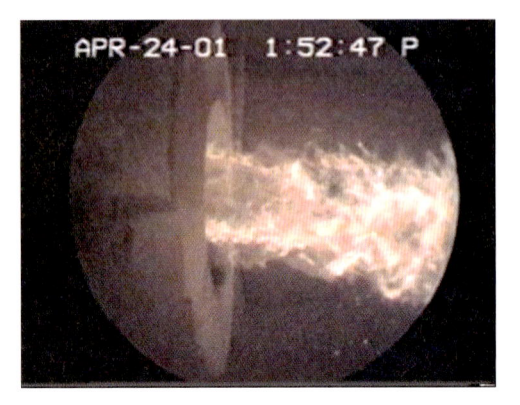

Figure 20 Neat wood flame (courtesy of RWE npower).

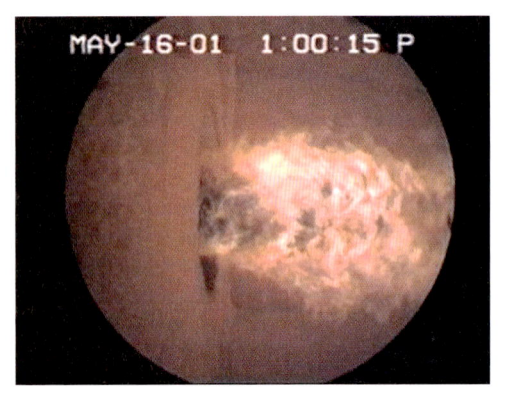

Figure 21 Neat coal flame (courtesy of RWE npower).

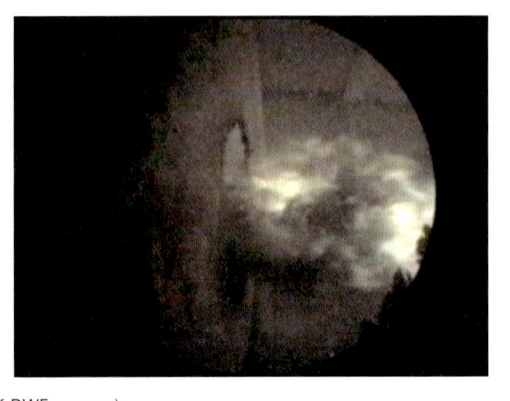

Figure 22 Unstable coal flame (courtesy of RWE npower).

However, many biomasses contain high moisture contents, which will increase the heat losses through moisture emitted from the chimney (which is dependent on the total moisture content of the fuel, as fired) and generated in the combustion reaction (which is a function of the chemical composition of the fuel). For very high moisture content fuel, predrying of the fuel with waste energy should be considered to improve the efficiency of the process.

5.04.10.3 Unburnt Carbon and Carbon Monoxide

Carbon monoxide emissions and high residual levels of unburnt solid char material are often indicators of incomplete combustion and are also indicators of potential operational or economic problems. High CO indicates that there may be areas within the furnace where reducing conditions are occurring and these may exacerbate corrosion of furnace walls or deposition, since ash tends to melt at lower temperature under reducing conditions. High unburnt carbon is indicated by increased carbon in ash, which, in addition to the lost fuel it represents, also potentially impacts precipitator performance. For combustion systems that burn waste biofuels such as waste wood, this is completely unacceptable as their license to operate will include stringent limits on unburnt material. In addition, if the level is above that set down in the relevant standard, it may preclude the sale of ash to the cement industry.

5.04.10.4 Impact of Biomass Combustion

The characteristics of the ash-forming material in biomass are of great concern with regard to longer term impacts of bed agglomeration, slagging, fouling, and corrosion. These problems can result in frequent maintenance requirements, reduced generating capacities, and unscheduled outages, and add substantially to the cost of power generation.

The incombustible material in biomass has a greater range of both concentration and chemical composition than in typical power station coals. Ash contents range from very low (< 1% for wood, few biomass fuels contain more than 5% ash) up to values equivalent to coal and are based on the chemical components required for plant growth, that is, generally in the form of salts or bound in the organic matter. The ash in biomass is present mainly as salts of calcium, potassium, and magnesium, although other elements are present in lesser amounts. Some salts are formed with the organic acid groups of the cell wall components, whereas others occur as carbonates, phosphates, sulfates, silicates, and oxalates. Some inorganic material can also be present as soil contaminants. There are also differences in the ash content and elemental compositions of biomass fuels due to the seasonal variations to which the foliage is subjected. For example, wood harvested in the summer typically contains higher levels of inorganic elements (e.g., K, Ca, Mg, P, Na, and S) required for plant growth. Herbaceous fuels contain potassium and silicon as their principal ash-forming constituents. They are also commonly high in chlorine relative to other biomass fuels. The dominant inorganic components in woody biomass fuels are calcium and potassium, which can contribute to around 60% of the inorganic fuel ash; the chlorine content is usually low.

The important aspect is that when heated the bonds that hold the inorganic atoms break down and liberate the atoms as a volatile species. This means that biomass is a very difficult material as the ash melts at low temperatures and also devolatilizes at low temperatures; therefore, it is very reactive and as such slagging, fouling, and corrosion must be carefully considered when selecting a source of biomass for use [21].

5.04.10.4.1 Ash-related problems

The type of problem faced depends on the design of plant. In grates and fluid bed combustors, the peak temperatures are lower but the material can remain in close contact on the grate or in the bed. With pulverized combustion, the combustion temperatures are nearly double those of the bed and grate.

In a fluidized bed, there is a risk that the bed does not fluidize properly. This is often caused by the agglomeration of the bed material (usually sand). The alkali species in the fuel are driven off and then condense and coat the bed material. This can lead to sand particles sticking together to form a clinker, which is too heavy to fluidize. This destroys the fluidization of the bed, which can lead to a hot spot forming in the bed that can in turn lead to further melting and fusion of the ash. The higher the concentration of the troublesome component in the biomass, that is, K, Na, and P, the greater the risk that bed agglomeration will occur [22].

The formation of slagging and fouling deposits will affect the operation of power plant in a number of ways. Most importantly, slagging and fouling deposits on water or steam tubes will lead to reduced heat transfer, which can impact adversely on efficiency or, in the extreme, reduce maximum load. Other important factors can include the cost of and damage caused by increased soot blowing frequency. The impact of deposits is determined by their rate of growth, ease of cleaning, and heat transfer resistance.

Ash deposition caused by the sintering of molten or partially molten ash components of a fuel is known as slagging. The ash deformation temperature as measured by the standard ash fusion tests can be very low for certain biomasses; for example, oats and barley can have an initial deformation temperature as low as 750–800 °C as compared to 1150–1350 °C for many coals (normal operating temperature for biomass-fired CFB boilers is 850–900 °C). Slagging deposits are generally very dense and the molten ash readily attaches itself to exposed refractory. This can lead to massive buildups (5–10 m^3, i.e., several tonnes), which eventually will cause major problems such as destroying the fluidization in a fluid bed (see **Figure 23**) or may lead to an ash bridge; both will result in the units being taken out of operation to clear the blockage. For massive ash bridges, this can take several weeks.

Fouling deposits are formed by the condensation of inorganic species driven off at high temperatures in the furnace. These volatile species then condense on cold surfaces, which can be water tubes or other ash particles. The effect of this is that the surfaces

Figure 23 Massive ash deposit formed in a circulating fluidized bed boiler (courtesy of RWE).

Figure 24 Deposit formed from condensing ash species from a peat boiler (courtesy of RWE npower).

or particles then become sticky. If other particles come into contact with the sticky surface or the sticky particles come into contact with other similar particles or a substrate, a deposit can start to build up. This is a slow process and the deposits can be consolidated by the chemical reaction with the deposit. **Figure 24** shows a deposit that formed within a circulating fluid bed. It is extremely hard and caused operational problems when it became dislodged.

5.04.10.4.2 Corrosion

The corrosion of boiler tubes is a major concern to power generators and can lead to unexpected costs as a result of unplanned outages. Traditionally, corrosion has been associated with the presence of chlorine and alkali species such as sodium and potassium, and biomasses can have significant amounts of both of these. The risk will depend on the plant operating conditions and material selection, for example, carbon steel/austenitic steel.

The sulfur to chlorine ratio of the fuel may also be an important factor in determining fuel fireside corrosion. Research has indicated that the corrosion potential can be reduced if alkali chlorides (primarily potassium) can interact with sulfur to form less corrosive alkali sulfates and gaseous HCl. However, in the absence of sulfur, alkali chlorides dominate and condense on water tubes, which can lead to aggressive corrosion. The peat-fired CFB boilers in Ireland suffered from chronic tube corrosion as a result of the lack of sulfur in the flue gases [23]

5.04.11 Environmental Impact

The burning of biomass can make a significant contribution to the government's objectives of CO_2 reduction. It will provide a dispatchable source of renewable energy at a time when the network is becoming more reliant on intermittent wind energy.

5.04.11.1 Gaseous Emissions

5.04.11.1.1 Oxides of sulfur (SO$_x$)

The main emission of sulfur is SO_2. This was identified as one of the main causes of acid rain and since that time the emissions have been heavily controlled. The European Commission introduced the LCPD that limited the emissions of sulfur, requiring most large power stations to fit FGD plant or opt to close. In the United Kingdom, the EA uses the BATREF document [24], which provides possible limits for new and existing plant. A new biomass plant would have to achieve stack emissions of less than 200 mg Nm^{-3} at standard conditions.

The sulfur dioxide emissions from a plant are a simple function of the sulfur content of the feedstock and the abatement technology used. In general, biomasses have low sulfur content, for example, sulfur content of wood would be typically 0.05% while in PKE it is around 0.2%. Fluidized bed technologies often use limestone injection to capture the sulfur, while other technologies would use a back end FGD.

5.04.11.1.2 Oxides of nitrogen (NO$_x$)

For large-scale combustion systems, the main nitrogen emission is NO. NO_x chemistry is complex; the emissions depend on the fuel type, the mixing of the combustion air, and the stoichiometry (commonly known as fuel NO_x). Fuels with high volatile content, even if they have high nitrogen content, will produce lower NO_x emissions on a combustion system design for low NO_x combustion; these systems are designed to stage the manner in which the fuel and air are mixed.

If the combustion temperature is high (> 850 °C), then oxidation of the nitrogen in the combustion air will occur (commonly known as thermal NO_x). Biomass fuels would also be expected to burn with a lower adiabatic flame temperature, reducing thermal NO_x formation rates.

Most modern boilers employ furnace staging using a low-NO_x combustion system to reduce the NO_x levels on the boilers. If this does not achieve the designed emission levels, then techniques such as SNCR can be used.

5.04.11.1.3 Carbon monoxide

The incomplete combustion of carbon produces CO. Operationally, this is used to optimize the combustion process as it indicates that there is a nonoptimum mixing of combustion air with the fuel. Traditionally, on large multiburner plants, getting the fuel and air right has been one of the ongoing problems. For this reason, most large plants operate with a level of excess air. The level of CO that can be achieved on biomass-only plant is strongly dependent on the chosen technology, with grate technology often giving high CO, while on circulating fluid bed the levels can be very low. The 'BAT ref' document [24] sets an emission limit of 50 mg Nm^{-3} for good combustion.

5.04.11.1.4 Volatile organic compounds

Volatile organic compounds (VOCs) together with NO_x play a role in the production of ozone from photochemical reactions in the atmosphere. Ozone is injurious to respiratory functions and is also a GHG. VOC emissions from efficiently operated plants are negligible.

5.04.11.1.5 Hydrochloric acid

During combustion, the majority of chlorine in any biomass will be volatilized as HCl and unabated emissions are therefore largely dependent on the chlorine content of the biomass. Where technologies for removing SO_2 have been installed, these can also be important control devices for acidic halogen gases. In wet FGD systems, flue gases are initially washed in a prescrubber, which removes most of the fly ash and soluble gases such as HCl.

5.04.11.1.6 Dioxins and furans

Dioxins and furans are carcinogenic agents, so their emissions are becoming carefully monitored. Dioxin/furan formation in furnaces is generally difficult to predict but does require the presence of chemical precursors. These are generally chlorinated compounds and hence fuel chlorine content is an important indicator of the propensity to form dioxin. However, in an efficient high-temperature combustion system, these compounds would also be expected to destroy any chemical precursors present and prevent the formation of dioxins within the furnace.

5.04.11.2 Solid Residuals

5.04.11.2.1 Particulates

Particulate emissions are heavily controlled. New plants would be expected to meet very tight limits, possibly emitting less than 10 mg Nm^{-3}. The ash content of many biomasses is low (< 5%) and the particle size generated by burning biomass can be fine. The traditional method of dust collection used on coal-fired plants of electrostatic precipitators is not suitable to capture this ash; therefore, bag filter technology is used. Very low emission levels can be easily achieved with this technology.

5.04.11.2.2 *Heavy metals*

Most biomass fuels contain considerably lower levels of heavy metals than coal or oil. Consequently, the concentrations of the trace elements in the ash and emissions of the more volatile trace elements (such as mercury) are low. This is not the case where waste is used such as demolition wood.

5.04.11.2.3 *Ash*

The ash from coal-fired power stations has had many uses over the years. One of the latest in the United Kingdom was in the reshaping of Celtic Manor Golf course in southern Wales. It has been used as cement replacement in concrete. The ash from pure biomass plants is completely different in nature and will be unsuitable for any of these uses. This is an important area that needs to be developed; otherwise, it may restrict the use of biomass in power generation.

Wood ash is used as a forest fertilizer and soil conditioner in countries with a tradition of large-scale wood burning, like Scandinavia and the United States [25].

5.04.12 Conclusions

There is a strong trend toward using more biomass-based power generation and less fossil fuels. The plants being built are of increasing size and efficiency. The nature of biomass with smaller fuel production units and low energy density favors smaller and more embedded generation plants and also CHP applications where district heating is possible.

New medium-sized and large plants are often fluidized beds. Larger units tend to be CFBs and plants for neat biomass firing up to several hundred MW_e are supplied. The trend is toward larger units and more advanced steam data but CFB technology for supercritical plant, which gives the highest available efficiency today, is currently offered for only coal or coal/biomass cofiring. This is due to the available tube materials which are not sufficiently resistant to corrosion at the high metal temperatures in such plants when used in biomass-only installations. Foster Wheeler has the view [14] that it is possible to achieve 800 MW_e with 20% biomass and 600 MW_e with 50% biomass depending on the type of biomass.

There is also a movement toward conversion of existing coal-fired power stations to fire wood pellets. This could very easily be limited by the available production capacity for wood pellets as the world production was around 12–15 million tonnes in 2008 and one power station generating 100 MW electricity continuously will require approximately 0.5 million tonnes a year. The production capacity for wood pellets is growing fast and new production facilities are built every year. A conversion from fossil fuel to wood pellets will usually be based on the reuse of existing equipment like mills and burners. Wood pellets can be processed in this type of situation and give satisfactory performance, but a derate in the order of 20–25% is expected in most cases.

Conversion of power stations designed for fossil fuels to burning neat biomass has been carried out in Sweden, The Netherlands, Denmark, and Belgium, and a number of projects for similar conversions are under way in Canada and the United Kingdom among others.

There are significant challenges in combustion, health, and safety aspects of burning biomass fuels and the logistics of moving it from the production site and delivering it to the user in a suitable format. The health and safety aspects include exposure of personnel to the dust, which can cause asthma and other diseases, and nut product-derived biomass such as peanut husks has to be handled in a way that ensures that nobody with a nut allergy is exposed to the dust unknowingly. The dust can also be explosive in high concentrations and dust layers accumulating on hot surfaces can self-ignite. It is also possible for a stockpile of biomass to self-heat and ignite if the moisture content is favorable for this. The logistics of using biomass as a fuel for power generation is dominated by the lower bulk density and heat content compared to fossil fuels as well as the fact that much of the production takes place at farms that are run as independent companies while the power companies are used to dealing with a few suppliers of large quantities. This gap in culture between supplier and end user must be bridged and a robust supply chain developed before biomass can become an established fuel for power generation. This has already taken place in some countries but needs to expand onto the international market.

References

[1] Mann MK and Spath PL (2000) *A Summary of Life Cycle Assessment Studies Conducted on Biomass, Coal, and Natural Gas Systems.* Golden, CO: National Renewable Energy Laboratory (NREL).

[2] Good practice guidelines for growing energy crops. http://www.defra.gov.uk/erdp/pdfs/ecs/src-guide.pdf; http://www.defra.gov.uk/erdp/pdfs/ecs/miscanthus-guide.pdf#search=%22Good%20practice%20guidelines%20for%20miscanthus%20production%22 (accessed 25 October 2010).

[3] Brierly E, Truckell I, Brewer T, Towers W, and Malcolm A (2004) Environmental impact of the extraction of forestry residues. DTI/PUB URN 04/1080. http://webarchive.nationalarchives.gov.uk/ and http://www.berr.gov.uk/files/file14944.pdf (accessed 13 September 2011).

[4] Semere T and Slater F (2005) The effects of energy grass plantations on biodiversity – A preliminary study, dti, February 2005. http://webarchive.nationalarchives.gov.uk/tna/+/http://www.dti.gov.uk/renewables/publications/pdfs/bcr007820000.pdf/ (accessed 25 October 2010).

[5] European Environment Agency (2006) How much bioenergy can Europe produce without harming the environment. EEA Report No. 7/2006, ISSN 1725-9177.
[6] RWE Engineering Report (2004) Life cycle analysis of biomass energy crops – SRC and perennial grasses. TECH/JJB/390/04, December 2004.
[7] Bates J, Edberg O, and Nuttall C (2009) Minimizing greenhouse gas emissions from biomass energy generation. Environment Agency, Bristol, UK. http://www.environment-agency.gov.uk/static/documents/Research/Minimising_greenhouse_gas_emissions_from_biomass_energy_generation.pdf (accessed 21 October 2011).
[8] Malmgren A and Goh B (2007) Guidance document on biomass co-firing on coal-fired power stations. DTI Project 324-2. London, UK: DTI.
[9] Sawin JL and Martinot E (2010) REN21.2010. Renewables 2010 Global Status report, Deutsche Gessellschaft fur Technische Zusammenarbeit (GTZ) GmbH. http://www.ren21.net/Portals/97/documents/GSR/REN21_GSR_2010_full_revised%20Sept2010.pdf (accessed 14 September 2011).
[10] Nind A and Cronin B (2010) Pöyry: The industrial emissions directive, a briefing note from Pöyry Energy Consulting. http://www.ilexenergy.com/pages/documents/reports/electricity/IED_Briefing_Note_v1_0.pdf (accessed 24 September 2010).
[11] Nind A and Cronin B (2010) industrial emissions directive, a briefing note from Pöyry Energy Consulting. http://www.ilexenergy.com/pages/documents/reports/electricity/IED_Briefing_Note_v1_0.pdf (accessed 2 January 2011).
[12] HM Revenue & Customs (2010) http://customs.hmrc.gov.uk/channelsPortalWebApp/channelsPortalWebApp.portal?_nfpb=true&_pageLabel=pageExcise_ShowContent&propertyType=document&columns=1&id=HMCE_CL_001174 (accessed 2 September 2010).
[13] Product description on suppliers official website. http://www.volund.dk/technologies_products/biomass_energy_systems/combustion_grates/vibration_grate_hvb_water_cooled (accessed 19 July 2010).
[14] Jäntti T, Sarkki J, and Lampenius H (2010) The utilisation of CFB technology for large-scale biomass firing power plant. *Power-Gen Europe 2010*, Amsterdam, The Netherlands, 8–10 June. http://www.fwc.com/publications/tech_papers/files/TP_CFB_10_03.pdf?bcsi_scan_3880D4A112C8751C=0&bcsi_scan_filename=TP_CFB_10_03.pdf (accessed 7 October 2010).
[15] Svedberg U, Samuelsson J, and Melin S (2008) Hazardous off-gassing of carbon monoxide and oxygen depletion during ocean transportation of wood pellets. *The Annals of Occupational Hygiene* 52(4): 259–266.
[16] Svedberg U, Petrini C, and Johanson G (2009) Oxygen depletion and formation of toxic gases following sea transportation of logs and wood chips. *The Annals of Occupational Hygiene* 53(8): 779–787.
[17] List of approved workplace exposure limits from EH40/2005 Workplace exposure limits, environmental hygiene guidance note EH40 (2007) Published on the UK Health and Safety's Executive's official website. http://www.hse.gov.uk/coshh/table1.pdf (accessed 14 September 2011).
[18] Adams RG, Baimbridge P, and Cahill P (2006) *Dangerous Substances and Explosive Atmosphere Regulations (2002): Power Generation Industry (Coal Fired Plant) Best Practice Document*.
[19] Marshall L, Fralick C, and Gaudry D (2010) OPG charts move from coal to biomass, POWER, 1 April 2010. http://www.powermag.com/coal/OPG-Charts-Move-from-Coal-to-Biomass_2570.html (accessed 19 December 2010).
[20] Van Loo S and Koppejan J (2002) *Handbook of Biomass Combustion and Co-firing*. Earthscan, London: Twente University Press.
[21] Baxter L, Miles T, Miles T, Jr., *et al.* (1998) The behaviour of inorganic material in biomass-fired power boilers: Field and laboratory experiences. *Fuel Processing Technology* 54: 47–78.
[22] Hiltunen M, Barisic V, and Zabetta E (2008) Combustion of different types of biomass in CFB boilers. *16th European Biomass Conference*. Valencia, Spain, June.
[23] Flynn G (2006) *Independent Newspaper*, Two ESB power plants facing closure over corroded pipes. 10 May 2006. http://www.independent.ie/national-news/two-esb-power-plants-facing-closure-over-corroded-pipes-97210.html (accessed 13 January 2011).
[24] Integrated pollution prevention control, reference document on best available techniques for large combustion plants, European Commission, July 2006. ftp://ftp.jrc.es/pub/eippcb/doc/lcp_bref_0706.pdf?bcsi_scan_EEC049581022EE5A=0&bcsi_scan_filename=lcp_bref_0706.pdf (accessed 13 January 2011).
[25] Pitman R, Wood ash use in forestry – A review of the Environmental Impacts, no year stated but references from 2002. http://www.forestry.gov.uk/pdf/use_of_ash_in_forestry.pdf/$FILE/use_of_ash_in_forestry.pdf (accessed 17 December 2010).

5.05 Biomass Co-Firing

A Nuamah, The University of Nottingham, Nottingham, UK; RWE npower, Swindon, UK
A Malmgren, BioC Ltd, Cirencester, UK
G Riley, RWE npower, Swindon, UK
E Lester, The University of Nottingham, Nottingham, UK

© 2012 Elsevier Ltd. All rights reserved.

5.05.1	Introduction	56
5.05.1.1	Global Trend	56
5.05.1.2	Challenges Facing the Power Industry	57
5.05.2	Available Biomass Materials	57
5.05.2.1	Wood-Based Fuels	57
5.05.2.2	Energy Crops	57
5.05.2.2.1	Short-rotation coppice	57
5.05.2.2.2	Miscanthus	57
5.05.2.3	Agricultural Residues	58
5.05.2.3.1	Olive residues	58
5.05.2.3.2	Oil palm residues	58
5.05.2.3.3	Shea residues	58
5.05.2.3.4	Rice husks	58
5.05.2.3.5	Straw	59
5.05.2.3.6	Grass	59
5.05.2.3.7	Bagasse	59
5.05.2.4	Processed Wood (Wood Pellets and Torrefied Wood)	59
5.05.2.5	Liquid Biomass	60
5.05.2.5.1	Tall oil	60
5.05.2.5.2	Tallow	60
5.05.2.5.3	Jatropha oil	60
5.05.2.5.4	Sewage sludge	60
5.05.2.6	Gaseous Biomass	61
5.05.3	Combustion Technology	61
5.05.3.1	Pulverized Coal Combustion	61
5.05.3.2	Fluidized Bed Combustion	61
5.05.3.3	Stoker Combustion	61
5.05.3.4	Cyclone Boilers	62
5.05.3.5	Gasification	62
5.05.3.5.1	Direct gasification	62
5.05.3.5.2	Indirect gasification	62
5.05.3.6	Gasification Techniques	62
5.05.3.6.1	Fixed bed gasifiers	62
5.05.3.6.2	Fluidized bed gasifiers	63
5.05.3.6.3	Entrained flow gasifiers	63
5.05.4	Co-firing Methods	63
5.05.4.1	Direct Co-firing	63
5.05.4.2	Parallel Co-firing	64
5.05.4.3	Indirect Co-firing	64
5.05.5	Global Overview of Biomass Co-firing Plant	64
5.05.5.1	United States	64
5.05.5.1.1	McNeil generating plant	65
5.05.5.2	Netherlands	65
5.05.5.2.1	Amer 9	65
5.05.5.2.2	Borssele	66
5.05.5.2.3	Maasvlakte 1 and 2	66
5.05.5.3	United Kingdom	66
5.05.5.3.1	Aberthaw power plant	66
5.05.5.3.2	Didcot power plant	68
5.05.5.3.3	E.ON (Kingsnorth)	68
5.05.5.3.4	Drax	68

5.05.6	**Health and Safety Issues Associated with Co-firing**	68
5.05.6.1	Spontaneous Fires	68
5.05.6.2	Exposure to Biomass and Coal Dust	69
5.05.7	**Technical Issues regarding Biomass Co-firing**	69
5.05.7.1	Fuel Delivery, Storage, and Preparation	70
5.05.7.2	Supply of Biomass	70
5.05.7.3	Properties of Biomass and Their Effects on Plant Operations	70
5.05.8	**Conclusions**	72
References		72
Further Reading		73

5.05.1 Introduction

The global demand for energy has increased drastically over the last decade. Coal is regarded as a major source of pollution, but continues to be one of the most reliable and widely available sources of energy in most countries. This, coupled with the changing phase of the BRIC countries (Brazil, Russia, India, and China) toward industrialization, contributes enormously toward global carbon emissions, thereby causing global warming and its associated problems. There is a growing acceptance that energy from renewable resources must replace the use of fossil fuels, in order to reduce the rate of global climate change.

There are, however, technologies that have the potential to mitigate these emissions, whether from coal, biomass, or other resources. Carbon capture and storage (CCS) and renewable energy technologies have been identified as carbon abatement technologies which could drastically reduce the carbon emissions from power plants. CCS, as innovative as it may be, still has a lot of technical challenges to overcome before it can be properly commercialized. However, carbon capture, while novel in the power generation sector, has already been employed in other sectors such as the oil and gas industry, where carbon is captured, transported, and stored in depleted oil and gas fields to increase the pressure and the flow of oil beneath the ground – this gives grounds for optimism for coal CCS [1].

This chapter limits itself to biomass co-firing as a renewable energy option and will not discuss other technologies in detail.

Biomass co-firing, as the name suggests, is the burning of biomass along with other fuels. The principal objective of adding biomass as a partial substitute fuel in high-efficiency coal boilers is that the combustion of biomass is carbon neutral if the biomass is grown in a regenerative manner. Moreover, there should be minimal changes in total boiler efficiency as a result of co-firing. Currently, co-firing is the most effective use of biomass for power generation, with efficiency ranging between 35% and 45% [2]. It has also been shown that the introduction of 5–10% biomass in co-firing requires only minor alteration of the handling equipment. If larger amounts of biomass are used (exceeding 10%), modifications in the mills, burners, and dryers may be needed [2]. Other advantages are that it promotes the use of renewable and/or other waste organic materials, thus augmenting the global effort to limit the use of land for landfilling activities. Legislation around landfilling may be an effective means of promoting the use of biomass in the fuels market.

While there are many forms of renewable energy, from tidal power to solar power, biomass is an important source of energy that can be transported and used as a solid, liquid, or gaseous fuel. Bioenergy, or energy from biomass, has huge potential, especially in countries with renewable forest resources, in wealthier countries with an excess of agricultural land, and in countries where specialized high-yielding biomass species can be grown.

5.05.1.1 Global Trend

Globally, about 10% of the total primary energy demand is met by biomass. Biomass dominates predominantly in developing countries where it is used for cooking and heating [2]. In industrialized countries, the use of biomass is below average although Finland, which is part of the International Energy Agency (IEA) member countries, meets 11% of its energy demand with solid biomass. The United States, which is the largest producer of biomass, meets only 1% of its energy demand with this renewable feedstock. Other European countries such as Sweden, Austria, and Portugal generate more than 2% of their total energy from biomass [3].

In recent years, many governments have encouraged the use of biomass for power generation by initiating incentives to entice power generators. The relatively high percentage of biomass usage enjoyed by Finland is as a result of government policy which saw the use of solid biomass being exempt from carbon tax on fossil fuels during the period 1990–97. In the United Kingdom, as part of the government effort to meet its stringent emission target, the government has set a target to increase the proportion of electricity generated from biomass from 3% in 2003 to 10.4% in 2011 [3]. The final target is 15% by 2015 [2, 4]. This is backed by a generous incentive package termed the Renewables Obligation, where power generators are issued with a Renewables Obligation Certificate (ROC) after generating 0.5–4 MWh$_e$ from renewable sources, depending on the ROC band, which can be sold to generate further revenue for the industry.

5.05.1.2 Challenges Facing the Power Industry

The major technical challenges in biomass co-firing lie in the storage, preparation, and handling of biomass. Many countries lack the necessary infrastructure to transport biomass to the power plants since such crops are generally grown over a large geographical area. The seasonal nature of biomass means that abundant supplies exist only around harvesting, with significantly reduced quantities being available during cultivation and growth. The high moisture content of biomass (up to 70%), coupled with its low bulk density and heating value [5], adversely affects the behavior of the fuel during combustion, handling, and transport. This also means that higher volumes of fuel will need to be collected, transported, stored, milled, and burned to achieve the same thermal heat output as coal, which has a very low moisture content.

Many of these drawbacks are reduced if biomass is co-fired with coal. Co-firing can avoid the need for the high capital cost of building a new plant. Retrofitted boilers can be altered to fire varying amounts of biomass with coal while maintaining its originally designed capacity. The energy conversion efficiency of biomass is significantly increased when co-fired in larger plants. This efficiency ranges between 35% and 45%, which is far higher than the efficiency in biomass-dedicated plants [2]. Apart from reduced carbon dioxide (CO_2) emissions, the sulfur and nitrogen content in biomass is very low, which subsequently reduces NO_x and SO_x emissions by diluting the contributions from coal [6]. In other scenarios, the operating cost associated with co-firing is likely to be higher due to the higher cost of some biomass fuels compared with coal; nevertheless, co-firing is usually the cheapest form of 'renewable' energy, which is another important factor that favors the use of biomass when seeking to meet the European Union (EU)-level regulations on emissions.

5.05.2 Available Biomass Materials

Traditionally, solid biomass fuels have been the main form of biomass used to generate energy. In most of the developing countries, solid biomass fuels have been utilized to provide heating and also for cooking. In co-firing, other forms of biomass materials have also been used, such as liquid and gaseous biomass fuels. While solid biomass still dominates the market, the liquid and gaseous biomass fuels are gaining some impetus as highly efficient energy sources.

5.05.2.1 Wood-Based Fuels

The characteristics, both physical and chemical, of wood-based fuels vary significantly in the form of sawdust, shavings, bark, and chips. Residues from forestry, sawmills, and the furniture industry have been identified as viable options for co-firing. The heating value of oven-dry sawdust is around $20.5\,MJ\,kg^{-1}$ (high heating value (HHV)) depending on the type and the percentage presence of bark [7]. Wood is one of the most widely spread sources of fuel for residential, commercial, or industrial utility boilers or furnaces for producing thermal and/or electrical energy. Locally, the United Kingdom produces large amounts of wood residue – it is estimated that it produces 10 Mt of waste wood each year [41]. While this amount is not significantly higher than in many countries, the United Kingdom does not have a large-scale producer of wood pellets, which is needed to maximize the potential of this fuel source. Wood pellets are mostly imported from Russia, North America, Scandinavia, and other northeastern European countries. Large-scale production facilities are under development, however, in Scotland [41].

The type of wood used varies from country to country, but the United Kingdom has indigenous supplies of pine and spruce, wood from fruit trees like apple and pear, and eucalyptus wood among others. Eucalyptus is a nonnative species and was first introduced into the United Kingdom in the late eighteenth century.

5.05.2.2 Energy Crops

Energy crops are specifically grown for use as a fuel and are therefore designed to maximize energy yields per hectare at the lowest cost possible. The commercial ones are usually densely planted monocultures with high yields. Short-rotation coppice (SRC) and miscanthus are popular choices for co-firing applications.

5.05.2.2.1 Short-rotation coppice

SRC cultures are high-density plantations with high-yielding varieties of willow and poplar. The shoots are harvested every 2–5 years, but the roots are left intact in order to avoid replanting. Approximately 3000 ha are planted with SRC across the United Kingdom. The shoots from SRC are produced in the form of rods, chips, or billets. The inherent moisture content, depending on the form, can be between 45% and 60%. A typical yield from a UK-based SRC can be between 5 and 18 oven-dry tonnes per hectare per year (or $odt\,ha^{-1}\,yr^{-1}$ for short).

5.05.2.2.2 Miscanthus

Miscanthus is native to Asia and is a perennial fast-growing grass. It uses the C4 photosynthesis pathway and hence is more efficient in fixing carbon and in water use than the majority of native species in Europe. It grows rapidly during the summer months to produce canes that can be harvested annually, rather than on a 2- to 5-year cycle as with SRC. The calorific value (CV) of oven-dry

Miscanthus is 19.0 MJ kg^{-1} (HHV), with a yield similar to the average SRC at 7–12 odt ha^{-1} yr^{-1}. It can continue to grow from the same rhizomes for at least 15–20 years. One advantage over SRC is that if the landowner decides to stop growing energy crops, Miscanthus can be removed easily by spraying a herbicide like glyphosate [8].

5.05.2.3 Agricultural Residues

Usually, agricultural processes produce waste residues, which can end up as compost or animal bedding. Reuse is a cheap source of biomass and is more benign since landfill sites will inevitably generate methane and other gaseous emissions that increase the environmental burden. Residues that have been used in co-firing applications include olive residues, oil palm residues, and shea residues. Other agricultural residues of interest include wheat straw, corn stalks, nutshells, sugarcane bagasse, orchard prunings, and vineyard stakes.

5.05.2.3.1 Olive residues

Olive residues are produced globally, but the main sources are from around the Mediterranean, with Spain, Italy, and Greece accounting for 97% of total production [7]. Olive oil production is the main source of olive residues, where only about 21% of the weight of an olive is actually oil, the rest being residues that are normally treated as waste [6]. The residues include crushed olive kernel, shell, pulp, skin, water, and any remaining oil. Olive plantations can produce between 500 and 10 000 kg olives per hectare [7].

The advent of a three- and two-phase production system of olive oil has generated new types of residues. In Spain, about 90% of olive production systems utilize the two-phase process, which produces residues called 'alpeorujo'. Alpeorujo is a solid residue from olive oil extraction and is made up of stones, skins, flesh, water (50–60%), oil (2–4%), and ashes (2%). High moisture content and high alkali metal content of alpeorujo create problems for boilers due to the low melting temperatures of the ash, although co-firing can reduce the problem.

5.05.2.3.2 Oil palm residues

Oil palms are mainly grown in Southeast Asia, South America, and Africa. Malaysia and Indonesia currently dominate the world market in the production of palm oil. Palm oil is extensively used in the food and chemical industries. Forty-five percent of the palm fruit remains after oil is extracted, which can be used as a fuel. This residual material consists of the empty fruit bunches, kernel, shell, and fibrous material. Palm residues can also be burned in oil palm processing mills to generate heat and power. The production of palm oil creates a vast amount of waste biomass after the milling and the crushing of palm kernel. Over the last decade, palm kernel expeller (PKE) was investigated by power generators as a potential biomass fuel for co-firing. It has now been burned commercially for at least 5 years by many generators as one of the most popular co-firing fuels in the United Kingdom. However, price fluctuations make its popularity more 'volatile' than other choices of biomass feedstock. PKE's lower moisture content and higher CV (compared with other biomass types) make it an excellent choice for co-firing with coal (**Table 1**). The kernel shell could also be used as a fuel during co-firing, but it is hard and therefore difficult to mill, thus making it less popular than PKE.

5.05.2.3.3 Shea residues

The shea tree is native to Africa, where its butter is extracted from the kernel for use in cosmetics and foods. After butter extraction, significant quantities of waste are produced in the form of shell, husk, and the fleshy mesocarp. These residues can be processed and used as fertilizers, domestic fuels, or as a waterproofing agent. Similar to palm wastes, the characteristics of the shea residue can vary according to the processing methods used to extract the butter. This material has been used for co-firing at a number of power stations in the United Kingdom, but there have been reports of issues with self-heating and dust handling problems.

5.05.2.3.4 Rice husks

Rice husks are the waste materials after the rice grains have been removed and are predominantly composed of silica. They can be used as an energy source, but the high ash content, relative to other biomass materials, makes their use problematic during

Table 1 Properties of palm biomass

	Moisture content (wt.%)	Calorific value (kJ kg^{-1})
Fiber	37	19 068
Shell	12	20 108
Empty fruit bunches	67	18 838
PKE cake	3	18 900

co-firing. Ash contents of 15–20% (on a dry basis) are not uncommon with >60–70% SiO$_2$ content. Pellets made from a mixture of rice husks and olive residues have also been marketed, but it is unclear as to whether this product has been commercially successful.

5.05.2.3.5 Straw

Straw is a product that is available in abundance in most farming-intensive countries. Denmark has been one of the leaders in the use of straw as a power station fuel. Denmark introduced legislation banning the practice of burning straw in the fields in 1990, which made straw a more practical fuel source. There are disadvantages with using straw in combustion processes since its ash has an extremely low melting point, which can result in slagging problems, and its fibrous nature makes it very difficult to handle during milling and transportation. Either specialist equipment is required for handling and grinding or the boiler needs to be reconfigured to burn straw bales.

5.05.2.3.6 Grass

Grass can be used as a biomass fuel since it is abundant in many countries. Switchgrass and reed canary grass are examples of popular varieties of rapidly growing grasses. As with straw, blending grass with coal can be problematic in terms of handling and milling, particularly without retrofitting existing equipment, thus making it less popular than other biomass types. Grasses do have the advantage that they can be grown outside the general harvest season and can also be harvested more than once a year.

5.05.2.3.7 Bagasse

Bagasse is the residue after sugarcane or sorghum stalks are crushed to extract their juice. It contains high amounts of fixed carbon due to the high bioconversion by the sugarcane plant during photosynthesis. Sugarcane is a major commercially grown agricultural crop in the vast majority of countries in Africa and in the southern part of America, in particular Mauritius and Brazil.

Table 2 shows details for different types of solid fuels in terms of elemental and proximate composition.

5.05.2.4 Processed Wood (Wood Pellets and Torrefied Wood)

Processed wood fuels, such as wood pellets and torrefied wood, can be generated from a variety of wood residues. Wood pellets have a higher and more uniform CV than raw wood. The production of uniform shape and size means that handleability problems are predictable. They also have a moisture content of 5–10% [7], which is considerably lower than the 60–70% moisture that is present in the fresh 'parent' material.

Torrefaction is a process of improving, or upgrading, the properties of lignocellulosic materials like wood (Table 3). The process involves slow pyrolysis of the feed material with a hold temperature between 200 and 300 °C. The process lowers the moisture content and increases the CV (around 21 MJ kg^{-1}, which is similar to subbituminous coal); removes the volatiles that cause smoke during combustion, resulting in a product that is still approximately 70% of its initial weight but with 80–90% of the original CV; and also increases the hydrophobicity, making it more durable while improving grinding properties. The additional investment and

Table 2 Properties of different solid fuels [6]

Property	Coal	Peat	Wood without bark	Bark	Forest residues	Willow	Straw	Reed canary grass	Olive residues
Ash content (db)	8.5–10.9	4–7	0.4–0.5	2–3	1–3	1.1–4	5	6.2–7.5	2–7
Moisture content	6–10	40–55	5–60	45–65	50–60	50–60	17–25	15–20	60–70
Net CV	26–28.3	20.9–21.3	18.5–20	18.5–23	18.5–20	18.4–19.2	17.4	17.1–17.5	17.5–19
C (% db)	76–87	52–56	48–52	48–52	48–52	47–51	45–47	45.5–46.1	48–50
H (% db)	3.5–5	5–6.5	6.2–6.4	5.7–6.8	6–6.2	5.8–6.7	5.8–6	5.7–5.8	5.5–6.5
N (% db)	0.8–1.5	1–3	0.1–0.5	0.3–0.8	0.3–0.5	0.2–0.8	0.4–0.6	0.65–1.04	0.5–1.5
O (% db)	2.8–11.3	30–40	38–42	24.3–40.2	40–44	40–46	40–46	44	34
S (% db)	0.5–3.1	<0.05–0.3	<0.05	<0.05	<0.05	0.02–0.1	0.05–0.2	0.08–0.13	0.07–0.17
Cl (% db)	<0.1	0.02–0.06	0.001–0.03	0.01–0.03	0.01–0.04	0.01–0.05	0.14–0.97	0.09	0.1 (in ash)
K (% db)	0.003	0.8–5.8	0.02–0.05	0.1–0.4	0.1–0.4	0.2–0.5	0.69–1.3	0.3–0.5	30 (in ash)
Ca (% db)	4–12	0.05–0.1	0.1–0.5	0.02–0.08	0.2–0.9	0.2–0.7	0.1–0.6	9	No data

db, dry basis; % on a weight basis.

Table 3 Properties of torrefied wood compared with others [9]

	Wood chips	Wood pellets	Torrefied wood
Moisture content (%)	35	5–10	3
NCV (MJ kg^{-1})	10.5	17	21
Bulk density (kg m^{-3})	550	600	800
Energy bulk density (GJ m^{-3})	5.8	9	16.7
Hygroscopic nature	Wet	Wet	Hydrophobic
Behavior in storage	Gets moldy, dry matter loss	Deteriorates, get moldy	Stable

loss of product during torrefaction are outweighed by the lower transportation costs and higher CV. Torrefaction also allows for a wider use of source material (including grasses and roots).

5.05.2.5 Liquid Biomass

Liquid biomass fuels are generally grouped into biodiesels and ethanol. Some of the liquid biomass fuels specifically used for co-firing operations include palm oil, raw vegetable oil, tall oil, waste vegetable oil, rapeseed oil, and jatropha oil. These fuels are converted into biodiesel by the process of transesterification, which is the chemical process of converting animal fat and vegetable oil into biodiesel. Ethanol is produced by fermentation of sugar-bearing and starch crops such as wheat, maize, potato, and sugar beet. In 2005, it was estimated that about 17% of biomass used in co-firing was liquid [10]. Disadvantages include lower CV and potentially higher NO$_x$ emissions. However, liquid biomass has advantages over conventional liquid fuels like petrol and diesel, particularly in that liquid biomass is renewable, biodegradable, and a superior lubricant (in the case of biodiesel) and has better solvent properties. Another vital advantage of bioethanol and biodiesel is that they can be mixed with conventional petrol and diesel, respectively, which allows the use of the same handling and distribution infrastructure [11]. Liquid biomass fuels have been tried, tested, and proven to be a very useful substitute for petrol and diesel in the transport industry; however, their application in the power generating sector is still in its infancy.

5.05.2.5.1 Tall oil

Tall oils are essentially by-products from the kraft pulping process in the papermaking industry. During this process, pulp is created by the digestion of wood, which is influenced by a combination of factors including the high cooking temperature of the chemicals and its elevated pH level. Black liquor is produced as a by-product of the pulping process, which contains cooking chemicals, residual pulp, and resin or pitch from the trees. Tall oil is therefore produced from the refined form of the resin or pitch and is used in the manufacture of soaps, lubricants, and emulsions. Moreover, it can easily replace, or be blended with, current energy fuels to supply energy. Its physical properties vary based on the type of tree it is obtained from and the processing method employed. Tall oil can be very corrosive and aggressive to low-grade steel. Care must therefore be taken before it is introduced to ensure that the integrity of the combustion system is not compromised.

5.05.2.5.2 Tallow

Tallow is a product from rendered animal by-products. The rendering process drives off water at high temperatures to separate the fat (or tallow) from the protein. About 30–35% of an animal's mass can be rendered, and of this, 24% is tallow. Tallow is generally used in the food and chemical industries, with around 250 000 t of tallow being produced annually in the United Kingdom with an average CV of 40.0 MJ kg^{-1} [41]. All grades of tallow can be used as liquid fuel in place of fossil fuel since the CV of tallow is just over 90% that of fuel oil and very little modification of combustion equipment is needed to burn it [12]. However, the use of tallow in co-firing applications has been prevented as a result of its classification as a nonwaste material according to the UK interpretation of the European Waste Incineration Directive (WID). It only becomes classed as a waste material if it is burned.

5.05.2.5.3 Jatropha oil

The jatropha plant is pest and drought resilient with a high tolerance to poor soil conditions. Enhanced growth rates have been shown to be achievable by applying fertilizers containing minerals such as magnesium, sulfur, and calcium. It is estimated that a hectare of land can grow 2200 jatropha plants producing 7 t of jatropha seed yielding 2.2–2.7 t of jatropha oil. The oil content of jatropha kernel is 63% [13], which is higher than palm oil (up to 45%). The fact that the plant cannot be used as a food source without detoxification makes it very attractive as an energy fuel source. Drax, a power generation company in the United Kingdom, has recently announced plans to develop and use jatropha oil in its plans for developing biomass-only power stations and units [14].

5.05.2.5.4 Sewage sludge

Sewage sludge is the final solid component produced during wastewater treatment. Approximately 1.5 Mt of sewage sludge is produced in the United Kingdom each year, which when processed is suitable for co-firing. After the sludge component has been separated from the water fraction, it is dried and pelletized. The drying is energy intensive since producing 1 t of sewage sludge pellets requires 20 t of sewage sludge. The CV of dry sewage sludge is highly variable, with an average of 12 MJ kg^{-1}. As a waste product, this falls under the control of the WID of the EU and can only be burned in a WID-compliant plant, which prevents its use in most co-firing plants as they tend to be not WID compliant.

5.05.2.6 Gaseous Biomass

Solid biomass can further be processed into gaseous forms by the process of gasification. The gasification of solid biomass implies incomplete combustion of the material resulting in production of combustible gases, such as carbon monoxide (CO), hydrogen (H$_2$), and traces of methane (CH$_4$). The technique of converting solid biomass into gaseous forms has been described in detail in subsequent sections.

5.05.3 Combustion Technology

Biomass co-firing relies on existing coal technologies to function, as it is not a stand-alone technology. This is achieved with slight or, in some cases, no modification at all to the parent plant. Common technologies employed in biomass co-firing are pulverized coal combustion (PCC), fluidized bed combustion (FBC), cyclone boiler, stoker combustion, and gasification.

5.05.3.1 Pulverized Coal Combustion

PCC technology is a widely utilized technology to generate energy from fossil fuel, especially coal [15]. In this technology, pulverized coal is injected to combust in a furnace in the presence of a controlled level of air. The heat generated is used to produce high-pressure steam driving a steam turbine to generate electrical power. The average efficiency for such plants is about 36% in the OECD (Organisation for Economic Co-operation and Development) countries and 30% in China [16]. The concept of PCC has been enhanced to operate at higher temperatures and pressures to produce supercritical (SC) steam and also ultra-supercritical (USC) steam (>374 °C and 218 atm). These two advanced technologies have efficiencies far greater than PCC, with efficiency ranging between 40% and 55%. However, the full commercialization of SC technology has been limited by the need for materials that can withstand high temperatures and pressures. These technologies are seen as a major carbon mitigation route, as it is estimated that a percentage point increase in plant thermal efficiency can lead to a double reduction in CO$_2$ emissions [17]. Therefore, replacing old pulverized fuel (PF) plants with SC pulverized coal plants has the potential of reducing emissions by 10–25% [15].

5.05.3.2 Fluidized Bed Combustion

FBC can be either a bubbling bed (BFBC) or a circulating bed (CFBC). BFBC is achieved by combusting the fuel with a bed material that has a depth of around 1 m operating at gas velocities sufficient to fluidize the fuel and the bed material. CFBC operates at higher gas velocities, high enough to entrain the fuel and bed particles in the gas flow leaving the combustion chamber, where the particles are separated in a cyclone or beam separator and recirculated to the combustion chamber.

These technologies result in lower NO$_x$ and SO$_x$ emissions than PF technology, which is due to the fact that FBC operates at temperatures (800–900 °C) below the temperatures required for thermal NO$_x$ formation [15] and also there exists an intimate contact between the fuel and the bed material. Moreover, SO$_2$ can be totally removed, negating the need for flue gas desulfurization or recirculation, by addition of limestone to the bed material. FBC technologies are ideal for high-ash coals or coals with poorer burnout properties. Their thermal efficiencies are normally about 3–4% below that of PF combustion. However, with the advent of pressurized fluidized bed combustion (PFBC) technology, which employs the same processes but with higher pressures, thermal efficiencies can exceed 40%. There is also the possibility of improving upon the PFBC by the application of combined cycle technology [15].

5.05.3.3 Stoker Combustion

In the stoker or grate-fired boiler system, the fuel is fed onto a moving grate while air is blown through the bed of fuel. Smaller particles burn out suspended above the grate while larger particles burn on the grate, as the fuel moves from the back to the front of the boiler. These boilers are capable of firing a wide range of fuels, including coal, peat, straw, waste, and wood residues in fairly large pieces (not more than 3 cm).

This technology has a low maintenance and operational cost, but it is limited to a maximum capacity of about 100 MW$_e$ and has a lower efficiency compared with PCC and FBC [18]. Modern stoker units are equipped with cyclones, electrostatic precipitators, or baghouses, sometimes with gas scrubbers to remove particulate from the stack phases. There are often problems when firing low-melting fuels in stokers, but these can be reduced by using mechanical or water-cooled grates and by avoiding the use of preheated combustion air in the final burning region.

5.05.3.4 Cyclone Boilers

Cyclone boilers are another combustion technology suitable for biomass co-firing. Here the mineral matter in the fuel forms a slag that holds and captures the large particles, allowing the volatile and fine particles to burn in suspension providing intense radiant heat for slag layer combustion. The burners for cyclone boilers are generally large, water-cooled, and horizontal with the combustion temperature in the external furnace ranging between 1650 and 2000 °C. For optimum cyclone performance, the fuels are specified to meet certain requirements, such as ash content must be greater than 6% (too high for many pure biomass types), volatiles must be greater than 15%, and the moisture content must be less than 20% unless the fuel is dried [41]. Cyclone boilers only need fuels to be crushed and not pulverized making them suitable for co-firing in that they require minimal modification for feeding and mixing the biomass and the coal [42].

5.05.3.5 Gasification

Gasification converts solid or liquid carbon-based fuels into a gas (syngas or biosyngas) in a high-temperature environment. The process is initiated in the presence of oxygen, air, or steam and also heat. The gas produced is mainly made up of CO and H_2, and other components including CO_2, H_2O, and CH_4. The percentage of these gases (CO, H_2, CO_2, H_2O, and CH_4) depends on the composition of the raw materials and the gasification conditions such as pressure and temperature. To obtain the highest efficiency for this technology, the gasification process is integrated with a combined gas turbine set, called the integrated gasification combined cycle (IGCC), where efficiency is maximized by using the syngas to drive a gas turbine as well as powering a steam turbine by utilizing the exhaust heat generated from the gas turbine. Work has been done to suggest that efficiencies of up to 56% can be achieved under IGCC [16]; however, it is understood that the practical thermal efficiency is about 40% [43].

5.05.3.5.1 Direct gasification

In direct gasification, reaction temperatures are produced by partial combustion of the feedstock in the presence of air or oxygen in the reactor. Usually, the syngas produced from this process is very dilute when air is used due to the high amount of nitrogen in air. The use of pure oxygen produces syngas with high CV, which is good for combustion purposes, but the process becomes considerably more expensive.

5.05.3.5.2 Indirect gasification

Here, the heat required for gasification is supplied by an external source outside the main gasifier usually by the use of steam. Steam contributes to increasing the CV of the product gas due to its high hydrogen content and, moreover, it is very attractive due to its low cost and easy production. An example of an indirect gasifier using gas as heat source is fluidized bed gasifier equipped with heat exchanger tubes. Here, part of the product gas is burned with air as oxidizing agent in a pulse combustor. The resulting heat is used to gasify the fuel that is fed into the reactor [19]. Two separate reactors are required when char is used as the heat source: a circulating fluidized bed steam gasifier converts fuel to produce gas and a circulating fluidized bed combustor burns residual char to provide heat which is needed to gasify the fuel. Bed material, usually silica sand, is circulated between the two reactors to facilitate better heat transfer.

5.05.3.6 Gasification Techniques

Based on the type of technique and equipment used, three basic types of gasifiers can be distinguished: fixed bed, fluidized bed, and entrained flow gasifiers.

5.05.3.6.1 Fixed bed gasifiers

Fixed bed gasifiers require mechanically stable fuel of smaller particle size (1–3 cm), such as pellets or briquettes [20], to ensure free and easy passage of gas through the bed. Depending on the direction of flow of the feedstock and the gas, these gasifiers are classified as updraft and downdraft gasifiers. In updraft fixed bed gasifiers, the fuel is fed from the top while air is blown into the bottom of the reactor. This arrangement can withstand biomass of higher moisture content (up to 40–50%) [19]. This is because the hot gas exiting the gasifier initiates the combustion process by drying and pyrolyzing the fuel as it moves down the gasifier until finally undergoing gasification and combustion at the bottom. The product gas is generally useful for heat and power generation through a steam turbine and not particularly applicable for synthetic fuel, chemical, or gas turbine applications, due to the amount of higher hydrocarbons (e.g., aromatic hydrocarbons and tars) contained in it.

Alternatively, in downdraft fixed bed gasifiers, the fuel is fed in from the top while air is introduced at the sides above the grate and combustible gas blown through the grate. The setup is very simple and of low cost. The gas produced (mainly CO, H_2, CH_4, CO_2, and N_2) is relatively clean compared with that produced in updraft fixed bed gasifiers and contains no or low amounts of tars or oils, making it suitable for application in heat and power generation using gas turbines.

5.05.3.6.2 Fluidized bed gasifiers

For biomass gasification in a fluidized bed, the temperature for successful gasification is at least 750 °C [44] while maintaining the bed temperature below the ash melting point of the fuel. Failure to adhere to this standard may produce sticky ash that might glue together with bed particles causing agglomeration and breakdown of fluidization. Hence, fluidized bed gasifiers are appropriate for woody biomaterials, which have a higher ash melting point (above 1000 °C) than herbaceous biomaterial (e.g., straw), whose ash melting point can be as low as 700 °C [21].

5.05.3.6.3 Entrained flow gasifiers

Entrained flow gasifiers operate at a very high temperature (1200–2000 °C) and pressure (about 50 bar) and turn the mixture of fuel and oxygen into a turbulent dust flame, producing liquid ash, which deposits on the walls of the gasifier. This is sometimes very problematic, especially when analyzing the ash melting behavior of solid biomass feedstock; another drawback is the high cost associated with oxygen production and the milling of the fuel to suitably fine sizes for easy entrainment [44]. Due to the operating conditions of this type of gasifier, only specific types of biomass are suitable to be applied. The technology is relatively mature and has been commercially utilized in the petroleum industry for the gasification of petroleum residues.

5.05.4 Co-firing Methods

There is no dedicated technology for co-firing, which implies that it utilizes the existing technology for generating power from fossil fuels. Some of these technologies have been described in the preceding sections. However, based on the different routes by which the coal and biomass blend can be introduced into the boiler, three other techniques have been identified: direct, indirect, and parallel co-firing.

5.05.4.1 Direct Co-firing

This is the most popular, simplest, and cost-effective way of co-firing coal with biomass. Here, the combustion of coal and biomass takes place in the same boiler producing blended coal and biomass ash. There are four possible ways to this technique [4]:

1. Co-milling of coal and biomass with existing coal mill equipment or with dedicated individual milling equipment and firing them through the existing coal feeding system
2. Direct injection of premilled biomass and firing of the biomass material through existing coal injection systems and burners
3. Installation of new, dedicated biomass milling equipment and firing the coal and the biomass through separate injection systems
4. Utilizing the biomass as a reburn fuel

Option 1 can be achieved in different ways depending on the milling system:

- *Milling and firing of blended biomass and coal fuel through existing coal milling and firing equipment.* Here, coal and biomass are milled and dried together in existing equipment to achieve the desired particle size. The blended fuel is then fired into the furnace for operation of the plant. It is the cheapest and most straightforward option. The main disadvantage of this technique is that the grinding performance of the coal mill degrades due to the presence of the biomass. It also carries the highest risk of malfunction of the fuel feeding system [42]. This option is suitable for biomass fuels such as olive/palm kernels or cocoa shells as well as sawdust [45] but not for herbaceous biomass.
- *Modifying existing coal mills on each boiler to mill biomass materials separately and firing the milled material through existing pulverized coal pipework and burners* [46].
- *Milling of the biomass in dedicated biomass mills and the introduction of the milled fuel into the existing coal-firing systems.*

With option 2, for the introduction of the premilled fuel into the furnace, three direct co-firing options can be applied:

- *Injection of the biomass directly into the furnace, with no flame stabilization and no additional combustion air.* This is relatively inexpensive and simple to install as it involves direct injection through the walls of the furnace, albeit it does involve the installation of new, small-diameter pipework for better furnace penetration [4]. The drawback of this process is that its application is limited by conventional wall- or corner-fired furnaces. This approach has been used in downshot boilers at RWE npower's Aberthaw power station in the United Kingdom.
- *Installation of new, dedicated biomass burners, with a combustion air supply.* Here, the premilled biomass is fed into the same boiler as the coal but through separate feeding systems. This option requires the installation of a number of biomass transport pipes across the boiler front, which may already be congested, creating difficulties in maintaining an adequate burner performance over the normal load curve. This is more capital intensive than co-milling, since it requires greater modification to existing coal plants. Again, there are a number of potential problems that need to be resolved such as the location of new burner, alterations to accommodate secondary air supply, and the lack of experience in large-scale biomass burners [4].

However, option 2 presents a relatively simple and cost-effective way of increasing the proportion of biomass co-fired in a typical coal plant. Moreover, unlike co-milling, where there is an undue pressure from the biomass on the mill and feed system, this option ensures that there is no interference on the existing coal milling and feeding system.

- *Pneumatic injection of premilled biomass into existing coal pipework downstream of the coal mills or at the burner and firing through the existing burners.* The introduction of additional fuel and air reduces the mill primary air and coal flow rate accordingly to maintain both the coal mills and the burners within their normal operating envelope. Albeit relatively inexpensive and simple to install, there are significant interfaces with the mill and combustion control system, which have to be carefully managed. The available options for the biomass injection points are directly into the burner, just upstream of the burner into the pulverized coal pipework, and into the mill outlet pipework.

5.05.4.2 Parallel Co-firing

Here, the biomass and the coal are separately combusted producing individual ashes, supplying steam to a common header. The fuel preparation and feeding are physically independent. The only potential limiting factor to this technique is the capacity of existing downstream infrastructure, such as the steam turbine. The amount of steam that could be co-fired could be limited by the capacity of the steam generator.

For this technique to be successful, there should be sufficient overcapacity of the steam turbine to accommodate the extra power from biomass or a reduction in the coal boiler capacity to make room for the biomass. Since the coal and the biomass are converted independently, an optimal system for each fuel can be chosen, for example, CFB for biomass and PC for coal. The capital investment of installing parallel co-firing is significantly higher than for direct co-firing; however, this technique attracts some interest due to its potential to optimize the combustion process, the ability to use fuels with high alkali and chlorine content, and the possibility of producing separate ashes.

5.05.4.3 Indirect Co-firing

The process of indirect co-firing involves gasifying biomass separately and injecting the produced gas into a coal boiler to be burned. Like parallel co-firing, this technique produces separate ashes while allowing very high co-firing ratios. Its main disadvantage is the high capital investment of installation. However, this approach may suit the future of co-firing, which will see, almost certainly, an increase in the biomass/coal ratio as well as in the range of different biomass fuels considered. Therefore, high capital investment could pay off in the future with more advanced co-firing configurations giving better operability and flexibility.

5.05.5 Global Overview of Biomass Co-firing Plant

The huge benefits of biomass co-firing as the most efficient renewable route and the corresponding incentives enjoyed by companies for generating electricity from renewables have globally stimulated the development of the technology at a considerable rate. This rate has been intensified in the past 5–10 years, which has seen the modification of existing plant to accommodate the biomass and the introduction of new plant designs with the capacity to co-utilize biomass with fossil fuels [22]. According to the IEA Bioenergy database (http://www.ieabcc.nl), a significant number of these plants are in the United States, with about 100 in Europe and 12 in Asia.

5.05.5.1 United States

Biomass co-firing has been practiced in the United States for a long period of time. It, however, gained impetus from the 1990s, where energy generators started enjoying incentives from the government for generating electricity from renewable sources [23]. A large range of biomass fuels, including residues, energy crops, and herbaceous and woody biomass, have been fired using PCC, stokers, and cyclone boilers. The introduction of the energy generated tax credit in 1992, which was exclusively targeted to support electricity generated from wind and closed-loop biomass, attracted electricity generators to invest in these technologies. Initially, the incentive package covered only closed-loop biomass – that is, energy or forest crops where what is harvested is regrown – but changes in legislation in 1999 allowed for extension and expansion of the existing incentive for electricity generated from biomass. The qualified biomass fuels for incentives included any solid, nonhazardous cellulosic waste material, pellets, crates, trimmings, and agricultural by-products and residues. Other incentives were introduced to encourage renewable technologies in the United States including exemptions from property tax, state sales tax, and income tax, with offers for loan and special grant programs, industry recruitment incentives, accelerated depreciation allowance, and net-metering provisions [3].

Over 40 plants in the United States have co-fired biomass and coal for several years mostly for testing and demonstration purposes. Five plants currently operate continuously for testing wood or switchgrass, and one plant has been operating commercially for the past 2 years burning wood-based fuels and coal [24]. Almost all the co-firing plants in the United States utilize the direct co-firing process, apart from the McNeil generating plant, which employs the indirect options (Table 4).

5.05.5.1.1 McNeil generating plant

The construction of this plant was by popular acclamation where residents in the city of Burlington, Vermont, USA, approved the construction of a 50 MW wood-fired power plant. Electricity was initially supplied by an aging coal-fired plant with poor emission records, and hence the idea of using locally available and environmentally friendly feedstock was widely accepted.

The McNeil generating plant operates by the indirect co-firing techniques, with an installed capacity of 50 MW$_e$. Wood chips are the main biomass fuel and contribute about 15% by heat to the co-firing plant. It utilizes a low-pressure Battelle gasification process that consists of gasification and combustion reactors. The gasification reactor is heated by an indirect source to generate medium-CV fuel of about 17–18 MJ m^{-3} and residual char at a temperature of 700–850 °C [25]. The combustion reactor burns the residual char to provide heat for gasification. Sand is used as a medium of heat transfer between the reactors by circulating the sand between the gasifier and the combustor. The product gas is co-fired in a stoker grate boiler for steam generation, which is used in steam turbines for power.

5.05.5.2 Netherlands

The Dutch government has set ambitious targets with 14% of its total energy from renewable sources by 2020 [26]. For that reason, the government has entered into an agreement with six utilities companies, which operate coal-fired power plants, to commit themselves to reduce CO_2 emission by an equivalent of 5.8 Mt yr^{-1} in the period 2008–12. It is envisaged that more than half of this target (3.2 Mt yr^{-1}) will be achieved by the substitution of coal by biomass [27].

In The Netherlands, 4 GW$_e$ out of the total power production of 14 GW$_e$ is generated by coal-fired power plants, which co-fire biomass. Table 5 shows the total number of coal-fired power plants and the types of biomass used. Apart from Amer 9, all co-fired power plants in The Netherlands utilize the direct injection technique.

5.05.5.2.1 Amer 9

The Amer 9 plant utilizes both direct and indirect co-firing configurations. The plant co-fires biomass pellets up to a maximum of 1200 kt yr^{-1}, generating 27% by heat through two modified coal mills. Only wood-based fuel has been used since 2006, due to reduced subsidies for agricultural by-products.

For the indirect co-firing option, low-quality demolition wood is gasified in a CFB gasifier at atmospheric pressure and a temperature of approximately 850 °C. The raw fuel gas is cleaned extensively and combusted in a coal boiler via specially designed low-CV gas burners. An advantage of this concept is that there is no contamination of the fuel gas as it enters the coal-fired boiler. This allows a wide range of fuels to be co-fired within existing emission constraints while avoiding problems with ash quality. The

Table 4 Major US biomass co-firing demonstration plants [3, 22]

Utility	Plant	Boiler type	Boiler size (MW$_e$)	Biomass type	Biomass heat input (%)
Alabama Power	Gadsden	Tangentially fired	70	Switchgrass	7
Allegheny Energy	Albright	Tangentially fired	150	Sawdust	7
Allegheny Energy	Willow	Cyclone	188	Sawdust	5–10
Alliant Energy Corporation	Ottumwa	Tangentially fired	704	Switchgrass	3
GPU	Shawville	Wall-fired	130	Wood	1.5
GPU	Shawville	Tangentially fired	160	Wood	1.5
GPU/RE	Seward	Wall-fired	32	Sawdust	10
La Cygne	KCP&L	Cyclone	840	Wood	5
NRG Energy	B. L. England	Cyclone	120	Wood	12 (mass)
NRG Energy	Dunkirk	Tangentially fired	100	Wood	10–15
NIPSCO	Michigan City	Cyclone	425	Wood	5.5
Nisource	Bailly	Cyclone	160	Sawdust	10
NYSEG/AES	Greenidge	Tangentially fired	105	Wood	10
Madison G&E	Blount St.	Wall-fired	50	Switchgrass	10
Otter Tail	Big Stone	Cyclone	450	Seed corn	1–4
Santee Cooper	Jefferies	Wall-fired	165	Wood	10–20 (mass)
Southern Company Services, Inc.	Hammond	Tangentially fired	120	Wood	5–14 (mass)
Southern Company Services, Inc.	Kraft	Tangentially fired	55	Wood	20–50 (mass)
Tampa Electric	Gannon	Cyclone	165	Wastepaper	5
TVA	Allen	Cyclone	270	Sawdust	10
TVA	Colbert	Wall-fired	190	Sawdust	1.5
TVA	Kingston	Tangentially fired	160	Sawdust	2.5
FERCO	McNeil	Stoker grate	50	Wood chips	15

Table 5 Biomass fuels power plants in The Netherlands [22]

Plant	Type of co-firing	Co-firing	Co-firing (%, thermal)	Status	Burner configuration
Gelderland	Direct	Demolition wood	3	Commercial	Wall-fired
Amer 8	Direct	Wood pellets	10–12	Commercial	Tangentially fired
Amer 9	Indirect	Demolition wood	27	Commercial	Tangentially fired
Borssele 12	Direct	Kernels, shells, fibers, paper sludge	10–15	Commercial	Tangentially fired
Maasvlakte 1	Direct	Biomass pellets	5	Commercial	Tangentially fired
Maasvlakte 2	Direct	Poultry litter	5	Commercial	Tangentially fired
Hemweg 8	Direct	Sewage sludge	3	Test phase	Wall-fired

challenge, as always, is working within the relatively stringent fuel constraints while avoiding the inevitable high investment costs [22]. Amer 8 also co-fires at high biomass feed levels but uses a standard hammer mill configuration.

5.05.5.2.2 Borssele

Borssele is a 420 MW$_e$, tangentially fired PCC unit, equipped with low-NO$_x$ burners with overfire air. This plant co-fires coal and phosphor oven gas, which is transported from a nearby phosphor production plant through a pipeline. About 80 000 t of gas are fired annually, which is equivalent to a 3.5% coal replacement. Initially, there were concerns over the quality of the fly ash, due to risk of contamination by the presence of phosphate; however, the concentration of phosphorus is sufficiently low, and as such, no adverse effects have been observed [27].

Lately, paper sludge, olive pulp, cocoa shells, palm kernels, and wood pellets have been co-fired over the coal belt through existing mills. It is also possible to co-fire these fuels through separate mills and burners. Sewage sludge has also been fired at Borssele 12, but it is no longer used due to odor problems [28].

5.05.5.2.3 Maasvlakte 1 and 2

Liquid organic waste from the petrochemical industry is co-fired with coal in the 518 MW$_e$ PCC, a tangentially fired plant fitted with flue gas desulfurization. The liquid waste is handled and fired separately from the coal and constitutes about 1% of the output of the plant. The disposal of the fly ash and the bottom ash produced is problematic due to molybdenum contamination of the liquid waste.

At Maasvlakte 2, the co-fired biomass pellets consist of a mixture of wood, composted sewage sludge, and paper sludge. The pellets are mixed with the raw coal and milled in the existing milling equipment. The pellet production plant is capable of manufacturing 150 000 t of pellets with a heating value of 16 MJ kg^{-1}, and is situated adjacent to the power station. During the demonstration trials, the operation of the mills was found to be normal and inspections revealed no damage or accumulation of woody material in the mills or transport lines. The quality of the fly ash, bottom ash, and gypsum produced was tested and they fulfilled their regular quality specifications. Also, no adverse effects on atmospheric emissions or wastewater effluent were observed. Co-firing started commercially in 1998 and the amount co-fired is equivalent to 5% of the output of the plant [3].

5.05.5.3 United Kingdom

The United Kingdom has, by law, set a stringent target to reduce its carbon emissions by 80% by 2050, with a preceding short-to-medium target, where 20% reduction is expected by 2020 and 10.4% and 15.4% by 2011 and 2016, respectively [41]. To meet this target, it is expected that about 30–40% of electricity would be generated from renewables, which is made attractive by the introduction of the Renewables Obligation, as power generators are awarded ROCs that are tradable. Table 6 shows the number of ROCs awarded for the production of 1 MWh of electricity by different technologies. The certificates were traded at a price of around £45 in 2010 [31]. If a supplier cannot provide the required number of ROCs, they have to pay a buyout fee, which was £37 per ROC in 2010 [32].

Currently, all the 15 coal-fired power plants have co-fired biomass, but several of them have stopped doing so. A wide variety of biomass fuels have been utilized, including baled straw, woody materials, poultry litter, residues, tallow, and bonemeal (Table 7).

5.05.5.3.1 Aberthaw power plant

This plant is located on the coast of south Wales in the Vale of Glamorgan. It is one of the three RWE npower power stations co-firing a range of biomass. Originally, the plant was designed to fire only coal and has been operating at full scale since 1971 with three operation units. It has the capacity to generate 1500 MW of electricity. As part of the company's effort to invest in lower carbon technologies, it has invested over £9.5 million in biomass co-firing technology to allow the substitution of some of the coal burned

Table 6 The ROC bands for different approaches that use biomass [29, 30]

Approach	Fuel type	ROCs (MWh^{-1})
Co-firing	Biomass	0.5
Co-firing of energy crops	Energy crop which is one of the following: (1) *Miscanthus giganteus*; (2) *Salix* (also known as SRC willow); or (3) *Populus* (also known as SRC poplar)	1
Co-firing with combined heat and power (CHP)	Biomass by a qualifying CHP generating station and where the fossil fuel and biomass have been burned in separate boilers	1
Co-firing of energy crops with CHP	Energy crop which is one of the following: (1) *Miscanthus giganteus*; (2) *Salix* (also known as SRC willow); or (3) *Populus* (also known as SRC poplar) by a qualifying CHP generating station and where the fossil fuel and energy crops have been burned in separate boilers	1.5
Dedicated biomass power generation	Electricity generated solely from biomass	1.5
Dedicated energy crops power generation	Energy crop which is one of the following: (1) *Miscanthus giganteus*; (2) *Salix* (also known as SRC willow); or (3) *Populus* (also known as SRC poplar) generating electricity solely from energy crops	2
Dedicated biomass with CHP	Electricity generated from biomass by a qualifying CHP generating station in a calendar month in which it is fueled wholly by biomass	2
Dedicated energy crops with CHP	As above but with energy crops	2

Table 7 Information on UK co-firing power plants [33]

Company	Power station	Installed capacity (MW)	Primary fuel	Co-firing fuel
AES	Kilroot	390	Coal/oil	Olive pellets
Alcan	Lynemouth	420	Coal	Wood pellets, olive pellets
British Energy	Eggborough	2000	Coal	2.5% PKE, olive pellets and pulp, shea pellets and meal
Drax Power Limited	Drax	4000	Coal	3% Energy crops/wood pellets
EDF Energy	West Burton	2000	Coal	5% Biomass blend – wood pellets, shea, miscanthus
EDF Energy	Cottam	2000	Coal	5% Biomass blend – wood pellets, olive cakess
E.On UK	Kingsnorth	2034	Coal/oil	Cereal residues
E.On UK	Ironbridge	964	Coal	Wood chips, PKE
E.On UK	Ratcliffe	2000	Coal	None
International Power	Rugeley	1000	Coal	None
RWE npower	Aberthaw B	1553	Coal	Tallow, sawdust, PKE, wood chips, small roundwood
RWE npower	Tilbury B	1029	Coal/oil	3% PKE, sawdust, olive residues
RWE npower	Didcot A	1940	Coal/gas	PKE, sawdust, olive residues, shea, wood pellets
Scottish and Southern Energy	Ferrybridge C	2034	Coal	10% Biomass – wood, olives, shea residues, PKE
Scottish and Southern Energy	Fiddler's Ferry	1995	Coal	10% Biomass
ScottishPower	Cockenzie	1200	Coal	Wood pellets
ScottishPower	Logannet	2400	Coal	Sewage sludge/wood pellets
Uskmouth1 Power Company	Uskmouth	393	Coal	Shea meal
	Littlebrook	685		Palm oil

with biomass fuels such as sawdust, PKE, and wood chips in a 55 MW existing generating plant [34]. It employs the direct injection technique, with 5% (thermal basis) of biomass. The biomass is milled in a separate biomass milling plant using hammer mills and then injected into the boilers through dedicated injectors and burns in the coal flames, rather than milling the biomass and coal together. This has been achieved without significant modification of the existing boiler. Liquid biomass fuels such as tallow and tall oil have also been co-fired at the plant for a number of years.

5.05.5.3.2 Didcot power plant

RWE npower invested over £3.5 million in the Didcot power plants to provide enough renewable electrical energy, through biomass co-firing, to over 100 000 homes each year [34]. It is estimated that this investment could replace about 300 000 t of coal and avoid 700 000 t of CO_2 emissions into the atmosphere. Didcot A has an installed capacity of about 2000 MW, which was originally designed to fire coal or gas. It has been modified to fire biomass materials such as PKE, sawdust, olive residue, shea residue, and wood pellets alongside coal in its co-firing operations. The biomass is co-milled with the coal at Didcot and burned through the existing unmodified coal burners.

5.05.5.3.3 E.ON (Kingsnorth)

Pelletized straw materials have been co-fired at the plant's four 500 MW_e, tangentially fired, low-NO_x units. The pelletized biomass fuel is preblended with the coal in the coal handling system and is fired through the existing handling and firing system. Before the commissioning of the plant, pretrials and health and safety checks had been completed, which led to the installation of temporary blend facilities and additional explosion suppression systems. During the pretrials, it was observed that for every percentage increment of biomass in the co-firing mixture, there was a corresponding 2% reduction in mill capacity, even though this depended largely on the type of biomass. There were also noticeable reductions in carbon, NO_x, and SO_x emissions, and the ash produced met salable standards [3].

5.05.5.3.4 Drax

Drax has invested in a multimillion-pound co-firing facility to allow the company to meet its set target of generating 12.5% of the total electricity from biomass co-firing, reducing carbon emissions by about 15% and saving over 2.5 million tonnes of CO_2 annually. This investment puts the company in the forefront of developments to establish alternative fuels technology for power generation in the United Kingdom. The company has again announced plans to build three biomass co-firing plants, with each having an installed capacity of 300 MW. This could result in the company being responsible for the supply of at least 15% of UK renewable energy and up to 10% of total UK electricity [35]. Drax Power Limited has been burning biomass since 2003, with its main fuel being sustainable wood-based products and residual agricultural products such as sunflower seed husks and peanut husks, which are secured through a supply agreement for biomass with local producer groups and supplier groups for all their required biomass fuels.

5.05.6 Health and Safety Issues Associated with Co-firing

5.05.6.1 Spontaneous Fires

Spontaneous combustion has always been one of the most serious hazards in the power generation industry, as recorded in the United States, France, Great Britain, and Australia from the 1950s to the 1990s [36]. Spontaneous combustion is most likely when deep deposits of coal have been heated and moistened by steam purges. For vertical-spindle mills, deposits of coal in the air inlet to the mill are particularly dangerous because the air inlet temperature is higher than the temperature in all other parts of the mill. In addition, smoldering could take place, without causing excessive increase in mill outlet temperatures, which could remain undetected for a considerable period of time. Biomass, like all materials with high-volatile matter, is often prone to spontaneous combustion, which makes storage, milling, and transport often problematic [37].

A combination of low humidity levels and dust particulate accumulation can expose the plant to a high fire risk due to the occurrence of combustion and deflagration. It has, however, been found that for an air/gas mixture, deflagration may fail if the ratio of gas to oxygen is too high (fuel-rich mixture) or too low (fuel-lean mixture). For a coal dust/air mixture, the lower explosive limit for lignite and bituminous coals is 30 and 140 $g\,m^{-3}$, respectively. Biomass fuels have a lower explosion limit similar to lignite at around 30–40 $g\,m^{-3}$ [37]. The concept of a fuel-rich upper explosive limit for any PF milling system is questionable if air is used as the transport medium due to the sufficiently energetic source of ignition. It has been suggested that PF particles can use the available air to continue to react, even in the fuel-rich region. Generally, for bituminous coals, the risk of deflagration occurring can be reduced if the air/fuel ratio within the PF supply system is limited. It has also been found, based on empirical data and laboratory analysis, that applying a similar operating restriction when co-milling biomass should not pose any additional threat during normal operation, provided that blend concentrations are kept within well-defined limits. This is due to the fact that the explosion characteristics of biomass/coal blends containing up to 15 wt.% biomass are dominated by the coal blend [37].

Work by Caini and Hules [38] found that suppression systems could be used to minimize or prevent the occurrence of fires and deflagration, especially in coal bunkers, feeders, and pulverizers. This system injects inert gases or particles like sodium bicarbonate to dilute the oxygen concentration to a level where fire and deflagration of the mixture are not possible [43]. It is very important that the oxygen level be reduced to a level below 15% and above 12%, as below 15% oxygen fire cannot thrive and below 12% visible signs of oxygen depletion might set in [39].

5.05.6.2 Exposure to Biomass and Coal Dust

Workers subject themselves to high risk of exposure to dust when working with biomass and coal. Dry biomass particles are easily suspended in air due to their low density and large drag coefficient. Exposure to dust at work contravenes the Control of Substances Hazardous to Health (COSHH) regulations, which clearly stipulate that workers should not unnecessarily be exposed to chemical, physical, or biological agents that may harm their health. Where it is impossible to prevent exposure, steps must be put in place to control the situation to reduce as much as possible the level of contamination and exposure. Moreover, workers must be given the necessary training and protective equipment to protect themselves from unnecessary exposure when it becomes inevitable. Information on suitable protective equipment against exposure can, in the UK, be provided by the Health and Safety Executive (HSE) where recommendation has been made for suitable protection against exposure to specific materials such as wood dust and grains. This information has been found to be applicable to biomass materials such as cereal pellet and wood pellet [37].

The effects of coal or biomass dust on health are very diverse, depending on the type of dust. But dust mainly affects the lungs and the respiratory systems through inhalation, creating the risk of nasal cancer. Other dust-associated health problems include dermatitis and soreness of the eyes, abrasion, and conjunctivitis. It is strongly advised that people who are allergic to dust must avoid exposure completely. Palm and shea residues originally contained nuts; hence, it is advisable for people who have a nut allergy to avoid working in storage areas or areas where dust inhalation is possible.

In general, the use of a disposable filtering facepiece respirator would be enough to provide adequate protection, unless personnel are exposed to high concentrations of dust that might be beyond the designed limit of the respirator. In such cases, dust levels must be continuously monitored to determine the risk of exposure. Dust formation can be suppressed or prevented by the use of suppression systems such as moisture or foaming agents. This system of dust prevention requires very low capital investment compared with full dust extraction systems. However, misting systems can also generate conditions that are favorable for mold growth on stored biomass. This problem clearly depends on biomass type, plant design, atmospheric conditions, and cleaning regimes.

Currently, there is limited information regarding the effects of mold on health, as well as human susceptibility which varies considerably. Even though the majority of the molds found on biomass are common species and pose no known harm to health, persons with impaired immune systems may be at risk when exposed to high levels of airborne molds and fungal spores.

Good housekeeping such as minimizing storage times, the immediate cleaning up of spillages, and minimization of dust and moisture levels can reduce the ambient spore loading in areas where biomass is handled. Currently, there is no regulatory limit on airborne levels for spores, even though the level of bacteria and microbiological organisms is covered by COSHH. This, however, does not negate the potential health hazards of working with biomass; hence, good housekeeping procedures and personal protective measures must be adhered to in order to mitigate these risks.

Under COSHH, hardwood dust is classified as a carcinogen which has the potential to cause lung and respiratory problems. However, only softwoods are usually used as biomass fuels and they present a significantly lower risk than hardwoods [37].

Mycotoxins and endotoxins are by-products from the growth of mold and breakdown of bacterial cells, respectively. They contribute to naturally occurring aerosols which are generally noninfectious. Nevertheless, they may cause irritations mainly of the respiratory tract such as mucous membrane irritation (MMI), immunotoxic diseases, and allergic diseases (e.g., asthma and allergic rhinitis). Like dust, there is no exposure limit; the general approach for protection against endotoxins and mycotoxins has been to limit exposure.

The release of volatiles from many volatile organic compounds (VOCs) in biomass materials gives them their characteristic smell. Some of these biomass materials, especially olive, may release substances such as carbon monoxide, hydrogen sulfide, methane, CO_2, and volatile fatty acids (e.g., acetic acid, propanoic acid, and butyric acid). In general terms, this may not be harmful, but there may be potential health and safety hazards when personnel are exposed in a confined space with poor ventilation. An employee from a power station in The Netherlands suffered carbon monoxide poisoning after unloading a consignment of olive cakes in a confined space. Risk could be reduced by conducting an appropriate laboratory screening of the fuel prior to delivery.

5.05.7 Technical Issues regarding Biomass Co-firing

There are vast characteristic differences between coal and biomass largely influenced by the behavior of coal and biomass blends under co-firing conditions. Apart from the heating value of coal being almost twice that of biomass and the corresponding bulk density of biomass being significantly less than that of coal, the moisture content of biomass is usually much higher than that of coal, ranging from 25% to over 50%. The ash content of biomass can also vary from less than 1% to over 20%. Moreover, the fuel nitrogen of biomass can vary from 0.1% to over 1%, but its sulfur content is usually very low [3].

5.05.7.1 Fuel Delivery, Storage, and Preparation

Work on the delivery, storage, and preparation of coal for power generation has been well documented. However, when coal is co-fired with biomass, new challenges arise, which are primarily due to the differences in their properties. The low bulk density of biomass requires different types of handling, storage, and preparation compared with coal. The low energy and high shear strength require a receiving pit as open as possible to allow sufficient unloading for the boiler capacity, and a screening device designed to meet the irregular shapes of the biomass material.

Storing biomass with moisture content greater than 20% for a long period of time can cause problems, which could lead to the growth of biological activity causing self-heating of the storage piles, loss of dry matter, and significant deterioration of the physical quantity of the fuel [4]. This means that moist biomass cannot be stored on-site for a long period of time; hence, co-milled mixtures of biomass and coal must be prepared shortly before the fuel is fired or else the quality of the feedstock will be deteriorated due to the degradation of the biomass [47]. There is also the possibility that high dust and spore concentration in the stored fuel can create health and safety issues during subsequent fuel handling operations [37].

Taking appropriate steps prior to delivery can minimize biological activity during long-term storage but significantly add to the cost of the fuel. Some of these steps are as follows [5]:

- Storage of biomass in billets or larger pieces, if possible, to reduce the surface area available for biological activity
- Using fungicides and other chemical agents to suppress biological activity
- Predrying of the fuel to a moisture level where biological activity cannot flourish
- Cooling the stored fuel by forced ventilation to temperatures where biological activity can be minimized

On the other hand, some biomass materials (such as PKE and wood pellets) have moisture content below 20% and are not affected by biological activity to the same extent as wet fuels.

Due to the nature of biomass and its high moisture content, there is a risk of spontaneous combustion occurring. This can be prevented by adhering to the following guidelines [3]:

- Storage piles should consist of a homogeneous material.
- Biomass piles should not be compacted.
- Temperature and the gas composition in the pile should be monitored.

Co-milling of blended coal and biomass with already existing coal mill equipment may require significant modification, since the equipment was designed to suit the brittle nature of coal. Since biomass is not brittle, the breakage mechanisms are different. Biomass/coal ratios may be limited if the biomass is not milled to the required specification. Moreover, the use of wet biomass can alter the heat balance in the mill and wet biomass also has the tendency to accumulate in the mill, which can be problematic during normal operation and when emptying. During milling and processing, biomass releases combustible volatiles at lower temperatures than coal, which can result in health and safety issues that need to be considered especially during start-ups, shutdowns, mill trips, and restarts [3].

5.05.7.2 Supply of Biomass

To meet the quantities of biomass suitable for co-firing, power generators usually rely on imported biomass fuels. Dried or pelletized wood is widely available in countries such as North America, Scandinavia, Russia, and specific European countries. Other biomass materials such as olive and palm residues can be sourced from countries with large olive or palm oil production such as Spain, Italy, Greece, Turkey, Tunisia, Portugal, Malaysia, and Thailand [40]. Oil, sugar, and starch energy crops can be used for the production of liquid fuels with high energy content as in biodiesel and bioethanol. However, they are a primary food stock; hence, their full-scale utilization may compete with and defeat their main purpose of serving as food for human consumption.

5.05.7.3 Properties of Biomass and Their Effects on Plant Operations

As mentioned earlier, biomass and coal have diverse characteristics. Generally, biomass has a higher moisture content (about 50–70% in fresh wood) than coal (about 3% in bituminous coal), resulting in low CV of the biomass fuel. The volatile matter content of biomass is close to 80% and 20% fixed carbon (on a moisture-free and ash-free basis), whereas bituminous coal has around 20–30% volatile matter and 70–80% fixed carbon [5]. Moreover, both particle size variations and the high fiber content of biomass contribute to the poor flow properties of biofuels. This means that, with the exception of pelletized fuel made from dry raw materials, high internal and external frictions will occur during movement of the material, making it more abrasive and somewhat corrosive [6].

Apart from the physical properties, the chemical properties of wood biomass set demanding requirements for power plant operation. These properties include total ash content, ash melting behavior, and the chemical composition of ash. Alkaline metals present in the ash are generally responsible for fouling the heat transfer surfaces and are abundant in wood fuel ashes which will be easily released in the gas phase during combustion [6]. It is known that a small concentration of chlorine in the fuel can result in the development of harmful alkaline and chlorine compounds on boiler heat transfer surfaces [6].

EUBIONET concluded that most of the problems with boiler performance when co-firing arise from the difference in properties between the coal and the biomass fuel (Table 8), which can be summarized as follows (Maciejewska 2006):

- Biomass has a higher inherent moisture content.
- Pyrolysis starts at lower temperatures with biomass than with coal.
- The volatile matter content of biomass is higher than that of coals, even that of high-volatile coals.
- The proportion of heat that is generated from the volatile fraction of biomass is approximately 70% compared with 30–40% for coal.
- The CV of the volatile matter from biomass is significantly lower than that from coal.
- Biomass char contains more oxygen than coal char and is also more porous and reactive.
- Biomass ash tends to be more alkaline, which increases the chances of fouling in the boiler.
- Biomass can have high chlorine content, but typically low sulfur and ash content.

These variations mean that if biomass is blended with coal, the following implications may be expected:

- Increased rate of deposit formation
- More frequent soot blowing
- Higher risk of corrosion of heat transfer surfaces
- Bed material agglomeration (in fluidized beds)
- Higher in-house power consumption, particularly with the mills
- Higher flue gas temperature

Table 8 Properties of biomass and their effects on power plants

Properties	Impacts
Physical	
Moisture content	Storage durability
	Dry matter losses
	Low CV
	Self-ignition
Bulk density	Fuel logistics (storage, transport, handling)
Particle dimension and size distribution	Determines fuel feeding system
	Determines combustion technology
	Drying properties
	Dust formation
	Operational safety during fuel conveying
Chemical	
Carbon (C)	Gross CV (GCV; positive)
Hydrogen (H)	GCV (positive)
Oxygen (O)	GCV (negative)
Chlorine (Cl)	Corrosion
Nitrogen (N)	NO_x, N_2O, HCN emissions
Sulfur (S)	SO_x emissions, corrosion
Fluorine (F)	HF emissions, corrosion
Potassium (K)	Corrosion (heat exchangers, superheaters)
	Lowering of ash melting temperature
	Aerosol formation
	Ash utilization (plant nutrient)
Sodium (Na)	Corrosion (heat exchangers, superheaters)
	Lowering of ash melting point
	Aerosol formation
Magnesium (Mg)	Increased ash melting temperature
	Ash utilization (plant nutrient)
Calcium (Ca)	Increased ash melting temperature
	Ash utilization (plant nutrient)
Phosphorus (P)	Increased ash melting temperature
	Ash utilization (plant nutrient)
Heavy metals	Emission of pollutants
	Ash utilization and disposal issues
	Aerosol formation

While the magnitude of these implications depends on the quality and the proportion of biomass in the fuel blend, the overall result is that operating and maintenance costs may increase. However, this can be reduced or avoided with appropriate fuel blend control, where optimum amounts of the biomass fuel in the fuel blend can be defined with appropriate combustion tests together with bed material and deposit quality assessment [6].

5.05.8 Conclusions

Coal will continue to play a critical role in the global energy mix for the foreseeable future, despite all the known impacts that come from its combustion. There are many technologies that are destined to mitigate emissions from coal. Co-firing of coal with biomass has been identified as a low-cost option for efficiently and cleanly converting biomass to energy by adding biomass as a partial substitute fuel in high-efficiency coal boilers. Moreover, it makes good use of materials that would otherwise end up in landfill, thereby serving a dual purpose of mitigating emissions and contributing toward a cleaner environment.

However, biomass co-firing cannot thrive without adequate financial support to entice power generators and favorable legislation from the government to allow the technology to prevail. This support is common to many new technologies; however, the huge benefits associated with biomass co-firing, in terms of its ability to use existing PF technologies and achieve direct and immediate results, make such support essential.

Biomass co-firing is not a stand-alone plant; it employs the already existing coal-fired technologies with slight modification, or no alteration at all if the biomass percentage is low. This chapter has discussed in detail the common technologies employed in biomass co-firing. It is found that, among the three main biomass co-firing options, the direct co-firing method is the simplest to operate and common among many biomass co-firing power stations. The indirect and parallel co-firing options also have some advantages; however, the complexity and the cost involved in their operations deter power generators from embarking on that route. Notwithstanding, there are pockets of plants, especially in Europe, where the technology is used.

Biomass co-firing technology, despite presenting numerous benefits, also presents significant challenges. Health and safety issues associated with the handling of the biomass and the coal have been discussed in this chapter, and it is generally accepted that adequate measures are needed to protect personnel, such as the wearing of personal protective equipment (PPE), and to prevent spontaneous fires. Coal bunkers, feeders, and pulverizers may be protected by injecting adequate amounts of inert gas by using suppression systems. This would dilute the oxygen concentration to a level where deflagration of the mixture is not possible. Another challenge faced by the technology is the effects of the properties of biomass on boiler equipment. Some of these effects include increased rate of deposit formation and soot blowing, risk of corrosion of heat transfer surfaces, and bed material agglomeration. These effects are found to be reduced in lower biomass percentage and very pronounced in higher biomass, and can be reduced if appropriate fuel blend controls are adhered to. Progressive developments based on an increasing awareness of biomass behavior will lead to increases in the optimum amount of the biomass that can be introduced into the blend, thus achieving maximum environmental benefit with minimal impact on the plant.

References

[1] McPherson B (2010) Development and application of carbon dioxide (CO_2) storage for improving the environmental impact of advanced power plants. In: Roddy D (ed.) *Advanced Power Plant Materials, Design and Technology*. Woodhead Publishing Ltd., UK. ISBN 1-84569-515-1.
[2] International Energy Agency (IEA) (2007) Biomass for power generation and CHP. *IEA Energy Technology Essentials*. http://www.iea.org/Textbase/Techno/essentials.htm (accessed 20 November 2011).
[3] Fernando R (2005) *Fuels for Biomass Co-firing*. IEA Clean Coal Centre, London, UK. CCC/102. ISBN 92-9029-418-3.
[4] Livingstone WR (2007) Advanced biomass co-firing technologies for coal-fired boilers. Renfrew, Scotland: Doosan Babcock, Technology and Engineering. http://www.see.ed.ac.uk (accessed 10 November 2010).
[5] Maciejewska A, Veringa H, Sander J, and Peteves SD (2006) Co-firing of biomass with coal: Constraints and role of biomass pre-treatment. European Commission Directorate General Joint Research Centre, Report No. EU 22461 EN, The Netherlands.
[6] European Bioenergy Network (EUBIONET) (2003) Biomass co-firing – An efficient way to reduce greenhouse gas emissions. Finland. http://eubionet.vtt.fi (accessed 5 January 2011).
[7] Woods J, Tipper R, Brown G, et al. (2006) Evaluating the sustainability of co-firing in the UK. DTI Report No. URN 06/1960.
[8] Caslin B, Finnan J, and McCracken S (2010) *Miscanthus Best Practice Guidelines*. Teagasc and the Agri-Food and Bioscience Institute, Northern Ireland. ISBN 1-84170-567-5.
[9] Mitchell P, Kiel J, Livingstone B, and Dupont-Roc G (2007) Torrefied biomass – A foresighting study into the biomass case study for pellets from torrefied biomass as a new solid fuel. http://www.all-energy.co.uk/UserFiles/File/2007PaulMitchell.pdf (accessed 20 January 2011).
[10] Biomass Energy Centre (2008) Co-firing fuels. http://www.biomassenergycentre.org.uk (accessed 20 November 2010).
[11] Kavalov B and Peteves SD (2005) Status and perspective of biomass to liquid fuels in the European Union. European Commission Directorate Joint Research Centre, Report No. EU 21745 EN.
[12] United Kingdom Renderers' Association (UKRA) (2010) Renewable fuel: Uses for tallow. http://www.ukra.co.uk (accessed 20 November 2011).
[13] Akbar E, Yaakob Z, Kamarudin SK, et al. (2009) Characteristic and composition of *Jatropha curcas* oil seed from Malaysia and its potential as biodiesel feedstock. *European Journal of Scientific Research* 29(3): 396–403.
[14] Yorkshire Post (YP) (2010) Power giant Drax close to deal on creating green fuel factory. *Yorkshire Post*, 2 August.
[15] Perry M and Rosillo-Calle F (2006) Co-firing report – United Kingdom. *International Energy Agency (IEA) Bioenergy Task 40: Sustainable International Bioenergy Trade – Securing Supply and Demand*. Report No. T40UK02R, London, UK.
[16] Wicks R and Keay M (2005) Can coal contribute to sustainable development? *Energy and Environment* 16(5): 767–779.
[17] World Coal Association (2011) Improving efficiencies. http://www.worldcoal.org/coal-the-environment/coal-use-the-environment/improving-efficiencies/ (accessed 25 February 2011).

[18] Khan AA, De Jong W, Jansens PJ, and Spliethoff H (2009) Biomass combustion in fluidized bed boilers: Potential problems and remedies. *Fuel Processing Technology* 90: 21–50.
[19] Belgiorno V, De Feo G, Della Rocca C, and Napoli RMA (2002) Energy from the gasification of biomass. *Waste Management* 23: 1–15.
[20] Vamvuka D (2010) Overview of solid fuels combustion technology. *Handbook of Combustion* 5: 31–84.
[21] Dai J, Sokhansanj S, Grace JR, et al. (2008) Overview and some issues related to co-firing biomass and coal. *The Canadian Journal of Chemical Engineering* 86: 367–386. doi:10.1002/cjce.20052.
[22] International Energy Agency (IEA) (2005) Biomass combustion and co-firing. *IEA Bioenergy Task 32*. http://www.ieabcc.nl/database (accessed 20 November 2010).
[23] Deal C (2007) Climate change technology transfer: Opportunities in the developing world. http://www.wise-intern.org (accessed 11 February 2011).
[24] Klara SM (2009) Biomass for thermal energy and electricity: A research and development portfolio for the future – Before the Committee on Science and Technology, Subcommittee on Energy and Environment, US House of Representatives. National Energy Technology Laboratory (US DOE), Pittsburgh, USA.
[25] Maniatis K (2001) Progress in biomass gasification: An overview. http://www.ec.europa.eu (accessed 11 February 2011).
[26] Jansen JC, Uslu A, and Lako P (2010) What is the scope for the Dutch government to use the flexible mechanisms of the Renewables Directive cost-effectively? Energy Research Centre of the Netherlands. http://www.ecl.nl (accessed 1 February 2011).
[27] Spliethoff H (2010) Power generation from biomass and waste. In: *Power Generation from Solid Fuels: Power Systems*, ch. 6, pp. 361–467. London: Springer. doi: 10.1007/978-3-642-02856-4_6.
[28] Beekes ML, Gast CH, Korevaar CH, et al. (1998) Co-combustion of biomass in pulverised coal fired boilers in the Netherlands. *Proceedings of the 17th Congress of the World Energy Council*, 13–18 September 1998, Houston, TX, USA.
[29] Department of Energy and Climate Change (DECC) (2010) http://chp.decc.gov.uk/cms/roc-banding (accessed 28 February 2011).
[30] Flower MF (2010) Combustion of Single Biomass Particles in a Heated Wire Mesh Apparatus with Video Based Measurements. PhD Thesis, Imperial College London, 288pp.
[31] UK Powerfocus (2010) *McCloskey* 125.
[32] Ofgem (2010) The renewables obligation buy-out price and mutualisation ceiling 2010–11. http://www.ofgem.gov.uk/Media/PressRel/Documents1/RO%20BuyOut%20price%202010%2011%20FINAL%20FINAL.pdf (accessed 28 February 2011).
[33] UK Department of Trade and Industry (DTI) (2006) The economics of co-firing. Final Report No. URN06/1959.
[34] RWE npower (2011) About Didcot A power station. http://www.npower.com/rwenpowercr (accessed 27 February 2011).
[35] Drax (2011) Corporate and social responsibility: Co-firing. http://www.draxpower.com (15 January 2011).
[36] Kuchta JM, Rowe VR, and Burgess DS (1980) Spontaneous combustion susceptibility of US coals. US Bureau of Mines, RI874. Washington, DC, USA.
[37] Colechin M (2005) Best practice brochure: Co-firing of biomass (main report). DTI Report No. COAL R287, DTI Pub. URN 05/1160.
[38] Caini KC and Hules KH (1986) Coal pulverizer explosions. Industrial dust explosions. ASTM STP 958. Cashdollar and Hertzberg (eds.) American Society for Testing and Materials, Philadelphia, pp. 200–216.
[39] FS (Fire Suppression) (2011) http://www.fire-suppression.co.uk (accessed 22 January 2011).
[40] Livingstone WR (2005) *A Review of the Recent Experience in Britain with the Co-firing of Biomass with Coal in Large Pulverised Coal Fired Boiler.* Mitsui Babcock. Copenhagen, Denmark: IEA Exco Workshop on Biomass Co-firing.
[41] DECC (2010) http://chp.decc.gov.uk/cms/roc-banding
[42] Fernando (2010) Co-gasification and indirect co-firing of coal and biomass. CCC/158, 37pp. ISBN 978-92-9029-478-8.
[43] Granatstein DL (2002) Case study on BioCoComb biomass gasification project, Zeltweg Power Station, Austria. IEA Bioenergy Task 36 Report, September.
[44] Heinrich E and Weirrich F (2004) Pressurised entrained flow gasifiers for biomass. Environmental Engineering Science 2153.
[45] Maciejewska A, Veringa H, Sander J, and Peteves SD (2006) Co-firing of biomass with coal: Constraint and role of biomass pre-treatment. European Commission Directorate General Joint Research Centre. EU 22461 EN.
[46] Livingstone WR (2007) Advanced biomass co-firing technologies for coal-fired boilers. Doosan Babcock, Technology and Engineering, Renfrew, Scotland. Available at http://www.see.ed.ac.uk (accessed 10 November 2010).
[47] Jenkins BM, Miles Jr TR, and Miles TR (1998) Combustion properties of biomass. Fuel Processing Technology 54(1–3): 17–46.

Further Reading

[1] Cliff D, Rowlands D, and Sleeman J (1996) *Spontaneous Combustion in Australian Coal Mine.* Queensland, Australia: SIMTARS.
[2] Department of Energy & Climate Change (DECC) (2009) Calculating the level of the Renewables Obligation. http://www.decc.gov.uk/assets/decc/what%20we%20do/uk%20energy%20supply/energy%20mix/renewable%20energy/renewable%20energy%20policy/renewables%20obligation/1_20091001145510_e_@@_calculatingthelevelotherenewablesobligation.pdf (accessed 15 January 2011).
[3] US Department of Energy (DOE) (2000) Biomass co-firing: A renewable alternative for utilities. National Renewable Energy Laboratory, DOE/GO-102000-1055. http://www.nrel.gov/docs/fy00osti/28009.pdf (accessed 15 November 2010).
[4] Gouws MJ and Knoetze TP (1995) Coal self-heating and explosibility. *Journal of the South African Institute of Mining and Metallurgy* 1995: 37–43.
[5] Kiel J (2009) Biomass co-firing in coal fired power plants: Status, trend and R&D needs. Energy Research Centre of the Netherlands. Bioenergy Seminar, Brussels, Belgium. http://www.ieabcc.nl (accessed 15 February 2011).
[6] Nasrin AB, Ma AN, Choo YM, et al. (2008) Oil palm biomass as potential substitution raw materials for commercial biomass briquettes production. *American Journal of Applied Sciences* 5(3): 179–183.
[7] Scurlock JMO (1999) Miscanthus: A review of European experience with a novel crop. US Department of Energy's Environmental Science Division, ORNL/TM-13732, Publication No. 4845. Tennessee, USA.
[8] Tillman D, Plasynski S, and Hughes E (2002) Biomass co-firing: Results of technology progress from co-operative agreement between EPRI and USDOE. *The 27th International Technical Conference on Coal Utilisation and Fuel Systems.* Clearwater, FL, USA, 4–7 March.

5.06 A Global Bioenergy Market

O Olsson and B Hillring, Swedish University of Agricultural Sciences, Skinnskatteberg, Sweden

© 2012 Elsevier Ltd.

5.06.1	Bioenergy	75
5.06.1.1	A Note on Bioenergy Policy Measures	75
5.06.2	Biofuels, Biomass, and Bioenergy: Definitions	76
5.06.3	Limitations	76
5.06.4	Bioenergy Markets and Trade	77
5.06.4.1	Wood Fuels	77
5.06.4.1.1	Trade in wood fuels: Early development	77
5.06.4.1.2	A note on transportation costs	78
5.06.4.1.3	Wood fuel trade in the 2000s	78
5.06.4.1.4	Wood fuel trade amounts and patterns	78
5.06.4.2	Liquid Biofuels	79
5.06.4.2.1	Background	79
5.06.4.2.2	Overview of the global markets for liquid biofuels	79
5.06.5	A Global Bioenergy Market? The Extent of Bioenergy Markets	79
5.06.5.1	Energy Market Integration in General	80
5.06.5.2	Bioenergy Market Integration	81
5.06.5.2.1	Internationalization: Good or bad?	81
5.06.6	Barriers to Bioenergy Trade	81
5.06.6.1	Import Tariffs, Export Subsidies, and the Like	81
5.06.6.2	Nonexplicit Trade Barriers	82
5.06.7	Discussion: The Future of Bioenergy Trade	82
References		83

5.06.1 Bioenergy

Biomass has been one of the first resources utilized for energy purposes by humankind. Its importance throughout history can hardly be overstated, having provided humanity with energy for many thousands of years. However, during the last 100 years, the share of bioenergy in the global energy mix has decreased from about one-third in the early 1900s to roughly 10% in 2006 [1, 2]. The reason for this decrease is largely due to the massive increase in the use of fossil fuels – oil, natural gas, and coal – that has taken place during this time period. For a number of reasons, this process cannot be continued in the twenty-first century.

First of all, fossil fuels are nonrenewable resources. The rate of depletion of the current reserve stock greatly exceeds the rate at which new reserves are being formed (note that there are radically different views on how acute the problem of resource depletion is [3, 4]). Second, the combustion of fossil fuels leads to emissions of carbon dioxide (CO_2) into the atmosphere. The increase in anthropogenic emissions of CO_2 is, according to the Intergovernmental Panel on Climate Change (IPCC), a cause for the increase in global average temperature that has occurred during the twentieth century. It is generally accepted that in order to avoid dangerous levels of climate change, emissions of fossil CO_2 need to be reduced [5]. Third, since the major remaining fossil fuel resources – oil and natural gas in particular – tend to be geographically concentrated in a rather small number of countries, many of the world's nations are dependent on imports of fossil fuels. Although dependence on energy imports need not be a problem if the supply is stable and reliable, this is not always the case. For example, the turbulence in recent years concerning the flow of Russian natural gas through Belarus and Ukraine has increased concerns among European policy makers and citizens about the potential risks of being overly dependent on imported energy (see, e.g., Reference 6).

Bioenergy is seen as an important part of the future global energy system because it can be a solution to many of the problems of fossil fuels. To begin with, bioenergy is a renewable form of energy which is an important factor in light of the debate on the eventual depletion of fossil fuel resources. Second, bioenergy does not contribute to the net increase of CO_2 in the atmosphere, provided that production is conducted in a sustainable manner, that is, that harvest does not exceed growth and that soil issues are handled properly [7]. Third, since bioenergy resources are not as concentrated geographically as, for example, oil and gas, an increased share of bioenergy in the energy mix can be an important tool to mitigate the problems of energy supply security.

5.06.1.1 A Note on Bioenergy Policy Measures

Apart from being motivated on the basis of concerns regarding fossil fuel depletion, global warming, and energy security, bioenergy implementation is promoted for a wide variety of reasons, including the potential of bioenergy to contribute to rural development [8, 9], improved air quality [10], and new markets for agricultural commodities [11–13].

However, the many purported advantages of bioenergy go against the logic formulated in the 'Tinbergen rule' named after the Dutch economist Jan Tinbergen [14]. The Tinbergen rule states that in order to fully achieve a multiple number of independent policy targets, an equal number of policy instruments is required. A policy measure with the objective to 'kill many birds with one stone' runs the risk of ending up a rather blunt tool [15]. This is imperative to have in mind, particularly in discussions on bioenergy trade – which we will discuss further in Section 5.06.7 – but also in the implementation of bioenergy in general. For example, as is discussed by Sterner et al. [16], bioenergy could possibly reduce unemployment on a local or regional level, but it is likely that policy measures specifically aimed at reducing unemployment would achieve a superior result. In other words, although bioenergy has many benefits, it is important to note that the way in which policy makers prioritize between their objectives has far-reaching implications for the outcomes of their policies [17].

5.06.2 Biofuels, Biomass, and Bioenergy: Definitions

Bioenergy markets are still a relatively new phenomenon. One symptom of this is the lack of terminological consensus in the literature on bioenergy markets. A typical example of this is the term 'biofuel', which according to the European standard is "any fuel produced directly or indirectly from biomass" [18] and according to Encyclopedia Britannica is "any fuel that is derived from biomass" [19]. However, in both research literature and mainstream media, the term biofuel is to a large degree synonymous with 'liquid biofuel' [13]. In the same vein, solid biofuels such as wood chips or wood pellets are often referred to as 'biomass'. As we do not wish to encourage this rather illogical terminology, we will use the term 'biofuels' for all forms of biomass used for energy purposes. This means that bioethanol and biodiesel are referred to as 'liquid biofuels', and wood pellets, firewood, and wood chips are referred to as 'solid biofuels', and biomethane as a 'gaseous biofuel'. An overview of different biomass resources and how they may be utilized for energy purposes can be found in **Figure 1** [20].

5.06.3 Limitations

As this article is focused on bioenergy trade, the discussions herein are limited to biofuels being traded across national borders. To the best of our knowledge, there is no international trade in gaseous biofuels taking place at the time of writing. (However, since, e.g., landfill gas or biogas derived from sewage waste can be refined into a substance chemically identical to natural gas – with methane (CH_4) as the principal energy-carrying component – existing natural gas infrastructure can very well be utilized for transport of biogas. In several countries, biogas produced from landfills or sewage waste is injected into the natural gas grid [21]. This means that the European natural gas pipeline network just as well can be utilized for transport of biogas–natural gas mixtures which in turn would bring about international trade in biogas.) This means that this article will be limited to liquid and solid

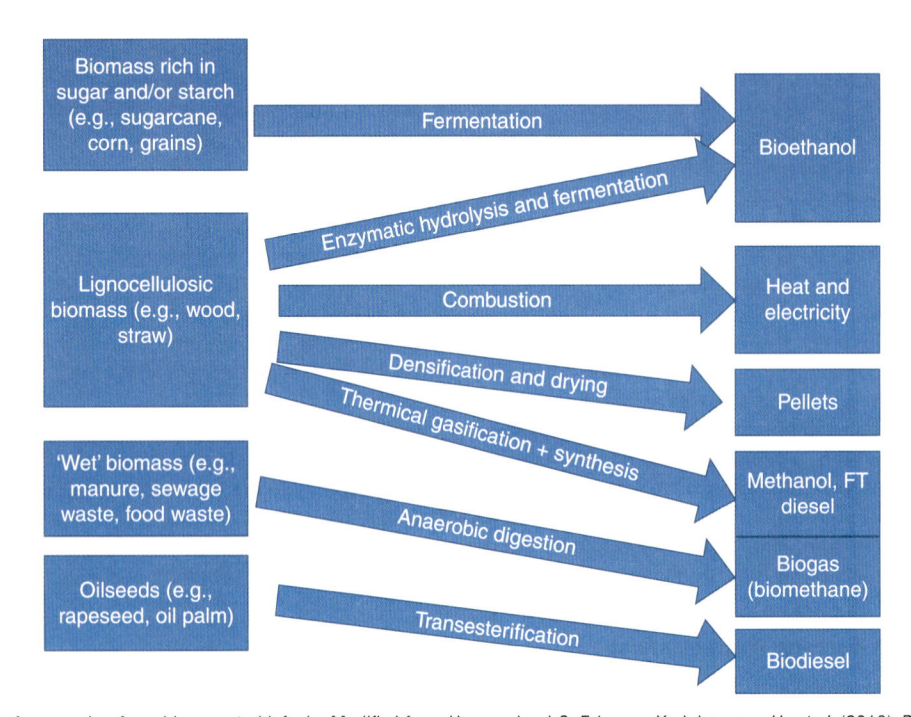

Figure 1 Means of conversion from biomass to biofuels. Modified from Hammarlund C, Ericsson K, Johansson H, et al. (2010) *Bränsle för ett Bättre Klimat: Marknad och Politik för Biobränslen (Fuel for a Better Climate: Biofuel Market and Policies).* Lund, Sweden: Agrifood Economics Centre.

biofuels. This is in our view a logical subdivision for several reasons. Liquid biofuels are predominantly of agricultural origins and are mainly used as transportation fuels. Contrastingly, solid biofuels are dominated by woody biomass and are mainly used for production of heat and electricity. (There are certainly exceptions to these generalizations. Straw is to a large degree used as fuel in the production of heat and electricity, e.g., in Denmark [22], and there are hopes that in the future it will be possible to produce liquid transportation fuels from lignocellulosic biomass such as wood on a commercial level [23].)

Furthermore, many examples presented will deal with biodiesel, bioethanol, or wood pellets, for the simple reason that studies analyzing the markets for these fuels dominate the relevant literature. Nevertheless, many of the patterns and problems discussed will apply to all forms of liquid and solid biofuels.

5.06.4 Bioenergy Markets and Trade

5.06.4.1 Wood Fuels

Wood is an extremely versatile natural resource. It can be used as a building material, for paper production, and as raw material for a wide range of different chemical products. Form a wide historical perspective however, the sector of application where wood has been most dominant has been energy. Houses and bridges can be built out of stone, and paper was for a long time produced mainly from discarded textile rags, but up until the rise of coal in the eighteenth and nineteenth centuries, wood totally dominated global energy supply. (Wind was, of course, extremely important for transportation purposes, as were wind mill and water mill for other purposes, but it has been estimated that biomass – mostly woody biomass – had a 95% share of global energy supply as late as the eighteenth century. Interestingly, it was the peat-fuelled economy of the seventeenth-century Dutch Republic that proved to be the first example of an economy not entirely dependent on wood for its energy needs [24].) Wood was used for cooking, heat production, and not least as the driver of many important proto-industrial processes. This meant that wood was a very strategic resource, not only since it was needed for shipbuilding but also for the production of charcoal and in turn, weaponry.

Throughout history, wood energy has been utilized predominantly through the combustion of firewood. (In the European standard for solid biomass fuels (EN-14961), firewood is defined as "cut and split oven-ready fuelwood used in household burning appliances like stoves, fireplaces and central heating systems" [25].) Still today, firewood is an important fuel for domestic heating and cooking in developing countries, but its importance in the industrialized world should not be underestimated. In France, for example, firewood alone makes up about 3% of total primary energy supply and is an important component of the residential heating market [26, 27]. However, an important characteristic of the firewood market in the developing as well as the industrialized world is that it is, to a large extent, informal and outside standard energy supply systems. Using France once more as an example, it can be noted that "… sixty percent of this [the country's] firewood is self-supplied or comes from non-commercial suppliers" [27].

However, a gradual commercialization of wood energy has taken place in the last 30–40 years. An increased use of bioenergy in the forest industry and in the district heating (DH) sector was an important part of the strategy to reduce Sweden's dependence on imported oil [28] after the oil crises of the 1970s. Similar strategies were used in other forest-rich countries such as Austria [29] and Finland [30]. This increasing industrialization and modernization of the wood energy sector has brought about significant growth in the use of wood fuels. For example, in Austria, Finland, and Sweden, energy derived from wood makes up 10–15% of total primary energy supply [31]. However, firewood is gradually losing its dominance of wood energy markets. A large share of the industrialized utilization of wood energy takes place in the forest industry itself through the combustion of bark ("… organic cellular tissue which is formed by taller plants (trees, bushes) on the outside of the growth zone (cambium) as a shell for the wooden body" [25]) and black liquor ("… liquor obtained from wood during the process of pulp production, in which the energy content is mainly originating from the content of lignin removed from the wood in the pulping process" [25]) for the production of process heat and electricity. Modern forms of wood fuels range from unrefined fuels such as firewood and wood chips ("… chipped woody biomass in the form of pieces with a defined particle size produced by mechanical treatment with sharp tools such as knives" [25]) to more sophisticated fuels such as wood pellets. (A pellet is a "… densified biofuel made from pulverized biomass with or without additives usually with a cylindrical form, random length typically 5 to 40 mm, and broken ends. The raw material for biofuel pellets can be woody biomass, herbaceous biomass, fruit biomass or biomass blends and mixtures" [25]. Note that the absolute majority of the global pellet market is made up of wood pellets.)

5.06.4.1.1 Trade in wood fuels: Early development

Although wood fuel use harks back many thousand of years, large-scale international trade in wood fuel is a phenomenon only a few decades old. Unrefined wood is a rather bulky product with a relatively low value per weight or volume unit. This is perhaps the most important reason why wood fuels traditionally have been utilized rather close to their origin. However, with the modernization of the wood energy sector that has taken place in recent decades, new fuel supply patterns have been developed as well. The countries surrounding the Baltic Sea in the North of Europe have among Europe's highest shares of bioenergy in their energy mixes. Hence, it is perhaps logical that this was the region where international trade in wood fuels first took place on a larger scale. As was mentioned above, Sweden was one country where an increased use of wood fuels became a keystone of energy policy from the late 1970s and onwards [28]. In the 1990s, the country also became a very large importer of wood fuels. This was by no means a result of a *per se* lack of domestic resources, but rather a price issue. Despite the transport cost, it made economic sense to purchase low-cost wood chips from the Baltic States as well as wood pellets from North America for use in DH and combined heat and power (CHP) plants located on the Swedish coast [32, 33]. It is estimated that 26% of the biofuels used in DH in 2000 was made up of imports [33].

5.06.4.1.2 A note on transportation costs

In order to understand how it could be profitable to transport wood pellets from the West Coast of Canada to Sweden – which became a standard trade route in the late 1990s – it is imperative to note the radical difference in transport costs between different means of transportation.

As can be seen in Table 1, it costs roughly as much to transport 1 metric ton of wood pellets 500 km by truck as it does to transport the same amount 20 times longer by ship [34]. These figures go a long way in explaining not only the logic behind the pioneering Swedish wood fuel import of the 1990s but also much of the trade patterns that dominate the present-day trade in wood fuels.

5.06.4.1.3 Wood fuel trade in the 2000s

With the rapidly increasing demand for renewable energy in the first decade of the twenty-first century, many countries see wood fuels as an important part of their future energy systems. This trend is particularly strong in Europe and is driven by the European Union's (EU) '20/20/20 in 2020' goals [35]. (According to the (legally binding) goals laid out in the Renewables Directive (Directive 2009/28/DC), the EU shall achieve a 20% reduction in greenhouse gas (GHG) emissions, a 20% share of renewable energy in the union's energy mix, and a 20% improvement in energy efficiency by 2020.) The early uses of wood energy on an industrialized scale was pioneered by countries with large domestic forest resources, but in the last decade, demand for wood fuels has increased at an exceptionally strong pace in countries with very little forest cover. A very important phenomenon is the introduction of wood fuels – wood pellets in particular – being co-fired with coal in large power stations, in particular, the Netherlands and Belgium. In many European power stations, up to 10–15% of the coal has been replaced with wood pellets without major adjustments to the boiler or the fuel handling systems [36]. Adding to this, there are many power stations in planning that will be constructed specifically to use biomass, and especially wood, as fuel. (It is estimated that in the United Kingdom alone, the increased demand for wood for energy purposes will lead to an import of up to 30 million tons of wood annually [37] in 2025 if current plans are realized.)

5.06.4.1.4 Wood fuel trade amounts and patterns

A problem with analyzing trade in wood fuel is that it is not always clear if a certain cargo of wood is destined for use as energy or as raw material for the pulp and paper industry. This makes it very difficult to estimate the world trade in wood fuels that can be used both as energy and as industrial raw material depending on the market conditions. A typical example here is the market for wood chips. There is a large intercontinental trade in wood chips – often transported in vessels designed specifically for this purpose, the so-called wood-chip carriers [38] – but historically, this has been a trade in wood chips for pulp and paper production. However, it should be noted that this might change in the future as many of the planned projects in the United Kingdom are to be based on wood chips [39, 40].

At present, the international trade in wood fuel is dominated by wood pellets. In 2008, the global wood pellet market was about 11.5 million metric tons (~200 PJ). United States, Sweden, Germany, and Canada are among the largest producer countries. About two-thirds of the global pellet consumption takes place in Europe, with Sweden as the single largest consuming country at approximately 1.8 million tons [41]. It is important to note that wood pellets are used in several different forms, which to some degree divide the pellet market into separate segments. In Austria, Germany, and Italy, wood pellets are predominantly used in residential boilers and stoves, whereas consumption in Belgium and The Netherlands is dominated by large-scale power plants where wood pellets in most cases are co-fired with coal in order to reduce emissions of fossil carbon dioxide [42]. In Sweden, large-scale consumption in DH and CHP plants dominated the wood pellet market in the 1990s, but the share of pellets consumed in single-family houses has successively increased to the point where it now makes up about 40% of the total market [43].

In general, international trade in wood pellets is dominated by flows aimed at the large-scale sector, whereas "… [the] logistics of pellet supply to the residential sector [...] still seems to be mainly based on national or even regional supply chains" [44]. About 4 million tons, or 35% of the total market, was traded internationally in 2008. Roughly, half of this is made up by internal EU trade and the rest is made up by North American exports which to some degree are directed toward Japan, but primarily to Europe. More than 1.5 million tons (~25 PJ) were exported from Canada and the United States to Europe in 2008. (It is likely that this amount has increased since 2008 with increasing demand in Europe and the construction of several large export-oriented wood pellet factories in the US South [45].)

The reason for the international and intercontinental trade flows in pellets is the arbitrage (defined at www.financialdictionary.net as "the buying of one item and the selling of the same item for a higher price, therefore making a profit on the difference") profits that

Table 1 Wood pellet transport costs in Euros per metric ton (2005)

Mode of transport (tons)	Distance (km)	Cost (€ ton^{-1})
Truck (40)	500	25.4
Train (1000)	2 000	20.5
Ship (22 000)	10 000	21

Source: Pigaht M, Liebich M, and Janssen R (2005) *Opportunities for Pellet Trade, Task 3.2.3., Deliverable 20.*

can be made from exploiting the price differences between countries and continents. The EU has so far been more ambitious in its support for renewable energy compared to Canada and the United States. This has led to European demand pushing prices up to a level where it is more profitable to import pellets from North America, where production costs are substantially lower. The latter is especially true in the newly constructed pellet factories in the United States which are several times larger than the largest pellet plants currently in operation in Europe. (It should, however, be noted that a pellet factory with a production capacity of 900 000 tons yr^{-1} is being constructed in Western Russia. When completed, this will be the world's largest pellet plant [46].)

5.06.4.2 Liquid Biofuels

5.06.4.2.1 Background

The use of biofuels for transportation purposes is a concept that is as old as the automobile itself. Early Otto engines could run on 'bioethanol' and the T-Ford of 1908 was in fact a flexifuel vehicle that could run on petrol, ethanol, or on blends between the two. However, after World War I, the car market shifted to petroleum-derived fuels which have dominated the market for automobiles ever since [47]. In the wake of the oil crises of the 1970s, interest in transportation fuels made from biomass was reawakened, most importantly in the United States and Brazil. In Brazil, the government introduced a program called 'Pró-Alcool' aimed at reducing the country's dependence on imported oil by replacing petrol with domestically produced sugarcane ethanol [48]. In the United States, production of ethanol from corn was supported – albeit on a more modest level – for similar reasons as well as to find new markets for an agricultural sector suffering from oversupply [13]. Another very important driver of US demand for ethanol since the 1990s is that ethanol has been blended with regular petrol as an environmentally benign method to increase the octane level and thereby ensure a cleaner combustion [10].

The history of biodiesel is equally as old as that of bioethanol. Rudolf Diesel, the inventor of the diesel engine, in fact demonstrated his engine at the World's Fair in Paris in 1900 on peanut oil. As with bioethanol, interest in biodiesel has increased in time periods of uncertainty regarding petroleum supply or acute oil shortages. Allegedly, the Japanese battleship *Yamato* used refined soybean oil as fuel toward the end of World War II. In recent decades however, biodiesel has been promoted for environmental reasons in both the United States and Europe [49].

Like bioethanol, biodiesel can be produced from a variety of different raw materials, and the raw material of choice is largely dependent on local conditions pertaining to geography, climate, and the structure of the agricultural sector. Consequentially, soybean oil has been the dominant raw material in the United States, Brazil, and Argentina, palm oil in Malaysia and Indonesia and oil from rapeseed in Europe [50, 51].

5.06.4.2.2 Overview of the global markets for liquid biofuels

The use of liquid biofuels for transportation purposes has grown remarkably in recent years. The ways in which they have been introduced do however differ significantly between regions. As was previously mentioned, bioethanol has been aggressively pursued in the United States and Brazil. These two countries completely dominated the world market in 2008 with approximately 91% of a total global bioethanol production of about 53 million tons (~1400 PJ). Compared to wood pellets, the world bioethanol market is distinctively more regional in that a relatively small share of global production is traded internationally, only about 7%. The largest producing countries are also the largest consumers, and are also among the most important in terms of trade. Brazil totally dominates global bioethanol exports with a market share of above 90%, whereas the United States has been the top importer in 2008 followed by the EU, Japan, and Canada [41, 52].

In some regard, the global market for biodiesel has more in common with the wood pellet market than with the bioethanol market, in the sense that a rather large share (27%) of the global production of 10.6 million tons (~380 PJ) is traded internationally (**Figure 2**) [53]. Another similarity is that the market is very much driven by European demand. About two-thirds of global biodiesel production and more than 85% of consumption took place in the EU in 2008 [41]. This is perhaps no surprise since diesel engines are much more widespread in Europe than in the United States, but it should, nonetheless, be noted as an important characteristic of the market. The European dominance of the biodiesel market may, however, be reduced somewhat in the near future. Both the United States and Brazil have introduced more ambitious programs for the promotion of biodiesel at the same time as Germany – which by far is the largest biodiesel market in the EU – has reduced its financial support for biodiesel [54, 55]. In 2008 however, the United States was the world's largest biodiesel exporter followed by Argentina. The US exports have to a large degree been going to the EU, but following a 2008 EU–US trade conflict, it is unsure how this will develop in the future (see Section 5.06.6 for more details on the US–EU biodiesel 'trade war'). Argentina, meanwhile, has had a very strong growth in terms of biodiesel production and exports in the recent few years, and according to FAPRI [54], it has now overtaken the United States as the world's largest net exporter of biodiesel. The Argentinean producer–exporters benefited greatly from the above-mentioned trade conflict between the United States and the EU, which opened up new export opportunities [56].

5.06.5 A Global Bioenergy Market? The Extent of Bioenergy Markets

Generally, as trade between countries increases, different national markets become integrated to a larger and larger degree. This means that the consequences of events affecting the supply or demand in a specific national market need no longer be limited to the country wherein the specific events took place. The coupling between national markets can be seen in how the prices of a specific

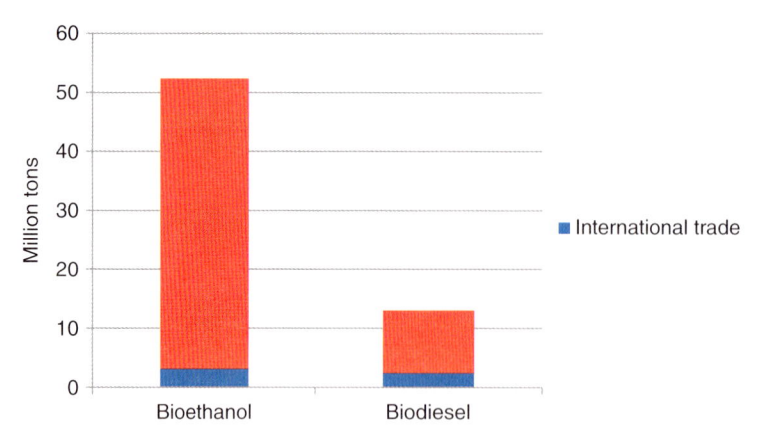

Figure 2 Total market size and share of international trade for bioethanol and biodiesel in 2008. The international trade in bioethanol in 2008 is estimated to lie in the range 2.8–3.1 million tons. In the graph, the high estimate is plotted. Source: Lamers P, Hamelinck CN, Junginger M, and Faaij A (2011) International bioenergy trade: A review of past developments in the liquid biofuels market. *Renewable and Sustainable Energy Reviews.*

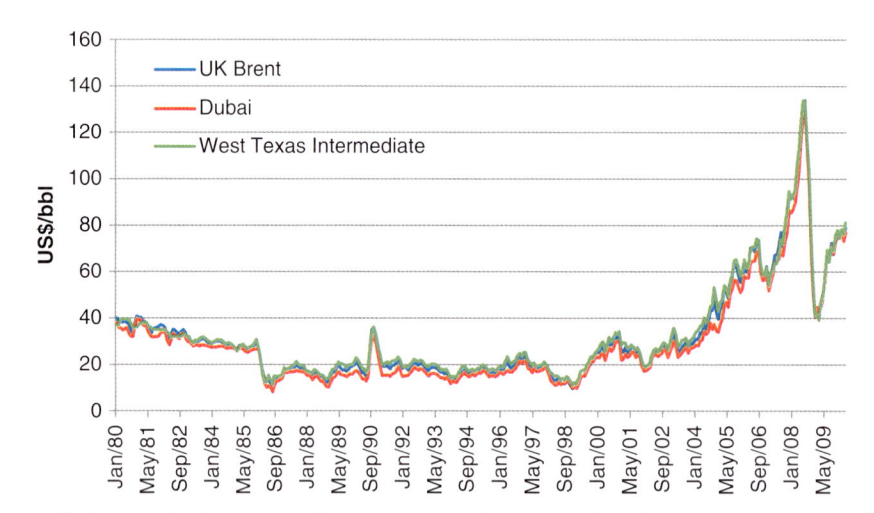

Figure 3 Price of crude oil in Dubai, United Kingdom, and West Texas, 1980–2010. Source: IMF. IMF primary commodity prices. http://www.imf.org/external/np/res/commod/index.asp.

commodity develop in the different countries. According to economic theory, if two markets are integrated by trade, prices in the two countries will have a tendency to converge to a common level, and not differ by more than the cost of transporting the commodity between the two countries. This is in economics referred to as the 'Law of One Price' (see, e.g., Reference 57). An example of this is the market for oil, which is a globally traded commodity and for which the entire world constitutes a common market [58]. This condition manifests itself in how the price of oil in different parts of the world moves almost consistently in unison over time, as can be seen in **Figure 3**. If an oil price shock occurs in one of the trading spots in the world, 90% of the price shock reverberates around the world immediately (**Figure 3**) [59, 60].

Although the prices may not follow each other exactly consistently, market forces will make sure that they can never decouple and move entirely independently. In econometrics and time series analysis, series that are related in this manner are said to be 'cointegrated'. The reason for the behavior in the price series is that if, for some reason, a price difference should appear, traders will eventually realize this and make use of the spread to make a risk-free profit which eventually will close the price gap (arbitrage).

5.06.5.1 Energy Market Integration in General

Studies of the extents of energy markets are common in the literature, and most have made use of time series analysis and cointegration analysis of price series in one way or another. In the oil market, Kim *et al.* [58], Bachmeier and Griffin [59], Weiner [61], and Gulen [62] are noteworthy examples. The general conclusion from these studies is that the global oil market to a large extent can be seen as a single market. Natural gas markets, which are more dependent on pipeline infrastructure, are not as integrated as oil markets. It is still too early to speak of a truly global natural gas market. The available literature has been primarily focused on determining whether the European (see, e.g., References 63–67) markets are integrated within themselves. In both cases, this seems not to be the case, although there certainly seems to be a trend toward increasing integration. As for the world coal markets, there is some dispute as to whether they are integrated or not. Whereas Kim [68] comes to the conclusion that the world by and large constitutes an integrated market for steam coal, Wårell [69] finds that although Japan and Europe previously were integrated into one market, they were separate markets in 2000.

5.06.5.2 Bioenergy Market Integration

Although there have been quite a few studies of market integration in markets connected with bioenergy (e.g., forest products markets [70–72] and agricultural commodities [73–75]), there are not many examples of analyses of the geographical extent of bioenergy markets. Liu [76] analyzed whether the ethanol prices in the United States, the EU, and Brazil are cointegrated in order to determine the connections between the ethanol markets in the respective regions. The conclusion is that the prices "… do not follow the same pattern in the long-term" [76] and the three markets cannot be considered integrated. However, there are certainly connections between the three markets in that price changes in both the US and Brazil spills over into the EU market. However, the Brazilian and US prices do not seem to interact and price changes in the EU do not change the other two markets. Olsson [77] analyzed the level of integration in European wood fuel markets with focus on the residential market for wood pellets and the large-scale (DH) market for unrefined wood fuels. The conclusion is that, in general, European wood fuel markets are separated along national borders. The only exception was the Austrian and German markets for residential market wood pellets, which can be considered integrated, whereas Sweden is separate from the other two countries included in the study. As for the large-scale market, the Estonian, Finnish, and Swedish markets for unrefined wood fuels are separated despite a rather active wood fuel trade in the Baltic Sea area. The study does, however, point to a gradual reduction of the price differences between the countries, which may indicate a process toward market integration.

As trade in bioenergy markets becomes increasingly international, it can, however, be expected that prices in different countries will over time converge to a common level. This is a prospect that has been discussed in relation to European wood pellet markets in a report from the 'Pellets for Europe' project [78]. The authors state that although there are obstacles to the development of the European wood pellet market and that price levels, "… as the international market and trade of pellets grows and international information becomes more available […] these differences are expected to diminish and slowly a 'European price' […] will form [78]." However, there are also studies that argue that wood energy markets are likely to remain regional. One of the conclusions that Toivonen *et al.* [79] draw about the future development of wood energy markets in Finland is that "… Demand and supply will develop differently in different regions and result in regional markets with regional prices unless storage and transportation technology of wood-based fuels will develop" [79].

5.06.5.2.1 Internationalization: Good or bad?

As for the effects on the bioenergy market of an increased internationalization, there are some different perspectives in different sources. Whereas some sources argue that internationalization is a means to improve security of supply and achieve higher stability in the bioenergy market, others claim that a globalized bioenergy market is likely to be more volatile. According to Ericsson and Nilsson [33], increased security of fuel supply acquired through diversification of suppliers was one important reason for why Swedish DH companies began importing biomass fuels in the 1990s. On the other hand, Kranzl *et al.* [80] conducted a study of price volatility of different bioenergy assortments and claim that "… the more standardised a product is, the higher its energy density and the more (international) trade of this product exists, the higher is the price volatility" [80]. It should, however, be noted that this latter assertion is disputed by general studies on the effect of globalization and international trade on price volatility. For example, Jacks *et al.* [81] have studied price series for nine different commodities over a period of 300 years and contend that market integration in fact leads to 'less' volatility and that "… economic isolation caused by war or autarkic policy has been associated with much greater commodity price volatility" [81]. Conclusively, Trømborg and Solberg [82] briefly discuss the potential effects on Norwegian wood energy prices on increased international bioenergy trade and conclude that "Import of biomass represents an opportunity for bioenergy producers in Norway, but international competition for biomass can also increase biomass prices in Norway" [82]. In other words, whether the effects of an increased internationalization of bioenergy markets will have positive or negative effects is a matter of perspective.

5.06.6 Barriers to Bioenergy Trade

Bioenergy trade is often promoted as an efficient tool to ensure cost-effective reductions in GHG emission as well as energy security [83]. Despite this, many obstacles to international bioenergy trade still remain.

5.06.6.1 Import Tariffs, Export Subsidies, and the Like

In terms of obstacles to free trade related to subsidies of domestic fuels and tariffs on imported biofuels, the bioethanol market is arguably the biofuel market most fraught with such barriers. Both the EU and the United States subsidize domestic production of domestic bioethanol to different extents and also apply import tariffs on imported bioethanol [41]. The reason for this is likely to be connected to the relation of bioethanol to the agricultural sector – in which promotion of domestic production is very common – as well as a prioritization of energy security [12]. Fuel ethanol production on a large scale was started in the United States in the late

1970s, not with the aim to mitigate climate change but to reduce the country's dependence on imported oil and to support the agricultural sector [84, 85].

Since production costs for Brazilian sugarcane-based ethanol is about one-third of the cost of producing ethanol from corn – as in the United States – or sugar beets as in the EU, domestically produced ethanol in Europe and America would be outcompeted without the import tariffs. According to Elobeid and Tokgoz [86], removal of the US import tariffs would lead to a doubling of US ethanol imports and a 7% reduction of domestic US ethanol production. However, despite the US import tariffs, substantial amounts of Brazilian ethanol make their way to the US market through a loophole in the trade barriers. This is done by export of Brazilian hydrous (i.e., ethanol with a water content of up to 5%) ethanol to countries participating in the trade agreement known as the Caribbean Basin Initiative (CBI, including Antigua, Aruba, Bahamas, Barbados, Belize, Costa Rica, Dominica, El Salvador, Grenada, Guatemala, Guyana, Haití, Honduras, British Virgin Islands, Jamaica, Montserrat, Netherlands Antilles, Nicaragua, Panama, Dominican Republic, Saint Kitts and Nevis, Santa Lucia, Saint Vincent and the Grenadines, and Trinidad and Tobago). Since CBI countries are exempt from the US import tariff on ethanol, the ethanol is dehydrated and then re-exported to the United States [41]. According to the Industrial Ethanol Association (IEA) [87], loopholes are also exploited in order to get around EU import tariffs. Ethanol is mixed with other chemicals and can thus be classified as under a different article of the EU customs regulation to avoid the ethanol import tariffs.

In the global biodiesel market, there are also a number of trade issues that are important to review. Most importantly, beginning in 2008, a small-scale trade war has been raging between the United States and the EU surrounding the flows of subsidized US biodiesel into the EU. This controversy, commonly referred to as 'splash-and-dash', is an unintended consequence of US support policies for the promotion of biodiesel. As part of the 2004 American Jobs Creation Act, a tax credit was introduced, amounting to US$1 per gallon biodiesel blended in the country. The tax credit was proportional to the percentage of biodiesel mixed with regular diesel fuel, that is, a 'B20' mixture, consisting of 20% biodiesel and 80% fossil diesel, would receive a tax credit of US¢20. This was exploited by cunning market actors who exported pure biodiesel from Malaysia to the United States, where a small amount, for example, 1%, of fossil diesel was 'splashed' into the pure biodiesel thereby making the cargo eligible for the US tax credit. After this, the blended B99 cargo was 'dashed' to Europe for sale on EU markets [88–91]. The European Biodiesel Board claimed that the imports hurt European biodiesel producers and filed a complaint to the European Commission, which decided on countermeasures in the form of anti-dumping fees on US biodiesel flows into the EU [41, 92]. However, there have reportedly been attempts to circumvent this by relabeling US-produced biodiesel exported to Europe as being of Canadian origin [55, 93].

5.06.6.2 Nonexplicit Trade Barriers

Apart from the barriers to trade directly related to tariffs and export subsidies, several issues surrounding bioenergy trade are accused of being trade barriers dressed up as something else. One such issue is that the EU standard for biodiesel is claimed to be designed to fit the chemical for biodiesel produced from rapeseed – which is the main feedstock for biodiesel produced in the EU – and to a degree excludes biodiesel made from palm oil or soy oil [94, 95]. Whether this has actually acted as a barrier to biodiesel imports is not fully clear [41], but the problem has been acknowledged by the European Commission and the standards are reportedly under review [94]. It is important to note that the lack of proper technical standardization can also act as a barrier to trade [96]. This has been observed as one obstacle to the development of international trade in wood pellets, particularly in high-quality wood pellets aimed at the residential market [41, 97]. However, with the recently introduced European standard for solid biofuels, it is likely that this problem will at least be partly mitigated [98].

As a result of the debate in recent years on the sustainability of bioenergy production [99], different certification systems have been developed. Initiatives have been launched by companies, NGOs, and governments with the aim to guarantee that biofuels meet certain criteria regarding the net GHG emission reductions and biodiversity (for an overview, see Reference [100]). In the 2009 EU directive on renewable energy, sustainability criteria for liquid biofuels are included in order to "… ensure sustainable provision and use of bioenergy" [35]. However, representatives of the palm oil production industry in Malaysia and Indonesia claim that the EU sustainability criteria on biofuels are in fact in violation of World Trade Organization (WTO) rules on free trade [41]. Malaysia and Indonesia have stated that "… both countries would bring up the EU RED discriminatory treatment matter to the World Trade Organisation (WTO) to ensure that the EU rules does not reduce exports of palm oil" [101].

'Phytosanitary issues' might also act as a barrier to trade [41]. One example of this is the strict EU restrictions on the import of nontreated coniferous wood products from countries infected with the pinewood nematode (*Bursaphelenchus xylophilus*). The pinewood nematode causes a disease in pine species called 'pine wilt', which can result in trees dying within weeks after infection. For example, this has led to drastic reductions in imports of wood chips from North America following the introduction of the restrictions in 1989. It is estimated that this has brought about an annual loss of $100 million in potential North American wood chip exports [102]. It should, however, be noted that wood chips from broadleaved trees may be imported into Europe. For example, Norwegian pellet producer *Biowood Norway* uses wood chips made from Canadian birch as raw material in their production process [103].

5.06.7 Discussion: The Future of Bioenergy Trade

The international trade in solid and liquid biomass fuels is growing rapidly, driven by national and supranational ambitions to reduce current dependence on fossil fuels in the global energy system. However, it is still too early to speak of a truly 'global bioenergy market'. Despite the fact that large international – as well as intercontinental – trade flows have been established in biomass fuels such as bioethanol and wood pellets, the biomass market exhibits several signs of immaturity compared to more traditional commodity markets. First of all, despite improvements in recent years, there are still some actual uncertainties regarding the definitions and standards of both liquid and solid biofuels. Needless to say, the lack of completely coherent and comprehensive global standards and classifications will continue to act as a barrier to liquidity in bioenergy markets until these issues are properly mitigated. Hitherto, it has, for example, been very difficult to obtain proper statistics of bioenergy trade flows as customs codes – upon which trade statistics rely – have not taken into account the actual end use of the good in question. Hence, trade in ethanol to be used in industrial processes has not been separated from trade in fuel ethanol, and woody biofuels, such as pellets and chips, have been bundled together in broad categories as "sawdust and wood waste and scrap, whether or not agglomerated in logs, briquettes, pellets or similar forms." For pellets, a specific customs code (44013020) has now been introduced on an EU level with trade statistics published by Eurostat, but this will not be introduced into the Harmonized System before 2012 [41].

The issue that hitherto primarily has dominated bioenergy markets and driven trade is policy measures that for one reason or another are introduced to increase the share of bioenergy in the energy systems of the world. The paths which the large economies of the world choose in terms of energy policies will determine the future of the global bioenergy market. The introduction of more aggressive climate legislation in the United States and Canada could, for example, bring about a swift reduction in the flows of wood pellets from North America to Europe. In a prognosis of the future of global bioenergy trade, Bradley *et al.* [23] forecast that "... [i]t is likely that US biomass will be destined for domestic biofuels and other bioenergy." [23]. Similarly, if the large economies of Asia decide to pursue co-firing to a degree similar to what is currently being done in Europe, European utilities might face tough competition for the biomass resources of the US South.

Another issue that must be taken into consideration when discussing the bioenergy trade patterns of the future is by exactly what means the trade in bioenergy will take place. In this article, 'bioenergy trade' has been used as synonym for 'trade in biomass fuels' but this is by no means the only manner in which bioenergy can be traded. Depending on transportation costs and energy use, integration of electricity grids, and the development of global markets for carbon emissions and/or green certificates, it might turn out to be both more profitable and more energy efficient to trade bioenergy in other forms than strictly by shipping fuel between continents [104, 105]. Furthermore, even if the discussion is limited to physical transport of biomass, it is not clear whether global trade in biomass energy resources will be dominated by trade in finished products (i.e., refined biodiesel or wood pellets) or intermediary materials such as unrefined soybean oil. According to Bradley *et al.* [23], the dominating cost component in the production of second-generation biofuels is the refining process. This means that producers may choose to locate their facilities not as close to the raw material as possible but instead choose the location of a cellulosic ethanol production plant on the basis of where the facility can be built and run as efficiently as possible, with raw material being shipped in from abroad. One example of this that can already be seen is the large wood pellet production facility run by *Biowood Norway* on the Norwegian west coast. This pellet plant is heavily reliant on imports of wood chips from Canada and West Africa for raw material, which are refined to pellets aimed at the European market [103].

Finally, one very significant issue regarding bioenergy trade flows and climate policies is what the effects would be if different forms of bioenergy were to be priced differently depending on their respective potential to reduce net GHG emissions. The production of sugarcane ethanol in Brazil is widely regarded to be not only the most cost-effective means of production but also the one with the most favorable energy balance as well as the largest GHG reduction potential [12]. Brazilian sugarcane ethanol has been classified as an 'advanced biofuel' on the basis that it reduces GHG emissions by up to 50% compared to fossil alternatives [106]. On the other hand, the net GHG emission reduction from corn ethanol in the United States is heavily debated to the point where some claim that corn ethanol actually increases the lifecycle of GHG emissions compared to petrol [107]. As UNCTAD [17] notes, stringent criteria on the carbon balances of transportation biofuels and inclusion of biofuel emissions in carbon markets may have a significant impact on the direction of trade flows. Focus on reduction of GHG emissions would, for example, lead to greater export opportunities for developing countries, since many of these are situated in warmer climates suitable for efficient production of bioethanol. However, this scenario rests on the assumption that the large economies of the world indeed do make reduction of GHG emissions the top priority of their biofuels policies rather than energy security or protection of domestic agricultural sectors.

References

[1] Smil V (2003) *Energy at the Crossroads: Global Perspectives and Uncertainties.* Cambridge, MA: The MIT Press.
[2] Industrial Ethanol Association (IEA) (2006) IEA energy statistics: Global shares of total primary energy supply in 2006. France: IEA. http://www.iea.org/textbase/stats/pdf_graphs/29TPESPI.pdf
[3] Deffeyes KS (2003) *Hubbert's Peak.* Princeton, NJ: Princeton University Press.
[4] Huber PW and Mills MP (2005) *The Bottomless Well: The Twilight of Fuel, the Virtue of Waste, and Why We Will Never Run Out of Energy.* New York, NY: Basic Books.
[5] Intergovernmental Panel on Climate Change (IPCC) (2007) Summary for policymakers. In: *Climate Change 2007: Synthesis Report. An Assessment of the Intergovernmental Panel on Climate Change.* Geneva, Switzerland: IPCC.
[6] Pirani S, Stern J, and Yafimava K (2009) *The Russo-Ukrainian Gas Dispute of January 2009: A Comprehensive Assessment.* Oxford: Oxford Institute for Energy Studies.
[7] Holmgren K, Eriksson E, Olsson O, *et al.* (2007) *Biofuels and Climate Neutrality: System Analysis of Production and Utilisation (Elforsk Rapport 07:35).* Stockholm, Sweden: Elforsk.
[8] Hillring B (2002) Rural development and bioenergy: Experiences from 20 years of development in Sweden. *Biomass and Bioenergy* 23: 443–451.
[9] Berndes G and Hansson J (2007) Bioenergy expansion in the EU: Cost-effective climate change mitigation, employment creation and reduced dependency on imported fuels. *Energy Policy*, 35: 5965–5979.
[10] Hertel TW, Tyner WE, and Birur DK (2010) The global impacts of biofuel mandates. *Energy Journal*, 31(1): 75–100.

[11] Salamon PB, Ledebur EV, Elmahdi K, and Klepper R (2006) *Renewable Energy: New Forces in Global Ethanol Trade?* Chania, Crete, Greece: European Association of Agricultural Economists.
[12] Walter A, Rosillo-Calle F, Dolzan P, et al. (2007) *Market Evaluation: Fuel Ethanol*. IEA Bioenergy Task 40, France: IEA.
[13] Balat M and Balat H (2009) Recent trends in global production and utilization of bio-ethanol fuel. *Applied Energy* 86: 2273–2282.
[14] Fridfinnson B and Rude J (2009) *The Effects of Biofuels Policies on Global Commodity Trade Flows*. Canada: Canadian Agricultural Trade Policy Research Network.
[15] Daly HE (1992) Allocation, distribution, and scale: Towards an economics that is efficient, just, and sustainable *Ecological Economics*, 6, 185–193.
[16] Sterner T, Johansson B, and Stenman-Johansson O (1998) Skall vi köra på sprit? (Should our cars run on liquor?). *Ekonomisk Debatt* 26: 603–616.
[17] UNCTAD (2009) *The Biofuels Market: Current Situation and Alternative Scenarios*. Geneva and New York: United Nations.
[18] CEN (2004) *Solid Biofuels: Terminology, Definitions and Descriptions (SIS-CEN/TS 14588:2003)*. Brussels, Belgium: CEN.
[19] Encyclopedia Britannica (2010) *Biofuel*. Chicago, IL: Encyclopedia Britannica.
[20] Hammarlund C, Ericsson K, Johansson H, et al. (2010) *Bränsle för ett Bättre Klimat: Marknad och Politik för Biobränslen (Fuel for a Better Climate: Biofuel Market and Policies)*. Lund, Sweden: Agrifood Economics Centre.
[21] Persson M, Jönsson O, and Wellinger A (2009) *Biogas Upgrading to Vehicle Fuel Standards and Grid Injection*. France: IEA.
[22] Boldt J (2009) *Fremtidige Priser på Biomasse til Energiformål*. Copenhagen, Denmark: Danish Energy Agency.
[23] Bradley D, Pelkmans L, and Cupyers D (2009) *Second Generation Biofuels and Trade: An Exploratory Study*. IEA Bioenergy Task 40, France: IEA.
[24] de Zeeuw JW (1978) *Peat and the Dutch Golden Age*. Wageningen, The Netherlands: Landbouwuniversiteit Wageningen.
[25] Alakangas E (2010) *Classification of Biomass Origin in European Solid Biofuel Standard*. Jyväskylä, Finland: EUBIONET III.
[26] Industrial Ethanol Association (IEA) (2010) *Share of Total Primary Energy Supply in 2007, France*. France: IEA.
[27] Barel C (2009) *Pellets@las Pellet Market Country Report France*. France: ADEME.
[28] Björheden R (2006) Drivers behind the development of forest energy in Sweden. *Biomass and Bioenergy* 30: 289–295.
[29] Kranzl L, Diesenreiter F, and Kalt G (2009) *IEA Bioenergy Task 40 Country Report Austria 2009*. IEA Bioenergy Task 40, France: IEA.
[30] Helynen S (2004) Bioenergy policy in Finland. *Energy for Sustainable Development* 8: 36–46.
[31] Junginger M, van Dam J, Alakangas E, et al. (2010) *Solutions to Overcome Market Barriers in Bioenergy Markets in Europe: Resources, Use and Market Analysis – D 2.2*. Jyväskylä, Finland: EUBIONET III.
[32] Hillring B and Vinterbäck J (2000) Development of European wood-fuel trade. *Holzforschung and Holzverwertung* 6: 98–102.
[33] Ericsson K and Nilsson LJ (2004) International biofuel trade: A study of the Swedish import. *Biomass and Bioenergy* 26: 205–220.
[34] Pigaht M, Liebich M, and Janssen R (2005) *Opportunities for Pellet Trade, Task 3.2.3., Deliverable 20*.
[35] European Commission (2009) *Directive 2009/28/EC of the European Parliament and of the Council of 23 April 2009 on the Promotion of the Use of Energy from Renewable Sources and Amending and Subsequently Repealing Directives 2001/77/EC and 2003/30/EC*. Brussels, Belgium: European Commission.
[36] Al-Mansour F and Zuwala J (2010) An evaluation of biomass co-firing in Europe. *Biomass and Bioenergy* 34: 620–629.
[37] John Clegg Consulting (2010) *Wood Fibre Availability and Demand in Britain 2007 to 2025*. Edinburgh, Scotland: John Clegg Consulting.
[38] Stopford M (2009) *Maritime Economics*. London and New York: Taylor & Francis.
[39] Moore C (2010) The future? A practioners ramble. *The Argus Biomass Markets Conference*. Brussels, Belgium: Argus Media Ltd., 15 April.
[40] Shankleman J (2010) Biomass boom threatens UK wood chip shortage. *BusinessGreen.com* April.
[41] Junginger M, van Dam J, Zarrilli S, et al. (2010) *Opportunities and Barriers for International Bioenergy Trade*. IEA Bioenergy Task 40, France: IEA.
[42] Peksa-Blanchard M, Dolzan P, Grassi A, et al. (2007) *Global Wood Pellets Markets and Industry: Policy Drivers, Market Status and Raw Material Potential*. France: IEA.
[43] Pi R Swedish association of pellet producers webpage. Stockholm, Sweden: Pelletsindustrins Riksförbund, http://www.pelletsindustrin.org.
[44] Hiegl W and Janssen R (2009) *Pellet Market Overview Report EUROPE*. Europe: Intelligent Energy.
[45] Pirraglia A, Gonzalez R, Saloni D, and Wright J (2010) Wood pellets: An expanding market opportunity. *Biomass Magazine* June.
[46] Argus Media (2010) World's largest pellet plant to start up in Russia. *Argus Biomass Markets* July.
[47] Solomon BD, Barnes JR, and Halvorsen KE (2007) Grain and cellulosic ethanol: History, economics, and energy policy. *Biomass and Bioenergy* 31: 416–425.
[48] Goldemberg J (2006) The ethanol program in Brazil. *Environmental Research Letters* 1: 014008.
[49] Knothe G (2001) Historical perspectives on vegetable oil-based diesel fuels. *Industrial Oils* 12.
[50] Industrial Ethanol Association (IEA) (2004) *Biofuels for Transport: An International Perspective*. France: IEA.
[51] Pousa GP, Santos AL, and Suarez PA (2007) History and policy of biodiesel in Brazil. *Energy Policy* 35: 5393–5398.
[52] Mussatto SI, Dragone G, Guimarães PMR, et al. (2010) Technological trends, global market, and challenges of bio-ethanol production-R1. *Biotechnology Advances* July.
[53] Lamers P, Hamelinck CN, Junginger M, and Faaij A (2011) International bioenergy trade: A review of past developments in the liquid biofuels market. *Renewable and Sustainable Energy Reviews*.
[54] FAPRI (2010) *FAPRI 2010 US and World Agricultural Outlook*. USA: FAPRI.
[55] Eur'ObservER (2010) *Biofuels Barometer 2010*. London: Eur'ObservER.
[56] Argentina Renovables (2009) *The State of the Argentine Biodiesel Industry. First Quarter 2009 Report*.
[57] Krugman PR and Obstfeld M (2008) *International Economics: Theory and Policy*. Pearson Education Limited.
[58] Kim J, Oh S, and Heo E (2007) A study on the regionalization of the world crude oil markets using the asymmetric error correction model. *Ninth IAEE European Conference*, Florence, Italy.
[59] Bachmeier LJ and Griffin JM (2006) Testing for market integration crude oil, coal, and natural gas. *Energy Journal* 27: 55–71.
[60] IMF. IMF primary commodity prices. http://www.imf.org/external/np/res/commod/index.asp.
[61] Weiner RJ (1991) Is the world oil market 'one great pool'? *Energy Journal* 12: 95.
[62] Gulen SG (1997) Regionalization in the world crude oil market. *Energy Journal* 18: 109.
[63] Asche F, Osmundsen P, and Tveterås R (2002) European market integration for gas? Volume flexibility and political risk. *Energy Economics* 24: 249–265.
[64] Neumann A, Siliverstovs B, and von Hirschhausen C (2006) Convergence of European spot market prices for natural gas? A real-time analysis of market integration using the Kalman Filter. *Applied Economics Letters* 13: 727.
[65] De Vany A and Walls WD (1993) Pipeline access and market integration in the natural gas industry. *Energy Journal* 14: 1.
[66] Serletis A (1997) *Is There an East-West Split in North-American Natural Gas Markets?* Germany: Munich Personal RePEc Archive.
[67] Brown SP and Yücel MK (2008) Deliverability and regional pricing in U.S. natural gas markets. *Energy Economics* 30: 2441–2453.
[68] Li R (2008) *International Steam Coal Market Integration*. Australia: Department of Economics, Macquarie University.
[69] Wårell L (2006) Market integration in the international coal industry: A cointegration approach. *Energy Journal* 27: 99–118.
[70] Toppinen A and Toivonen R (1997) *Cointegration in Testing Market Integration: An Empirical Analysis of Finnish Roundwood Markets*. Helsinki, Finland.
[71] Alavalapati JRR, Adamowicz WL, and Luckert MK (1997) A cointegration analysis of Canadian wood pulp prices. *American Journal of Agricultural Economics* 79: 975–986.
[72] Toppinen A, Viitanen J, Leskinen P, and Toivonen R (2005) Dynamics of roundwood prices in Estonia, Finland and Lithuania. *Baltic Forestry* 11: 88–96.
[73] Mohanty S, Peterson EWF, and Smith DB (1996) Relationships between U.S. and Canadian wheat prices: Cointegration and error correction approach. *Canadian Journal of Agricultural Economics* 44: 265–276.
[74] Mainardi S (2001) Limited arbitrage in international wheat markets: Threshold and smooth transition cointegration. *Australian Journal of Agricultural and Resource Economics* 45: 335–360.

[75] Pippenger J and Phillips L (2008) Some pitfalls in testing the law of one price in commodity markets. *Journal of International Money and Finance* 27: 915–925.
[76] Liu X (2008) Impact and competitiveness of EU biofuel market: First view of the prices of biofuel market in relation to the global players. *107th Seminar*. Sevilla, Spain: European Association of Agricultural Economists, January 30–February 1.
[77] Olsson O European bioenergy markets: Integration and price convergence. Alnarp, Skara, Umeå and Uppsala: SLU. http://diss-epsilon.slu.se:8080/archive/00002185/.
[78] Dahl J (2005) *Final Progress Report from the Project "Pellets for Europe"*. Denmark: Force Technology.
[79] Toivonen R, Tahvanainen L, Pelkonen P, and Bahabur Magar S (2008) *Wood-Based Bioenergy: Demand and Supply Trends in Europe*. Joensuu, Finland: University of Joensuu.
[80] Kranzl L, Kalt G, Diesenreiter F. *et al*, (2009) *Does Bioenergy Contribute to More Stable Energy Prices?* Vienna.
[81] Jacks DS, O'Rourke KH, and Williamson JG (2009) Commodity price volatility and world market integration since 1700. *National Bureau of Economic Research Working Paper Series*, Vol. 14748, USA: SSRN.
[82] Trømborg E and Solberg B (2010) Forest sector impacts of the increased use of wood in energy production in Norway. *Forest Policy and Economics* 12: 39–47.
[83] Faaij AP and Domac J (2006) Emerging international bio-energy markets and opportunities for socio-economic development. *Energy for Sustainable Development* 10: 7–19.
[84] Jull C (2007) *Recent Trends in the Law and Policy of Bioenergy Production, Promotion and Use*. Rome, Italy: Food and Agriculture Organization.
[85] Keeney D (2009) Ethanol USA. *Environmental Science and Technology* 43: 8–11.
[86] Elobeid A and Tokgoz S (2008) Removing distortions in the U.S. ethanol market: What does it imply for the United States and Brazil? *American Journal of Agricultural Economics* 90: 918–932.
[87] Industrial Ethanol Association (IEA) (2007) *Customs Inconsistencies Destabilise European Bioethanol Industry*. France: IEA.
[88] Kram JW (2007) The end of 'Splash and Dash'? *Biodiesel Magazine* October.
[89] Abbot C and Wiessner C (2008) Bailout bill pulls plug on biodiesel splash and dash. *Reuters* October.
[90] Ng J, Ng HK, and Gan S (2009) Recent trends in policies, socioeconomy and future directions of the biodiesel industry. *Clean Technologies and Environmental Policy* 12: 213–238.
[91] Smith S (2008) EU pursues legal action against US-subsidized biodiesel. *Biodiesel Magazine* February.
[92] Eur'ObservER (2009) *Biofuels Barometer 2009*. London: Eur'ObservER.
[93] Sims B (2010) Balancing act. *Biodiesel Magazine* October.
[94] Ericsson K (2006) Prospects for Bioenergy in Europe: Supply, Demand and Trade. Doctoral Thesis, Lund University.
[95] Oosterveer P and Mol AP (2010) Biofuels, trade and sustainability: A review of perspectives for developing countries. *Biofuels, Bioproducts and Biorefining* 4: 66–76.
[96] Swann G (2010) *International Standards and Trade: A Review of the Empirical Literature*. France: OECD.
[97] Hiegl W, Janssen R, and Pichler W (2009) *Advancement of Pellets-Related European Standards (D 7.5)*. Pellets@las. Europe: Intelligent Energy.
[98] Alakangas E (2010) European pellet standards: Multipart standard EN 14961. *Bioenergy International* April, pp. 24–25.
[99] Grunwald M (2008) The clean energy scam. *Time* March.
[100] van Dam J (2010) *Update: Initiatives in the Field of Biomass and Bioenergy Certification*. IEA Bioenergy Task 40, France: IEA.
[101] Adnan H (2010) M'sia unhappy with EU green directive for palm oil. *The Star* May.
[102] Cram M and Hanson J How to identify and manage pine wilt disease and treat wood products infested by the pinewood nematodes. Washington, DC: USDA. http://swww.na.fs.fed.us/spfo/pubs/howtos/ht_pinewilt/pinewilt.htm.
[103] Markhus T (2010) *Presentation at Biowood Norway's Pellet Plant in Averøy*, Norway, April.
[104] Schlamadinger B, Faaij A, and Daugherty E (2004) *Should We Trade Biomass, Electricity, Renewable Certificates or CO_2 Credits?* IEA Bioenergy Task 38, France: IEA.
[105] Laurijssen J and Faaij A (2009) Trading biomass or GHG emission credits? *Climatic Change* 94: 287–317.
[106] GreenMomentum (2010) EPA designates sugarcane ethanol as advanced biofuel. *GreenMomentum.com* February.
[107] Searchinger T, Heimlich R, Houghton RA, *et al* (2008) Use of U.S. croplands for biofuels increases greenhouse gases through emissions from land-use change. *Science* 319: 1238–1240.

5.07 Biomass CHP Energy Systems: A Critical Assessment

M Börjesson and EO Ahlgren, Chalmers University of Technology, Gothenburg, Sweden

© 2012 Elsevier Ltd. All rights reserved.

5.07.1	Introduction	87
5.07.2	Biomass CHP Options	88
5.07.2.1	Combustion	89
5.07.2.2	Gasification	89
5.07.2.3	Summary of Technology Properties	90
5.07.3	Bioenergy System Aspects	90
5.07.3.1	Biomass Markets and CO$_2$ Effects	91
5.07.3.2	Biomass Competition between Sectors	92
5.07.4	Biomass CHP Technology System Aspects	93
5.07.4.1	Competitiveness of Biomass CHP Options	94
5.07.4.2	Scale Effects of Biomass CHP	95
5.07.5	Concluding Remarks	96
References		97
Relevant Websites		97

Glossary

Combined cycle A process in which a gas turbine and a steam turbine cycle are used in combination. The exhaust fumes from the combustion in the gas turbine are utilized to produce steam for the steam turbine cycle. Electricity is generated in both the gas turbine and steam turbine cycles.
Exergy The amount of useful work a certain quantity of energy can perform.
Exogenous Relates to a factor originating from outside the studied system. The factor can influence but cannot be influenced by the activities in the system.

Gasification A process in which a solid hydrocarbon feedstock is heated under substoichiometric conditions, that is, with low supply of oxygen (or air), and is converted into a gas (consisting of, among other components, carbon monoxide and hydrogen). The gas can be an intermediate product in the production of chemicals or be used as fuel.
Steam cycle A process in which a medium (usually water) is heated by the combustion of a fuel into high-temperature, pressurized steam and subsequently used to drive a steam turbine to generate electricity.

5.07.1 Introduction

Biomass is a renewable resource and constitutes as such an option for reduced use of fossil fuels and a way to decrease greenhouse gas emissions. For many countries and regions, increased use of biomass also offers a possibility to improve the energy security of supply by reducing the need for imported energy carriers such as oil. However, despite its renewability, biomass is a limited resource in the sense that the annual potential is constrained by practical, economical, and environmental boundaries. With future more stringent greenhouse gas emission constraints as well as higher energy service demands, an increased pressure on efficient biomass resource utilization is thus likely.

Biomass for energy purposes can refer to an array of different types of resources, including wood wastes from forestry and industry, agricultural residues, residues from food and paper industries, organic municipal wastes, sewage sludge, as well as dedicated energy crops such as short rotation coppice, grasses, sugar crops, starch crops, and oil crops. Since CO$_2$ emitted in biomass combustion have been absorbed from the atmosphere through the photosynthesis in the growth of the plant, the process can be considered carbon neutral. Regrowth is, however, a condition for ensuring a complete carbon cycle and a sustainable biomass use. Regarding modern use of biomass for energy purposes, organic wastes and residues have been the main types of biomass resources used, but energy crops are increasing in significance. Residues and wastes have so far mainly been used for heat and power generation, while sugar, starch, and oil crops are primarily used for fuel production [1]. Although new biomass resources based on energy crops have larger potential than, for example, wood waste, they are more expensive and also compete with other potential use of the arable land, such as for food production.

There are a number of possibilities for the conversion of biomass to useful energy outputs. Often, the cost-effectiveness and suitability of different biomass conversion routes depend on factors such as resource availability, feedstock quality, transportation costs, and plant size. If sufficient biomass is available, biomass-based combined heat and power (CHP) generation is generally considered as a clean and reliable heat and power source suitable for base load service [1]. Furthermore, CHP generation is commonly referred to as a measure to increase the efficiency of energy systems. Simply put, the basic advantages of CHP is that joint production of heat and power requires considerably less fuel input than if the two outputs were to be produced in separate plants. Biomass-fueled CHP represents thus an appealing alternative for the combination of an efficient energy technology with a renewable and climate-neutral fuel. Many governments and intergovernmental organizations have recognized the benefits of CHP, and, for example, the European Union (EU) administration has identified CHP as a way of saving energy, avoiding grid losses, reducing emissions, as well as increasing security of supply, and therefore encourages a larger CHP deployment [2]. CHP based on renewables is also mentioned in the context of meeting the so-called '20–20–20' goals within the EU, that is, to 2020 reduce primary energy use by 20%, increase the share of renewables to 20%, and reduce greenhouse gas emissions by at least 20% [3].

Despite the many benefits of CHP, and despite the fact that the principles of the technology have been well-known for a long period of time, the increase in CHP deployment has not been as fast as that of energy business in general or of electricity or steam-generating industries in particular, as highlighted by Verbruggen [4]. Furthermore, the degree to which CHP is applied differs widely between nations, also when comparing countries with similar economic development [5]. The uneven distribution of CHP, in combination with the high accessibility and relatively low complexity of many CHP technologies, suggests that CHP deployment may not be an issue of technology character as much as being linked to policy and economy-related system issues [4].

Although the biomass CHP option seems to be a straightforward way to efficient and climate-friendly energy systems, the deployment is linked to a number of complex issues of importance for the analysis of biomass CHP benefits, as well as of biomass use in general. Often, different views emerge from diverging perspectives and assumptions about the system surroundings rather than about the technology *per se*. Factors that can have significant influence on the estimated performance of biomass CHP include time horizon, valuation of heat and electricity, choice of system boundaries, and assumptions regarding marginal effects. In this chapter, different aspects of biomass CHP energy systems are analyzed and discussed. Covered areas include questions related to technology choice, for example, what biomass CHP technology alternatives are suitable under different conditions? What are the benefits of advanced technologies such as biomass integrated gasification combined cycle (BIGCC) plants compared to conventional steam turbine (ST) plants? Furthermore, reflections are made on issues linked to biomass use, for example, how is a limited potential of biomass resources most effectively used? Should biomass be used for heat and/or electricity generation or perhaps as transport biofuels in vehicles? Aspects related to plant scales are touched upon, as well as difficulties linked to choices in systems and technology analyses of biomass CHP, for example, what impact has the choice of system boundaries and boundary conditions on the view on biomass CHP performance?

The chapter is organized according to the following. In Section 5.07.2, an overview of properties of biomass CHP technologies are given. In Section 5.07.3, aspects of bioenergy systems, especially implications connected to limitations in biomass availability, are analyzed. This includes an exploration of the many complex factors involved in determining the likelihood of affordable biomass supplies keeping pace with demand. It also explores issues involved in assessing how much of a limited biomass resource is likely to be available for biomass CHP. In Section 5.07.4, the perspective is narrowed down to the biomass CHP technology systems, and aspects related to the competitiveness of biomass CHP options as well as to plant scale are considered. It also illustrates the difficulty of comparing a technology which is still under development (e.g., gasification-based CHP) with one that is already deployed (e.g., combustion-based CHP). Concluding remarks are given in Section 5.07.5.

5.07.2 Biomass CHP Options

There are several potential conversion routes for the generation of biomass-based power and CHP. Examples include direct combustion in combination with steam cycles, organic Rankine cycles (ORCs) or Stirling engines, gasification in combination with gas turbines, gas engines, or both a gas turbine and an ST in combined cycles (CCs). The technologies are, however, at different stages of development and deployment. Today, combustion in combination with a steam cycle is the dominating conversion route in commercial use, while the other mentioned options are in the demonstration or early commercialization phase [6]. Other options for power production based on biomass resources include, for example, anaerobic digestion in combination with gas engines as well as co-combustion of biomass in coal-fired plants.

Regardless of generation technology, CHP generation renders two outputs with significant differences in characteristics: heat and electricity. From a thermodynamic perspective, but also to high degree from an economic point of view, electricity is a high-value energy carrier, which can be converted to all other forms of energy, while heat is less valuable. The value of heat depends on the temperature level. At high temperature levels, for example, in the form of process steam, heat can be utilized to perform work; at lower temperatures, it can be used for, for example, space heating; while at ambient temperatures, the technical usefulness, as well as the economic value, is gone [4].

Storage and transportation of high-temperature heat is associated with high costs and major losses. Storage and transport of low-temperature heat, such as district heating, is less complicated and losses are smaller but investment costs for distribution networks as well as pumping costs are still significant. For low-temperature heat, some degree of storage capacity is available through heat distribution networks and buildings, which function as a buffer. Due to the limitations in heat distribution, heat markets for CHP plants are at best of local character or at worst, in cases when distribution networks do not exist and/or are uneconomical to invest in (heat loads are too sparsely located, etc.), nonexistent. In many countries, this fact has been a key problem for large-scale extension of CHP [4].

Storage of electricity normally requires energy conversion and is associated with high investment costs as well as considerable losses. Pumped water storage connected to hydropower has been one of few economical options. Although balancing of power supply and demand certainly presents a challenge and needs to be handled at a system level, seen from the perspective of individual CHP plants, connection to regional, national, or international power grids to a large degree solves the problems attached to electricity storage and offers a large market for generated electricity [4].

In the following sections, a brief review of biomass CHP technologies based on combustion and gasification is given along with some examples of applications. The presentation focuses on dedicated biomass plants, and co-combustion with fossil fuels is thus not treated explicitly.

5.07.2.1 Combustion

Direct combustion of biomass in a boiler generates heat that can be used to produce electricity via an ST. If there is an economic use for the generated waste heat, that is, a heat demand, CHP generation is an option that can improve the overall energy efficiency and economic performance of the plant significantly. Although the electrical efficiency of the steam cycle is lower than for alternative technologies, such as gasification-based alternatives, it is currently considered to be the cheapest and most reliable option [6].

Although trade of refined biomass resources over long distances is increasing in importance, biomass markets are still to a large degree local or regional in their character. Scarce availability of local biomass feedstock and high transportation costs have led to biomass plants being small compared to, for example, coal-fired plants. Typical sizes of biomass ST CHP plants are in the range 1–100 MW$_{th}$ [1]. However, a few larger-scale biomass CHP plants are in operation. One of these is the Alholmen Kraft plant, located in Jakobstad, Finland, which has a capacity of 550 MW$_{th}$. The Alholmen Kraft plant, which was taken into operation in 2001, uses a fuel mixture of about 45% wood fuels (bark, wood chips, and other wood wastes), 45% peat, as well as about 10% pit coal as supplementary fuel. The plant generates electricity, process steam to the nearby paper mill, as well as district heat, and has high steam data: 165 bar/545 °C. The Igelsta plant, located in the Stockholm area of Sweden, has a capacity of 240 MW$_{th}$ and was taken into operation in 2009. It uses mainly forest residues as fuel and produces electricity and district heating. The plant has steam data of 90 bar/540 °C. In Port Talbot in South Wales, United Kingdom, the world's largest biomass-fired power plant with a capacity of 350 MW$_e$ is constructed. As a comparison, advanced pulverized coal power plants are typically built in capacities of 400–1000 MW$_e$.

The generally small plant sizes of biomass CHP plants approximately double the specific investment cost and also result in lower electrical efficiency compared to coal power plants. The electrical efficiency of biomass ST CHP is often around 30% depending on plant size, but in modern biomass CHP plants, using high-quality wood chip fuels, it can be as high as 34% (on lower heating value (LHV) basis). For electricity-only production, up to 40% efficiency is achievable [1]. With technical development, higher steam data, and thus higher electrical efficiency, should be possible to achieve in the future. In the 2020 time frame, steam data of about 100 bar/600 °C could be reasonable for small biomass CHP plants (about 10 MW$_e$) and correspondingly 190 bar/600 °C for larger plants (about 80 MW$_e$), according to Hansson *et al.* [7]. In the latter case, this would result in an electrical efficiency of about 35.5% [7]. It should be noted that the prospect of increasing electrical efficiency is not only a technical issue but is also to a large degree a trade-off between potential to increase revenues and additional costs. The revenues are in turn dependent on factors such as future energy prices and energy policies.

The utilization of municipal solid waste (MSW) as fuel in CHP generation calls for robust technologies and rigorous controls of emissions, which lead to relatively high costs [6]. MSW is a highly heterogeneous and usually heavily contaminated fuel, and MSW plants have comparably low electrical efficiencies since corrosion problems limit the steam temperature. Around 22% electrical efficiency is common for MSW CHP plants, but new designs can reach 28–30% [1]. Even though combustion of MSW is a mature technology and emissions of pollutants can be effectively controlled, the relatively high cost of electricity generation, in combination with the absence of appropriate waste management and incentives, means that MSW, in many countries, remains a largely unexploited energy resource despite a large potential [6]. Furthermore, MSW combustion often faces problems with public acceptance and is seen as competing with recycling [1].

The Stirling engine and the ORC are two technologies that are currently at the demonstration stage, but could be interesting options for future small-scale, distributed CHP generation. Important aspects for increased competitiveness of these technologies from the current state include improvements in conversion efficiency, higher reliability, and lowered costs [6].

5.07.2.2 Gasification

Gasification is a process in which a solid fuel (biomass, coal, etc.) is heated under substoichiometric conditions, that is, with a limited amount of oxygen or air available, with the result that a gas containing carbon monoxide and hydrogen, among other components, is produced. After upgrading, a gas mixture referred to as synthesis gas or syngas is obtained. Biomass resources can generally be gasified into syngas with an energy conversion efficiency of 85–95% [6]. The syngas is an intermediate product which, in different ways, can be further converted into a range of energy products, including electricity as well as gaseous or liquid high-quality fuels, which can be used as transport fuels.

There are several possibilities of power or CHP generation in connection with biomass gasification. The syngas can, after cleaning, be combusted in a gas engine resulting in an electrical efficiency in the range of 22–35%. Another option is to combust the syngas in a gas turbine, which gives an electrical efficiency of up to 40%. Even higher electrical efficiency can be reached by utilizing both gas turbine and ST in a CC plant; about 42% electrical efficiency is fully possible [6]. The syngas can also be further upgraded into methane in a methanation process. This product is often referred to as substitute or synthetic natural gas (SNG). The SNG could be fed into the natural gas grid and be used in conventional stationary gas utilities, or alternatively, as fuel in the transportation sector. As indicated, also liquid transport biofuels can be produced from the syngas, including, for example, Fischer–Tropsch diesel and methanol.

As mentioned, biomass gasification offers possibilities of higher electrical efficiencies than with direct combustion. For small-scale plants of less than 5–10 MW$_e$, fairly simple units with gas engines are interesting alternatives to ST-based systems, which at these scales experience significant diseconomies of scale [6]. CC plants are more complex. There are so far only a small number of successful demonstrations of the technology and still no large-scale commercial applications [8]. One demonstration plant of the BIGCC technology is located in Värnamo, Sweden. The plant, which has a capacity of 6 MW$_e$ and 9 MW$_{heat}$, is based on a pressurized air-blown gasifier, and has been successfully run with different wood and straw fuels. A BIGCC CHP plant with a capacity of 2 MW$_e$ and 4.5 MW$_{heat}$, equipped with a steam-blown gasifier and fueled with wood chips, is located in Güssingen, Austria. Except for BIGCC plants entirely fed with biomass, there are also examples of 'co-gasification'. A 253 MW$_e$ coal-fueled integrated gasification combined cycle (IGCC) plant in Buggenum, the Netherlands, has been tested for co-gasification of a number of biomass and waste fuels [8]. Out of the 5.25 GW$_e$ IGCC plant capacity existing globally in 2006, about 0.15 GW$_e$, or less than 3%, was based on biomass fuels [6]. Several commercial-scale projects are, however, reported to be 'in the pipeline' in Northern Europe, United States, Japan, as well as in India.

5.07.2.3 Summary of Technology Properties

In Table 1, conversion efficiencies and costs are summarized for different biomass CHP, MSW CHP, and, for comparison, coal condensing power plants. The table presents both typical data of today and estimated future values for a time perspective of around 2020. Due to the uncertainties involved, cost data are only provided for current conditions. Data are based on Hansson *et al.* [7] for all technologies except for BIGCC CHP, for which data are based on Marbe *et al.* [9].

5.07.3 Bioenergy System Aspects

The fact that biomass in a closed system can be considered climate neutral does not imply that all kinds of biomass use are efficient from a climate perspective with a systems viewpoint applied. Limitations in biomass supply suggest that use of biomass in one part of the system can have consequences in another part of the system and that different allocations of biomass resources are linked to different levels of environmental and economical efficiency. Although also direct and indirect land use change effects can be important aspects of the environmental performance of biomass use (as highlighted in several studies in recent years), this aspect is not covered in the present chapter.

Table 1 Plant data for biomass CHP, MSW CHP, and coal condensing plants for current conditions as well as estimated future values for the 2020 time frame

	Size (MW$_e$)	Electrical efficiency (%)	Total efficiency (%)	Specific investment cost (kEUR kW$_e^{-1}$)	Fix. O&M (% inv. cost)	Var. O&M (EUR MWh$_{fuel}^{-1}$)
Today						
Biomass ST CHP	10	27	110	3.7	1.5	3
	30	30	110	2.8	1.5	3
	80	34	110	2.2	1.5	3
MSW ST CHP	3	15	89	11.1	3	10
	30	22	91	5.6	3	10
Coal condensing	400	47	47	1.2	2	3
Future – 2020						
Biomass ST CHP	10	28.5	105–113			
	30	32.5	105–113			
	80	35.5	105–113			
MSW ST CHP	3	20	91			
	30	24	93			
Biomass Stirling CHP	0.05–0.1	23–27	80–90			
BIGCC CHP	10–100	43	90			
Coal condensing	400	50	50			

Efficiencies are on LHV basis; values for biomass ST refer to plants equipped with flue gas condensation (explaining the total efficiency of above 100%). Heat production included in total efficiency refers to district heating. Values are based on Hansson *et al.* [7] and Marbe *et al.* [9]. A currency exchange rate of 10 SEK = 1 EUR has been used.

5.07.3.1 Biomass Markets and CO$_2$ Effects

Even though biomass is a renewable resource, it is also a limited resource. In a future with more ambitious CO$_2$ reduction objectives, this will most probably lead to increased competition for biomass resources and increasing biomass prices. Although this view is getting increasingly acknowledged, it is far from obvious how to handle this in an environmental evaluation of biomass use. Some of the difficulties involved are connected to how the workings of biomass markets should be looked upon; how should potential effects of alternative biomass use be handled, that is, if the biomass was not used in a specific application under consideration, how would it then be used; and should potential emission effects linked to this be accounted for? Different approaches on how to understand biomass markets can lead to very different outcomes regarding the environmental performance of biomass technologies. Although there are few right or wrong answers regarding these issues, it is essential to be aware of which assumptions different views rely on.

The commonly used, straightforward assumption that all biomass use is climate neutral (except for emissions generated in extraction, distribution, etc.) is implicitly based on the assumption that indirect emission effects of biomass use are nonexistent or can be neglected. With this approach, the supply of biomass at a certain price is often considered 'unlimited' from the perspective of the activities considered. Furthermore, the biomass price is generally not assumed to change as a function of the activities in the concerned system, that is, the biomass price is seen as an exogenous parameter. This means that whether a lot of biomass or a very small amount is used within the system has, with this point of departure, no implications on the price of biomass. Numerous studies apply this or similar approaches; two examples, which in different ways focus on biomass CHP, are studies by Marbe *et al.* [9] and Knutsson *et al.* [10], from 2004 and 2006, respectively. The former study examines possible economic synergy effects that can be achieved if biomass CHP is used for delivering both process heat to industry and district heat to district heating networks and basically applies a plant-level perspective. The latter study analyses effects of green certificates and CO$_2$ emission trading on investments in CHP generation in the Swedish district heating sector as a whole, and thus applies a national perspective.

By assuming that biomass use is CO$_2$ neutral, it is also implicitly assumed that biomass is not a constrained resource under the conditions considered, for instance, regarding time horizon. The reasoning behind this is that if biomass is a constrained resource, then additional biomass use in one part of the energy system would offset a response in another part of the energy system since the biomass market would be affected. In theory, an increased use of biomass for one specific application would lead to a price effect and a decreased use of biomass for the marginal biomass user. This marginal biomass user might then substitute the decreased biomass use with some other energy option available. In view of the dominance of fossil fuels in many energy systems, it is not unlikely that the marginal biomass user then would increase its fossil fuel use. Under such circumstances, additional use of biomass in one part of the energy system would indirectly lead to increased fossil fuel use and thereby CO$_2$ emissions in another part of the energy system.

Following the above assumptions, an approach with CO$_2$-neutral biomass use thus suggests that the full biomass potential is not met and a change in the energy system, for instance, from an investment in a new biomass CHP plant, would not affect the marginal biomass use. This is not necessarily a controversial assumption, for instance, if the time perspective is short and the availability of biomass is large and/or if small changes in biomass use are considered, that is, if the impact on biomass price and availability could be considered negligible. There can certainly be empirical evidence from many regions that supports the view that there presently are unused biomass resources also at comparably low costs. However, in the case of large-scale increases in biomass utilization, the perspective might be more questionable, although this is dependent on the potential size and characteristics of the biomass market in question.

An approach in which biomass use does not give rise to indirect CO$_2$ emissions and the biomass price is treated as an exogenous parameter not affected by the activities of the studied system, could suggest one of the two following biomass market characteristics: biomass supply is in the biomass quantity range considered very elastic, or; if biomass demand increases then, as a response, also biomass supply increases, that is, if the demand curve shifts to the right in a supply–demand diagram, then also the supply curve shifts to the right. A shift of the biomass supply curve to the right basically implies that the cost of extracting or producing biomass decreases; this could be due to the development of more efficient ways of growing energy crops or due to other reasons. With either one of these biomass market characteristics, the assumption of a change in biomass use without effects on indirect CO$_2$ emissions or on price is adequate. However, if these features, for one reason or another, are not representative for the system under consideration, another perspective might be more appropriate.

At times, although not that common, indirect marginal effects of biomass use are included also in static energy systems scenario analyses. In such studies, marginal effects on the biomass market are taken into account with an approach that resembles the more frequently applied view of linking changes in electricity use with marginal effects in the electricity system. In the case of electricity, the point of departure is to establish which electricity generation technology is on the margin in the electricity system. An increase in electricity use, somewhere in the system, is then linked to emissions corresponding to the emission level that the marginal production technology gives rise to in order to generate the amount of electricity required to meet the increase. The marginal electricity generation technology is generally also assumed to set the electricity price on the market. In the case of biomass, in a similar way, a biomass user (a technology) on the margin is assumed. Furthermore, a change in biomass use somewhere in the system is assumed to affect this biomass marginal user, for example, an increase in biomass use will lead to a decreased use of biomass for the marginal user. As indicated earlier, the assumed measures that the biomass marginal user will take in response to the change in the biomass market will, with this way of thinking, determine the emission effect associated with a change in biomass use. In accordance with the above, the biomass marginal use is often also assumed to determine the biomass price.

A conceptual difference between electricity and biomass, which to some degree makes the analogy between marginal electricity emissions and marginal biomass emissions arguable, is that electricity is a secondary energy carrier while biomass is a primary energy source. While electricity by definition is constrained in the sense that electricity use equals electricity generated and a change in electricity use has a strong linkage to change in production, the linkage between biomass use, and the potential biomass supply is weaker. An approach in which an increase in biomass use somewhere in the system does not give rise to an increase in the total biomass use of the system, and thereby a potential indirect CO_2 effect if substitution to fossil fuels occurs, in terms of biomass market characteristics could imply the following: biomass supply is highly inelastic in the biomass quantity range considered (large biomass price effect); or alternatively, the marginal biomass demand is very elastic (small biomass price effect); and furthermore, an increase in demand, that is, a shift of the demand curve to the right, does not lead to a change in supply, that is, the supply curve does not shift.

The illustrated view is, for instance, provided by Axelsson *et al.* [11] in their presentation of a modeling tool for creating energy market scenarios for evaluation of investments in energy-intensive industry. The presented energy market scenarios are intended to reflect future conditions; a time frame of 2020 is mentioned. In the work, an increased (or decreased) use of biomass in a studied utility is by definition assumed to imply decreased (or increased) biomass use for a marginal biomass user, which determines the indirect level of CO_2 emissions associated with changes in biomass use. Furthermore, the marginal biomass user's willingness to pay for biomass determines the biomass price. In the study, two future potential marginal users of biomass are identified in a European context: coal power plants in which biomass is co-combusted and transport biofuel production. In the first case, increased biomass use thereby results in indirect CO_2 emissions in a magnitude corresponding to coal combustion and, in the second case, corresponding to use of oil-based transport fuels (petrol/diesel). Accordingly, in the first case the biomass price is assumed to be connected to the coal price and in the second case to the oil price (with appropriate conversion efficiencies and assumed energy policies taken into account) [11].

There are several implications involved in assuming that a change in biomass use by definition influences a marginal biomass use. If co-combustion in coal power plants is considered to be the marginal biomass use, this suggests that biomass use from a climate perspective could equal coal use. Consequently, from this perspective, many (if not most) applications of biomass use do not contribute to lower greenhouse gas emissions. For instance, the approach suggests that, from a climate perspective, it is better to use natural gas or oil than biomass. The question arises, with this type of analysis, what would the incentives of using biomass be in the first place? Obviously, biomass use needs to reach a certain level for this way of thinking to be logical, and there is thus a time aspect to this. However, to assume a future state, in which the biomass supply cannot be increased and where biomass use becomes a question of allocation of a constrained resource, without taking the development from the current situation to this future state into account, in this sense, implies at least a pedagogical problem as well as a risk of missing options that might be advantageous in the short run. On the other hand, biomass technologies that are identified to perform well from a climate perspective also with the described scenario setup are likely to be robust, efficient choices also in a longer time horizon.

The above discussion highlights that the time perspective linked to climate ambitions and the potential availability of biomass resources are factors of great importance for the environmental performance of biomass technologies if indirect market effects are taken into account. A dynamic systems view, in which a time scale from the current situation with comparably high biomass availability in relation to biomass demand to a future situation with more ambitious climate targets and potentially lower resource availability in relation to the demand is considered simultaneously, seems as a beneficial framing of the problem. Such perspective should allow for the possibility that different potential use of biomass might be advantageous in different time perspectives. One technology option might be advantageous and capable to cut CO_2 emissions in the short run but inefficient as a long-term solution when biomass competition increases. Just as the possibilities of bridging technologies should not be neglected, the risk of lock-in effects should also be acknowledged.

5.07.3.2 Biomass Competition between Sectors

Since all energy technologies are part of a larger system, the system suitability of a technology will to a large degree determine the level of its deployment. In this way, the future deployment of biomass CHP depends on the purposes for which a limited potential of biomass resources for the most part will be used in the future, that is, will biomass available for energy purposes primarily be used in the stationary energy sector for heat and power generation, and thereby enable a high biomass CHP deployment, or will it primarily be used for other purposes, for example, as feedstock for transport fuel production? Due to the growing interest for transport biofuels in recent years, this question has received increasing attention.

From a greenhouse gas emission savings point of view, a comparatively straightforward reasoning can lead to the conclusion that biomass is better used for heat and power generation than as biofuels in the transportation sector. The basic explanation for this is connected to the losses associated with conversion of solid biomass to liquid (or gaseous) fuels suitable for vehicles. If assuming that biomass could be converted, for example, through biomass gasification, to transport fuel with an energy conversion efficiency of about 50%, it would take about two 'energy units' (GWh, MJ, etc.) of biomass to replace one energy unit of fossil energy, in this case oil-based transport fuels (petrol or diesel). In contrast, in many stationary energy applications, such as heat or power plants, it would only take one energy unit of biomass to replace one energy unit of fossil energy, for example, oil boilers could be converted to run on biomass pellets and biomass could be co-combusted in coal power plants with a negligible impact on efficiency. From this perspective, it can thus be concluded that it is more efficient to use biomass resources in the stationary energy system than for transport purposes. The fact that coal, per energy unit, gives rise to higher CO_2 emissions than oil, and consequently that the CO_2 emission savings are higher when coal is replaced, furthermore strengthens this conclusion.

There are, however, objections to the reasoning above. For one thing, the assumption of an energy conversion efficiency of 50% may, for some potential biofuel production technology routes, be too low (although for other routes, it is also too high). For instance, several studies suggest that SNG could potentially be produced with a conversion efficiency approaching 70%. Furthermore, a large part of the waste heat could be utilized, for example, as district heating, and in such way an even higher total efficiency is obtained. Although yet to be proven in commercial applications, figures indicating that also transport biofuel could be part of a system that at least approaches a 'one-to-one' exchange ratio between biomass and fossil energy (i.e., when including use of waste heat) certainly improves the attractiveness of the option. However, regarding gas as vehicle fuel, it should also be mentioned that costs for distribution and fueling infrastructure and costs for gas vehicles are substantial.

The last point above reminds us of the fact that not only energy efficiency and CO_2 reduction potential are of importance but also economical efficiency is. When introducing economical parameters in the analysis, the conclusions could very well be altered. In other words, economical efficiency is in many cases not the same as energy efficiency. So far, the deployment of biofuels for transport has heavily relied on policy measures promoting an introduction. If, however, an extensive period of continuously high oil prices would take place, conversion of solid fuels to liquid (or gaseous) transport fuels would at some point be a cost-effective solution even without subsidies. Since low-cost coal resources are abundant, the extent to which biomass would be chosen over coal, should to large degree be dependent on the level of a CO_2 emission penalty or on other policy measures. It could be noted that in a situation in which coal is used for transport fuel production, so-called coal-to-liquids or coal-based syngas, biomass could be used to replace coal for transport fuel production with the same efficiency and CO_2 emission abatement as is obtained when biomass replaces coal in heat or power generation.

Future potentially high and/or volatile oil prices link to the argument for biomass use as a means of increasing energy security of supply. Obviously, use of biomass resources for biofuels in the transportation sector is a more efficient measure to reduce oil dependence than, for example, to use biomass to replace coal in power generation. However, as described above, replacement of coal in power generation is currently a more efficient measure for reducing greenhouse gas emissions. Since there are multiple objectives with different optimal solutions, tradeoffs are inevitable.

Another important issue regarding the sectors in which biomass resources are most cost-effectively used relates to which technology alternatives will be available at competitive costs in the future. If assuming that technology development in the future leads to the supply of cheap, climate-neutral electricity through, for instance, fossil fuel combustion with carbon capture and storage (CCS), solar or nuclear, it can be reasonable to think that the demand for biomass-based power generation will not be as high as if such technology development did not occur. In a similar manner, breakthroughs in fuel cell technology and hydrogen production through electrolysis or in battery technology would decrease the future need for transport biofuels. Predictions of potential future key technology development breakthroughs are of course associated with gigantic difficulties. Any forecasts based on assumptions of a certain technology development should certainly be interpreted as being of an explorative or 'what if' kind of nature, rather than as likely predictions of the future. Nevertheless, such scenarios could be valuable for a further understanding of the system dynamics at work and also to provide indicative quantitative insights, for example, regarding at what cost-levels certain technologies become cost-effective, or regarding how large a share of the estimated energy supply potentials biomass might secure given a certain total energy demand increase.

A number of such scenarios are provided by Grahn et al. [12] in their study on future cost-effective transport fuel and vehicle choices under stringent carbon constraints. In line with the discussion above, the study investigates the potential impact on cost-effective fuel and vehicle choices in the transportation sector by future low-carbon electricity generation technologies in the stationary energy sector (CCS and concentrating solar power), with the help of an optimizing, global energy systems model, which is run to 2100. In accordance with earlier results from the same research group, as well as several others making similar kinds of model assessments, transport biofuels gain comparably low shares of the transport energy supply in many model cases. In these cases, instead, electricity and hydrogen gain significant shares of the transport energy supply in the second part of the century. Biomass is mainly used in the stationary energy system. However, in scenarios that include low-cost, low-carbon electricity generation options, the amount of transport biofuels is considerably higher. Although many of the scenarios show a diversified transportation sector fuel and technology mix, breakthroughs for certain technologies can also lead to the dominance of specific options; for example, low battery costs could very well lead to an almost complete electrification of the light duty road transport sector [12].

Even though any firm predictions regarding the future allocation of biomass between sectors should be avoided, biomass use in the stationary energy system, including CHP, has a benefit due to the conversion losses linked to transport biofuel production. The future development is, however, dependent on the future valuation of the different kind of energy products, by the market as well as by policy makers.

5.07.4 Biomass CHP Technology System Aspects

As described in earlier sections, there are a number of different possible technology options for biomass CHP generation. Since the technologies have different properties in terms of conversion efficiencies, technology costs, level of development, and so on, a number of system aspects have implications for their competitiveness and relative advantages.

5.07.4.1 Competitiveness of Biomass CHP Options

While biomass combustion based technologies, such as biomass ST CHP, dominate the bioenergy sector of today, biomass gasification can potentially be a future key technology for not only efficient renewable production of heat and electricity but also for production of refined, liquid, or gaseous biofuels, for example, usable as transport fuels. The technology is versatile in the sense that a range of different types of biomass feedstock can be used and that a multiple of outputs can be produced from the intermediate gas obtained in the gasification process. As pointed out in earlier sections, advanced biomass gasification based technologies, such as the BIGCC technology, are still at a demonstration stage and no large-scale commercial applications are yet in place. Even so, analyses of future potential possibilities, system suitability, and economic performance of such technologies have in recent years been numerous and gained interest in academia as well as in industry. The basic question addressed in these studies is often related to the competitiveness of advanced biomass gasification based technologies, such as BIGCC, in comparison with more conventional options, such as biomass ST, in regard to costs and environmental performance. This section discusses the approaches of such assessments, and seeks to clarify the influence of different system perspectives for analysis outcomes as well as to elaborate on possible robust insights concerning the competitiveness of biomass combustion contra biomass gasification.

One benefit of gasification is that it makes it possible to use biomass in combination with gas turbines and in gas CC plants and, thereby, to reach a significantly higher electrical efficiency than in conventional biomass ST plants. However, regarding CHP production, the heat efficiency as well as the total efficiency (electricity and heat) is lower than in a conventional biomass ST CHP plant with flue gas condensation. If also introducing biomass heat-only boilers (HOBs) into a comparison, we thus have three options with substantial differences in output: one alternative with high electrical output but low heat output (BIGCC CHP), one alternative with 'medium' electrical output as well as 'medium' heat output (biomass ST CHP), and finally, one alternative with no electrical output but high heat output (biomass HOB).

From an exergy point of view, it makes sense to argue that the BIGCC technology is the most beneficial alternative among the three options; electricity is a higher-value energy carrier than heat, and to obtain a significantly higher electrical efficiency at the expense of a somewhat lower total efficiency seems as an advantageous trade-off. This reasoning to a high degree reflects the main incentive for BIGCC CHP over biomass ST CHP. If quantitative values for energy prices and technology costs are introduced in the analysis, a more thorough analysis can be made. In such analysis, a number of thresholds could be estimated, regarding at which combinations of energy prices, energy policies, technology costs, and so on, one or the other option would be the most economically beneficial. It is here argued that if an energy price scenario close to, for example, a European average would be chosen for such comparative analysis (a price scenario in which a higher price for electricity than for heat is assumed, etc.), the competitiveness of the BIGCC option would to a large degree be determined by the BIGCC technology costs. Related to this, the appropriate discount rate would also be of great significance.

Since BIGCC is not a mature technology, the technology cost is marred by large uncertainties. Often in a technology assessments, two kinds of technology costs are estimated and used: either the plant cost under current conditions, that is, a sort of 'first-of-a-kind' plant cost, or the plant cost under the condition that the technology has reached (a certain amount of) maturity. Due to the higher complexity of the BIGCC technology compared to the biomass ST and biomass HOB technologies, the plant cost of the BIGCC technology will regardless of approach be higher than the plant costs of the other options. However, needless to say, a mature technology cost would make the BIGCC technology far more competitive than with the former approach with current technology costs.

If the cost of a mature technology, sometimes referred to as the cost of the '*n*-th' plant (as opposed to first generation of plants, etc.), and a social discount rate, that is, a discount rate that reflects a societal perspective rather than a private investor perspective, are chosen for the analysis, BIGCC CHP frequently turns out as a very competitive alternative to the conventional alternatives of biomass ST CHP and biomass HOB. For instance, studies by Marbe *et al.* [9], Dornburg and Faaij [13], Börjesson and Ahlgren [14], and Difs *et al.* [15] show overall quite positive pictures of the potential future economic, environmental, and energetic performance of the BIGCC technology. The BIGCC technology is, of course, even more competitive where promotion of 'green' electricity through policy measures, such as green certificates or feed-in tariffs, is taken into account to reflect the current policy situation in many countries. What conclusions that can be drawn and what recommendations can be made based on this kind of analysis are, however, not obvious since the results to a large degree are dependent on the chosen perspective, which in itself is not entirely uncomplicated.

Techno-economic assessments that assume technology properties that are supposed to be achievable, rather than what actually have been achieved already, do only illustrate the competitiveness of a technology once technology maturity has been reached. Analyses which under such conditions indicate benefits of certain options, such as of BIGCC, should rather be interpreted as providing or confirming incentives for a continued and possibly accelerated research and development [15] than as ensuring profitability of projects in the short term. In order for new technologies to reach maturity and thus lowered costs, learning investments are necessary. The willingness for actors to take on risks and learning costs and/or the possibilities to find niche markets is thus essential to reach a possible future potential. Furthermore, private investors generally require a higher return on invested capital and apply a higher discount rate than is used in energy systems analyses applying a societal perspective, making technological change less economically advantageous from an industry perspective than from a societal viewpoint.

When placing a technology assessment in a system surrounding and moving toward a more dynamical systems view, aspects such as system feedbacks, relationships between elements of the system, and system limitations, for example, regarding feedstock supply and level of energy demands, should be taken into account. The earlier mentioned competing technology options, BIGCC CHP, biomass ST CHP, and biomass HOB, all use biomass as feedstock and all deliver heat, and two of them also deliver electricity. As mentioned in earlier sections, biomass markets as well as heat markets are to a large degree local, while electricity markets generally are of a regional, national, or international character. In an undeveloped biomass market, the cost of obtaining large amounts of biomass may rise significantly with increasing distance to suppliers and the supply can thus, under certain conditions, be quite inelastic. In a similar manner, the demand for heat, for example, district heating, can in the short run be relatively insensitive to price increases since, even though some conservation measures can be taken, the investment cost required for the individual consumer to change heating system is substantial.

If technology capital costs, and uncertainties related to these as discussed earlier, for a moment are neglected, the choice between BIGCC CHP, biomass ST CHP, and biomass HOB is, with a higher valuation of electricity contra heat, to a large extent dependent on the size of the local biomass supply in relation to the size of the heat demand. If a large biomass supply exists, the BIGCC CHP gives the highest electrical output while at the same time the heat demand can be met. The option seems under these conditions as an advantageous alternative. However, given a situation with lower biomass supply, the choice would at some point have to shift to an alternative with higher heat output per biomass input in order to meet the local heat demand. In this case, the first-hand option would then be the biomass ST CHP alternative, but with even scarcer biomass supply, biomass HOB would eventually be the only feasible option. This holds given that a certain heat demand should be met with either one of the three considered technology alternatives and under the assumption of an undeveloped biomass market. Obviously, also other technology options, such as heat pumps, are of relevance in a complete optimization of a district heating system. A combination of heat pumps and CHP could very well give the highest heat output also with low biomass availability. However, due to local conditions, cost reasons, etc., heat pumps may not be a suitable option in all cases. The example shows that even if one technology alternative, such as the BIGCC CHP, might be the preferable option when comparing alternatives one against another in a static analysis, specific system surroundings regarding, for example, feedstock supply and energy service demand, can alter the intuitive technology ranking.

An objection to the relevance of the above reasoning could be linked to the fact that no concern of meeting an electricity demand, which also can be quite inelastic, has been given. As mentioned, there are, however, important differences in characteristics between electricity markets and heat markets connected to the ability to distribute the respective energy product. The possibility of long-range electricity distribution allow for more alternatives for electricity generation, also renewable alternatives, than might be the case for heat production in specific local district heating systems.

The reasons for a small biomass availability for CHP generation, which can trigger a situation in which the higher heat efficiency of the ST CHP is valued more than the higher electrical efficiency of the BIGCC CHP, can be both actual physical biomass supply constraints but also that available biomass resources are used for other purposes, for example, due to energy policies. This effect is highlighted by Börjesson and Ahlgren [14] in a study from 2010. Using energy systems optimization modeling, the study contrasts different biomass gasification based energy technologies connected to district heating, including BIGCC CHP as well as transport biofuel production with district heating delivery, and conventional district heating plant options, including biomass ST CHP. The geographical focus of the study is the Västra Götaland region of Sweden. In the study, policy measures for CO_2 reduction and for promotion of 'green' electricity are assumed, and required subsidy levels for large-scale production of transport biofuels are estimated.

The results of the study indicate a trade-off between biomass CHP generation with high electrical output and transport biofuel production. The trade-off situation is mostly due to the limitations in the supply of local, lower-cost biomass; when a large part of the available lower-cost biomass resources, through high transport biofuel subsidies, is allocated to biofuel production, conventional biomass ST CHP is, due to its high heat efficiency, relatively more competitive compared to BIGCC CHP than in a situation without biofuel production. The results are obtained even though an 'unlimited' supply of slightly more expensive imported biomass pellets is included in the model. This means that a higher production of transport biofuels can potentially be linked to a lower generation of biomass-based electricity. If biomass-based electricity generation is replaced by coal-based electricity generation, which to some extent could be argued to constitute the marginal production in the Nordic electricity system, the climate benefits of transport biofuels are small [14].

5.07.4.2 Scale Effects of Biomass CHP

There are a number of factors governing the optimal size and distribution of biomass CHP plants in a system with at least some degree of decentralization (without the possibilities for decentralized generation it is of course not even possible to discuss large- vs. small-scale and, further, as mentioned, heat markets are always to at least some, though normally to a large, extent decentralized). In general terms, some factors improve with increased plant scale, while other factors do not. For biomass CHP, biomass-to-electricity conversion efficiencies and specific plant costs, that is, costs per output, generally belong to the first category; conversion efficiencies increase with plant scale and costs per output decrease. To the category of factors that deteriorate with larger scale belong different types of distribution costs, both distribution of the biomass feedstock to the plant and distribution of the plant outputs, that is, heat and electricity. As mentioned, while electricity can be distributed long distances without severe cost increases, many biomass resources are still local in their character, either due to difficulties in transportation or due to undeveloped biomass markets, and this has constrained the size of biomass plants. Since it is likely that biomass markets will develop strongly in the not too distant future, there is thus also a time aspect to this. It should also be noted that the different scale effects depend on the type of biomass CHP considered, such as ST CHP or BIGCC CHP.

A CHP plant scale optimization will depend on the valuation of waste heat; if maximum plant resource efficiency is considered, all waste heat should be utilized when this is possible, that is, the heat demand in a district heat system will, in such case, determine the maximum operation time of the plant. However, if the resource efficiency of a higher system level instead is used as the measure, there might be good reasons to run a highly efficient biomass CHP plant for a longer period of time than there is a heat demand in order to substitute for power generation from less efficient (or more polluting) plants elsewhere in the system. In practical operation, economical considerations will of course determine the operation and thus also biomass cost and revenues from sales of secondary energy carriers will eventually be critical parameters.

The energy infrastructure is a further factor that can influence the large- versus small-scale discussion. For instance, regarding the power grid, decentralized options might require costly grid extensions, but on the other hand, there are arguments for a more dispersed power generation since this might reduce the risk of power failures in certain areas where the grid is weaker. The natural gas infrastructure plays a role for large- versus small-scale options through the competition between natural gas and biomass on the heat markets, but also when biomass gasification based polygeneration plants with multiple products (heat, electricity, transport fuel, etc.) are concerned. If SNG is one of the products of such plants, the access to a large market through connection with a natural gas grid improves robustness as well as the possibility for optimization of revenues.

Interactions with the transportation sector might also play a role in influencing the scale of future biomass CHP. This is particularly the case in a country like Sweden, where biogas, produced locally through digestion of sewage sludge and/or agricultural waste, to high degree is used as a transportation fuel and less for generation of heat and electricity in CHP plants, and where there is no national gas grid. In most other European countries, such locally produced biogas is often used in small-scale CHP plants or fed into the natural gas grid. If there were no traditions and subsidies for use of gas in the transportation sector in areas with no national gas grid, it would thus be a stronger incentive for the deployment of small-scale CHP. Generally, dependent on applied energy policies, it might be more advantageous to invest in biorefineries for production of biofuels for the transport market, than to invest in biomass CHP. Furthermore, if the waste heat generated from these plants is delivered to local heat markets, a certain share of the heat markets will be utilized and somewhat less room will be left for CHP. Since the heat output of biorefineries optimized for transport fuel production is relatively small compared to the biomass input, also large-scale biorefineries could be located in connection to comparably small-sized district heating systems and still make use of economies of scale. This could also allow for the utilization of biomass resources, such as forest residues, close to its source and thus keep down the requirements for transport of unrefined biomass. Large-scale biomass CHP, with potentially high electrical efficiency, is, on the other hand, naturally restricted to larger size district heating systems with high heat demands.

Due to the different properties of conventional biomass CHP, on the one hand, and BIGCC CHP, on the other hand, the relative economical and environmental performance of the technologies in regard to different scales is not obvious. Although the outcomes are related to site-specific conditions regarding biomass and heat markets and general characteristics of the surrounding energy system, a further understanding of factors involved is helped by quantitative examples. A study on this subject has been performed by Dornburg and Faaij in 2001. More specifically, the study investigates the efficiency and economy of wood-fired biomass energy technologies, including heat boilers, ST plants, and BIGCC plants (both condensing and CHP) with focus on the effects of scale.

Dornburg and Faaij show that scale effects related to biomass energy systems are significant. At the thermal input scale range considered (0–300 MW_{th-inp}), larger scale improves the environmental performance, measured as relative fossil energy savings, of the studied energy technologies. In other words, the higher plant conversion efficiencies achievable with larger scales outweigh the higher energy use of logistics as well as the increased losses of heat distribution also linked to larger scales. In the study, BIGCC plants give the highest savings of fossil energy among the tested options, that is, higher than different types of biomass ST plants and heat plants. Furthermore, CHP is in this respect found to be more effective than the corresponding condensing, power only options. Regarding the economic indicators studied, it is found that the total costs per unit primary fossil energy savings for some technologies, including BIGCC CHP, decrease for the whole scale range studied, while other technologies, including conventional biomass ST CHP and heat plants, show a cost minimum at medium scales and then rising costs as fuel logistics and heat distribution increases their impact on total costs. The study concludes that combustion technologies can neither compete with respect to economical nor energetic performance with studied gasification technologies in the scale range of 10–200 $MW_{th-input}$. However, the caveat is given that gasification technologies (BIGCC) are still in the demonstration stage and it is not certain that the projected performances and costs used in the analysis will ever be realized [13]. Even if the study dates a few years back, this caveat seems to be appropriate still.

5.07.5 Concluding Remarks

CHP generation is generally considered a measure to increase the overall efficiency of energy systems. The basic advantage of CHP is that joint production of heat and power requires considerably less fuel input than if the two outputs were to be produced in separate plants. Biomass CHP represents thus an alternative for the combination of an efficient energy technology and a renewable, climate-neutral fuel. In this chapter, system aspects of bioenergy systems including CHP has been analyzed and discussed. This section summarizes some main insights and reflections.

While biomass CHP based on direct combustion and steam cycle is the dominant biomass CHP technology of today, gasification-based technologies, such as BIGCC CHP, might become more influential in the future. The basic benefit of gasification-based CHP technologies is the possibility of a higher biomass-to-electricity conversion efficiency than conventional options. Many studies suggest that when the BIGCC technology has reached maturity, it will be a cost-competitive option and have an advantageous environmental performance. However, so far the technology has suffered from too high technology costs to enable a larger scale deployment. As often with new technologies, the willingness for actors to take on the learning costs and/or the possibilities to find niche markets are thus essential. Given the potential benefits, the incentives for further development and cost reduction from a societal perspective appear high.

In a situation with undeveloped biomass markets and high costs of biomass distribution, biomass-based heat generation is to a high degree dependent on locally available resources. This can lead to inefficient technology choices from the perspective of a higher system level; for instance, high electrical efficiencies can be disfavored over high heat efficiencies. It is, however, likely that biomass markets will develop and that biomass (in the same way as other feedstock options) to a higher degree will be traded over longer distances. This trend is already observed; for instance, wood pellets are today transported to Europe from Canada. Advances in pretreatment methods such as torrefaction and pyrolysis, which increase the energy density and thus lower transportation costs, can furthermore accelerate such development.

Better opportunities for low-cost biomass transport also benefit large-scale biomass CHP plants. With larger scales, the efficiency of biomass CHP plants generally increases while, at the same time, the specific investment cost decreases. Naturally, large CHP plants do, however, also require large heat demands. Heat connections between different district heating systems are one way of increasing the opportunities for large-scale plants, although the costs involved in such expansions can be significant.

Although biomass can be traded globally, it is important to acknowledge that if future stringent greenhouse gas emission constraints are applied on a global scale, biomass will be a constrained resource. Thus, even if biomass in a closed system can be considered climate neutral, not all kinds of biomass use are equally advantageous from a systems perspective; different allocations of biomass resources are linked to different levels of environmental and economical efficiency. In energy systems analyses looking forward in time, this should be considered, in principle, regardless of studied system level (such as plant level, the global energy system, etc.). It should be noted that the conclusions regarding environmental performance of a specific biomass application will differ radically depending on whether the biomass use is assumed to affect other alternative biomass uses or whether the increased demand is assumed to be met by an increased biomass supply.

Connected to the prospect of a future situation in which biomass resources are scarce, and thus cannot be used for all purposes without limits, the question arises in what sectors and for what purposes a limited amount of biomass should be used. The main alternatives are basically either to use the biomass for heat and power generation in stationary energy systems or to convert the biomass to liquid or gaseous fuels for use in the transportation sector. Certainly, a mixture of these options is the most likely future scenario since local and regional circumstances and incentives will favor different solutions. Even so, identifying drivers for one or the other option can be useful for achieving an understanding of general tendencies. Although subject to a number of uncertainties, many studies come to the conclusion that biomass is used more effectively in heat and power production than as transport biofuels. The basic reason for this is connected to the losses associated with conversion of biomass to liquid or gaseous fuels suitable for vehicles. On the other hand, the willingness to pay for fuel is very high in the transportation sector, and high oil prices can lead to an increased deployment of the conversion of solid fuels to transport fuels. However, in a future with growing energy service demands as well as high ambitions regarding greenhouse gas emission abatement, the pressure on efficient biomass utilization will be high, and so will the demand for high exergy energy carriers such as electricity. In this context, the properties of biomass CHP in general and of biomass CHP options with high electrical efficiency in particular seem advantageous.

References

[1] IEA (2007) *IEA Energy Technology Essentials: Biomass for Power Generation and CHP.* Paris, Cedex, France: OECD/IEA.
[2] European Parliament and the Council (2004) European parliament and the council, directive 2004/8/EC of the European parliament and of the council on the promotion of cogeneration based on a useful heat demand in the internal energy market and amending directive 92/42/EEC. *Official Journal of the European Union* L 52: 50–60.
[3] European Commission (EC) (2008) *European Commission (EC) Communication from the Commission: Energy Efficiency: Delivering the 20% Target, COM (2008) 772 Final.* Brussels, Belgium: European Commission.
[4] Verbruggen A (1992) Combined heat and power: A real alternative when carefully implemented. *Energy Policy* 20: 884–892.
[5] Verbruggen A (2008) The merit of cogeneration: Measuring and rewarding performance. *Energy Policy* 36: 3069–3076.
[6] Bauen A, Berndes G, Junginger M, et al. (2009) Bioenergy – A sustainable and reliable energy source. *Main Report.* Paris, France: IEA Bioenergy.
[7] Hansson H, Larsson S-E, Nyström O, et al. (2007) El från nya anläggningar 2007. Stockholm, Sweden: Elforsk.
[8] Fahlén E and Ahlgren EO (2009) Assessment of integration of different biomass gasification alternatives in a district-heating system. *Energy* 34: 2184–2195.
[9] Marbe Å, Harvey S, and Berntsson T (2004) Biofuel gasification combined heat and power – New implementation opportunities resulting from combined supply of process steam and district heating. *Energy* 29: 1117–1137.
[10] Knutsson D, Werner S, and Ahlgren EO (2006) Combined heat and power in the Swedish district heating sector – Impact of green certificates and CO_2 trading on new investments. *Energy Policy* 34: 3942–3952.
[11] Axelsson E, Harvey S, and Berntsson T (2009) A tool for creating energy market scenarios for evaluation of investments in energy intensive industry. *Energy* 34: 2069–2074.
[12] Grahn M, Azar C, Williander MI et al. (2009) Fuel and vehicle technology choices for passenger vehicles in achieving stringent CO_2 targets: Connections between transportation and other energy sectors. *Environmental Science and Technology* 43: 3365–3371.
[13] Dornburg V and Faaij APC (2001) Efficiency and economy of wood-fired biomass energy systems in relation to scale regarding heat and power generation using combustion and gasification technologies. *Biomass and Bioenergy* 21: 91–108.
[14] Börjesson M and Ahlgren EO (2010) Biomass gasification in cost-optimized district heating systems – A regional modelling analysis. *Energy Policy* 38: 168–180.
[15] Difs K, Wetterlund E, Trygg L, and Söderström M (2010) Biomass gasification opportunities in a district heating system. *Biomass and Bioenergy* 34: 637–651.

Relevant Websites

http://www.alholmenskraft.com – The Alholmen Kraft plant
http://www.soderenergi.se – The Igelsta plant

5.08 Ethics of Biofuel Production

I Waller, FiveBarGate Consultants Ltd, Cleveland, UK

© 2012 Elsevier Ltd.

5.08.1	Introduction	99
5.08.2	A Model for Sustainability Management Systems	99
5.08.3	RTFO	103
5.08.4	RED	103
5.08.5	ISCC	104
5.08.6	RSB	104
5.08.7	RSPO	104
5.08.8	RTRS	105
5.08.9	CEN Standard on Biomass for Transport Biofuels	105
5.08.10	ISO Standard on Biomass for Energy	105
5.08.11	Various Standards in the Retail Sector	106
5.08.12	International Labor Laws	106
5.08.13	Indirect Land Use Change	107
5.08.14	Conclusions	107
References		107

5.08.1 Introduction

The issue of ethical aspects of biofuels production requires consideration of multiple and varied factors. These include the impact of a biofuels production pathway on the stakeholders affected by the supply chain and the environment within which the supply chain operates.

The scope of influence of any biofuels supply chain has effectively been drawn wider and wider as debate on the extent of actual and potential impacts develops. For example, impact assessment is considered at local level, around a biofuels production pathway in terms of emissions to water sources or use of energy to dry crops or producing a fuel. Discussion has however also considered global impacts as the consideration of land use change practices turns from direct impacts of clearing land to grow a crop to the potential indirect effects of using crops from one unit of land for biofuels and therefore having to clear further forest land in order to produce sufficient crop for other uses.

These factors are generally considered within a framework of sustainability management and reporting. Sustainability is itself widely defined. However, at a very high and conceptually simple level with regard to biofuels, it can be considered as delivering fuels today in a way that does not undermine our planet's future.

The breadth of this definition requires further development in order to make it useful and provide rigorous and appropriate measures that can help resolve the potential direct and indirect impacts of biofuels production. Working toward more useful definitions of sustainability has been the subject of intense activity in the biofuels sector over recent years.

A framework for evidence of sustainability management systems may be drawn from a number of regulations and standards in existence or in development. Many of these are European regulations or standards. It is generally recognized that European policy and markets are well ahead of other regional policy and industrial practice with regard to sustainability assurance. This stems from concerns raised through the late twentieth century relating to the application of genetically modified (GM) technology within human food supply chains.

This chapter begins by proposing a model for sustainability management systems in general. It then goes on to examine eight specific sustainability standards that have been used in various ways in the biofuels sector, drawing out similarities and differences in emphasis. The chapter concludes by looking at a number of voluntary standards used in the retail sector, some relevant aspects of international labor laws, and the impact of indirect land use change (iLUC) on biofuels sustainability.

5.08.2 A Model for Sustainability Management Systems

In general, sustainability management systems are defined at a national or regional policy or regulatory level in order that societal concerns are managed consistently. This approach has developed following growing understanding of society's impact on the environment and a desire to reduce the impact of road transport on global warming. Occasionally, these management systems are more international in nature, developed from multistakeholder or environmental groups. However, all these systems have become more involved and detailed in nature as the requirements to provide assurances regarding the potential direct and indirect impacts have surfaced.

A generic model of a sustainability management system is illustrated in Figure 1, with the first step being to establish standards.

100 Issues, Constraints & Limitations

Figure 1 A generic model for a sustainability management system.

This approach has been taken in a number of regions, starting with the United Kingdom in developing the Renewable Transport Fuel Obligation (RTFO). **Figure 2** provides some more detail on the RTFO as developed with the Low Carbon Vehicle Partnership.

The RTFO approach to sustainability management developed from the original European Biofuels Directive, which was later superseded by the Renewable Energy Directive (RED). The RED sets a reporting standard, defining biofuel properties according to sustainability criteria and then requiring European Community Member States to gradually introduce more and more biofuels meeting this standard into the transport fuel pool.

This type of approach to sustainability management has developed a range of standards. The standards are generally constructed from a top-down approach to concepts, married with a bottom-up approach which considers how to find evidence that helps make the concepts measurable. **Figure 3** illustrates this generic model for construction of standards.

This generic model allows high-level principles to be developed into detailed indicators of performance through criteria developed for each principle. The kinds of principles generally considered are broadly shown in **Figure 4**.

Looking across a range of sustainability standards that have been developed or adapted for biofuels, a pattern begins to emerge as illustrated in **Figure 5**.

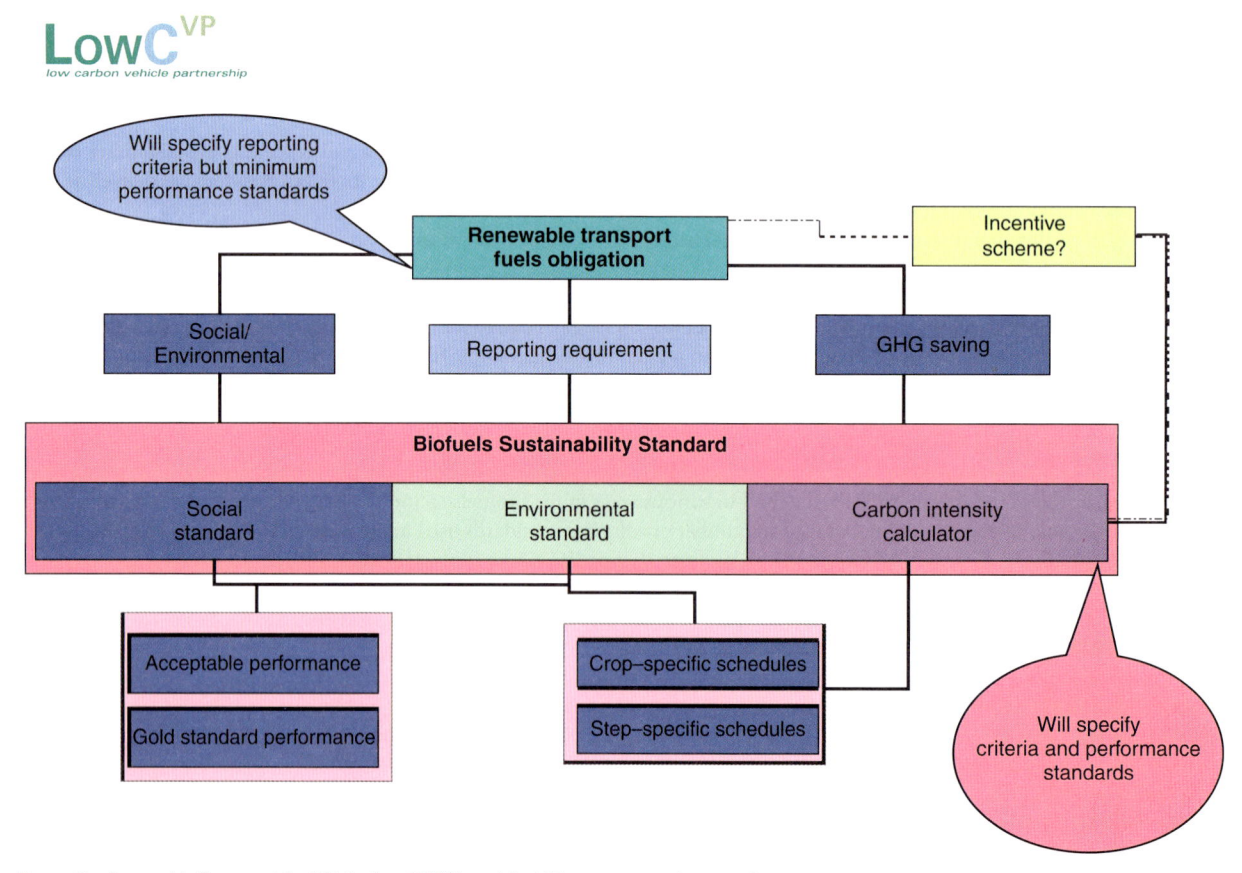

Figure 2 Renewable Transport Fuel Obligation (RTFO) sustainability management approach.

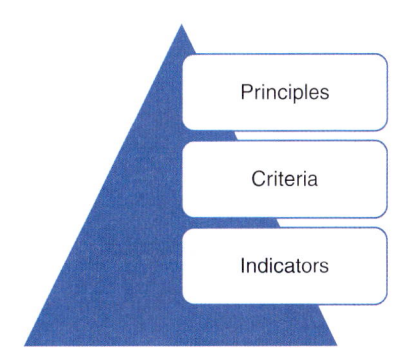

Figure 3 Generic model for construction of standards.

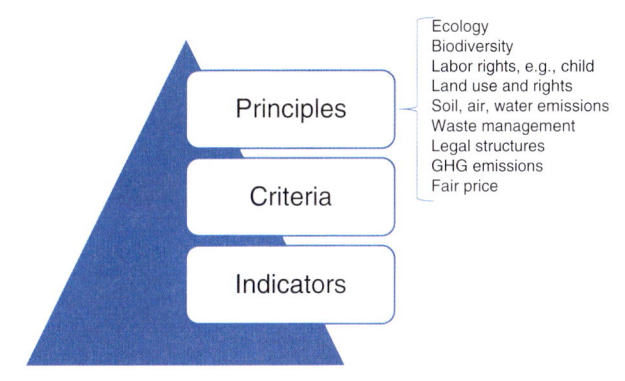

Figure 4 Typical principles included within sustainability standards.

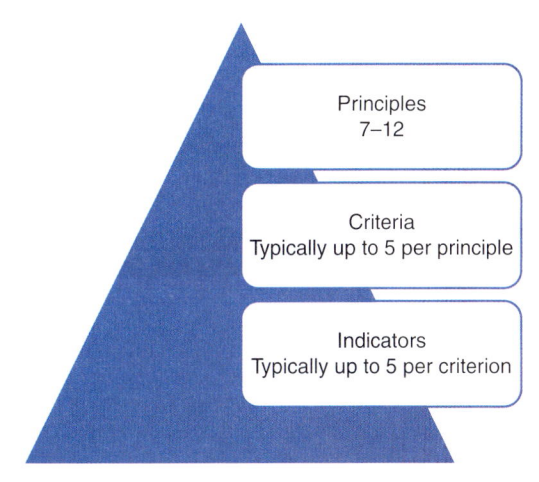

Figure 5 Typical structure observed across a range of sustainability standards.

This kind of structure enables verification, as the indicators are items that a suitably qualified and experienced auditor can seek objective evidence for (see **Figure 6**).

The requirement for third-party verification raises a number of questions and challenges for supply chains. Generally, this verification is required at the point that a biofuel is placed into the market. However, in order to demonstrate compliance with the standard, the party placing the fuel into the market must have knowledge of the land use history relating to the soil in which the biomass from which the fuel was derived was grown. Third-party verification must be able to demonstrate product provenance all the way back to the soil.

This gives rise to the concept of a chain of custody, which passes ownership of different products or commodities along a supply chain, from soil to fuel (see **Figure 7**).

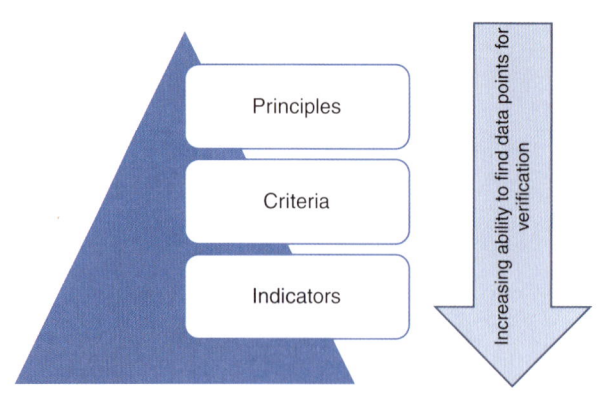

Figure 6 Approach to verification in an auditing context.

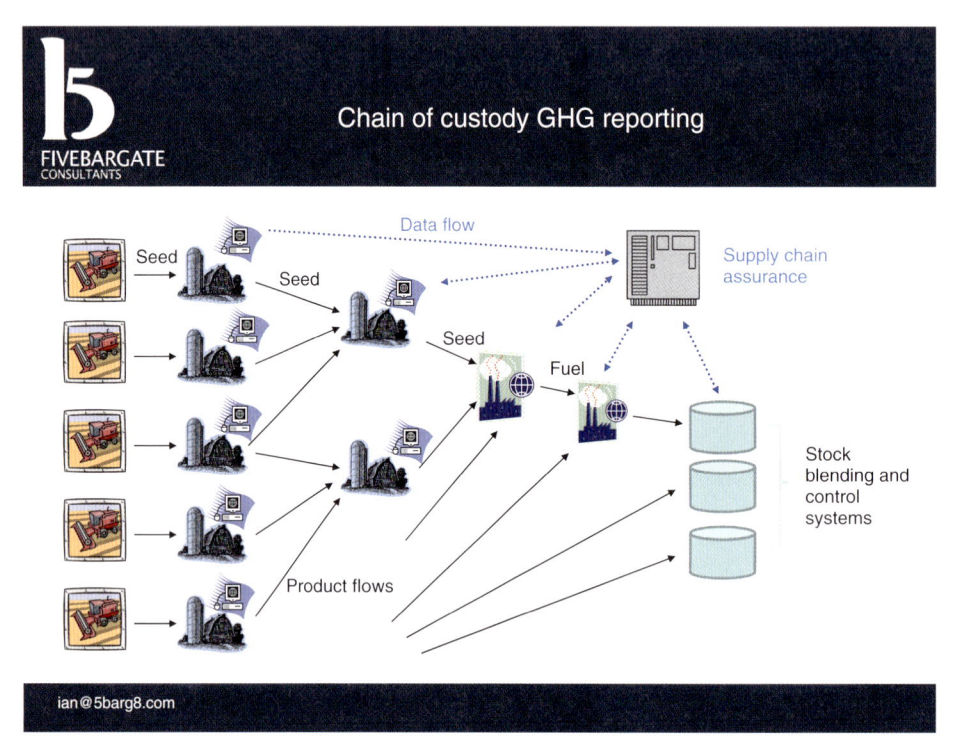

Figure 7 'Chain of custody' greenhouse gas reporting.

This chain of custody must enable a third party to assess information transmitted along the chain of custody and information retained within the chain of custody in order to demonstrate that claims made relating to the finished fuel can be justified with objective evidence.

These chains of custody may be very long. For example, a land owner A may grow a crop and harvest it. They may then sell their crop to a trader B, who in turn aggregates this crop with other similar crops and sells the total to another trader C, who further aggregates crops and then sells to a further trader D before the crop arrives with a biofuels producer E, who is buying crops from multiple aggregated sources. The biofuel producer may sell their product to a trading partner F, who subsequently sells the biofuels to a further trader G, who blends the biofuels with other biofuels and sells a blend onto a further trader H. This trader then finally sells to a party I, who mixes the biofuels with fossil fuel and sells this blended fuel to a party J, who uses it as transport fuel. Generally it is the final party, J, who has to demonstrate compliance with a standard. Party J in this example is 10 steps away from the soil where the crop was grown but needs to have objective evidence of the sustainability characteristics of the land in which the crop was grown on in order for the biofuels to have sound provenance and qualify as sustainable biofuels. Such a supply chain would not be uncommon, given the global trade in agricultural commodities and fuels.

The following sections review a range of relevant standards, examining the linkages between principles, criteria, and indicators.

5.08.3 RTFO

RTFO is the policy that has set the precedent within bioenergy sectors for carbon and sustainability (C&S) reporting of bio-based energy vectors [1]. This policy was developed during the early years of the twenty-first century in response to the European biofuels policy and came into force in April 2009. In addition to implementing the EU biofuels policy, the RTFO sets a framework for reporting the provenance of the biofuels placed on the market and sets targets for both the level of sustainability achieved and the transparency of the information made available.

The RTFO approach to C&S reporting was developed by adopting a multistakeholder approach to setting a benchmarking standard against which all biofuels can be measured. The standard developed included a greenhouse gas (GHG) assessment methodology as well as environmental and social criteria indicators. The GHG methodology is not considered here as it is addressed elsewhere in this volume. The environmental and social criteria and indicators were set into a framework that was developed by drawing consistent themes from multiple existing similar standards. This approach created a 'standard of standards', or meta-standard, against which all standards can be benchmarked. The RTFO meta-standard has retained its industry leading profile as it has been revised in order to enable comparison with a broader set of standards.

The meta-standard considers seven broad principles as listed in Table 1.

Up to the time the RTFO was introduced, energy markets enabled the use of biomass in energy applications, such as power and transport, but did not require the power or transport sectors to be accountable for the broader environmental impact of the supply chains they engage with. This arguably led to some potential unintended consequences associated with the opportunity for suppliers of biomass-based feedstocks to indirectly create consequential environmental harm.

The example often quoted is the use of palm-based products in energy, where the rate of expansion of palm forests may have caused adverse destruction of long-established forests which have retained high carbon stocks and supported highly biodiverse ecosystems. Whether this is the case is unclear, as protagonists argue that the palm sector is growing rapidly due to continuing demand for palm oil for food and oleochemical applications. However, what is clear is the wide-ranging press opposition to the RTFO biofuels promotion policy that was instigated by single interest groups working in partnership to influence decision makers.

5.08.4 RED

The RED has developed a wide response to the concerns raised in response to the development of the RTFO C&S reporting framework [2]. This is particularly evident in the definition of a liquid biofuel. A series of requirements relating to the use of biofuels is defined within Articles 17 and 18 of the Directive.

Article 17 provides sustainability characteristics of a biofuel as properties of the fuel itself.

- The fuel properties shall
  - exclude wastes and residues derived from everything except agriculture, aquaculture, fisheries, and forestry
  - have a minimum GHG saving of at least 35%, rising to 50% and then 60%
  - not come from land of high biodiversity, including
    - primary forest
    - designated areas for
      - nature protection
      - species protection
    - highly biodiverse grassland
    - where the land use is classified from January 2008
  - not come from land of high carbon stock, including
    - wetland
    - continuous forest
    - woodland of more than 1 ha in size with average tree height greater than 5 m

Table 1 The seven broad principles in the RTFO meta-standard

Biomass production will not destroy or damage large above- or belowground carbon stocks
Biomass production will not lead to the destruction of or damage to high-biodiversity areas
Biomass production does not lead to soil degradation
Biomass production does not lead to the contamination or depletion of water sources
Biomass production does not lead to air pollution
Biomass production does not adversely affect workers' rights and working relationships
Biomass production does not adversely affect existing land rights and community relations

RTFO, Renewable Transport Fuel Obligation.

- where the land use is classified from January 2008
- peatland as defined in January 2008
– Where derived from within the European Community the fuel must be demonstrably grown according to EU common agricultural policy environmental protection standards and the fuel must be shown to deliver at least a default GHG emission reduction when assessed at a regional level. The region is defined according to a European Union National Unit of Territory level 2.

Article 18 then requires all these properties to be assured by third-party verification. Parties providing third-party assurance must be able to demonstrate independence from the supply chain and demonstrate suitable organizational and individual qualifications and experience.

The RED allows any party to develop a scheme of sustainability assurance that may seek approval by the European Commission. Such a voluntary scheme, once approved, must be accepted by all parties within the European Union. There are no approved schemes at the time of writing.

5.08.5 ISCC

The International Sustainability & Carbon Certification (ISCC) System has developed in response to the RED [3]. It is intended to deliver all the requirements of the RED, including verification, by providing assurance at each stage of the supply chain. ISCC has applied for recognition as a voluntary scheme.

In order to demonstrate ISCC compliance, a member company must pay fees to ISCC and undergo an audit of the management systems they have in place, to demonstrate that they meet the requirements of ISCC. Audits are provided by audit companies recognized by ISCC. The requirements of the management systems are set out in detailed documents, covering requirements for data capture and data flow.

5.08.6 RSB

Roundtable on Sustainable Biofuels (RSB) was established with broad stakeholder involvement including environmental activists [4]. The RSB standard offers a set of principles and a verification structure. The standard offers 12 principles as listed in **Table 2**.

5.08.7 RSPO

The Roundtable on Sustainable Palm Oil (RSPO) is a voluntary standard established by parties trading palm oil [5]. RSPO originally had seven principles, which have developed to the eight principles defined in **Table 3**.

Governance of the RSPO is via membership and active contribution to standard setting. Membership includes environmental activists, who tend to have shown deep concern for biodiversity as well as human rights.

Table 2 The 12 principles in the RSB standard

Legality	Biofuels operations shall follow all applicable laws and regulations
Planning, monitoring, and continuous improvement	Sustainable biofuel operations shall be planned, implemented, and continuously improved through open, transparent, and consultative impact assessment and management process and an economic viability analysis
GHG emissions	Biofuels shall contribute to climate change mitigation by significantly reducing life-cycle GHG emissions as compared to fossil fuels
Human and labor rights	Biofuel operations shall not violate human rights or labor rights, and shall promote decent work and the well-being of others
Rural and social development	In regions of poverty, biofuels operations shall contribute to the social and economic development of local, rural, and indigenous people and communities
Local food security	Biofuel operation shall ensure the human right to adequate food and improve food security in insecure regions
Conservation	Biofuel operations shall avoid negative impacts on biodiversity, ecosystems, and conservation principles
Soil	Biofuel operations shall implement practices that seek to reverse soil degradation and/or maintain soil health
Water	Biofuel operations shall maintain or enhance the quality and quantity of surface water and groundwater resources and respect prior or customary water rights
Air	Air pollution from biofuels operations shall be minimized along the supply chain
Use of technology, inputs, and management of waste	The use of technologies in biofuels operations shall seek to maximize production efficiency and social and environmental performance and minimize the risk of damage to the environment and people
Land rights	Biofuel operations shall respect land rights and land use rights

GHG, greenhouse gas; RSB, Roundtable on Sustainable Biofuels.

Table 3 The eight principles in the RSPO standard

No.	Principle
1.	Commitment to transparency
2.	Compliance with applicable laws and regulations
3.	Commitment to long-term economic and financial viability
4.	Use of appropriate best practice by growers and millers
5.	Environmental responsibility and conservation of natural resources and biodiversity
6.	Responsible consideration of employees and individuals and communities affected by growers and mills
7.	Responsible development of new plantings
8.	Commitment to continuous improvement in key areas of activity

RSPO, Roundtable on Sustainable Palm Oil.

5.08.8 RTRS

The Round Table on Responsible Soy (RTRS) covers five broad principles as listed in Table 4 [6].

The RTRS structure is therefore similar to other standards, offering parties the opportunity to be assured against RTRS and subsequently to offer RTRS-assured product to market. The standard has been established over many years of stakeholder engagement including environmental activists.

5.08.9 CEN Standard on Biomass for Transport Biofuels

The EN standard-setting body began work on developing a supply chain assurance standard for all biomass-based energy vectors in parallel with development of the RED [7]. However, as the CEN process is a multistakeholder, multination process that seeks consensus between industry bodies, the committee structure was unable to develop appropriate standards in a time frame that met with the requirements of the RED. Therefore, the CEN process has now reduced the scope of its efforts to consider bioliquids only, in order to feed into the RED requirements where further clarification is required by industry and Member States in order to deliver the RED.

The CEN process initially developed a workgroup approach with the following broad working areas: nomenclature; GHG accounting methodology; environmental impacts; social impacts; chain of custody assurance; indirect effects. Work continues in the areas of environmental impacts and chain of custody assurance.

Table 5 lists some of the factors included in the CEN process.

5.08.10 ISO Standard on Biomass for Energy

During 2009, the broader international community recognized the importance of developing broad-based carbon and sustainability assurance standards [8]. This has developed into an agreement to produce an international standard on these issues via ISO (International Organization for Standardization). The high-level work for this global standard-setting process has not fully

Table 4 RTRS principles

Responsible community relations
Legal compliance and good business practice
Good agricultural practice
Responsible labor conditions
Environmental responsibility

RTRS, Round Table on Responsible Soy.

Table 5 Some factors considered in the CEN process

Does the biomass come from a region that has defined protection, including grassland, peatland, or other registered nature protection/conservation area since January 2008?
Does the biomass come from a region that has terrestrial or aquatic biodiversity value?
Does the biomass come from a region that has a management plan in place to manage the impact on the environment? This includes impacts on soil, water, and air and considers nutrient management and agricultural practice

commenced at the time of writing. However, it is likely to build on the early work of the CEN looking at biomass for energy in the broadest sense and potentially may build on the CEN workgroup structure.

The timescale for an ISO PC248 process is likely to conclude in a standard being accepted in the time frame from 2015 to 2020, which is within the time frame of the RED.

5.08.11 Various Standards in the Retail Sector

There are a number of voluntary standards in the retail sector. These include the Rainforest Alliance standard [9], Traidcraft [10], Fairtrade [11], Linking Environment and Farming (LEAF) [12], Little Red Tractor mark [13], and the Forestry Stewardship Council (FSC) mark [14]. These standards generally allow a retail product to carry an approved mark or label, once the supply chain has been reviewed for conformity assessment with the managing agent's standard requirements. Since they are already in use for other products, they provide a quick route to product assurance for biofuels and their feedstocks.

Some of these standards cover environmental sustainability, while others cover social aspects of sustainability. The FSC mark for forestry products defines broad principles of compliance with environmental and social factors (see Table 6). These again fit very well with the RTFO meta-standard.

The LEAF mark is another well-developed, structured, and detailed standard, this time associated with agricultural production. The LEAF mark covers the principles listed in Table 7. Again, there is a strong fit with the RTFO meta-standard.

Some of these standards focus more on human capital, such as land and labor rights and workforce needs. Specific social supply chain requirements found here tend to align with those of the RTFO and the RED, with the social requirements offering standards guidance in relation to the principles of paying a fair price to cover costs of production, paying a premium that allows investment in future production, and entering long-term contracts to provide stability.

5.08.12 International Labor Laws

The International Labour Organization defines a series of standards aimed at improving the rights, livelihoods, security, and opportunities of people, families, and communities around the world. Since 1919, the International Labour Organization has maintained and developed a system of international labor standards aimed at promoting opportunities for women and men to obtain decent and productive work, in conditions of freedom, equity, security, and dignity. In today's globalized economy, international labor standards is an essential component in the international framework for ensuring that the growth of the global economy provides benefits to all. The list of standards developed is detailed and complex (see Table 8).

These standards offer a much more detailed structure than the RTFO.

Table 6 FSC compliance principles (environmental and social)

Compliance with laws and FSC principles
Tenure and use rights and responsibilities
Indigenous peoples' rights
Community relations and worker's rights
Benefits from the forest
Environmental impact
Management plan
Monitoring and assessment
Maintenance of high conservation value forests
Plantations

FCS, Forestry Stewardship Council.

Table 7 LEAF principles

Organization and planning – integrated farm management
Soil management and crop nutrition
Crop protection
Pollution control and waste management
Energy and water efficiency
Wildlife and landscape
Animal husbandry and the environment

LEAF, Linking Environment and Farming.

Table 8 Standards developed by the International Labour Organization

Freedom of association, collective bargaining, and industrial relations
Forced labor
Elimination of child labor and protection of children and young persons
Equality of opportunity and treatment
Tripartite consultation
Labor administration and inspection
Employment policy and promotion
Vocational guidance and training
Employment security
Wages
Working time
Occupational safety and health
Social security
Maternity protection
Social policy
Migrant workers
Seafarers
Fishermen
Dockworkers
Indigenous and tribal peoples
Specific categories of workers
Final articles conventions

5.08.13 Indirect Land Use Change

The final aspects to consider with regard to biofuels supply chains are captured within the thinking relating to iLUC. Providing useful methods for objectively assessing indirect effects and their impact has proven to be very difficult. Recent work has developed from economic analysis published by Searchinger et al. [15]. Searchinger et al. postulated that biofuels use drives land use change by creating additional demand. There has been a flurry of academic, political, and press activity following this work. The Gallagher [16] review aimed to build on Searchinger et al.'s work by calling for scientific and technical submissions to consider indirect effects. This led to a great deal of work within the European Community [17]. Further work has been developed by the Low Carbon Vehicle Partnership [18] also.

In general, there is consensus that there may be indirect effects of creating additional demand for products of agricultural production, including the potential for this demand to lead to land use change. However, the supply chain mechanisms and influence through which this additional demand may create this land use change are varied and complex. Some aspects of biofuels use may have created additional demand for land use. Some aspects of biofuels use may reduce demand for land use. The complex nature of the supply chains therefore makes agreement and resolution of the underlying science base complicated.

What is generally agreed is that land use demand is created by a broad set of factors, including biofuels, but more widely associated with other demands, such as food and materials. It is also generally agreed that if all land-based sectors were to assess the direct impacts of their operations on the environment, in a similar way to the many and varied biofuels sustainability standards, then indirect effects might well be eliminated. To put it another way, every indirect impact is a direct impact from another land-based sector.

5.08.14 Conclusions

The factors impacting upon biofuels sustainability are many and diverse. There is broad agreement on the high-level principles that should apply to sustainable biofuels production, with signs of increasing convergence. Because of the range of possible feedstocks and the length and complexity of supply chains, several different standards have been developed. They draw to varying extents on existing, tried-and-tested assurance mechanisms. The ultimate requirement is for verifiable, auditable data that assure regulators that fuels sold comply with evolving sustainable production principles. A generic model linking those high-level principles to measurable, auditable data has been proposed here and exemplified with reference to existing approaches and some topical developments.

References

[1] http://www.renewablefuelsagency.gov.uk/abouttherfa
[2] Directive 2009/28/EC of the European parliament and of the council of 23 April 2009 on the promotion of the use of energy from renewable sources and amending and subsequently repealing Directives 2001/77/EC and 2003/30/EC.

[3] http://www.iscc-system.org/
[4] http://rsb.epfl.ch/
[5] http://www.rspo.org/?q=page/9
[6] http://www.responsiblesoy.org/
[7] http://www.cen.eu/cen/Sectors/TechnicalCommitteesWorkshops/CENTechnicalCommittees/Pages/TCStruc.aspx?param=648007&title=CEN/TC%20383
[8] http://www.iso.org/iso/pressrelease.htm?refid=Ref1282
[9] http://www.rainforest-alliance.org/
[10] http://www.traidcraft.co.uk/
[11] http://www.fairtrade.org.uk/
[12] http://www.leafuk.org/leaf/home.eb
[13] http://www.redtractor.org.uk/site/REDT/Templates/Home.aspx?pageid=1&cc=GB
[14] http://www.fsc-uk.org/
[15] Searchinger T, Heimlich R, Houghton RA, *et al.* (2008) Use of U.S. croplands for biofuels increases greenhouse gases through emissions from land-use change. *Science* 319(5867): 1238–1240, DOI: 10.1126/science.1151861.
[16] http://www.renewablefuelsagency.gov.uk/reportsandpublications/reviewoftheindirecteffectsofbiofuels
[17] http://ec.europa.eu/energy/renewables/biofuels/land_use_change_en.htm
[18] FWG-p-11-02.

5.09 Life Cycle Analysis Perspective on Greenhouse Gas Savings

N Mortimer, North Energy Associates Ltd, Sheffield, UK

© 2012 Elsevier Ltd. All rights reserved.

5.09.1	Biofuel Potential	109
5.09.2	Life Cycle Assessment	110
5.09.3	Net Energy Balances for Biofuels	114
5.09.4	Greenhouse Gas Emissions Results	115
5.09.5	Land Use Change	117
5.09.6	Direct Land Use Change	117
5.09.7	Indirect Land Use Change	120
5.09.8	Soil Nitrous Oxide Emissions	121
5.09.9	Sources of Processing Energy	123
5.09.10	Coproducts	126
5.09.11	Future Biofuel Technologies	127
5.09.12	Conclusions and Recommendations	130
References		130

Glossary

Biofuels Any liquid or gaseous fuel that can be derived from organic material to replace, directly or indirectly, conventional transport fuels.

Biomass feedstocks Any source of organic material that is used to provide products or services, such as energy.

Life cycle assessment (LCA) A technique for evaluating the total natural resource and environmental impacts of a product or service over its defined life cycle.

Attributional life cycle assessment Evaluation of natural resource and environmental impacts of an activity in terms of their allocation to the economic operators of that activity mainly for regulatory purposes.

Consequential life cycle assessment Evaluation of the global natural resource and environmental impacts of an activity mainly for policy analysis purposes.

Primary energy Energy derived from depletable resources such as fossil and nuclear fuels.

Greenhouse gas (GHG) emissions A collection of gases, including carbon dioxide, methane, and nitrous oxide that cause global warming and global climate change.

System boundaries An imaginary line drawn around an activity under investigation by life cycle assessment which specifies the extent of analysis of natural resource and environmental impacts associated with the main activity.

Reference system An activity which, in the context of life cycle assessment, would take place if the activity under investigation had not been undertaken.

Coproduct allocation Means of dividing total natural resource and environmental impacts between numerous products and/or services that are generated by an activity under investigation by life cycle assessment.

5.09.1 Biofuel Potential

There are many definitions and uses of the term 'biofuel'. One relevant definition is that a biofuel is any liquid or gaseous fuel that can be derived from organic material, often referred to as 'biomass feedstocks', to replace, directly or indirectly, conventional transport fuels. However, it needs to be appreciated that the term 'biofuel' is sometimes extended to cover, additionally, solid fuels, in various forms, that can be used to generate heat and/or electricity. In this context, only biofuels that are produced for transport applications will be considered here. Biofuels include bioethanol and biobutanol, which are possible replacements for petrol or gasoline, and biodiesel and synthetic diesel, or syndiesel, which can be used in place of diesel fuel, diesel engine road vehicle (DERV) fuel, marine fuels, and aviation fuels. These are liquid fuels but methane-rich gas can also be produced from biomass feedstocks, in the form of biogas, biomethane, or biosynthetic natural gas (bioSNG), as an alternative to conventional fuels in modified versions of existing vehicles, usually for road transport.

One common feature of these biofuels is that they contain, totally or partially, carbon, which has been derived from biogenic sources. The incorporation of biogenic carbon is important to the concept that such fuels effectively recycle carbon dioxide (CO_2) between the atmosphere and biomass feedstocks. As such, the use of these fuels does not contribute directly to additional CO_2 in the atmosphere, although indirect contributions to CO_2 and other greenhouse gases (GHGs) also need to be taken into account as will be explained shortly. Another complication to the definition of biofuels is that hydrogen (H_2) can also be produced from biomass feedstocks for use in a variety of applications, including transport, by means of modified internal combustion engines or fuel cells. While fuel in the form of H_2 does not contain any carbon, its production from organic material will have involved the generation and possible release of CO_2, which can be reabsorbed by the subsequent growth of biomass feedstocks. Hence, biomass-derived H_2 can also be regarded as a biofuel.

Biofuels can be produced from an extremely large and diverse range of biomass feedstocks by means of a number of different processing technologies. Some of these technologies, such as fermentation, are well established and, indeed, quite old. Other technologies are very new and are currently the subject of research and development. The enduring attraction of biofuels as major sources of energy is due to their prospective benefits:

- they can potentially provide alternative sources of transport fuel, which can be used in existing vehicles without major modification;
- they can be derived from many diverse, potentially renewable sources of energy;
- they can potentially reduce dependence on crude oil, thereby contributing to national or regional energy security and assisting the transition away from depletable energy resources; and
- crucially, they can potentially reduce GHG emissions, which are responsible for global climate change.

It is in this last regard that the attraction of biofuels has been most strongly recognized. Total GHG emissions from transport are rising globally and this trend is expected to be maintained into the foreseeable future unless significant, practical means can be found to eliminate or reduce such emissions while ensuring access to sustainable mobility. However, achieving this is a very substantial challenge. Most analysts and policy makers realize that there is no single means of addressing this challenge, especially within the relatively short timescales required. Biofuels have been seen by many as one possible option that, in combination with other solutions, can be implemented relatively quickly to initiate the urgently needed move toward sustainable mobility.

The most apparently attractive feature of all biofuels is their 'carbon neutrality', which is based on reabsorption of CO_2, released during their production and/or combustion, by growth of succeeding biomass feedstocks. However, it has long been realized that GHG emissions are associated with the cultivation or provision of biomass feedstocks and their conversion into suitable biofuels. Hence, determination of the actual 'carbon benefits' of any particular biofuel depends on evaluation of all the GHG emissions, including, predominantly, methane (CH_4) and nitrous oxide (N_2O) as well as CO_2, from all stages of its production or process chain. For certain biofuels under specific circumstances, these associated GHG emissions can be very significant. In particularly extreme cases, more GHG emissions can be released during the production of a biofuel than those emitted in the production and use of the conventional transport fuels that they are intended to replace. Clearly, from the perspective of global climate change mitigation, it is imperative to avoid such undesirable and unintended outcomes. Consequently, assessment of total GHG emissions associated with biofuels has become a fundamentally important consideration for their development and deployment as well as for the policy and regulatory frameworks that promote their production and utilization.

5.09.2 Life Cycle Assessment

The fundamental basis for determining the relative benefits or disbenefits of biofuels is life cycle assessment (LCA). This is a well-established technique for evaluating the total natural resource and environmental impacts of a product or service over its defined life cycle. The basic principles of LCA are documented within International Organization for Standardization (ISO) 14040 Series (see, e.g., References 1 and 2). Over recent times, there has been increasing use of LCA, especially with regard to demonstrating the claims of 'green' products and services. Providing conclusive proof of benefits, in terms of sustainability, for any given product or service is not a trivial task since a very considerable amount of information is required in a full LCA study. Apart from demanding data requirements, uncertainties can arise due to lack of complete scientific knowledge of some environmental pathways that connect emissions to impacts. These and other considerations qualify the results of LCA as a means of informing decisions by policy makers on sustainable development. Despite possible limitations, LCA finds ever-increased application in the specific evaluation of total GHG emissions as the need for effective mitigation measures grows in response to global climate change.

Although LCA principles are well known, their specific application in practice is open to a necessary degree of interpretation. This enables subsequent results to address, appropriately, the different specific questions to which LCA studies can be applied. For this reason, numerous evaluation procedures and computer-based tools, based on different calculation methodologies, are available. In terms of evaluating total GHG emissions associated with biofuels, differences between calculation methodologies focus mainly on the following issues:

- *Systems boundary.* This is an imaginary line drawn around the process under consideration which specifies the extent of analysis of GHG emissions along and beyond the main process chain associated with the production of a biofuel. For example, the systems boundary will establish whether GHG emissions related to the manufacture, maintenance, and decommissioning of plant, machinery, and equipment are included in or excluded from calculations.
- *Reference system.* This relates to whether any account is taken of the GHG emissions effects of the potential alternative use of a main resource input or inputs to the production of a biofuel. For example, GHG emissions may be avoided or increased when land is used to cultivate biomass feedstocks or when disposal is avoided by using wastes in biofuel production.
- *Coproduct allocation.* This is a procedure that is required when more than one product is produced by a process. For example, it is the stated means by which the total GHG emissions of production are, in effect, attributed to or otherwise divided between a biofuel, as the main product, and by-products, such as animal feed.

- *Surplus electricity.* Sometimes, surplus electricity is available for sale from biofuel production processes that use combined heat and power (CHP) units, and this has to be accounted within the GHG calculations. This is sometimes achieved by subtracting a given amount of GHG emissions, derived using stated assumptions, that are effectively avoided when this electricity displaces electricity from another source.

Specific GHG calculation methodologies and tools adopt different approaches to these and other issues. A summary of the main differences on these issues for a selection of methodologies and tools is presented in Table 1 (further explanation of the terminology used in Table 1 is given later in this chapter). The Renewable Fuels Agency (RFA) Technical Guidance [3] provided the basis for evaluating GHG emissions for biofuels during the introduction of the Renewable Transport Fuel Obligation (RTFO) in the United Kingdom. However, this approach has been modified accordingly [7] to comply with the requirements of the European Commission (EC) Renewable Energy Directive [4]. While these two methodologies have been specifically developed for biofuels, a more broadly applicable approach is offered by the British Standards Institution (BSI) Publicly Available Specification 2050 (PAS 2050), which can be used for assessing total GHG emissions for any product or service [5]. Among the tools available for evaluation of total GHG emissions of biomass energy technologies, generally, and biofuels, specifically, the Biomass Environmental Assessment Tool version 2.0 (BEAT$_2$) has been prepared in the United Kingdom for application to a variety of relevant biomass energy technologies including biofuels [6]. Globally, other tools exist and new ones are being developed in response to the expanding use of biofuels.

The existence of different methodologies and tools and, more crucially, the derivation of clearly different results for apparently the same biofuel have generated much confusion, debate, and controversy. There are often numerous reasons for differences in results, in the form of total GHG emissions. Sometimes, this involves differences in important assumptions and/or values for key parameters that have not been openly stated and emphasized. This can be resolved quite easily by ensuring adequate transparency in calculations as a fundamental principle at the heart of any meaningful evaluation that is expected to engender confidence. However, a more widespread cause of discrepancies is the adoption of different approaches to the calculation of total GHG emissions. Unfortunately, the justification of a chosen approach is sometimes not explained comprehensively and explicitly. This can give the

Table 1 Summary of the main differences of a selection of GHG emission calculation methodologies and tools

Methodology	Systems boundary: plant, equipment, and machinery	Reference system: land use	Reference system: waste disposal	Coproduct allocation	Surplus electricity
RFA Technical Guidance [3]	Excluded	Not taken into account	Not taken into account	Substitution credits wherever possible with price allocation otherwise	Avoided GHG emissions based on marginal electricity generation[a]
EC Renewable Energy Directive [4]	Excluded	Direct land use change taken into account and indirect land use change under consideration	Waste products and residues assumed provided without GHG emissions	Energy content allocation	Avoided GHG emissions based on generation of electricity using the same fuel as CHP unit in conventional plant[b]
PAS 2050 [5]	Excluded	Direct land use change taken into account	Taken into account in comparisons	Price allocation chiefly with substitution credits for electricity surpluses	Avoided GHG emissions based on displaced average grid electricity[c]
BEAT$_2$ [6]	Included	Assumes maintained fallow set-aside where relevant	Landfill with energy recovery where relevant	Price allocation unless substitution credits possible and significant	Avoided GHG emissions based on displaced net grid electricity[d]

[a] Credit for surplus electricity from any cogeneration within the biomass energy technology based on displaced marginal electricity generation.
[b] Credit for surplus electricity from any cogeneration within the biomass energy technology based on avoided GHG emissions for the generation of electricity using the same fuel as the cogeneration plant within biomass energy technology.
[c] Credit for surplus electricity from any cogeneration within the biomass energy technology based on displaced average grid electricity, although there is some disagreement over whether this is interpreted on a gross or net basis.
[d] Net credit for surplus electricity from any cogeneration within the biomass energy technology based on difference in GHG emissions for electricity generation by the combined heat and power plant and average grid electricity.
CHP, combined heat and power; GHG, greenhouse gas.

impression that such choices are arbitrary and ignore the essential requirement of any given application of LCA that it must state and address the particular question it seeks to answer. This is not a trivial or academic issue since the rules chosen in GHG emissions calculations can have a very fundamental influence over subsequent results, their interpretation, and their meaningful comparison.

Before examining some of the details of differences in approaches, it is instructive to set this discussion in the context of the purposes behind the calculation of total GHG emissions. Although the principles of LCA emphasize the need to adopt the correct approach that actually answers the specific question being asked, it is often not immediately apparent what this means in practice. This is usually because the specific question under consideration is not stated or clarified sufficiently. There is ongoing deliberation about this in the general field of LCA among academics and practitioners. However, it has been the debate over biofuels, and whether or not they reduce overall GHG emissions, that has begun to draw out the basic foundations on which choices between different calculation methodologies should be made.

In this regard, there are important distinctions between types of LCA, which, in particular, include consequential LCA and attributional LCA [8]. The purpose of consequential LCA is to determine the complete and, in effect, global impacts of introducing a new product or new activity. Hence, consequential LCA tends to be an *ex ante* approach that is specifically relevant to policy analysts. It is particularly relevant to answering 'what if' questions and, as a result, GHG emissions calculations should be all encompassing. This involves tracing and quantifying all the implications, and their relevant connections, that have been induced by policies that support new products or activities. This is frequently much more challenging than might be imagined as it can require the detailed modeling of consequences on a truly global scale. Such modeling can often be highly demanding in terms of data requirements, which far exceed existing capabilities.

In contrast, the purpose of attributional LCA is to allocate total GHG emissions to a specific product or service. This evokes the concept of establishing responsibility for or 'ownership' of GHG emissions by those who provide a given product or service. As such, it can be seen that attributional LCA is most suitable for *ex post* evaluation of a product or service that is specifically relevant to regulation. The challenge that this presents is what basis should be used to 'attribute responsibility'. Clearly, this needs to be related to the practicalities of decision making by those who are directly involved with the provision of a product or service. In the parlance of regulation, these decision makers are the 'economic operators' and their responsibility or ownership usually has an economic or financial aspect. Hence, it can be argued that, in the regulatory context, GHG emissions should be attributed on an economic basis.

Consequential and attributional LCA have very different purposes, involve very different approaches, and usually produce quite different results. Both are valid in terms of the specific questions they seek to answer. However, the basic foundations that they provide have rarely been adopted with necessary rigor in the development of existing, official methodological frameworks or most previous LCA studies. This is demonstrated in **Table 2** by summarizing those aspects of methodologies for calculating total GHG emissions for biofuels that should be adopted for strict compliance with the purposes and logic of these types of LCA. By comparing **Tables 1** and **2**, it can be seen that existing methodologies and tools are not completely suitable for either policy analysis or regulation.

Among the many differences between calculation methodologies and tools is the treatment of coproduct allocation. Such allocation procedures are important because by-products are often generated during the production of prominent biofuels and should, therefore, carry part of the GHG emissions burden associated with the biofuel production process. A variety of coproduct allocation procedures can be adopted including the use of substitution credits and allocation by energy content and price. The use of substitution credits first involves calculating the total GHG emissions for the entire process chain. Then, GHG emissions that would have been associated with the normal generation of alternative products which are displaced by the by-products of biofuel production are subtracted from this total. As such, this is an accounting procedure rather than strict allocation. Additionally, in order to determine the substitution credit, it is necessary to identify the displaced product and evaluate the total GHG emissions

Table 2 Summary of aspects of calculation methodologies for compliance with consequential and attributional LCA

Type of LCA and question answered	Suitable application	Systems boundary: plant, equipment, and machinery	Reference system: land use	Reference system: waste disposal	Coproduct allocation	Surplus electricity
Consequential LCA: What are the complete GHG emissions impacts of introducing a new policy?	Policy analysis	Included	Taken into account	Taken into account	Substitution credits	Substitution credits[a]
Attributional LCA: Who is responsible for these GHG emissions?	Regulation	Excluded	Possibly not taken into account[b]	Possibly not taken into account[b]	Price allocation	Price allocation[c]

[a] Derivation of the substitution credit for surplus electricity from any cogeneration within the biomass energy technology has to be based on the specific details of the question being addressed, such as whether the surplus electricity displaces existing electricity supplies by the switching off or closure of a particular power station or whether it adds to the general mix of electricity supply.
[b] Inclusion or exclusion of reference systems depends on whether the economic operator has any direct influence over land use or waste disposal.
[c] In this context, surplus electricity is no different from any other coproduct and, hence, it is subjected to price allocation.
GHG, greenhouse gas; LCA, life cycle assessment.

associated with its production. Apart from this extra analysis, which is, in effect, the result of expanding the systems boundary, it should be noted that substitution credits can vary over time as displaced products and their means of production change.

Allocation by energy content, price, or other characteristic attribute simply involves dividing the total GHG emissions for a process between coproducts on an effective percentage basis. The energy content of a product is a fixed characteristic and allocation is performed by forming percentages based on the energy content (calorific or heating value) of each coproduct multiplied by their respective masses. Unless technical conditions alter, such allocation does not change with time because the data involved consist of the physical properties of the coproducts. However, the choice of energy content allocation is rarely explained or justified and, indeed, any physical characteristic could have been selected as a basis for allocation. While it is sometimes suggested that the choice of energy content allocation reflects the fact that coproducts could be burnt for energy generation, it is quite clear that, in most instances, this does not happen. Furthermore, some coproducts may not have an energy content and, in such cases, this allocation procedure would not be appropriate. Similar criticisms apply to the choice of other physical properties, even mass, which is occasionally used, but is also not universally suitable since it fails to accommodate the generation and sale of electricity as a coproduct.

Allocation by price involves multiplying the amount of each coproduct by its respective price to determine percentage contributions to total economic value as a basis for dividing total GHG emissions. The main justification for using price allocation is that it, in effect, assigns responsibility for GHG emissions in line with financial benefits. The most obvious drawback of this allocation procedure is that it varies over time in response to changes in the relative prices of coproducts. Additionally, some coproducts may not actually be sold directly from the process, thereby requiring the derivation of 'shadow prices', which may introduce further uncertainty into the calculations. It can also be argued that, even where market prices are available and known, they may not accurately attribute responsibility based on financial benefits because market failure can mean that 'price' does not reflect 'profit' as an indicator of financial worth to the economic operator. Finally, commercial companies may prefer to avoid using price allocation because it could reveal financially sensitive data if such information has to be revealed to a third party in the regulatory process.

Regardless of which coproduct allocation procedure is adopted, it is apparent that most existing calculation procedures and tools are not wholly consistent in their specific details. In particular, from **Table 1**, it can be seen that allocation procedures are often hybrid forms which mix specific approaches together in a fairly arbitrary way. Only the EC Renewable Energy Directive appears to apply a single coproduct allocation procedure. However, it could be argued that special treatment of surplus electricity, which, after all, is a by-product, introduces a degree of inconsistency even in this calculation methodology. Another potential source of discrepancy is the approach adopted for waste products that are used to produce some biofuels. In particular, it is assumed that no actual or avoided GHG emissions are associated with the provision of these biomass feedstocks. This may not reflect what happens in practice and it may also imply that such sources of biofuels are 'free' when in fact they are likely to have a real economic value.

It should be apparent from this brief discussion of some of the details of GHG calculation methodologies and tools that there are fundamental differences, which will ultimately lead to differences in the final results. This is unfortunate because it can create confusion and mistrust in the results of GHG emission calculations. Hence, the basis of calculations, including their intended purpose, should always be clearly stated so that subsequent users can understand what may be causing differences between published results. It also needs to be appreciated that calculation methodologies and tools can produce a wide variety of forms of results. Usually, they report absolute results in the form of total GHG emissions measured in equivalent CO_2 (eq. CO_2). This means that all other GHG emissions, such as CH_4 and N_2O, have been converted using their relevant global warming potentials (GWPs). Ideally, the values of the GWPs used should also be stated since these can vary depending on the time period under consideration and their original source. Normally, a 100-year time horizon is chosen and relevant values are taken from the Assessment Reports of the Intergovernmental Panel on Climate Change (IPCC). A summary of these is given in **Table 3** along with the combination of GWPs adopted by selected methodologies and tools.

To simplify the presentation of results and the establishment of targets, net GHG emissions savings are often quoted and these will be used predominantly here (the current target for biofuels used in the European Union is for net GHG emissions savings of at least 35%, increasing to 50% by 1 January 2017 for existing biofuel plants and to 60% for new biofuel plants that start production on or after 1 January 2017 [4]). Net GHG emissions are derived as the percentage difference between total GHG emissions

Table 3 Global warming potentials for methane and nitrous oxide (100-year time horizon)

Source of data	Methane (kg eq. CO_2 kg^{-1} CH_4)	Nitrous oxide (kg eq. CO_2 kg^{-1} N_2O)	Adoption by methodology or tool
Second Assessment Report [9]	21	310	
Third Assessment Report [10]	23	296	RFA Technical Guidance [3]
			EC Renewable Energy Directive [4][a]
			BEAT$_2$ [6][b]
Fourth Assessment Report [11]	25	298	PAS 2050 [5]

[a] These are the GWPs cited in the EC Renewable Energy Directive although quoted default and typical values are derived using the GWPs from the Fourth Assessment Report [11].
[b] BEAT$_2$ incorporates the option to change GWPs from these default settings.

Table 4 Examples of current baseline values of total greenhouse gas emissions for conventional fuels

Conventional fuel	Total greenhouse gas emissions (kg eq. $CO_2 MJ^{-1}$) Petrol/gasoline	Diesel/DERV fuel
RFA Technical Guidance [3]	0.0848	0.0864
EC Renewable Energy Directive [4]	0.0838	0.0838

DERV, diesel engine road vehicle.

associated with biofuel production and the total GHG emissions of production and use of the conventional fuels (petrol/gasoline, diesel/DERV, etc.) that they displace. The relevant expression for this is given as follows:

$$S = \frac{G_c - G_b}{G_c} \times 100\%$$

where S is the net GHG emissions savings of biofuel (%), G_c the total GHG emissions of conventional fuel (kg eq. $CO_2\ MJ^{-1}$), and G_b the total GHG emissions of biofuel (kg eq. $CO_2\ MJ^{-1}$).

In order to determine net GHG emissions savings, it is necessary to have baseline values for the total GHG emissions associated with the production and use of conventional fuels. Examples of the baseline values for petrol and diesel currently recommended in the United Kingdom for the RTFO [3] and by the EC Renewable Energy Directive [4] are illustrated in **Table 4**. For consistency, the EC values are adopted here in the derivation of net GHG emissions savings.

Given the diversity of factors that can affect the evaluation of net GHG emissions savings of biofuels, a single accessible tool for deriving results and illustrating considerations, in the form of BEAT$_2$, is adopted here. For this, the approach adopted in BEAT$_2$ has been modified to reflect the EC Renewable Energy Directive [4]: specifically, excluding GHG emissions associated with the manufacture, maintenance, and decommissioning of plant, machinery, and equipment; assuming that no GHG emissions are associated with the use of waste and residues for biofuel production; coproduct allocation is based on energy content; avoided GHG emissions of surplus electricity are based on those of electricity generated by conventional means from the same fuel as used in CHP units that serve biofuel plants; and GWPs are adopted from the IPCC Third Assessment Report [10]. The BEAT$_2$ approach has also been extended to cover other current and future biofuels [12–15].

5.09.3 Net Energy Balances for Biofuels

The assessment of the prospective benefits, or otherwise, of biofuels has a long history and has often attracted controversy. This goes back to the 1970s, at least, when a number of studies were conducted in the United States on the net energy balances of bioethanol production from corn/maize (see, e.g., References 16 and 17). Some studies concluded that more energy was required, from fossil fuel sources, than would be available from bioethanol (net energy balance >1). It became apparent that assumptions about the source of heat and electricity used in proposed US bioethanol plants was a crucial consideration in the net energy balance. Indeed, it was suggested that the possible use of agricultural residues, in the form of corn stover, could result in net energy balances in which primary energy consumption of production was less than delivered energy in the bioethanol (net energy balance <1).

More recent studies have revisited this issue and found that current US bioethanol production from maize, based predominantly on the use of coal as a source of energy in processing, has a net energy balance greater than unity, as well as unfavorable environmental impacts, including worse total GHG emissions than those of petrol/gasoline [18]. However, it is necessary to set this conclusion in its proper context of the US biofuel policy, which has fostered recent bioethanol production in the United States. This was motivated by an intention to reduce foreign oil imports and to support agriculture rather than by action to avoid fossil fuel resource depletion and to mitigate global climate change. It could be argued that this policy has been successful in its intended purpose of, in effect, turning US coal into bioethanol as an alternative to petrol/gasoline derived from imported crude oil. There are obvious dangers in drawing broad conclusions from specific cases that are relevant only within particular policy frameworks.

A range of different net energy balances are possible depending on the particular biomass feedstock and the details of how it is converted into a biofuel. This can be demonstrated with the results from adjusted versions of BEAT$_2$ workbooks (or spread-sheets) which provide estimates of primary energy consumption as well as GHG emissions. (It should be noted that, unlike the derivation of GHG emissions within frameworks such as the RFA Technical Guidance and the EC Renewable Energy Directive, there is no 'official' methodology for evaluating net energy balances. However, to be consistent with the approaches used in other studies [18], reference systems for land use were excluded, the manufacture, maintenance, and decommissioning of plant, equipment, and machinery were included (although these contributions are often excluded from GHG emissions calculations), and primary energy substitution credits were used for coproducts (animal feed and surplus electricity from CHP).) In this context, primary energy is the energy available from fossil and nuclear fuels, and, as such, is a measure of energy resource depletion. The net energy balance can be found by dividing the primary energy consumption of biofuel production by the delivered energy, or energy content, of the biofuel. A selection of such net energy balances generated in this way is shown in **Figure 1**. It can be seen that in both instances where a

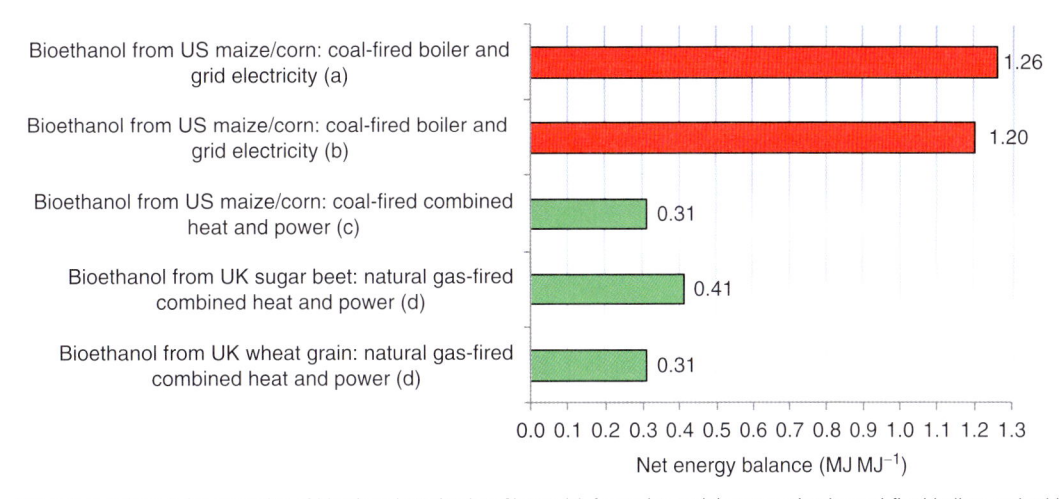

Figure 1 Net energy balances for examples of bioethanol production. Notes: (a) Assuming mainly processing by coal-fired boilers and grid electricity [18]. (b) Simulated using BEAT$_2$ [6] with a substitution credit of 7.967 MJ kg^{-1} protein for animal feed [18]. (c) Simulated using BEAT$_2$ [6] with a substitution credit of 7.967 MJ kg^{-1} protein for animal feed [18] and a substitution credit for US grid electricity of 2.540 MJ MJ^{-1} [19] displaced by surplus electricity from the combined heat and power unit. (d) Simulated using BEAT$_2$ [6] with a substitution credit of 7.967 MJ kg^{-1} protein for animal feed [18] and a substitution credit for UK electricity of 2.952 MJ MJ^{-1} [20] displaced by surplus electricity from the combined heat and power unit.

coal-fired boiler with imported grid electricity is used for bioethanol production from US maize/corn, net energy balances are greater than unity. However, a net energy balance of less than unity arises if it is assumed that a natural gas-fired CHP unit supplies all the heat and electricity requirements of the bioethanol plant. Other examples of bioethanol production that produce favorable net energy balances are also shown in **Figure 1**.

5.09.4 Greenhouse Gas Emissions Results

As with net energy balances, estimated net GHG emissions savings of the production and use of biofuels depend on many factors including the original biomass feedstock and the source of processing heat and electricity. This is demonstrated in **Figure 2**, which presents typical values for net GHG emissions savings for current biofuels (biodiesel, bioethanol, and biogas) as quoted in the EC Renewable Energy Directive [4]. Although the basic assumptions used to derive these default values are only partially explicit, they can be compared directly with the results from modified versions of BEAT$_2$ workbooks for specified examples of biofuel production. In general, estimated net GHG emissions savings from these two sources are similar, as will be shown shortly. For the time being, a number of trends are immediately apparent from **Figure 2**. It will be noted that relatively high net GHG emissions savings (>80%) can be achieved with biodiesel derived from recycled vegetable oil and biogas from dry and wet manure. Much lower net GHG emissions savings are realized with biodiesel produced from oil palm without CH$_4$ capture, soybean, and oilseed rape (ranging from 36% to 45%). For biodiesel production from oil palm, considerable amounts of CH$_4$ can be released from ponds that store effluent from oil mills, resulting in large contributions to total GHG emissions. Such emissions can be reduced significantly by collecting the CH$_4$ and either flaring it to CO$_2$ (which is biogenic and, therefore, 'neutral' as it is reabsorbed by subsequent oil palm growth) or using it as a supplementary energy source in the mill. The improvement in net GHG emissions savings, from 36% to 62%, from this mitigation measure is clear in **Figure 2**. The influence of the source of heat and electricity used in the production of bioethanol from wheat grain is also demonstrated in **Figure 2**, which indicates that using a lignite-fired CHP unit achieves only modest net GHG emissions savings (32%) while these can be increased markedly (69%) by using a straw-fired CHP unit. Of all the liquid biofuels derived from cultivated biomass feedstocks, the highest net GHG emissions savings are realized by bioethanol production from sugarcane (71%). However, it is important to avoid overly generalizing conclusions from **Figure 2** since actual net GHG emissions savings can depend on the specific details of biomass feedstock provision and processing.

The origins of some differences between net GHG emissions savings for particular biofuels can be suggested by examining relative contributions to their estimated total GHG emissions. This was achieved using modified versions of BEAT$_2$ workbooks and methodology of the EC Renewable Energy Directive. The results are illustrated in **Figure 3**. It will be seen that very high contributions to total GHG emissions are associated with N fertilizer manufacture and soil N$_2$O emissions for biodiesel production from UK oilseed rape (56%) and French sunflowers (40%) and for bioethanol produced from UK wheat grain (63%), US maize/corn (54%), and sugarcane (42%). (It should be noted that relative contributions to total GHG emissions can be affected by the details of calculation methodologies in complex ways. For example, by applying the RFA Technical Guidance [3], different patterns of contributions can be generated [21]. The reason for this is mainly due to the treatment of surplus electricity from the CHP units of the biofuel production plants (see **Table 1**).) The contribution from other cultivation inputs to total GHG emissions for biodiesel production from US soybean is high (63%) because nitrogen (N) fertilizer application rates are low and the contribution from

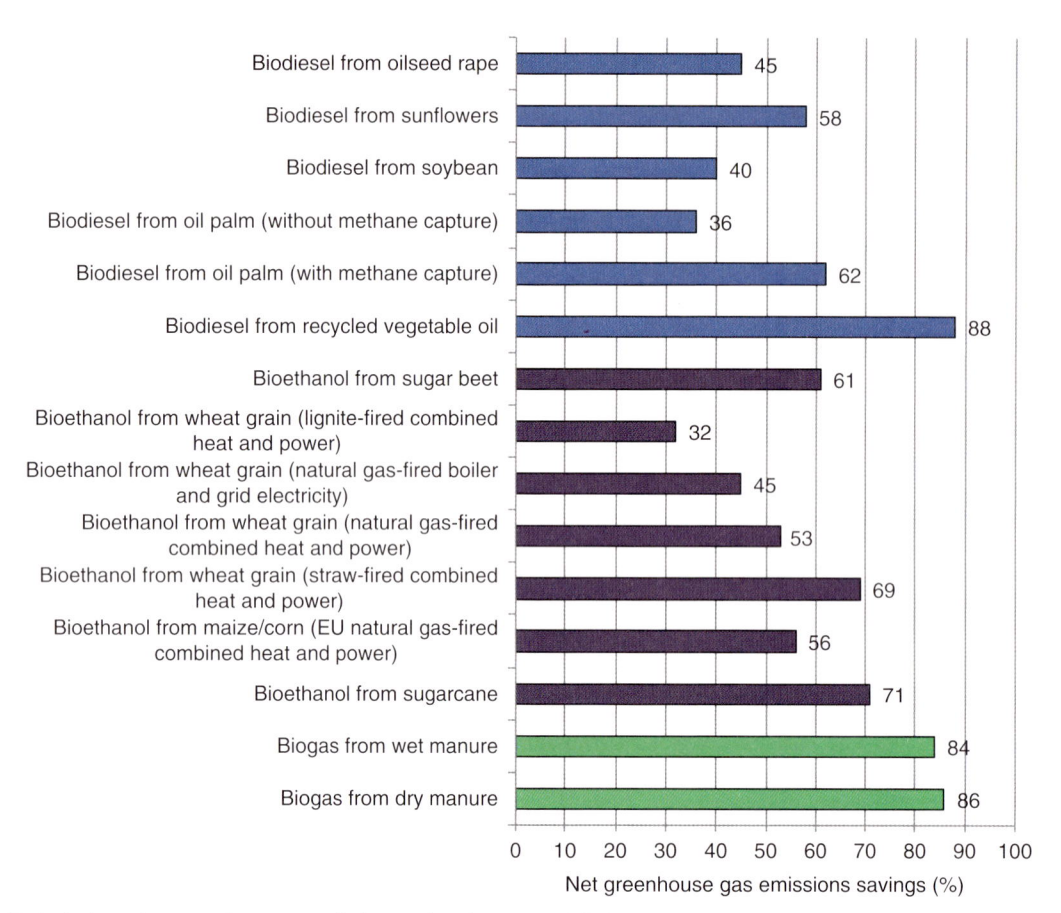

Figure 2 Typical values of net greenhouse gas emissions savings for current biofuels.

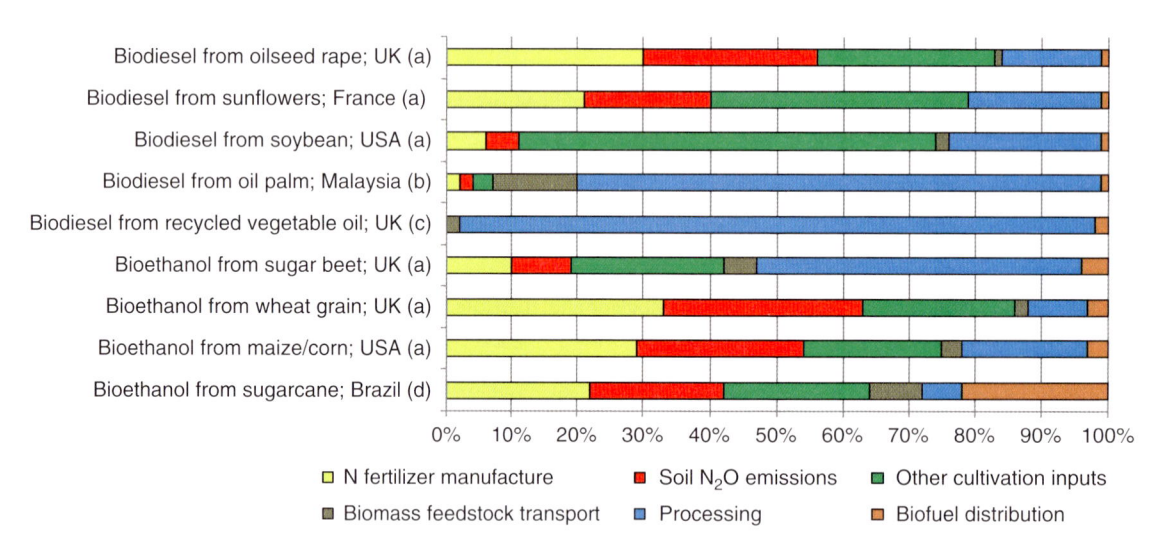

Figure 3 Relative contributions to typical values of total greenhouse gas emissions for current biofuels. Notes: (a) Processing with a natural gas-fired combined heat and power unit. (b) Processing with a natural gas-fired combined heat and power unit and no methane capture for oil mill effluent. (c) Processing with natural gas-fired boiler and grid electricity. (d) Processing with a bagasse-fired combined heat and power unit.

processing (oil extraction, refining, and esterification) is relatively low. Relative contributions from processing are high for biodiesel production from oil palm, mainly due to CH_4 emissions from oil mill effluent ponds, and for biodiesel production from recycled vegetable oil, because all other contributions are small. It should be noted that in all cases where CHP units are used in processing, the estimated contribution from processing includes deduction of avoided GHG emissions from the sale of surplus electricity. Additionally, it can be seen from **Figure 3** that most contributions from transportation of biomass feedstock and biofuel distribution are relatively minor. The main exception to this is bioethanol production from Brazilian sugarcane where transport distances are assumed to be comparatively higher than in biofuels produced in other countries.

Among the many factors that can affect estimates of net GHG emissions savings of biofuels, the most prominent are

- consideration of systems boundaries, in particular, direct (dLUC) and indirect (iLUC) land use change;
- details of biomass feedstock cultivation, especially with regard to N fertilizer application rates, N fertilizer manufacture, and N_2O emissions from soil;
- source of processing energy, as related to specific fuels used to provide heat and electricity for biomass feedstock conversion to biofuels;
- methods of GHG emissions calculation, mainly as affected by the choice of coproduct allocation procedures;
- nature of biomass feedstocks, specifically, differences between cultivated crops and waste products;
- treatment of reference systems, with regard to accounting or otherwise of avoided GHG emissions; and
- advances in biofuel production, as represented by future technologies.

The effects of all these important factors are examined and discussed in the remainder of this chapter, with illustrations by means of estimated net GHG emissions savings based on BEAT$_2$-type workbooks.

5.09.5 Land Use Change

Arguably the most controversial and problematic issue for the global climate change mitigation potential of biofuels concerns land use change. This is because potential GHG emissions from land use change can eliminate any estimated benefits of biofuels or, indeed, make them worse than conventional transport fuels even without taking account of the GHG emissions from the rest of the production process or chain. Land is a major constraining factor in the production of any biofuel that is derived from cultivated crops. Dependence on cultivation has, of course, the attractive feature that it enables the amount of biofuels that can be produced, on a regular (mainly annual) basis, to be predetermined and, if necessary, varied or, specifically, increased, to a certain degree. Depending on the mechanism by which biofuel demand translates into biomass feedstock supply, various levels of production can be planned and controlled. This contrasts with the production of biofuels from waste products, including agricultural, forestry, and arboricultural residues, the ultimate availability of which depends on other factors that cannot be varied at will as they usually depend on other, separate considerations. In particular, the normal economic mechanism by which increases in price bring forward supply does not operate completely with respect to wastes and residues. In the short term, such sources of biomass feedstocks are fixed whereas cultivated feedstocks can respond to price signals over a period of 1–5 years, depending on the nature of the particular crop.

Despite this attractive feature, cultivated biomass feedstocks are affected by a potentially major negative implication because the land on which they are grown could be used for other purposes. Obviously, there is competition over land between biomass feedstocks and crops for food, materials, and other purposes. There is also possible conflict over land for completely different uses including urban and infrastructure development. As discussed previously, alternative land use is normally addressed in LCA studies by means of reference systems, which, in effect, expand the systems boundaries applied to the activities under consideration. However, evaluation of the effects on GHG emissions calculations can be extremely complicated and can have far-reaching consequences as it is necessary to account for the actual changes to any given area of land and, potentially, its subsequent impact on global land use. Such analysis is not trivial and final impacts may be large or small, depending on circumstances and assumptions. Overall, consideration of land use change can introduce considerable uncertainties into the assessment of net GHG emissions savings for biofuels.

5.09.6 Direct Land Use Change

Of the two broad types of land use change, dLUC is more easy to accommodate with regard to estimating total GHG emissions associated with biofuels. The issue of dLUC arises when land is converted specifically for the cultivation of biomass feedstocks for biofuel production. Both negative and positive changes in net GHG emissions can result from dLUC. For example, within BEAT$_2$, the default setting is that land for growing oilseed rape, sugar beet, wheat grain, etc., was previously maintained set-aside that had been withdrawn from agricultural production due to EC policy measures. Typically, this land is assumed to be fallow and mown every year. GHG emissions occur from tractor use in mowing operations (71 kg eq. CO_2 ha^{-1} a^{-1}; [22]) and N_2O emissions are released from the soil (0.95 kg N_2O ha^{-1} a^{-1}; [23]). In total, these GHG emissions account for 353 kg eq. CO_2 ha^{-1} a^{-1}. These relatively low emissions are, effectively, avoided by cultivating such land for biofuels so they constitute a negative net emission, or a 'credit' in the GHG emissions calculations for the subsequent biofuel. However, because of changes in EC agricultural policy, such land designation has disappeared over a period of time. Hence, this adjustment in calculations is now less meaningful.

Apart from its effect on GHG emissions calculations, the possible elimination of 'spare land' presents a particular problem for biofuels. This is because, in response to existing policy measures and targets that will increase pressure for biofuel production, land will need to be found for biomass feedstock cultivation. While some of this will be current food cropland, which will generate other problems (see below), it may also be necessary to convert other forms of land to biomass feedstock cultivation. This may include certain categories of land, such as grassland, woodland, peatland, and wetland, which may be available in relatively large areas and may be considered to have a low economic value, in narrowly defined terms. Leaving aside other important environmental impacts, such as the loss of habitat and reduction in biodiversity, the conversion of such land can present significant issues for GHG emission calculations. Depending on the specific nature of this land and how it is converted to cultivation, substantial quantities of GHGs can be released as below- and above-ground carbon stocks are destroyed. These GHG emissions can consist of CH_4 and N_2O as well as CO_2 emissions. The percentage of carbon stocks released and the timescale over which this occurs has to be taken into account, especially in terms of allocation to subsequent cultivated crops. Additionally, foregone opportunities to sequester carbon by this land in its previous form have to be considered, although this may be partially counterbalanced by the carbon sequestration potential of certain biomass feedstocks.

In the United Kingdom, the possible implications of dLUC on GHG emissions associated with biofuel production were addressed in the Gallagher Review [24]. This indicated very significant GHG emissions from carbon stock changes through the conversion of certain types of land, especially grassland, to biomass feedstock cultivation for current biofuel production. It was apparent from the Gallagher Review that a systematic and comprehensive approach would need to account for all possible land use conversion to all types of biomass feedstock. Such an approach is now available in the form of EC Guidelines for the calculation of carbon stock changes [25]. Calculation procedures are based, generally, on those outlined by the IPCC for evaluating GHG emissions from land use change in the context of formulating national inventories [26]. The approach adopted involves estimating the carbon stock of the soil and vegetation (above- and below-ground) before and after conversion to biomass feedstock cultivation. This takes into account the climate region, soil type, land management factors which are intended to reflect type of land use, degree of tillage and level of organic inputs, and the nature of the vegetation. Default values for these factors are based on IPCC data supplemented with data specific to the cultivation of relevant biomass feedstocks for current biofuel production. To assist application, global maps of climate regions and soil types are also provided. The resulting net carbon stock change per unit area (t C ha^{-1}) is then converted into CO_2 emissions, spread over a 20-year time period and allocated to the subsequent biofuel on the basis of its biomass feedstock yield [4].

The effect of such net carbon stock changes resulting from dLUC on net GHG emissions savings varies depending on circumstances, particularly in terms of the biomass feedstock yield, which is related to the specific biofuel, and the original land use. Examples of this are provided in **Figures 4** and **5**, which illustrate, respectively, the hypothetical conversion of UK grassland to wheat cultivation for bioethanol production and Malaysian forest/scrubland to oil palm cultivation for biodiesel production. Figure 4 compares the net GHG emissions savings of 56% for bioethanol from UK wheat grain without dLUC with savings

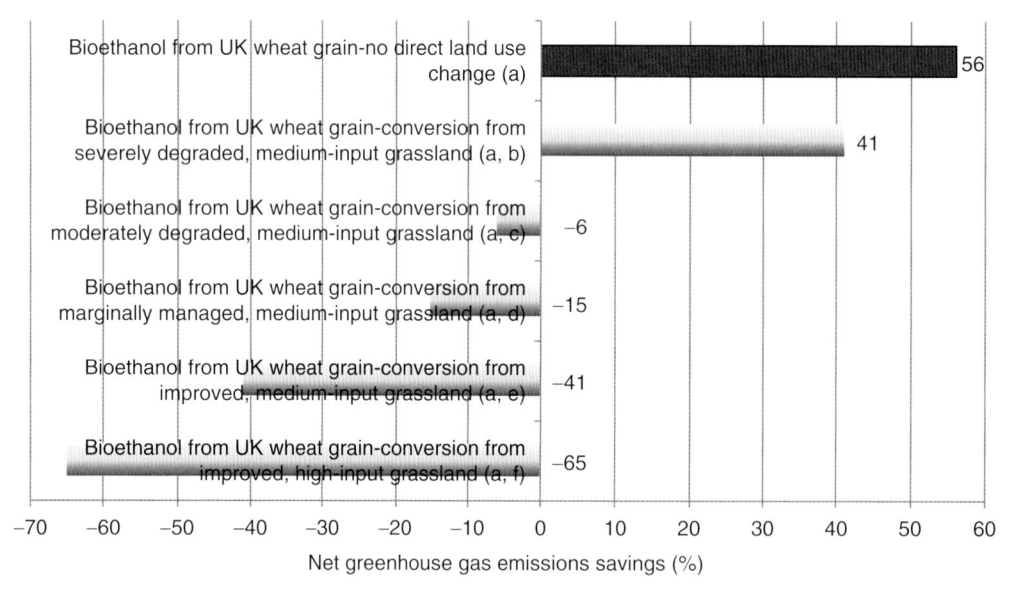

Figure 4 Net greenhouse gas emissions savings for bioethanol from UK wheat grain with direct land use change. Notes: (a) Simulated using modified BEAT$_2$ workbook [6] for bioethanol from wheat grain with a yield of 8.00 t ha^{-1} a^{-1} at 20% moisture content, processing with a natural gas-fired combined heat and power unit, bioethanol productivity of 62 617 MJ ha^{-1} a^{-1} and 56.3% coproduct allocation to bioethanol. (b) Estimated net carbon stock change of 73.3−65.5 = 7.8 t C ha^{-1} [25] for conversion of severely degraded, medium-input grassland to full-tillage, medium-input cropland on high-activity clay soils in a cool, temperate, moist/wet climate. (c) Estimated net carbon stock change of 97.0−65.5 = 31.5 t C ha^{-1} [25] for conversion of moderately degraded, medium-input grassland to full-tillage, medium-input cropland on high-activity clay soils in a cool, temperate, moist/wet climate. (d) Estimated net carbon stock change of 101.8−65.5 = 36.3 t C ha^{-1} [25] for conversion of marginally managed, medium-input grassland to full-tillage, medium-input cropland on high-activity clay soils in a cool, temperate, moist/wet climate. (e) Estimated net carbon stock change of 101.8−65.5 = 36.3 t C ha^{-1} [25] for conversion of marginally managed, medium-input grassland to full-tillage, medium-input cropland on high-activity clay soils in a cool, temperate, moist/wet climate. (f) Estimated net carbon stock change of 127.0−65.5 = 61.5 t C ha^{-1} [25] for conversion of improved, high-input grassland to full-tillage, medium-input cropland on high-activity clay soils in a cool, temperate, moist/wet climate.

Figure 5

Scenario	Net GHG emissions savings (%)
Biodiesel from Malaysian oil palm-conversion of Asian insular tropical moist forest with between 10% and 30% canopy cover (a)	91
Biodiesel from Malaysian oil palm-conversion from Asian insular tropical scrubland (a, b)	73
Biodiesel from Malaysian oil palm-no direct land use change (a)	51
Biodiesel from Malaysian oil palm-conversion from Asian insular deciduous forest with > 30% canopy cover, and with shifting cultivation and shortened fallow (a, d)	−98
Biodiesel from Malaysian oil palm-conversion from Asian insular deciduous forest with > 30% canopy cover, and with shifting cultivation and mature fallow (a, e)	−110
Biodiesel from Malaysian oil palm-conversion from Asian insular native deciduous forest with > 30% canopy cover (a, f)	−124

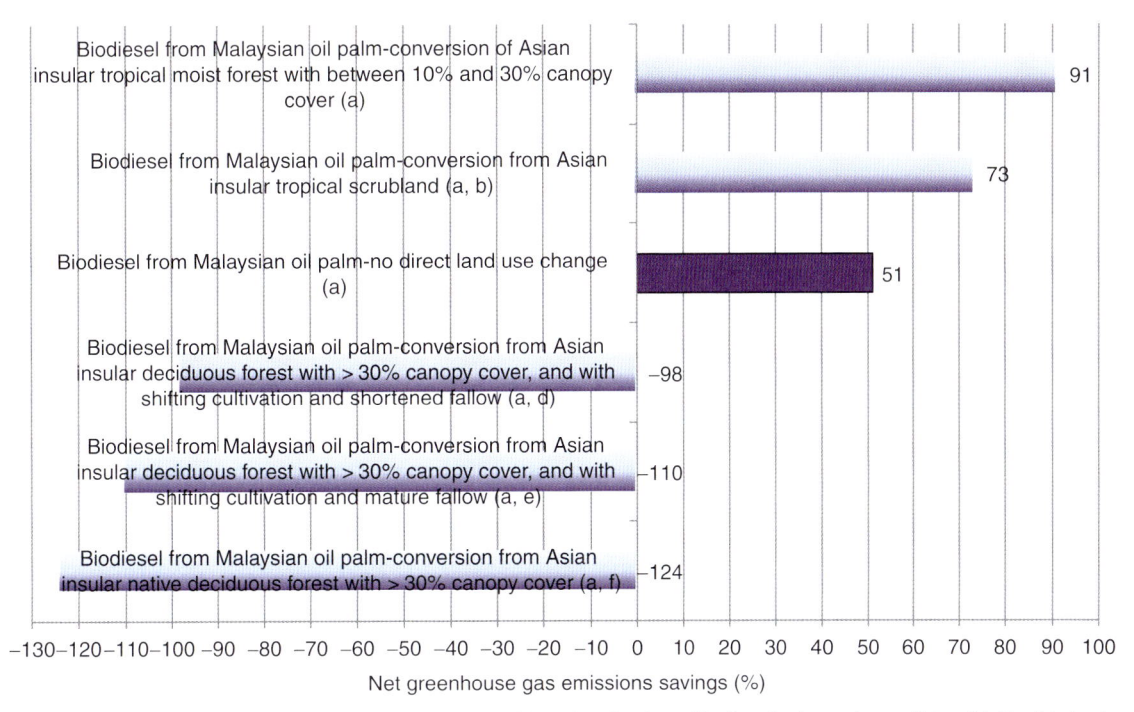

Figure 5 Net greenhouse gas emissions savings for biodiesel from Malaysian oil palms with direct land use change. Notes: (a) Simulated using BEAT$_2$-type workbook [14] for biodiesel from oil palm with a yield of 4.08 t ha^{-1} a^{-1} at 22% oil content, processing with a fuel oil-fired combined heat and power unit and methane capture, biodiesel productivity of 122 708 MJ ha^{-1} a^{-1} and 31.2% coproduct allocation to biodiesel. (b) Estimated net carbon stock change of 81.0−107.0 = −26.0 t C ha^{-1} [25] for conversion of Asian (insular) tropical moist forest with between 10% and 30% canopy cover to full-tillage, medium-input perennial cultivation on low-activity clay soils in a tropical, moist climate. (c) Estimated net carbon stock change of 93.0−107.0 = −14.0 t C ha^{-1} [25] for conversion of Asian (insular) tropical scrubland to full-tillage, medium-input perennial cultivation on low-activity clay soils in a tropical, moist climate. (d) Estimated net carbon stock change of 204.1−107.0 = 97.1 t C ha^{-1} [25] for conversion of Asian (insular) moist, deciduous forest with greater than 30% canopy cover, and with shifting cultivation and mature fallow, to full-tillage, medium-input perennial cultivation on low-activity clay soils in a tropical, moist climate. (e) Estimated net carbon stock change of 211.6−107.0 = 104.6 t C ha^{-1} [25] for conversion of Asian (insular) moist, deciduous forest with greater than 30% canopy cover, and with shifting cultivation and mature fallow, to full-tillage, medium-input perennial cultivation on low-activity clay soils in a tropical, moist climate. (f) Estimated net carbon stock change of 221.0−107.0 = 114.0 t C ha^{-1} [25] for conversion of Asian (insular) moist, native (nondegraded) or managed deciduous forest with greater than 30% canopy cover to full-tillage, medium-input perennial cultivation on low-activity clay soils in a tropical, moist climate.

including the effects of dLUC associated with the conversion of different types of grassland. In all instances, the net GHG emissions savings are lower. Furthermore, with the exception of one case, the CO$_2$ emissions from net carbon stock changes are so high that these savings are negative, meaning that the bioethanol has higher GHG emissions than petrol derived from conventional crude oil. The one exception with dLUC involves conversion of severely degraded grassland to wheat cultivation. In this context, 'severely degraded grassland' has suffered "long-term loss of productivity and vegetation cover, due to severe mechanical damage to vegetation and/or soil erosion" [25]. It seems unlikely that such grassland is prominent in the United Kingdom although there are other countries where such land may exist.

The situation illustrated in **Figure 5** is somewhat different. Although there are instances of land use conversion that result in negative net GHG emissions, there are two cases in which savings are higher than the comparative value of 51% for biodiesel production from Malaysian oil palms. In these particular instances, consisting of Asian insular moist forest with between 10% and 30% canopy cover and Asian insular tropical scrubland, the carbon stock prior to conversion is lower than that for the oil palm plantation. In this regard, the assumed value for the above- and below-ground vegetative carbon content of the biomass feedstock is a critical consideration. However, from such evaluation of the effects of dLUC, it can be seen that there are specific forms of land use conversion that should be avoided if necessary net GHG emissions savings are to be achieved with biofuels. Hence, the EC Renewable Energy Directive specifically states that, as part of sustainability criteria, biofuels should not be derived from biomass feedstocks that have involved the conversion of wetlands, continuously forested areas, area with 10–30% canopy cover, and peatland [4, 27]. The inclusion or exclusion of conversion of forested areas with between 10% and 30% canopy cover depends on particular circumstances depending on the existing carbon stock and the type of biomass feedstock cultivated.

In the EC Guidelines for the calculation of carbon stock changes associated with dLUC, it has been assumed that the carbon in elements of the stock, such as trees, is actually released in the form of CO$_2$. This would be the case if existing trees were burnt or allowed to decay. Consequently, the CO$_2$ released should be attributed to the following crop that is assumed to be the reason for such land clearance. However, much of the timber may be recovered for a variety of uses which might, in fact, store carbon for many decades or even centuries. Indeed, logging may well be the actual reason for such land clearance, in which case any net CO$_2$

emissions should be allocated mainly or wholly to the timber produced rather than exclusively to subsequent crops. Regardless of the reason for land clearance, it is still the case that removing trees eliminates a future 'sink' for CO_2 emissions. Hence, in many instances, the reasons for dLUC and its consequences may be complex and interrelated, causing fundamental problems for attributing GHG emissions from land conversion.

5.09.7 Indirect Land Use Change

The other form of land use change, which consists of iLUC, is considerably more controversial and potentially more serious for current biofuels in terms of their proclaimed benefits for mitigating global climate change. The impact of iLUC on total GHG emissions associated with the production of biofuels is based on the concept of land use displacement. With this concept, the cultivation of a biomass feedstock on land that has been previously used to grow another crop will cause the production of this crop to be displaced elsewhere, which, in turn, may cause yet other crops to be displaced. This process of displacement continues until previously uncultivated land has to be converted to agriculture due to global constraints on the availability of such land. At this point, dLUC occurs and there can be a net reduction in carbon stocks, which causes CO_2 emissions to be released. The magnitude of these emissions depends, crucially, on the nature of the carbon stock that has been disturbed or destroyed. If, for example, the destruction of tropical rain forest is involved, then the subsequent CO_2 emissions are very substantial. However, no matter what their magnitude, these CO_2 emissions are, according to the concept of iLUC, attributed to the very first action that initiated this sequence of land use changes. Hence, in the current context, any CO_2 emissions from iLUC are allocated to the cultivation of biomass feedstocks for biofuel production.

This concept was originally articulated in 2008 when a number of studies were published that attempted to quantify the effect on total GHG emissions associated with biofuels from iLUC. Particularly prominent studies concluded that the additional GHG emissions from iLUC were so large that many current biofuels had total GHG emissions greater than those of diesel and petrol derived from conventional fossil fuels [28, 29]. More recent work has suggested that the member states of the European Union will not be able to meet both the targets for biofuel supply and net GHG emissions savings required by the EC Renewable Energy Directive if iLUC is taken into account [30]. Conclusions from the original studies prompted considerable activity on the topic of iLUC and its possible impact on biofuel policy. This included preparation of the Gallagher Review in the United Kingdom [24] and an iLUC exercise conducted by the EC [31–33]. The EC exercise examined existing literature of the subject [33], investigated existing global land use models [32], and evaluated the possible implications of EC biofuel policy [31, 34]. At the end of 2010, provisional findings from the exercise to date were drawn together [35]. These concluded that the contribution from iLUC to the total GHG emissions associated with current biofuels could be large but there were considerable uncertainties about the actual magnitude.

The basic reason for such uncertainties is the challenge presented by attempting to model land use change globally. This requires an extremely large amount of detailed data for all relevant countries, their land designations, and their existing land use. Furthermore, a credible and reliably functioning model of land use displacement effects is needed that can address all the interactions of complex agricultural decision making. Since it was apparent by the end of 2010 that neither existing data nor adequate models were available, the EC was unable to resolve the issue of iLUC on GHG emissions for biofuels. Instead, the EC set out options that it could adopt in responding to iLUC in 2011. These included taking no action but monitoring developments; increasing the target net GHG emissions savings for biofuels in the EC Renewable Energy Directive; introducing additional sustainability criteria requirements for certain biofuels, which would, in effect, mean that iLUC would be avoided or minimized; and applying a 'penalty' GHG emissions factor to biofuels which, somehow, reflects the estimated impact of iLUC [35].

It will be appreciated that the iLUC issue is complex and, possibly, intractable. However, it can be argued that, by addressing iLUC in this manner, the EC and similar bodies are attempting to make inappropriate adjustments which conflict with the basis of their regulatory aims. As discussed previously, there are clear distinctions between GHG emissions regulation, which needs to be based on attributional LCA, and policy analysis, which has to be based on consequential LCA. Practical regulation, in particular, has to recognize the decision-making framework of the 'economic operators' who are regulated, especially in terms of their ability to take responsibility for or 'ownership' of GHG emissions. However, most proposed approaches to the issue of iLUC for biofuels ignore the disparity between the attribution of subsequent GHG emissions and the actual ability of economic operators to influence the exceedingly remote consequences of their own actions. It could be said that there is a lack of clear thinking about the official methodologies for GHG emissions calculations because they appear to be attempting to address regulation and policy analysis simultaneously. Instead, it is essential to accept that these are two quite different purposes based on different types of LCA, which will, by their very nature, generate different results.

In the parlance of LCA, the correct and consistent approach depends on where systems boundaries are drawn around the processes under investigation. It has to be accepted that, as systems boundaries are expanded to include increasingly remote activities, the level of effective responsibility or ownership of subsequent GHG emissions declines. Hence, the establishment of the systems boundary, and its subsequent inclusion or exclusion of GHG emissions, should reflect the ability of the economic operator to control, directly or indirectly, these emissions. In current market situations, this suggests that the systems boundary should be based on economic responsibility. Hence, if iLUC is an issue that is caused by global constraints on the availability of agricultural land, this should factor into the economic considerations of those who decide to grow biomass feedstocks through land prices. If this link is tenuous, then the effect on GHG emissions for biofuels is weak, and conversely so. However, it could also be argued that land prices reflect many influences of which the possible global shortage of agricultural land is just one factor. An additional problem is that, at the moment, only biofuels are subject to regulation with respect to GHG emissions. The lack of universal application of GHG emissions reporting and targets for all products and services leads to obvious market distortions, market failures, and inappropriate decision making. It can be proposed that, ideally, effective carbon pricing would correct this by internalizing the impact of all sources of GHG emissions. Unfortunately, current prospects for this globally are not encouraging.

A radically alternative approach is to recognize the fundamental source of the problem, which is actual ongoing destruction of carbon stocks, due to land use change, throughout the world. There are many causes of land use change and, indeed, a few ameliorating influences. Among those factors that drive land use change are increasing requirements for food (due to a growing world population), changing dietary preferences (in response to increasing wealth and switch to food products that use proportionally more land), expanding use of land for nonfood production (materials and chemicals as well as biofuels), degrading agricultural land (so that it is no longer productive), and continued urbanization (causing direct and indirect degradation and loss of land for cultivation). Those factors that can alleviate pressure on land use change include improving yields (resulting in less land being required for the same output) and the ability of restoring abandoned and degraded land to cultivation (causing the stock of land for agriculture to expand). These and other causes of, and means of, alleviating pressure on land use change can be compounded and further complicated by issues surrounding the control of land use, such as ownership, or lack thereof, and the absence of effective land use monitoring and policing, which result in illegal land grabs, illegal logging, and so on.

Currently, biofuels only play a very minor role in this complex global situation. It is clearly unrealistic to expect that the regulation of one factor through GHG emissions calculations and targets will address the much larger-scale problem of carbon stock destruction from all causes of land use change. Hence, instead of incorporating iLUC into GHG emissions calculations through biofuel regulation, it is much more appropriate to focus efforts on preventing land use change and its impacts directly. This has to be achieved through the creation, implementation, monitoring, and policing of appropriate global and national protocols and mechanism for the protection of all significant carbon stocks. In the current absence of necessary global agreement, the most practical action should be applied to the issue of dLUC rather than iLUC. This consists of excluding from production quotas or targets those biofuels derived from biomass feedstocks that have been cultivated on land converted through the destruction of high-carbon stocks. In essence, this is the approach already adopted in the EC Renewable Energy Directive by excluding biofuels obtained from crops involving certain types of land use conversion [4, 27]. Another consequence of the uncertainty surrounding the issue of iLUC has been to encourage interest in biofuels that can be derived from biomass feedstocks that require less or no land use. This includes the production of biofuels from wastes and residues, using new conversion processes, and from novel sources such as algae. The possible benefits of using such biomass feedstocks depend on the evaluation of their associated GHG emissions, which has to be based on reliable assumptions about their subsequent commercial implementation.

5.09.8 Soil Nitrous Oxide Emissions

Another significant consideration in the evaluation of GHG emissions associated with certain biofuels concerns the release of N_2O emissions from soils. The importance of this issue is that relatively small N_2O emissions can result in large contributions to total GHG emissions due to the high GWP for this particular gas. Up to now, the main concern has been soil N_2O emission resulting from the application of artificial or mineral N fertilizers. The reason for this is that N fertilizer application rates for certain biofuel crops can be quite significant. The normal approach to estimating these emissions is to use the procedures outlined by the IPCC [26]. These consist of three possible procedures, referred to as IPCC Tier 1, Tier 2, and Tier 3. Under IPCC Tier 1, soil N_2O emissions are related to the original N fertilizer application rate through a simple linear relationship which takes into account the different pathways by which N converts to N_2O. (These pathways consist of direct N_2O emissions and two forms of indirect N_2O emissions consisting of volatilization and atmospheric deposition, and leaching and runoff [26].) This simple relationship applies to all soil types, climatic conditions, land management practices, and forms of artificial N fertilizer. With IPCC Tier 2, a more sophisticated method of calculation is used based on the availability of more detailed or specific data on sources of nitrogen and their generation of N_2O emissions from soils. Adopting IPCC Tier 3 involves actually measuring soil N_2O emissions, which can be very time consuming and expensive, and/or deriving estimates with suitable models, such as the denitrification–decomposition (DNDC) computer simulation [36].

Considerable concern has been raised about the use of a universal, simple relationship, as specified under IPCC Tier 1, in GHG emissions calculations for biofuels [37]. This is largely because of the possibility of substantially underestimating the release of N_2O associated with the application of artificial N fertilizers and other sources of N in biomass feedstock cultivation. Hence, this issue is currently under further investigation. However, in the absence of any broadly accepted and agreed alternative, the IPCC Tier 1 approach is commonly applied in GHG emissions calculations. In some instances, the IPCC Tier 1 approach is used selectively, as there is uncertainty about the reliability of the evaluation of indirect N_2O emissions from leaching and runoff, for example. The actual mechanisms involved in determining total N_2O emissions from soil are clearly complex and depend on many specific considerations. In contrast, the IPCC Tier 1 approach is intentionally simple and, it must be recalled, was derived for application in the generation of national GHG emissions inventories rather than, particularly, biofuel regulation. To a certain degree, uncertainty is reflected in the wide variation in the IPCC Tier 1 default values for soil N_2O emissions. For example, the simple relationship produces an average emissions factor of 0.0208 kg N_2O kg^{-1} N, whereas the full range, which reflects the best and worst combination of default values, extends from 0.0091 to 0.0527 kg N_2O kg^{-1} N. The effect on this variation can have a significant impact on the net GHG emissions savings of certain biofuels, as illustrated in **Figure 6**. In particular, it can be seen that bioethanol production

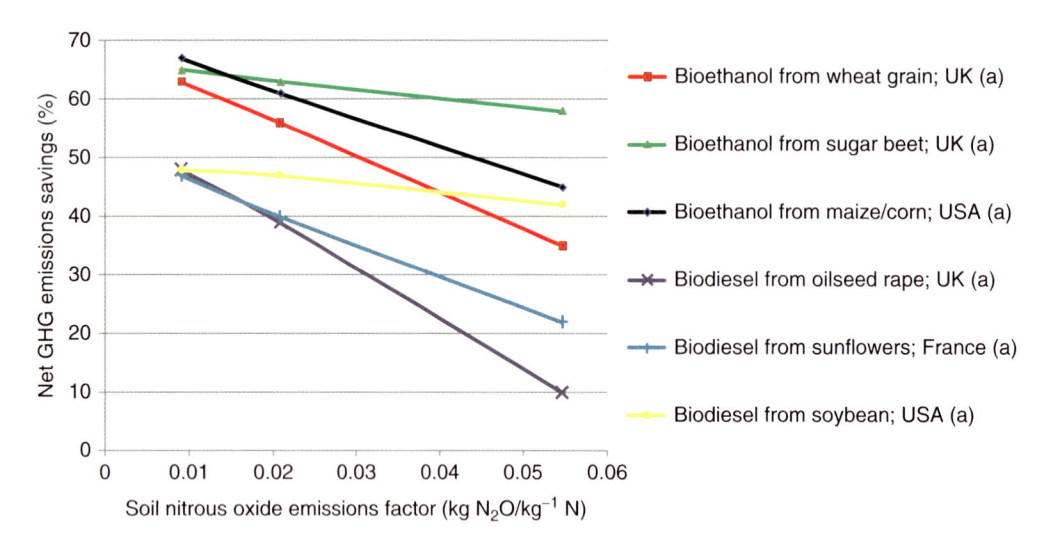

Figure 6 Variation of net greenhouse gas (GHG) emissions savings for current biofuels with soil nitrous oxide emissions from artificial nitrogen fertilizer application. Note: (a) Processing with a natural gas-fired combined heat and power unit.

from UK wheat grain and US maize/corn and biodiesel production from French sunflowers and UK oilseed rape are all adversely affected by the assumed soil N_2O emissions factor.

Hence, improvements in the evaluation of soil N_2O emissions for a number of current biofuels are an urgent priority. Fundamental work in this area has been initiated to derive a more reliable approach to estimating soil N_2O emissions and, if possible, to reduce them. For example, in the United Kingdom, a major research study, referred to as the MIN-NO project, funded by the Department for Environment, Food and Rural Affairs and the Scottish Government, is undertaking field measurements and these will be used with the DNDC model to generate, if necessary, a more representative relationship between N fertilizer application rates and soil N_2O emissions [38]. This study is planned to report final results in 2014. Other studies have focused on specific aspects of the issue and the potential effects of particular mitigation measures. A review of existing knowledge and its implications for current biofuels was conducted for the RFA during 2009 [21]. From this and other work, it is apparent that any future evaluation of soil N_2O emissions will have to take into account a number of very specific factors including the nature of the soil, the details of cultivation, the form of artificial N fertilizer, and the type of weather following application. In particular, it appears that the timing of fertilizer applications and the possibility of soil waterlogging are important considerations. Hence, a more reliable and representative approach to evaluation may well be a complex procedure rather than a simple relationship. This could affect the possibility of generating soil N_2O emission default value maps or atlases which would, ideally, be very helpful for estimating GHG emissions for biofuel production.

In addition to these complexities, there are other aspects that may need to be taken into account. Among these is whether soil N_2O emissions from the incorporation of crop residues and the application of organic manures and composts should be included in GHG emissions calculations for biofuels. Currently, standard calculators promoted by the EC and national regulators do not seem to include these sources of N_2O emissions (see, e.g., References [39–41]). Previously, the issue of crop residue incorporation has been addressed in GHG emissions calculation only through adjustments for possible effects on the artificial fertilizer requirements of following crops. However, a clear approach to this based on sound evidence has not been devised. Hence, this is normally excluded from most GHG emissions calculations. However, it is possible to account for effects of crop residue incorporation using IPCC Tier 1 default values [26] and assumptions concerning the N content of the residues and the amount incorporated. It should be noted that the removal of some of these residues for other purposes, obviously, reduces any soil N_2O emissions attributed to the biofuel.

The consequences for soil N_2O emissions of applying organic manures have also been discounted previously in GHG emissions calculations for biofuels. When explicit, the justification for this was that these are attributed to the livestock that originally produced them, as they would not exist otherwise. The only GHG emissions accounted for have been those associated with the actual process of applying these manures. However, a counterargument is that these manures provide N for the biofuel crop and this reduces the need for artificial N fertilizer. Hence, related soil N_2O emissions should be taken into account. Again, this can be achieved using IPCC Tier 1 default values [26], standard data on the N content of various manures (see, e.g., Reference 42), and assumptions about N losses during storage prior to application. In the context of this last point, it seems to be reasoned that N losses during storage, leading to N_2O emissions, are attributed to the livestock from which they originated.

A further consideration related to the soil N_2O emissions from the incorporation of crop residues and the application of organic manures and composts is that such activities can introduce and maintain carbon in the soil. Hence, it can also be argued that this is a beneficial effect that, under certain circumstances, results in a degree of carbon sequestration, which should also be accounted for, as a 'credit', in GHG emissions calculations. This argument might seem to find some possible traction within the details of the EC Renewable Directive [4] and treatment of carbon stocks in relation to dLUC [25]. However, the acceptance of this approach depends on the level of carbon sequestration that might be achieved and how evidence might be collected and reported to support this. It should be noted that there is current scientific debate over levels of carbon sequestration, which are affected by the type of soil, its past history, and any ongoing buildup or saturation of carbon. Additionally, while carbon sequestration accredited to the biofuel crop might be justified through the incorporation of its residues, there is potential disagreement concerning whether any benefits from organic manure application can be regarded in the same way. It has been argued that any carbon sequestration cannot be attributed to a crop treated with organic manures since this really involves moving carbon from one place (where the livestock obtained their food) to another (where the treated crop is grown). The reason why considerations about possible carbon sequestration are important is that the estimated carbon credit can counterbalance the negative impacts of related soil N_2O emission. These issues require detailed scientific investigation and sound evidence for their resolution in terms of GHG emissions calculations for biofuels.

Another issue related to soil N_2O emissions is the contribution made to total GHG emissions from the manufacture of artificial N fertilizers. This contribution can be significant for certain current biofuels, as shown previously in **Figure 3**. The GHG emissions factor for an artificial N fertilizer depends on the type of fertilizer and the nature of the technology used in its manufacture. The most common forms of artificial N fertilizers are ammonium nitrate and urea. As summarized in **Table 5**, there are a number of different estimates for the GHG emissions factors of these forms of fertilizer. Two particular features will be seen in **Table 5**. The first is that the GHG emissions factors for urea are substantially less than those for ammonium nitrate. From this, it might be concluded that, from a GHG emissions perspective, it would be advantageous to use urea instead of ammonium nitrate. However, leaving aside differences in the suitability of these particular N fertilizers and their take-up by certain crops in specific situations, the overall benefits of this potential switch are less obvious in terms of total GHG emissions, which reflect both artificial N fertilizer manufacture and application [45]. This is because urea application generates soil CO_2 emissions as well as N_2O emissions. Additionally, lime may also have to be applied to counteract possible acidification effects of urea application, resulting in GHG emissions from both lime manufacture and related soil CO_2 emissions. Furthermore, it has been suggested that there are differences in soil N_2O emissions caused by different forms of artificial N fertilizers [46]. The second feature apparent in **Table 5** is that there is a significant difference in the GHG emissions factor for ammonium nitrate manufacture between average production and best available technology (BAT). It is generally expected that, in the European Union at least, the fertilizer manufacturing industry will move quickly toward BAT as a result of involvement in the European Union Emissions Trading Scheme. Hence, the GHG emissions factors for BAT are likely to be more relevant in GHG emissions calculations in the foreseeable future. The possible effect of this on the net GHG emissions savings of current biofuels is demonstrated in **Figure 7**. It will be seen that there are marked improvements in the net GHG emissions savings of specific biofuels, for example, biodiesel production from UK oilseed rape.

5.09.9 Sources of Processing Energy

Another factor that influences the net GHG emissions savings of biofuels is the source of energy normally used to provide heat and electricity in the conversion process. Various sources of heat and electricity can be adopted and illustrations of their effects on net GHG emissions savings are provided for bioethanol and biodiesel in **Figures 8** and **9**, respectively. The options chosen for these illustrations consist of providing heat by means of coal-, oil-, natural gas-, straw-, and wood-fired boilers with electricity derived from the relevant national grid in each case and also from coal-, oil-, natural gas-, straw-, and wood-fired CHP units. A number of

Table 5 Selection of greenhouse gas emissions factors for ammonium nitrate and urea fertilizer manufacture

Form of artificial nitrogen fertilizer	Emissions factor Carbon dioxide emissions (kg CO_2 kg^{-1} N))	Methane emissions (kg CH_4 kg^{-1} N)	Nitrous oxide emissions (kg N_2O kg^{-1} N)	Total greenhouse gas emissions[a] (kg eq. CO_2 kg^{-1} N)
Ammonium nitrate				
NNFCC database[b]	2.245	0.0121	0.0147	6.875
BIOGRACE database[c]	2.827	0.0087	0.0096	5.869
EFMA EU 2006[d]	2.343	0.0062	0.0125	6.186
EFMA EU BAT[e]	1.771	0.0050	0.0028	2.715
Urea				
EFMA EU 2006[d]	1.391	0.0076	0	1.568
EFAM EU BAT[e]	0.978	0.0066	0	1.130

[a] Using global warming potentials of 23 kg eq. CO_2 kg^{-1} CH_4 and 296 kg eq. CO_2 kg^{-1} N_2O from the IPCC Third Assessment Report [10] as consistent with the EC Renewable Energy Directive [4].
[b] Average production in Western Europe [43].
[c] BIOGRACE list of standard values [44].
[d] European Union's average value for 2006 [45].
[e] European Union's best available technology [45].

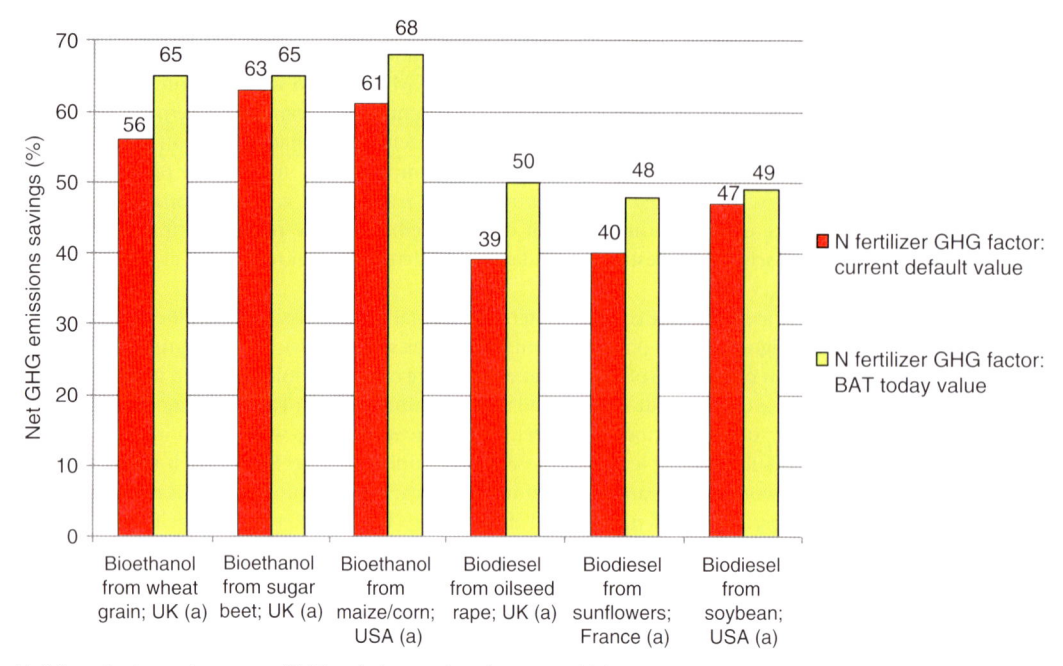

Figure 7 Variation of net greenhouse gas (GHG) emissions savings for current biofuels with total GHG emissions from ammonium nitrate fertilizer manufacture. Note: (a) Processing with a natural gas-fired combined heat and power unit.

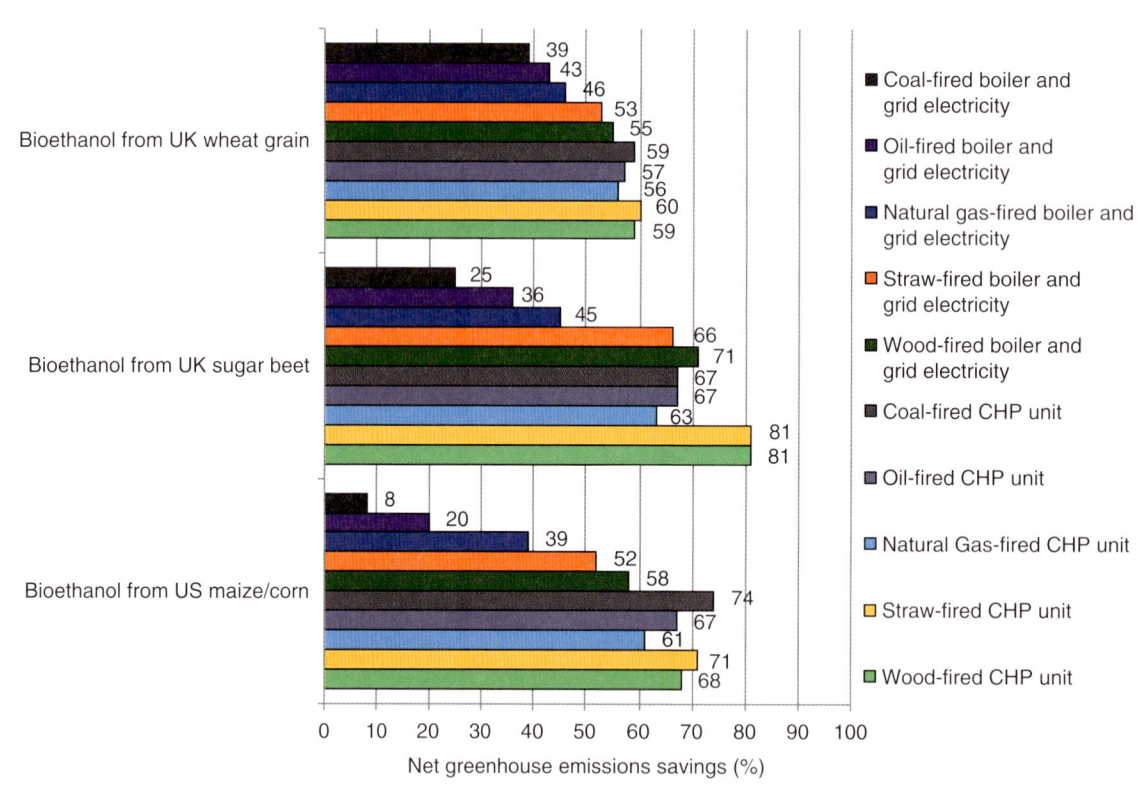

Figure 8 Net greenhouse gas emissions savings of bioethanol with different sources of processing energy. CHP, combined heat and power.

important features are apparent in these illustrations. Probably the most obvious is that there are differences in the net GHG emissions savings for either bioethanol or biodiesel production from different biomass feedstocks using the same source of processing energy, in the form of either a boiler with grid electricity or CHP. As already discussed, this is mainly due to differences in GHG emissions associated with the provision of the original biomass feedstocks. However, some differences can arise in

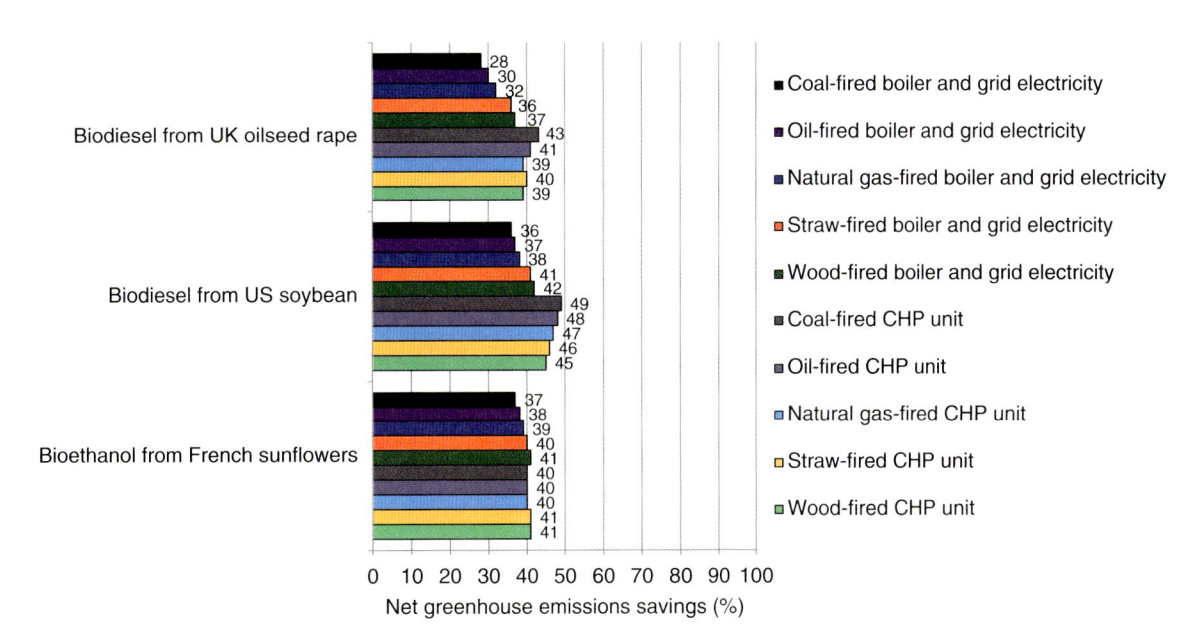

Figure 9 Net greenhouse gas emissions savings of biodiesel with different sources of processing energy. CHP, combined heat and power.

processing for the same biofuel, which, for example, result from different fermentation dynamics for different biomass feedstocks. Furthermore, in cases where grid electricity is used, national differences in GHG emissions factors have to be taken into account.

Such considerations can be relatively minor compared with differences between the sources of processing energy used to derive a given biofuel from each specific biomass feedstock. In particular, due to their greater overall energy efficiency, the use of CHP units, generally, results in higher net GHG emissions savings than with the use of a separate boiler and grid electricity. Comparisons are, of course, affected by whether the basic source of fuel in the CHP plant and boiler is a fossil fuel or a biomass fuel. However, the effect of this may be less pronounced than might, at first, be expected. This is primarily a consequence of applying the EC Renewable Energy Directive methodology for GHG emissions calculations to the specific treatment of surplus electricity generated by CHP units and sold to the grid. In many situations, including most biofuel production plants, CHP units are principally designed to meet process heat requirements. These are often quite large while the process electricity requirements are relatively small. Hence, depending on particular circumstances, the CHP unit has surplus electricity, which can be exported to the grid, thereby improving the overall economics of the process.

With the EC Renewable Energy Directive methodology, such surplus CHP electricity is accounted for in GHG emissions calculations by means of a substitution credit. However, unlike some methodologies that base this credit on the GHG emissions factor for grid electricity, the EC Renewable Energy Directive adopts a quite different approach. This involves establishing a credit based on a GHG emissions factor of a power-only unit using the same fuel as the CHP unit. It appears that the justification for this somewhat convoluted approach is to account for alternative uses of any given fuel. If such is the justification, then it would seem the methodology is attempting, incorrectly, to address both regulatory and policy analysis objectives simultaneously. Be this as it may, the overall effect of this particular approach within the EC Renewable Energy Directive is that the substitution credits for surplus electricity from biomass-fired CHP units is lower than those associated with fossil fuel-fired CHP units. Of course, there are direct benefits, in terms of reduced GHG emissions, from the operation of biomass-fired CHP units, but these can be moderated by reduced indirect benefits from surplus electricity sales.

The overall effect of this is demonstrated in **Figure 10**, which shows the net GHG emissions savings from bioethanol produced using CHP from UK wheat grain with different emissions factors for surplus electricity. In this particular case, the surplus electricity from the CHP unit is relatively high at 642 kWh per tonne of bioethanol. With a natural gas-fired CHP unit, the resulting credit based on the EC Renewable Energy Directive equates to 12% of the total GHG emissions. In **Figure 10**, net GHG emissions savings are compared for those using the approach of the EC Renewable Energy Directive and those with a credit based on UK grid electricity in 2006 equal to 0.581 kg eq. CO_2 kWh^{-1}. With a coal-fired CHP unit, the net GHG emissions savings decrease when a grid electricity credit is used. There is no significant change for an oil-fired CHP unit. However, in the case of natural gas-, straw-, and wood-fired CHP units, the net GHG emissions savings all increase. This is most pronounced for biomass-fired CHP units.

Figure 10 demonstrates that by adopting equivalent sourced electricity for surplus CHP electricity within the provisions of the EC Renewable Energy Directive, differences in net GHG emissions savings are relatively limited, ranging between 56% and 60% for fossil fuel- and biomass-fired CHP units used in the production of bioethanol from UK wheat grain. However, if UK grid electricity is displaced, differences are somewhat enhanced, ranging from 54% for coal-fired CHP to 67% for wood-fired CHP. This would seem to reflect, more realistically, the advantages of biomass-fired CHP units in terms of GHG emissions savings. Indeed, this approach is more relevant as it communicates the benefits of such CHP units to the economic operators who decide the sources of

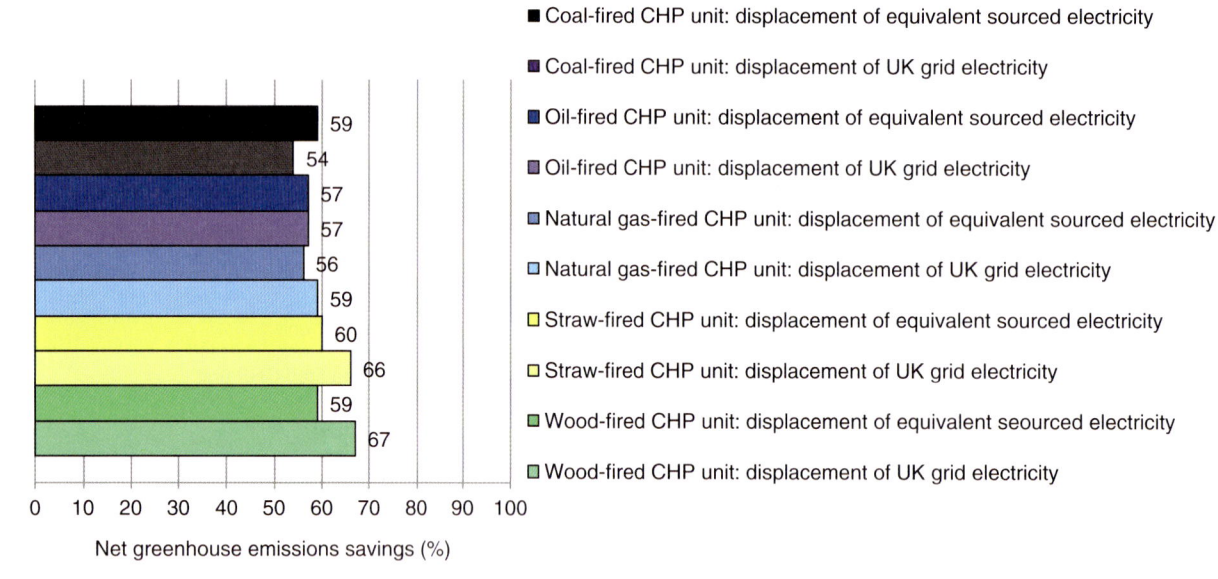

Figure 10 Effect of emissions factor for surplus electricity credit on net emissions savings for bioethanol from UK wheat grain. CHP, combined heat and power.

processing energy for biofuel plants. However, adopting the current approach specified in the EC Renewable Energy Directive could, perversely, discourage the use of biomass-fired CHP units. This is particularly the case when differences in net GHG emissions savings between biofuel production using biomass-fired and fossil fuel-fired CHP units are relatively small, and the economics of the former is significantly less favorable relative to the latter.

5.09.10 Coproducts

The production of many current biofuels generates other products, referred to as coproducts or by-products depending mainly on their economic significance. These other products have to be taken into account in the calculation of GHG emissions. As discussed previously, this is achieved through the application of allocation procedures, which, as the phrase suggests, is an attempt to share GHG emissions between all the products that emerge from any given process. However, among all the possible allocation procedures proposed, one method does not strictly comply with the concept of 'sharing' GHG emissions. This allocation procedure consists of using substitution credits for all coproducts apart from the main product. With this particular procedure substitution credits are subtracted from the total GHG emissions process. As such, the use of substitution credits is an accounting mechanism rather an allocation procedure. As explained previously, the use of substitution credits complies with consequential LCA, which is relevant to policy analysis. In contrast, true allocation procedures reflect attributional LCA, which is necessary for regulation.

Leaving aside the fundamental differences and relevance of allocation procedures, it has been suggested that their application has no significant effect on the estimated net GHG emissions savings of biofuels. For example, in justification of its use of coproduct allocation based on energy content, it is stated in the EC Renewable Energy Directive that

> The substitution method is appropriate for the purposes of policy analysis, but not for the regulation of individual economic operators and individual consignments of transport fuels. In those cases, the energy allocation method is the most appropriate method, as it is easy to apply, is predictable over time, minimises counter-productive incentives and *produces results that are generally comparable with those produced by the substitution method* [4, para 81, p. 18].

However, as demonstrated in **Figure 11**, this last aspect is not necessarily correct. **Figure 11** summarizes the net GHG emissions savings of current biofuels using coproduct allocation by energy content, mass, price, and substitution credits. Apart from these differences in allocation procedures, these results are based on the same assumptions as those shown previously for these particular biofuels. Very substantial differences in net GHG emissions savings are apparent for some biofuels, especially between allocation by energy content and adoption of substitution credits.

The essential details of the substitution credits used to generate the results shown in **Figure 11** are summarized in **Table 6**. Various considerations affect the detailed application of substitution credits in GHG emissions calculations. In particular, it is necessary to identify the specific product that the coproduct under consideration is expected to displace, its means of production, and, therefore, its emission factor. There are many possible options for displacement and the choice needs to be appropriate for the specific context of the policy analysis that is being undertaken. This determines the realistic alternatives and the timescales in question. It is also necessary to determine the 'equivalence' of the coproduct to the displaced product because one may not be an

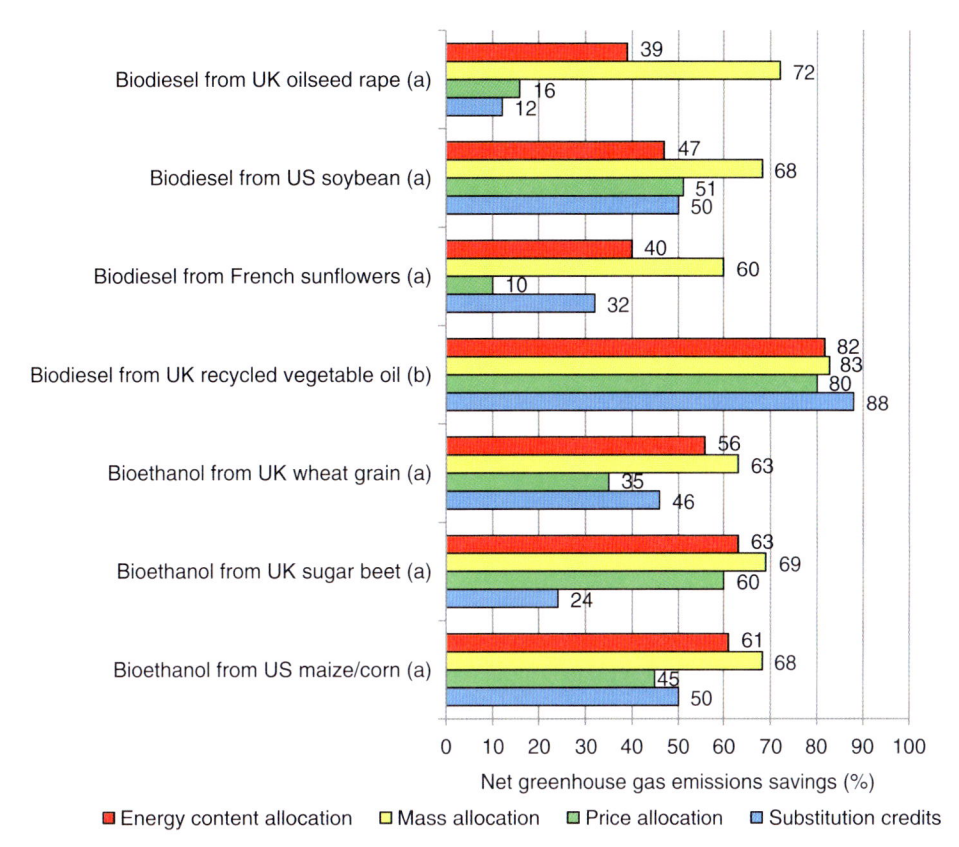

Figure 11 Effect of coproduct allocation procedures on net greenhouse gas emissions savings of current biofuels. Notes: (a) Processing with a natural gas-fired combined heat and power unit. (b) Processing with a natural gas-fired boiler and grid electricity.

exact replacement of the other. This requires a meaningful basis for comparing alternative products. For example, for coproducts that are animal feeds, calorific value, protein content, digestibility, etc., may feature separately or in combination when establishing equivalence as part of GHG emissions calculations. Finally, any extra processing of coproducts has to be taken into account when using substitution credits in GHG emissions calculations. This is because comparisons are, in effect, being made between finished products. Hence, in the case of animal feeds, drying to an equivalent moisture content has to be included. This contrasts with the approach adopted in other allocation procedures that do not need to take into account any GHG emissions associated with a coproduct once it has been separated from the main product. These and other considerations mean that the net GHG emissions for biofuels determined using substitution credits can vary substantially depending on the basic assumptions incorporated into the calculations. These assumptions should reflect the nature of the policy analysis that is being conducted and, as such, should be stated clearly and comprehensively when results are quoted. The appropriate approach to such analysis needs to incorporate global modeling, similar to that necessary to address the effects of iLUC, in order to accommodate the dynamic and interactive consequences of product displacement and substitution.

5.09.11 Future Biofuel Technologies

In addition to current biofuels, there are a number of new technologies under development and commercialization that have the potential to avoid some of their negative impacts, in terms of GHG emissions. These future biofuel technologies often involve the utilization of different and, in some cases, novel biomass feedstocks and advanced conversion techniques that do not rely on fermentation or esterification. Many of the possible biomass feedstocks enable the impacts of dLUC, iLUC, and soil N_2O emissions to be reduced, by using nonfood crops that can achieve higher yields than conventional crops required for current biofuels. Such biomass feedstocks include cultivated sources of wood, such as short-rotation coppice (SRC), short-rotation forest (SRF) and conventional forests, and grasses, such as reed canary grass, miscanthus, and switchgrass. Other possible biomass feedstocks offer the opportunity to avoid the impacts of dLUC, iLUC, and soil N_2O emissions completely by using noncrop sources, such as agricultural residues, wood wastes, other waste products and municipal solid waste (MSW), and novel sources such as algae. The potential utilization of these types of biomass feedstocks for biofuel production is not without some important implications and considerations, however. For example, land availability may constrain the cultivation of nonfood crops. Additionally, the availability of residues and wastes is governed by factors other than the demand for biofuels and they may have significant competing

Table 6 Summary of substitution credits for coproduct allocation

Biofuel and coproduct	Coproduct output (tonne coproduct per tonne biofuel)	Substitution credit (kg eq. CO_2 per tonne coproduct)
Biodiesel production from UK oilseed rape		
Rape meal	1.58	504[a]
Glycerin	0.20	2170[b]
Biodiesel production from US soybean		
Soy meal	3.76	373[c]
Glycerin	0.15	2170[b]
Biodiesel production from French sunflowers		
Sunflower meal	0.45	504[a]
Glycerin	0.15	2170[b]
Biodiesel production from UK recycled vegetable oil		
Glycerin	0.20	2170[b]
Bioethanol production from UK wheat grain		
Distillers' dark grains and solubles	1.14	491[d]
Bioethanol production from UK sugar beet		
Beet pulp	1.25	337[e]
Bioethanol production from US maize/corn		
Distillers' dark grains and solubles	0.93	283[f]

[a] Based on displacement of soy meal from soybeans grown in the United States and milled in the United Kingdom and a substitution credit of 504 kg eq. CO_2 per tonne rape or sunflower meal [3]. This can be compared with displacement of 0.80 t soy meal per tonne rape meal and an emissions factor for US soy meal imported into the European Union of 65 kg eq. CO_2 per tonne soy meal [47].
[b] Based on an emissions factor for propylene glycol of 2170 kg eq. CO_2 per tonne [47].
[c] Based on displacement of wheat grain grown in the European Union and a substitution credit of 373 kg eq. CO_2 per tonne soy meal [3].
[d] Based on displacement of soy meal from soybeans grown in the United States and milled in the United Kingdom and a substitution credit of 491 kg eq. CO_2 per tonne distillers' dark grains and solubles [3]. This can be compared with displacement of 0.78 t soy meal per tonne distillers' dark grains and solubles and an emissions factor for US soy meal imported into the European Union of 65 kg eq. CO_2 per tonne soy meal [47].
[e] Based on displacement of UK wheat grain and a substitution credit of 337 kg eq. CO_2 per tonne beet pulp [3].
[f] Based on displacement of US corn gluten feed and a substitution credit of 283 kg eq. CO_2 per tonne distillers' dark grains and solubles [3].

applications. The utilization of all these sources depends on new processing technologies that can extract suitable materials in sufficient quantities from biomass and convert them into suitable biofuels. In some cases, instead of extracting and processing oils, starches, or sugars, these new technologies exploit abundant lignocellulosic material either by means of enzymes or through gasification, as in Fischer–Tropsch processing, to obtain biofuels such as syndiesel and, with biomethanization, bioSNG. In the case of algae, it may be possible to extract natural oils directly and convert them into suitable biofuels.

Future biofuel technologies are at various stages of development and commercialization. Hence, it is not possible to establish definitive estimates of their net GHG emissions savings since, realistically, this requires basic, proven information on the actual provision of relevant biomass feedstocks and on the actual performance of conversion techniques. However, indicative estimates of net GHG emissions savings, based on proposed or speculative data for future biofuel technologies, can be derived. An example of this is illustrated in **Figure 12**, which presents estimated net GHG emissions savings for the production of syndiesel and bioSNG from a variety of biomass feedstocks using the methodology of the EC Renewable Energy Directive [13, 15]. In general, **Figure 12** indicates the potential to achieve very high net GHG emissions savings. However, this requires some qualification. In particular, it should be noted that any impacts of dLUC and iLUC have not been incorporated in these estimates. Depending on the actual choices in sourcing specific biomass feedstocks, this could affect the net GHG emissions savings for syndiesel and bioSNG derived from SRC, SRF, timber, miscanthus, and switchgrass. Although high net GHG emissions savings are indicated for most residues and wastes, some, such as those for syndiesel and bioSNG derived from straw and MSW, are noticeably lower. This is due to the combination of relatively low net calorific values for these biomass feedstocks and the GHG emissions associated with their provision consisting of collecting, baling, and transporting, in the case of straw, and pelletizing, in the case of MSW.

The results presented in **Figure 12** are based on the GHG emissions calculation methodology of the EC Renewable Energy Directive which excludes the effect of so-called reference systems. This is appropriate for calculations that are used for regulatory purposes and, hence, are based on attributional LCA. However, in the context of policy analysis which requires the application of consequential LCA, the overall or global impacts of an activity have to be taken into account. This involves establishing reference systems that determine the GHG emissions implication of the chains of consequences that an activity initiates, in the same way that the impacts of iLUC have to be addressed. However, unlike most of the effects of iLUC, sometimes activities can promote positive consequences, such as the avoidance of GHG emissions. Such is the case when considering the use of wastes in biofuel production. In such instances, the need to dispose of wastes means that significant GHG emissions can be avoided. The importance of this, from a policy analysis perspective, is illustrated in **Figure 13**, which shows estimated net GHG emissions for syndiesel and bioSNG generated from a selection of wastes without and with the effect of reference systems [13, 15]. In this instance, it has been

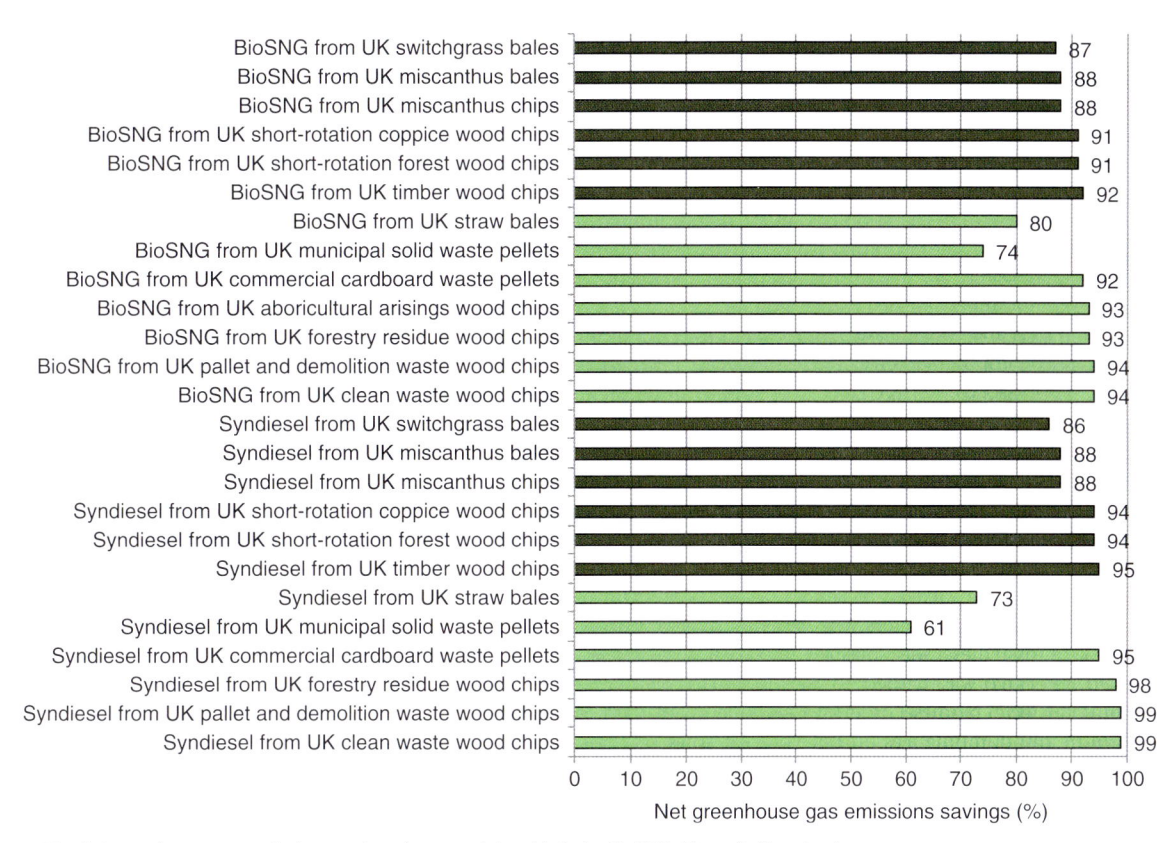

Figure 12 Net greenhouse gas emissions savings for some future biofuels. BioSNG, biosynthetic natural gas.

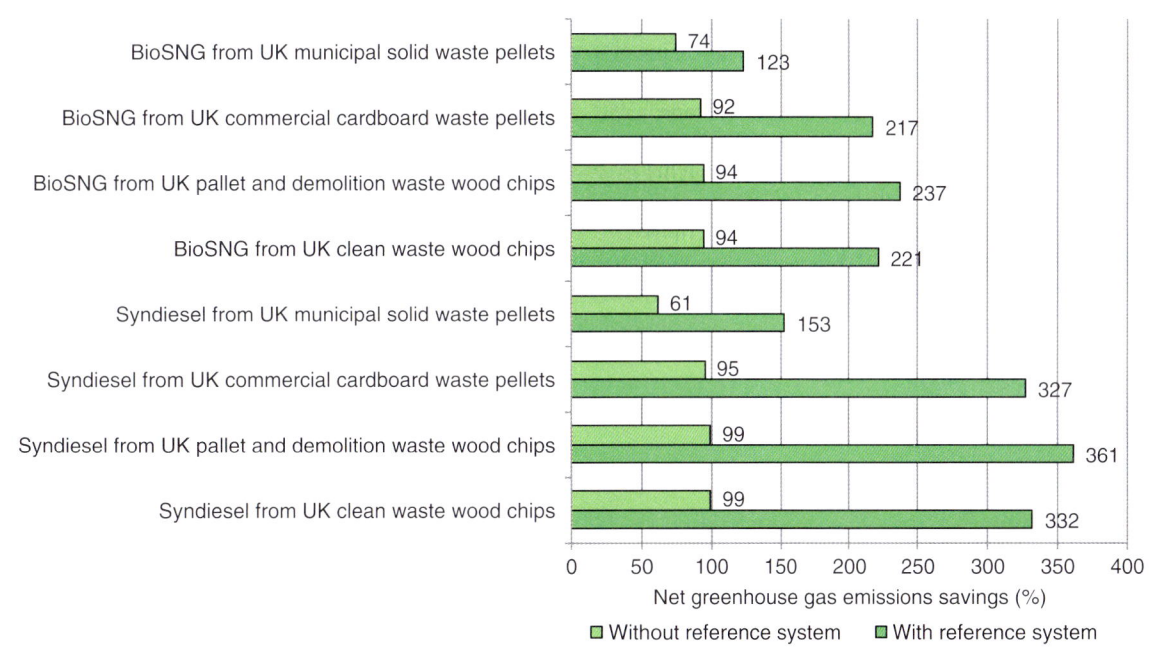

Figure 13 Net greenhouse gas emissions savings for future biofuels from wastes without and with reference systems. BioSNG, biosynthetic natural gas.

assumed that the alternative to biofuel production is disposal to landfill with subsequent methane capture and electricity generation, which, subsequently, displaces national grid supplies. The effect of this is to moderate the GHG emissions benefits compared with simple disposal to landfill. **Figure 13** demonstrates that, by taking the reference system into account, net GHG emissions savings can exceed 100%.

5.09.12 Conclusions and Recommendations

It has been shown that there are many factors that can influence the evaluation of total GHG emissions and net GHG emissions savings for biofuels. These can cause small or large differences in results. They can also combine together to generate a considerable range of results for any particular biofuel. Hence, it is absolutely essential to qualify any results with the basic assumptions that have been made about the details of the biofuel, its biomass feedstock, how this is obtained, processed, and converted, and, crucially, the GHG emissions calculation methodology adopted and, ultimately, the reasons behind the generation of results. In the currently contentious debate surrounding biofuels, it is vital that such matters are clearly stated and that adequate transparency is displayed in the publication of results. Ideally, this means that all details of GHG emissions calculations should be made available within the accepted constraints of commercial confidentiality.

However, the issue of potential variations in results is not simply an academic concern. Even small changes in results can be very important when set in the context of specific targets for net GHG emissions savings for commercially produced biofuels. For example, the EC Renewable Energy Directive specifies minimum net GHG emissions savings of 35% for current biofuels supplied in the European Union, rising to 50% from 1 January 2017, with a target of at least 60% for biofuels and bioliquids produced from plants starting production on or after 1 January 2017 [4]. From the results illustrated here, it can be seen that a change or combination of changes in the specific details of the production of a biofuel could make a significant difference on whether it complies with current or future net GHG emissions savings targets.

Such sensitivity also explains why there is concern among commercial biofuel producers over the possibility of modifying existing GHG emissions calculations and net GHG emissions savings targets in the light of further scientific knowledge, especially regarding the effects of iLUC and, to a lesser degree, soil N_2O emissions. To an economic operator, this introduces considerable policy risk into an already demanding decision-making process that includes both technology and financial risk. While it is necessary to ensure that biofuels provide positive benefits in terms of GHG emissions mitigation, it is important to realize that targets for the supply of biofuels will not be achieved without substantial commitment and investment by such economic operators.

This does not mean that new scientific understanding should be ignored. Instead, uncertainty should be reduced by appreciating the distinction between the fundamental purposes, principles, and application of attributional and consequential LCA. Hence, in the regulation of biofuel producers with respect to the declared net GHG emissions savings of their products, attributional LCA should be applied, rigorously and consistently. One particular result of the strict application of the logic of attributional LCA is that the evaluation of net GHG emissions savings from biofuels for regulatory purposes should exclude the effects of iLUC as these are well outside the control or clear influence of economic operators. However, evaluation of the effects of iLUC is obviously and legitimately within the scope of policy analysis which sets the targets for levels of biofuel production. Such matters are most appropriately addressed by consequential LCA.

In addition to these fundamental issues, the further development and implementation of biofuels will depend on a number of important considerations, which include

- 'low-carbon' biomass feedstock cultivation techniques such as enhancing crop yields without increasing nitrogen fertilizer application rates,
- advanced biofuel processing technologies that can increase overall conversion efficiencies and utilize a wider range of biomass feedstocks,
- improved scientific knowledge concerning the effect of dLUC and soil N_2O emissions,
- agreement on the effects of iLUC through establishment of reliable global land use change modeling,
- international harmonization of appropriate GHG emission calculation methodologies and their relevant databases, and
- application of robust and widespread certification procedures that support GHG emissions calculations for regulatory purposes [48, 49].

References

[1] ISO (1999) Environmental management – life cycle assessment – goal and scope definition and inventory analysis. BS EN ISO 14041. London, UK: British Standards Institute.
[2] ISO (2006) Environmental management – life cycle assessment – principles and framework. BS EN ISO 14040. London, UK: British Standards Institute.
[3] RFA (2009) Carbon and sustainability reporting within the renewable transport fuel obligation: Technical guidance parts 1 and 2, version 2.0. St. Leonards-on-Sea, UK: Renewable Fuels Agency. http://www.renewablefuelsagency.gov.uk (accessed March 2009).
[4] EC (2009) Directive 2009/28/EC of the European parliament and of the council of 23 April 2009 on the promotion of the use of energy from renewable sources and amending and subsequently repealing directives 2001/77/EC and 2003/30/EC. Brussels Belgium: European Commission.
[5] BSI (2008) PAS 2050 – specification for the assessment of life cycle greenhouse gas emissions of goods and services. Publicly Available Specification. London, UK: British Standards Institution, October 2008.
[6] DEFRA (2008) Biomass environmental assessment tool, version 2.0. Prepared by AEA Group plc and North Energy Associates Ltd for Department for Environment, Food and Rural Affairs and the Environment Agency, London, UK. http://www.biomassenergycentre.org (accessed November 2008).
[7] RFA (2010) Carbon and sustainability reporting within the renewable transport fuel obligation: Technical guidance parts 1 and 2, version 3.2. St. Leonards-on-Sea, UK: Renewable Fuels Agency. http://www.renewablefuelsagency.gov.uk (accessed April 2010).

[8] Brander MT, Hutchinson C, and Davis G (2009) Consequential and attributional approaches to LCA: A guide to policy makers with specific reference to greenhouse gas LCA of biofuels. Technical Paper TP-090403-A. Edinburgh, UK: Ecometrica Press. http://www.ecometrica.co.uk (accessed April 2009).

[9] IPCC (1996) Climate change 1995: Second assessment report of the IPCC. *Intergovernmental Panel on Climate Change.* Cambridge University Press, Cambridge. http://www.ipcc.ch/ipccreports/assessment-reports.php (last accessed 7 December 2009).

[10] IPCC (2001) Climate change 2001: The scientific basis; Contribution of working group 1 to the third assessment report of the IPCC. *Intergovernmental Panel on Climate Change.* Cambridge, UK: Cambridge University Press. http://www.ipcc.ch/ipccreports/assessment-reports.php (last accessed 7 December 2007).

[11] IPCC (2007) Climate change 2007: Synthesis report: Fourth assessment report. *Intergovernmental Panel on Climate Change.* Cambridge University Press, Cambridge. http://www.ipcc.ch/pdf/assessment-report/ar4/ar-syn.pdf (last accessed 7 December 2009).

[12] Hill N, Mortimer ND, Bates J, *et al.* (2008) Implementation of the EU biomass action plan and the biofuel strategy: Comparing GHG emission reduction performance of different bio-energy applications on a life cycle basis. Brussels, Belgium: AEA Technology plc for the Directorate-General for the Environment, European Commission.

[13] Mortimer ND, Evans AKF, Shaw VL, and Hunter AJ (2009) Life cycle and techno-economic assessment of the north east biomass to liquids project. Contract No. 08/016. York, UK: North Energy Associates Ltd for the National Non-Food Crops Centre. http://www.nnfcc.co.uk (accessed February 2009).

[14] Mortimer ND, Evans AKF, Ashley A, *et al.* (2010) Comparison of the greenhouse gas benefits resulting from use of vegetable oils for electricity, heat, transport and industrial purposes. Project Code NNFCC10-016. York, UK: North Energy Associates Ltd for the Department for Energy and Climate Change via the National Non-Food Crops Centre. http://www.nnfcc.co.uk (accessed February 2010).

[15] Mortimer ND, Evans AKF, Mwabonje O, *et al.* (2010) Analysis of the greenhouse gas emissions for thermochemical BioSNG production and use in the United Kingdom. Project Code NNFCC10-009. York, UK: North Energy Associates Ltd for the National Non-Food Crops Centre. http://www.nnfcc.co.uk (accessed June 2010).

[16] Dritschilo W, Monroy M, Nash E, *et al.* (1983) Energy versus food resources ratios for alternative energy technologies. *Energy* 8(4): 255–265.

[17] Johnson MA (1983) On gasohol and energy analysis. *Energy* 8(3): 225–233.

[18] Pimental D (2003) Ethanol fuels: Energy balance, economics and environmental impacts are negative. *Natural Resources Research* 12: 2.

[19] Wang M (1999) GREET 1, version 8a. Chicago, IL: Argonne National Laboratory, University of Chicago.

[20] Mortimer ND (2009) Primary energy and greenhouse gas multipliers for fuels and electricity, United Kingdom 2002. Part of the Statistical Analysis Database for Project NF0614. York, UK: North Energy Associates Ltd for the Department for Environment, Food and Rural Affairs via the National Non-Food Crops Centre. http://www.nnfcc.co.uk (accessed October 2009).

[21] Mortimer ND, Mwabonje O, and Hunter AJ (2009) Nitrous oxide emissions from biofuel feedstock cultivation. St. Leonards-on-Sea, UK: North Energy Associates Ltd for the Renewable Fuels Agency. http://www.renewablefuelagency.gov.uk (accessed November 2009).

[22] Spirinckx C and Ceuterick D (1996) *Comparative Life-Cycle Assessment of Diesel and Biodiesel.* Mol, Belgium: VITO (Flemish Institute for Technological Research).

[23] Edwards R, Griesemann J-C, Larivé J-F, and Mahieu V (2003) Well-to-wheels analysis of future automotive fuels and powertrains in the European context: Tank-to-wheels report (version 1). Ispra, Italy: Institute for Environment and Sustainability, Joint Research Centre.

[24] RFA (2008) The Gallagher review of the indirect effects of biofuel production. St. Leonards-on-Sea, UK: Renewable Fuels Agency. http://www.renewablefuelsagency.gov.uk (accessed July 2008).

[25] EC (2010) Commission decision of 10 June 2010 on guidelines for the calculation of land carbon stocks for the purpose of annex V to directive 2009/28/EC. *Official Journal of the European Union* L151: 19–41.

[26] IPCC (2006) IPCC guidelines for national greenhouse gas inventories: Volume 4: Agriculture, forestry and other land use. Edited by Eggleston S, Buendia L, Miwa K, *et al.* Kanagawa, Japan: Institute for Global Environmental Strategies. http://www.ipcc-nggip.iges.org.jp (last accessed 27 May 2008).

[27] EC (2010) Communication from the European Commission on the practical implementation of the EU biofuels and bioliquids sustainability scheme and on counting rules for biofuels. *Official Journal of the European Union* C160: 8–16.

[28] Fargione J, Hill J, Tilman D, *et al.* (2008) Land clearing and the biofuel carbon debt. *Science Express.* http://www.sciencexpress.org (accessed 7 February 2008).

[29] Searchinger T, Heimlich R, Houghton R, *et al.* (2008) Use of US croplands for biofuels increases greenhouse gases through emissions from land use change. *Science Express* 319(5867): 1238–1240.

[30] Bowyer C (2010) Anticipated indirect land use change associated with expanded use of biofuels and bioliquids – an analysis of the national renewable energy action plans. London, UK: Institute for European Environmental Policy. http://www.ieep.eu (accessed November 2010).

[31] Al-Riffai P, Dimaranan B, and Laborde D (2010) Global trade and environmental impact study of the EU biofuels mandate. Washington, DC: ATLASS Consortium, International Food Policy Institute. http://ec.europa.eu/energy/renewables/studies/land_use_change.en.htm (accessed March 2010).

[32] Fonseca MB, Burrell A, Gay H, *et al.* (2010) Impacts of the EU biofuel target on agricultural markets and land use: A comparative modelling assessment. EUR 24449 EN. Sevilla, Spain: European Commission Joint Research Centre, Institute for Prospective Technological Studies. http://ec.europa.eu/energy/renewables/studies/land_use_change.en.htm (accessed June 2010).

[33] EC (2010) The impact of land use change on greenhouse gas emissions from biofuels and bioliquids. Brussels, Belgium: Directorate-General for Energy, European Commission. http://ec.europa.eu/energy/renewables/studies/land_use_change.en.htm (accessed July 2010).

[34] Edwards R, Mulligan D, and Marelli L (2010) Indirect land use change from increased biofuels demand: Comparison of models and results for marginal biofuels production from different feedstocks. EUR 24485 EN. Ispra, Italy: European Commission Joint Research Centre, Institute for Energy. http://ec.europa.eu/energy/renewables/studies/land_use_change.en.htm (last accessed 14 October 2010).

[35] EC (2010) Report from the commission on indirect land-use change related to biofuels and bioliquids. COM(2010)811 Final. Brussels, Belgium: European Commission. http://ec.europa.eu/energy/renewables/studies/land_use_change.en.htm (accessed 22 December 2010).

[36] UNH (2007) User's guide for the DNDC model, version 9.1. Durham, NH: Institute for the Study of Earth, Oceans and Space, Complex Systems Research Center, University of New Hampshire. http://www.dndc.sr.unh.edu (accessed 15 April 2007).

[37] Crutzen PJ, Mosier AR, Smith KA, and Winiwarter W (2008) N_2O release from agrobiofuel production negates global warming reduction by replacing fossil fuels. *Atmospheric Chemistry and Physics* 8: 389–395.

[38] ADAS (2011) Minimising nitrous oxide intensities of arable crop products. LINK Research Project LK09128, ADAS UK Ltd, Boxworth, UK. http://www.adas.co.uk/Home/Projects/MINNO/tabid/283/Default.aspx (accessed 2 March 2011).

[39] BIOGRACE (2011) Harmonised calculation of biofuel greenhouse gas emissions in Europe: Excel greenhouse gas emission calculation tool; Version 3-public. http://www.biograce.net (accessed 2 March 2011).

[40] JEC (2011) JEC biofuel pathways RED method; Version 3.0, 14 November 2008. Ispra, Italy: Joint Research Centre-EU CAR-CONCAWE collaboration, Institute for Environment and Sustainability, European Commission Research Centre. http://.ies.jrc.ec.europa.eu/jec_research-collaboration/downloads-jec.html (accessed 2 March 2011).

[41] RFA (2011) RFA_Calculator_RED_Ready_Setup.exe: Carbon calculator RED ready. St. Leonards-on-Sea, UK: Renewable Fuels Agency. http://www.renewablefuelsagency.gov.uk (accessed 2 March 201).

[42] DEFRA (2010) Fertiliser manual: RB209, 8th edn. London, UK: Department for Environment, Food and Rural Affairs. http://www.defra.gov.uk (accessed June 2010).

[43] NNFCC (2009) NF0614NFert02open.xls: Ammonium nitrate production 1996. York, UK: National Non-Food Crops Centre. http://www.nnfcc.co.uk (accessed 2 March 2011).

[44] BIOGRACE (2011) Harmonised calculation of biofuel greenhouse gas emissions in Europe: List of standard values; Version 2-public. http://www.biograce.net (accessed 2 March 2011).

[45] Brentrup F and Pallière C (2008) GHG emissions and energy efficiency in European nitrogen fertiliser production and use. *Proceedings of the International Fertiliser Society*, No. 639, York, UK. (Paper presented to International Fertilizer Society at a conference in Cambridge, UK, on 11 December 2008).

[46] Bouwman AF, Boumans LJM, and Batjes NH (2002) Modeling global annual N_2O and NO emissions from fertilized fields. *Global Biochemical Cycles* 16(4): 1–9.

[47] JEC (2007) Well-to-wheels analysis of future automotive fuels and powertrains in the European context. Well-to-Tank Report, Version 2c, WTT Appendix 1. Ispra, Italy: Institute for Environment and Sustainability, European Commission Research Centre. http://.ies.jrc.ec.europa.eu/jec_research-collaboration/downloads-jec.html (accessed 13 March 2011).

[48] Kindred D, Mortimer N, Sylvester-Bradley R, *et al.* (2008) Understanding and managing uncertainties to improve biofuel GHG emissions calculations. Project Report No. 435, Part 2. London, UK: Home Grown Cereals Authority.

[49] Mortimer ND, Ashley A, Evans AKF, *et al.* (2008) Support for the review of the indirect effects of biofuels. Sheffield, UK: North Energy Associates Ltd for the Renewable Fuels Agency. http://www.renewablefuelsagency.gov.uk (accessed June 2008).

5.10 Biomass Gasification and Pyrolysis

DJ Roddy, Newcastle University, Newcastle upon Tyne, UK
C Manson-Whitton, Progressive Energy Ltd., Stonehouse, UK

© 2012 Elsevier Ltd. All rights reserved.

5.10.1	Introduction	134
5.10.2	Historical Development	134
5.10.3	Basic Gasification Technology	135
5.10.4	Gasifier Designs	136
5.10.4.1	Fixed Bed	136
5.10.4.2	Fluidized Bed	137
5.10.4.2.1	Bubbling fluidized bed	137
5.10.4.2.2	Circulating fluidized bed	137
5.10.4.2.3	Dual fluidized bed	138
5.10.4.3	Entrained Flow	138
5.10.4.4	Plasma	139
5.10.4.5	Choice of Oxidant	139
5.10.5	Gasifier Feedstock Supply	139
5.10.5.1	Waste Biomass Feedstocks	140
5.10.5.1.1	Solid recovered fuel	140
5.10.5.1.2	Mixed waste wood	140
5.10.5.2	Virgin Biomass Feedstocks	141
5.10.5.2.1	Virgin woodchip	141
5.10.5.2.2	Forestry and arboricultural arisings	141
5.10.5.2.3	Sawmill coproduct	141
5.10.5.2.4	Energy crops	141
5.10.5.3	Typical Fuel Characteristics and Key Contaminants	141
5.10.5.4	Feedstock Reception and Handling	142
5.10.6	Gas Processing	142
5.10.6.1	Contaminants and Their Impacts	142
5.10.6.2	Gas Cleaning Technologies	145
5.10.6.2.1	Cyclones	145
5.10.6.2.2	Bag house filters	145
5.10.6.2.3	Candle filters	145
5.10.6.2.4	Packed bed filters	145
5.10.6.2.5	Wet scrubbers	145
5.10.6.2.6	Electrostatic precipitation (wet and dry)	145
5.10.6.2.7	Specialist tar removal and tar destruction techniques	146
5.10.6.2.8	Specialist sulfur treatment	146
5.10.6.2.9	Activated carbon treatment	146
5.10.6.2.10	Water gas shift	146
5.10.6.2.11	Methane reformation	147
5.10.6.2.12	Cooling	147
5.10.6.2.13	Flare	147
5.10.6.2.14	Water treatment	147
5.10.7	Overview of Gasification Technology Options	147
5.10.8	Pyrolysis	148
5.10.9	Case Studies	149
5.10.9.1	Entrained Flow Gasifier	149
5.10.9.1.1	Freiburg, Germany	149
5.10.9.2	Fluidized Bed Gasifiers	149
5.10.9.2.1	Skive, Denmark (BFB)	149
5.10.9.2.2	Lahti, Finland (CFB)	150
5.10.9.2.3	Güssing, Austria (dual fluidized bed)	150
5.10.9.3	Fixed Bed	150
5.10.9.3.1	CHP plant at Harboore, Denmark (updraft gasifier)	150
5.10.9.4	Plasma	151
5.10.9.4.1	Advanced Plasma Power	151

5.10.9.4.2	Hitachi Metals Ltd., Japan	151
5.10.10	**Recent and Future Developments**	151
5.10.11	**Further Reading**	152
References		152

5.10.1 Introduction

Globally, economic development during the last century has been inextricably dependent on abundant supplies of oil and gas. These resources provide not only heat and power but also transport fuels and feedstock for chemicals and materials. The imperatives of the need to tackle climate change and to address the dwindling abundance of readily accessible supplies of oil and gas are driving the need to seek alternative sources of energy and hydrocarbon building blocks.

Biomass is one such alternative resource. It is renewable since it provides carbon from the biosphere rather than reintroducing carbon from long-term storage, and may be replenished on a time frame of years and decades rather than millennia. Although biomass is not a major industrial fuel, it supplies 15–20% of the total fuel use in the world, mostly in developing countries for domestic heating and cooking.

However, biomass in its natural state is a very different resource from oil and gas. It is a distributed, heterogeneous fuel with a low gravimetric and volumetric calorific value (CV). It is not a direct replacement and is therefore not a fungible resource.

Biomass can be used in its natural state for the direct provision of heat via combustion, which can in turn be converted to motive power using the Rankine cycle. However, this is a limited use of a valuable, renewable hydrocarbon resource, and does not address the need for liquid fuel, chemical feedstock, or even readily deployable heat or power generation at moderate scale with acceptable efficiencies.

Converting biomass to a resource that has similar characteristics to the oil and gas it seeks to replace is a valuable strategic intent. Techniques such as gasification and pyrolysis can provide gaseous, liquid and solid analogues for natural gas, oil, coal, and derivatives.

A number of such 'substoichiometric technologies' have been developed for coal in the past few hundred years. The worldwide gasification capacity at scale (plants above $100\,MW_e$) now stands at 70 817 MW thermal (MW_{th}) of syngas output at 144 operating plants with a total of 412 gasifiers [1]. Equivalent developments for biomass offer the prospect of converting biomass into an energy-dense material that can be moved at low cost to the places where its energy and other attributes can be best used in high-efficiency operations.

This chapter begins with a review of the history of gasification and pyrolysis technology development in Section 5.10.2 before moving on to an outline of the basic science and technology that underpins gasification and pyrolysis processes in Section 5.10.3. Section 5.10.4 explores the main types of gasifier design (fixed and fluidized beds, entrained flow (EF), and plasma). Many of the challenges with gasification lie in the provision of suitable feedstocks (covered in Section 5.10.5) and in processing the gas stream to the standards required in various end uses (covered in Section 5.10.6). After recapping on the main gasification system options (Section 5.10.7) and pyrolysis arrangements (Section 5.10.8), a series of case studies is presented in Section 5.10.9 to illustrate how the various elements have come together in practice. The chapter concludes with a review of recent and likely future developments and some suggestions for further reading.

The material presented in this chapter provides a critical link between other chapters in the Biomass/Biofuels volume of this major reference work. Other chapters examine different ways of growing various types of biomass and ensuring their carbon and sustainability credentials, limitations on the ability of biofuels to meet all future demands without a migration from first-generation fuels toward synthetic fuels, technologies for producing synthetic fuels from synthesis gas, and alternative uses for synthesis gas for sustainable production of organic chemicals in addition to fuels. At the center of all of that stands the pyrolysis and gasification system required for converting biomass into good quality synthesis gas.

5.10.2 Historical Development

While there are tens of thousands of gasifiers operating globally across a range of scales, the majority of the capacity is fueled by coal. Of those that operate on biomass, most have been used for heat and some power applications via steam raising rather than for production of high-quality syngas. There is very limited experience of biomass gasifiers providing the quality of syngas necessary for power generation in engines or for conversion to biofuel.

Significant advances were made during the oil crisis of the 1970s, although oil price decline halted significant further developments. Today's oil price, in addition to the recognition of the need to address climate change is driving activity in this sector. It is only over the past 5 years that biomass gasifier systems have come close to commercial operation, with probably fewer than 50 operating worldwide generating biofuels or power in excess of $1\,MW_{th}$ input rating. This relative infancy is due to a number of factors discussed in Section 5.10.10. However, a number of suppliers are currently installing their first 'commercial'-scale products.

The production of gas from coal began in 1665 in England [2]. In early processes, the coal was converted into coke (the main product) and coal gas (a by-product) by heating it in an airtight furnace (or coke oven) using additional coal as an external fuel. This was effectively a pyrolysis process. Larger-scale gasification processes were developed toward the end of the eighteenth century to provide gas in large quantities, based on converting coke into hydrogen and carbon monoxide [3]. Coal gas was first used for lighting purposes in Philadelphia in 1796. The first work on studying gas production from wood was done by P. Lebon in 1791. By the 1850s, 'town gas' (produced from the gasification of coal) was widely used in London for lighting. Winkler started developing the fluidized bed coal gasifier in 1922. The growth of gas works continued until the oil and gas industry started to introduce cheap fuels. Over time, the use of industrial gas extended from direct use in lighting and cooking to heating, and then as a chemical feedstock for producing ammonia, methanol, and their many derivatives including various fertilizers. More recently, it has been used for electricity generation and ultimately for liquid transport fuel production.

Parallel developments took place in steam drum and piping technology, leading to gastight equipment that could be operated at pressures above 2 bar – and therefore more compact installations. Fully continuous gasification became possible with the commercialization of cryogenic separation of air into oxygen and nitrogen in the 1920s. This led to developments like the Lurgi moving-bed pressurized gasification process in 1931 and the Koppers-Totzek EF process in the 1940s [3].

Terminology usage has varied over time and between countries. 'Town gas' is usually derived from coal, 'wood gas' from biomass, and 'water gas' from coke. Many prefer to reserve the term 'synthesis gas' for mixtures of hydrogen and carbon monoxide (only) irrespective of the feedstock. Some people use the term 'producer gas' to cover all of the above: others reserve it for partial oxidation of coke using humidified air. Producer gas was first used to power an internal combustion engine in 1881, with the engine 'sucking' the gas from a gasifier – hence the additional term 'suction gas'.

During the Second World War, there was an upsurge in interest in gasification as a source of fuels at a time when fuel supply was problematic. Small gasifiers running on charcoal and wood were readily available in the 1940s with more than a million small units in operation [4]. Fuel quality and exhaust emissions are likely to have been highly variable. Once liquid fuels became readily available again, interest in gasification fell away. However, work continued in developing countries such as China, and then South Africa, Brazil, the Philippines, and Indonesia.

The oil crisis in 1973 triggered new interest in coal and biomass gasification, and this was sustained by the 1980 oil crisis. In South Africa, Sasol used coal gasification and Fischer–Tropsch synthesis [5] as the basis of their synthetic fuels and petrochemicals industry, making their facility the largest gasification center in the world [6]. Commercial facilities with high-value end products have tended to be more immune to downward swings in oil and gas prices [7]. While interest in biomass gasification in developed countries has been intermittent, developing countries have tended to demonstrate an ongoing interest in gasification of agricultural wastes, particularly for energy supply in remote areas. Developed countries are now looking more widely at their increasing levels of organic waste production in the context of resource conservation and climate change abatement, and see gasification as a versatile process for converting organic waste into a range of energy forms, including high-specification transport fuels via the latest gas-to-liquids technologies [8].

5.10.3 Basic Gasification Technology

Gasification is a process in which a solid material containing carbon (e.g., biomass) is converted into a gas by reacting it at high temperature with oxygen which is present at levels insufficient to support complete combustion. The aim is to produce a synthesis gas (or syngas) consisting mainly of hydrogen and carbon monoxide. Syngas can then be used for chemical or fuel synthesis (hence the name), or as a fuel for direct combustion.

The main steps are:

Biomass is heated in a pyrolysis stage to drive off the volatile components that typically make up 70–86% of the dry biomass, leaving a solid char (or biochar). Depending on the details of the gasifier, the heat can come from external sources or from combustion of some of the pyrolysis products. The volatile components are mainly hydrogen, carbon monoxide, carbon dioxide, methane, hydrocarbon gases, tar, and water vapor. Gas stream composition depends on pyrolysis temperature, pressure, and residence time, as well as the nature of the biomass feedstock. Where the heat for the gasification stage comes from combustion of a proportion of the pyrolysis char inside the gasifier, the exothermic reactions are represented by the equations:

$$C + O_2 \rightarrow CO_2 \quad \Delta H = -393.8 \text{ kJ mol}^{-1} \quad [1]$$

$$C + \frac{1}{2}O_2 \rightarrow CO \quad \Delta H = -123.1 \text{ kJ mol}^{-1} \quad [2]$$

Next comes the gasification stage proper, where higher temperatures crack tars and hydrocarbons in the pyrolysis gas stream and char are partially oxidized. Carbon is converted into CO and hydrogen in a reaction called the water gas reaction in which carbon reacts with water vapor derived from the original biomass:

$$C + H_2O \leftrightarrow CO + H_2 \quad \Delta H = 118.5 \text{ kJ mol}^{-1} \quad [3]$$

Another key gasification reaction is the Boudouard reaction:

$$C + CO_2 \leftrightarrow 2CO \quad \Delta H = 159.9 \text{ kJ mol}^{-1} \quad [4]$$

In these reversible, endothermic reactions (3 and 4), higher temperatures favor the production of hydrogen and carbon monoxide. Lower pressures also favor the production of carbon monoxide, while higher pressures favor the production of carbon dioxide.

The other main reaction is the exothermic water gas shift reaction in which CO reacts with steam to form CO_2 and additional hydrogen:

$$CO + H_2O \leftrightarrow H_2 + CO_2 \quad \Delta H = -41 \text{ kJ mol}^{-1} \quad [5]$$

There is also an important methanation reaction:

$$C + 2H_2 \leftrightarrow CH_4 \quad \Delta H = -87.5 \text{ kJ mol}^{-1} \quad [6]$$

The above reactions and others involving feedstock impurities take place simultaneously during the gasification process. The relative proportions of gases at the gasifier exit depend on process conditions and the composition of the biomass feedstock. The position of the steady-state equilibrium depends in the normal way on temperature and pressure, but at low temperatures the rate of reaction may be so low that equilibrium compositions are never reached in practice. For example, below 700 °C, the water gas shift reaction proceeds so slowly that the product composition is said to be 'frozen' [2]. Gas–solid reactions are slow compared with the gas-phase reactions. Another key parameter affecting the outlet gas composition is the amount of oxygen relative to what is required to support complete combustion.

5.10.4 Gasifier Designs

A wide range of gasifier configurations have been developed globally, each tailored to different feedstock materials (type and form), different scales, and different required qualities of syngas. There are three basic forms of gasification system: fixed bed (updraft and downdraft), fluidized bed, and EF.

The main points of difference relate to where biomass is fed into the gasifier (top or side), how it is moved around (under gravity or via gas flow), the temperature at which it is operated (and in particular whether it is above or below the ash/char melting point), the operating pressure, and the choice of oxidant (oxygen, air or steam).

Some people draw a major distinction between low-temperature gasification (< 1000 °C) and high-temperature gasification (>1200 °C). With low-temperature gasification, the desired products (hydrogen and CO) typically contain only half of the energy in the gas stream, with the remainder being contained in the methane and higher hydrocarbon tars [3]. With high-temperature gasification there is limited methane and/or tar formation, and the gas cleanup and recovery system is therefore simpler. Gasification processes typically seek to operate either below the ash softening point (above which it starts to become sticky and prone to agglomeration) or above the slagging temperature (whereupon it becomes fully liquid and therefore removable).

In addition, there are slight variants using techniques such as indirect gasifiers (where heat is applied externally rather than autothermally from partial combustion of the biomass in the gasification stage), plasma arcs, and molten metal baths, either as a core part of the gasification process or as a means of cleanup.

5.10.4.1 Fixed Bed

In a fixed bed gasifier, gas flows relatively slowly through a bed of fuel, which therefore must have good permeability. This means that 'lumpy' feedstock is required rather than crushed or pulverized form. The oxidant can be air or oxygen, although commonly for biomass facilities air is used. In a fixed bed gasifier, there are four distinct thermal zones. In the drying zone, remaining moisture in the fuel is evaporated. In the pyrolysis zone, the material is heated to 300–400 °C with no added oxygen, generating a pyrolysis gas laden with liquid hydrocarbon tar and a char. In the gasification (reduction) zone, typically in excess of 800 °C, the majority of the char is converted to a syngas. In the combustion zone, in excess of 1000 °C, the remaining char is fully combusted, providing the heat required for the reactions in the other zones.

There are two main versions of the fixed bed gasifier: 'updraft' and 'downdraft'. In both cases, fuel is added into the top of the gasifier. In an updraft gasifier, the oxidant is injected into the base of the vessel and the syngas exits from the top (so the biomass and gases move in opposite directions), and some of the char burns as it falls to provide heat. In a downdraft gasifier, the syngas exits through the base of the vessel, while the oxidant is fed in at the top or the side (so the biomass and gases move in the same direction). Some of the biomass is burnt as it falls, and then forms a bed of hot charcoal. The different configurations dictate the relative positions of the four zones discussed above.

Both types of gasifier are relatively simple, and therefore lend themselves to smaller-scale facilities. Updraft gasifiers have high thermal efficiencies (due to high charcoal burnout and good internal heat exchange), can accommodate higher moisture feedstocks (as the countercurrent gas flow dries it from the point of entry), and the relatively low temperature of the raw syngas is suited to the gas cleanup units. Additionally, updraft gasifiers can be configured at a wide variety of scales from 10 kW$_e$ to > 30 MW$_e$. However, in an updraft gasifier, the tar laden gas from the pyrolysis zone passes out in the syngas, whereas in a downdraft gasifier, the tar passes through the combustion zone and therefore can be cracked at temperature. Crudely, updraft gasifiers generate of the order of 100 g Nm^{-3} of tar, whereas downdraft gasifiers produce only 1 g Nm^{-3}. This has a significant impact on the downstream syngas cleanup required.

This major advantage tends to outweigh the disadvantages of downdraft gasification that include higher particulate carryover, slightly lower gasifier efficiency (due to the relatively high temperature of the exit gases), some scale-size limits, and tighter constraints on feedstock quality in terms of particle size and moisture content. Pelletization or briquetting of the biomass is often necessary. The gasifier throat configuration is critical in ensuring tar destruction. In general, this constrains the maximum gasifier size to approximately 8–10 MW$_{th}$ (and often smaller), although the units lend themselves to multiple trains to increase capacity.

Excessive tar formation can occur during unsteady operation or periods of part-load operation [2]. Care needs to be taken before restarting a fixed bed gasifier to ensure that all combustible gases have been vented. Fuel blockages and high-temperature corrosion are other common problems. They sometimes suffer from product gas nonuniformity as a result of flow maldistribution, but generally they offer high levels of thermal efficiency albeit at relatively low throughputs. Slight variations on fixed bed gasifier configurations, particularly with regard to oxidant injection points and gas flow, can offer further optimization of the various attributes. Such developments tend to be proprietary.

5.10.4.2 Fluidized Bed

This technology was originally developed by Winkler in 1926 for large-scale coal gasification. In a biomass fluidized bed gasifier, solid crushed fuel particles are suspended together with a much larger mass of fine inert bed material (e.g., silica sand, dolomite, or even the ash from the fuel itself) in high gas flow. New feed particles are mixed with those already undergoing gasification. The ash can be discharged dry or agglomerated. The low temperatures (< 900 °C) in this gasifier allow the use of reactive feedstock. Some fluidized bed gasifiers are designed to be operated under pressure. The high gas volumes required for fluidization mean that these gasifiers are often air-blown although oxygen-blown systems are feasible. The gas exits the chamber at the top. In this type of gasifier, the four stages (drying, devolatilization, gasification, and combustion) are not stratified as in a fixed bed gasifier, but occur simultaneously. The tar levels in this type of gasifier are at an intermediate level between up- and downdraft systems at a nominal ~10 g Nm^{-3}.

At start-up, an external means of bringing the sand up to temperature is required. During normal operation, a proportion of the injected biomass is combusted in a controlled flow of oxidant in order to maintain the bed temperature. Fluidized bed gasifiers are more compact than fixed bed because the intensive mixing in the bed leads to good heat exchange and high reaction rates. They can operate at lower reaction temperatures and can thereby tolerate biomass feedstocks with a lower ash melting point or a highly corrosive ash. A drawback is that carbon burnout is incomplete because of the range of residence times seen by individual particles. There are several types of fluidized bed gasifier.

5.10.4.2.1 Bubbling fluidized bed

Biomass is fed in from the side (see **Figure 1**), with air, oxygen, or steam being blown upward through the bed at a rate that is just high enough to keep the material agitated – typically 1–3 m s^{-1}. Good mixing leads to a faster pyrolysis reaction than in a fixed bed gasifier [10]. Oxygen gives a higher quality syngas than air. The modest temperatures result in reasonably high levels of methane production. Reactors designed to have a larger head space above the bubbling bed tend to produce lower tar levels in the syngas stream [10]. Particulate levels can be high as a result of particle attrition in the fluidized bed. A cyclone at the syngas exit point catches the ash and char particles. Bubbling fluidized bed (BFB) gasifiers have run on many different biomass feedstocks and tend to be quite tolerant of variation in particle size and moisture content because of the quality of the mixing. One of the main risks is bed agglomeration, which can occur when biomass feedstocks with too low an ash melting temperature are employed.

Technology providers for BFB gasifiers include Carbona, Foster Wheeler, Enerkem, TRI, EPI, and Iowa State University [9].

5.10.4.2.2 Circulating fluidized bed

Biomass is fed in from the side (see **Figure 2**). A higher air/oxygen/steam velocity is used (typically 5–10 m s^{-1}) in order to keep the biomass suspended, with the particulates being returned to the fluidized bed via a cyclone and siphon. Higher velocities lead to higher levels of particle attrition and therefore higher concentrations of particulates. The gasifier needs to be designed against

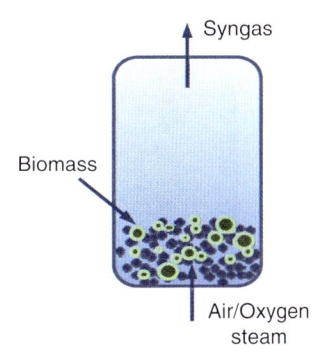

Figure 1 Bubbling fluidized bed gasifier. Reproduced with permission from E4Tech (2009) Review of technologies for gasification of biomass and wastes. NNFCC Project 09/008. www.nnfcc.co.uk.

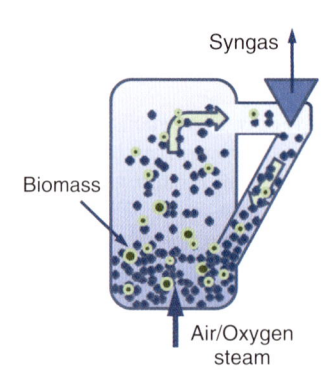

Figure 2 Circulating fluidized bed gasifier. Reproduced with permission from E4Tech (2009) Review of technologies for gasification of biomass and wastes. NNFCC Project 09/008. www.nnfcc.co.uk.

erosion by high-velocity particles. Circulating Fluidized Bed (CFB) gasifiers tend to switch easily between different feedstocks provided the size is kept below 20 mm. The cyclone is designed to separate out both the ash and the bed material and return them to the reactor.

Smaller particles tend to be gasified on the first pass and carried over while larger particles remain behind until they have become sufficiently consumed to be carried over into the external recycle loop. This makes CFBs particularly suited to the gasification of biomass where particle size and shape can be difficult to control. Carbon burnout is considerably better than with a BFB gasifier.

Pressurized operation is also possible, and is cost-effective if the syngas is required to be pressurized for downstream use [3]. A 20 bar system has been developed by Foster Wheeler, using lock hoppers for pressurizing the biomass feed and for primary ash removal.

The most prominent technology provider for CFB gasifiers at present is Foster Wheeler, but designs are also being developed by VTT, CUTEC, Fraunhofer, VVBGC, and Uhde/TUB-F [9].

5.10.4.2.3 Dual fluidized bed

Here there are separate, but linked, CFB reactors for gasification and combustion. Biomass is fed into the gasifier and converted into syngas and char using steam. Suspended char and sand drop into the combustor where the char is burnt in air whose velocity is sufficiently high to keep the heated particles of sand suspended and drive them through a cyclone. The cyclone returns the hot particles to the gasifier while releasing syngas. The use of steam not only boosts the concentration of hydrogen in the syngas but also increases the methane content. The main advantages are the ability to optimize gasification and combustion separately, and the ability to produce a relatively low-nitrogen syngas using air rather than oxygen for the combustion part. Cracking catalysts are used to break down any heavy hydrocarbons in the syngas stream, along with a scrubber for alkali and particulate removal.

The technology is at a relatively early stage of development, with REPOTEC, SilvaGas, and Taylor Biomass among the active players [9].

5.10.4.3 Entrained Flow

In an EF gasifier (see **Figure 3**), pulverized fuel particles and gas flow concurrently and rapidly with inherently short residence times (a few seconds) in the gasifier reactor. This type of gasifier can also process atomized liquid feedstock or slurries. It is the most common technology for processing coal, and has featured very prominently in successful coal gasifiers since the 1950s [1]. All EF

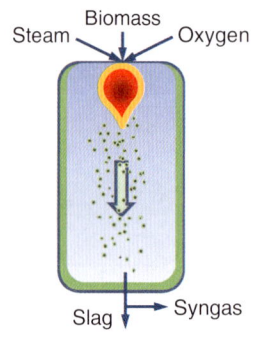

Figure 3 Entrained flow gasifiers. Reproduced with permission from E4Tech (2009) Review of technologies for gasification of biomass and wastes. NNFCC Project 09/008. www.nnfcc.co.uk.

gasifiers are slagging (resultant ash is fused and discharged as molten slag) as the processing temperature is higher. This is an important aspect of the design since the formed slag serves as part of the inner vessel wall, providing a heat and corrosion protection layer. Liquid slag viscosity must be controlled such as by adding a suitable fluxing agent such as limestone. These gasifiers generally use pure oxygen as an oxidant, but many are not suited to waste or biomass streams because these cannot be slurried, and the biomass particles (compared with coal) do not lend themselves to dry-feed. Therefore, they are usually only used for biomass in conjunction with pyrolysis preprocessing. The majority of EF gasifiers were developed for coal operation and are large-scale, typically at 600 MW_{th} or larger [1].

The high temperatures (typically 1200–1600 °C) of an EF gasifier provide extremely low levels of tar as a result of extensive thermal cracking [11] and very low methane content. High temperatures also favor hydrogen and CO production over methane and CO_2. A drawback is that the extensive cooling required prior to gas cleanup reduces the thermal efficiency. The cost (and energy) penalty associated with satisfying the high oxygen demand of an EF gasifier is significant. Operating pressure can be up to 100 bar.

EF gasifiers may be able to accept a mixture of feedstocks provided the particle size is adequate and the composition remains reasonably steady over time. Given the short residence time involved, it is normal to grind the biomass down to a particle size of less than 1 mm. Typically, the feedstock moisture content must be below 15%. Unlike other gasifiers, the EF gasifier needs a pilot flame to provide the initial injection of energy. The advantage of a high-quality syngas is offset by the need for a pulverized feedstock. EF gasifiers designed for coal operation can sometimes accept 10–15% biomass in a coal blend [2].

Several companies are developing EF gasifier designs for biomass gasification. The most prominent are Choren and Range Fuels, with a number of other companies at an earlier stage of development, for example, Pearson Technology, FZK/KIT, and Mitsubishi Heavy Industries [9].

5.10.4.4 Plasma

Plasma is generated by high-voltage discharge between graphite electrodes. The torch can reach temperatures of 6000–10 000 °C, which will convert hydrocarbon solids, liquids, and gases to H_2 and CO. Syngas composition can be regulated by controlling the plasma torches to compensate for variations in feed rate and composition and achieve a steady gasifier temperature. Such systems can be configured such that the plasma is generated in the core gasification vessel, with a body of feedstock not dissimilar to an updraft gasifier configuration, in which case no oxidant is required at all. Any inorganic matter is vitrified into an inert slag. Alternatively, the plasma can be applied in a separate vessel, downstream of a more conventional gasifier, where the impure syngas, liquids, and residual char are converted to carbon monoxide and hydrogen – high-quality syngas. Plasma gasifiers are normally designed to run on waste, with a particular initial interest in medical waste. Any heavy metals contained within the waste tend to come out in the vitrified slag.

The biggest players at present are Westinghouse and Plasco, with InEnTec, Startech, and Solena Group also active in the field [9].

5.10.4.5 Choice of Oxidant

Gasifiers can use oxygen or air as the oxidant. Systems that use oxygen tend to be more costly (10–15% increase in capital cost), and also entail the cost or parasitic load of oxygen production (equivalent to 5–7% on operating costs) [7]. However, for liquid fuel or Bio-SNG production, oxygen tends to be necessary to avoid nitrogen dilution in the gas stream and to keep the cost of high-spec gas cleanup within acceptable bounds. Nitrogen is, however, not a problem where the intended end use is ammonia synthesis. Most EF gasifier developers opt for an oxygen-blown design, particularly where fuel synthesis is the aim. Fluidized bed developers tend to offer both air and oxygen depending on the application. Steam can also serve as an oxidant as well as an indirect heat source, or it can serve as a moderator to reduce the gasification temperature relative to a pure oxygen system.

5.10.5 Gasifier Feedstock Supply

It is particularly important to understand the properties of candidate biomass fuels in undertaking process design and specification, especially with respect to fuel preparation and handling and gasifier operations. Standards do exist for solid biofuels of all types: the EU has developed via CEN/335 a comprehensive approach to the classification and standardization of solid biofuels and this should be used in transactions between seller and buyer and by process designers in order to assure reliable and certifiable operational conditions.

The essential first condition that must be satisfied is that feedstock specification and the process design are matched; the gasifier in particular cannot be omnivorous. For gasification, important feedstock attributes are:

- morphology (size, shape) – affecting pressure drop across the bed and consistency of operation
- moisture content – drier feedstocks give a higher quality gas
- energy content – on a dry and ash-free basis most biomass provides about 19 MJ kg^{-1}, but in practice the figures vary considerably
- volatile matter content – important for tar production levels
- elemental composition – important for energy content and for critical contaminants (particularly levels of halogens, sulfur, arsenic, and mercury)
- ash fusion characteristics – both the quantity of ash and its melting characteristics are important
- bulk density – important for energy density, ease of material handling, storage costs and transport costs.

Here waste biomass feedstocks are considered first, followed by virgin biomass feedstocks before looking at feedstock handling and reception requirements for a reliable gasification facility.

5.10.5.1 Waste Biomass Feedstocks

Over 98% of the potential UK biomass resource is from waste products [12]. Municipal, commercial, and industrial waste therefore provide a valuable and ubiquitous source of biomass fuel. Waste is increasing in the United Kingdom. Annual municipal arisings have been predicted to grow from ~40 million tonnes to in excess of 50 million tonnes by 2020 [13]. Across the spectrum of municipal, commercial, and industrial waste arisings, the key biomass waste fuels are:

- Solid recovered fuel (SRF) in its wet and dry forms
- Mixed waste wood
- Sawmill coproduct and other discarded clean wood.

5.10.5.1.1 Solid recovered fuel

SRF is nonhazardous waste that has been processed to provide a consistent, market-orientated fuel with a higher CV, lower moisture and ash content, and controlled chemical content and biomass fraction.

In its raw state, municipal waste is typically 50% biomass due to the organics, paper, wood, and textile content. Its composition depends very much on local regulations and approach to separation and recycling of household waste. Such material is of relatively low CV with uncontrolled form and composition.

The production of SRF from nonhazardous wastes creates the opportunity to utilize waste-derived fuels in thermal applications that are more sophisticated than the classical waste disposal route via incineration; in particular SRF is being regarded increasingly by a number of producers and users as a potential feedstock in gasification.

The term SRF arises from work undertaken by the European Commission under CEN/343 to provide a systematic basis for the classification and standardization of fuels derived from nonhazardous wastes. This work was undertaken in the anticipation that the energy content of nonhazardous wastes should be exploited in pursuit of increased resource efficiency within the EU CEN/343 therefore set out to define a scientifically informed basis for describing the properties of waste-derived fuels for the purpose of facilitating trade between producer and user, for informing process design, environmental permitting, communication with stakeholders, and for quality management.

It will be readily appreciated that it is not feasible to design a piece of sophisticated plant such as a gasifier without tailoring the design to the known properties of the fuel. This is true for a conventional coal gasifier and it is equally the case for a gasifier intended for operation on biomass or a waste-derived fuel. Given the variable provenance and properties of waste materials, it becomes an indispensable condition that some method must be applied by which the physical and chemical properties of a waste-derived fuel can be specified and assured, if they are to be used as a gasifier feedstock. The CEN/343 approach provides a rigorous method to do this.

The production of SRF is usually carried out by mechanical biological treatment (MBT). This process is a combination of mechanical sorting and biological stabilization of the residue. Alternatively, it can be provided by an autoclave process. In this case, the biogenic content of the primary fuel output tends to be higher but wetter, and requires significantly higher input energy for production. Importantly, manufacturers of SRF are starting to provide fuel to a European quality specification. Example processes are EcoDeco and Herhof. MBT material has a CV of 15–20 GJ te^{-1} (EcoDeco indicate 17 GJ te^{-1} [14]) and a biomass content of at least 60%.

5.10.5.1.2 Mixed waste wood

Waste wood arises from various sectors including municipal arisings, retail, the wood and wood products sector, furniture, transport, and packaging. The majority of this residual waste wood is mixed, containing contaminants in the form of glues and resins in chipboard and medium-density fiberboard (MDF), paint, plastic coatings, and so on. These contaminants inhibit recycling and widespread energy recovery from the arisings in the United Kingdom, since Waste Incineration Directive compliant plant is required.

Waste wood is an important source of biomass feedstock, although there is debate over available resource. In the Carbon Balances Report [15], ERM estimates that there are ~7.5 million tonnes of waste wood produced annually in the United Kingdom, of which only 1.2 million tonnes is recycled or reused and 0.3 million is incinerated with energy recovery. This leaves ~6 million tonnes or 80% that is currently disposed of to landfill. In line with other waste sources, waste wood arisings are not envisaged to decrease. However, a significant number of proposed renewable energy plants are predicated on waste wood for all or part of the feedstock stream.

Waste wood has a CV of ~15 GJ te^{-1} depending on the exact moisture and storage condition, and a biomass content of ~90% or more, depending on exact sourcing of the material. Waste contractors commonly chip the material for ease of transport, and seek small gate fees or zero cost disposal routes for this chipped, prepared material. This often includes local delivery within a 25 mile radius.

Waste wood does not receive the same level of gate fees as most types of SRF, and may even command a price. However, the typically higher biogenic content and reduced ash content can offer enhanced outturn product revenues and lower costs. This can partially offset the loss of revenues on the weighbridge.

5.10.5.2 Virgin Biomass Feedstocks

This subject is covered in great detail in Perlack's chapter, so all that appears here is a brief UK perspective.

5.10.5.2.1 Virgin woodchip
In the United Kingdom, half of the commercial forestry is operated by the forestry commission, with the balance under private management. Approximately 9 million green tonnes are extracted per annum for timber production. Green timber has 50–55% of moisture as harvested, although with seasoning it can be reduced to 30% naturally over time, without additional heat. This material can be utilized as woodchip, although its use is in direct competition with sawlog. Small roundwood is less valuable than sawlog, so woodchip can be sourced from this material.

5.10.5.2.2 Forestry and arboricultural arisings
Other than saw-wood, there is a variety of lower grade timber available from forestry and the urban environment. In managing forestry, brash (removal of ancillary stems), thinning (trees which are too small for extraction), and poor quality final crops can be extracted. The arboricultural arisings in England, Scotland, and Wales by forest district is estimated to be ~670 000 [16] oven-dried tonnes per annum. This is equivalent to 1 300 000 green tonnes.

Similarly, in the urban environment and on road and rail-sides, tree management produces arboricultural arisings. These are usually chipped, and often landfilled, but are increasingly being viewed as another energy biomass source.

5.10.5.2.3 Sawmill coproduct
Sawmill coproduct is an alternative and valuable source of woody biomass. Sawmills recover ~50% of the input material as sawn product, with the balance being coproduct in the form of bark, sawdust, and woodchip. With the latest equipment and sawing efficiency improvements, sawmill recoveries are improving slightly, but this still represents a significant source of biomass material.

Current outlets from sawmills have been historically to the boardmill industries for the production of chipboard and MDF. Increases in levels of using recycled material have put pressure on this market, which is dominated by a few large players in the United Kingdom. Increased board production in other parts of Europe with lower manufacturing costs continues to apply downward pressure on the coproduct price. Therefore, sawmills are considering other outlets, such as onsite combustion for energy generation and pellet manufacture.

Sawmill coproduct has a high moisture content, up to 55% since much of the sawn softwood produced in the United Kingdom is unseasoned. Therefore, the CV is relatively low at ~7.5 GJ te^{-1}. It also means that transport costs per gigajoules for this material can be relatively high.

In 2004, UK sawmills consumed 5.1 million tonnes of softwood to produce ~2.5 million tonnes of sawn log [17]. Therefore, ~2.5 million tonnes of coproduct was generated, of which ~1.7 million tonnes was utilized by the UK panel board industries. This coproduct was generated by 235 sawmills nationally, of which 18 sawmills individually produced over 40 000 tonnes of coproduct per annum. This material commands a price, and an increasingly higher one, as the number of biomass projects seeking pure materials increases.

5.10.5.2.4 Energy crops
There are a wide range of energy crops grown both for biomass and as feedstock for biofuels. In the United Kingdom, the main biomass crops are miscanthus and short rotation coppice (willow).

Short rotation coppice is usually a form of willow that provides a woody perennial crop. It is normally harvested every 3 years and once established can provide a crop for a further 30 years. Yields naturally vary according to local conditions, but are usually estimated to be between 8 and 12 oven-dried tonnes (odt) per hectare per year. Early experience in the United Kingdom has been of lower yields than this, often below 5 odt ha^{-1} yr^{-1}, including losses during harvesting and storage, although more recent developments in strains of willow and improved husbandry and handling indicates that 9 odt ha^{-1} yr^{-1} could be attainable. The nominal CV in the dry state is assumed to be 18 GJ te^{-1}, although it is usually harvested at ~50% moisture, and dried to ~25% to provide a feedstock of 12 GJ te^{-1}.

5.10.5.3 Typical Fuel Characteristics and Key Contaminants

Table 1 collates and compares UK data on key biomass feedstock characteristics for both waste and virgin materials.

Although many of the macroscopic properties of biomass are remarkably similar across a number of species, it is important to note that minor constituents can vary with the species and undoubtedly with the environment and soils in which they are grown. (Scientific literature is prolific on the subject of mineral take-up from the environment, with some plant species being especially effective in accumulating, lead, zinc, mercury, etc.)

This is particularly important when considering the properties of biomass ashes, which in themselves are notably dissimilar to coal ashes, both in the amount and also their chemical composition. Biomass ash is generally quite different to coal ash, and tends to contain large quantities of salts. Typical components are potassium, calcium, phosphorus, sodium, magnesium, iron, and silicon. This has implications for chosen gasifier operating conditions, especially with respect to ash fusion temperatures and the volatile

Table 1 Summary of key biomass feedstock characteristics

	SRF	Waste wood	Virgin wood
Prepared moisture content	20%	15%	30% (partial drying)
Ash content	20%	3%	1.5%
Net CV	15 GJ te^{-1}	14 GJ te^{-1}	12 GJ te^{-1}
Bulk density	300 kg m^{-3} (pelletized) < 100 kg m^{-3} (floc)	250 kg m^{-3}	250 kg m^{-3}
Biomass fraction (by energy)	60%	95%	100%
Chlorine	0.6% (up to 1%)	0.03% (up to 0.4%)	0.01% (up to 0.04%)
Sulfur	0.15% (up to 1%)	0.03% (up to 0.2%)	0.01% (up to 0.1%)
Heavy metals	Hg 0.5 mg kg^{-1} (up to 10 mg kg^{-1}) As 1.0 mg kg^{-1} (up to 100 mg kg^{-1})	Hg 0.05 mg kg^{-1} (up to 0.2 mg kg^{-1}) As 1.0 mg kg^{-1} (up to 10 mg kg^{-1})	Hg 0.05 mg kg^{-1} (up to 0.2 mg kg^{-1}) As 0.10 mg kg^{-1} (up to 2 mg kg^{-1})

behavior of certain alkali metal oxides at elevated temperatures. Furthermore, gas processing operations may be sensitive to small levels of both alkali metals and heavy metals in the deactivation of catalysts.

5.10.5.4 Feedstock Reception and Handling

Feedstock must be safely admitted into the facility, and stored in a way which satisfies both the technical requirements of the processing plant and also any regulations regarding odor, leaching, and wind disturbance issues.

An important factor in any biomass system is feedstock processing. This is dictated by the feedstock type, delivered form, and gasifier form requirements. Fixed bed gasifiers require lumped fuel (large chips, pellets, or briquettes), fluidized bed gasifiers require a finer particle or floc, and EF gasifiers require very fine particle size capable of being injected in dense phase flow or as a liquid.

Therefore, the feedstock must be supplied in, or processed into the appropriate form. This can be achieved by shredding, hammer-milling, pelletizing, or briquetting. The separate use of heat is often necessary since moisture content is critical, ideally using waste heat from the process to control humidity of the fuel. It is normal to aim for a moisture content in the range 10–20%. Above that range the thermal efficiency of the gasifier begins to drop away: below that range the energy required for drying grows rapidly. Thermo-mechanical options that combine both aspects of fuel conditioning include pyrolysis and torrefaction.

Each of these processes has an energy penalty that can add significantly to the operational cost. An EF gasifier that may offer superior syngas characteristics will require either very finely milled solid material (possibly torrefied) or a pyrolysis oil. These processes in particular decrease the overall process efficiency significantly and increase costs. A gasification system that can handle a relatively simple shredded or chipped material may offer efficiency and cost advantages upstream, although if this comes with a significant gas quality penalty, the cost of subsequent downstream gas processing may be higher.

The storage and handling of lump fuel is relatively straightforward. Woodchip or pellets can be tipped directly onto flat floors, bunkers, moving floor systems, or even blown into silos. Floc is difficult to handle: it is extremely low density that makes it volumetrically inefficient to handle; it must be carefully handled to prevent wind disturbance and escape; and it is difficult to move out of containers and through process plant. Storage facilities are typically designed for at least 10 days feedstock supply.

Other important elements of the feedstock handling system can include controlling biomass supply rate into the gasifier, controlling biomass distribution across the inlet, maintaining gasifier pressure and temperature conditions during feedstock injection, conveying of biomass over extended vertical and horizontal distances, removal of foreign objects, and automating the whole process to reduce labor costs and possible health risks. Common problems are material bridging, plugging, tar accumulation on entry valves, and physical damage to conveying screws.

5.10.6 Gas Processing

The gas processing chain is also critical, and often overlooked. In addition to the primary components in the syngas (CO, H_2, CH_4, N_2, CO_2), there are a variety of impurities which are a function of feedstock and gasifier configuration. These have an impact on the operability and longevity of downstream equipment, particularly the power generator or catalyst, the final emissions to air and water from the facility, and quality of output fuel. The critical impurities are tars, particulates, sulfur, and chlorine compounds, nitrogen compounds such as HCN and NH_3, heavy metals, alkali metals, and polyaromatic hydrocarbons including dioxins. Additionally, it may be necessary to adjust the ratios of CO and H_2 in the gas stream, and even reduce or remove components such as CO_2.

5.10.6.1 Contaminants and Their Impacts

Table 2 lists the main contaminants in a raw gasifier product stream and summarizes their impacts when left untreated.

Table 2 Impurities and their impact

Impurity	Cause	Impact
Tar	Incomplete conversion to a gas, especially from updraft and fluidized bed gasifiers. Tars include a wide range of hydrocarbons with dew points of ~300 °C and below.	Severe impact on downstream equipment, particularly heat exchangers, catalysts, and engines. As syngas passes through the dew points of the tars, they condense on surfaces, becoming increasingly viscous with reducing temperature, causing fouling and blockages. Under certain conditions (particularly where condensed tar is subject to elevated temperatures), it may also solidify nonreversibly. Additionally, the tars tend to contain other impurities such as chlorides, giving rise to corrosive properties. Poorly controlled tar levels are the single biggest cause of facility failure, often within tens of hours of operation. (Note: where gasifiers produce syngas for operation into a boiler, tars may be fully combusted and therefore may not be such a significant issue).
Particulates	Particulates include small particles of char, ash, and also, where gas temperatures are below 600 °C, alkali salts which condense onto other particles. These are carried over from the gasifier, especially from downdraft and fluidized bed gasifiers.	Particulates have an impact on downstream equipment, contributing to blockages and coating of surfaces, and can combine with tars to form composite materials, which are even more challenging to remove.
Nitrogen-containing compounds, particularly ammonia	Formation within the gasifier, particularly from high nitrogen-containing feedstocks such as barks. Ammonia is formed in the reducing atmosphere in the presence of hydrogen, as is cyanide (HCN), where certain fuels are burnt (such as melamine).	Nitrogen-bearing compounds can cause poisoning of catalysts. Ammonia can have an impact on engines, causing the oil to degrade. Furthermore, high levels of NH_3 and HCN compounds contribute to the levels of nitrogen oxides (NO_x) emitted to air. Since this is a commonly controlled pollutant at levels that are hard to meet from a gas engine (due to the high levels of thermal NO_x generated), controlling ammonia levels is beneficial.
Sulfur compounds	Most fuels contain some sulfur, although the quantity in naturally occurring biomasses is limited. During gasification, these form two compounds: H_2S and COS. It should be noted that the removal of these compounds is relatively challenging compared with removal of SO_x downstream of combustion.	Sulfur is a key poison leading to catalyst deactivation. The sulfur deactivates iron, cobalt, and copper catalysts by forming metal sulfides that are no longer active. As far as engine operation is concerned, sulfur can lead to corrosion problems, and will also poison flue gas treatment catalysts. Sulfur oxides (SO_x) are also a controlled pollutant. Any sulfur compounds that are combusted, whether in a boiler, gas engine, or gas turbine, form such oxides.
Chlorine compounds	Chlorine exists in many naturally occurring biomasses, as well as in wastes. PVC in waste streams is a notable contributor to chlorine levels Within the gasifier these form HCl.	Many catalysts are poisoned by the presence of chlorine, and the level of control necessary for methanol and Fischer–Tropsch reactors is particularly stringent. HCl causes corrosion in downstream equipment and must be controlled in gas engines.
Dioxins	Dioxins are a family of chlorinated organic compounds and furans, which form rapidly in the gas phase between 250 and 400 °C. They arise mainly from chlorinated waste materials such as PVC rather than natural biomass.	These compounds are extremely toxic, and their emission is strictly controlled.
Metals	Heavy metals such as mercury, lead, and vanadium will vaporize in the gasifier and be carried out in the gas phase. While they occur at low levels in natural biomass, they can be present at higher levels in certain waste streams.	Such materials can cause severe damage to downstream equipment due to liquid metal embrittlement of high strength steels. Additionally, they are toxic pollutants that are specifically controlled.
Alkali metals		These poison catalyst material as well as causing degradation of engine oil.

The degree of gas cleanup required depends not only on contaminant level but also on syngas end-use specification. **Table 3** tabulates the typical syngas quality required for three example downstream processes: power generation using a gas engine; biofuel synthesis via the Fischer–Tropsch (F-T) process; and methanol synthesis.

For most heat or power production configurations via steam raising, the syngas can be used in its raw form – especially if it remains at high temperature and therefore does not condense on its way to the burner – with conventional postcombustion flue gas treatment. This is the way in which gasification has been used extensively around the world. However, for power generation in a high-efficiency gas engine, the raw syngas needs to be cleaned to the levels indicated in **Table 3** and **Figure 4**. While the demands for biofuel production are more stringent than for a gas engine, sweetening a gas quality from the level acceptable by the engine to a level acceptable for biofuel production is feasible, and routinely undertaken on fossil fuel gas trains prior to catalytic processes.

Table 3 Syngas quality requirements

	Typical levels raw syngas (RDF)	Engine limits	F-T limits	Methanol limits
Tars	1000–10 000 mg Nm^{-3}	15 mg Nm^{-3}	1 mg Nm^{-3} (15 °C below dew point)	Same as F-T
Particulates		15 mg Nm^{-3}	0.1 mg Nm^{-3}	Same as F-T
Sulfur	750 mg Nm^{-3}	50 mg Nm^{-3}	0.1 mg Nm^{-3}	0.1 mg Nm^{-3}
Halides	2500 mg Nm^{-3}	15 mg Nm^{-3}	0.01 mg Nm^{-3}	0.001 mg Nm^{-3}
Alkali metals		Controlled	0.01 mg Nm^{-3}	0.1 mg Nm^{-3}
Heavy metals	Hg: 0.3 mg Nm^{-3} As: 1 mg Nm^{-3}	Waste incineration directive limits dominate	Poison	Poison
NH$_3$		10 mg Nm^{-3} including HCN	10 mg Nm^{-3}	10 mg Nm^{-3}
HCN		Inc. above	0.01 mg Nm^{-3}	0.01 mg Nm^{-3}
N$_2$	Up to 50%. Depends on air vs. O$_2$ and on direct vs. indirect heating	~50% max due to overall min fuel CV	Inerts reduce efficiency. So low as possible	Inerts reduce efficiency. So low as possible
CO$_2$	Up to 15%	Effect with N$_2$ on overall CV	Inerts reduce efficiency. Low as possible	4–8% for max activity/selectivity
H$_2$:CO ratio	0.5–1.5:1	No issue	1.5–2:1	(H$_2$-CO$_2$): (CO + CO$_2$) 2:1
CH$_4$	0–5% v/v (depending on gasifier)	No issue	Reduces efficiency. So < 2%.	Reduces efficiency. So low as possible
Temperature	500 °C ex-gasifier	25 °C	200–350 °C	150–270 °C
Pressure	Atmospheric – 40 bar	Atmospheric	10–50 bar	50–100 bar

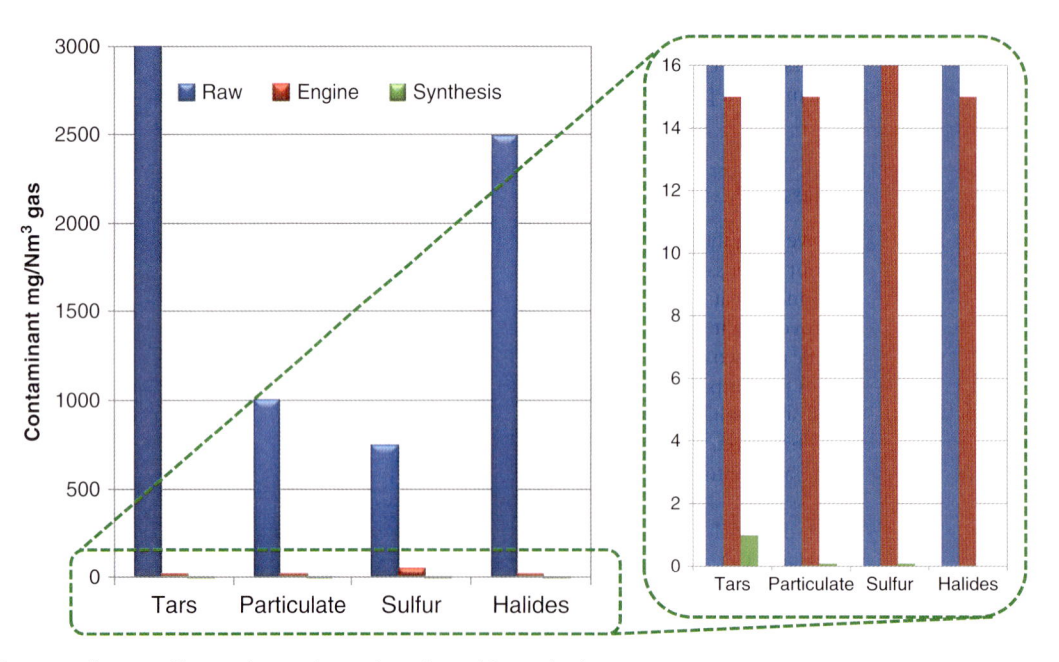

Figure 4 Syngas quality ex-gasifier, requirement for use in engine and for synthesis.

5.10.6.2 Gas Cleaning Technologies

The exact cleanup requirements are strongly related to the nature of the gasification process used and the feedstock. The following techniques are used, some of which can be used to remove multiple contaminants.

5.10.6.2.1 Cyclones

Cyclonic separators are ideal for primary, bulk particulate removal. The gas is forced into a circular motion separating out more than 90% of the larger particles (> 5 μm) by inertia. Additionally, they can operate at high temperature, thus retaining thermal energy in the gas (if required) and also allowing installation early in the process flow adjacent to the gasifier [18]. Finally, they collect the particulates in a form that is readily removable and dry. Cyclones are therefore used in many gasification systems. However, cyclones are not sufficient in isolation since smaller particles below about 40 μm are not removed.

5.10.6.2.2 Bag house filters

Bag house filtration is an alternative and complementary approach for particulate removal. These filters are made of woven fibers. Even small particulates (0.5–100 μm) are trapped in the mesh, and are back-flushed periodically with an inert gas or syngas. The larger particles are removed by upstream cyclones, such that only the finer particulates are trapped by the filter. While bag filters are effective in particulate removal, they can become clogged over time, particularly where subject to tars. Coatings have been developed which act as a barrier between the tars and filter material, limiting this effect and allowing some removal of low levels of tars. Coatings of lime or sodium bicarbonate and charcoal/activated carbon can also be added to provide a chemical removal effect where required. The lime neutralizes HCl, while the charcoal or activated carbon removes heavy metals. Baghouse filters can usually only operate below 350 °C, but this is more than sufficient for HCl and mercury removal duty.

5.10.6.2.3 Candle filters

Candle filters are an alternative approach for removing fine particles. These are rigid porous ceramic or metal barriers that are usually suspended like candles in the flow stream. Like baghouse filters, the gas passes through them forming a cake on the surface which is then periodically back-flushed to remove the trapped material. Ceramic filters can operate at higher temperatures, although they are at greater risk of catastrophic failure particularly due to thermal shock. Metal filters require lower temperature operation but are more robust. It is usually advisable to provide some form of guard system to ensure that if the filter fails, the system shuts down and uncontrolled ingress of material into the downstream equipment is avoided.

5.10.6.2.4 Packed bed filters

In small-scale gasifiers extremely simple filters can be used, usually comprising woodchips or sand. Such filters are not regenerable, and are disposed of (or even regasified) once they have caked.

5.10.6.2.5 Wet scrubbers

Wet scrubbers rely on mixing the product gas and its contaminants with droplets of liquid, which are then removed from the stream by coalescence. The removal medium is usually water, sometimes doped with chemicals, but also other fluids are used such as rape methyl ester (RME). Scrubbing can be effective at removing a wide range of contaminants: particulates; chemical contaminants such as ammonia; heavy metals; chlorides; potentially sulfides; and tars.

Chemical removal is improved by doping with sodium hydroxide (for chlorides) or sulfuric acid (for ammonia). While a degree of H_2S and COS can be removed with the dosing by hydrogen peroxide or sodium hypochlorite, this is unlikely to be suitable for removal of substantial levels of sulfur due to the quantity of dosing required, and handling the downstream consequences of the sulfur contamination in the waste water.

For particulate and chemical removal, scrubbers can operate at relatively high temperatures, often acting as a cooling quench for the syngas, reducing it from >400 °C down to ~200 °C. This rapid quenching effect is also beneficial for constraining dioxin formation.

Overall, scrubbing provides good gas cleaning. The disadvantage of scrubbing is that it can result in large quantities of contaminated liquid for disposal. Some systems recycle this back into the gasifier. Others, where the scrubbing medium is water-based, use evaporative systems or water treatment to separate the contaminant from the medium, such that it can be recycled and reused. Where tar levels are inherently low, this approach is feasible. Where tar levels are high, it becomes challenging to process economically the quantities of waste liquid involved.

5.10.6.2.6 Electrostatic precipitation (wet and dry)

In these systems, the gas passes through a high-voltage gap, which provides a charge to the particles, which are then attracted to a collector plate of the opposite polarity. In a dry system, the particles are mechanically removed from the plate periodically. In a wet system, the particles are trapped in liquid and flushed away. The dry system is effective for completely dry particles but less effective where there is tar contamination. Wet systems provide good removal for particulates as well as aerosol tars. This is an effective approach for providing high-quality gas, particularly for polishing after upstream operations.

5.10.6.2.7 Specialist tar removal and tar destruction techniques

In addition to conventional aqueous scrubbing techniques (as used for removal of chemical contaminants), there have been developments in alternative techniques for tar removal. These are proposed to offer two advantages – the possibility of enhanced tar removal by better compatibility with the tar and avoiding the subsequent removal of hydrocarbons from the waste water. One approach is to use RME as a scrubbing medium in a conventional scrubbing tower, which is reported to have a better affinity for tars. The used RME blowdown may then be able to be recycled into the gasifier. The Energy Research Centre of the Netherlands (ECN; http://www.ecn.nl) have also developed a more sophisticated tar removal technique that cools the syngas through the critical dew point temperatures with a regenerable solvent and a modified electrostatic system [19]. This process has recently been commercialized.

Rather than removing tars from the gas stream, it is possible to crack them into lighter hydrocarbons. Thermal destruction requires a high temperature, often 1200 °C. This not only forms a significant heat demand, but also can cause combustion of some of the energetic gas compounds. Alternatively, catalytic destruction can be employed, with the added bonus of ammonia destruction. Even catalytic approaches require fairly high-temperature operation, for example, over 900 °C for rhodium and 750–900 °C for nickel, and are also susceptible to poisoning [20]. Although there has been significant research in this field, particularly with regard to Ni-based catalysts, there are no commercial plants currently operating with such a device. The most advanced at scale is a catalyst developed by Condens Oy, planned for use on two projects that are under construction at the time of writing.

5.10.6.2.8 Specialist sulfur treatment

High levels of sulfur (usually in the form of H_2S or COS) can be removed by a variety of means. Techniques include:

Solid state scavengers. Sulfides can be removed using solid state scavengers such as ferrites that form iron pyrites. These are disposable systems where the output is a stable product, and suitable for processes below the 5 MW_e scale if sulfur is a particular problem.

Redox reactors. Here hydrogen sulfide is oxidized to elemental sulfur in an alkaline solution containing an oxygen carrier. Iron chelate is used as a solvent, which is mixed with the gas, removing the sulfur and allowing free passage of the other compounds. The solvent is flashed off and reoxidized with air, such that the elemental sulfur precipitates and is removed by filtration.

Physical and chemical solvents. These are liquids that also adsorb the H_2S preferentially over the other gaseous compounds. Chemical solvents strip compounds by forming chemical bonds, which are then subsequently broken during the thermal regeneration process. The solvents are usually solutions of amines in water. Physical solvents capture components in the syngas stream interstitially rather than through chemical bonds. The gas is mixed with the solvent at higher pressure, removing the contaminants, and allowing the pure gas to pass through. The solvent is then flashed off to regenerate it, and release the contaminant. Both processes then require a subsequent stage to convert the H_2S to elemental sulfur, such as a Claus plant. Unless the facility is of large scale (> 50 MW_e), this type of approach is unlikely to be economic.

5.10.6.2.9 Activated carbon treatment

Activated carbon removes a wide variety of trace components from the gas stream. For naturally occurring biomasses, this is unlikely to be necessary, but it may be beneficial for uncontrolled waste feedstocks, particularly for heavy metal removal. These are trapped on the active surface. Although the bed will eventually saturate, it is more likely to require changing due to degradation and contamination. It cannot be regenerated, but must be disposed of. Where a system includes a water quench or wash, this can be done by adding it as a feed to the gasifier, given the high carbon content, and in this case the vast majority of the heavy metal is then captured in the quench and disposed of in the waste water treatment. Alternatively, it can be shipped offsite for disposal. Activated carbon can remove other trace components from synthesis gas, for example, carbonyls. Iron and nickel carbonyls ($Fe(CO)_5$, $Ni(CO)_4$) are undesirable trace components in syngases.

5.10.6.2.10 Water gas shift

The water gas shift process enables adjustment of the CO/H_2 ratio by reacting the syngas with steam. The water is broken down into hydrogen and oxygen, the latter reacting with some of the CO in the syngas stream to produce CO_2. Thus the H_2/CO ratio is adjusted, although excess CO_2 may need to be separated from the gas stream.

There are two main configurations of the gas shift reaction; the clean gas shift and the raw gas shift. The former requires sulfur content below 100 ppm for high-temperature conversion and below 0.1 ppmv in the low-temperature version. The raw gas (or dirty) shift actually requires sulfur loading on the catalyst to maintain it in the activated sulfided state. Therefore, the different types of shift reaction are suitable for different parts of the process; the dirty gas shift takes place immediately downstream of the gasifier, whereas the clean gas shift must be positioned downstream of the sulfur removal plant.

High-temperature shift uses desulfurized syngas from the sulfur removal plant that will be near ambient temperature. This is heated and saturated using process steam to about 360 °C, which is the catalyst inlet temperature. The catalyst is iron oxide based and promoted with chromium or copper. Additional steam is added to the reactor. The exothermic reaction in the reactor provides an outlet temperature of ~500 °C, and the CO levels are reduced to a fifth of the original level. The dirty gas shift uses a cobalt–molybdenum catalyst, and the unit is placed downstream of the gasifier ideally after the quench, where used. The input temperature is ideally 260 °C with a fully saturated gas, where no further steam is required in the process, and the outlet temperature is again ~500 °C.

5.10.6.2.11 Methane reformation

Where a gasification process provides significant levels of methane, it may be necessary to reform this for biofuel catalysis. Methane is reacted with steam or oxygen to produce CO, H_2, and CO_2. The use of steam (steam methane reforming, or SMR) is a standard approach. It is carried out at ~600 °C and 20–30 bar pressure. This has a critical influence on the flow scheme. The process also requires external heat with corresponding costs for steam generation. Alternatively, oxygen or autothermal reformation may be adopted. This generates significant heat exothermically, but does require oxygen.

5.10.6.2.12 Cooling

For syngas use in biofuel production, the catalysts operate between 150 and 300 °C. In that regard, cooling the syngas is not necessarily the most efficient process. However, it is critical that no further tars condense from the gas stream, a condition which can be achieved by reducing the gas temperature to 25 °C and then reheating to the operating temperature. This reheating can be assisted by recovering heat from the upstream cooling to improve efficiency.

For use in an engine, the gas requires cooling to ~40 °C. Some of the gas cleaning processes outlined above result in significant levels of cooling, particularly scrubbing. Heat exchangers can also be utilized, although the position of these must be designed carefully to ensure that they do not foul with tars and particulates in the gas stream. Typically, these will be placed downstream of the major gas cleaning equipment, such as cyclones and quenches.

5.10.6.2.13 Flare

While not strictly part of the gas treatment system, a flare is necessary to protect the processing equipment, catalysts, and engine during start-up and for emergency shutdown. The syngas is diverted to the flare after a cyclonic or quench-scrubber stage since the relatively cool gas in cold equipment can lead to tar deposition, fouling, and damaging of downstream equipment.

5.10.6.2.14 Water treatment

Waste water arisings can contain different types of organic and nonorganic substances, although the quantity depends on the type of gasification and the combination of gas cleaning technologies used. In terms of organic substances, downdraft, fixed bed gasifiers are likely to produce only small amounts of tars and some particulates, a large proportion of which may be removed in the dry state and therefore not be found in the waste water. Conversely, fluidized bed systems or updraft gasifiers may contain significant levels of both tar and particulate, much of which will be found in any waste water. The primary inorganic substance is ammonia, with potentially some levels of sulfides and hydrogen chloride, depending on feedstock. Where uncontrolled waste feedstocks are used, heavy metals may also be vaporized in the gas stream, most of which will be dissolved in any scrubbing system.

In general, feedstock control (such as limiting to virgin biomass, particularly with nitrogen content) combined with good gasification systems, and dry containment removal where possible, can significantly reduce the complexity of any waste water treatment required. Where feedstocks are more complex, or the gasifier technology prone to high levels of particulates and particularly tars, then more sophisticated water treatment is required (sedimentation, membranes, etc.), which is feasible, but entails costs. In most systems, the quantity of waste water to be treated and/or disposed of is mainly a function of the moisture content in the incoming feedstock. Predrying to levels typically below 20% and ideally around 15% is beneficial.

5.10.7 Overview of Gasification Technology Options

The various gasifier technologies are available at a range of overlapping sizes [9] – see Table 4.

E4Tech considers each gasifier type in terms of feedstock flexibility, syngas quality, potential for scale-up and cost, and provided an approximate ranking – see Table 5.

The fixed bed systems offer the opportunity of lower cost solutions at modest scale. This allows cost-effective provision of syngas for direct combustion, and potentially operation in an engine. However, achieving process control, the demands on downstream gas processing and the typical scale of synthesis stages mean that fixed bed systems are not the natural choice for gas-to-liquids conversion from biomass feedstocks.

Table 4 Gasifier technology capacity range

Gasifier type	Capacity range (odt day^{-1} biomass input)
Fixed bed, downdraft	0.2–10
Fixed bed, updraft	5–60
BFB, atmospheric pressure	10–100
Plasma	15–300
Atmospheric CFB and dual	60–400
Pressurized BFB, CFB, and dual	200–1800
Entrained flow	400–10 000

Table 5 Gasifier type comparison, with each type ranked from * (poor) to **** (good)

Gasifier type	Feedstock tolerance	Syngas quality	Scale-up potential	Costs
EF	*	***	****	***
	Preparation to <1 mm, 15% moisture, low ash, composition unchanging over time	Very low CH_4, C_{2+} and tars, high H_2 and CO	Very large gasifiers and plants possible	High efficiency. Expensive pretreatment if decentralized
BFB	***	**	***	**
	<50–150 mm, 10–55% moisture, care with ash	C_{2+} and tars present, high H_2 and CO only if O_2 blown. Particles	Many large projects planned	Possible higher gasifier capital costs and lower efficiency
CFB	***	**	***	**
	<20 mm, 5–60% moisture, care with ash	C_{2+} and tars present, high H_2 and CO only if O_2 blown. Particles	Many large projects planned	Possible higher gasifier capital costs
Dual	***	**	**	***
	<75 mm, 10–50% moisture, care with ash	C_{2+} and tars present, high H_2, but high CH_4. Particles	Some projects planned, but only modest scale-up	Potential for low syngas production costs
Plasma	****	****	*	*
	No specific requirements	No CH_4, C_{2+} and tars. High H_2 and CO	Only small-scale, modular systems	Very high capital costs, low efficiency

Reproduced from E4Tech (2009) Review of technologies for gasification of biomass and wastes. NNFCC Project 09/008. www.nnfcc.co.uk.

The BFB solutions will be somewhat more expensive, but are likely to be able to span a reasonable range of scales, such that the same fundamental gasifier technology could be applied to a larger, commercial biofuel's facility. By definition, these technologies will require a higher level of downstream tar abatement.

Plasma systems have been designed to target the challenges of handling waste feedstocks, and should not have tar issues in the processed gas stream. It should be noted that a plasma system will still require credible chemical contaminant removal. The key disadvantages with a plasma system relate to the increased capital cost and reduced efficiency due to the parasitic loads.

EF systems are the most expensive systems at small scale. For wastes, they will almost inevitably require an upstream pyrolysis stage that increases costs and reduces efficiency. However, it is likely that EF systems may be serious contenders at larger scale.

5.10.8 Pyrolysis

Pyrolysis is distinct from gasification in that *no* oxygen is used for the thermal conversion (as opposed to partial oxidation in the case of gasification) [21]. Heat is applied externally causing the breakdown of fuel into a gas, a liquid, and a residual char. The exact thermal conditions dictate the proportions of these components. Pyrolysis systems therefore require efficient transfer of heat into the fuel. Three configurations are standard: rotary kilns, fixed bed vessels, and vessels containing a heat transfer medium such as sand. Typically, these systems require separate combustion to provide the necessary heat.

Fast pyrolysis (or flash pyrolysis) is a somewhat different proposition, where the system is designed to produce mainly biooil – up to 75% by mass. The process involves rapid heating to a temperature of 450–600 °C followed by rapid quenching of the pyrolysis vapors.

Two key drivers for pyrolysis to liquid are the production of biooil as an intermediary for subsequent gasification or as a biooil for direct upgrading to a liquid fuel product.

As gasifiers become bigger and draw their feedstocks from within a larger radius, attention focuses on finding low-carbon ways of transporting feedstocks in an energy-dense form to the gasifier. The importance of this becomes clear when it is noted that the energy density of biomass (typically 3.7 GJ m^{-3} bulk product) is an order of magnitude lower than that of crude oil (typically 36 GJ m^{-3} bulk product) [3]. Fast pyrolysis provides an energy-dense liquid feedstock (around 20 GJ m^{-3}), while slow pyrolysis or torrefaction provides an energy-dense solid feedstock.

Biomass pyrolysis processes are still at an early stage of development. The largest currently in operation are:

- ENSYN, Canada – 2 × 45 te day^{-1}, CFB
- Pyrovac, Canada – 35 te day^{-1}, vacuum pyrolysis
- Fortnum/Vapo, Finland – 12 te day^{-1}, vacuum pyrolysis
- Dynamotive, Canada – 10 te day^{-1}, stationary fluidized bed.

5.10.9 Case Studies

A few examples are included here to show how some of the technologies described above have been deployed in recent years.

5.10.9.1 Entrained Flow Gasifier

5.10.9.1.1 Freiburg, Germany

Choren emerged from a series of gasification ventures predicated on UET Umwelt und Energietechnik Freiberg GmbH formed in 1990. In their Carbo-V® process (see **Figure 5**), the feedstock is first pyrolyzed (also referred to as low-temperature gasification) at 400–500 °C in one chamber that provides both a gas and a char. The gas is then partially oxidized at the top of the gasification chamber at high temperature above the ash melting point (1200–1500 °C). This section of the reactor is water-cooled and slag-protected. Then the reaction is 'quenched' chemically by the introduction of the char (which has been ground into a combustible dust) into the middle of the EF gasifier chamber. The temperature drops in a matter of seconds to 700–900 °C as syngas forms in an endothermic reaction. Residual char removed from the syngas is then fed back into the high-temperature zone of the gasifier where the ash melts and forms a protective layer on the walls.

It has been operated and is commercially available for both oxygen-blown and air-blown applications. In principle, it is suitable for all carbon-containing feedstocks, while the current marketing emphasis is on different types of wood. The process is suitable for power applications and offers specific advantages for syngas applications (e.g., Fischer–Tropsch and methanol) requiring high-quality syngas. The reported gas composition (by volume) when running on woodchips from forest timber and plantations, sawmill coproduct, and recycled wood is 37.2% H_2, 36.4% CO, 18.9% CO_2, 7.3% H_2O, 0.1% N_2, and 0.06% CH_4.

Starting in 1998, Choren ran a 1 MW_{th} Alpha plant for a number of years, running on woodchips, waste wood, municipal waste, bone meal and black coal [2]. The gasification unit cost €2.5 million. They are currently completing a 45 MW_{th} Beta plant, due for completion in early 2011 at a capital cost of €100 million [10]. The Beta plant will run initially on dry woodchips from recycled wood and residual forestry wood. It includes a Shell SMDS Fischer–Tropsch unit with a rated output of 13 500 tonnes yr^{-1} of liquid fuels (diesel and naphtha). Their ultimate objective is the development of very large-scale biofuel refinery projects at 600 and 3000 MW_{th}.

5.10.9.2 Fluidized Bed Gasifiers

5.10.9.2.1 Skive, Denmark (BFB)

Carbona was formed in Helsinki in 1996, having bought out Enviropower (a Finnish gasification company with license rights to the RENUGAS gasification technology developed by GTI). Andritz Oy acquired minority ownership of Carbona in 2006. This is a BFB gasification system. The basic configuration is air/steam-blown although an oxygen/steam-blown system is feasible – see **Figure 6**. It operates at 20–30 bar depending on the requirements of the downstream process.

The first commercial-scale facility is in Skive, Denmark. It is 20 MW_{th} input scale and operates on wood pellets, although the technology is reputed to be able to operate on other feedstocks. The feedstock is chips or pellets, fed in by a screw conveyor. The scope of supply includes the full process chain from fuel feeding through to gas distribution. As embodied at Skive, the gas processing train is relatively limited as the feedstock is inherently low in contaminants. However, the process does include a novel

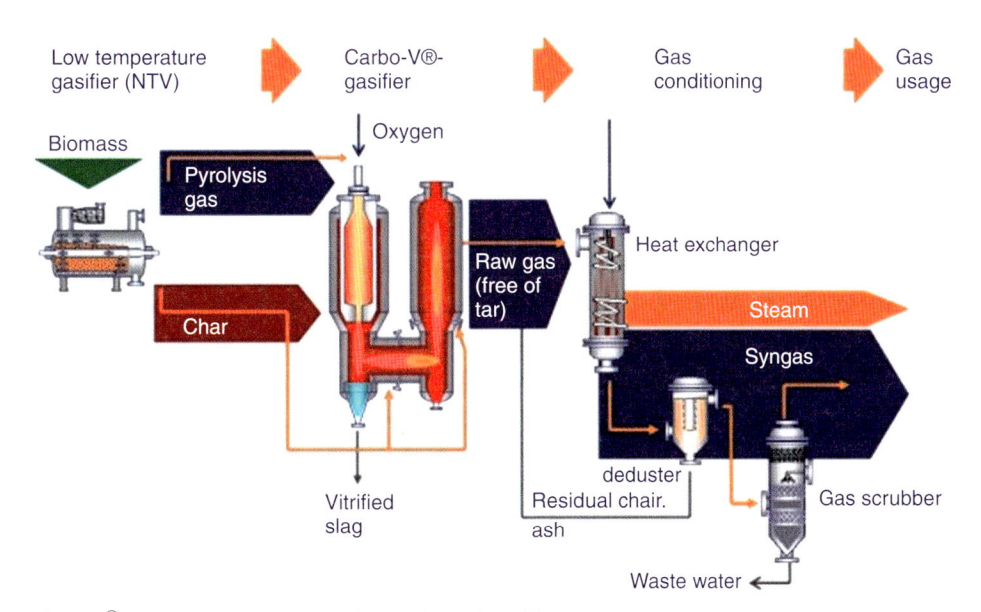

Figure 5 Choren Carbo-V® gasification process. Used with permission from Choren.

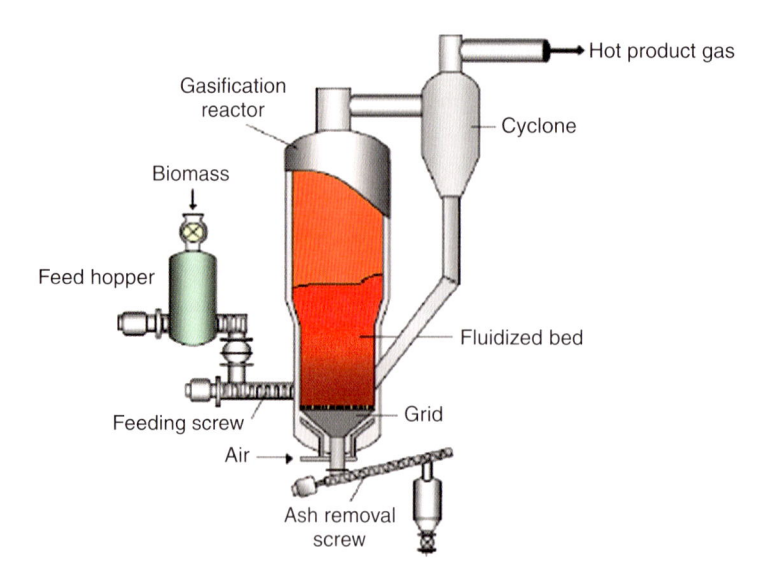

Figure 6 RENUGAS bubbling fluidized bed gasifier. Reproduced with permission from E4Tech (2009) Review of technologies for gasification of biomass and wastes. NNFCC Project 09/008. www.nnfcc.co.uk.

tar cracker system developed by Carbona and VTT. This uses a nickel catalyst to produce hydrogen, CO, and ammonia that are subsequently cooled, dedusted, and scrubbed.

The unit is configured with three Jenbacher engines to run as CHP, producing 5.5 MW$_e$ along with 11.5 MW$_{th}$ for a district heating scheme.

There are aspirations to develop the technology for use in biofuel applications.

5.10.9.2.2 Lahti, Finland (CFB)

The Kymijärvi power station in Lahti, Southern Finland, uses a CFB gasifier to produce raw syngas, which is then fed directly to a pulverized coal boiler. The aim is to reduce the overall carbon footprint of the power station and associated district heating scheme by effectively co-firing biomass with coal. Built in 1997 using Foster Wheeler technology at a cost of €12 million, the gasifier has a capacity of 70 MW$_{th}$, thereby providing about 15% of the boiler's average heat input [2]. The circulating bed material serves as a heat carrier and stabilizes the temperatures in the process. Feedstocks have included bark, woodchips, sawdust, and uncontaminated wood waste at various times. Gasifier capacity is determined by the biomass feed rate, and gasification temperature by the air feed rate. The gasifier has run since 1998 with an annual availability factor close to 97.5%. Biomass co-firing has been found to reduce SO$_x$ and NO$_x$ emissions. A larger unit (about twice the size) is now planned for the same site.

5.10.9.2.3 Güssing, Austria (dual fluidized bed)

Based on REPOTEC technology, a pilot plant has been running in Güssing since 2002, demonstrating high levels of reliability. It is a good example of a CHP facility based on gasification and running on regional feedstocks. When running at a feed rate of 40 odt day^{-1}, a gasification temperature of 900 °C, a combustion temperature of 1000 °C, and atmospheric pressure, it produces 2 MW$_e$ along with 4.5 MW$_{th}$, which is used to supply the town of Güssing with domestic and industrial heat. With its 4000 inhabitants, Güssing lies in a region that enjoys 40% tree cover and hence a ready supply of biomass feedstock. The unit runs on woodchips and wood industry residues, and uses a Jenbacher gas engine for CHP. Steam fluidizes the gasification zone, while air fluidizes the combustion zone. Hot sand is circulated between the reactors to provide the heat for gasification. The gas cleanup system consists of a fabric filter followed by a scrubber. Scrubber effluent is vaporized and fed into the combustion zone of the gasifier. Typically, the CV of the dry syngas is 12 MJ Nm^{-3} and the tar content is 10–40 mg Nm^{-3}. The plant is reported to have cost €10 million [2].

The unit is also used for testing and development purposes using a 7 Nm^3 h^{-1} slipstream, looking at Fischer–Tropsch synthesis, methanation of syngas, and the use of syngas to run a solid oxide fuel cell. The F-T unit has been running since 2005 using a cobalt catalyst to produce diesel and sometimes an iron-based catalyst to produce other products. Gas cleanup on the slipstream unit consists of drying, compression to 25 bar, chlorine removal, and sulfur removal [10].

5.10.9.3 Fixed Bed

5.10.9.3.1 CHP plant at Harboore, Denmark (updraft gasifier)

The original plant built in 1993 was designed to run on woodchips and supply district heating to 750 subscribers [2]. Since that time, the system has been optimized for gasification, a new wet gas cleaning unit has been developed and two Jenbacher gas engines have been installed. The facility is now rated at 5 MW$_{th}$ input, producing 3.4 MW$_{th}$ of heat output and 1.4 MW$_e$ of electricity. Ash is removed via a rotating grate. The gas from the gasifier can be burnt directly in a boiler to supply the district heating system.

Alternatively, the system can be operated in CHP mode with the gas being fed via several stages of cooling and cleaning to the Jenbacher gas engines. In this mode, the gas is cooled in shell-and-tube heat exchangers connected to the district heating system in which a large amount of tar and water is separated out. There is then an electrostatic precipitator to remove tar aerosols, dust, and any remaining water upstream of the gas engines. The collected tars are used as fuel for supplying peak heat demand via the boiler. There is also a facility for reinjecting light tars into the gasifier reaction zones. In order to meet local environmental standards on effluent discharge, there is a patented process for high-temperature cracking of remaining traces of tar.

5.10.9.4 Plasma

5.10.9.4.1 Advanced Plasma Power

Advanced Plasma Power was founded in 2005 to commercialize the proven Gasplasma technology originally developed by Tetronics Ltd. This is a two-stage gasification process: first, gasifying the pretreated waste feedstock in an EPI fluid bed gasifier producing a syngas contaminated with tars and soot as well as solid chars and ash, and second, using a plasma arc treatment to convert the residual soot tars and chars into further syngas which has consistent CVs while simultaneously vitrifying the ash. Downstream gas processing is still necessary for removal of chemical contaminants. The system is designed for operation on waste materials. Advanced Plasma Power have a small-scale (0.5 MW$_{th}$) pilot facility demonstrating operation on a range of waste materials. By definition, this process is designed to produce a high-quality syngas, and therefore the production of biofuels is considered to be a possible future development. The key issues with this approach are the heavy cost penalty and the reduced efficiency due to the parasitic electrical loads.

5.10.9.4.2 Hitachi Metals Ltd., Japan

On a much larger scale, the Utashinai plant in Japan uses two Westinghouse plasma gasifiers to produce steam and electricity from municipal solid waste (MSW). It was built in 2002 at a capital cost of $65 million. When running at its maximum feed rate of 280 tonnes day^{-1} of MSW, the plant exports 3.9 MW to the grid while supplying 4 MW internally. The technology is basically a combination of a moving bed gasifier and plasma torches pointing down into the gasifier bed. Unprocessed feedstock is fed in at the top of the reactor, molten glass and metal flow out of the bottom of the reactor, residual tars are cracked in the middle of the reactor, and syngas flows out the top. The maximum temperature is 5500 °C.

5.10.10 Recent and Future Developments

The investment environment is difficult to predict as levels of commitment to national CO_2 emissions reductions rise and fall, mechanisms for setting a carbon price remain undefined, and societal views on the sustainability of biomass as a feedstock for electricity, heat, fuels and organic chemicals remain unsettled. Given the versatility of the gasification process for matching a range of feedstocks to a range of end uses, it is not yet clear which routes will attract the most investment internationally.

As has been shown earlier, a successful gasification solution comprises not only the gasifier itself but also a complete engineered process. This comprises feedstock preparation, through the conversion unit itself, the processing and refinement of the solid, liquid, and gaseous product streams, and the balance of plant required to handle responsibly the emissions to air, land, and water.

In most cases, biomass-fueled systems are at a much more moderate scale than their fossil fuel counterparts. The commercial horizons of such projects are therefore also smaller, making it challenging to apply the necessary rigor in the process design phases, and to deploy the complex and often expensive process equipment. This is exacerbated as many waste and biomass gasification technology companies are small enterprises. They do not always have the wide range of technical or commercial expertise to tackle what would be in any other circumstances a job of considerable complexity that really demands the capability of a multidiscipline process engineering contractor. Such problems can be exacerbated by poor contracting strategies. This has unfortunately led to a somewhat checkered history in the sector.

It is within the competence of a proficient process engineering industry to analyze and resolve these issues. However, securing funding, for what are still often considered to be 'unproven' technologies, is a challenge. The perceptions of risk and strategies for mitigation of risk have changed markedly over the past three decades. Modern norms for project finance seek to devolve as many risks as possible via commercial arrangements to contracting counterparties – for example, equipment suppliers, contractors, and banks – while demanding unequivocal delivery of performance guarantees. These trends undoubtedly facilitate the efficient use of capital, and reduce the number of unanticipated cost over-runs but with the corollary that under such circumstances it is more difficult, or even impossible to arrange project finance for first-of-a-kind energy projects. Thus, contemporary norms for project finance sit uncomfortably with the emerging demand to deploy new energy infrastructure that incorporates novel and unproven technologies or even novel process configurations. Equally, corporate balance sheets tend to be insufficiently strong to undertake large capital projects on balance sheet; the recent history of infrastructure developments being undertaken with a combination of debt and corporate equity. In the post-2006/8 risk-averse banking climate, it is even more the case that conventional financing arrangements could only be used to deliver infrastructure energy projects that use tried and tested (i.e., 'proven') technologies and designs.

Technically, developments are required to provide reliable, cost-effective gasification systems that produce syngases with a high level of gas purity. Many of the associated challenges are already obvious.

Much of the relevant technology has been developed for coal gasification, but biomass gasification presents some specific and different challenges of its own [3]. Biomass ash in its molten state tends to be highly aggressive due to the alkali metal and alkaline earth metal content that can react with refractory material. It can also have a high chloride content, which can damage downstream components. Biomass tends to be more reactive than coal. Vegetable-based biomass tends to be fibrous, which can make the size reduction required for EF gasification difficult to achieve. Compared with coal, biomass gasification generates high levels of tar, especially in the lower temperature ranges. There is therefore a question as how best to produce high volumes of high-purity syngas for liquid biofuels and (to a lesser extent) for engine or gas turbine power generation. One approach would be to address the above issues and find a way of making EF gasifiers work for biomass. The other would be to opt for fluid bed technologies and find different ways of reducing tar content outside of the gasifier. Straight adoption of coal gasification technologies is unlikely to work since the operating gasifier temperature range will be constrained by biomass' wide ash melting point window.

There is also the question of whether to aim to feed a dry feedstock to an EF gasifier or whether to opt for liquid biooil or a slurry of char in biooil as feedstock [2]. The choice is complicated by the fact that the reactor operates under pressure (typically 60 bar) as the most effective way of supplying downstream high-pressure fuel synthesis plants. Given the low energy density of biomass compared with coal (which is six times higher), the cost/energy penalty involved in supplying an inert pressurizing agent for a solid feed is significant. Biooil from flash pyrolysis processes can be highly corrosive. The likely performance of a biooil/char slurry is largely untested.

There is a general challenge in the whole area of gas cleanup and overall energy efficiency. This arises because most raw syngas streams are produced at high temperature, and many purified syngas end uses require a high-temperature feedstock, but most of the common gas cleanup technologies are designed to run at relatively low temperatures.

Other challenges relate to the desire to use waste biomass streams, leading often to a need to handle heterogeneous, variable feedstocks and comply with particularly onerous regulations on emissions. One approach is to adapt gasifier technology developed for coal service to handle refuse-derived fuels as at the 650 te day^{-1} Schwarze Pumpe facility in Germany [22] or adapt liquid waste gasification technology as with use of a Siemens gasifier to handle organic nitrogen compounds in the United Kingdom [23]. Another approach is to use a separate pyrolysis process upstream of the gasifier in order to provide a more consistent feedstock.

Interesting papers have appeared recently on co-gasification of plastic waste with woodchip [24], co-pyrolysis of short rotation coppice willow with biopolymer waste [25], combinations of BFBs and CFBs for biomass gasification [26], use of dolomite as a tar removal catalyst in sewage sludge gasification [27], and linking biomass gasification to fuel cell technology for combined heat and power [28, 29].

5.10.11 Further Reading

A comprehensive, informative, and up-to-date introduction to the subject of gasification is provided by Christopher Higman and Maarten van der Burgt in their book [3].

Harry Knoef concentrates specifically on biomass in his handbook on biomass gasification that arises from the work of the European Gasification Network [2].

E4Tech have produced a useful and up-to-date (2009) review of technologies for gasification of biomass and wastes, including a wealth of case studies [9].

References

[1] NETL (2010) Worldwide gasification database. http://www.netl.doe.gov/technologies/coalpower/gasification/worlddatabase/index.html (accessed 10 January 2011).
[2] Knoef HAM (2005) *Handbook Biomass Gasification*. BTG (ISBN: 90-810068-1-9; www.btgworld.com).
[3] Higman C and van der Burgt M (2008) *Gasification*. London, UK: Elsevier/GPP.
[4] Egloff G and Van Arsdell P (1943) Motor vehicles propelled by producer gas. *Petroleum Engineer* 14: 645.
[5] Fischer F (1925) Liquid fuels from water gas. *Industrial and Engineering Chemistry* 17: 574.
[6] van Dyk JC, Keyser MJ, and Coertzen M (2006) Syngas production from South African coal sources using Sasol-Lurgi gasifiers. *International Journal of Coal Geology* 65: 243.
[7] Well KS. Coal gasification and IGCC technology: A brief primer. *Proceedings of the Institution of Civil Engineers: Energy, EN1* 163: 7–16.
[8] Juniper Consultancy Services Ltd (2000) *Technology and Business Review: Pyrolysis and Gasification of Waste – A Worldwide Technology and Business Review*, vols 1&2. Juniper Consultancy Services Ltd, Stroud, UK.
[9] E4Tech (2009) Review of technologies for gasification of biomass and wastes. NNFCC Project 09/008. wwww.nnfcc.co.uk.
[10] IEA (2010) Status of 2nd generation biofuels demonstration facilities in June 2010. Report T38-P1b, July 2010. http://biofuels.abc-energy.at/demoplants/.
[11] Hotchkiss R (2003) Coal gasification technologies. *Proceedings of the Institution of Mechanical Engineers – Journal of Power and Energy* 217: 27.
[12] Gill B, MacLeod N, Clayton D, *et al.* (2005) *Biomass Task Force: Report to Government*. London, UK: Defra.
[13] Lee P, *et al.* (2005) Quantification of the potential energy from residuals (EfR) in the UK. Commissioned by the Institution of Civil Engineers, London. The Renewable Power Association Oakdene Hollins Ltd.
[14] Juniper Consulting (2005) *MBT – A Guide for Decision Makers – Processes, Policies and Markets*. Stroud, UK: Juniper.
[15] ERM (2006) Carbon balances and energy impacts of the management of UK wastes. *Defra R&D project WRT 237*.
[16] McKay H, Hudson JB, and Hudson RJ (2003) Wood fuel resource in Britain: Main report (FES B/W3/00787/REP/1, DTI/Pub URN 03/1436) http://www.berr.gov.uk/files/file15006.pdf.
[17] Forestry Commission. http://www.forestry.gov.uk/website/foreststats.nsf/byunique/ukgrown.html.
[18] Stevens D (2001) Hot gas conditioning: Recent progress with larger-scale biomass gasification systems. Report NREL/SR–510–29552. Golden, CO: NREL.

[19] Boerrigter H, van Paasen SVB, Bergmann PCA, *et al.* (2005) 'OLGA' tar removal technology: Proof of concept for application in integrated biomass gasification combined heat and power systems. Petten: ECN. wwww.olgatechnology.com.
[20] Corrella J, Toledo JM, and Padilla R (2004) Catalytic hot gas cleaning with monoliths in biomass gasification in fluidized beds:1. Their effectiveness for tar elimination. *Industrial and Engineering Chemistry Research* 43: 2433–2445.
[21] McKendry P (2001) Energy production form biomass (part 2): Conversion technologies. *Bioresources Technology* 83: 47–54.
[22] Greil C, Hirschfelder H, Turna O, and Obermeier T (2002) Operational results from gasification of waste material and biomass in fixed bed and circulating fluidized bed gasifiers. *Gasification: The Clean Choice for Carbon Management.* Paper Presented at the Fifth European Gasification Conference, 8–10 April 2002, Noordwijk, The Netherlands.
[23] Schingnitz M (2003) Gasification: An opportunity to design environmentally compatible processes in the chemical and pulp paper industry. *Chemical Engineering and Technology* 26: 9.
[24] Ahmed II, Nipattummakul N, and Gupta AK (2011) Characteristics of syngas from co-gasification of polyethylene and woodchips. *Applied Energy* 88(1): 165–174.
[25] Kuppens T, Cornelissen T, Carleer R, *et al.* (2010) Economic assessment of flash co-pyrolysis of short rotation coppice and biopolymer waste streams. *Journal of Environmental Management* 91(12): 2736–2747.
[26] Srinivasakannan C and Balasubramanian N (2011) Variations in the design of dual fluidized bed gasifiers and the quality of syngas from biomass. *Energy Sources Part A: Recovery Utilization and Environmental Effects* 33(4): 349–359.
[27] de Andres JM, Narros A, and Rodriguez ME (2011) Behaviour of dolomite, olivine and alumina as primary catalysts in air-steam gasification of sewage sludge. *Fuel* 90(2): 521–527.
[28] Abuadala A and Dincer I (2010) Investigation of a multi-generation system using a hybrid steam biomass gasification for hydrogen, power and heat. *International Journal of Hydrogen Energy* 35(24): 13146–13157.
[29] Sadhukhan J, Zhao YR, Leach M, *et al.* (2010) Energy integration and analysis of solid oxide fuel cell based microcombined heat and power systems and other renewable systems using biomass waste derived syngas. *Industrial and Engineering Chemistry Research* 49(22): 11506–11516.

5.11 Biomass to Liquids Technology

G Evans and C Smith, NNFCC, Biocentre, Innovation Way, Heslington, York, UK

© 2012 Elsevier Ltd. All rights reserved.

5.11.1	Introduction	156
5.11.1.1	Biofuels Drivers and Issues	157
5.11.1.1.1	Drivers	157
5.11.1.1.2	Issues	158
5.11.2	The BtL Process	159
5.11.3	A Brief History of FT	160
5.11.4	Steps in Biomass Conversion to Liquids via FT	162
5.11.4.1	Feedstock Preparation and Pretreatment	162
5.11.4.1.1	Size reduction (comminution)	162
5.11.4.1.2	Drying	162
5.11.4.1.3	Feedstock pretreatment	163
5.11.4.2	Gasifiers for FT	168
5.11.4.2.1	Entrained flow gasifiers	169
5.11.4.2.2	Fluidized bed gasifiers	170
5.11.4.2.3	Plasma gasifiers	171
5.11.4.2.4	Scales of operation	172
5.11.4.2.5	Conclusion	172
5.11.4.3	Syngas Cleanup for FT	172
5.11.4.3.1	Syngas contaminants	172
5.11.4.4	Syngas Conditioning for FT	177
5.11.4.5	FT Process	177
5.11.4.5.1	FT catalysts	178
5.11.4.5.2	Reactors for FT	180
5.11.4.5.3	Summary	183
5.11.5	Alternative BtL Fuel Options	183
5.11.5.1	Methanol	183
5.11.5.2	Dimethyl Ether	184
5.11.5.3	Gasoline	185
5.11.5.4	Mixed Alcohols (via Catalysts)	185
5.11.5.5	Alcohols (via Fermentation)	186
5.11.5.6	Hydrogen and BioSNG	186
5.11.5.6.1	Hydrogen	186
5.11.5.6.2	BioSNG	186
5.11.5.7	Summary	187
5.11.6	Timescales and Development of BtL Processes	187
5.11.7	BtL Implementation Progress	188
5.11.7.1	BioMCN	189
5.11.7.2	Enerkem	190
5.11.7.3	Choren	190
5.11.7.4	Range Fuels	190
5.11.7.5	INEOS Bio	190
5.11.7.6	NSE Biofuels	191
5.11.7.7	Chemrec	191
5.11.7.8	Summary	191
5.11.8	Outline of BtL Economics	191
5.11.8.1	Capital Costs	191
5.11.8.2	Feedstock Cost Analysis	194
5.11.8.3	Economies of Scale	196
5.11.8.4	Summary	196
5.11.9	Environmental Issues	197
5.11.9.1	GHG Savings	197

5.11.9.2	Comparative Technology GHG Saving Effectiveness	200
5.11.9.3	Comparative Land Use Effectiveness	200
5.11.9.4	Summary	201
5.11.10	**Summary and Outlook**	203
References		204
Further Reading		204

Glossary

Advanced biofuel A biofuel that is produced by a novel method and/or that gives a better product than current biofuels.

Advanced pretreatment In the context of thermochemical conversion of biomass, this refers to torrefaction, pyrolysis, and pelletizing, which convert biomass to a more dense energy carrier and can result in the production of a feedstock that is more amenable for use in gasification systems.

Biomass to liquids An advanced process to produce biofuels, in which biomass is converted to liquid fuels or chemicals via syngas, including dimethyl ether, methanol, ethanol, synthetic natural gas, and synthetic diesel.

BioSNG (biosynthetic natural gas) A methane-rich gas derived from gasification of biomass materials and that has been upgraded to a quality similar to that of natural gas.

Fischer–Tropsch A high-temperature and high-pressure catalytic process that converts syngas into heavy hydrocarbon wax. This can be subsequently converted into finished fuels, typically by hydrocracking (a standard refinery procedure). The Fischer–Tropsch process can produce a high-quality diesel and/or other valuable hydrocarbon products including kerosene and naphtha.

Gasification Production of a combustible gas via the partial combustion of a feedstock.

Pyrolysis Transformation of a substance by the action of heat, in the absence of an oxidant (e.g., air, oxygen). This procedure always yields solid, liquid, and gaseous products, the yields of which depend on the conditions (e.g., heating rate, temperature, pressure) applied to the feedstock. It can be used as a densification strategy to allow biomass to be transported to a refinery, or, if upgraded, as a drop-in (or direct replacement) fuel.

Syndiesel (synthetically manufactured diesel) It can be derived from biomass via the biomass-to-liquids process using the Fischer–Tropsch process, and is also known as FT diesel.

Syngas A designed mixture of carbon dioxide and hydrogen produced by gasification, also known as synthesis gas.

Torrefaction A low-temperature slow pyrolysis carried out at around 300 °C that completely dries and devolatilizes biomass to give a dry and friable form of biomass.

5.11.1 Introduction

Increasing concerns over the environmental impact of using fossil fuels, security of supply, and price volatility have led to a growing interest in the production of alternative fuels from renewable resources. Greenhouse gas (GHG) emissions from the transport fuel sector are a particular concern because currently they account for a quarter of annual worldwide carbon dioxide (CO_2) emissions and are growing, while emissions from other sectors are declining or stable. Biofuels are the only near-term option to decarbonize the transport system, particularly for the existing car fleet, yet concerns have been raised over the sustainability of current 'first-generation' biofuels made from oilseeds, starch, and sugar crops.

Advanced biofuels, which are produced from biomass using a novel method of processing or which offer a superior product compared to existing biofuel routes, can be produced from a range of lignocellulosic materials including wood, agricultural residues, and the organic fractions of waste streams such as municipal solid wastes (MSWs). Compared with the feedstocks used to produce first-generation biofuels, these lignocellulosic feedstocks are typically cheaper and less subject to price fluctuations, have the potential to avoid competition with food resources, and yield greater GHG savings. For these reasons, legislation in many countries is increasingly favoring the production and utilization of advanced biofuels from lignocellulosic biomass and wastes.

Advanced processes for producing fuels from biomass can be broadly split into either biological (e.g., lignocellulosic ethanol production, anaerobic digestion) or thermochemical routes (e.g., pyrolysis, gasification). The various routes for the production of biofuels from biomass to end product are summarized in **Figure 1**. Thermochemical routes have a number of advantages over biochemical processes, in particular the ability to produce diesel substitutes and jet fuel. Furthermore, thermochemical methods have a greater flexibility with regard to feedstocks compared to biochemical methods, which is of significant advantage in terms of supply, and can convert all organic compounds in the biomass feedstock. Finally, thermochemical processes can produce a range of end products. This is a key advantage allowing a plant to tailor end products to demand, known as the biorefinery concept. These products can be exactly the same as are used today.

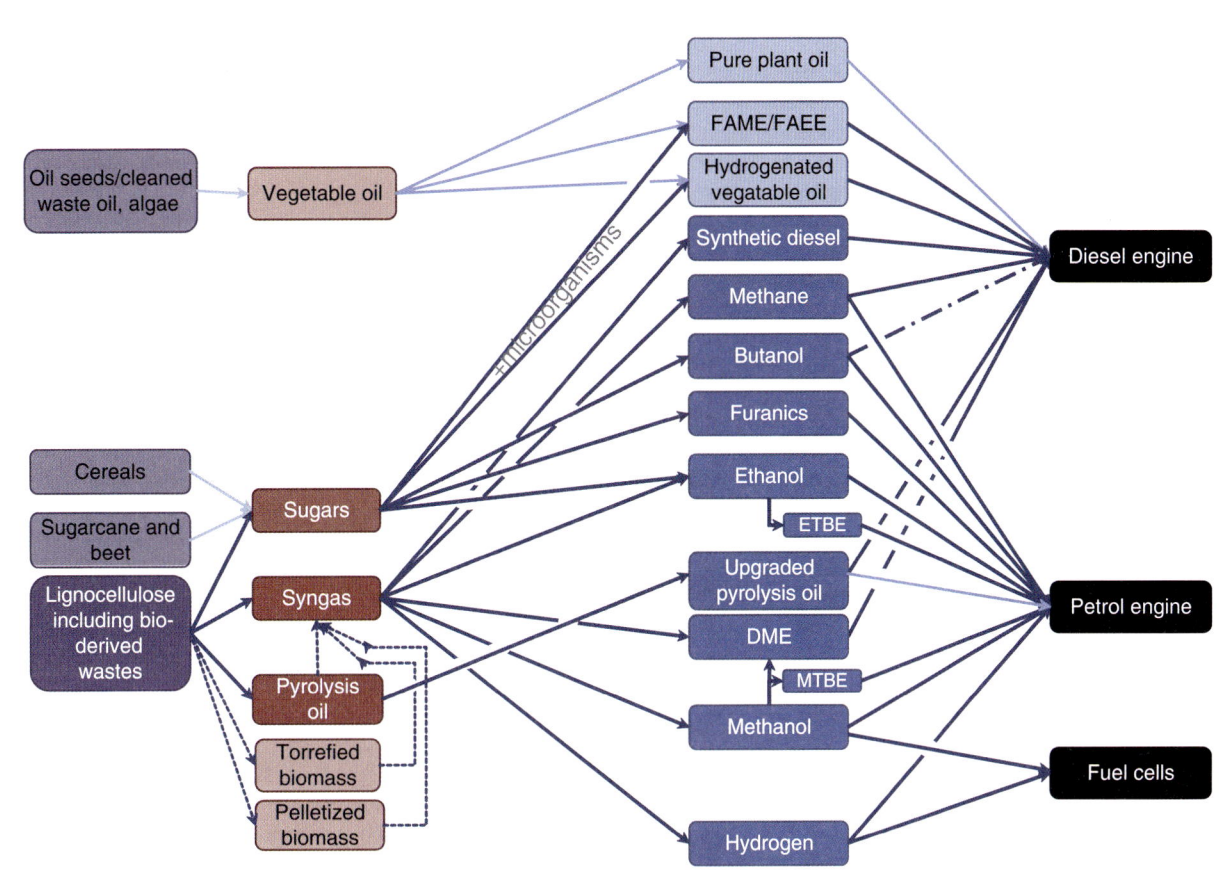

Figure 1 Potential biofuel pathways. Light blue lines indicate existing pathways for the production of biofuels; dark blue lines indicate alternative pathways to current biofuel products that may become commercially feasible in the near to mid-term (in particular before 2020); and dashed lines indicate pathways to biofuel products not currently in use but potentially feasible in the near to mid-term. Redrawn with permission from LowCVP and NNFCC (2010) Biofuels Pathways. *LowCVP Report*.

5.11.1.1 Biofuels Drivers and Issues

The biofuels industry is a relatively new industry that shows considerable potential for the future in terms of meeting various policy objectives and technology requirements. Uptake is being driven by a number of drivers as shown in **Figure 2**. However, there are a parallel range of issues that need to be addressed to ensure that the emerging biofuels industry builds into a robust and sustainable industry.

5.11.1.1.1 Drivers

Biofuels have the potential to address a wide range of environmental, socio-economic, political, and technological drivers. The relative importance of each of these factors varies according to geographical location, and can change with time.

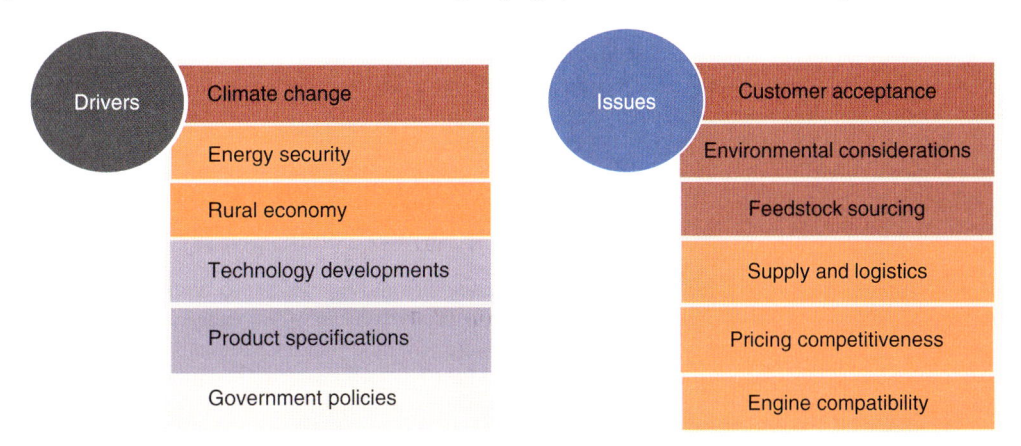

Figure 2 Biofuels drivers and issues. Red shading indicates drivers and issues of very high importance, orange indicates high importance, purple indicates medium importance, and white indicates low importance. Redrawn from Nexant Inc. (2007) Feasibility of Second Generation Biodiesel Production in the United Kingdom. *NNFCC Report*.

The principal strategic driver for the adoption of biofuels in the European Union (EU) is to mitigate climate change. Given that transport accounts for almost a quarter of worldwide GHG emissions, and since these emissions are rising, this is a key sector for any climate change policy to focus on. Most biofuels have been shown to provide GHG savings, but these are highly dependent on a range of factors including the crop used, processing methodology, and the parameters used in calculation. An increasing focus is on quantifying the GHG emissions associated with biofuels production and this is becoming an increasingly important part of complying with biofuel incorporation targets.

The second most significant driver for biofuels uptake in the EU is energy security – in the United States and China, this is the primary driver for biofuels use. The EU typically does not produce enough mid-distillate fuels and an opportunity exists for biomass-to-liquids (BtL) technologies to produce additional quantities of road diesel and jet fuel to meet increasing demands for these products.

Improving competitiveness and rural economics is the third driver for developing biofuels in the EU. The production of biofuels requires large amounts of biomass and this provides a way to diversify and rejuvenate the rural sector by providing an alternative income stream for farmers and landowners. The development of a biofuels industry also provides an opportunity to drive increased R&D in a wide range of sectors and to expand industrial infrastructure.

In addition to these well-known drivers, new technology developments and new fuel specifications also drive an increasing need for alternative fuels including biofuels. For example, Ricardo and Lotus are currently developing E85 (85% ethanol/15% petrol mix) engines that can take advantage of ethanol's high octane level with the potential to produce vehicles that will give close to diesel economy when fueled with E85. Such a development could drive the increased use of E85 and hence the increased production of ethanol. Engines that utilize synthetic fuels are being investigated as a potential avenue by Volkswagen (Fischer–Tropsch (FT) diesel-type fuels) and by Volvo Trucks (dimethyl ether (DME)).

BtL fuels can also deliver benefits to refiners who will increasingly need to source fuels from crude oils that are more difficult to access and refine. Synthetic fuels such as FT diesel can potentially help refiners to meet increasingly stringent fuel specifications such as on sulfur content. In addition to maintaining the status quo, high-quality blendstocks such as BtL diesel with high cetane and low sulfur can be used to increase margins by allowing more lower grade diesel blending components to be incorporated into higher value diesel streams.

The day-to-day use of biofuels is generally driven by government policies. In the United States, the Renewable Fuels Standard 2 (RFS2) was established for this. In the EU, the Renewable Energy Directive (RED) will require that 10% of the energy of transport fuels is provided from renewable sources by 2020. Increasingly, there are also added incentives such as capital cost loans, duty differentials, and/or tradable certificates, which promote the use of biofuels.

5.11.1.1.2 Issues

During the development of the biofuels industry in the 2000s, a number of issues were highlighted and continue to be addressed. These include, for example, biofuels sustainability, engine compatibility, and economic competitiveness (**Figure** 2).

While biofuels are now an integral and growing part of the fuel mix in many countries, many customers are not aware that they are using biofuels, albeit in low blends with fossil fuels. Conservatism among consumers, who often stick to products they are familiar with, may hinder the future larger scale uptake of biofuels. This is exacerbated by the often negative press coverage of biofuels with respect to perceived issues of environmental damage and those affecting the quality of biofuels. In particular, there has been concern over formulation issues and the effect this could have on engine performance.

Sustainability concerns include concerns over potential direct and indirect effects of biofuel production. These effects include possible impacts on food prices and deforestation. A considerable desire is on the part of many biofuel producers is to ensure sustainable sourcing of biomass and the use of waste materials and residues so that undesirable impacts are avoided. Thus, the prospects for advanced biofuels such as BtL are potentially beneficial, as BtL plants can utilize waste materials, residues and crops grown on marginal and degraded lands. However, BtL plants require around 5 tonnes of biomass for 1 tonne of output and given the current expected size of commercial plants is around 200 000 tonnes per annum (tpa) of products, this brings with it considerable logistic issues to ensure economic and sustainable supply of biomass to a plant, especially given that in many countries, biomass supply chains are undeveloped. Research is ongoing to address this issue; this research includes looking at smaller scales of operation and increasing conversion efficiency.

Biofuel production is a rapidly developing, but still largely immature sector, especially with regard to advanced biofuels. Capital costs of advanced biofuel production are high, and provide a considerable barrier to investment, although this is, to a certain extent, offset by the potential to use lower cost feedstocks. This is in contrast to fatty acid methyl ester (FAME) and first-generation ethanol plants where the capital cost of a plant may be lower, but this is offset by higher and more volatile feedstock pricing.

Finally, engine compatibility must be considered. Introducing a new fuel into that sold at forecourts brings challenges within both the existing and the future vehicle fleet. Ethanol, for example, acts as an oxygenate at low concentrations but at higher blends may begin to exhibit incompatibilities with some materials of construction in some vehicles. Although many of the challenges with respect to ethanol utilization at low ethanol concentrations in petrol have been resolved, R&D continues to establish and address other effects, which may for example arise during combustion, particularly with respect to higher ethanol blends in petrol such as E10, E20, and so on. Even where drop-in BtL fuels such as FT diesel are incorporated into the existing fuel infrastructure, they may still exhibit differences during use and these will need to be identified and addressed through R&D. These differences could manifest themselves, for example, in atomization and in cold flow performance.

5.11.2 The BtL Process

BtL is a member of the XtL (X to liquids) family where X can represent C for coal, G for gas, or B for biomass. It is one of a range of thermochemical technologies that can be used to produce valuable products from biomass. These products include liquid transport fuels, methane, heat, electricity, chemicals, and materials, or a mixture of two or more of these as shown in **Figure 3**. In general, however, BtL is typically focused toward liquid fuels production. In particular, BtL is often associated with the production of synthetic diesel via the FT process. In this chapter, BtL is defined as any process that utilizes biomass gasification to produce a syngas, which is subsequently converted into a fuel. However, BtL will refer mainly to the FT example – alternatives will be discussed in Section 5.11.5.

For each of the XtL processes, the first stage is to convert the feedstock into a clean syngas having a designed mixture of carbon monoxide and hydrogen; FT processes using a cobalt catalyst typically require a ratio of two moles of hydrogen to one mole of carbon monoxide (other downstream fuel synthesis processes will require different ratios). Once this has been achieved, the feedstock from which the syngas was derived effectively becomes irrelevant. A key feature of this technology, therefore, is that whatever feedstock is used, the final fuel, for which a number of options are available, is the same.

Syngas is produced from biomass by gasification. Gasification is a very flexible process with respect to feedstock and, in principle, many different carbon sources can be used to produce syngas. These include natural gas, coal, wood, straw, and refuse. The syngas is subsequently converted into usable fuel (or chemical) forms such as synthetic diesel or ethanol. A key advantage of BtL is the potential for the end fuels to be used in a range of existing end-use sectors with little or no modification; this includes the marine, rail, and aviation sectors. This range of products is a long-term advantage, especially for sectors where there is no ready drop-in alternative, such as in aviation.

FT is a technologically mature process for converting coal and natural gas into liquid fuels. For coal, the process has been used since before the Second World War, primarily to provide a source of liquid fuels when crude oil was not available. More recently, gas-to-liquids (GtL) technology has been developed to produce synthetic diesel from gas in large stranded gas fields. For biomass, however, FT experience is limited with just a few projects currently moving from the pilot stage to the demonstration stage across the world.

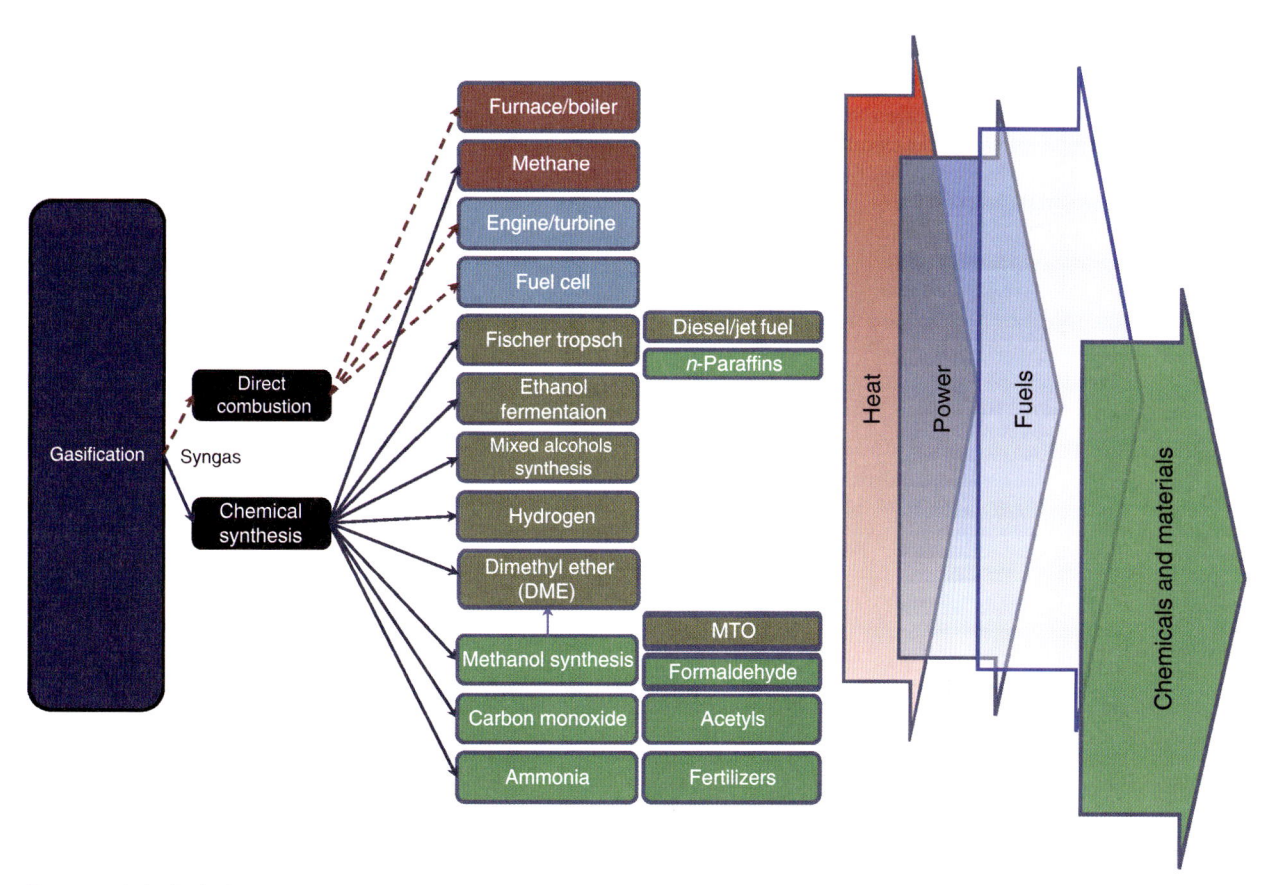

Figure 3 Derivative fuels, energy, and chemicals from biomass gasification. Dotted lines represent alternative gasification pathways not discussed in this chapter. Reproduced from NNFCC presentation (2010) Inputs, technology and biomethane utilization: An overview. *Biorenewable Fuel and Fertiliser: Realising the Potential*, 24 March. York: FERA. http://www.soci.org/

5.11.3 A Brief History of FT

The formation of hydrocarbons from carbon monoxide and hydrogen using transition metal catalysts has been known since the experiments of Sabatier and Sanderens in 1902. These experiments, at the beginning of the twentieth century, showed that methane could be produced from carbon monoxide and hydrogen using a nickel catalyst. It was not until 1923, though, that the production of liquid hydrocarbons from coal feedstocks was demonstrated by Fischer and Tropsch (**Figure** 4) using iron, cobalt, and ruthenium catalysts at high pressure. This was followed in 1936 by the development of a process that could be carried out at medium pressure by Fischer and Pilcher. A timeline of FT development is presented in **Figure** 5.

The uptake of FT processes has historically been linked to the need to develop liquid fuels when access to domestic natural resources or imports has been limited such as in Germany during the 1940s and in South Africa during the 1950s, 1960s, and 1970s. The first commercial FT plants were commissioned in the late 1930s in Germany, with a combined output of 660 000 tpa of FT products. While these plants closed down after the Second World War due to the competition with crude oil, they still provide the first examples of commercial production of FT products via coal-to-liquids (CtL) approaches. The modern development of FT technologies based on CtL has been pioneered by Sasol in particular. The first CtL plant in South Africa was commissioned in 1955 in Sasolburg, South Africa (Sasol I) and had a capacity to produce 6 million tpa FT products from coal, before it converted to the use of natural gas in 2004. Despite tough economic competition with the newly discovered oil reserves in the Middle East in the 1950s, the success of the Sasolburg operation was attributed to the production of several high-quality linear waxes and the development of an associated chemical processing infrastructure to utilize the FT products to produce value-added chemicals. Both Germany and South Africa remain the leaders in FT technology today.

In recent decades, there has been a renaissance of interest in the FT process due to successive oil crises coupled to concerns over security of supply and price. Both CtL and GtL projects have been developed in this period. In 1980 and 1982, Sasol followed the Sasolburg plant with the commissioning of two plants at Secunda, known as Sasol II and III. The Secunda plants have a total capacity of 150 000 barrels (bbl) day^{-1} (6 million tpa), and there are plans to expand this to 180 000 bbl day^{-1} (7.25 million tpa) by 2014. Sasol has plans for expansion of CtL to China, with plans for a plant to be commissioned in 2013 and potentially in Indonesia at 80 000 bbl day^{-1} (3.22 million tpa).

The identification of 'stranded' gas reserves, which have little or no local use, promoted interest in GtL technologies in the 1970s and 1980s. The Mossgas GtL project at Mossel Bay in South Africa (now operated by PetroSA) was commissioned in 1992, and was the first large-scale GtL plant to be commissioned. The plant, which has an estimated capacity of 36 000 bbl day^{-1} (1.45 million tpa), converts natural gas via a high-temperature, iron catalyst FT process developed by Sasol to a wide range of FT products, including unleaded gasoline, ultra-low-sulfur diesel, kerosene, low middle distillates, liquefied petroleum gas (LPG), and waxes. The Mossgas project was followed in 1993 by the commissioning of the Shell plant at Bintulu, Malaysia. The Bintulu plant uses a low-temperature GtL process in conjunction with a proprietary cobalt catalyst to specifically target middle distillate products. The capacity is 13 000 bbl day^{-1} (0.5 million tpa). Like the Mossgas plant, the Bintulu plant uses FT to produce a range of automotive fuels, specialty chemicals, and waxes, and is based on the use of offshore gas reserves. The BP GtL demonstration plant at Nikiski, Alaska was commissioned in 2002, and has an output of 300 bbl day^{-1} (12 000 tpa). More recently, the Sasol Oryx project in Qatar was commissioned in 2006 at an estimated cost of around $1 billion (bn). The Oryx project has a capacity of 34 000 bbl day^{-1} (1.37 million tpa) and uses the Sasol slurry phase distillate process, based on low-temperature FT.

Both Sasol and Shell are now building upon their experiences and developing further GtL projects using FT technology. The Pearl GtL project is a joint venture between Qatar Petroleum and Shell, which will convert natural gas, using the same process used in Bintulu, to produce 140 000 bbl day^{-1} (5.64 million tpa) liquid fuels and other products. This is expected to be commissioned in 2010, with a total capital cost of $12–$18 bn. In Nigeria, Sasol has formed a partnership with Chevron to develop a plant with a

Figure 4 Fischer and Tropsch. Reproduced with kind permission from Max Planck Institute of Coal Research.

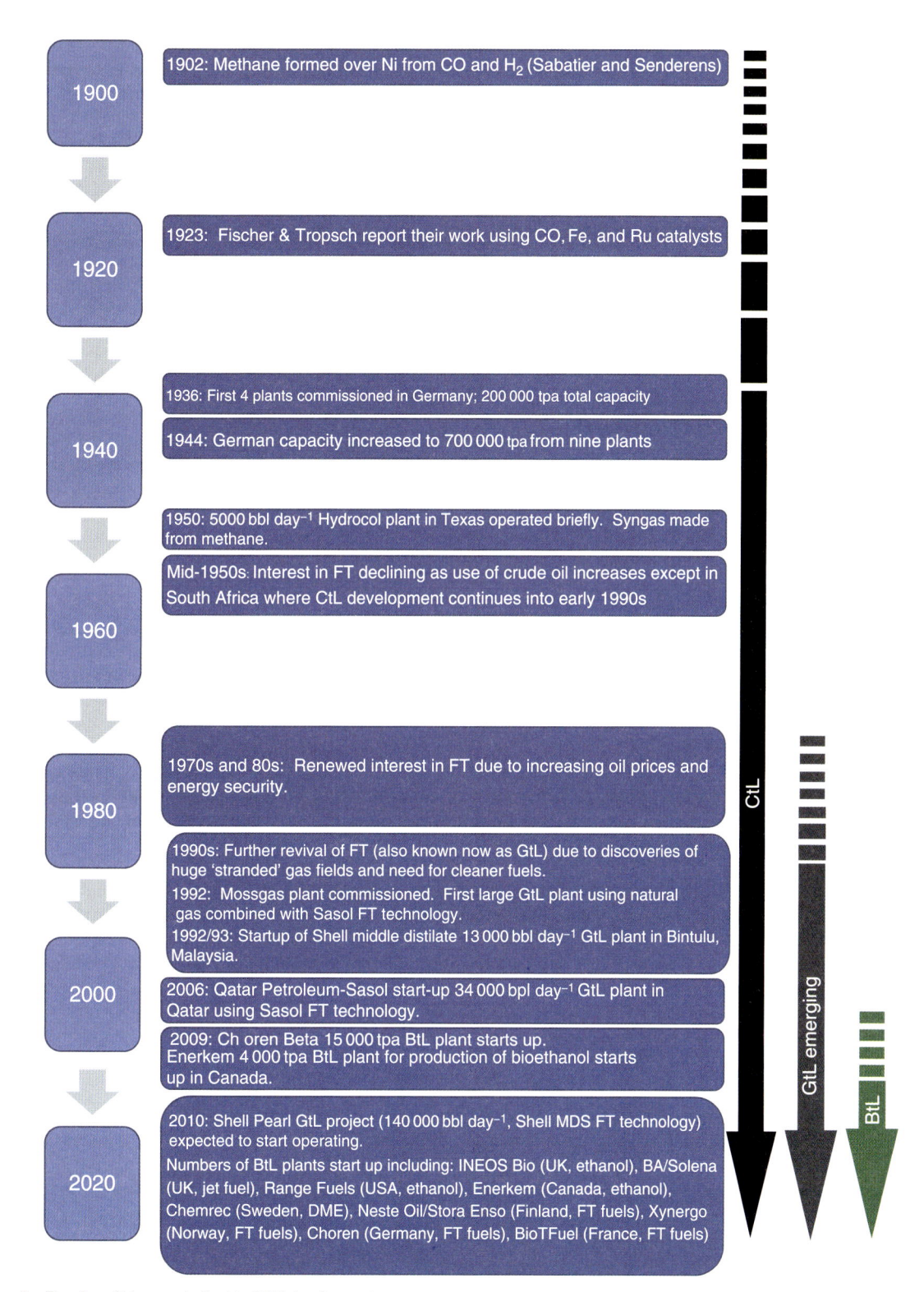

Figure 5 Timeline of biomass-to-liquids (BtL) development.

capacity of 34 000 bbl day^{-1} (1.37 million tpa) at Escravos, which will combine Sasol's slurry phase distillate FT technology with Chevron's proprietary biocracking process. This plant is expected to be commissioned in 2011 at an estimated cost of $1.7 bn.

Both CtL and GtL are now established technologies with developments progressing throughout the world. BtL processes have begun to develop more recently, principally due to environmental concerns including the need to reduce GHG emissions from the transport sector. BtL (utilizing FT) development is most advanced in Germany, where, for example, Choren Industries is in the process of commissioning its new 15 000 tpa synthetic diesel demonstration plant. Elsewhere, Neste in Finland is building an FT demonstration facility at Stora Enso's Varkaus paper mill. Several companies have announced their intention to build demonstration facilities such as Flambeau Paper Mill in Wisconsin, USA, which has announced its plan to build a plant with a capacity of 51 000 tpa for 2012, and Xynergo in Norway, which has plans for a 100 000 tpa diesel plant. Others, not based around FT, include Range Fuels (wood to mixed alcohols, primarily ethanol), Enerkem in Canada (MSW to ethanol), INEOS Bio in the United Kingdom (MSW to ethanol), and Chemrec in Sweden (wood to DME). All these examples are explained in more detail in Section 5.11.7.

5.11.4 Steps in Biomass Conversion to Liquids via FT

BtL processes consist of a number of distinct but highly integrated steps as shown in **Figure 6**. The first stage is feedstock preparation. This is followed by the production of a syngas from the biomass by a process known as gasification. The syngas is cleaned of contaminants and conditioned before it is catalytically converted to, in the case of low-temperature FT combined with a cobalt catalyst, a waxy hydrocarbon by the FT process. This wax can then be hydrocracked, a standard refinery process, to create the desired product. Each of the steps in the conversion of biomass to FT diesel is described in more depth in the following section.

5.11.4.1 Feedstock Preparation and Pretreatment

The type and degree of biomass preparation needed, in particular size reduction and drying, will vary depending on the requirements of the gasifier and the biomass used. Biomass varies in its physical characteristics including its moisture content, resistance to crushing, and bulk density, and this affects the type of processing and the amount of processing required. Feedstock preparation, and any subsequent pretreatment, has a significant effect on the efficiency of the BtL process and thus the importance of careful and correct feedstock preparation should not be understated.

5.11.4.1.1 Size reduction (comminution)

Biomass, as received, is often highly irregular in its size and shape. Most gasification systems require some degree of size reduction to ensure that the biomass has the correct size and shape for subsequent conversion. Size reduction can be carried out using chopping or shredding, hammer mills, or disk and knife milling. These are all well-established techniques. The tolerance to variations in size varies significantly between different gasifiers. As shown in **Table 1**, entrained flow gasifiers have the most stringent size requirement, whereas for plasma gasifiers size is less important.

Size reduction is an energy-intensive step, and thus can be costly both economically and in terms of GHG balance of the fuel. Often a trade-off is needed between the cost of size reduction and the benefits accrued in gasification. After size reduction, sieving and screening are necessary to ensure a homogeneous feedstock prior to gasification. Screening is also used to ensure that any contaminants, such as metals, are removed although other separation processes will also be used if such tramp material is likely.

5.11.4.1.2 Drying

As received, biomass can contain high levels of moisture. For example, fresh wood has a moisture content of around 40–50%, and straw around 15%. Most gasification systems require a relatively dry feedstock, although as shown in **Table 1**, systems vary in the acceptable moisture content. Biomass with high moisture contents will lower gasification efficiencies and increase the amounts of methane and tars in the syngas. However, some moisture can be beneficial in the gasification process to help control gasification temperatures and to modify the syngas composition.

Biomass drying can improve gasification by:

1. Reducing feedstock moisture contents to an acceptable level for a particular gasifier.
2. Aiding long-term storage and reducing the costs of biomass transportation.

Biomass drying is typically carried out at 100–120 °C, and is costly due to the amount of energy required to drive off excess moisture. While gasification improves with drier biomass feedstocks, drying beyond a specified level may be too costly and impractical.

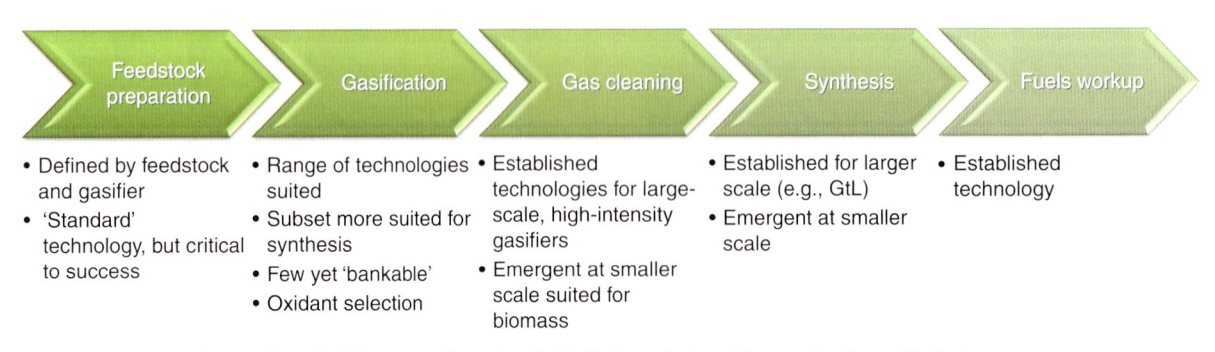

Feedstock preparation	Gasification	Gas cleaning	Synthesis	Fuels workup
• Defined by feedstock and gasifier • 'Standard' technology, but critical to success	• Range of technologies suited • Subset more suited for synthesis • Few yet 'bankable' • Oxidant selection	• Established technologies for large-scale, high-intensity gasifiers • Emergent at smaller scale suited for biomass	• Established for larger scale (e.g., GtL) • Emergent at smaller scale	• Established technology

Figure 6 Steps in the Fischer–Tropsch (FT) process. Reproduced with kind permission of Progressive Energy Limited.

Table 1 Specifications of biomass for gasification

Gasifier	Size	Moisture (%)	Composition	Other
Entrained flow	<1 mm	15	Should not change over time. Limited proportion of high-ash agricultural residues	Pretreatment steps being used
Bubbling fluidized bed (and dual with BFB gasifier)	<50–150 mm	10–55	Can change over time. Care needed with some agricultural residues	
Circulating fluidized bed (and dual with CFB gasifier)	<20 mm	5–60	Can change over time. Care needed with some agricultural residues	
Plasma	Not important	Not important	Not important, can change over time. Higher energy content feedstocks preferred	Used for a variety of different wastes, gate fees common

BFB, Bubbling fluidized bed; CFB, circulating fluidized bed.
Reprinted from Table 3 in E4tech (2009) *Review of Technologies for Gasification of Biomass and Wastes*. York: NNFCC.

5.11.4.1.3 Feedstock pretreatment

Pretreatment technologies are an optional step in feedstock preparation. Pretreatment can be used to aid biomass handling and storage and to ease the use of biomass in downstream BtL processes, hence reducing the capital costs of BtL plants (although these cost savings must be balanced against the extra costs incurred by pretreatment). Biomass pretreatment plays a significant role with respect to biomass use in BtL by:

1. facilitating material transport, handling, and storage by producing a bio-oil or uniformly shaped particles,
2. increasing the biomass energy density,
3. reducing comminution costs by reducing the energy required for milling or by converting biomass into a liquid form,
4. making biomass more amenable for specific gasification processes; for example, liquids are more easily fed into pressurized gasifiers,
5. permitting a range of biomass types from different sources to be effectively blended, thereby ensuring a biomass feed of consistent quality to a gasifier, and
6. adjusting the chemical composition of biomass, for example, to enable biomass to be used in gasifiers designed for coal gasification or to remove or modify the ash to enable fluidized bed gasifiers to be operated at higher temperatures (thereby avoiding the danger of ash melting).

Three predominant methods of pretreatment could be utilized for BtL applications. These, in the order of pretreatment intensity, are pelletization, torrefaction, and pyrolysis. The type of feedstock pretreatment performed will depend on a number of requirements including costs and the needs of the gasifiers used.

5.11.4.1.3(i) Pelletizing

Pellets are a condensed form of biomass, of specified shape and size, produced by forcing milled biomass through a die at high pressure. As pellets are often made from wood, many pellets are currently produced from sawdust to avoid the cost of comminution. Pellets are also often made from other dried and milled biomass sources including straw, willow, and *Miscanthus*.

Wood pellets have a number of advantages over wood as a feedstock for BtL plants. Pellets have a high energy density, around 15–16 GJ tonne^{-1}, compared to wood chips, which have an energy content around 12 GJ tonne^{-1} at 30% moisture content; have a specified ash content; and a low moisture content of around 10% (**Table 2**). Pellets have a uniform size and shape, typically

Table 2 Characteristics of densified biomass

Biomass form	Moisture content	Bulk density $(kg\,m^{-3})$	Energy density $(GJ\,m^{-3})$
Chips	35	550	5.8
Pellets	10	600	9.0
Torrefied pellets	3	800	16.7
Pyrolysis oil	25–30	1200	30.0

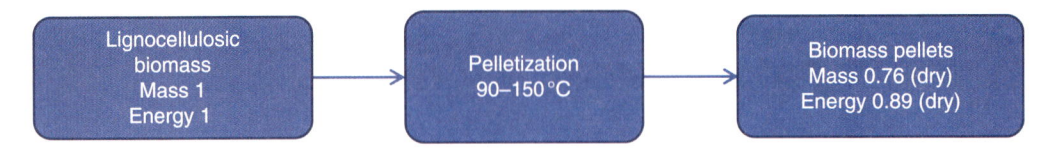

Lignocellulosic biomass Mass 1 Energy 1 → Pelletization 90–150 °C → Biomass pellets Mass 0.76 (dry) Energy 0.89 (dry)

Figure 7 Pelletizing mass and energy balance. Based on an original diagram from Kiel J, ECN Netherlands, presented in the presentation Torrefaction for biomass upgrading into commodity fuels, presented at IEA Bioenergy Task 32 workshop 'Fuel storage, handling and preparation, and system analysis for biomass combustion technologies, Berlin, 7 May 2007. Reproduced and modified with permission.

6–8 mm, although 10–12 mm is common for large industrial use. This facilitates ease of flow, allowing automatic/semiautomatic handling of the materials. A key benefit of using pellets for gasification processes is that they are easier to grind than wood chips, which retain their fibrous nature, and so use of pellets brings cost savings in biomass feeding operations where grinding is needed. Pellets also allow better packing in storage and transportation because of their uniform shape. The mass and energy balance of pellet production from wood is shown in **Figure 7**.

The disadvantage of wood pellets is that they are relatively high in price compared to other woody feedstocks such as logs and chips. No devolatilization occurs during pelletization, so the only mass loss is as a result of moisture loss during drying and pelletization. Thus, it is important to note that, while, physically, wood pellets may bring some advantages to the BtL process, the chemical composition of the wood, apart from a reduction in water content, remains the same. Any feedstock quality issues from the source biomass such as heavy metal contents will remain the same in the pellet product.

Key beneficial features for BtL provided by pelletization are as follows:

1. Local milling requirements/costs prior to gasification are reduced as the biomass needs to be milled prior to pelletization.
2. Pelletized biomass has an increased energy density and is easier to handle and transport, having a uniform size and shape.
3. The biomass moisture content is low and controlled.
4. Pellets can be produced and sold against a standard specification.

Undesirable features that remain after pelletization and/or arise as a result of the pelletization process are as follows:

1. The chemical composition of biomass remains the same. In particular, the ash remains in the pelletized product and is unchanged.
2. Blending pelletized biomass produced from different biomass sources will only be marginally improved.
3. Pelletized biomass must be protected from the elements and is subject to biological degradation.
4. BtL feedstock costs will be increased.

Pelletization is the most mature technology of the pretreatment technologies described in this chapter and is of the lowest cost. An estimate by Evans (2008) suggested that the capital costs of a 66 000 tpa (feed input) plant would be on the order of £3 million (£2006).

5.11.4.1.3(ii) Torrefaction

Torrefaction is the thermal treatment of biomass at temperatures of between 200 and 300 °C and at atmospheric pressure and in the absence of oxygen to produce a solid product (biocoal) with enhanced properties compared to the biomass feedstock. The end product (which is not charcoal) has a stable moisture content of about 3%, a reduction in mass by about 30%, retention of 90% of the original energy content, and removal of smoke-producing agents (**Figure 8** and **Table 2**). In addition, the product is hydrophobic and not subject to biological degradation, which allows it to be stored out of doors, and is highly friable. It should be noted though that torrefaction does not address the issues related to biomass chemical properties such as ash slagging, fouling, sintering, and corrosion caused by sodium and potassium salts. However, more oxygen and hydrogen is removed by torrefaction than carbon; this leads to an increase in calorific value of the end product.

Key beneficial features for BtL provided by torrefaction are as follows:

1. The increased friability reduces milling requirements/costs prior to gasification.
2. The torrefied product has a very low and consistent moisture content (around 3%).

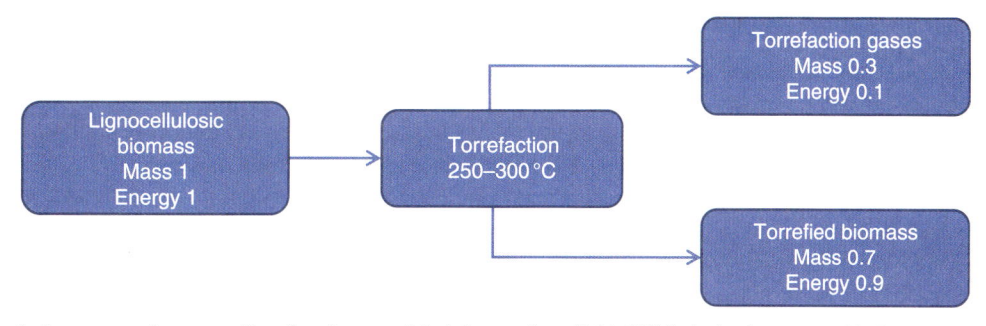

Figure 8 Torrefaction mass and energy outline. Based on an original diagram from Kiel J, ECN Netherlands, presented in the presentation Torrefaction for biomass upgrading into commodity fuels, presented at IEA Bioenergy Task 32 workshop 'Fuel storage, handling and preparation, and system analysis for biomass combustion technologies, Berlin, 7 May 2007. Reproduced and modified with permission.

3. There is a reduction in the hydrogen and oxygen contents – this moves the composition of the biomass closer to that of coal and so facilitates the use of gasifiers designed for coal.
4. If pelletized, torrefied biomass has an increased energy density and is easier to handle and transport.
5. The hydrophobic nature of torrefied biomass permits outside storage.
6. Torrefied biomass can be stored over long periods as it is not subject to biological degradation – this eases the effects of biomass seasonality.
7. Torrefied biomass can be produced and sold against a specification.

Undesirable features that remain after torrefaction and/or arise as a result of the torrefaction process are as follows:

1. The biomass ash remains in the torrefied product and is little changed.
2. Unless pelletized, the energy density of torrefied biomass is lower than that of the source biomass.
3. Blending torrefied biomass produced from different biomass sources will only be marginally improved.
4. BtL feedstock costs will be increased and overall system conversion efficiency will be reduced.

Torrefaction is an emerging technology, so capital costs for torrefaction plants are not well understood. An estimate by Evans (2008) suggested that the capital costs of a 60 000 tpa (feed input) plant would be on the order of £4.25–5.75 million (£2006).

5.11.4.1.3(iii) Pyrolysis for the production of liquids

Fast or flash pyrolysis is the thermal treatment of biomass in the absence of air or oxygen with the aim of producing an energy-dense liquid product, sometimes known as bio-oil. This oil can be used directly, for example as a fuel to fire a furnace, upgraded into transport fuels; or used as a route to facilitate gasification to produce syngas.

In the fast pyrolysis process, dried and size-reduced organic materials are rapidly heated to 450–600 °C in the absence of air or oxygen resulting in the production of organic vapors, pyrolysis char, and a bio-oil. Around 70–75% by mass of the biomass is converted to oil (contains around 65% of the energy of the original biomass), around 20% is converted to gases, and 10% is converted to a char, as shown in **Figure 9**. Energy for the process is typically provided by utilizing the evolved permanent gases and some of the char.

The suitability of a wide range of materials has been tested for pyrolysis including wood, sugarcane bagasse, switchgrass, and straw.

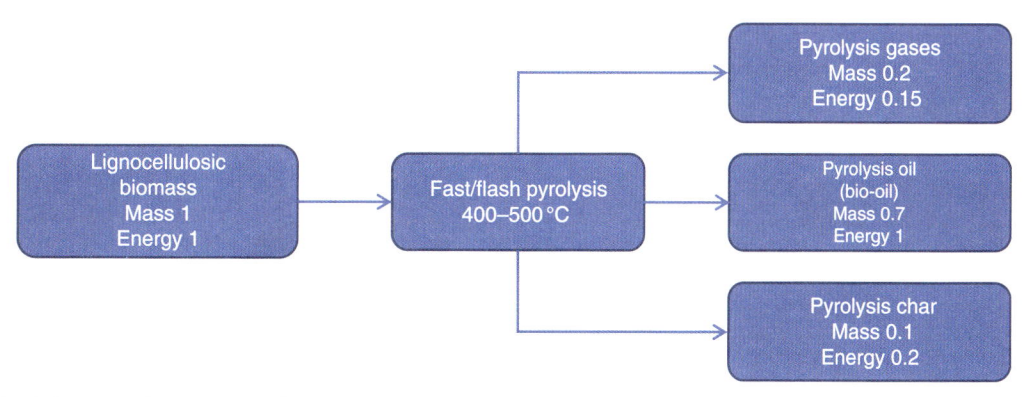

Figure 9 Pyrolysis mass and energy outline. Based on an original diagram from Kiel J, ECN Netherlands, presented in the presentation Torrefaction for biomass upgrading into commodity fuels, presented at IEA Bioenergy Task 32 workshop 'Fuel storage, handling and preparation, and system analysis for biomass combustion technologies, Berlin, 7 May 2007. Reproduced and modified with permission.

Key beneficial features for BtL provided by pyrolysis are as follows:

1. Liquid pyrolysis oil is easier to feed into pressurized and entrained flow gasifiers, such as those that could be utilized for BtL. As a liquid will atomize, no milling equipment is needed prior to gasification.
2. Pyrolysis oils from different sources can be easily blended to provide a gasification feedstock that has limited variation in composition and specifications and to provide a method to control the effects of biomass seasonality.
3. The mineral matter from within the biomass is retained in the char product; this means that the pyrolysis oil is relatively free of ash, chlorine, and silica, which could all be problematic in gasification and gas cleanup. The remaining char could, for example, be used as a fuel for electricity generation or as a fertilizer (biochar). These benefits, though, are negated if the char is mixed back into the oil prior to gasification although energy yields will be maximized.
4. Pyrolysis oil has a high energy density and is relatively easily transported and stored.
5. Pyrolysis oil can be produced and sold against a specification.

Undesirable features that remain after pyrolysis and as a result of the pyrolysis process are as follows:

1. If an ash-free feedstock to the gasifier is desired, then there will be a reduced system conversion efficiency.
2. Pyrolysis oil is highly oxygenated and high in moisture (25–30%) content.
3. Pyrolysis oil is highly acidic (pH 2–3 is typical).
4. As the most intensive pretreatment technology, more energy is lost across pretreatment compared to pelletization and torrefaction. Pyrolysis oil is also the highest cost pretreatment method.

As with torrefaction, pyrolysis is also an emerging technology, and capital costs are not well understood with a wide variation in estimates. An estimate by Evans (2008) suggested that the capital costs of a 66 000 tpa (feed input) plant would be on the order of £8.6 million (£2006).

5.11.4.1.3(iv) Biomass requirement

In terms of biomass requirement for each of these approaches, it is clearly preferable to utilize unprocessed biomass over other pretreatment options. For example, a 425 000 tpa BtL plant would require in the region of 3.8 million tonnes of wood if used directly, 4.3 million tonnes of wood if used torrefied, and 5.6 million tonnes of wood if used pyrolyzed. Evidently, the amount of biomass required for each of these options is considerable, and while from a feedstock point of view using untreated biomass is preferable, in terms of energy and bulk density for transport, and as shown in **Table 2**, it is preferable to use torrefied pellets or pyrolysis oil as intermediates. There is, therefore, a trade-off between the amount of feedstock required, costs, transport logistics, and processing characteristics, which must be carefully considered when assessing the feasibility of a BtL project.

5.11.4.1.3(v) Centralized versus decentralized approaches to biomass collection

In addition to facilitating gasification by altering the physical and chemical characteristics of biomass, biomass pretreatment can potentially help facilitate the supply of biomass to a BtL facility by increasing its energy density. Two models of biomass collection have been proposed to supply a major BtL plant – the decentralized and the centralized approach.

The decentralized approach (**Figure 10**, left) allows biomass to be aggregated and pretreated at satellite pretreatment facilities, and then shipped to a centralized BtL plant. This has the potential to reduce transport costs, reduce traffic movements and provide additional local employment. It should be noted, though, that transport costs are typically only a small percentage of the overall BtL product cost, so the cost benefits of pretreatment must be carefully assessed against the added pretreatment costs (see overleaf). The decentralized approach is being championed by IFP in France and Karlsruhe Institute of Technology in Germany, which, in conjunction with Lurgi, are planning to build a BtL plant, scheduled for completion in 2012, which will work in conjunction with approximately 50 regional densification centers.

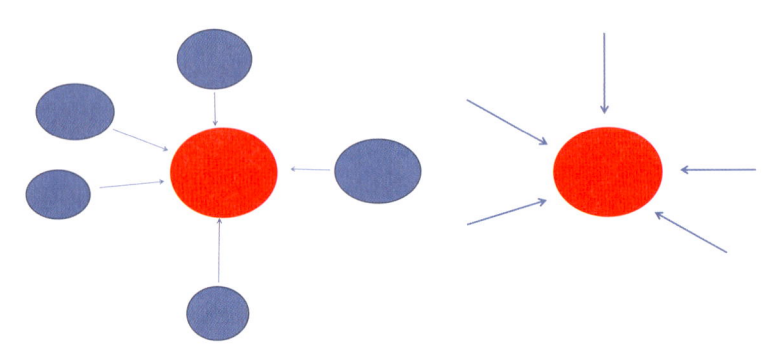

Figure 10 Decentralized and centralized models for biomass supply to a centralized biomass-to-liquids (BtL) refinery.

In the centralized approach (Figure 10, right), biomass is transported directly to a centralized refinery for processing to fuels and may include, depending on the gasifier type employed, an on-site pretreatment facility. This approach maximizes the overall BtL system efficiency and hence reduces the total amount of biomass needed to produce each liter of BtL product.

5.11.4.1.3(vi)   Economics of pretreatment

One of the principal challenges when assessing the feasibility of BtL plants is to source sufficient biomass of the right quality and at the lowest possible cost. Both centralized and decentralized approaches can be considered, although the cost and GHG benefits of pretreatment must be carefully examined.

North Energy Associates [1] investigated the differences in total capital investment (TCI) costs for a BtL plant using a pyrolysis distributed hub approach compared to a centralized BtL facility and compared these against the transportation cost savings achievable by pretreatment. This study estimated that the capital costs for a 200 000 tpa (of diesel product) plant would be £562 million (£2008) for a centralized plant consuming 1.4 million tpa of feedstock and a total of £977 million (£2008) for a decentralized setup consisting of a centralized biorefinery consuming 2.3 million tpa of feedstock converted into pyrolysis oil by 10 decentralized pyrolysis plants (Table 3). Although the North Energy study did not adjust the capital costs of BtL plant to account for the benefits accrued from pretreatment, the project does give an indication of the significantly higher capital costs that will need to be recovered if the decentralized approach were to be selected.

The scale of the cost savings that can be realized by pretreatment is illustrated in Figure 11. The data in Figure 11 have been obtained from a modification of the North Energy Associates model in which capital cost savings accrued through the use of pretreated biomass have been incorporated, using data obtained from Magalhães *et al.* (2009). Figure 11 indicates that untreated biomass is a more economic option for BtL for biomass transport distances up to about 300 km. Above 300 km, pyrolysis starts to become economic. The model indicates that torrefaction is generally less attractive economically.

In addition to assessing potential cost savings that may be realized via biomass pretreatment, potential GHG savings must also be considered. With the potential for financial rewards for biofuels with higher GHG savings, any GHG savings realized via biomass pretreatment could have an impact on cost of production.

Based on the same model and assumptions as for Figure 11, Figure 12 shows that at distances of less than 1000 km, BtL diesel GHG savings are maximized with the use of untreated wood (at 25% moisture content) as a feedstock, while above 1000 km, pyrolysis gives greater GHG savings. Torrefaction, based on this model, generally provides the least favorable option in terms of % GHG savings.

Table 3   Feedstock requirement, product output, and total capital costs for a BtL plant using pyrolyzed and untreated feedstock

	Dry feedstock (tonne yr^{-1})	Syndiesel output (tonne yr^{-1})	Naphtha output (tonne yr^{-1})	Total capital costs (£ million 2008)
BtL/pyrolyzed feedstock	2.3 million	208 000	52 000	977
BtL/untreated feedstock	1.4 million	208 000	52 000	562

BtL, Biomass to liquids.

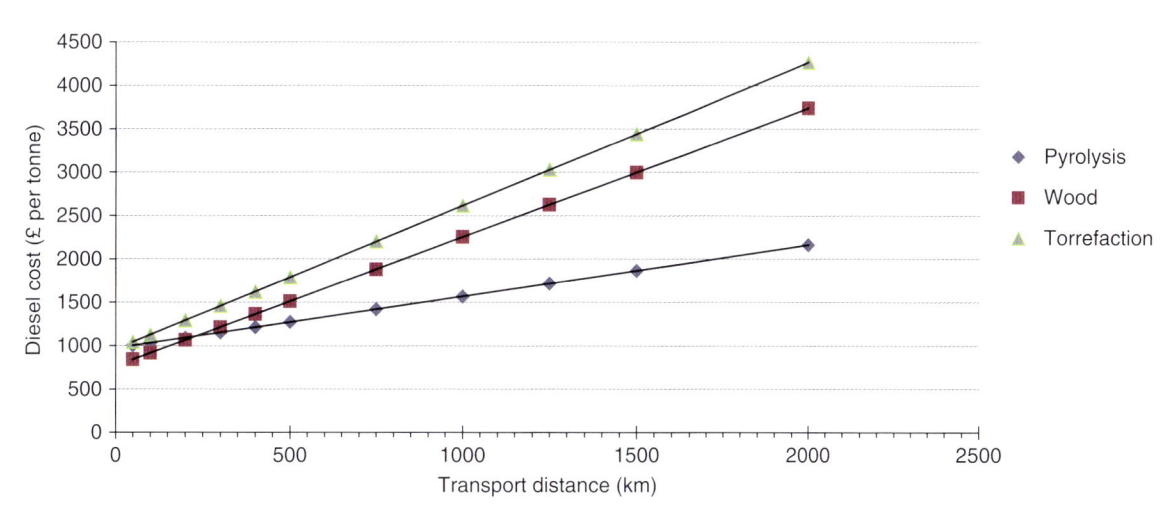

Figure 11   Effect of transport distance and advanced pretreatment on the cost of diesel from Fischer–Tropsch (FT) processes.

168 Technology Solutions – New Processes

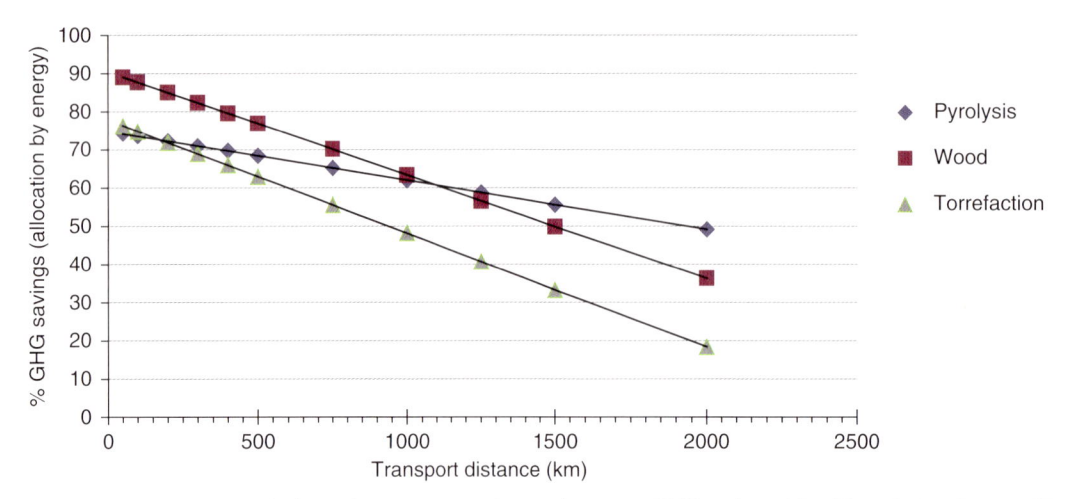

Figure 12 Effect of transport distance and advanced pretreatment on the greenhouse gas (GHG) savings of diesel from Fischer–Tropsch (FT) processes compared to fossil diesel.

5.11.4.1.3(vii) Effect of biomass pretreatment on BtL system efficiency

Figure 13 shows the energy retained across a BtL process incorporating FT chemical synthesis. The chart indicates that overall system conversion efficiency decreases with increasing pretreatment intensity with the overall system efficiency reduced to about 30% if pyrolysis is used as a pretreatment step compared to 44% if no pretreatment is utilized.

5.11.4.1.3(viii) Summary

Advanced biomass pretreatment can make biomass easier to use in gasification, and facilitate its transport to a processing plant. Such pretreatment comes at a cost, and there needs to be careful consideration of the economic and GHG benefits that accrue through pretreatment as opposed to direct feeding. Research in the United Kingdom has shown that while pyrolysis can be a feasible option for moving biomass long distances, it does not necessarily lead to improvements in BtL GHG emissions. Thus, the benefits of employing a pretreatment step will depend on whether the rationale is purely economic, driven by GHG savings, or a combination of the two.

5.11.4.2 Gasifiers for FT

Following biomass preparation, the next stage in the BtL process involves the conversion of the biomass into syngas via gasification. Gasification is a mature technology for coal with a wide range of different types of gasifiers available. These types differ mainly in their mode of operation, operating temperature and pressure, suitability for different feedstocks, and oxidant used.

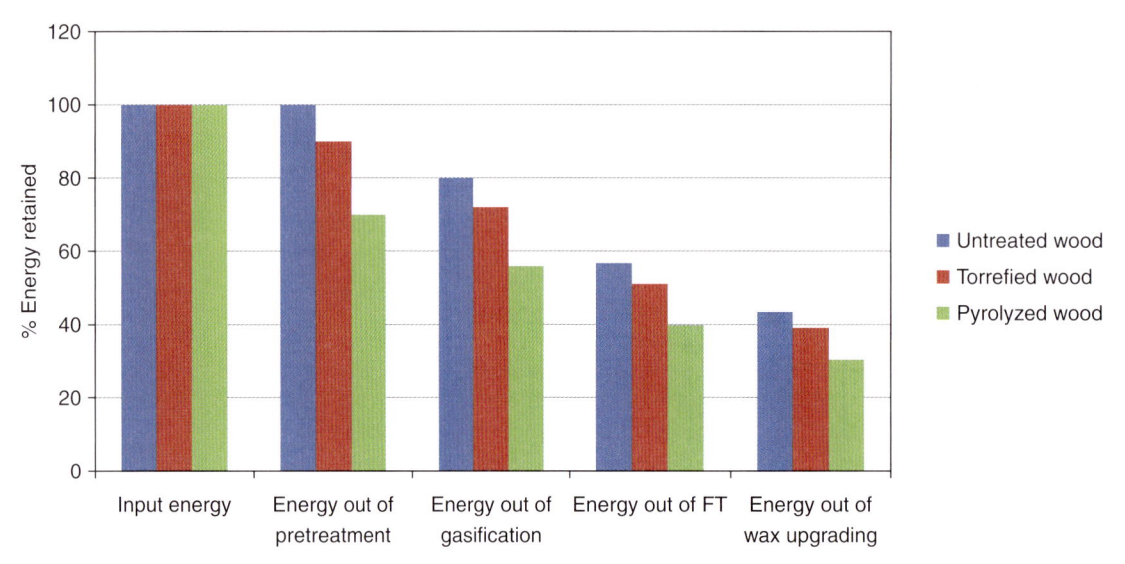

Figure 13 Fischer–Tropsch (FT) energy conversion efficiency of direct use and using biomass pretreatment.

The majority of gasifiers for biomass have been developed at smaller scale compared to coal gasifiers and primarily for heat and power applications where product gas quality requirements will be different from those needed for chemical synthesis applications. Biomass gasifiers more suited to BtL are being developed and these include:

- Entrained flow gasifiers.
- Fluidized bed gasifiers.
- Plasma gasifiers.

The advantages and disadvantages of these gasifiers are shown in Table 4. While other gasifiers are also available, these are at different stages of development and only some will be appropriate for BtL applications. Apart from those listed above, rotary kiln, cyclonic or vortex reactors, and screw auger reactors may also be used depending on the application. Key determinants for suitability include scale of operation, economics, feedstock requirements, and product quality capabilities. For a fuller description of gasifiers and gasification, see Chapter 5.14.

5.11.4.2.1 Entrained flow gasifiers

Of the variety of gasification technologies available, entrained flow gasifiers are potentially the most suited to BtL applications due to their ability to produce a syngas low in tars and hydrocarbons.

Table 4 Gasification reactor types

Reactor type	Mode of operation	Advantages	Disadvantages
Entrained flow gasifier	Powdered or atomized feedstock gasifiers in dense cloud within reactor. Can be run as a cyclonic reactor	Design permits operation at high temperature to produce effectively tar-free syngas – ash is designed to slag. Syngas has low methane content. High conversion efficiency	Carbon loss with slag. Feed must be powdered (fed dry or as a paste) or atomized. Poor gas – solid contact. Operates at pressure. For syngas production, requires oxygen
Bubbling fluidized bed (BFB)	Relatively low gas velocity, inert bed material stays in reactor	Good heat and mass transfer rates. High specific heat capacity. Good temperature control. Can accommodate variations in fuel quality. Good turndown. Easy start-up and shutdown	Carbon loss with ash. Feed preprocessing required (to achieve small particle size). Scale limited to between 1 and 25 MWth
Circulating fluidized bed (CFB)	Inert bed material is elutriated, separated, and returned (recirculated) back to reactor	As for the BFB. Can be designed for very large scale (5 to >100 MWth)	As for the BFB except for scale-up

(Continued)

Table 4 (Continued)

Reactor type	Mode of operation	Advantages	Disadvantages
Dual fluidized bed (indirect)	Char material is heated in the combustion chamber and is transferred to the gasification chamber to indirectly heat the biomass	As for BFB	Low temperatures needed to avoid potential problems with ash slagging Higher methane in syngas
Plasma gasifier	Feedstock is gasified in a high-energy electric arc	Design permits operation at high temperature to effectively produce tar-free syngas – ash is designed to slag Syngas has a low methane content High conversion efficiency Can process a variety of biomass types, including waste	High energy consumption by torches Waste feedstocks can result in high chlorine levels Scale-up has been limited so far

Reprinted from Table 25 by Evans G (2008) *Techno-Economic Assessment of Biomass 'Densification' Technologies.* Nottingham: *emda* using diagrams from E4tech (2009) *Review of Technologies for Gasification of Biomass and Wastes.* York: NNFCC.

Entrained flow gasifiers can be imagined to be a burner firing a powdered or atomized feedstock into a furnace with insufficient oxygen provided for full combustion. The insufficient oxygen and high gasification temperatures of around 1200–1500 °C result in high conversion efficiency to carbon monoxide and hydrogen with reduced production of undesirable constituents such as tars, hydrocarbons, and carbon dioxide.

Ash, which for biomass applications can often be an issue as it melts at low temperatures causing corrosion problems, is removed as a liquid slag by design. This liquid slag also protects the gasifier vessel.

Entrained flow gasifiers require a powdered (or atomized) feedstock, which is difficult to achieve with solid biomass. As noted above, it is possible to pretreat biomass, for example by torrefaction or pyrolysis, to facilitate its use in an entrained flow gasifier. Pyrolysis produces a liquid bio-oil product, which could easily be atomized for gasification – a number of organizations are driving this approach (e.g., ECN, FZK, IFP). Alternatively, torrefaction, which produces a friable solid product, often termed biocoal, could be used.

A number of entrained flow gasifiers are available, and have been well utilized for coal, but there is limited experience of using entrained flow gasifiers for biomass. They are usually specified for larger throughputs of around 150 000 tpa biofuel or 200 megawatt electricity (MWe). Entrained flow gasifiers are being used in BtL applications by Choren, Range Fuels, Karlsruhe, Mitsubishi, and Pearson.

5.11.4.2.2 Fluidized bed gasifiers

A fluidized bed operates when a quantity of fine, solid particulate material such as silica, sand, or alumina is forced to behave as a fluid, by the forced introduction of pressurized gas through the particulate material. This results in the medium having many of the properties and characteristics of fluids, resulting in high heat and mass transfer rates. Catalysts may also be used in the gasifiers, allowing increased conversion efficiency and reduced tar formation, although this limits the temperatures that can be employed and requires robust catalysts that are not poisoned by contaminants. Fluidized bed gasifiers are relatively well established and several are available for use with biomass.

Fluidized bed gasifiers can accept a wide range of materials. They operate below about 900 °C to prevent ash slagging and sintering in the reactor. Lower temperature operation increases hydrocarbon yields in the product gases and medium amounts of tar can be produced. To maximize the carbon efficiency, since methane passes through an FT reactor unchanged, the unreacted methane should be converted to carbon monoxide and hydrogen in a downstream catalytic reforming step.

Fluidized bed gasifiers fall into three main categories:

1. Bubbling fluidized bed

   A bubbling fluidized bed gasifier consists of a reactor with a layer of fine inert bed material at the bottom. Steam, oxygen, or another gas is blown up through the bed at around 1–3 m s^{-1} to agitate the bed but without causing any significant carryover of the bed material out of the reactor. Biomass is fed into the bubbling bed where it reacts to form syngas. Combustion of a portion of the gases evolved provides the energy for the gasification reactions within the bubbling bed. Syngas typically leaves the chamber through the top of the reactor. Bubbling fluidized bed reactors can operate at atmospheric pressure or above.

   Bubbling fluidized bed gasifiers can accept a wide range of feedstocks, including wood pellets and chips, stover, sludge, and other crop residues. The particle size of feed materials can be relatively large compared to other gasifiers, typically between <50 and 150 mm in diameter. Materials used vary widely in their moisture content, which ranges from 10% to 55%, although 10–15% is preferred – a certain quantity of moisture is desirable to provide some steam for steam gasification reactions. Bubbling fluidized bed gasifiers have high specific heat capacity, and have good temperature control. They are also tolerant of variations in feed quality.

   Bubbling fluidized bed gasifiers do have several disadvantages. While they may be able to accept a wide range of feedstocks, high-ash feedstocks such as straw with a low ash melting temperature can result in sintering if the reactor is operated at too high a temperature. Several remedial actions can be used to overcome this problem, including the use of temperatures less than 900 °C to avoid ash slagging, or using a range of biomass materials in combination that have a mixture of high and low ash contents with higher ash melting points. The addition of dolomite to the bed to bind minerals, or mixtures of feedstocks to counteract the high ash content in some materials, may also be used to control sintering. Bubbling fluidized bed gasifiers result in a syngas with a greater proportion of methane, hydrocarbons, and tars, and relatively high levels of particulates such as bed material ash and soot. While particulates can be removed, this is a challenge at high temperature and requires extensive gas cleaning compared to other gasifier types that can produce cleaner syngas directly such as the entrained flow gasifier.

   Bubbling fluidized bed gasifiers have been widely used for power applications, but there is limited experience in using biomass in these gasifiers. These gasifiers are usually considered to be suitable for operation at an order of magnitude lower in scale compared to circulating fluidized beds (CFBs), around 7–30 MWe as shown in **Figure 12** or, assuming successful process intensification, 8000–30 000 tpa of fuels. Despite this design criterion, however, it should be noted that, to date, the largest gasifiers installed for biomass applications are bubbling fluidized beds. The use of bubbling fluidized bed gasification for biomass is being pursued by Carbona, Foster Wheeler, Energy Products of Idaho, Enerkem, Iowa State University, and Thermochem Recovery International, albeit primarily for energy applications.

2. Circulating fluidized bed

   CFB gasifiers use air, steam, or oxygen blown upward through a bed of fine inert material in the gasifier at such a velocity that the bed material escapes from the reactor after which it is collected and recycled back into the reactor. The biomass is suspended in this material and reacts to form syngas. The syngas and the unreacted bed material are removed from the top of the gasifier where a cyclone is used to separate the syngas and the bed material, which is returned to the base of the gasifier, in a circulating process. CFB gasifiers can be pressurized, and operate at less than 900 °C to avoid ash melting and sticking. Typical CFB gasifiers that operate at slightly smaller scales are developed than entrained flow gasifiers (**Figure 12**) although if pressurized they can operate at similar scales to entrained flow gasifiers. CFB systems are being developed by Foster Wheeler, Vaxjo Varnamo, VTT, CUTEC, Fraunhofer Institute, and Uhde, primarily for energy generation, although Uhde is planning to build a BtL demonstration unit in France utilizing torrefied biomass as a feedstock (BioTfuel project).

3. Dual fluidized bed

   Dual fluidized bed systems consist of two parts – a gasification chamber and a combustion chamber. Biomass is fed into the gasification chamber, and using steam it is converted to syngas and char. The char moves out of the gasification reactor and is burned in the combustion chamber, where the bed particles are heated. The bed particles are then recycled back into the gasification chamber, providing indirect heat for the process. Dual fluidized bed gasifiers can be pressurized and operate at less than 900 °C to avoid ash slagging and typically produce a gas richer in methane with a higher calorific value. As they produce higher levels of methane compared to other gasifier types, they are particularly suited to the production of methane (biosynthetic natural gas (bioSNG)) via a downstream methanation synthesis step. Dual fluidized bed systems are being developed by Repotec, Silvagas, Taylor Biomass Energy, and ECN, primarily for energy applications. The combined heat and power (CHP) unit at Gussing incorporates a dual fluidized bed gasifier.

5.11.4.2.3 *Plasma gasifiers*

Plasma gasifiers operate by gasifying the feedstock in plasma generated by a high-energy electric arc. Inert gas is passed through the arc, heating the process gas to 1500–5000 °C. Biomass is added into the gasifier where it comes into contact with the arc. The organic components are converted to organic gases, while the inorganic components are converted to a vitreous slag. A slight negative pressure is used in processing, with a gas removal system and a removal system for solids. Plasma gasifiers usually do not need gasification oxidants, although some gas is needed to produce the arc.

The ability to adjust the plasma torches means that plasma gasification is extremely flexible with regard to feedstock composition, size, and moisture content. Indeed, almost any type of material can be utilized and broken down to its elemental components in gaseous form. This flexibility means that plasma gasification is particularly suitable for waste materials, which may be highly heterogeneous in composition, possess considerable variation between batches, and may be difficult to use in any other process. The high temperatures used ensure that no tars and furans are produced, and that the gas is lower in trace contaminants compared to other gasifier types.

Plasma gasifiers do have a number of disadvantages. Energy consumption may be high as a result of the electricity requirement to power the plasma torches. However, some systems are able to recoup some of this energy through the process. Chlorine levels in the product gas can be high if waste feedstocks, particularly nonbiological, are used and this can lead to high levels of impurities such as dioxins and metals, although the heavier components are vitrified in the ash.

Plasma gasifiers are established in the power industry. Westinghouse, Plasco, Startech, Solena, and InEnTec are all developing biomass-based applications, with all except Plasco developing fuel applications. Scale-up has been limited so far, with the majority of applications at smaller scale. Solena is working in partnership with British Airways to establish a UK plasma gasification facility, likely to be located in East London. This plant, estimated to be commissioned from 2014, will produce 16 million gallons (around 60 000 tpa) of jet fuel, using 500 000 tpa of waste.

5.11.4.2.4 Scales of operation

Biomass gasifiers range widely in scale as shown in **Figure 14**. At larger scale, entrained flow and pressurized CFB reactors are perhaps most suited. Fluidized bed reactors and plasma gasifiers are generally considered to be suited for scales between 1 and 100 MW although it should be noted that, to date, the largest biomass gasifiers built are fluidized bed gasifiers. Scaling up of gasifier outputs may be achieved by employing a modular approach, such as that by several technology providers including Choren.

5.11.4.2.5 Conclusion

A wide range of different gasifiers are suitable for BtL applications. Each type varies in its feedstock requirements, operating temperature range, scalability, commercial development, and syngas quality. There is limited experience of using biomass in gasifiers for applications other than for energy generation. **Figure 15** summarizes the current status of biomass gasification technologies in terms of technology development and market strength. Fluidized bed technologies are most well developed, but, from a syngas quality aspect, they are less attractive for BtL applications. Entrained flow gasifiers are less well developed, but offer advantages in terms of syngas quality. Plasma gasifiers may also be highly suited to BtL applications, particularly since they are very flexible with respect to feedstock and do not need an expensive oxygen plant, although these are a relatively new development.

5.11.4.3 Syngas Cleanup for FT

The syngas produced from the BtL process needs to be cleaned up of contaminants to avoid downstream catalyst poisoning. Contaminants that must be removed include tars (which are a typical contaminant from biomass gasification and which increase with reducing gasification temperature), acidic gases such as sulfur, and particulates.

5.11.4.3.1 Syngas contaminants

Figure 16 illustrates the relationship between the typical levels of tars, particulates, sulfur, and halides typically arising from biomass gasification and the maximum level of tolerated contaminants for gas engine applications and for chemical synthesis applications, while **Table 5** shows tolerance levels for contaminants in more detail. At present, producing a gas suitable for reliable use in an

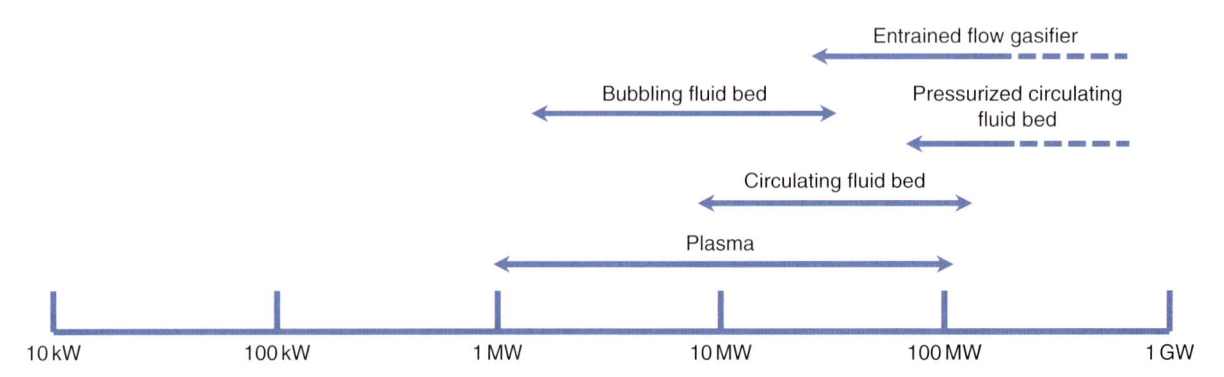

Figure 14 Gasifier size ranges. Redrawn with permission from Table 1 in Bridgwater AV (2002) The future for biomass pyrolysis and gasification: Status, opportunities and policies. http://ec.europa.eu/energy/renewables/studies/doc/bioenergy/2002_report_p536.pdf (accessed 14 January 2010).

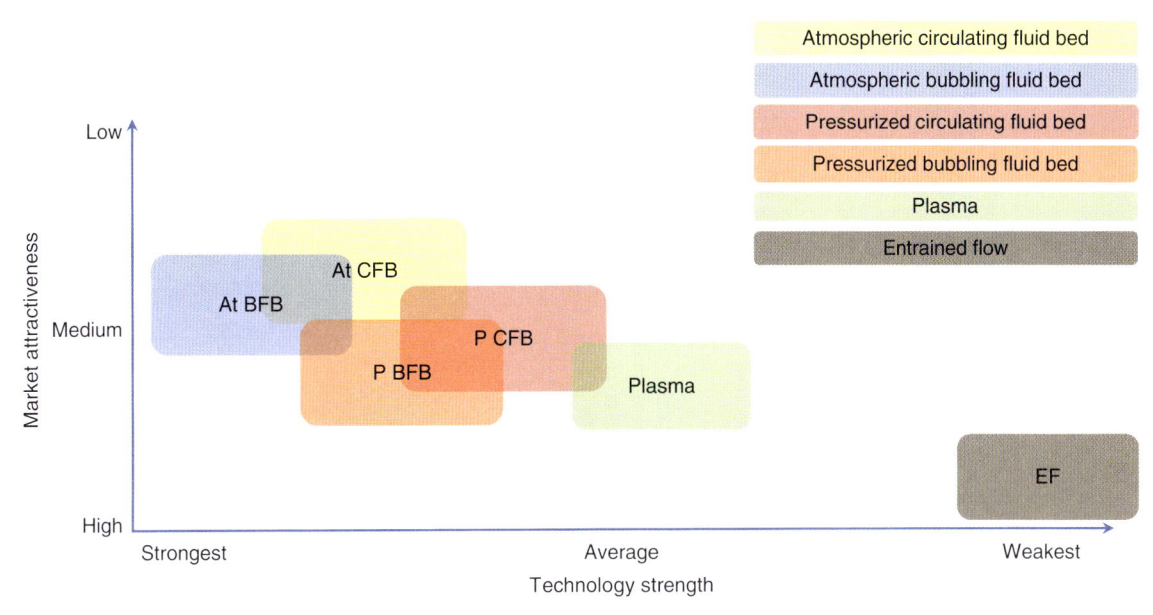

Figure 15 Technology status for power production from biomass. Redrawn with permission from Figure 1 in Maniatis K (2001) Progress in biomass gasification: An overview. In: Bridgwater AV (ed.) *Progress in Thermochemical Biomass Conversion*. Oxford, UK: Blackwell.

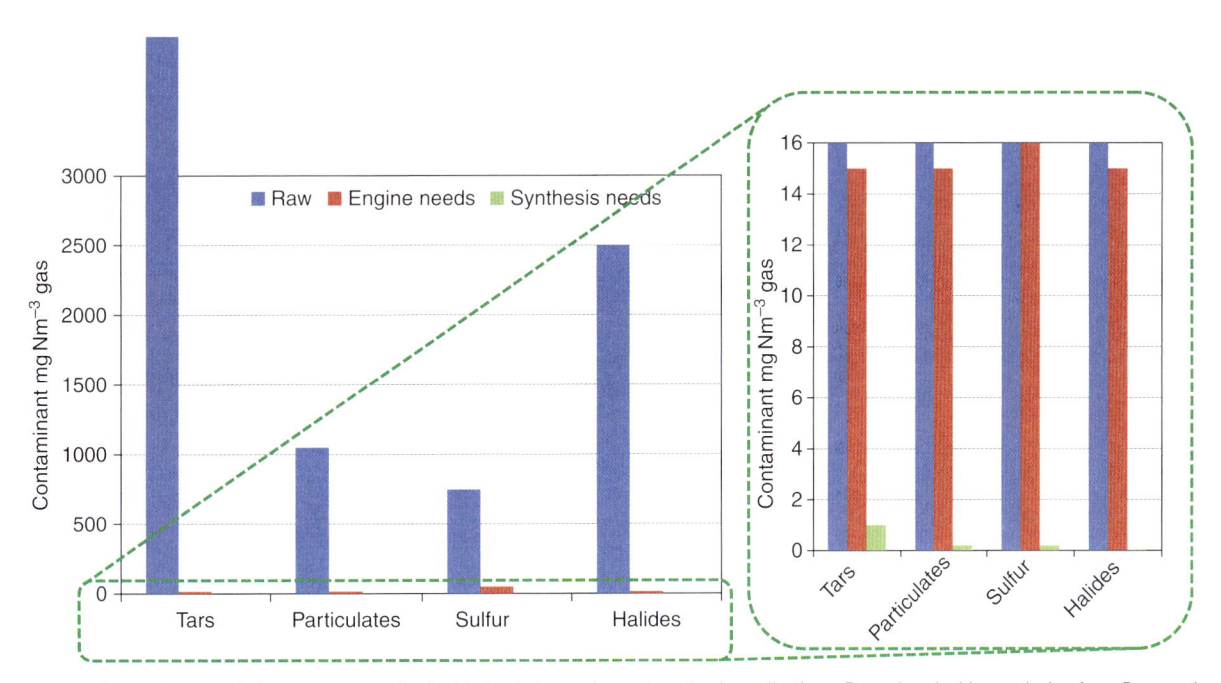

Figure 16 Contaminant levels in raw syngas and tolerable levels for engine and synthesis applications. Reproduced with permission from Progressive Energy Ltd.

engine is challenging, so producing a gas an order of magnitude cleaner again for chemical synthesis is a significant challenge to the development of BtL applications. However, apart from tars, the majority of these impurities are present in syngas streams from coal and oil albeit at differing concentrations, so commercially available technologies exist for their removal. The most significant of these contaminants are acidic gases, alkaline compounds, tars, and particulates.

5.11.4.3.1 (i) Acidic gases (sulfur and ammonia)
The principal acidic gases in syngas are sulfur and nitrogenous compounds. Sulfur in biomass can be converted to hydrogen sulfide or sulfur oxides during gasification. Sulfur causes permanent loss of FT catalyst activity, reducing catalyst lifetimes. It can also cause problems with the activity of downstream tar cracking catalysts. The level of tolerable sulfur contaminants in the syngas varies

Table 5 Syngas contaminant levels for a range of BtL applications

Conversion	Fischer–Tropsch		Methanol		Mixed alcohol Mixture of ethanol and higher alcohols				Fermentation
Products	Olefins + CO$_2$	Paraffins + H$_2$O	Methanol	Methanol					Ethanol
Catalyst	Fe	Co	Cu/ZnO/Al$_2$O$_3$ (gas contact)	Cu/ZnO (liquid contact)	Alkali/Cu/ ZnO(Al$_2$O$_3$)	Alkali/ZnO/ Cr$_2$O$_3$	Alkali/CuO/ CoO	Alkali/MoS$_2$	Biological
Temp (°C)	300–350	200–250	220–275	225–265	275–310	300–425	260–340	260–350	20–40
Pressure (bar)	20–40	10–40	50–100	50	50–100	125–300	60–200	30–175	1–2
H$_2$/CO ratio	0.6–1.7	Slightly >2	Unimportant Slightly >2	Low ratios ~0.68	1–1.2				Not sensitive
(H$_2$ – CO$_2$)/ (CO + CO$_2$) ratio	Unimportant	Unimportant			Same as methanol (gaseous)	Same as methanol (gaseous)	Same as FT (Co catalyst)	Unimportant	Unimportant
CO$_2$	5%	5%	4–8% (very slow reaction without any CO$_2$, but also inhibited if too much present)					5% (avoid promotion of methanol)	Aids initial growth rates
H$_2$O	Low (slowly oxidizes catalysts, very large amounts inhibit Fe-based FT synthesis)		Low (excessive amounts block active sites, reducing activity but increasing selectivity)					Same as FT (Co catalyst)	Most reactors use an aqueous solution
Hydrocarbons	Recycle to produce smaller molecules (to improve efficiency)		Recycle to produce smaller molecules (to improve efficiency)						None
C$_2$H$_2$	Low (inert)		Low (inert)	<5 ppmv					Unknown
CH$_4$	<2% (inert)		Low (inert)						Low (inert)
N$_2$	Low (inert)		Low (inert)						Low (inert)
HCN	<10 ppb (poison)		<10 ppb (poison)						Unknown
NH$_3$	<10 ppb (poison)		<10 ppb (poison)						Can help organism growth
NO$_x$	<100 ppb (poison)		<100 ppb (poison)						<40 ppmv, since >150 ppmv inhibits bacterial enzymes
Sulfur (COS, H$_2$S, CS$_2$)	<100 ppb (most important poison)	<60 ppb (most important poison)	<100 ppb (poison, permanent activity loss), COS only a poison in liquid phase, Zn can scavenge 0.4% of its weight in S while maintaining 70% activity					Resistant, 50–100 ppmv is actually needed	Tolerant (up to 2% H$_2$S, since S can help certain organisms' growth

Halides (HCl, Br, F)	<10 ppb (poison, can lead to structural changes in the catalyst)	<1 ppb (poison, leads to sintering)	<10 ppb (poison, leads to sintering)	Should be removed, although some organisms tolerant to Cl compounds
Alkali metals (Na, K)	<10 ppb (promotes mixed alcohol reaction)	Low (avoid due to promotion of mixed alcohol reaction)		Unknown
Tars	Concentration below dew point (otherwise condense on surfaces)	Concentration below dew point (otherwise tars will condense on catalyst and reactor surfaces)		Must be removed – similar requirements to FT
Particulates	<0.1 ppm	<0.1 ppm		Must be removed
Particulate size	<2 μm	Unknown	Low	Must be removed
Other trace species:	Unimportant	Avoid: As, P, Pb (lower activity, as with other heavy metals); Co (forms CH$_4$, activity reduced); SiO$_2$ (promotes wax with surface area loss); free Al$_2$O$_3$ (promotes DME); Ni and Fe (promote FT)	Co (beneficial methanol to ethanol conversion)	Must be removed

FT, Fischer–Tropsch; ppb, parts per billion; ppm, parts per million; ppmv, parts per million volume.
Reprinted from Table 3 in E4tech (2009) *Review of Technologies for Gasification of Biomass and Wastes*. York: NNFCC. http://www.nnfcc.co.uk/tools/review-of-technologies-for-gasification-of-biomass-and-wastes-nnfcc-09-008 (accessed 3 March 2011).

according to end application and catalyst type. In general, cobalt FT catalysts are more sensitive to sulfur than iron FT catalysts. Sulfur should be removed to less than 100 parts per billion (ppb) for FT applications using iron catalysts and less than 60 ppb for cobalt FT catalysts.

High-protein feedstocks can result in high nitrogen contents in the syngas. Nitrogenous compounds in biomass can be converted to ammonia, nitrous oxides, nitrogen, and hydrogen cyanide. All can be problematic for downstream catalyst activity. Ammonia should be reduced to less than 100 ppb in the syngas, nitrous oxides to less than 100 ppb, and hydrogen cyanide to less than 10 ppb. In general, nitrogen itself is inert and has no effect on catalyst activity although it acts as a dilutant, reducing the efficiency of conversion of the syngas to products.

Two methods of removing acid gases in syngas are physical methods such as Rectisol and Selexol, where the gases are dissolved in a solvent; and amine-based processes, which rely on a chemical reaction of the gases with the solvent. Physical methods use high pressure to dissolve the acid gases in a solvent. The gas-containing solvent is then reduced in pressure to release and recover the gases. These processes are very flexible and can selectively recover a range of products for downstream uses. Three principal technologies, namely, Rectisol, Selexol, and Purisol, differ in the solvent used, processing conditions, and cost. Rectisol uses cold methanol, which is relatively inexpensive, while Selexol and Purisol use proprietary formulations and are correspondingly more expensive. Amine-based acid gas systems include the Sulfinol and ADIP-X processes developed by Shell, and use a combination of alkanolamines and a range of additional chemicals depending on the process used.

5.11.4.3.1(ii) Alkaline compounds
Some biomass feedstocks, for example straw, can have high levels of alkaline compounds such as potassium and other salts. These can have detrimental effects on FT processes. Vaporized alkali compounds can be deposited on tubes causing alkaline metal corrosion problems. Alkali materials can also affect the activity of tar cracking catalysts. Alkaline materials should be removed to less than 10 ppb for FT applications. Alkali materials are removed from gasification systems by cooling the hot syngas to below 600 °C so that alkali materials can condense to particulates and be removed by particulate filters such as those discussed under the heading 'Particulates'.

5.11.4.3.1(iii) Tars
Tars are a range of oxygenated organic materials produced through the incomplete gasification or combustion of a biomass feedstock. They are particularly problematic for synthesis applications such as fuels and chemical production where the syngas is cooled, because as the syngas cools, tars condense onto cool surfaces, resulting in fouling of pipes, plugging, or formation of small aerosol droplets. Tars can also deactivate reforming catalysts. They also have a high energy content and may reduce overall process efficiency. The presence of tar within syngas is less problematic where the syngas is directly used for combustion purposes as there is typically little or no cooling of the syngas prior to use.

Tar composition and amount vary according to gasifier type and feedstock and thus gasifier choice should be matched to end-user applications. For all applications, tars must be reduced to such a concentration where no condensation occurs in the reactor.

The most common method of tar removal is to cool the syngas and then to physically remove condensed tars using wet scrubbers, electrostatic precipitators, or other technologies such as washing in organic liquids, as exemplified by the OLGA process developed by ECN. Other methods include catalytic and thermal methods of tar destruction and may involve the recycling of tars back into the gasifier where they are broken down to form gas and energy. Catalytic methods can be used to remove both vaporized and condensed tars and are generally carried out at 750–900 °C. Thermal processes use temperatures in excess of 1200 °C to break down tars without using catalysts.

5.11.4.3.1(iv) Particulates
Particulates are solid materials in the gas stream derived from ash in the feedstock, char, and material from the gasifier bed. CFB and bubbling fluidized bed gasifiers produce higher levels of particulates compared with entrained flow gasifiers because they use moving bed materials. Therefore, the amount of particulates produced varies according to the amount of ash in the biomass and the reactor design. Particulates can damage downstream equipment and their removal is often needed to comply with emission regulations. Ideally, particulate levels in the syngas should be reduced to less than 0.1 ppb.

Particulates can be removed using a range of different systems, although they are typically removed using either cyclonic or barrier filters. Cyclonic filters allow the removal of bulk particulates from a gas stream. These are usually employed as an initial removal step in gasifier systems and are an integral part of some gasifier systems. These can handle gases at a range of temperatures, typically removing particles of 5 mm diameter; removal of particles 1–5 mm may be less efficient. Cyclonic filters can also be used to remove condensed tars and alkali materials.

Barrier filters consist of a range of porous materials that are gas permeable and may be either rigid, bag or packed bed constructions. Gases are passed over the barrier and particulate materials are blocked from passing through. Generally, barrier filters are used for the removal of smaller diameter particulates and are employed after cyclonic filters. They are less suitable for wet and sticky materials such as tars owing to the propensity for these to block the filter. Further cleanup of finer particulates can be achieved using electrostatic filters and wet scrubbers.

5.11.4.3.1(v) Other products

Other products that do not take part in FT reactions are also ideally removed from the syngas as they dilute the gas and may also affect the activity of catalysts. These include carbon dioxide, nitrogen, and hydrocarbons such as methane and ethane. Methane is removed for most applications unless bioSNG is required.

5.11.4.4 Syngas Conditioning for FT

The ratio of hydrogen to carbon monoxide in the syngas is one of the crucial factors affecting the efficiency and outputs of the downstream FT process and therefore needs to be optimized accordingly. Cobalt-based catalysts require the molar ratio of hydrogen to carbon monoxide to be just above 2. Iron-based catalysts are more tolerant of variations in the hydrogen to carbon monoxide ratio because they have an intrinsic water–gas shift activity. Other processes such as syngas fermentation will require different hydrogen to carbon monoxide ratios; these are presented in **Table 5** and discussed in Section 5.11.5.

The water–gas shift reaction is used to achieve the correct molar ratio of hydrogen to carbon monoxide. Carbon monoxide in the syngas is released by reacting it with steam to yield carbon dioxide and additional hydrogen (eqn [1]). This process operates at around 300 °C and 15–25 bar pressure and is commercially available, being in common use in the petrochemical industry.

$$\text{water-gas shift reaction:} \quad CO + H_2O + \text{heat} = CO_2 + H_2 \tag{1}$$

5.11.4.5 FT Process

Once cleaned and conditioned, the syngas can be converted to a range of products via either a chemical synthesis step or a biological processing step. FT (**Figure 17**) is the most commonly described chemical synthesis option, and results in the production of hydrocarbons, which can be upgraded to products such as naphtha, kerosene, diesel, and wax components.

FT is a well-established, commercial process having been practiced for many years, albeit with coal- and gas-derived feedstocks. A number of suppliers of this technology are as shown in **Table 6**. Different suppliers differ in the processes, reactors, and catalysts employed.

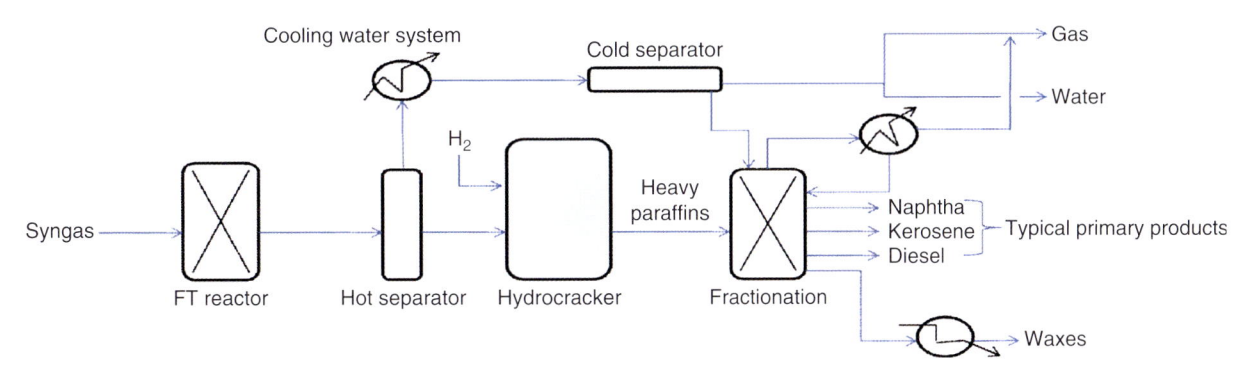

Figure 17 Simplified process flow diagram of once-through Fischer–Tropsch (FT) process.

Table 6 FT process developers

Company	Process	Reactor type	Catalyst
BP	Fixed bed/slurry	FBR/SBCR	Co
ConocoPhillips	Slurry	SBCR	Co
Exxon (AGC-21)	Slurry	SBCR	Co
IFP/ENI	Slurry	EBR/SBCR	Co
PDVSA/Intevep (DISOL)	Slurry	EBR	Co
PetroSA (Synthol)	Fluidized bed CFB	CFB	Fe
Rentech	Slurry	SBCR	Fe
Sasol (Arge/SAS/SPD)	Fixed bed/fluidized bed/slurry	FBR/FFB/SBCR	Fe or Co
Shell (SMDS)	Fixed bed	FBR	Co
Statoil	Slurry	SBCR	Co
Oxford Catalysts		Microchannel	
CompactGtL		Microchannel	

EBR, Ebullating bed reactor; FBR, fluidized bed reactor; FFB, fast fluid bed reactor; SBCR, slurry bed reactor. Reproduced from NNFCC report (08/017). Evans G (2007) International Biofuels Strategy Project. Liquid Transport Biofuels – Technology Status Report. York: NNFCC. http://www.nnfcc.co.uk/tools/international-biofuels-strategy-project-liquid-transport-biofuels-technology-status-report-nnfcc-08-017 (accessed 3 March 2011).

FT processes have been developed around large-scale processes for CtL and GtL applications. Such scales are not necessarily appropriate for biomass, which is a relatively dispersed, low-energy resource. There is a desire to reduce the scale of FT plants to be more appropriate for biomass use. Similarly, contaminant levels in syngas differ between different feedstocks and there is a need to consider systems that are more accepting of typical biomass feedstock contaminants.

5.11.4.5.1 FT catalysts

In the FT process, clean syngas is catalytically converted to form liquid hydrocarbons. Commercially, iron and cobalt catalysts are used because of their wide selectivity and cost, although other group VIII transition metals such as ruthenium and nickel can also be used. Although ruthenium has a high activity and selectivity for high-molecular-weight products, it is expensive and in short supply. Nickel gives high methane yields, desirable for SNG production, but does not have the wide selectivity exhibited by the other group members.

Iron catalysts have historically been widely used in commercial coal-based FT processes, for example in South Africa, and although an older technology compared to cobalt, they continue to be the preferred choice for FT processes using coal. Typically, iron catalysts are of lower cost compared to the alternatives and can be operated over a wide range of temperatures (220–350 °C), which can be useful for use in fluidized bed reactors since FT products will remain more volatile, avoiding the potential for catalyst agglomeration although selectivity to methane increases with increasing temperature. A useful property is their intrinsic water shift activity, which makes variations in the ratio of hydrogen to carbon monoxide in the syngas less important although this does increase FT reactor carbon dioxide production – hydrogen to carbon monoxide ratios down to 0.6 are potentially acceptable. This intrinsic water–gas shift activity feature is of particular interest where coal- or biomass-derived syngas is to be processed.

Iron catalysts are less robust than cobalt catalysts, making them less suited for use in slurry reactors. They also gradually deactivate, possibly after only 3 months of operation and cannot be regenerated. As with cobalt catalysts, iron catalysts can be poisoned. Of most concern is sulfur, which causes irreversible deactivation.

Products produced using iron catalysts are typically branched liquid hydrocarbons with higher levels of oxygenates and olefins compared to cobalt catalysts. The olefins make up about 10–30% or more of the compounds a carbon chain length of less than 30.

Cobalt-based catalysts are a newer technology compared to iron catalysts and are generally preferred for use with natural gas-derived syngas (since reforming of natural gas typically produces a syngas with a hydrogen to carbon monoxide molar ratio of about 2:1), particularly since they have a low water–gas shift activity. They are used commercially, for example, in the Shell FT plant in Malaysia. Cobalt catalyst supports are generally aluminum dioxide, silicon dioxide, and titanium dioxide, which have a high surface area absorbancy. Noble metal promoters are used to facilitate the reduction of cobalt oxide to metal during catalyst oxidation and regeneration. Oxide promoters are used to stabilize the dispersion of cobalt on the catalyst surface, to promote hydrocarbon chain growth, and to provide more selectivity to wax products.

Cobalt catalysts are operated at lower temperatures (200–240 °C) and lower pressures compared to iron catalysts. These lower temperatures combined with the cobalt catalyst promote the production of heavier waxy products, whereas the higher temperatures combined with the use of iron catalysts promote the production of lighter products. As they have a low intrinsic water–gas shift activity, they have a narrower acceptable hydrogen to carbon monoxide molar ratio range, typically needing a ratio of about 2:1. FT reactors utilizing cobalt catalysts, therefore, produce less carbon dioxide than those utilizing iron catalysts.

Cobalt catalysts are more stable and robust than iron catalysts and can be regenerated, making them well suited for use with tubular reactors, for example. However, they are more expensive. Products produced using cobalt catalysts are mainly straight chain heavy/waxy hydrocarbons with no aromatics, which need further upgrading by hydrocracking to yield the desired product slate.

In summary, the principal differences in catalysts are due to price, life span, and specificity. Iron catalysts are cheaper, but catalyst lifetime is reduced. Cobalt catalysts are more expensive, but have longer life spans. Generally, iron catalysts result in a larger amount of light olefin products, whereas cobalt catalysts result in a greater amount of wax products, which must subsequently be hydrocracked to produce the desired range of products.

5.11.4.5.1(i) FT reaction

FT processes convert synthesis gas with a given hydrogen to carbon monoxide ratio into hydrocarbon liquids and waxy solids with water as a coproduct via a stepwise polymerization process. As noted above, the process is carried out in the presence of an iron or cobalt catalyst at moderate temperature (200–350 °C) and pressure (c. 20–50 bar).

The FT chemistry involves a series of complex reactions, which can be summarized as follows:

Fischer-Tropsch reaction:
$$n\mathrm{CO} + 2n\mathrm{H}_2 + \text{heat} = n(\mathrm{CH}_2) + n\mathrm{H}_2\mathrm{O} \qquad [2]$$

The first step of the FT process involves adsorption of carbon monoxide onto the catalyst surface, followed by cleavage of the C–O bond to form carbides and oxides, followed by ligand hydrogenation to form a hydrocarbon with water as a by-product. The sequential addition of carbon, followed by hydrogen to form hydrocarbon groups, allows the nascent hydrocarbon chain to grow. Selective production by the FT process is dependent on the ability of the catalyst to promote chain elongation and to prevent termination reactions.

In addition to the hydrocarbon products, very small quantities of oxygen-containing hydrocarbons and some light gases (methane, ethane, etc.) are formed. The choice of catalyst and operating conditions influences the physical nature of the hydrocarbon product, that is, either a liquid or wax product is formed or some combination of both.

5.11.4.5.1(ii) FT products

The product distribution of the wax or liquid hydrocarbon products from the FT process is determined by the 'alpha' value (Anderson–Schulz–Flory theory) set by reaction conditions, including reaction temperature, catalyst type, and the hydrogen to carbon monoxide ratio of the synthesis gas (**Figure 18** and eqn [3]). Lower FT temperatures associated with cobalt catalysts typically produce waxy products with longer chain lengths, which can be hydrocracked to diesel (**Figure 19**). Higher FT temperatures associated with iron catalysts produce more gasoline range products and methane, and with more branching and oxygenation. Maximum selectivity with a cobalt catalyst to diesel is around 40% while with an iron catalyst to gasoline products is around 15–40%.

Anderson – Schultz – Flory distribution:
$$mn = (1-\alpha)^2 \alpha^{n-1} \qquad [3]$$

where mn represents the mole fraction of a hydrocarbon with a chain length of n carbons and a growth probability factor α, which determines the total carbon number in the FT products.

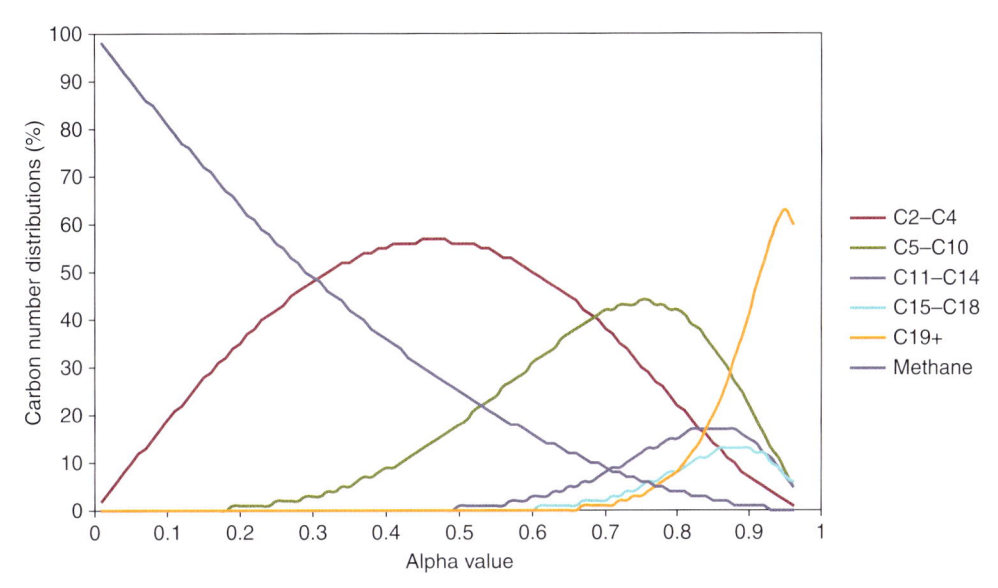

Figure 18 Product slate from Fischer–Tropsch (FT) reactions. Redrawn from Nexant Inc. (2007) Feasibility of Second Generation Biodiesel Production in the United Kingdom. *NNFCC Report*.

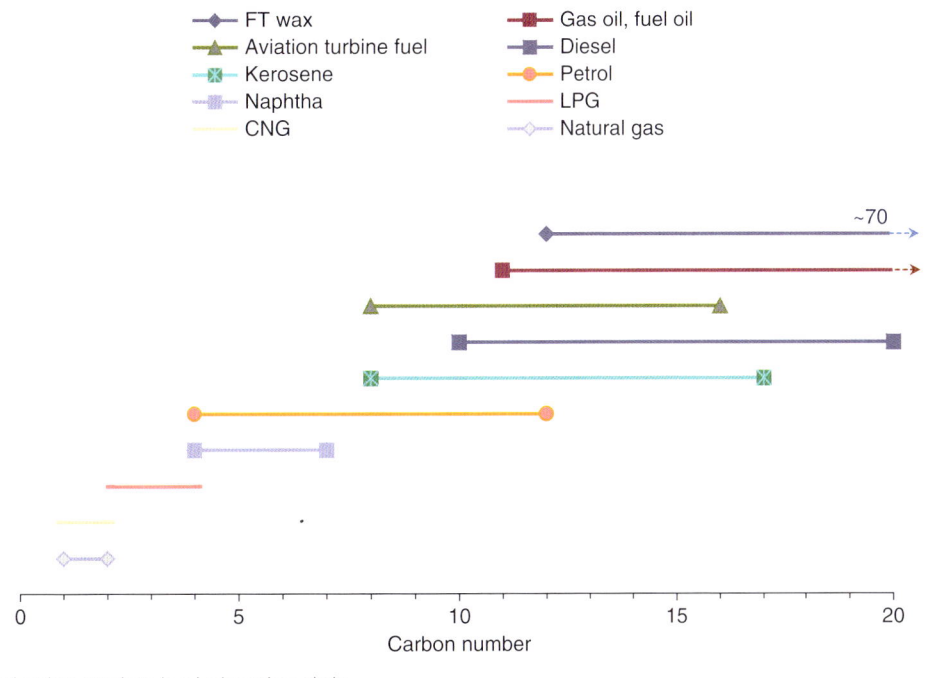

Figure 19 Typical carbon numbers in a hydrocarbon chain.

For different product slates focused on different refined products, the alpha value will be different. The higher the value of α, the longer the average chain length will be (**Figure 18**). However, in reality, FT products, as shown in **Figure 18**, often vary from that predicted by the Anderson–Schulz–Flory distribution, for example with undesirable C1 yields higher than predicted and C2 yields lower than predicted.

Low-temperature FT processes are now of key interest due to the international need for mid-distillate products. Such processes produce a wax product, which is subsequently hydrocracked to produce the desired hydrocarbon products – these products can include diesel, jet fuel, and/or naphtha as well as fuel gas. The conversion of carbon monoxide in syngas to FT products is between 50% and 90% if the off gas is recycled back to the FT reactor input stream.

When tuned to make diesel or jet fuel, a highly paraffinic fuel molecule is produced from the waxy product, which is low in aromatics, contains no sulfur, and is completely compatible with existing fuel infrastructures. These valuable properties provide a very high cetane number and low emissions (sulfur compounds, particulates, etc.) on combustion, making FT diesel, for example, a high-quality blendstock potentially enabling refiners to realize increased blending margins. These benefits, though, must be balanced against less favorable features such as poorer cold flow performance as a result of the low aromatic content, low density, and poor lubricity. The low aromatic content is an additional issue for jet fuel users because aromatics are believed to result in seal swelling during flight, thereby helping to avoid potential fuel system leaks. Some of these less favorable features can be offset by blending, particularly in the nearer term, since FT fuels, and in particular BtL, would be expected to be in limited supply. Additives can also be used to offset the effects of poor lubricity and cold flow performance.

Although FT diesel is off specification on density against EN590, pure FT diesel has a density around 780 kg m^{-3} compared to the EN590 specification of 820–845 kg m^{-3}; engine tests have indicated that engines will work well with low-density FT diesel yielding lower emissions.

In addition to the primary products described above, the FT process produces a range of other products, which can and will include the following:

- Fuel gas: This would typically be burned on-site to raise electricity, renewable in the case of a BtL process.
- Naphtha: In addition to synthetic fuel, the FT route also produces a paraffinic naphtha, which, when cracked, maximizes the production of the most valuable ethylene and propylene streams, which are further processed to make products such as polyethylene and polypropylene – these would be renewable plastics in the case of a BtL process.

5.11.4.5.2 Reactors for FT

A variety of reactors are available for FT processing, each with advantages and disadvantages. These generally fall into four categories and are at different stages of development, operate at different scales, and have differing appropriateness for BtL FT processing. The reactors most suitable for biomass applications are shown in **Figure 20**. These are:

- Slurry bed reactors.
- Fluidized bed reactors.
- Fixed bed tubular reactors.
- Microchannel reactors.

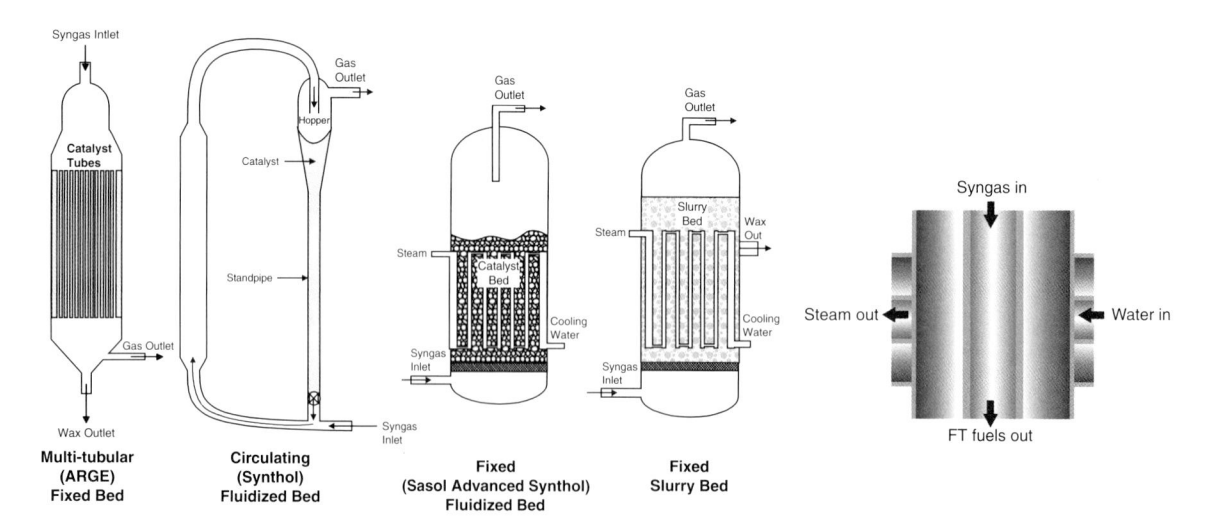

Figure 20 Types of Fischer–Tropsch reactors. The four images on the left have been reprinted from National Renewable Energy Laboratory Technical Report (NREL/TP-510-34929) *Preliminary Screening – Technical and Economic Assessment of Synthesis Gas to Fuels and Chemicals with Emphasis on Potential for Biomass-Derived Syngas*, by Spath PL and Dayton DC (December 2003). http://www.nrel.gov/docs/fy04osti/34929.pdf (accessed 14 January 2010). The image on the right is taken from http://www.velocys.com/media/video.php and reproduced by kind permission of Oxford Catalysts.

FT processes for use with biomass will ideally be viable at the smaller scale, have robustness to contaminants in the syngas, and have a good selectivity for products in the diesel and jet fuel range. Importantly, as the FT reaction is highly exothermic, it is imperative that the reactor has effective mechanisms for heat control to permit safe and reliable operation. This section examines the different FT reactors available and how suitable they are for different products and for dealing with variations in syngas quality.

5.11.4.5.1(iii) Fixed tubular bed reactors (multitubular trickle bed reactor)

In this type of reactor, syngas is introduced at the top of the reactor and flows down through up to 2000 tubes that are filled with catalyst, usually made from cobalt. The hydrocarbon products exit at the bottom of the reactor. Typical conversion efficiencies are around 70%, with over half of the products as waxes. The catalyst-filled tubes are immersed in boiling water for heat removal and pressures of around 20–30 bar are used to maintain the temperature of the water bath. Tubes are limited to around 25–50 mm diameter due to heat transfer limitations with wider diameter tubes. High gas velocities and gas recycling are used to improve conversion efficiency.

The fixed tubular bed reactors were the first to be introduced commercially, and were introduced in the 1950s. They have a relatively simple design, and there is no need for product separation from catalysts as it simply flows out of the bottom of the reactor, and performance is easily and reliably scaled up from single-tube studies. The fixed tubular bed system was the first to be commercially exploited, at Sasol I (the Sasol Arge reactor) and later at the Shell plant in Malaysia, in the Shell middle distillate synthesis (SMDS) system. Issues with catalyst poisoning are less problematic in fixed bed tubular systems than other systems such as slurry bed reactors, due to contaminants being confined to the upper sections of the catalyst bed.

Tubular bed reactors suffer from a number of problems including differentials in pressure and temperature across the tubes, leading to problems with catalyst sintering and deactivation. This is a particular problem for iron catalysts as only a fraction of the bed will be optimum for catalysis, while other parts may be either too cold or too hot. Catalyst replacement is also reportedly a major problem, especially for iron catalysts where life span is significantly lower than that for cobalt catalysts.

5.11.4.5.1(iv) Slurry bed reactors (slurry bubble column reactors and ebullating bed slurry reactors)

In a slurry bed reactor, syngas is bubbled up through a slurry made up of molten FT wax with catalyst suspended in it. This allows good contact between catalyst and syngas. Gaseous products are removed from the top of the reactor, while heavy nonvolatile waxes are separated from the catalyst. The slurry bed system was first deployed in 1993 and is optimized for low-temperature production of wax products.

Slurry bed reactors are the most advanced FT reactors, with good temperature control and good selectivity for long-chain products. These reactors are mainly used in conjunction with cobalt catalysts as in Exxon's AGC-21 process and Statoil and ConocoPhillips technologies, but can also use iron catalysts as in the Sasol single slurry phase distillate process. The simple design and construction and high capacities (10 000–20 000 bbl day^{-1}, 400 000–800 000 tpa) are significant advantages and these systems are up to 75% cheaper than fixed tubular reactors.

Slurry bed FT reactors have a number of disadvantages. These issues principally relate to catalysts. The low level of catalysts used in slurry bed reactors means that catalyst poisons can have serious effects on efficiency and life span. Effective syngas cleanup is, therefore, vital. Separation of the catalysts from the wax is also a challenge, and there are issues surrounding the design of external filters to allow catalysts to be reintroduced into the reactor without breakage. Catalysts need to be of sufficient size and robustness to prevent fines formation.

A modification of the slurry bed reactors is the ebullating bed slurry reactors. These are three-phase systems that contain liquid, vapor, and catalyst components, which are continuously mixed. They have a number of similarities with slurry bubble column reactors including temperature control and heat transfer efficiencies, although productivity may be lower. Key differences include the catalyst particle size, which for ebullating bed reactors is around 200 μm, compared to the 50–80 μm catalyst size needed for slurry bubble column reactors, and that the catalyst is suspended by the action of the circulating liquid. IFP and ENI have been developing ebullating fluidized bed processes in conjunction with a cobalt catalyst.

5.11.4.5.1(v) Fluidized bed reactors

Both CFB reactors and fixed fluidized bed reactors can be used for FT. Fluidized bed reactors are better suited for higher temperature processes, which are favorable for the production of gasoline and α-olefin range products, often called high-temperature FT (HTFT) processes. These beds are less suitable for long-chain hydrocarbon production because nonvolatile hydrocarbons can accumulate on catalyst surfaces, resulting in agglomeration of catalysts and defluidization of the bed.

Fixed fluidized bed reactors, such as the Sasol Advanced Synthol (SAS) reactor, feed syngas into the reactor through the vessel bottom. The gas flows through the fluidized bed of catalyst and product gases leave through the top of the reactor. Heat is controlled through a number of internal heat exchanger tubes within the fluidized catalyst bed. Thermal efficiency is superior to that of CFB reactors, so thermal and pressure gradients are reduced. Furthermore, catalyst consumption is reduced compared to circulating systems. Operating costs are lower, and product distribution can be more easily controlled. Capital costs of fixed fluidized beds are about 40% lower than those of CFB reactors.

In CFB reactors, syngas is again fed through the bottom of the vessel. High fluidization rates cause the FT reaction products (vapors and gases) and the catalyst to be separated from the bed where they exit the reactor into a cyclone separation system where the products are separated from the catalyst. The catalyst is then recycled back into the main reaction vessel. Reactors typically operate at 350 °C and 25 bar pressure. While these are well-established systems, they require a large amount of catalyst to be used. These are also very complex systems. The SAS process is a CFB FT reactor, which was used in Sasol I and II and the PetroSA plant in Mossel Bay. The PetroSA plant uses an iron-based catalyst, yielding a range of hydrocarbons from C1 to C20. These hydrocarbons are then split into three fractions for further processing to fuels and chemicals. The C2-rich stream is used in the production of polypropylene and ethylene, α-olefins C5, C6, and C8 are recovered for a range of fuels and chemicals, and longer chain olefins are used in fuels. Oxygenates in the aqueous stream are separated and used in the production of alcohols, acetic acid, and ketone-based products.

5.11.4.5.1(vi) Microchannel reactors

Microchannel reactors are the newest FT reactor development. These reactors consist of parallel arrays of channels between 0.1 and 5.0 mm in diameter. Thousands of microchannels containing catalyst are interleaved with boiling water-filled channels for cooling; this arrangement increases the efficiency of heat transfer in the process and correspondingly helps maintain steady temperatures and high rates of catalyst activity and life. Multiple reactors are used in parallel to provide commercial production volumes. Methane production is comparable with conventional FT reactors at about 9%.

Microchannel reactors reportedly allow process efficiencies to be increased 10- to 1000-fold compared to conventional systems. The increased reactor productivity per tonne of reactor and catalyst activity allow a concomitant reduction in both capital and operating costs associated with FT processes, and with microchannel technology, economies of scale can be reached faster, allowing FT to be carried out at smaller scales than the reactors traditionally used for CtL and GtL. This is especially valuable for BtL processes where there are inherent limits on the amount of biomass that can be sourced or economically transported to a centralized plant. Indeed, it is suggested that microchannel technology can allow economic production of fuels at scales of 500–2000 bbl day^{-1} (20–80 000 tpa) or 500–2000 tpd (tonnes per day) of biomass. A microchannel reactor can be typically 1.5 m diameter by 8 m long compared to conventional FT reactors, which are 9 m in diameter and 60 m long. **Figure 21** shows the SAS reactors at Sasol's Secunda CtL plant and the Oryx GtL plant, and the sheer scale of the reactors used in conventional FT processes.

A number of companies are driving the use of microchannel technology for FT processes, with perhaps the technologies of Velocys and CompactGtL the most applicable and advanced for FT biomass applications. Velocys has a pilot plant, with an output of 8 l day^{-1} (2600 tpa), which operates at 210–250 °C and 20 bar pressure and has a carbon monoxide conversion per pass of greater than 70%. Conventional catalysts cannot be used in the Velocys process, so the company has developed its own. However, it is more sensitive to sulfur and requires sulfur in the syngas to be reduced to less than 20 ppb. A typical reactor size will be about 0.6 m by 0.6 m, and a number of reactors could typically be used together in a containment shell for commercial operation.

Velocys is partnered with SGC Energia to examine the use of microreactor channel technology at the Gussing BtL plant in Austria for the production of around 10 000 gallons per year (35 tpa) of FT diesel from wood chips. CompactGtL is also developing microchannel reactors, but in this case this is for GtL applications, allowing gas produced in oilfields, which would otherwise be flared, to be converted into FT products. A pilot plant has been operational at Wilton in the northeast of England since 2008. In addition, Petrobras is also building a pilot plant, which is due to come online in mid-2010.

Figure 21 Sasol's advanced synthol reactor at Secunda in South Africa (left) and Oryx GtL in Qatar (right). These images have been reprinted with kind permission from Sasol.

5.11.4.5.3 Summary

The FT process is possibly the most well-described application of BtL and has been based on modifications of the FT process employed for both CtL and GtL applications. However, biomass use poses a number of unique technological and scale challenges. The scale needed for current commercial FT reactors to be economic is a particular issue for biomass use, and thus it is encouraging that there is a drive toward developing smaller scale applications more appropriate to biomass scales.

5.11.5 Alternative BtL Fuel Options

Although conversion of syngas to fuels via the FT process is the most commonly described option for BtL, a number of other options exist as shown in **Figure 22** to convert clean syngas into fuels, each of which can be described as a BtL process. These alternatives include methanol, ethanol, mixed alcohols, and gases such as DME, bioSNG, and hydrogen. Each of these end uses has differing syngas cleaning and processing requirements and requires different catalysts and/or different conversion conditions. This section describes the alternatives available, how they are produced, and factors affecting their uptake as fuels and chemicals.

5.11.5.1 Methanol

Methanol is a commodity chemical with a wide range of end applications, including use as a fuel and as a chemical. The global market for methanol is well over 35 million tpa. The principal market for methanol, accounting for around 65% of production, is in the production of formaldehyde for the construction sector.

Methanol has a high octane and a low cetane number; it is therefore better suited to spark ignition engines rather than compression ignition (CI) engines. It may be blended up to 3% by volume under the European Fuel Quality Directive, or may be used as a fuel in flexible fuel vehicles at up to an 85% blend with petrol known as M85. Methanol has a higher oxygen content relative to petrol; this improves combustion and reduces pollution from emissions. It was for this reason it was historically used as an oxygenate in fuels, either alone or in methyl *tert*-butyl ether (MTBE). It is also viewed as a potential hydrogen carrier for fuel cell vehicles, because it has a hydrogen to carbon ratio of 4:1 and has a lower reforming temperature than other fuels, simplifying the layout of the reformer and reducing its costs. However, methanol has a number of disadvantages as a fuel. It has only around half the energy content of petrol and there are a number concerns regarding health and safety, handling, and the potential for environmental damage from spillage. These concerns have resulted in its elimination from transport fuels in most countries worldwide.

Methanol can be used as a raw material for the production of a number of fuels, including the production of biodiesel, DME, MTBE, gasoline (via the methanol-to-gasoline (MTG) process or Topsoe integrated gasoline synthesis (TIGAS) process), and

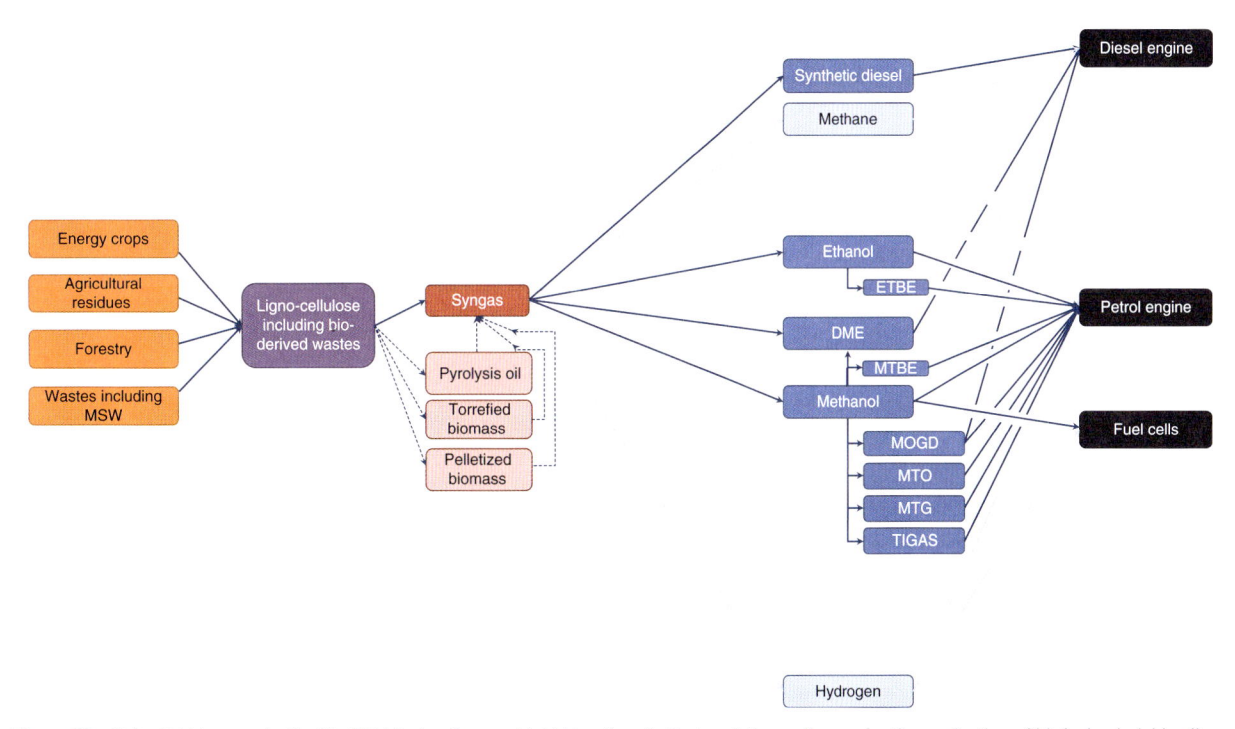

Figure 22 Potential biomass-to-liquids (BtL) fuel pathways. Light blue lines indicate existing pathways for the production of biofuels; dark blue lines indicate alternative pathways to current biofuel products that may become commercially feasible in the near to mid-term (in particular before 2020); and dashed lines indicate pathways to biofuel products not currently in use but potentially feasible in the near to mid-term. Reproduced with permission from LowCVP and NNFCC (2010) Biofuels Pathways. *LowCVP Report*.

gasoline and diesel (via the Mobil olefins to gasoline and distillate (MOGD) process), and in the Lurgi MtSynfuels process where methanol is an intermediary product. Processes for the direct production of DME and gasoline have been developed where syngas is converted to the end product using bifunctional catalysts where both methanol production and product conversion are integrated into a single step. The latter methods are explained in more depth in the following sections.

The technology for methanol production from fossil fuels is mature and exploits economy of scale in huge plants (mega-methanol plants) with production capacities measured in millions of tonnes. Methanol production is based on three steps: gasification to produce syngas, conversion of the syngas to crude methanol, and the subsequent distillation of the crude methanol to produce the desired purity. Around 75% of methanol is currently produced from steam methane reforming of natural gas, while some is produced from coal, particularly in China. The ready availability of refined production technologies and distribution infrastructure, along with the growing concerns over security of energy supply, could facilitate the penetration of biomass as a feedstock for methanol synthesis.

The conversion of syngas to methanol is achieved using copper/zinc-based catalysts, such as copper oxide or zinc oxide. Process conditions vary depending on the catalyst used – zinc oxide catalysts work at a temperature of 350 °C and at a pressure of 250–350 bar, whereas copper oxide catalysts work at a temperature of 220–275 °C and lower pressures of 50–100 bar. Biomass gasification can, depending on the catalysts used, result in a gas that is too high in carbon for methanol synthesis. Ideally, when copper/zinc oxide/alumina catalysts are used, the syngas stoichiometric ($H_2 - CO_2$) to ($CO + CO_2$) ratio should be greater than 2 (see Table 5). Carbon monoxide, therefore, needs to be removed from the gas and/or hydrogen added to it. The two principal methods for adjusting the hydrogen to carbon monoxide ratio in the derived syngas for methanol production are carbon monoxide separation, whereby an acid gas separation process is used to remove the excess carbon monoxide, or the addition of hydrogen so that carbon monoxide is hydrogenated. Copper oxide or zinc oxide catalysts are less sensitive, requiring a ratio of around 0.68 (Table 5).

The catalysts used for methanol synthesis are sensitive to poisoning by contaminants, so it is important that the synthesis gas from biomass is of sufficient purity. Sulfur levels in the syngas should be less than 100 ppb and halides should be less than 1 ppb volume as indicated in Table 5. Chlorinated compounds are a particular issue for the production of methanol from BtL processes as these can result in the sintering of copper, blocking of copper catalyst sites, and increased sulfur poisoning.

The production of methanol from syngas has a selectivity more than 99.5% and a thermal efficiency of around 79%. The theoretical syngas carbon monoxide conversion yield is around 25%, although actual values are around 4–7%. Yields of 99% can be achieved by recycling unreacted components (syngas, carbon monoxide, volatiles, water, and higher alcohols) back into the reactor (via a recycle loop) after methanol production. Production of methanol is an exothermic reaction, generating significant amounts of steam. Consequently, consideration for the efficient removal and control of heat is necessary in reactor design.

To the authors' knowledge, the only commercial BtL biomethanol plant, at the time of writing, is the BioMCN BtL biomethanol plant in Delfzijl, the Netherlands, which produces biomethanol from glycerin. Other facilities appear to be at a pilot and experimental scale, utilizing a wide range of different feedstocks. A range of agricultural wastes have been tested at the Nori Biomass No. 1 test plant in Nagasaki, Japan, with reported methanol yields between 36% and 55% depending on the biomass source, with woody materials reportedly giving higher methanol yields. Mitsubishi Heavy Industries have developed a process known as the biomass gasification methanol synthesis (BGMS) process and tested wood chips and waste wood at a 2 oven dry tonnes (odt) day^{-1} pilot plant in Japan in 2002, although the current status of this project is unknown.

5.11.5.2 Dimethyl Ether

DME is a synthetic fuel, gaseous at ambient conditions, which can be liquefied at moderate pressure allowing it to be handled as a liquid in a similar way to LPG. DME has a cetane number of 55–60 (which is higher than that of the standard EN590 diesel specification at 51), has a higher oxygen content, and produces low emissions of soot and nitrous oxides in comparison with fossil diesel. This makes it a suitable clean burning fuel for diesel engines although it is also a potential LPG substitute. DME has a carbon to hydrogen ratio of 3:1, which makes it a potential candidate as a hydrogen carrier for onboard fuel cells. The use of DME as a fuel, however, has a number of drawbacks. DME has only half the energy of fossil diesel; requires modification of engines, particularly plastic and rubber components; has poor lubricity and viscosity, requiring the possible use of additives; and is difficult to pump at high pressures. Conventional vehicles require dedicated onboard storage. Large-scale private vehicle uptake of DME as a fuel would require a new distribution, storage, and refueling infrastructure to be built and the introduction of modified vehicles. It is therefore less likely that it will become a common fuel in the nearer term. However, DME could be an attractive option for captive fleets and trucks where a lower cost refueling infrastructure can be put in place.

DME can be synthesized from syngas either through a direct or by an indirect process. The indirect process predominates, and allows the production of DME from syngas via dehydration of a methanol intermediate. This process requires aluminum catalysts and a syngas stoichiometric ($H_2 - CO_2$) to ($CO + CO_2$) ratio of greater than 2. It is an established technology (e.g., the Air Products' liquid phase DME process (LPDME®)), and because it is produced from a methanol intermediate, the end product can be varied as economic conditions dictate. The single-stage production of DME from syngas is a newer development, resulting in higher conversion efficiencies and utilizing a mixed functional catalyst. In contrast to the indirect route, the required syngas stoichiometric ($H_2 - CO_2$) to ($CO + CO_2$) ratio is 1 (see Table 5), which is closer to that derived from the gasification reaction; thus, it is assumed that there will be less need to perform syngas conditioning for this process.

The conversion of methanol to DME has been commercialized in the Far East at scales of around 100 000 tpa. Chemrec is investigating the use of black liquor gasification (BLG) to produce DME for biofuels for truck use as part of the EU BioDME project. It has a pilot plant with a capacity of 1600 gallon per day (1841 tpa) in Pitea, Sweden, for testing this concept, expected to start operations in mid-2010.

5.11.5.3 Gasoline

The BtL process is less suited for the direct production of gasoline products, principally due to the low octane value obtained from the resulting paraffinic molecules. However, gasoline can be produced from syngas via methanol and DME, both through direct conversion techniques where gasoline is produced directly from syngas in a single step (as exemplified by the TIGAS process) and through indirect conversion technologies where gasoline is produced via an intermediate (as exemplified by the Mobil MTG process and Lurgi MtSynfuel processes). Given that direct conversion technologies have been developed from the indirect route, it is perhaps pertinent to first consider the indirect routes from syngas to gasoline prior to direct routes.

The MTG process is a two-step process. It first produces methanol, which is dehydrated using a γ-alumina catalyst to give DME. This is, in turn, further dehydrated with a zeolite catalyst (ZSM-5) that has high selectivity for molecules in the gasoline range (C4–C10). This produces a high-quality, high-octane, low-sulfur gasoline range product containing aliphatic and aromatic components. However, the high aromatic content means it does not conform to current petrol specifications. By changing the catalyst and process conditions, the MTG process can be modified to produce either light olefins or a mixture of gasoline and diesel. The MTG process was commercialized in New Zealand during the early 1980s, although this was subsequently abandoned due to the rising price of natural gas, which made the process uneconomic.

The MOGD process is derived from the methanol-to-olefins (MTO) process and uses olefins from the MTO process, which are oligomerized over a ZSM-5 catalyst. The process has a selectivity to hydrocarbon products in the gasoline and diesel range greater than 95%. The proportions of each product can be changed depending on the mode of operation used, allowing considerable flexibility in the product slate produced. Low-temperature, high-pressure processes (200–300 °C, 20–105 bar) are known as the distillate mode. The distillate produced from the MOGD process, after hydrogenation, can produce diesel and aviation fuels. High-temperature, low-pressure processes result in the production of gasoline products. MOGD processes have been developed by both Exxon Mobil and Lurgi; and although the technologies have been demonstrated at small scale, they have not yet been commercialized.

The Haldor Topsoe TIGAS process is a development from the MTG process where syngas is converted to gasoline in a single synthesis loop via methanol and DME. The key difference is that in the TIGAS process, methanol reacts to form DME directly, while the MTG process requires the separate isolation of a methanol intermediate. Integration of the conversion of synthesis gas to methanol, and DME to gasoline steps, allows a saving on process equipment and requirement for pressure. Integration allows unconverted syngas to be recycled in the process and this increases the efficiency of the process, with an estimated 60% of the energy in wood potentially converted into transportation fuel. Due to the flexibility of the methanol/DME synthesis, a variety of synthesis gas compositions may be applied, although the highest DME yield and lowest methanol and water yields are obtained with a hydrogen to carbon monoxide ratio of 1.

The TIGAS process was demonstrated in the 1980s in a demonstration unit producing 1 tonne of gasoline per day from natural gas-derived syngas. Haldor Topsoe is collaborating with the Gas Technology Institute in Des Plaines, USA, to demonstrate the feasibility of producing gasoline from wood via the TIGAS process. Their planned demonstrator will convert 25 tonnes of wood per day into transportation fuel.

5.11.5.4 Mixed Alcohols (via Catalysts)

Mixed alcohol synthesis processes produce a mixture of methanol, ethanol, propanol, butanol, and smaller amounts of heavier alcohols from syngas. The ratio of alcohols produced varies according to the technology used; in some cases, ethanol can be the most significant component, whereas in other cases, it may be methanol. Mixed alcohol synthesis techniques were developed to provide a blendstock for octane enhancement of petrol fuels, but their development was superseded by the use of methanol via MTBE. As a fuel, higher alcohols have a lower vapor pressure, better solubility, increased water tolerance, and higher heating value compared to methanol. Interest in both mixed alcohol and ethanol production from synthesis gas has been rekindled recently due to the increased profile of biofuels.

The production of mixed alcohols via the catalytic route has been developed to demonstration scale over the past 30 years. In general, production of single alcohol streams is poor due to low catalyst selectivity. A number of research groups have attempted to selectively produce ethanol from synthesis gas with varying degrees of success, with most suffering from poor economics due to low catalyst selectivity. The conversion of syngas to mixed alcohols is achieved using catalysts similar to those used in FT and methanol production, but including alkali metals to promote mixed alcohol production. The required ratio of hydrogen to carbon monoxide is 1–1.2 (Table 5), so there is less need for a water shift reaction compared to other conversion processes. Depending on the catalyst used, some sulfur may be beneficial. For example, for an alkali molybdenum sulfide catalyst, between 50 and 100 parts per million volume of sulfur is required, while for other catalysts sulfur must be removed.

Ethanol and methanol are the major products of this process. The higher alcohols are only a small percentage of total production. A small distillation column separates ethanol and the higher alcohols from methanol, which is recycled to the synthesis reactor inlet. The yields of single-pass conversions are generally around 10–40%, but produce mainly methanol. The selectivity varies due to hydrocarbon production, but on a carbon monoxide-free basis is around 60–90%. The mixed alcohol products must be separated prior to utilization.

A number of companies are now pursuing the commercialization of mixed alcohol synthesis from bio-derived synthesis gas, including Pearson Technologies, Range Fuels, and Syntec. Of these, Range Fuels appears to be the closest to commercial deployment and, as such, is explained in more detail in Section 5.11.7. The feedstocks and technologies used vary from provider to provider. Pearson Technologies has tested a range of feedstocks including waste wood, sawdust, manure, and lignite, and it is likely that other waste biomass could be used, while Range Fuels is focusing on wood and waste wood. Both Pearson and Range Fuels are investigating the use of indirectly heated entrained flow gasifiers using steam, but while the Pearson technology appears to be a single-gasifier process, the Range Fuels process consists of two separate gasifiers using a low-temperature and a high-temperature reaction step.

5.11.5.5 Alcohols (via Fermentation)

In contrast to the high-temperature catalytic routes described above, the conversion of synthesis gas to alcohols can also be accomplished by fermentation with anaerobic bacteria such as *Clostridium ljungdahlii* and *Clostridium carboxidivorans* P7. Alcohol production is based on three steps: gasification to produce syngas, conversion of the syngas to crude alcohol via fermentation, and the subsequent distillation of the alcohol to produce the desired purity.

The fermentative route has a number of distinct advantages over the catalytic route. Fermentative processes operate at low pressures and temperatures, which reduces costs. High yields of a single product are achieved, enhancing economic attractiveness. The fermentative route is understood to be less sensitive to contaminants such as sulfur in the syngas and variations in syngas flow rate. Nevertheless, depending on the organism used, syngas may need to be cleaned to remove tars and light hydrocarbons as these may adversely affect cell growth and fermentation. In contrast to catalytic approaches, microorganisms can tolerate a range of hydrogen to carbon monoxide ratios in the syngas. There is, therefore, less need for the water shift reaction. In general, microorganisms prefer carbon monoxide to hydrogen, but both can be used simultaneously. The tail gas, which can be burned in an engine to provide power, could, therefore, be more hydrogen rich and could potentially be used for fuel cells in the future. The conversion efficiency depends on the microorganism and growth conditions, but in general ethanol concentrations need to be kept below 3% in the reactor since ethanol is toxic to microorganisms. The reaction time from biomass to distilled ethanol has been proven to be short (7–8 min) compared to fermentation of sugars, which often lasts for 1–2 days.

This technology is being developed by Coskata, General Motors, AlterNRG, INEOS Bio, and BRI Energy. Coskata is reportedly building a syngas fermentation to ethanol plant in Madison, Pennsylvania, using a Westinghouse Plasma Gasifier, at around 1500 odt day^{-1} through a modular system. INEOS Bio is planning to build a 25 000 tpa ethanol plant at Wilton in the northeast of England, which will use about 200 000 tpa of waste biomass.

5.11.5.6 Hydrogen and BioSNG

The BtL process can also produce a number of gaseous fuels in addition to liquid fuels of which hydrogen and bioSNG are the most advanced.

5.11.5.6.1 Hydrogen

Hydrogen is a clean burning gas that could be used in fuel cell vehicles, or in modified diesel and gasoline engines, albeit with low efficiency. Currently, it is not widely used as a transport fuel, except in a small number of pilot projects. The energy density of hydrogen is very low and is dependent on the pressure at which it is stored. Thus, conventional vehicles would require dedicated storage, which would be a major technical challenge and would require a dedicated refueling infrastructure. It is therefore unlikely that hydrogen will be a common vehicle fuel in the near to medium term in most locations, although Germany is reportedly investing heavily in the implementation of a hydrogen infrastructure, which could be deployed as early as 2015.

Hydrogen is used in a large number of oil refinery and chemical manufacturing processes. The principal use for hydrogen, accounting for 60% of hydrogen use, is for ammonia production via the Haber–Bosch process, oil refining (23%), and then methanol production (9%). The majority of hydrogen currently produced is from fossil sources such as natural gas and coal through XtL processes with around 77% of hydrogen derived from petrochemicals and around 18% from coal. Production of hydrogen from biomass feedstocks by application of the water–gas shift reaction to cleaned syngas is more difficult and costly compared to its production from natural gas. Thus, currently, there is little interest in hydrogen production from biomass.

5.11.5.6.2 BioSNG

Methane produced by the methanation of syngas and prepared to a standard suitable for use via the existing natural gas grid is termed bioSNG. BioSNG mainly consists of methane and can be used as a vehicle fuel although, compared to petrol and diesel, its use is likely to remain limited in the near to medium term. Methane is gaseous and can be used as compressed natural gas (CNG) or liquefied natural gas (LNG) in vehicles fitted with modified spark ignition engines or in dual fuel diesel/LNG CI engines. In dual fuel CI engines, 50–80% of the diesel can be replaced by gas; the diesel is needed to ignite the fuel mixture. As with DME, the use of biomethane as a transport fuel would require a new dedicated infrastructure for refueling, storage, and transportation, and unless refueling through the gas grid occurs, uptake in the nearer term may be limited to captive fleets where a lower cost refueling infrastructure can be put in place.

The production of methane from biogenic sources is increasing. Anaerobic digestion, which typically utilizes wet feedstocks, is well established and many plants are in operation around the world. Gasification followed by syngas methanation, which utilizes dry feedstocks, is currently moving from the pilot stage to the subeconomic demonstration stage and the first commercial operations are expected to start before 2015.

Methane is considered to be a key way of meeting renewable energy targets for heat, power, and transportation, and there is an increasing amount of R&D in this area, particularly in Sweden, the Netherlands, and Austria. In Sweden, the GoBiGas project, led by Goteburg Energi, is being developed in two phases. The first phase aims to build a 20 MW gasification plant, which will convert low-grade biomass from forestry into 160 GWh of bioSNG with an efficiency of 60–70% by 2012. The bioSNG will be injected into the Swedish natural gas grid. In the second phase, an 80 MW plant producing 640 GWh of biomethane/bioSNG is planned, although the design for this phase is not yet finalized. In the Netherlands, ECN has been actively pursuing bioSNG development, using a stepwise scale-up approach, with plans to build demonstration units in 2012 and, at full scale, in 2015. The EU bioSNG project aims to realize the development of a 1 MW bioSNG process development unit, which allows the demonstration of the complete process chain from wood to bioSNG at half-commercial scale at Gussing, Austria.

5.11.5.7 Summary

One of the intrinsic advantages of the BtL process is the wide range of chemicals and fuels that can be produced from syngas, including ethanol, FT diesel, FT jet fuel, DME, gasoline, mixed alcohols, and methanol. A wide range of technologies are currently being developed worldwide for each of these different end uses and these are at varying stages of development. Currently only the production of methanol from biomass is commercial at present.

The eventual implementation of each technology will depend on the development of markets and technologies. Technologies differ in their tolerance to syngas contaminants and variations in syngas composition and scale. Thus, there is no one-size-fits-all approach within BtL. Similarly, the market for each product varies considerably, from fuels that are fully or increasingly able to be mixed into the existing supply infrastructure such as ethanol and diesel, to those that would require significant investments such as bioDME and bioSNG. These represent longer term opportunities for the general transport sector, although captive applications may develop in the short to medium term.

5.11.6 Timescales and Development of BtL Processes

Policy and legislation are driving targets for the development of biofuels production around the world. In some cases, these targets include a specific element for advanced biofuels, which includes BtL. Of particular relevance to EU and US biofuels uptake are the forthcoming EU RED and USA RFS2.

The principal influence on forthcoming biofuels deployment in the EU is the RED, which stipulates that by 2020, 10% of the energy of each member states' transport fuels must be derived from renewable sources. To qualify as a biofuel that can contribute to the government's renewable energy target and be eligible for financial support, the RED states that, from April 2010, biofuels must comply with the environmental sustainability criteria that were defined by the European Commission at the end of 2009. Under these criteria, biofuels will have to save at least 35% GHG emissions compared to the fossil fuels they replace from April 2013, increasing to 50% by 2017. Alternatives to liquid fuels, such as electric and biogas vehicles, are predicted to be only a small part of the transport fuel mix by 2020, so it is likely that this target will primarily be met through the use of biofuels compatible with the existing supply chain. However, one of the principal issues in meeting this target will be that the EU is increasingly, and likely to remain, short of diesel, while having an excess supply of petrol. Analyses for the UK Renewable Energy Association [2] have shown that it is unlikely that the EU can meet a 10% target for diesel solely through FAME routes, and alternative biodiesel sources including algae-based fuels are unlikely to be available by 2020 as these are currently at an early stage of development. BtL fuels are probably the most well-developed alternatives to FAME biodiesel and first-generation ethanol, and as such may be able to contribute to the EU targets. Recognizing this and hoping to incentivize deployment, the RED states that fuels derived from residues, wastes, or lignocellulosic materials should count twice toward the 10% target.

The principal driver for biofuels deployment in the United States is the RFS2, which stipulates that by year 2022, 36 bn US gallons (approximately 120 million tonnes) of biofuel should be blended into road transport fuels, and is expected to displace around 7% of the total projected gasoline and diesel demand. Of this, 16 bn US gallons (approximately 56 million tonnes) should be derived from advanced processes such as BtL. To qualify toward meeting these targets, minimum GHG savings should be met, with cellulosic biofuels (including BtL) needing to demonstrate savings of 60% relative to the fossil fuels they replace. A wide range of fiscal incentives, both for subsidizing the building of plants and for the cost of the finished fuel, are available.

Despite these targets, it is acknowledged that many barriers stand in the way to BtL deployment. These challenges encompass technical, political, and economic issues, and concerted action is needed from policy makers, investors, end users, and the biomass supply chain to overcome these issues and promote development in this sector. These issues fall into four main categories:

- *Biomass supply.* It is a significant issue for a BtL plant, especially considering the scale of biomass typically expected to be required. Incentives for use of biomass in electricity and small-scale heat production can mean that biomass is preferentially directed to these markets. This means that BtL facilities may have a disadvantage in procuring sufficient feedstock. This problem is

exacerbated by the currently immature nature of biomass supply chains, which need to be further developed to meet the large volumes of biomass that will be needed in the future.
- *Cost*. Financially, it is acknowledged that BtL capital costs are typically high relative to alternatives and that R&D and commercialization are expensive. These are further affected by uncertainty over fuel prices, as BtL products are intrinsically linked to crude oil prices, and the uncertainty over the incentives, which can be used in this sector.
- *Policy*. Policy relating to biofuels is rapidly developing and has given rise to uncertainty, which has reduced investor confidence in biofuels. Developers need longer term assurance from governments of how technologies can meet specific policies.
- *Technology*. Although BtL has significant parallels in its approach and infrastructure requirements to existing and well-established CtL and GtL applications and several aspects are well established, it is important to note that the complete process is insufficiently developed. This means that a stepwise approach in the commercialization of BtL is needed. There are significant challenges to overcome, including large-scale gasification of biomass, gas cleaning, optimizing catalyst performance for biomass feedstocks, and demonstrating reliable integrated operation. Demonstration is required to give confidence to investors of the bankability of projects.

The influence of these factors will depend on local issues. **Figure 23** shows a projected scenario for the development of a commercial-scale BtL plant in the United Kingdom by 2020. This scenario assumes that a subcommercial demonstration plant would be needed before a larger commercial-scale plant would be built. Planning for both commercial-scale plants and subcommercial-scale plants would typically take place in parallel.

The development, construction, and operation of a small-scale demonstration plant are used to test systems and show the feasibility of all aspects of the value chain. The first commercial plant can be designed and the performance guaranteed based on the performance of the demonstration plant. Work on the commercial plant may be carried out in parallel (as exemplified by Choren and Neste Oy) or after sustained operation of the demonstration plant depending on the perceived risks of the project. If some risks in a project are considered too high, the final investment decision for a first-of-a-kind commercial-scale plant may be delayed until sufficient experience has been gained from the operation at the demonstration scale, especially where operational evidence is needed for financial backers. Alternatively, where the commercial plant is planned at the same time as work on the demonstration plant, the work may be limited in scope initially until there has been sufficient experience with the demonstration facility. In both cases, any delays in the development of the demonstration plant would be expected to lead to associated delays in the development of the first commercial-scale plant. Given the time frames above, implementation of a new BtL facility, given that individual BtL elements such as gasification are available, if begun now, or by 2013 at the latest, could be commercial by 2020.

An alternative option for development of a new BtL industry is to license technologies developed abroad. Although this option gives less flexibility to take advantage of indigenous strengths, it does provide the potential to build a BtL industry more quickly. BtL projects are being developed around the world and are expected to be commercialized by 2015. These projects are described in the next section.

5.11.7 BtL Implementation Progress

A number of BtL projects are being developed around the world as shown in **Figure 24**. Typically, most of these projects are in the process of building or starting up small-scale demonstration facilities at about the 10 000–20 000 tpa (products) scale with larger, commercial-scale operations expected to start operating around 2015 (**Figure 25**). The most advanced BtL project is perhaps BioMCN, which began production of methanol from glycerol, a coproduct of the FAME biodiesel industry in 2009. Elsewhere in the

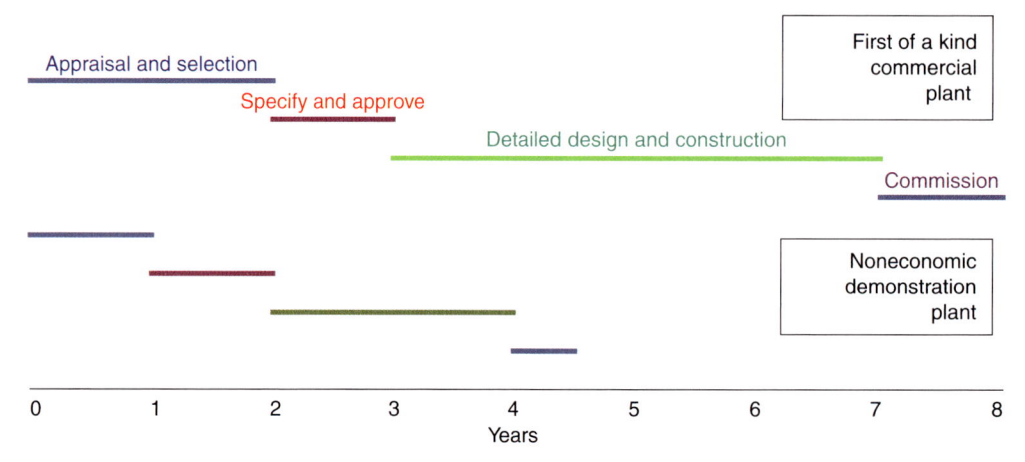

Figure 23 Timescales for the development of Fischer–Tropsch (FT) plants. Reproduced from Figure 12 in NNFCC report. Evans G and Nattrass L (2009) *Advanced Thermochemical Biofuels Roadmap and Challenge*. York: NNFCC. http://www.nnfcc.co.uk/tools/advanced-thermochemical-biofuels-roadmap-and-challenge-nnfcc-09-014 (accessed 3 March 2011).

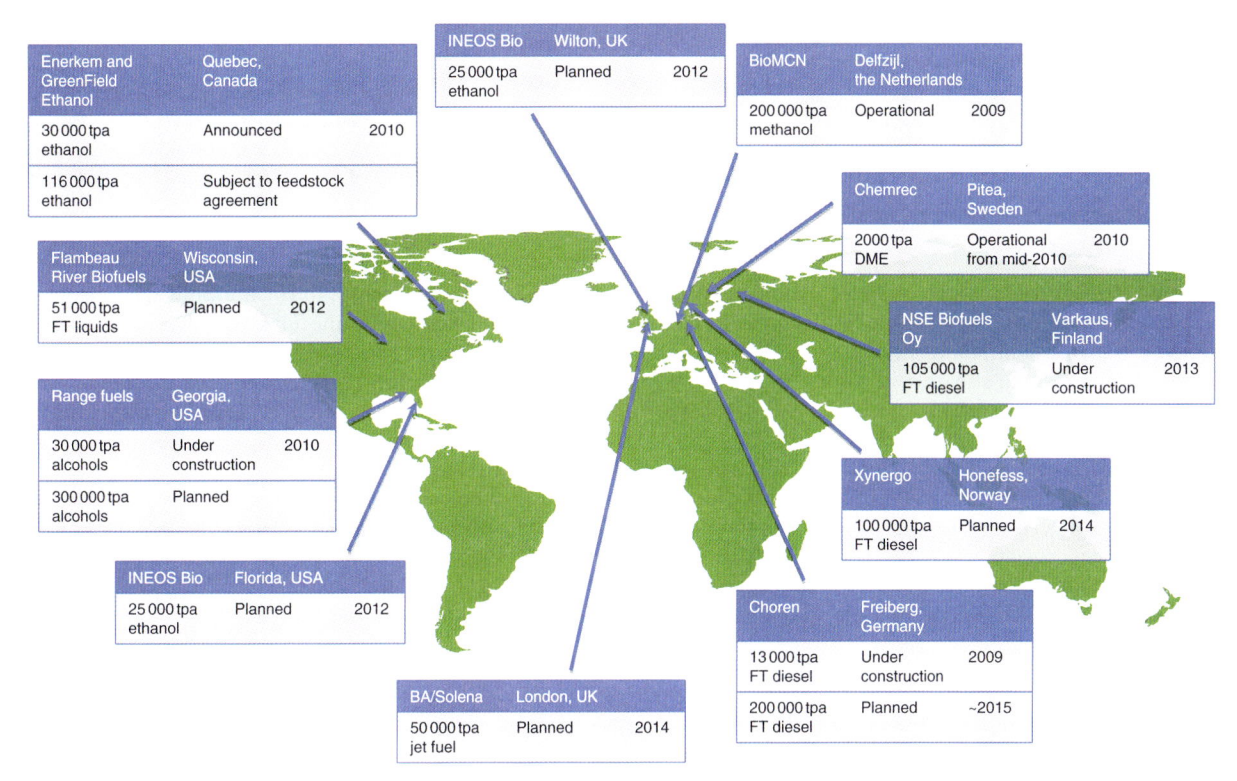

Figure 24 Worldwide developments in BtL processes. Reproduced from Figure 1 of Evans G and Nattrass L (2009) *Advanced Thermochemical Biofuels Roadmap and Challenge*. York: NNFCC. http://www.nnfcc.co.uk/tools/advanced-thermochemical-biofuels-roadmap-and-challenge-nnfcc-09-014 (accessed 3 March 2011).

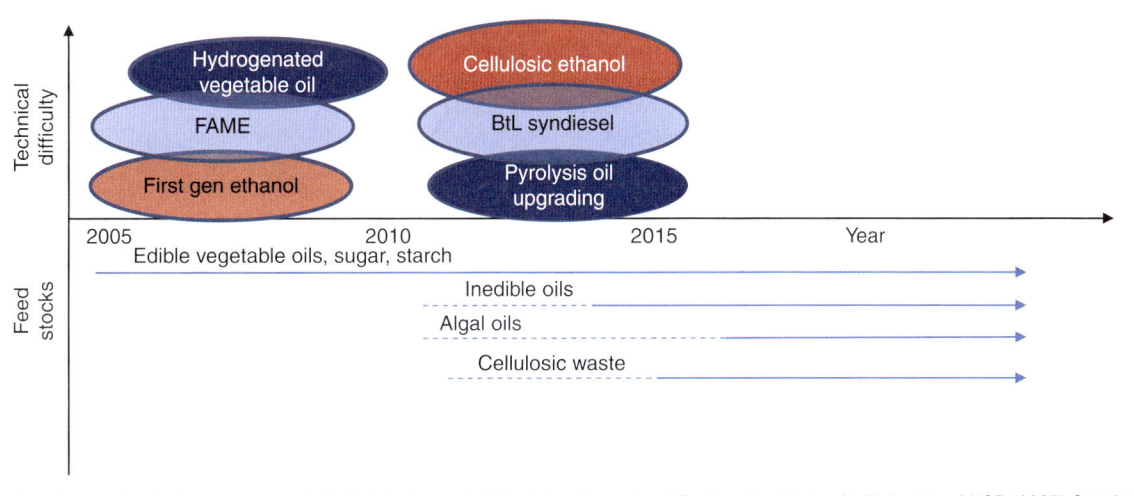

Figure 25 Timescales for the development of Fischer–Tropsch (FT) plants. Reproduced from a presentation by Holmgren, J UOP (2007) Creating a Sustainable Biofuels Future. Presented at Next Generation Biofuels Markets, Amsterdam. http://www.greenpowerconferences.com/biofuelsmarkets/NextGeneration_download.html (accessed 16 February 2010).

EU, Choren, Xynergo, and NSE Biofuels Oy are developing FT diesel processes and INEOS Bio is developing a BtL ethanol process. In North America, Enerkem in Canada is developing ethanol via BtL, Flambeau Mills is developing FT diesel, and Range Fuels is developing mixed alcohol production.

5.11.7.1 BioMCN

BioMCN has been producing 200 000 tpa of methanol via a BtL process since 2009, using waste glycerin from the biodiesel industry at Delfzijl, the Netherlands. Crude glycerin is purified, evaporated, and cracked to form syngas, and using a proprietary catalyst, the resulting biomethanol is distilled ready for sale. While the process is designed to run on glycerin, a range of other feedstocks could be utilized, for example waste wood and algae.

This plant is based on a conventional methanol plant that used natural gas as a feedstock. The plant was acquired by BioMCN in 2006, the feasibility of the glycerin-to-methanol process was demonstrated on a pilot plant scale in March 2008, and the commercial-scale plant was opened in 2009. There are plans to convert the remaining natural gas methanol production facilities to using glycerin, increasing capacity to 800 000 tpa.

5.11.7.2 Enerkem

Enerkem's Biosyn gasification process uses a bubbling fluidized bed gasifier to convert biomass to ethanol, although other green chemicals and fuels including synthetic diesel, synthetic gasoline, and DME may be produced in the future. A wide range of biomass types have been tested including sorted MSW, construction and demolition wood, treated waste wood, and forest and agricultural residues. The process can also process plastics. The process is carried out at low temperatures (700 °C) and <10 bar pressure. It can accept 'fluffy' material, so there is no need for pelletizing, and both slurries and liquids can be processed. Oxygen-enriched air and steam are used as the gasification medium.

Enerkem's Sherbrooke Pilot Plant in Canada has been operating since 2003 and has a production capacity of 475 000 l of alcohol per year (375 tpa). The company's Westbury plant at Greenfield, Quebec, is a commercial-scale plant due to open in 2010 and will produce 5 million liters (4000 tpa) of methanol from spring 2010, followed by ethanol production. The principal feedstock for this plant will be treated wood waste. Two further plants are planned, both with a capacity of 36 million liters (28 500 tpa). The first is planned for Edmonton, Alberta, using MSW and is due to be operational in 2011. The second is planned for Pontotoc, Mississippi, again using MSW, where there are plans to double the capacity to 72 million liters (57 000 tpa).

5.11.7.3 Choren

Choren Industries in Germany is perhaps the most advanced in the development of FT products from BtL. It is producing a high-cetane FT diesel, also known as SunDiesel, primarily from wood, although a range of agricultural feedstocks can be utilized. The Choren Carbo V technology is a three-stage gasification process consisting of a low-temperature gasification step, a high-temperature gasification step, and an endothermic entrained flow gasification step. In the first step, carried out at 400–500 °C, biomass is first subjected to slow pyrolysis to yield solid char and volatile gases. The volatile gases are then fed into an entrained flow combustion chamber where partial oxidation at 1200–1500 °C is used to release energy from the gases. In the third stage, the hot gases are fed into an entrained flow gasifier where they react with the pulverized char to produce syngas. The syngas can be used as a gas for combustion or upgraded to produce FT diesel known as SunDiesel. In its 'Beta' plant, Choren is using the SMDS FT technology, which has also been used in GtL applications such as in Bintulu, Malaysia, since 2003. This technology is a low-temperature FT process, using a cobalt catalyst.

Further research is investigating the potential for torrefaction to be used as an alternative to low-temperature gasification, allowing direct feeding of the torrefied biomass into the entrained flow gasifier.

Choren has operated a 1 MW, 200 tpa alpha pilot plant at Freiberg, Germany, since 2003. Production at its 45 MW, 13 000 tpa 'Beta' plant in Freiberg, Germany, is expected to start early in 2010. The first commercial-scale plant is due to come online in 2011, at Lubmin, Germany, with a capacity of 200 000 tonnes of FT diesel or 640 megawatt thermal (MWth). The company has plans to build a further five plants of the same size from 2013.

5.11.7.4 Range Fuels

Range Fuels uses the R2 BtL process, linking entrained flow gasifiers with an ethanol reactor to produce mixed alcohols (predominantly ethanol and methanol). Woody biomass is the preferred feedstock although a range of materials have been tested. The R2 process consists of two steps: an initial step in which the biomass is treated at 230 °C under pressure to release volatile gases, followed by gasification in a reforming reactor by superheated steam at 815 °C to produce syngas. The staged temperature process is used to ensure that there is a low level of contaminants such as tars in the syngas. A proprietary catalyst is used to produce a mix of alcohols including ethanol, methanol, propanol, and butanol, but designed to maximize ethanol and methanol yields.

Range Fuels has operated a demonstration facility at Denver, Colorado, since 2008. It recently announced the start of construction of a 113 000 tpa thermochemical ethanol and methanol production facility near Soperton, Georgia, USA. This is due online in the second quarter of 2010. The company has further plans for plants, including a 30 million US gallon per year (110 000 tpa) plant and a 100 million US gallon per year plant (360 000 tpa). These plants will initially utilize waste wood and wood residues.

5.11.7.5 INEOS Bio

INEOS Bio is commercializing the use of gasification to produce ethanol from waste materials. The process uses a two-stage gasification step to produce syngas. The biomass is first gasified in oxygen to produce a syngas that is low in furans and dioxins. The hot gas is then cleaned and quenched and the waste heat produced is recovered to provide power for use in the process. The syngas is then processed in a fermentation process, using naturally occurring anaerobic bacteria at 37 °C and at atmospheric pressure to produce ethanol at high specificity. The low temperatures and the use of atmospheric pressure, combined with the high specificity of the bacteria for the end product, mean that the process is expected to be of lower cost compared to other BtL processes such as FT. The process is feedstock flexible and allows a wide range of biomass feedstocks to be used.

The INEOS Bio technology has been developed over 5 years of operation at a pilot plant in the United States and there are plans for commercial plants in both the EU and the United States. A small commercial-scale facility with a capacity of 8 million US gallons (28 000 tpa) of ethanol is due to open in 2011 in Indian River County, Florida, using wood and vegetable wastes as its feedstock, while a second plant is planned for the United Kingdom (Teeside) producing 25 000 tpa of ethanol from biomass waste.

5.11.7.6 NSE Biofuels

Neste and Stora Enso are working together as NSE Biofuels to develop the production of BtL fuels from wood residues. A 12 MWth pilot plant has been developed at Stora Enso's Varkaus paper mill in Finland, in collaboration with Foster Wheeler Energy and VTT and was inaugurated in 2009. The facility uses wood residues as its principal feedstock and is using a CFB reactor, with pressurized oxygen- and steam-based gasification. Initially, the plant will primarily produce heat and power for the mill alongside small test quantities of fuels. If the fuel production tests are successful, commercial implementation producing 105 000 tpa of FT wax products is planned for 2013 with plans for further plants from 2015 onward. A key focus of NSE Biofuels is the integration of the process with the existing wood supply chain including forest industry residues and by-products. The demonstration plant will be highly integrated with the paper mill so as to gain maximum cost benefits and to leverage benefit from the existing biomass supply chain to the paper mill. Bark, energy crops, and refuse-derived fuels may also be utilized as feedstocks for the plant.

5.11.7.7 Chemrec

The Chemrec technology uses Kraft black liquor, a waste product from the pulp and paper industry, to produce DME. The technology is based on air- or oxygen-blown gasification systems that are employed either as a supplement to or as a replacement for existing recovery boilers at Kraft pulp mills.

In late 2009, Chemrec began building a DME biofuel plant in Pitea, Sweden, with a capacity of 4–5 tpd. This plant is expected to begin production in 2010. The Black Liquor Gasification with Motor Fuels Production (BLGMFP) project showed that the production of methanol (for DME) as a fuel was cost effective with current gasoline prices at €0.32 per liter, and could be produced at a biomass-to-methanol efficiency of 66%. Chemrec is collaborating with NewPage Corporation, the American paper and pulp manufacturer, carrying out a feasibility study on setting up a plant for BLG at NewPage's pulp mill in Escanaba, Michigan.

5.11.7.8 Summary

A wide range of different technologies are under development, utilizing a wide range of different feedstocks and at different scales. There is no common approach being taken, and developments so far encompass a range of proprietary technologies adapted for a specific application. In many cases, BtL projects have been developed by leveraging the infrastructure of an existing user, for example Chemrec and Flambeau Mills, or retrofitting an existing plant, for example BioMCN. This allows for cost savings through integration with the existing enterprise or through using waste products, an important aspect for BtL. Waste materials, such as waste wood and MSW, are the basis for many plants. As shown in the following sections, integration and use of wastes can significantly enhance the economic attractiveness of the BtL process.

5.11.8 Outline of BtL Economics

In general, BtL, particularly FT, is acknowledged to have higher capital costs and risks compared to other lignocellulosic and first-generation biofuels processes with clean syngas production being one of the largest cost elements within BtL. The scale of plants often requires substantial quantities of feedstock, which must be sourced at a competitive price. However, BtL has a number of beneficial features including the ability to accept a wide range of feedstocks and to be able to produce a wide range of products. This section reviews each of these factors, benchmarks BtL against other relevant technologies, and assesses the influence of each factor on BtL economics and investment risk.

5.11.8.1 Capital Costs

The varying scales and costs associated with different biofuels production options are shown in **Table 7**. As noted above, BtL facilities generally have the highest capital costs while FAME plants and pyrolysis plants the lowest. However, although pyrolysis is predicted to be the cheapest biomass liquefaction process in terms of capital costs, an upgrading unit would be needed in addition to upgrade the raw pyrolysis oil to usable transport fuels.

The available cost estimates that do exist for BtL have largely been based on cost data derived from recent major GtL and CtL projects, but because biomass gasification and the cleaning of biomass-derived raw syngas have not been proven at scale, this results in a high degree of uncertainty. Capital cost estimates depend on the exact configuration used, for example whether pretreatment, storage, and handling of the feedstock are included, and thus they are often not directly comparable. Indeed, it is

Table 7 Typical size, cost, and product quality of different biofuel technologies

Technology	Size (tonne yr^{-1})	Approximate cost level Euros	Relative direct product usability
First generation (FAME)	250 000	50–100 million	Medium
Pyrolysis	70 000	10 million	Very low
Hydrogen	200 000	275 million	Low
Methanol	200 000	325 000	Low-medium
First-generation and lignocellulosic ethanol	200 000	350–450 million	Medium
Syndiesel (BtL)	200 000	400–650 million	Very high

BtL, Biomass to liquids; FAME, fatty acid methyl ester.
Reproduced from NNFCC report (08/017). Evans G (2007) *International Biofuels Strategy Project. Liquid Transport Biofuels – Technology Status Report.* York: NNFCC. http://www.nnfcc.co.uk/tools/international-biofuels-strategy-project-liquid-transport-biofuels-technology-status-report-nnfcc-08-017 (accessed 3 March 2011).

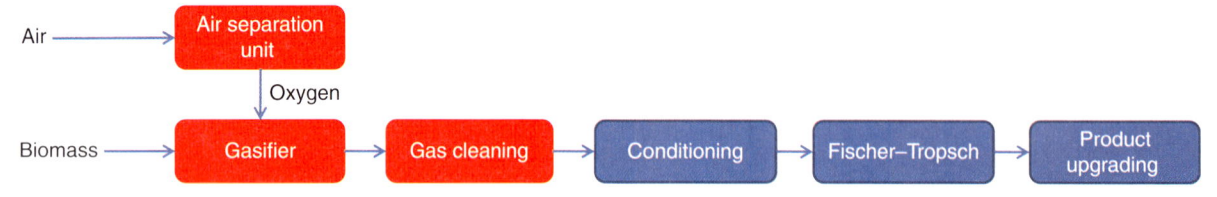

Figure 26 Steps in the conversion of biomass to diesel using Fischer–Tropsch (FT) process. Reproduced from Boerrigter H (2006) *Economy of Biomass-To-Liquids (BtL) Plants. An Engineering Assessment.* The Netherlands: ECN. http://www.thermalnet.co.uk/docs/2G-1 ECN-C-06-0191.pdf (accessed 16 February 2010).

suggested that supporting processes can increase total gasification costs by 70–80%; however, these are often excluded from capital cost estimates.

Boerrigter [3] used the 34 000 bbl day^{-1} (1.37 million tpa) Oryx1 GtL plant as a reference system to estimate the cost of a BtL plant. The Oryx plant had a TCI of US$1.1 billion. The use of biomass in place of natural gas requires several, predominantly front-end changes to processing parameters, highlighted in red in **Figure 26**. The equipment needed for a CtL plant is similar to that used for a BtL plant; thus, Boerrigter reasoned that this would be a suitable proxy for the equipment needed for a BtL plant:

- Coal requires around 50% more oxygen than that for natural gas. This higher oxygen demand requires a larger air separation unit, estimated to be around 50% more expensive than for a GtL plant.
- Coal gasification requires an entrained flow gasifier, which is around 50% more expensive than a reformer for natural gas.
- Syngas derived from coal contains more impurities than natural gas-derived syngas, adding additional costs.

These changes have consequent effects on the capital costs of the plant, and Boerrigter calculated that, at an equivalent scale, total costs would be 60% more expensive than the Oryx GtL plant.

The TCI price of the BtL plant is made up of costs for plant equipment, known as the inside battery limits (ISBL) costs; costs for supporting infrastructure outside of the plant itself, known as the outside battery limits (OSBL) costs; and a margin for owners' costs. In a typical cost estimation, the OSBL costs are set at 100% of the ISBL costs and owner's costs around 20%. In the example in **Table 8**, the air separation unit is the most capital intense item at 11.7% of TCI, followed by the gas cleanup Rectisol unit at 9.1%. Others have investigated the costs associated with other layouts of BtL plants, including the costs where pyrolysis and torrefaction have been used to preprocess the biomass feedstock for the plant. For example, North Energy Associates investigated BtL capital costs but assumed that the ISBL costs were the same regardless of pretreatment technology. This approach has some benefits, as there

Table 8 Capital cost of equipment for a BtL plant

Equipment	Item	ISBL (%)	TCI (%)
ISBL	Air separation unit	28	11.7
	Gasifier	19	7.8
	Syngas conditioning	6	2.6
	Rectisol	22	9.1
	Fischer–Tropsch	16	6.5
	Upgrading	9	3.9
OSBL			41.7
Owners cost			16.7
TCI			100.0

ISBL, Inside battery limits; OSBL, outside battery limits; TCI, total capital investment.

is no 'one-size-fits-all' costing for BtL plants, and capital and operating costs will depend on gasifiers used, end product, and whether the plant is on a greenfield site, where there is limited or no scope for integration with existing enterprises, or on an existing site where infrastructure integration may be possible.

Opportunities to reduce operating and capital costs may arise as a result of technological or integration opportunities, for example:

- Syngas fermentation to ethanol is reported as having greater tolerance to syngas contaminants and varying hydrogen to carbon monoxide molar ratio. Syngas cleaning and conditioning units for this technology will, therefore, likely be less costly than those for a BtL FT process for example.
- Biomass pretreatment could facilitate the use of an entrained flow, slagging gasifier, which can potentially provide a cleaner syngas, thereby reducing syngas cleanup requirements.
- Both small and large BtL plants can benefit from integration into existing infrastructure. For instance:
  ○ There may be potential to locate a BtL plant at a site with excess air separating capacity, to avoid the expenditure associated with the installation of new capacity.
  ○ There may be potential to refine hydrocarbon biofuel products within an existing refinery.
  ○ Smaller BtL plants can be integrated into existing pulp mills by replacing Tomlinson water tube boilers with BLG systems with excess heat from the FT process being utilized by the paper mill.
  ○ Benefits in energy efficiency and process economics may possibly be accrued by integrating both power generation and BtL fuel production. This can be achieved by utilizing the off-gas (light hydrocarbons) from the FT process to generate heat and electricity. The integration of power production within the BtL process also allows the possibility of other process configurations. For example, the FT unit itself operates on a relatively low conversion per pass of synthesis gas with large recycles. With integrated power production, it may be feasible to operate the FT unit on a once-through basis and feed the unconverted synthesis gas to a gas turbine for heat and power generation.

As shown in **Figure 27**, BtL processes can have similar overall total costs per tonne of product to an equivalently sized FAME plant based on rapeseed. However, the cost component breakdown is different. While BtL has a lower feedstock, utility, and direct fixed costs than FAME plants, the amount needed to cover return on investments, depreciation, and direct costs are significantly higher for the BtL plant. The high cost of BtL plants results in a high investment risk and this limits interest from the financial community. High return on investment percentages is required to encourage investors to invest in the plant where the technology is unproven at scale. This is a major barrier in the development of commercial BtL processes.

What is particularly noticeable from **Figure 27** is that relative to FAME plants, the cost of raw materials for a BtL complex is significantly less. This underlines one of the key strengths of BtL, principally its ability to utilize a range of feedstocks, including low-cost feedstocks such as waste, black liquor, and cheaper woods, to produce a wide range of high-quality products. Hence, while BtL plants may be necessarily at a large scale and be significantly more expensive compared to other biofuels options, lower feedstock costs can help mitigate some of the higher capital costs associated with BtL plants. This paradigm is shown by the large number of near- to medium-term enterprises planning on utilizing wastes for BtL processes, including INEOS Bio (using biomass waste), Chemrec (black liquor), and Range Fuels (waste wood and agricultural residues).

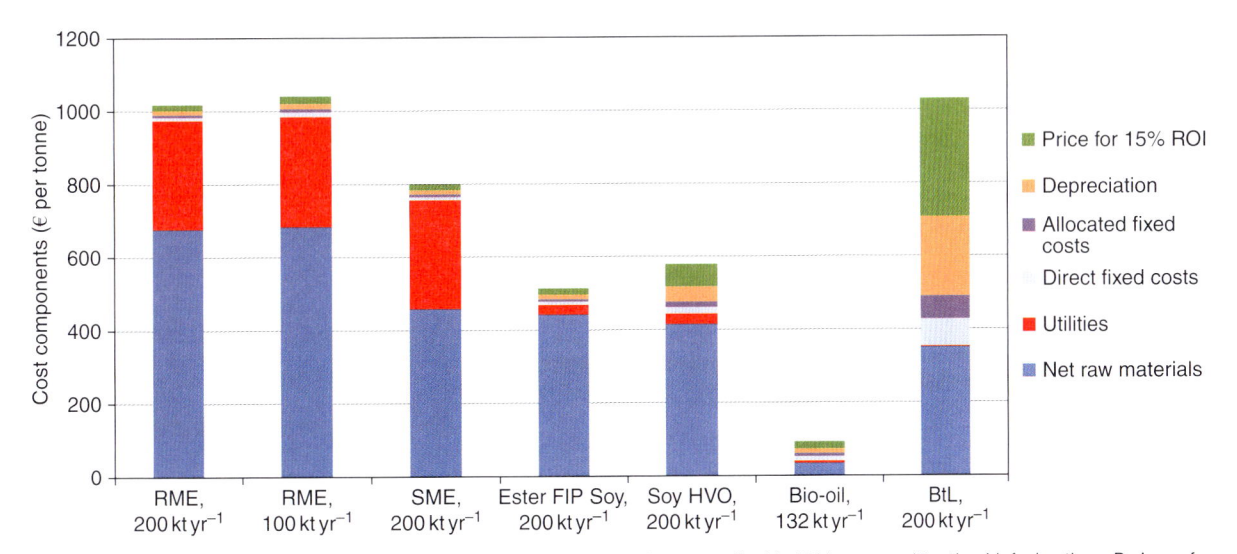

Figure 27 Relative influence of cost components on the final product cost of biomass-to-liquids (BtL) compared to other biofuel options. Redrawn from Nexant Inc. (May, 2007) Feasibility of Second Generation Biodiesel Production in the United Kingdom. *NNFCC Report*.

5.11.8.2 Feedstock Cost Analysis

BtL can, in theory, accept a wide range of different feedstocks and this inherent flexibility is one of the factors that makes the thermochemical production of fuels through BtL attractive. A variety of biomass materials could be used within the BtL process including dry residues such as straws (a by-product from cereal grain and oilseed production), energy crops (*Miscanthus* and short-rotation coppice), wood materials from forestry operations, and the organic fractions from waste streams such as MSWs. Despite the ability to use a variety of feedstocks including many low-cost feedstocks, their procurement in large volumes remains a challenge to BtL developers.

The cost to a processor of a particular biomass type depends on a number of factors including the cost of producing the feedstock, the time and thus cost of storage, haulage cost to a plant, seasonality, and, probably most importantly, the relative demand for that material from other end users. A BtL operator will require sufficient material at an economically favorable and stable price to ensure that the feedstock can be sourced year-round and that margins in the production process can be maintained. Preferably, that feedstock should be available on a consistent basis year-round. Typical biomass cost ranges per dry tonne on a consistent basis are illustrated in **Figure 28** (£2008).

It can be seen from **Figure 28**, there are clearly three different groupings of biomass according to their relative prices. UK waste materials, grouped in blue in the figure, vary in price from less than £50 per tonne (typically higher quality waste wood and waste papers), to organic wastes such as green and catering wastes, which attract a gate fee for their use. Virgin lignocellulosic materials, grouped in red, vary in price from around £30 to £75 per tonne, depending on the crop used, form, and tonnage. Wood chips, for example, are typically available at around £60 per dry tonne but can be available for less than this depending on demand. Agricultural commodities, grouped in green, are significantly more expensive and show considerable variations in price, from around £90 to just under £200 per tonne for wheat grains, to just under £250 to £350 per tonne for oilseed rapeseeds (or £610–£872 for the oil). BtL can utilize most of these feedstocks, but in terms of price, it is advantageous if possible to utilize waste materials as these are available at the lowest cost or even command a gate fee, as this maximizes the margins and profits for the producer. However, if designing a BtL plant capable of using wastes, the nonhomogeneity of wastes on a temporal and spatial basis must be considered, which will add to capital costs, particularly in the area of syngas cleanup, compared to a plant designed for a single feedstock such as wood. Comparing the data presented in **Table 7** and **Figure 28**, it can be seen that although first-generation plants can be built more cheaply than BtL processes, their feedstock costs are significantly higher resulting in differing cost component breakdowns and similar overall costs of production shown in **Figure 27**.

A further advantage of utilizing lignocellulosic and waste biomass for BtL plants is the general stability in feedstock pricing. **Figure 29** shows the prices of oilseed rape, wheat, wheat straw, and catering waste in the United Kingdom for the period 2005–10. As shown in the diagram, while straw and catering waste have been relatively stable in price, there is significant volatility in the prices for oilseed rape and wheat, particularly at the end of 2007, where wheat prices increased worldwide due to a number of issues including droughts affecting the harvest in Australia. Prices for UK wood chips have been quoted at a flat price of around £60 per tonne throughout this period. The intrinsic volatility of markets for wheat and oil feedstocks means that there is less certainty over the expected return from a first-generation biofuel process because the feedstock makes up a large proportion of the costs of the final product. The volatility surrounding the price of commodity feedstocks can result in considerable uncertainty for investors, especially when feedstock prices are high, as this can erode operating margins and profits.

Biomass from waste and lignocellulosics is currently an attractive feedstock for BtL plants because of favorable price and price stability. However, this may not always be the case. Biomass is perceived as a key way in which to mitigate climate change, so there has been an increased use of biomass for a wide range of 'new' renewables industries including power generation and production of other biofuels. The feedstock demand from these rapidly developing new markets needs to be balanced against the demand from traditional industries such as wood for pulping and straw for livestock. Increasing demand for biomass will result in increased price for the feedstock, and it follows that biomass will be directed toward the end users who can pay the most for the resource.

As biofuels are a high-volume/low-value commodity, there may be significant concerns over the ability to procure sufficient feedstock for a plant at an economically advantageous cost, especially when compared to other higher value markets and markets where financial incentives are employed. The disparity in financial incentives between different markets for biomass is well illustrated by the incentives in place and commodity prices for electricity and liquid fuels in the United Kingdom in 2009 as

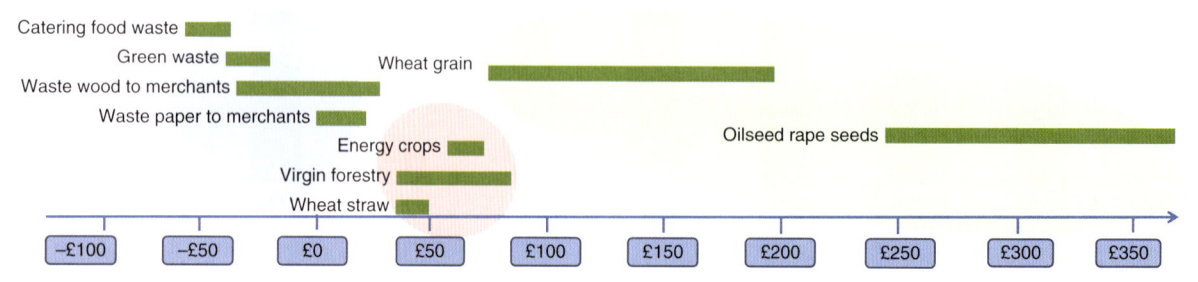

Figure 28 Indicative costs of a range of biomass feedstocks.

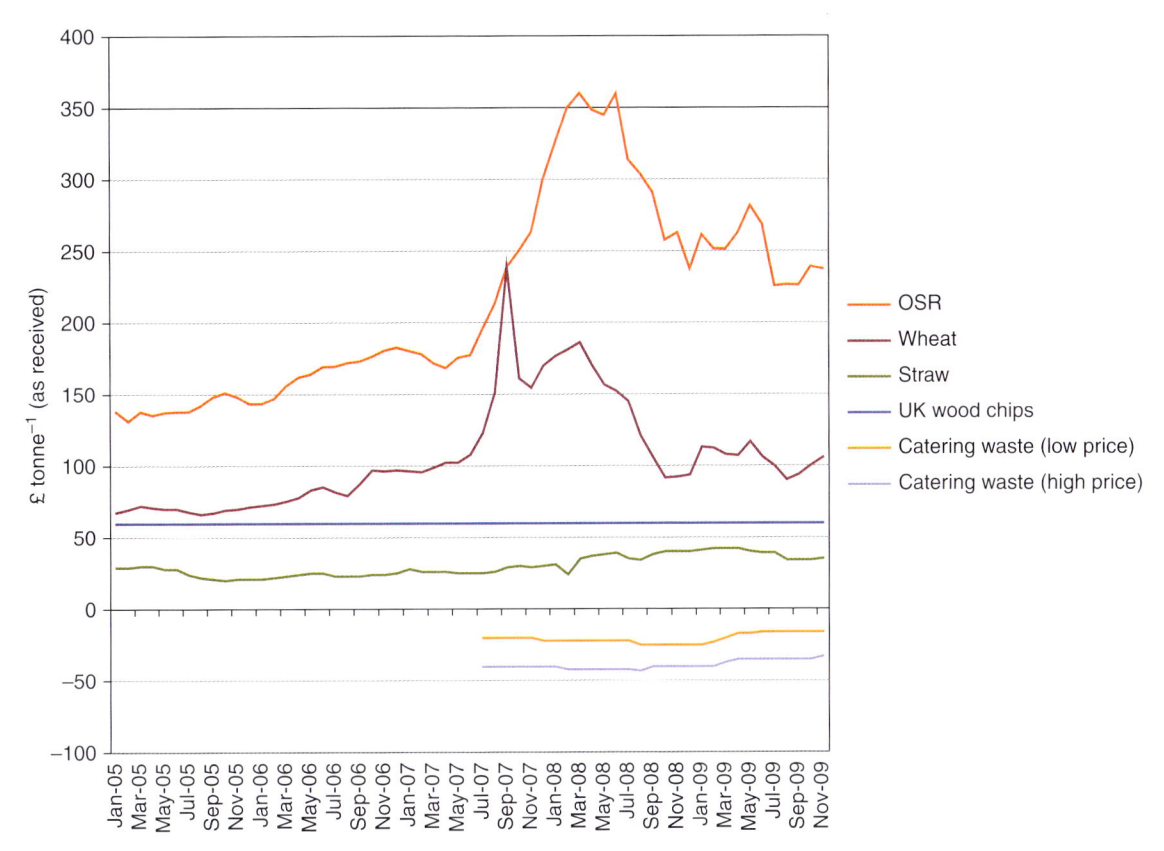

Figure 29 Price volatility for range of biomass feedstocks.

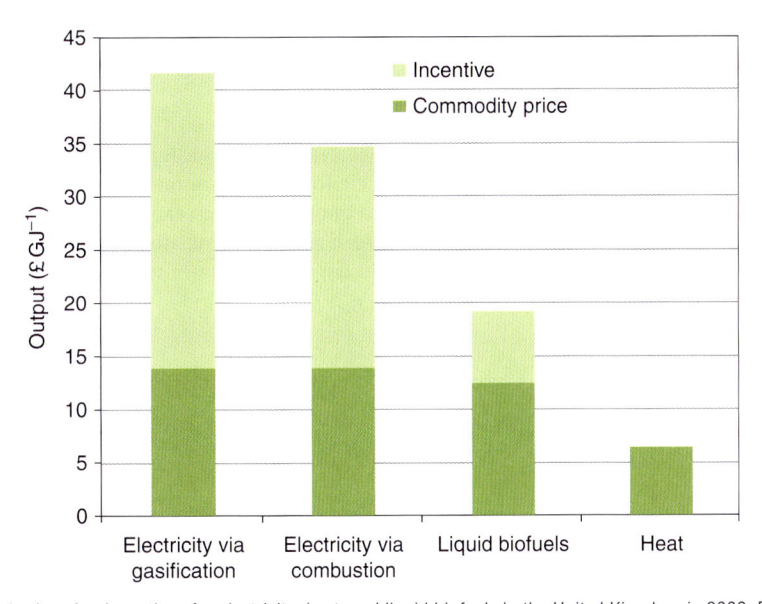

Figure 30 Relative price and price after incentives for electricity, heat, and liquid biofuels in the United Kingdom in 2009. Reproduced with permission from Progressive Energy.

shown in **Figure 30**. This shows that while the prices for electricity and liquid biofuels were similar on a £ per GJ output basis, the incentives employed mean that higher prices can be paid by electricity producers for biomass, which, if passed down the supply chain, means that biomass will be preferentially directed to these markets. Such financial incentives do little for the economics of emerging technologies for fuels production, especially as they are not necessarily related to the capital and operating costs associated with plants, and as a result can unfairly skew the economics of the process.

5.11.8.3 Economies of Scale

Based on current technologies, it is expected that BtL plants will need to be very large to be economic. Current developments around the world indicate that early commercial-scale developments will range in scale from 100 000 to 200 000 tpa of biofuel.

Figure 31 shows the change in unit cost per GJ of product with scale for an FT plant based on the use of wood derived from construction and demolition waste. The graph shows that there are three distinct zones where scale has a more pronounced effect on costs. The first zone, in this case to around an annual output of 100 000 tpa, indicates a steep decline in costs with scale. The influence of increasing scale becomes less pronounced at scales between 100 000 and 500 000 tpa, and beyond 500 000 tpa becomes still shallower. Choren, one of the leading developers of BtL via the FT route, estimates that the minimum economic scale for an FT plant would be around half of the scale of its Sigma plant, which corresponds to 100 000 tonne yr^{-1} BtL fuel output, or around 1520 odt day^{-1} biomass input. While this seems a significant output, it should be noted that even the largest BtL biofuels plants are significantly smaller than oil refineries, which manufacture transport fuels on massive scales. The largest of the UK oil refineries, ExxonMobil Fawley, has a throughput of 320 000 bbl day^{-1}, equivalent to around 14 million tonnes of products per year. Large-scale commercial BtL plants, such as the Choren Sigma plant, will produce around 200 000 tpa. This is around 64 times smaller than the throughput of the largest UK oil refinery. The size of biofuels plants is limited by the state of development and the feedstock supply chain, especially in the case of lignocellulosic technologies.

Two approaches are being developed to address the dichotomy between the need to build large FT plants for economy of scale and the need to build smaller FT plants to match the needs of the biomass supply chain. These are

1. biomass pretreatment to increase the biomass energy density so that it can be transported more economically over greater distances thereby potentially enabling larger FT plant scales and
2. FT process intensification, which enables the economic use of smaller scale FT plants.

Pretreatment to densify biomass was discussed in Section 5.11.4.1. Pyrolysis and torrefaction can be used to increase the energy density of biomass and hence reduce transport costs. However, biomass transportation costs form only a small part of overall BtL costs. Careful analysis is therefore needed on a project by project basis to confirm that pretreatment will reduce overall costs sufficiently.

Alternatively, process intensification may help reduce the size at which plants can economically operate and the corresponding amount of biomass required per plant. A challenge is whether this can be made to work technically and economically at smaller scale. A number of developers are pursuing the development of technologies for process intensification and such microreactors were discussed under the heading 'Microchannel reactors'. The Velocys technology acquired by Oxford Catalysts has been estimated to allow FT catalysts to be viable at outputs of 500–2000 bbl day^{-1} (20 000–80 000 tpa), which would correspond to biomass inputs of 300–1220 odt day^{-1}. Other similar microreactor technologies such as that developed by CompactGtL for GtL applications may also be applicable to biomass.

5.11.8.4 Summary

BtL plants are capital intensive and expensive compared to other biofuel options. The relatively undeveloped nature of this technology means that there is a considerable risk for investors. However, despite this high initial capital cost, the ability of BtL to accept a range of feedstocks, including low-cost wastes and lignocellulosic materials, means that feedstock costs are both cheaper than first-generation plants and less subject to volatility. These can mitigate the high capital costs. A key concern is ensuring that, in the face of increasing demand for biomass from other sectors such as power generation, BtL is able to compete financially for feedstock. Current BtL technology is based on the CtL and GtL industry, which operates at large scales. Concomitantly this requires

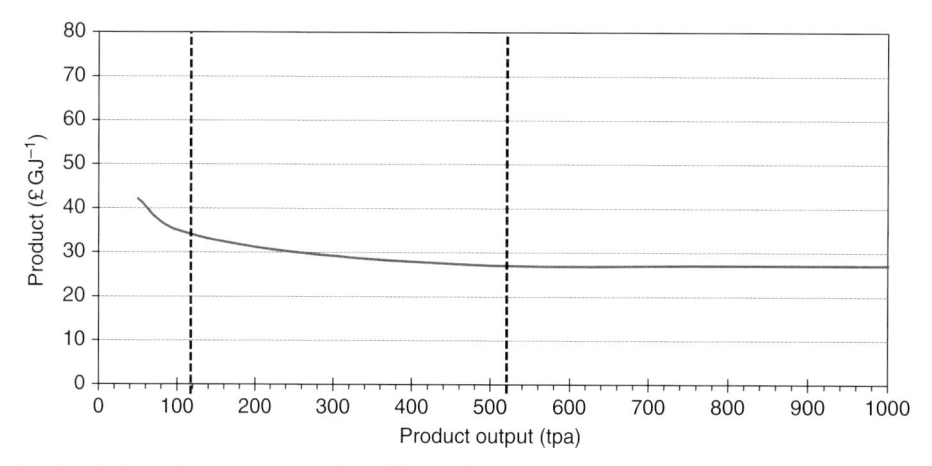

Figure 31 Effect of scale and advanced pretreatment on prices of Fischer–Tropsch (FT) diesel.

huge amounts of biomass for economic production scales of products. The development of FT microreactors, which allow economic production at lower feedstock volumes, is a promising technology that can allow a better match between feedstock availability and plant size.

5.11.9 Environmental Issues

Biofuels provide one element in an overall strategy to reduce GHG emissions in the transport sector. However, there have been significant concerns over the magnitude of these savings, the environmental and social impacts of feedstock procurement, and the direct and indirect effects of biofuel feedstock production. These concerns have been addressed in several policies worldwide and the sustainable production of biofuels will become increasingly important given the introduction of mandatory carbon and sustainability standards. This section briefly outlines the potential GHG savings that can be gained through BtL diesel compared to fossil diesel and other biofuels, the robustness of these assumptions, and the most effective use of land in terms of biomass use compared to other uses.

5.11.9.1 GHG Savings

The principal driver for the use of biofuels, especially in the EU, is reducing GHG emissions in the transport sector. It is, therefore, important to ensure that biofuels provide a net GHG saving relative to the fuels they replace.

Biomass absorbs carbon dioxide as it grows, which is then released when it is burnt. The use of biomass for energy delivery, therefore, does not increase the net amount of carbon dioxide in the atmosphere over short timescales. This means that biofuels can result in lower GHG emissions than fossil fuels, because when fossil fuels are completely oxidized, the carbon released has been stored for millions of years, thus adding to the global atmospheric carbon dioxide level. However, combustion of the fuel is only part of the picture. Biomass-based materials require energy and incur GHG costs in growing, harvesting, and transporting the crop to a centralized processing plant. Life cycle assessment (LCA) is used to investigate, from cradle to grave, the energy, GHG emissions, and environmental effects associated with biomass growth and processing. LCA is increasingly being used in the development of reporting criteria to determine the environmental sustainability of biofuels production. A fuller description of this topic is provided in **Chapter 5.10**.

It is generally assumed that lignocellulosic technologies such as BtL provide the potential for enhanced GHG savings relative to both their fossil fuel counterparts and first-generation biofuels. This is shown in **Figure 32**, which has been prepared from data published by Concawe/JRC and EUCAR [4]. Both GtL and CtL fuels have greater GHG emissions than fossil diesel in this analysis, especially CtL, which has over twice the amount of GHG emissions. Fuels derived from biofuels have lower GHG savings than fossil diesel (usually between 10% and 60%), and BtL potentially has very high GHG emission savings – close to 100% for the example shown in **Figure 32** (diesel produced from woodchips).

Biofuels produced from lignocellulosic materials yield higher GHG savings mainly because:

- The energy used within their production processes is derived from the biomass feedstock as opposed to a fossil fuel such as natural gas.
- Of lower fertilizer usage for feedstock production.
- Of the higher biomass production rate per hectare.

However, the savings that can be realized by BtL and other biofuel technologies can vary and are subject to intense debate and research. GHG savings can vary according to feedstock type, how and where it was grown, and the effects of growing the biofuel feedstock on agricultural system dynamics (indirect land use change effects). In addition to these physical effects, there are different LCA calculation methodologies that can be used which will yield different LCA results.

Biomass type is important since different biomass types will have received different treatments and different levels of processing during production, upstream of a BtL plant. Straw, for example, is grown with the aid of nitrogen fertilizers, which result in significant GHG emissions to atmosphere. If a portion of these emissions is allocated to the straw component of the crop, then this negatively affects the potential GHG savings achievable for BtL diesel produced from straw. For wastes, an alternate disposal scenario should also be considered, the reference scenario. If, for example, a waste would alternatively be land filled where it would decompose resulting in the emission of some methane to atmosphere, then this avoided emission can be applied as a GHG credit to the BtL process. This avoided emission credit can result in negative GHG savings versus diesel as shown in **Figure 33**. Note that pyrolyzing the biomass upstream of a BtL yields bigger GHG savings for waste materials in the examples shown in **Figure 33**. This is because more biomass is needed if the biomass is first pyrolyzed resulting in a larger avoided emission credit. However, it should be noted that under the current EU RED guidelines, waste materials and residues including straw will be assumed to have a zero reference scenario. As a result, the calculated results from the RED for biofuels produced from wastes will not look as favorable as shown in **Figure 33**.

The effects of direct and indirect land use change are a growing area of concern and research. Direct land use change concerns GHG emissions caused by changing the use of an area of land from one use, such as permanent grassland or forest, to energy crops (**Figure 34**, area A). The GHG emissions typically arise if the carbon stocks locked up in the soil are disturbed, for example by plowing. Indirect land use change is more complex and concerns potential GHG emissions caused by a sequence of events arising

Technology Solutions – New Processes

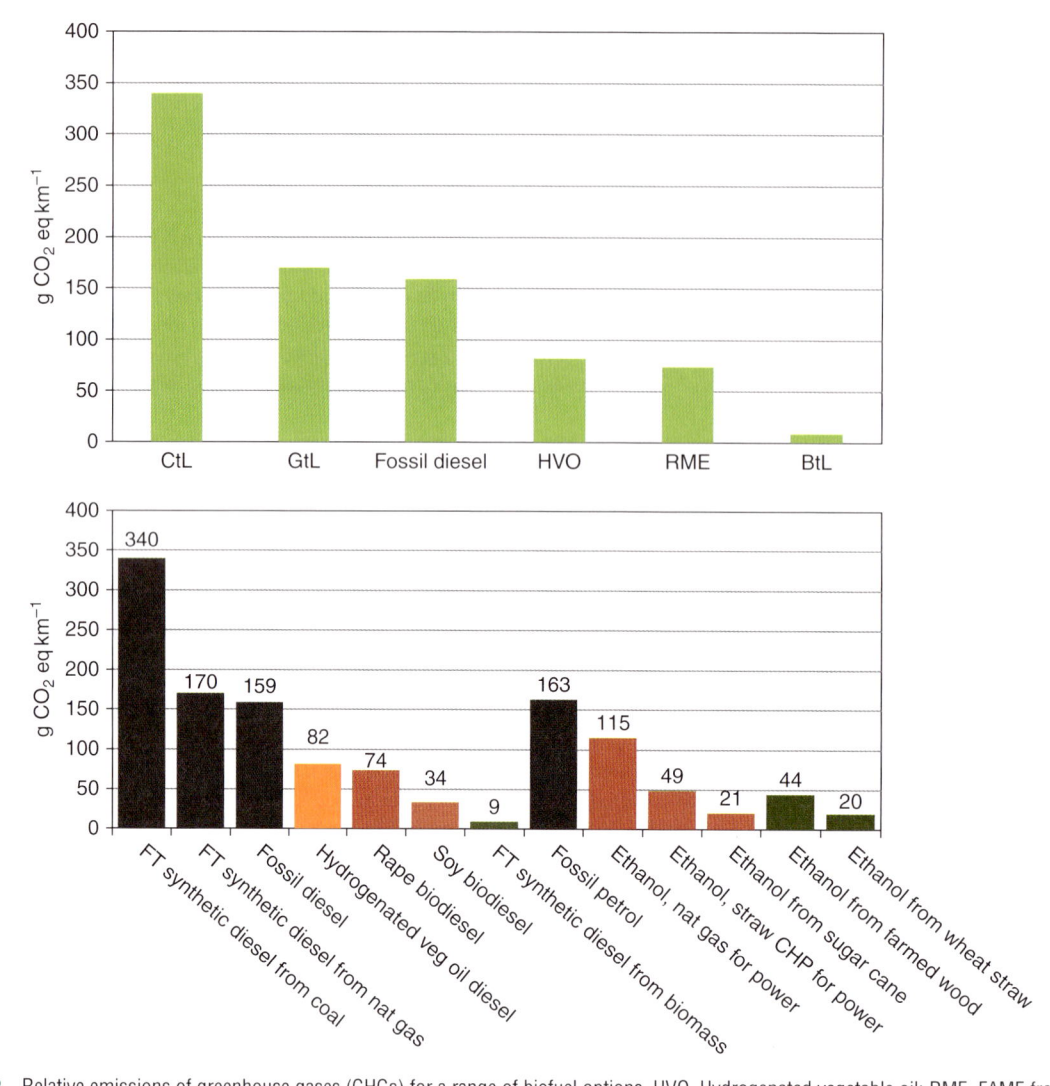

Figure 32 Relative emissions of greenhouse gases (GHGs) for a range of biofuel options. HVO, Hydrogenated vegetable oil; RME, FAME from rape oil. Reproduced from Evans G (2007) *International Biofuels Strategy Project – Liquid Transport Biofuels, Technology Status Report.* NNFCC report (08/017). York: NNFCC. http://www.nnfcc.co.uk/tools/international-biofuels-strategy-project-liquid-transport-biofuels-technology-status-report-nnfcc-08-017 (accessed 3 March 2011).

from the change in use of an area of land to produce crops destined for biofuel production as shown in **Figure 34** (energy crop production in area B results in crop previously grown in area B to be grown in forest area B*).

Calculated LCA results are also affected by the methodology used to carry out the LCA calculation, in particular the allocation procedure. The same LCA input data can yield different results for GHG savings when using different methodologies.

Allocation is defined as the partitioning of the environmental effects according to the inputs and outputs of the system under study. Briefly, allocation methodologies may fit into four main types:

- In allocation by substitution (also known as system expansion), as used by Concawe and the Technical Guidance produced for biofuel reporting by the UK Renewable Fuel Agency for the Renewable Transport Fuels Obligation (RTFO), it is assumed that by-products will substitute for an alternative product in another process and will therefore gain a credit that can be assigned back to the product.
- In the case of allocation by energy, GHGs are split between main products and by-products according to their relative energy flows. This is the methodology expected to be used in the EU RED.
- In allocation by mass, GHGs are split between products and by-products according to their relative mass flows.
- Similarly, for allocation by price, as used in the British PAS 2050 standard, GHGs are split between products and by-products according to their relative prices.

The effects of allocation procedure on LCA can be illustrated by reviewing the data provided by North Energy Associates for NNFCC. Based on a hypothetical UK BtL plant producing 500 000 tpa of products fed with pyrolysis oil produced by a network of 10 pyrolysis plants, each sourcing their feedstocks from a radius of 20 km or untreated biomass, **Table 9** shows that potential

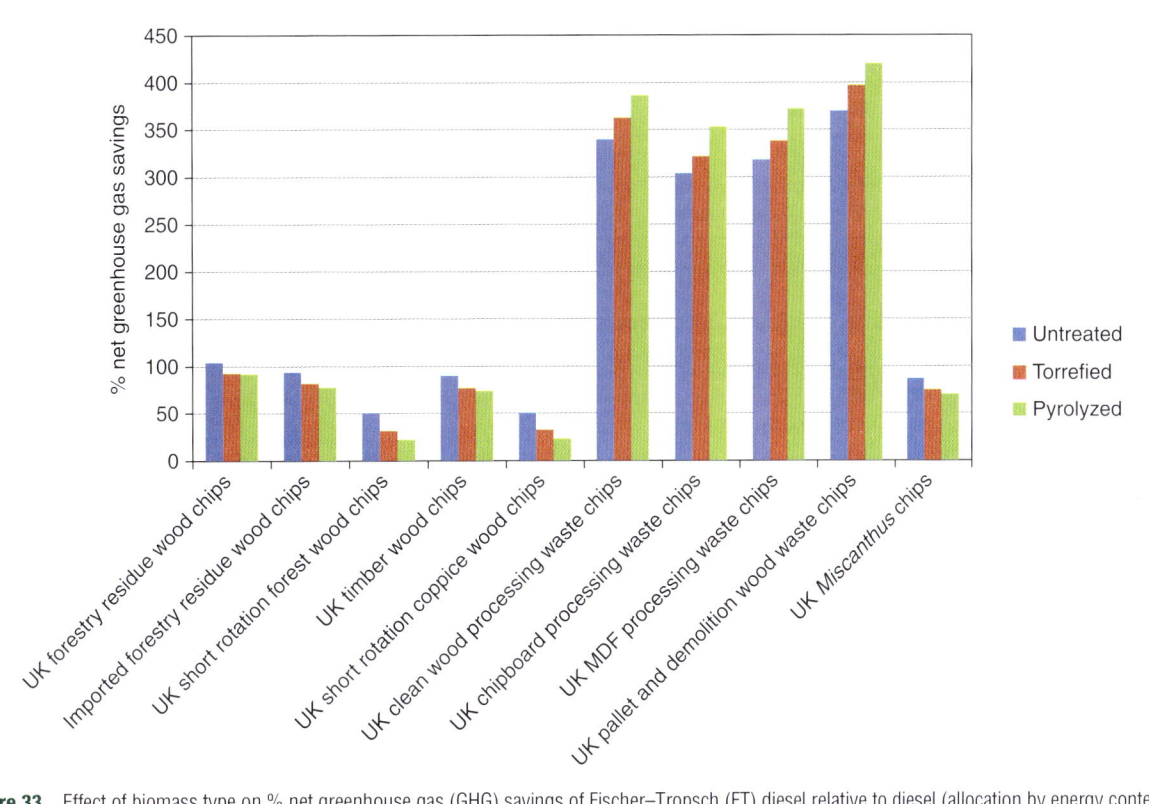

Figure 33 Effect of biomass type on % net greenhouse gas (GHG) savings of Fischer–Tropsch (FT) diesel relative to diesel (allocation by energy content).

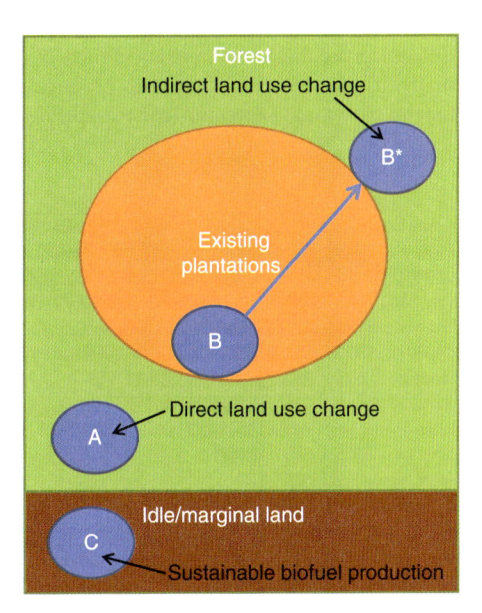

Figure 34 Direct and indirect land use change.

GHG savings of between 102% and 191% versus crude oil-derived diesel can be calculated for the pyrolyzed biomass feedstock case and between 112% and 141% for the untreated biomass feedstock case.

Of all the allocation procedures included in the North Energy study, the use of substitution credits generates the highest net GHG emission savings relative to fossil diesel, especially when pyrolysis is used. This is because the excess char produced by the pyrolysis process has been assumed to replace coal in a coal-fired power station, thereby gaining a large GHG savings credit. However, on an energy allocation basis, pyrolysis is less favorable because by densifying the biomass, there is loss of energy content, so more biomass is needed compared to the untreated biomass case.

This variation in LCA results by methodology, as highlighted by this example, illustrates the need to ensure that consistent methodologies are used when comparing LCA data.

Table 9 Effect of allocation procedure on GHG emission savings relative to fossil diesel

Allocation procedure	Substitution	Energy	Price
Used by	RTFO/Concawe	RED	PAS2050
BtL/pyrolyzed feedstock	191%	102%	103%
BtL/untreated feedstock	141%	112%	113%

BtL, Biomass to liquids; RTFO, Renewable Transport Fuels Obligation.

5.11.9.2 Comparative Technology GHG Saving Effectiveness

BtL must compete for biomass with other utilization options including power generation and heat. Fiscal and legislative incentives are increasingly focusing on the carbon cost of biofuels and bioenergy production; therefore, it is important to assess the relative contributions each can make in terms of GHG savings.

BtL provides an effective and efficient way to use biomass, particularly if the BtL plant is able to sell fuel, power, and heat. On a gram CO_2 equivalent per megajoule of fuel produced (gCO_{2eq} MJ^{-1}), as shown in **Figure 35**, BtL syndiesel production compares well with electricity production from biomass produced by a conventional steam cycle without CHP, although it should be noted that electricity can be used more efficiently than fuels in many applications. This is because syndiesel is produced at an energy efficiency of about 47% compared to about 25% for electricity produced from biomass using a conventional steam cycle.

Alternatively, the effectiveness of the BtL process can be determined by evaluating the gCO_{2eq} MJ^{-1} saved compared with a comparator as shown in **Figure 36**. In this case, electricity production typically emerges as the stronger case because the comparator used, EU-mix electricity, includes a strong element of coal-derived electricity.

A comparison of **Figures 34** and **35** highlights the need to ensure that when considering the 'best use of biomass' a range of pertinent parameters are taken into account. The use of 'GHG emissions saved' may lead to unintended consequences.

5.11.9.3 Comparative Land Use Effectiveness

An often quoted benefit of advanced or lignocellulosic biofuels is the fact that more fuel is produced per hectare of land since the whole plant can be used to produce fuel compared to just the oil seed or wheat grain for first-generation biodiesel and bioethanol made from oilseed rape and wheat. These differences are illustrated in terms of liters of diesel equivalent produced per technology per hectare per year in **Figure 37**. Additionally, if biomass was first used to produce a material (such as a bioplastic) that was subsequently gasified to produce fuels and energy, we would expect the land use effectiveness to be increased compared to the case where biomass is used directly as a fuel.

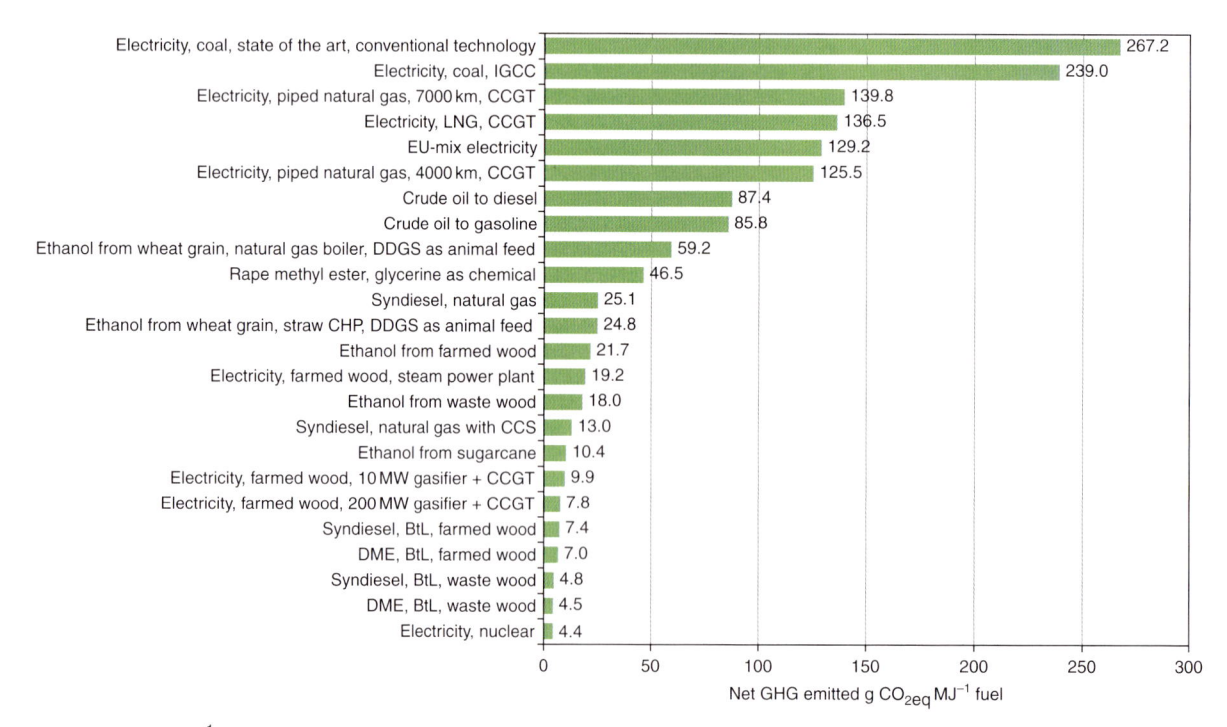

Technology	Net GHG emitted g CO_{2eq} MJ^{-1} fuel
Electricity, coal, state of the art, conventional technology	267.2
Electricity, coal, IGCC	239.0
Electricity, piped natural gas, 7000 km, CCGT	139.8
Electricity, LNG, CCGT	136.5
EU-mix electricity	129.2
Electricity, piped natural gas, 4000 km, CCGT	125.5
Crude oil to diesel	87.4
Crude oil to gasoline	85.8
Ethanol from wheat grain, natural gas boiler, DDGS as animal feed	59.2
Rape methyl ester, glycerine as chemical	46.5
Syndiesel, natural gas	25.1
Ethanol from wheat grain, straw CHP, DDGS as animal feed	24.8
Ethanol from farmed wood	21.7
Electricity, farmed wood, steam power plant	19.2
Ethanol from waste wood	18.0
Syndiesel, natural gas with CCS	13.0
Ethanol from sugarcane	10.4
Electricity, farmed wood, 10 MW gasifier + CCGT	9.9
Electricity, farmed wood, 200 MW gasifier + CCGT	7.8
Syndiesel, BtL, farmed wood	7.4
DME, BtL, farmed wood	7.0
Syndiesel, BtL, waste wood	4.8
DME, BtL, waste wood	4.5
Electricity, nuclear	4.4

Figure 35 gCO_{2eq} MJ^{-1} of fuel produced by technology.

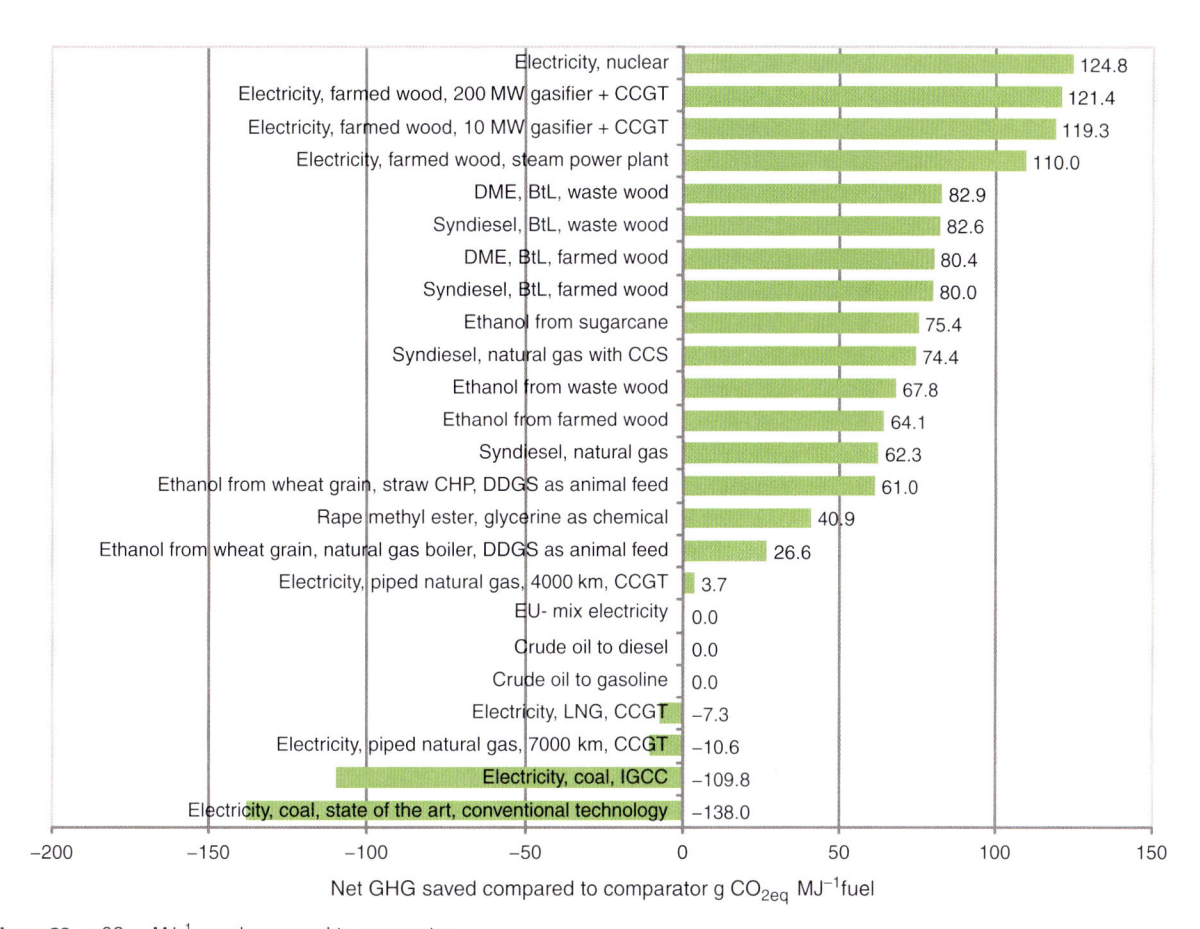

Figure 36 gCO$_{2eq}$ MJ^{-1} saved compared to comparator.

Electricity, nuclear	124.8
Electricity, farmed wood, 200 MW gasifier + CCGT	121.4
Electricity, farmed wood, 10 MW gasifier + CCGT	119.3
Electricity, farmed wood, steam power plant	110.0
DME, BtL, waste wood	82.9
Syndiesel, BtL, waste wood	82.6
DME, BtL, farmed wood	80.4
Syndiesel, BtL, farmed wood	80.0
Ethanol from sugarcane	75.4
Syndiesel, natural gas with CCS	74.4
Ethanol from waste wood	67.8
Ethanol from farmed wood	64.1
Syndiesel, natural gas	62.3
Ethanol from wheat grain, straw CHP, DDGS as animal feed	61.0
Rape methyl ester, glycerine as chemical	40.9
Ethanol from wheat grain, natural gas boiler, DDGS as animal feed	26.6
Electricity, piped natural gas, 4000 km, CCGT	3.7
EU- mix electricity	0.0
Crude oil to diesel	0.0
Crude oil to gasoline	0.0
Electricity, LNG, CCGT	−7.3
Electricity, piped natural gas, 7000 km, CCGT	−10.6
Electricity, coal, IGCC	−109.8
Electricity, coal, state of the art, conventional technology	−138.0

Net GHG saved compared to comparator g CO$_{2eq}$ MJ^{-1}fuel

For each of the lignocellulosic technologies shown in **Figure 37**, the liters of diesel equivalent produced per hectare per year have been calculated at low, medium, and high crop yields based on a mixed or polyfeed plant fed on the assumption that the plant feedstock is made up of 47% short-rotation coppice, 24% *Miscanthus*, and 29% straw, which could potentially be representative of a northeast UK BtL plant. The low crop yield figure represents today's production of biomass on less than ideal land, medium represents today's production on ideal land while high represents a near-future, optimized position for the UK production of biomass. It should also be noted that conversion process efficiency is variable. Reported process efficiencies for BtL, for example, vary between 40% and 55%.

Figure 37 indicates that the use of biomass for CHP production and to produce heat, as is well known, produces the most energy per hectare because high efficiencies of about 80% for CHP and up to about 90% for heat can be achieved. However, heat is a low-exergy energy type, and while natural gas remains a relatively low-cost fuel, it is less likely to see large-scale uptake, particularly in on-gas grid areas. Additionally, heat cannot be used as a transport fuel and it is unlikely that electricity will see widespread uptake as a transportation fuel in the near term. Of the biofuel technologies, BtL diesel, methanol, and hydrogen from wood have the highest area-related potentials. Ethanol production from straw achieves low yields due to the low yield of straw per hectare compared to wood (short-rotation coppice). However, if the whole wheat crop (i.e., the wheat grain plus the straw) were to be used to make biofuel (i.e., the whole crop biorefinery concept), then the volume of diesel equivalent that could be produced per hectare rises to 2950 l ha^{-1}. Electricity production (without CHP) gives lower yields than BtL and other lignocellulose-based fuels because of lower energy efficiencies.

5.11.9.4 Summary

The key driver for introducing biofuels, particularly in the EU, is the potential to reduce GHG emissions in the transport sector. However, the development of biofuels has raised a number of concerns, which are in the process of being addressed.

Of the variety of advanced biofuel technologies expected to be commercial within this decade, FT diesel derived from BtL has the potential to deliver significant GHG savings relative to both mineral diesel and first-generation biofuels. Syndiesel produced via the BtL process delivers good GHG savings per megajoule of fuel. However, BtL typically delivers fewer GHG savings when compared against a comparator (fossil diesel) when compared against electricity production.

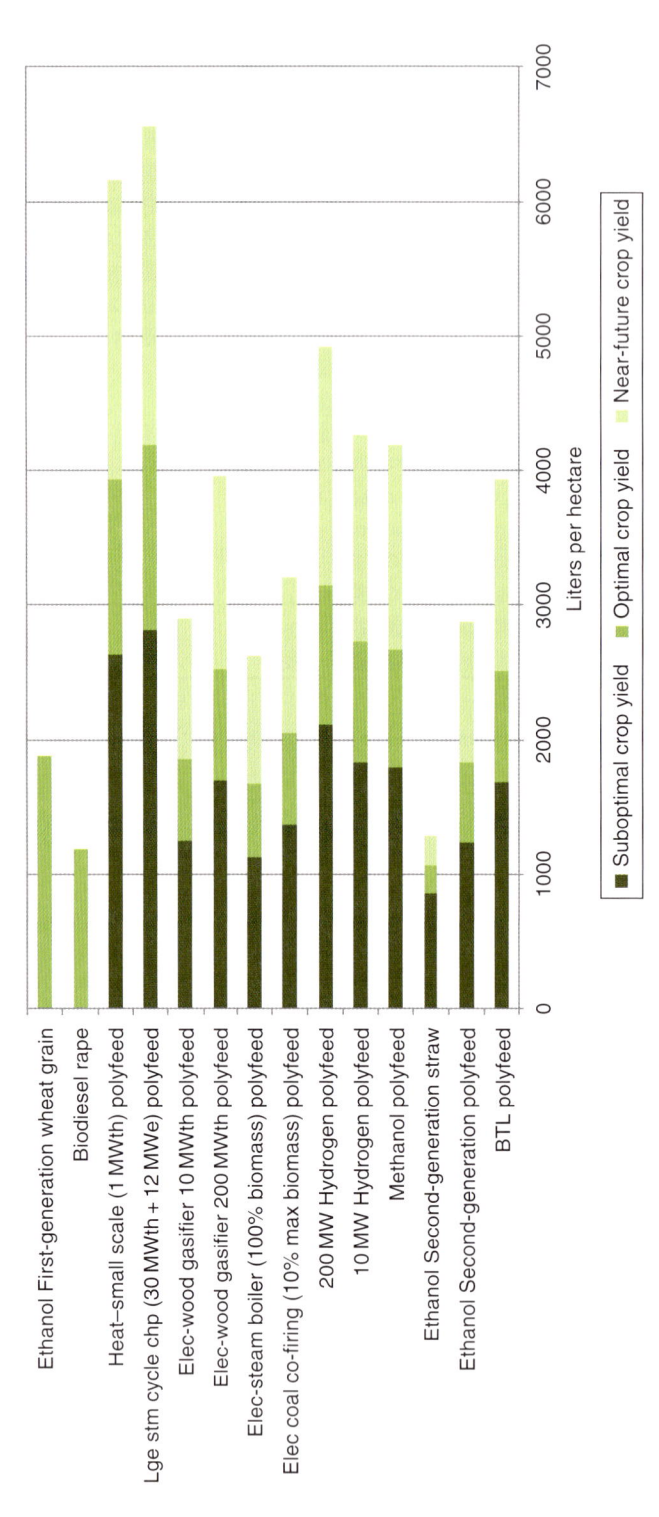

Figure 37 Liters of diesel equivalent produced per hectare per year by technology. Reproduced from Evans G (2007) *International Biofuels Strategy Project – Liquid Transport Biofuels, Technology Status Report*. NNFCC report (08/017). York: NNFCC. http://www.nnfcc.co.uk/tools/international-biofuels-strategy-project-liquid-transport-biofuels-technology-status-report-nnfcc-08-017 (accessed 3 March 2011).

5.11.10 Summary and Outlook

BtL development is now progressing from pilot-scale projects through to subeconomic demonstration projects whose aims are to support the development of the first commercial-scale reference plants, showing what works and what does not.

The most advanced BtL projects are, perhaps, Choren in Northern Germany, which, as of March 2010, is about to start full-scale operation, and BioMCN in the Netherlands. The Choren process is designed to convert woodchips into syndiesel ('Sundiesel') and naphtha using the FT process, while the BioMCN BtL process converts glycerol into methanol. Around the world, advantage is being taken of regional strengths and needs to drive BtL uptake. For example, in North America, BtL is being developed to produce ethanol from woody biomass; in Scandinavia, it is being developed to produce fuels including DME, synthetic diesel, and bioSNG from wood and wastes from the wood processing industry; and in the United Kingdom, it is being developed at smaller scale to produce BtL fuels (ethanol and jet fuel) from waste feedstocks such as MSW. For the future, though, ways to produce mid-distillate substitutes are needed, particularly in the EU and for the aviation and heavy duty sectors.

BtL technologies provide an opportunity to produce a variety of additional biofuels from an alternative range of feedstocks compared to first-generation biofuels produced from sugars, starches, and oil crops. They can produce more easily assimilated fuels such as synthetic diesel as well as used for processing waste materials, which would otherwise perhaps be landfilled. They typically offer GHG savings of about 90% compared to the fossil fuels they replace although the savings achievable depend on a number of factors including, for example, the biomass feedstock used.

However, the use of biomass brings a series of technical, logistic, economic, and sustainability challenges that need to be addressed. Technical challenges include how to ensure tars in syngas are removed prior to chemical synthesis and demonstrating reliable syngas production. Logistic issues include procuring and transporting sufficient biomass while balancing both economic and GHG costs. Perhaps one of the most significant issues to address is the high capital costs and associated risk. It is expected that commercial-scale BtL plants using FT synthesis will cost in the region of £500 million or more. Opportunity exists for developers to develop lower cost BtL projects that would be more economic at smaller scale and thereby better balanced with the scale of the biomass supply chain. In terms of sustainability issues, important and challenging work is ongoing to address the impacts of biofuels feedstock production, in particular in terms of direct and indirect land use change impacts. Limitations on biomass availability mean that effective and efficient use of biomass must be made while at the same time ensuring that low-carbon technologies are available to address all sectors including chemical and material production. BtL technology is well placed to meet and be part of this need, for example by being able to process used biomaterials while also producing a combination of fuel, chemical, power, and heat outputs as illustrated in **Figure 38**.

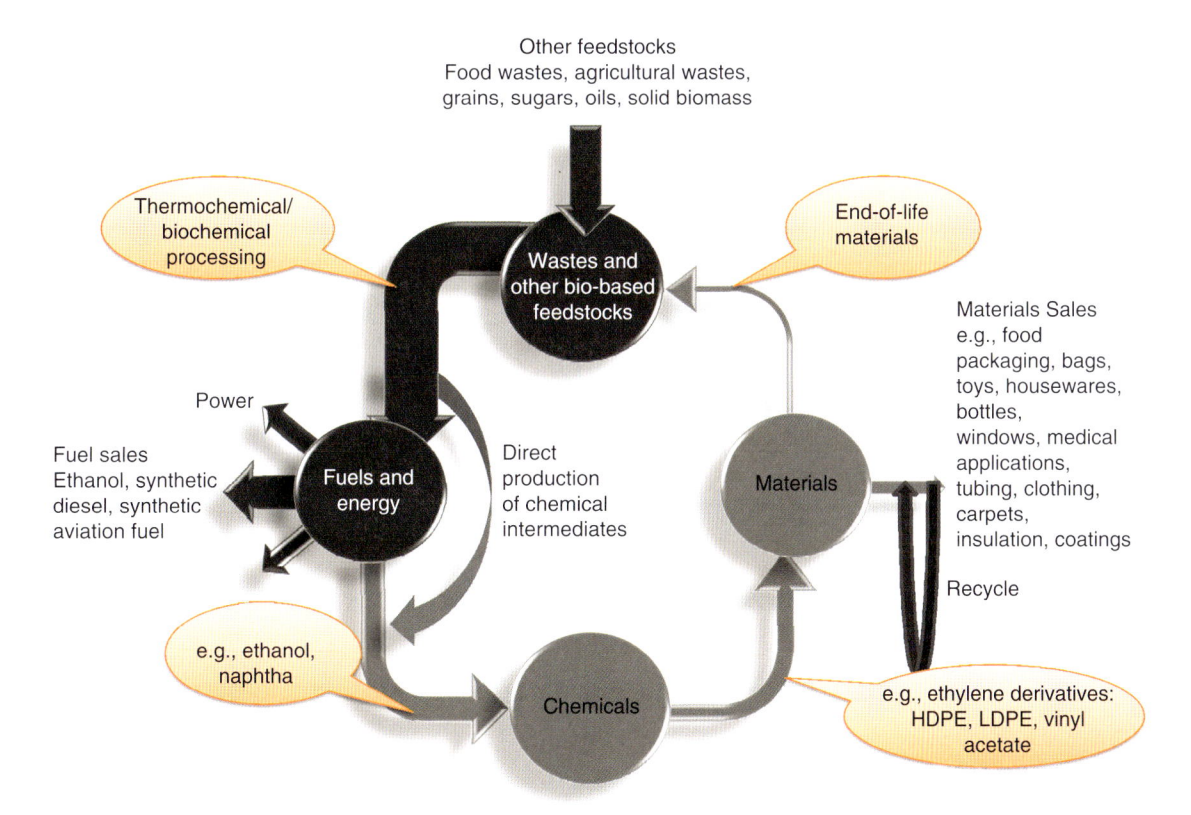

Figure 38 Integrated biomass-to-liquids (BtL) model for production of fuels, energy, chemicals, and materials. Reproduced from NNFCC presentation (2010) Inputs, technology and biomethane utilization: An overview. In: *Biorenewable Fuel and Fertiliser: Realising the Potential.* 24 March. York, UK: FERA. http://www.soci.org/

References

[1] Mortimer ND, Evans A, Shaw AL, and Hunter AJ (2009) *Life Cycle and Technoeconomic Assessment of the North East BtL Project (Report)*. York: NNFCC.
[2] Wenner C and Knibbs D (2009) Sustainably Achieving the RED 10% Energy Mandate for Transport. http://www.biofuelsnow.co.uk/resources.php (accessed 1 March 2011).
[3] Boerrigter H (2006) *Economy of Biomass-to-Liquids (BtL) Plants. An Engineering Assessment*. The Netherlands: ECN.
[4] Concawe, EUCAR, and JRC (2007) *Well-to-Wheels Analysis of Future Automotive Fuels and Powertrains in the European Context*. Petten, the Netherlands: European Commission Directorate General Joint Research Centre.

Further Reading

[1] Boerrigter H and Rauch R (2006) *Review of Applications of Gases from Biomass Gasification*. The Netherlands: ECN.
[2] Bridgwater AV, Hofbauer H, and van Loo S (eds.) (2010) *Thermal Biomass Conversion*. Newbury, Berkshire: CPL Press.
[3] Bridgwater AV (2002) The future for biomass pyrolysis and gasification: Status, opportunities and policies. http://ec.europa.eu/energy/renewables/studies/doc/bioenergy/2002_report_p536.pdf (accessed 14 January 2010)
[4] E4tech (2009) *Review of Technologies for Gasification of Biomass and Wastes*. York: NNFCC.
[5] Evans G (2007) *International Biofuels Strategy Project. Liquid Transport Biofuels – Technology Status Report*. York: NNFCC.
[6] Evans (2008) *Techno-Economic Assessment of Biomass 'Densification' Technologies*, NNFCC 08-015. York: NNFCC
[7] Evans G and Nattrass L (2009) *Advanced Thermochemical Biofuels Roadmap and Challenge*. York: NNFCC.
[8] Kavalov B and Peteves SD (2005) *Status and Perspectives of Biomass-to-Liquid Fuels in the European Union*. Petten, the Netherlands: European Commission Directorate General Joint Research Centre.
[9] Kumar A, Jones DD, and Hanna MA (2009) Thermochemical biomass gasification: A review of the current status of the technology. *Energies* 2: 556–581.
[11] Magalhães AIP, Petrovic D, and Rodriguez AL (2009) Techno-economic assessment of biomass pre-conversion processes as a part of biomass-to-liquids line-up. *Biofuels, Bioproducts Biorefining* 3: 584–600.
[10] LowCVP and NNFCC (2010) *Biofuels Pathways*. London: LowCVP.
[12] Maniatis K (2001) Progress in biomass gasification: An overview. In: Bridgwater AV (ed.) *Progress in Thermochemical Biomass Conversion*. Oxford, UK: Blackwell.
[13] Nexant Inc. (2007) *Feasibility of Second Generation Biodiesel Production in the United Kingdom*. York: NNFCC.
[14] NNFCC (2010) Inputs, technology and biomethane utilisation: An overview. In: *Biorenewable Fuel and Fertiliser: Realising the Potential*. 24 March. York, UK: FERA.
[15] Olah GA, Goeppart A, and Surya Prakash GK (2006) *Beyond Oil and Gas: The Methanol Economy*. Weinheim: Wiley-VCH.
[16] Spath PL and Dayton DC (2003) *Preliminary Screening – Technical and Economic Assessment of Synthesis Gas to Fuels and Chemicals with Emphasis on the Potential for Biomass-Derived Syngas*. Golden, CO: NREL.
[17] Stevens DJ (2001) *Hot Gas Conditioning: Recent Progress with Larger-Scale Biomass Gasification Systems*. Golden, CO: NREL.
[18] Steynberg A and Dry M (2004) *Studies in Surface Science and Catalysis, Vol. 152: Fischer Tropsch Technology*. Amsterdam, the Netherlands: Elsevier.
[19] Tonkovich AL, Mazanec T, Jarosch K, et al. (2008) *Improved Fischer–Tropsch Economics Enabled by Microchannel Technology*. Plain City, OH: Velocys Inc.
[20] van der Drift A and Boerrigter H (2006) *Synthesis Gas from Biomass for Fuels and Chemicals*. The Netherlands: ECN.
[21] Zwart RWR, Boerrigter H, and van der Drift A (2006) The impact of biomass pretreatment on the feasibility of overseas biomass conversion to Fischer Tropsch products. *Energy and Fuels* 20(5): 2192–2197.

Relevant Websites

http://tinyurl.com/IEA-task33 – IEA Bioenergy
http://www.fischer-tropsch.org – Fischer-Tropsch Archive
http://www.renew-fuel.com/ – RENEW

5.12 Intensification of Biofuel Production

AP Harvey and JGM Lee, Newcastle University, Newcastle upon Tyne, UK

© 2012 Elsevier Ltd. All rights reserved.

5.12.1	Biodiesel	205
5.12.1.1	Introduction: The Biodiesel Reaction	205
5.12.1.2	A Generic Biodiesel Flowsheet	206
5.12.1.3	Reactors	206
5.12.1.3.1	Oscillatory baffled reactors	206
5.12.1.3.2	Heterogeneous catalysis	207
5.12.1.3.3	Supercritical reaction	208
5.12.1.3.4	Reactive extraction/*in situ* transesterification	208
5.12.1.4	GRP/BRP Separation	209
5.12.1.5	Other Downstream Processing Steps	209
5.12.2	Bioethanol	210
5.12.2.1	Ethanol Dehydration	210
5.12.2.1.1	Extractive distillation	210
5.12.2.1.2	Membranes	211
5.12.2.1.3	Adsorbents	211
5.12.2.2	Integrating Alcohol Removal with Fermentation	212
5.12.2.2.1	Solvent extraction	212
5.12.2.2.2	Membrane processes	214
References		214

5.12.1 Biodiesel

5.12.1.1 Introduction: The Biodiesel Reaction

Biodiesel is a renewable transport fuel made by reacting triglyceride oils, usually of vegetable origin, with alcohols in the presence of a base catalyst. This converts the triglyceride molecule into three molecules of alkyl ester (the biodiesel) and one molecule of glycerol via a series of three equilibrium reactions. In almost all processes, methanol is the alcohol used, as it is the least expensive and results in the most rapid reaction.

1. *Triglyceride + Methanol ↔ Methyl Ester + Diglyceride*
2. *Diglyceride + Methanol ↔ Methyl Ester + Monoglyceride*
3. *Monoglyceride + Methanol ↔ Methyl Ester + Glycerol*

Vegetable oil has a high enough calorific value to be used as a fuel, but is unsuitable for modern diesel engines for two main reasons:

1. It does not flow well at lower temperatures, leading to problems with operating diesel vehicles during winter.
2. It does not atomize well in the combustion chamber, leading to waxing of the chamber and injection nozzles, and increased emissions (see Reference [1]).

In the reaction scheme above, it should be noted that each step is at a genuine equilibrium. The significance of this in terms of biodiesel production is that all plants are operated using an excess of methanol to drive the reaction to the product side. Typically molar ratios of methanol in the range 4.5:1 to 9:1 are used. This has implications for the cost of biodiesel, as the leftover methanol must be recycled, which is usually achieved by distillation.

It should be noted that the reaction can also be performed using an acid catalyst, but seldom is in practice, as the reaction takes an order of magnitude longer to reach completion. Not only is this a cost in itself (larger reaction vessels), but further material costs are incurred as the reactor has to be able to withstand sulfuric acid, the acid of choice for this reaction. A potential advantage of acid catalysis is that it can not only convert triglycerides to biodiesel but also any free fatty acids (FFAs). Indeed, above a certain percentage of FFAs, use of an acid catalyst should be economically advantageous. Higher FFA levels such as this are a problem for alkaline catalysts, as they react with the catalyst, thereby not only reducing the reaction rate, but also producing water, which is undesirable in the reaction. Indeed one of the challenges for biodiesel manufacturers is keeping water out of all streams: both solid NaOH (the usual form in which it is used in these processes as a base catalyst) and dry methanol are hygroscopic. Water is undesirable as it takes part in an undesired side reaction to produce soap. This could of course be hydrolysis of the biodiesel or the triglyceride itself. Both reactions lead to a decrease in yield, and complicate downstream processing considerably, as the downstream processing usually includes a water washing step. Typically biodiesel producers try to ensure that water is less than 0.1% of their reaction mixture.

5.12.1.2 A Generic Biodiesel Flowsheet

A generic flowsheet for a continuous plant is shown in **Figure 1**.

Solid sodium hydroxide is mixed with >99.9% methanol. Sodium hydroxide solutions cannot be used, as the water in the solutions is undesirable, as mentioned above. This is also the reason for the relatively high purity of the methanol (impurities are predominantly water).

Downstream of the reactor, the settler at its most simple design is an unmixed vessel that gives the reaction mixture sufficient time to separate by gravity, as glycerol (specific gravity (SG) = ~1.26) is substantially denser than biodiesel (SG = 0.88). It separates the reaction mixture into a 'biodiesel-rich phase' (BRP) and a 'glycerol-rich phase' (GRP).

Washing is usually achieved using water, resulting in wastewater of typically very high BOD (biological oxygen demand) and COD (chemical oxygen demand). The process is often a two-stage wash with freshwater at each stage. It reduces (by varying degrees) a range of contaminants in the BRP, including soap, methanol, and catalyst.

Polishing refers to the last step in the process in which various low-level contaminants are removed. In particular, metal ions from the catalyst and various soaps are removed. It is usually achieved using an ion exchange resin, notably Rohm and Haas's 'BD10Dry', specifically developed for this application.

GRP is the glycerol-rich phase, which contains much of the catalyst and various species extracted from the vegetable oil, often colored compounds such as carotene. Consequently, the GRP is typically brown rather than colorless (as pure glycerol would be), and the BRP is paler in color than the feedstock vegetable oil. The BRP itself will contain a range of contaminants that must be removed before it can be of saleable quality (as defined by EN14214 in the European Union, and similar standards worldwide). The methanol is usually recovered from the GRP for economic reasons. This is most easily achieved via a simple one-stage flash distillation. Further to this, the GRP will typically require neutralization prior to sale, although some processors go much further than this.

Glycerol in the past was a valuable by-product of biodiesel, capable of being refined and sold on to the cosmetics industry, but as the biodiesel industry has grown in the last 10 years, a mismatch between supply and demand has emerged, resulting in not only generally significantly lower prices for glycerol, but often extreme volatility in the price, making it a difficult feedstock to base future plans on. With a more stable price, glycerol could be a 'green' feedstock for a range of chemicals. It is now on the market in unprecedented quantities, and in principle it is versatile, as it is a small molecule with a functional group on each carbon. The range of potential products is very large, including, for example, epichlorohydrin, propane-1,3-diol, hydrogen, and methanol. The term 'glycerochemistry' has been coined to describe this area. As a sugar, the glycerol, or even the raw GRP, can be used as a substrate for biological processes. It can also be used as a fuel itself in diesel generators.

5.12.1.3 Reactors

Biodiesel, as a bulk chemical, is mostly produced at large scales, with a 'typical' plant having a production rate of 100 kte yr^{-1}. The plants therefore would be expected to be fully continuous, but often are not. The reactors are often operated in batch mode with reaction times (as part of batch cycles) of 1–2 h. The reaction kinetics determined at laboratory scale [2] imply that the reaction can reach completion in 10 min at typical conditions. Such rates are not achieved in large batch reactors or continuous stirred tank reactors, due to unavoidable mixing limitations at such scales. If the reaction could proceed at its inherent rate, the reactor could be reduced in size by an order of magnitude. Industrial-scale batch reactors can operate at 2 h reaction times. If the rates at laboratory scale could be reproduced at industrial scale, the size reduction would be a factor of 12 due to the increased rate of reaction, and typically a further factor of 2 by moving from batch to continuous (in losing the nonreaction time parts of the batch cycle, such as filling, heating, cooling, and emptying the vessel). This represents an overall decrease in volume of 24.

Converting a batch process to continuous is perhaps the most common form of process intensification.

5.12.1.3.1 Oscillatory baffled reactors

Oscillatory baffled reactors (OBRs) are an intensified form of plug flow reactor (PFR). They allow 'long' batch processes to be converted to more efficient continuous processing. Designs of conventional PFR have extremely high length-to-diameter ratios when they are to accommodate very long reactions. This is because the establishment of plug flow is dependent on achieving a high

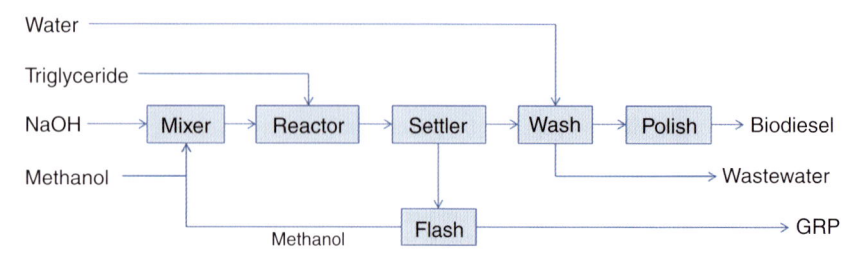

Figure 1 Generic biodiesel production flowsheet.

degree of turbulence, which requires the flow to exceed a certain velocity. Maintaining a high velocity for a long period leads to a long reactor. Long reactors, for example, exceeding hundreds of meters in length, have a range of practical problems including large effective footprint and high pumping costs. (The designs tend to be narrow also.)

Harvey *et al.* [3] were the first to demonstrate continuous production of biodiesel in an OBR. The reactor used was constructed from 2 × 1.5 m lengths of 0.024 m internal diameter jacketed glass, vertically oriented and connected by an inverted U-bend (see **Figure 2**).

It was demonstrated that saleable biodiesel could be produced from rapeseed oil at 15 min residence time when operating at 50 °C and in 10 min at 60 °C. Furthermore, the OBR is an ideal reactor for suspending solids, so it could be an advantageous design if a practical solid catalyst for biodiesel transesterification is developed (see Section 5.12.1.3.3). A general design methodology for OBRs is presented by Harvey and Stonestreet [4].

5.12.1.3.2 Heterogeneous catalysis

Heterogenizing the catalysis of triglyceride transesterification could substantially improve the economics of the process, as, in principle, if the ideal catalyst can be found, numerous unit operations will be greatly reduced in size or removed from the flowsheet altogether.

The process advantages are twofold:

1. Unlike a conventional homogeneous catalyst-using process, a solid catalyst-based process allows the remaining methanol to be distilled immediately after the reactor. This cannot happen in the conventional process, because as the methanol is removed the equilibrium adjusts and moves back toward the reactant side, thereby reducing conversion. But this equilibrium shift can happen only in the presence of the catalyst. In a heterogeneous process, the reaction mixture would no longer be in contact with the catalyst the moment it left the reactor. More methanol would be recovered in the minimum number of unit operations. Conventional processes either use only one flash distillation to recover methanol from the GRP (which contains most of the methanol) or require expensive multistage distillation columns to perform the separation.

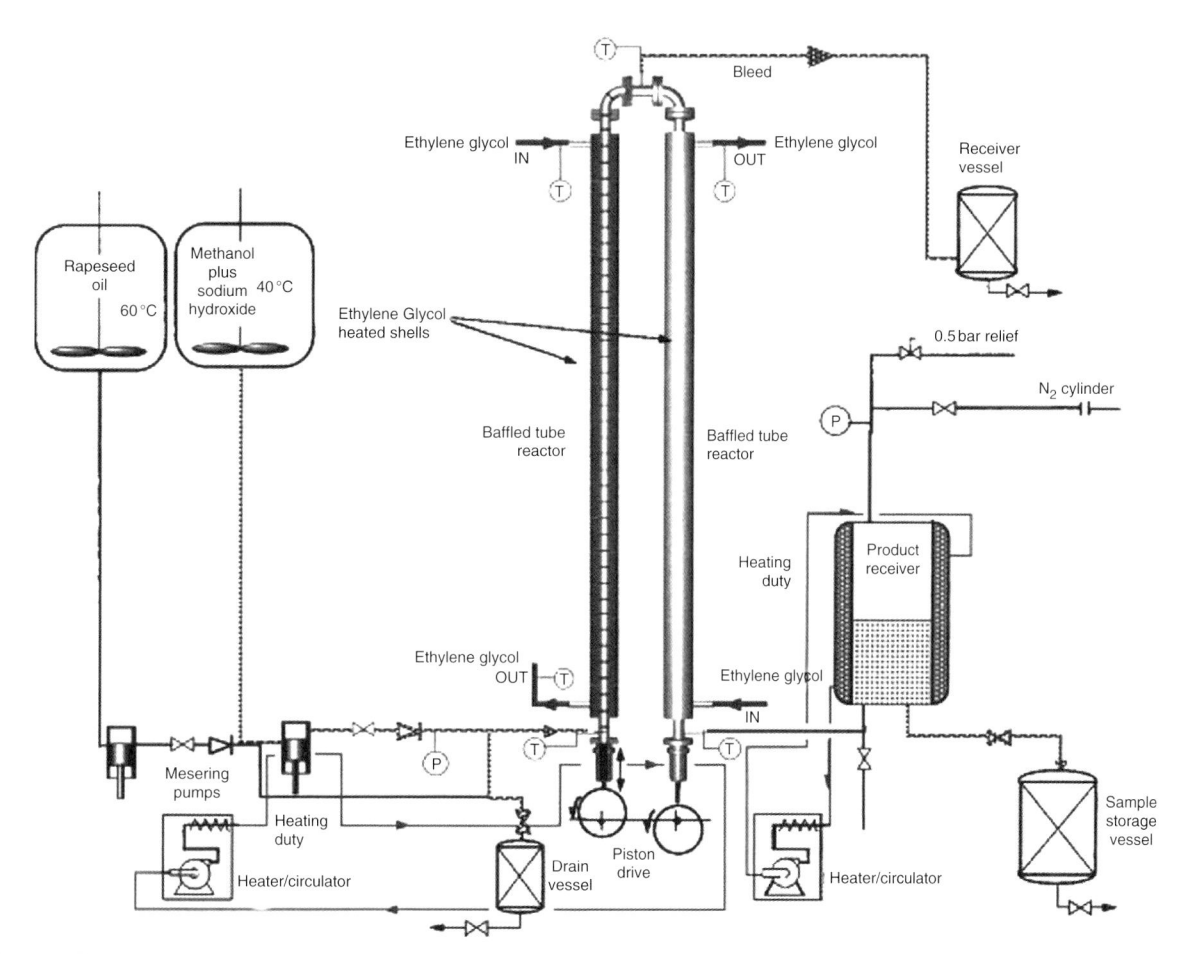

Figure 2 Process flow diagram for oscillatory baffled reactor production of biodiesel [3].

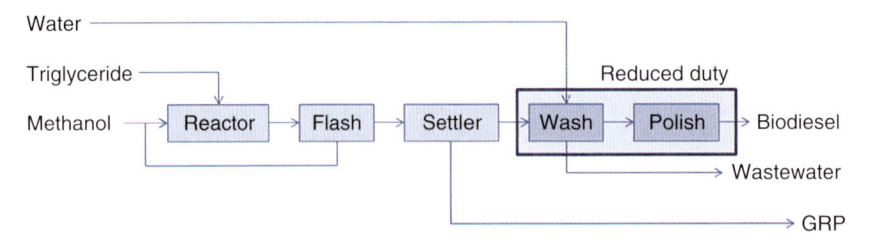

Figure 3 Ideal process flow diagram for a heterogeneously catalyzed biodiesel process.

2. As the heterogeneous catalyst remains entirely in the reactor, glycerol-rich product will not require neutralization downstream, thereby removing at least one unit operation from the process. In conventional processes, the raw glycerol-rich product contains much of the basic catalyst used, so the first step in its upgrading to a saleable product is to neutralize the base with acid.

The advantages can be seen in the process flow diagram of **Figure 3**:

1. The mixer step has been removed.
2. More of the methanol is recycled, as the entire reaction mixture is subject to distillation.
3. The duties on the washing and polishing steps are reduced, as the catalyst itself does not have to be removed from the BRP, and the catalyst itself is not responsible for soap production (as with NaOH). So in practice these downstream unit operations would be significantly smaller, thereby reducing the plant's capital cost and certain running costs. Conceivably, the polishing could be removed altogether as its role is largely the removal of metal ions originating in the homogeneous catalyst.

These clear potential advantages have led to a great deal of research in this area. However, finding the correct catalyst has proven extremely difficult. All candidates so far have been precluded on the grounds of unacceptable rate of leaching, cost, or insufficient activity. Axens' Esterfip process [5] is one example of a commercial biodiesel process using a solid catalyst, but it requires temperatures around 200 °C and high pressures. This kind of process is likely to be commercially viable only at larger scales.

The types of catalyst investigated so far include alkali metal oxides, doped alkali metal oxides, ion exchange resins, enzymes, and others. There have been a number of reviews on this subject. The reader is directed to Lam *et al.* [6] for a fairly recent comprehensive review.

5.12.1.3.3 Supercritical reaction

Supercritical processing can greatly speed up the transesterification reaction and does not require a catalyst, but it does require very high temperatures and/or pressures. Hence the capital cost advantage of a shorter reaction (smaller reactor) and running cost reductions achieved by removing the catalyst must be weighed against the increased costs of the equipment required to operate in such conditions. Typically supercritical processing can only be envisaged at large scales due to the higher capital costs of the equipment, or at smaller scales in niche markets for higher added-value products (where the processing cost is less of an issue, and supercritical processing is favored for other reasons).

There are a great number of studies on biodiesel production in supercritical methanol. The conditions range from 270 to 450 °C and 10 to 35 MPa, with an interplay between the various process conditions. Lower molar ratios (e.g., 6:1 to 9:1, MeOH:triglyceride) and lower pressures (e.g., 10 MPa) can be used at higher temperatures (400–450 °C); conversely, lower temperatures can be used at the cost of increased molar ratio and pressure. There are costs associated with achieving both temperatures and pressures, and the economic optimum is unclear. Much of the research work of the last 10 years is summarized in an excellent review by Sawangkeaw *et al.* [7].

5.12.1.3.4 Reactive extraction/In situ transesterification

A common form of process intensification is to combine process steps, thereby reducing the total number of steps in a process and reducing capital cost, plant size, and surrounding infrastructure. In most cases, this involves combining reaction with some other step, often separation.

Reactive extraction is an example of process intensification that begins with consideration of not just the process, but the whole supply chain. In this process, ground seeds are contacted directly with a methanol/catalyst mixture, rather than having their oil extracted by crushing and solvent extraction. This removes a number of significantly capital- and running cost-intensive processes from the supply chain, as well as eliminating the use of an organic solvent (hexane) in the solvent extraction step (see **Figure 4**). There is also evidence that this process negates the need for a drying step, or at least can tolerate a considerably higher percentage of water than conventional transesterification of liquid triglycerides. The key problem with reactive extraction is that currently it does not economically compete with conventional processing, as the cost savings in getting rid of the crushing and solvent extraction steps are outweighed by the costs associated with the very large excess of methanol required, typically 200:1 as compared to 6:1 in conventional liquid phase processing. A range of new projects are under way to try to diminish this disadvantage.

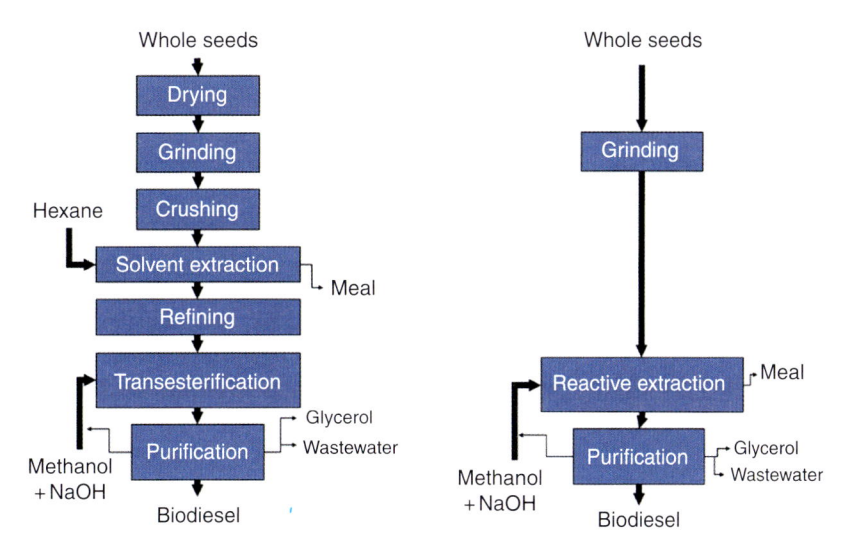

Figure 4 Comparison: conventional supply chain vs. reactive extraction.

So far reactive extraction has been successfully performed on a range of oilseeds including rapeseed, soy, *Jatropha*, and *Pongamia*, using either methanol or ethanol. Other oil-bearing materials such as sewage sludge and algae [8] are also being studied.

Supercritical reactive extraction is an interesting development, as it requires no catalyst and appears to be relatively water-tolerant. The first reports of this technology have appeared very recently, in processing algae [9] and *Jatropha* [10].

It may be that production by (nonsupercritical) reactive extraction lends itself to small-scale 'distributed production', as it does not require solvent extraction and crushing, both of which are usually performed in large-scale centralized facilities.

Reactive extraction for biodiesel production is extensively reviewed by Harvey *et al.* [11].

5.12.1.4 GRP/BRP Separation

The most obvious physical property difference to exploit in separating glycerol and biodiesel is density. Glycerol has a density of $1.26 \, \text{kg l}^{-1}$ and biodiesel $0.88 \, \text{kg l}^{-1}$. The simplest unit operation is a gravity settler, which is simply a vessel designed to give the mixture enough time to separate. If this step can be intensified, there are perhaps cost savings to be made in the capital cost of the vessel and via the impact of cleaner separation on downstream unit operations. The options for intensifying settling are as follows:

1. *Centrifuges*: Use of a centrifuge would result in a size reduction between 1 and 2 orders of magnitude, so would easily qualify as process intensification. In general centrifuges are not used, as they are relatively expensive in both running and capital costs, particularly compared to the low-cost settling tank, which is inexpensive and has no associated running costs. The Connemann/Westfalia biodiesel process [12], however, involves a number of Westfalia centrifuges, which are used at different stages for both washing and settling.
2. *Coalescer*: Coalescers speed up settling by forcing glycerol to coalesce into larger globules, which settle more quickly. There are a variety of means of promoting coalescence, normally involving forcing the mixed fluid to flow through constrictions, sometimes with hydrophilic or hydrophobic surfaces. Designs include arrays of closely spaced flat plates ('plate coalescers'), sand beds (narrow channels within a bed of sand), and fiber coalescers. Simple design calculations in-house, assuming a fiber bed design, indicate that more than an order of magnitude reduction in volume can be achieved compared to a passive settling tank. There are no reports of research into coalescer design for BRP/GRP separation in the academic literature. However, such products are commercially available. In particular, the Pall corporation (http://www.pall.com) provides coalescers of the fiber bed design specifically for the biodiesel/glycerol separation.

Another possible option is the hydrocyclone, but there appears to have been little study of the device for this application, nor any industrial suppliers for this specific application.

5.12.1.5 Other Downstream Processing Steps

1. *Distillation*: Separation of methanol from glycerol is relatively straightforward as the boiling points are significantly different, 64.7 and 290 °C, respectively. That is why it is often performed in a one-step 'flash' distillation. The water–methanol separation is more difficult, albeit easier than ethanol–water separation (a reason why methanol is used rather than ethanol in this process), as it does not form an azeotrope. As the boiling points of methanol and water are considerably closer than the boiling points of

glycerol and methanol, flash distillation is not sufficient. However, if the distillation step can be avoided, it should be. The first question that should be posed is whether the amount of water being recycled can be tolerated by the process. If not, then options for intensification of the process include technologies such as pervaporation and techniques for water removal by ad/absorption, for example, by molecular sieve.

2. *GRP treatment*: An interesting method of neutralizing glycerol to some extent while simultaneously removing FFAs from incoming vegetable oil feeds is simply to contact the two streams, thereby allowing the sodium hydroxide, which mainly ends up in the glycerol stream, to react with the FFAs. In principle this will neutralize one stream or the other, and in so doing remove the need for either an FFA removal step or a glycerol neutralization step (often required if the glycerol is to be sold), so this is a clear example of process intensification.

3. *Washing*: Washing can be intensified by countercurrent operation or by integration with separation using centrifuge or in theory a hydrocyclone. It is also possible that the washing step can be removed altogether and the load put onto the 'polishing step'. Saleh *et al.* [13] report use of an ultrafiltration membrane for removing intransigent suspended glycerol from the BRP, and Wang *et al.* [14] report a similar achievement using a ceramic membrane. These technologies could replace some of the washing duty, as could development of a heterogeneous catalyst as mentioned in Section 5.12.1.3.2. The washing step should perhaps be the subject of more investigation as in developed countries the costs of disposal of wastewater can be significantly high, so reducing the effluent, or its COD/BOD, or replacing the step altogether could enhance biodiesel's profitability.

5.12.2 Bioethanol

5.12.2.1 Ethanol Dehydration

The product stream from a typical fermentor will contain less than 5–8 mass% of ethanol. The remainder of the stream comprises water (> 85 mass%), carbon dioxide, and secondary alcohol products usually referred to as 'fusel oil'. The carbon dioxide and fusel oil are easily separated from the water and ethanol. The water and ethanol are separated in a two-step process because the water–ethanol system forms an azeotrope that prevents the production of pure ethanol from water in a single distillation column. In the primary water–ethanol separation, a distillation column is used to produce a mixture of 80–95 mass% ethanol. The choice of ethanol composition depends to a certain extent on the technology used in the second step. There are three options for producing high-purity ethanol:

1. extractive distillation to break or bypass the azeotrope;
2. membrane separation;
3. addition of a solid adsorbent to remove the residual water.

Each process is discussed in the following sections.

5.12.2.1.1 Extractive distillation

Extractive distillation refers to the addition of a third component to a system to facilitate the breaking or bypassing of an azeotrope. For the separation of ethanol from water, there are two possibilities: addition of a salt and addition of an organic entrainer.

The addition of a salt or any hygroscopic material reduces water–ethanol interactions and can lead to the removal of the azeotrope so that it is possible to separate ethanol and water + salt in a single distillation column. However, additional process units are required to recover the salt from the water and this affects the economics and operation of the process. Many salts have been proposed although $CaCl_2$ is most effective. In the 1930s, sodium acetate and potassium acetate were used but proved hard to recycle.

A more popular method is the addition of an entrainer. Two types have been used. The first type consists of high-boiling components such as glycerol and ethylene glycol where a large amount of the entrainer is added such that distillation produces pure ethanol and a water–entrainer mix. The water has to be removed from the entrainer, usually by evaporation, and this adds significantly to the energy cost of the process. The second type of entrainer is immiscible with water and causes the formation of a second liquid phase and a heterogeneous azeotrope. For commonly used entrainers of this type, such as cyclohexane and *n*-alkanes, the ethanol forms an additional binary homogeneous azeotrope and a ternary water–ethanol–entrainer azeotrope. The effect of this is best summarized in the diagram for the water–ethanol–cyclohexane system shown in **Figure 5**.

In **Figure 5**, the pure components are at the vertices of the triangle, the binary azeotropes are the points on the side of the triangle, and the ternary azeotrope is the single point within the triangle. The triangle is split into three distillation regions and no single distillation process can cross the boundary between regions. The initial distillation step is shown as a horizontal red line on the base of the triangle. The product stream from this step (80–95 mass% ethanol) is mixed with the entrainer (in this case cyclohexane) and distilled. The second distillation column operates in distillation region 3 in **Figure 5**, as shown by the red line, and produces pure ethanol as a bottom product and a mixture whose composition is close to that of the ternary azeotrope at the top of the column. When this mixture is condensed, it forms a water-rich liquid phase and a cyclohexane liquid phase. The cyclohexane-rich phase is recycled. It should be noted that these processes were developed to produce very pure alcohol for human consumption and that extensive energy recovery/integration is required to render them economically viable for the production of fuel.

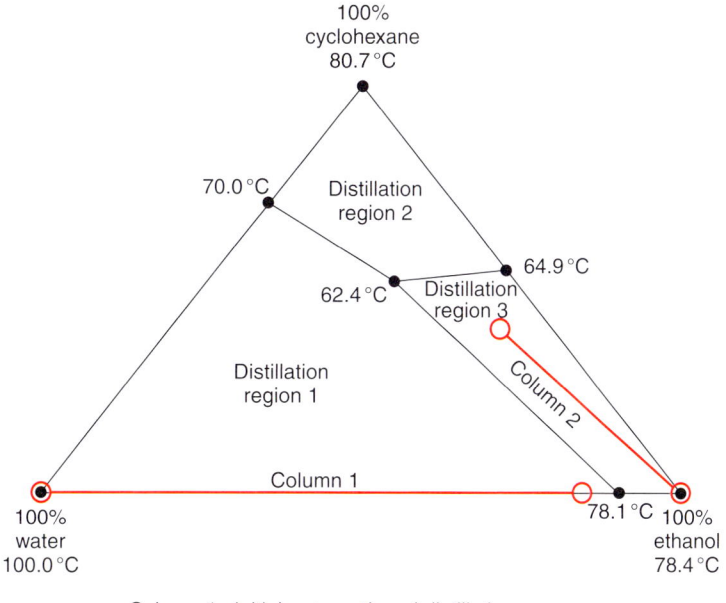

Figure 5 Distillation regions for the water–ethanol–cyclohexane system at 101.3 kPa.

5.12.2.1.2 Membranes

The second way to bypass the water–ethanol azeotrope is to use a membrane. A hybrid process combining distillation and membrane separation is used to produce high-purity ethanol. There are two options:

1. vapor permeation;
2. pervaporation.

In vapor permeation, the distillate from the primary water–ethanol separation is vaporized and fed to a membrane separation unit, whereas for a pervaporation process, the distillate from the primary ethanol distillation column is fed as a liquid and vaporizes as it passes through the membrane. For membrane separations, the material that passes through the membrane is called the permeate and the material that is left behind is called the retentate. In general, water–ethanol membrane separations use a membrane that is hydrophilic and water is preferentially transported through it. Several comparisons of vapor permeation and pervaporation [15–17] have shown that the flux (flow per unit area) of material through the membrane is higher for pervaporation but that the selectivity for water is better for vapor permeation. There are no reported industrial applications of vapor permeation, and pervaporation has been applied industrially since the mid-1980s.

In a hybrid pervaporation–distillation process, a membrane unit is placed after the primary water–ethanol distillation column. Pervaporation stands for permeation and evaporation and the membranes used in ethanol processes are usually selective for water. Some ethanol is transported through the membrane with the water and the permeate will be a mixture of water and ethanol, which is recycled to the distillation column. The retentate is almost pure ethanol. Hybrid pervaporation–distillation processes have been in commercial use since the late 1980s. In general, capital costs for enhanced distillation and pervaporation–distillation processes are the same but the operating costs are between 16% and 66% less for fuel-grade ethanol (99.9 wt.% ethanol). A thorough review of the applications and economics of hybrid pervaporation–separation processes is given by Lipnizki et al. [18].

Recently, zeolite membranes have been proposed for separating water–ethanol mixtures in a hybrid distillation–vapor permeation system [19]. The main advantage of a zeolite membrane is its longer life span due to its chemical stability as well as an improved flux over organic vapor permeation membranes.

5.12.2.1.3 Adsorbents

In all adsorber-based ethanol dehydration processes, the water is adsorbed onto the surface of solids that have an affinity for water. This solid is called the adsorbent. The adsorbent has a finite capacity for water and when this point is reached it must either be regenerated or disposed of. This choice is dependent on the purchase cost of the new adsorbent plus disposal costs and the cost of the regeneration process.

The most well-known solid drying agent for alcohol–water solutions is calcium oxide. This can be added to the water–alcohol mixture, where it reacts with the water to produce calcium hydroxide, which is removed by filtration. Calcium hydroxide is no longer used for this purpose for two reasons. First, the energy requirement for the removal of water from the calcium hydroxide is high, and second, the cost of the calcium hydroxide is too high to use it only once. If the adsorbent is to be used only once, then it should be cheap and preferably biodegradable. Examples of such adsorbents are starch and cellulose, both of which are found in many types of biomass. An ethanol–water vapor mixture is fed to a packed bed of biomass particles that adsorb the water to produce a pure ethanol product. The use of biomass to dehydrate ethanol is well known [20, 21] and improves the energy balance for the production of bioethanol. Originally ground corn was used as the adsorbent because it is a good source of both starch and cellulose and can be fed directly to ethanol fermentation after use as an adsorbent for water. Recently, interest in this technology has been revived and it has been shown that it is possible to use and regenerate wheat flour (starch) and straw (cellulose) without affecting their performance as adsorbents [22]. It is also possible to use various types of pretreatment to improve the water-adsorbing capacity of the biomass [23]. When water is detected at the outlet of the biomass bed in the ethanol product, it must be replaced/regenerated [24].

Both natural and synthetic zeolites were first proposed as adsorbents for water in the late 1970s [25]. Since then, there has been a huge expansion in the number of synthetic zeolites available and zeolites are now produced with pores that can adsorb small water molecules while excluding the larger ethanol molecules [26]. Zeolites with pore sizes of 3 Å (3×10^{-10} m) are very effective drying agents that can be added to ethanol–water mixtures at room temperature [27]. Unfortunately, the energy cost associated with regenerating the zeolite, by removing the water as vapor at elevated temperatures, is prohibitive.

In the past 20 years, zeolite-based pressure swing adsorption processes have been developed and have been found to be the most economical in terms of the energy consumed per kilogram of anhydrous ethanol produced. In the pressure swing adsorption process, the vapor stream from the top of the primary water–ethanol distillation column is fed to a packed bed of zeolite particles that adsorb the water. The zeolite can only adsorb a certain amount of water before it is saturated and must be regenerated. For this reason, two adsorbers are used in turns, as illustrated in **Figure 6**. Each adsorber bed can be used for just under 6 min before it needs to be regenerated. The regeneration process consists of depressurization, purging of the adsorbed water using ethanol vapor from the product stream, and finally repressurization. Pressure swing processes were developed commercially and little data is available from the companies who design and build them. However, adsorption data for the water–ethanol system on 3 Å molecular sieves is now available in the literature [29, 30] and a number of mathematical models have been published [28, 31] that can be used to design the adsorption system.

5.12.2.2 Integrating Alcohol Removal with Fermentation

The dehydration processes described in the previous section rely on a primary distillation step to increase the concentration of ethanol from around 5 mass% in the broth leaving the fermentor to over 90 mass%. The ethanol concentration in the broth is low because at higher ethanol concentrations the yeast responsible for producing the ethanol is poisoned by the ethanol. Even by using the most tolerant yeast strains it is only possible for concentrations in the broth to reach 14 mass% ethanol. There is evidence that by maintaining the ethanol concentration at a low level during fermentation, ethanol productivity increases [32]. Therefore, it would be logical to seek a method of continuously removing ethanol from the fermentation process while at the same time concentrating it to lessen the separation duty for the dehydration system. The technologies that have been investigated for this purpose are solvent extraction and membrane processes.

Membrane processes were discussed in the previous section on ethanol dehydration: the difference is that here they are used to selectively remove ethanol rather than water. Other options exist for the *in situ* removal of ethanol and these are discussed by Roffler *et al.* [33]. In general, the ethanol removal process can take one of two forms:

- *In situ* removal in which the ethanol removal process is placed within the fermentor. An ethanol-rich product stream is continuously removed from the fermentor.
- Side-stream removal in which broth is continuously removed from the fermentor and pumped through a separate ethanol removal process before being returned to the fermentor.

The advantages and disadvantages of both processes are given in **Table 1**.

5.12.2.2.1 Solvent extraction

The first reported use of extractive fermentation, as it was called by the authors, is by Minier and Goma [34]. In their system, ethanol was produced by fermenting glucose using *Saccharomyces cerevisiae*, which they claim was immobilized on porous bricks within a continuous fermentor. The flow through the fermentor was pulsed to generate good mixing and dodecanol was added as a solvent. The results show that the continuous removal of ethanol by dodecanol led to complete conversion of the glucose in the medium fed to the reactor and a 300% increase in the rate of ethanol production. Dodecanol flow rates were 14–36 times the culture flow rate and the improved performance should be set against the dilute ethanol–dodecanol stream produced by this process. The dodecanol also extracts glucose, salts in the culture medium, water, and biomass. Whether solvent extraction is used in a continuous fermentor as above or operating on a side stream from the fermentor, there is also the problem of continually having to sterilize the solvent ethanol recovery.

The use of a solvent that is highly selective for ethanol and biocompatible with the yeast being used would be desirable. This problem was studied by Kollerup and Daugulis [35], who after a paper and experimental study recommended 19 solvents that may be suitable for extractive fermentation of ethanol. In an attempt to overcome some of the problems associated with having a solvent

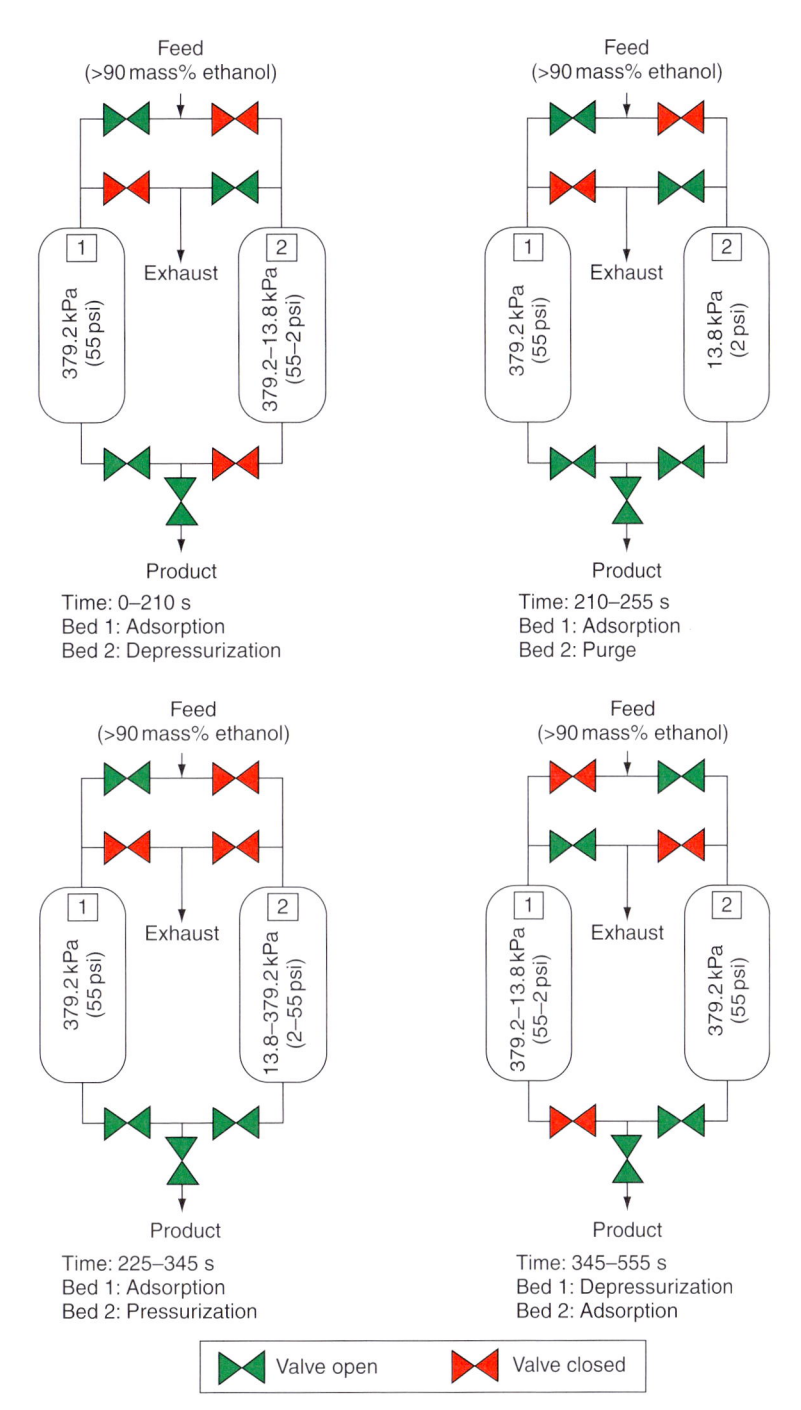

Figure 6 Pressure swing adsorption cycle for water from ethanol. Adapted from Simo M, Brown CJ, and Hlavacek V (2008) Simulation of pressure swing adsorption in fuel ethanol production process. *Computers and Chemical Engineering* 32: 1635–1649 [28].

Table 1 Advantages and disadvantages of *in situ* and side stream removal processes

Layout	Advantages	Disadvantages
In situ removal	No circulation loop required Simple to operate	The size of the removal system is limited by the size of the fermentor Hard to maintain
Side stream removal	No size limitation for the removal system Easy to maintain	Risk of oxygen limitation in the side stream and removal process Physical stress on the cells during circulation through the removal process Sterilization of the side stream and removal process may be a problem

in direct contact with the fermentation broth, a number of authors have suggested the use of supported liquid membranes. These systems use a porous membrane (polytetrafluoroethene (PTFE) or hollow fiber) to separate the broth from the solvent. While they could be thought of as membrane processes, they will be classified here as extraction processes, because the solvent and the broth are still in direct contact. Christen *et al.* [32] reported the use of isotridecanol as solvent, supported by a porous PTFE sheet. The authors report high conversion of glucose and a 250% increase in the rate of ethanol production. In addition, the combination of the membrane and solvent was claimed to be more selective for ethanol with a maximum separation factor of 4. The separation factor is the ratio of the concentration in the solvent to the concentration in the broth. Bandini and Gostoli [36] report the use of propylene glycol as a solvent supported with a flat PTFE membrane. Neither the solvent nor the fermentation broth wets the membrane, so a small air gap is maintained between the two liquids within the pores of the membrane. The air gap becomes saturated with volatile components from both liquids but because propylene glycol preferentially absorbs ethanol, it diffuses through the air gap. This arrangement prevents the transport of biomass and salts into the solvent phase. The data reported are for a water–ethanol system and this may well change for a broth containing ethanol. The maximum reported separation factor is 3.

An economic study of extractive fermentation [37] showed that for large-scale plants (100 million liters), the energy and water savings were significant compared to a conventional fermentation–distillation process. Despite this, there are no reports of extractive fermentation being applied to industrial bioethanol processes.

5.12.2.2.2 Membrane processes

Two membrane technologies have been proposed for integrated alcohol removal with membranes: membrane distillation and pervaporation. In both cases, the membrane material must be hydrophobic (water rejecting). The difference between the two processes is the size of the pores in the membrane. For membrane distillation, the membrane is considered to be porous (pore size 10^{-7} m) and liquid enters the pores. The process is one of evaporation from a large surface area within the membrane. For pervaporation, dense membranes are used (pore size 10^{-9} m or less). Individual molecules will enter/dissolve in the membrane and diffuse to the other side where they evaporate. The chemical composition and physical structure of the membrane affect the composition in the vapor.

The performance of a porous PTFE membrane in separating water–alcohol mixtures has been investigated by Hoffmann *et al.* [38]. There are two disadvantages of membrane distillation that preclude its use in fermentor systems. First, the permeate ethanol concentration is at most the same as that produced by distillation. Under atmospheric conditions, the permeate from a broth containing 2.5 mass% ethanol would contain around 21 mass% ethanol. Second, the broth would be open to the vapor side of the membrane, dramatically increasing the risk of contamination. For these reasons, there have been no reported applications of membrane distillation for ethanol removal.

When dense membranes are applied to ethanol removal from fermentation broths, pervaporation is used. Ethanol dehydration by pervaporation uses temperatures in the range 70–80 °C such that the ethanol is produced as a vapor at close to atmospheric pressure. These temperatures are too high for the microorganisms used to produce ethanol. Instead a selective permeation membrane is used with a vacuum on the ethanol side so that the ethanol vapor is produced at temperatures of around 30 °C. Shabtai *et al.* [39] report the use of a silicone rubber membrane for the continuous removal of ethanol. The mass fraction of ethanol in the culture was 3% and the permeate from the membrane was 12–20 mass% ethanol. Nomura *et al.* [40] reported the use of a silicalite zeolite membrane for the removal of ethanol from a continuous culture. The results were very promising with an ethanol concentration of 5 mass% in the culture resulting in a permeate containing 80 mass% ethanol. This performance was better than that achieved using only water and ethanol solutions. The enhancement was attributed to a high concentration of salts from the fermentation in the membrane resulting in a salt effect that enhanced the ethanol separation. In both cases, membrane performance decreases over time due to the formation of a gel layer.

References

[1] Mittelbach M and Remschmidt C (2004) *Biodiesel, the Comprehensive Handbook.* Martin Mittelbach.
[2] Freedman B, Butterfield RO, and Pryde EH (1986) Transesterification kinetics of soybean oil 1. *Journal of the American Oil Chemists' Society* 63(10): 1375–1380.
[3] Harvey AP, Mackley MR, and Seliger T (2003) Process intensification of biodiesel production using a continuous oscillatory flow reactor. *Journal of Chemical Technology and Biotechnology* 78: 338–341.
[4] Harvey AP and Stonestreet P (2002) A mixing-based design methodology for continuous oscillatory flow reactors. *Chemical Engineering Research and Design* 80: 31–44.
[5] Axens Esterfip-H. http://www.axens.net/html-gb/offer/offer_processes_104.html (accessed 1 February 2011).
[6] Lam MK, Lee MT, and Mohamed AR (2010) Homogeneous, heterogeneous and enzymatic catalysis for transesterification of high free fatty acid oil (waste cooking oil) to biodiesel: A review. *Biotechnology Advances* 28(4): 500–518.
[7] Sawangkeaw R, Bunyakiat K, and Ngamprasertsith S (2010) A review of laboratory-scale research on lipid conversion to biodiesel with supercritical methanol (2001–2009). *The Journal of Supercritical Fluids* 55(1): 1–13.
[8] Patil PD, Gude VG, Mannarswamy A, *et al.* (2011) Optimization of direct conversion of wet algae to biodiesel under supercritical methanol conditions. *Bioresource Technology* 102(1): 118–122.
[9] Levine RB, Pinnarat T, and Savage PE (2010) Biodiesel production from wet algal biomass through *in situ* lipid hydrolysis and supercritical transesterification. *Energy and Fuels* 24: 5235–5243.
[10] Lim S, Hoong SS, Teong LK, and Bhatia S (2010) Supercritical fluid reactive extraction of *Jatropha curcas* L. seeds with methanol: A novel biodiesel production method. *Bioresource Technology* 101(18): 7180–7183.
[11] Harvey AP, Kasim FB, and Zakaria R (2010) Biodiesel production by *in situ* transesterification – A review. *Biofuels* 1(2): 355–365.
[12] Westfalia http://www.westfalia-separator.com/applications/renewable-resources/biodiesel.html (accessed 1 February 2010).

[13] Saleh J, Tremblay AY, and Dube MA (2010) Glycerol removal from biodiesel using membrane separation technology. *Fuel* 89(9): 2260–2266.
[14] Wang Y, Wang XG, Liu YF, *et al.* (2009) Refining of biodiesel by ceramic membrane separation. *Fuel Processing Technology* 90(3): 422–427.
[15] Okamoto K, Tanihara N, Watanabe H, *et al.* (1992) Vapor permeation and pervaporation separation of water ethanol mixtures through polyimide membranes. *Journal of Membrane Science* 68(1–2): 53–63.
[16] Suematsu H, Kimura S, and Nitta T (1998) Cost estimation of pervaporation and vapor permeation membrane separation systems for ethanol–water mixtures. *Kagaku Kogaku Ronbunshu* 24(6): 881–887.
[17] Wang YH, Teng MY, and Lee KR (1998) Application of pervaporation and vapor permeation processes to separate aqueous ethanol solution through chemically modified nylon 4 membranes. *Separation Science and Technology* 33(11): 1653–1665.
[18] Lipnizki F, Field RW, and Ten P (1999) Pervaporation-based hybrid process: A review of process design, applications and economics. *Journal of Membrane Science* 153: 183–210.
[19] Sato K, Sugimoto K, and Nakane T (2008) Mass-production of tubular NaY zeolite membranes for industrial purpose and their application to ethanol dehydration by vapor permeation. *Journal of Membrane Science* 319(1–2): 244–255.
[20] Hong J, Voloch M, Ladisch MR, and Tsao GT (1982) Adsorption of ethanol–water mixtures by biomass materials. *Biotechnology and Bioengineering* 24: 725–730.
[21] Ladisch MR and Dyck K (1979) Dehydration of ethanol: New approach gives positive energy balance. *Science* 205: 898–900.
[22] Vareli G, Demertzis PG, and Akrida-Demertzi K (2000) Effect of regeneration thermal treatment of cellulosic and starchy materials on their capacity to separate water and ethanol. *Journal of Cereal Science* 31: 147–154.
[23] Beery KE and Ladisch MR (2001) Chemistry and properties of starch based desiccants. *Enzyme and Microbial Technology* 28: 573–581.
[24] Chang H, Yuan X, Tian H, and Zeng A (2006) Experiment and prediction of breakthrough curves for packed bed adsorption of water vapor on cornmeal. *Chemical Engineering and Processing* 45: 747–754.
[25] Hartline FF (1979) Lowering the cost of alcohol. *Science* 206: 41–42.
[26] Bein T (1996) Synthesis and applications of molecular sieve layers and membranes. *Chemistry of Materials* 8: 1636–1653.
[27] Teo WK and Ruthven DM (1986) Adsorption of water from aqueous ethanol using 3-Å molecular sieves. *Industrial & Engineering Chemistry Process Design and Development* 25: 17–21.
[28] Simo M, Brown CJ, and Hlavacek V (2008) Simulation of pressure swing adsorption in fuel ethanol production process. *Computers and Chemical Engineering* 32: 1635–1649.
[29] Kupiec K, Rakoczy J, Zielinski L, and Georgio A (2008) Adsorption–desorption cycles for the separation of vapour-phase ethanol/water mixtures. *Adsorption Science and Technology* 26: 209–224.
[30] Llano-Restrepo M and Mosquera MA (2009) Accurate correlation, thermochemistry, and structural interpretation of equilibrium adsorption isotherms of water vapor in zeolite 3A by means of a generalized statistical thermodynamic adsorption model. *Fluid Phase Equilibria* 283: 73–88.
[31] Kupiec K, Rakoczy J, and Lalik E (2009) Modeling of PSA separation process including friction pressure drop in adsorbent bed. *Chemical Engineering and Processing* 48: 1199–1211.
[32] Christen P, Minier M, and Renon H (1990) Ethanol extraction by supported liquid membrane during fermentation. *Biotechnology and Bioengineering* 36(2): 116–123.
[33] Roffler SR, Blanch HW, and Wilke CR (1984) *In situ* recovery of fermentation products. *Trends in Biotechnology* 2(5): 129–136.
[34] Minier M and Goma G (1981) Production of ethanol by coupling fermentation and solvent extraction. *Biotechnology Letters* 3(8): 405–408.
[35] Kollerup F and Daugulis AJ (1986) Ethanol production by extractive fermentation – solvent identification and prototype development. *Canadian Journal of Chemical Engineering* 64(4): 598–606.
[36] Bandini S and Gostoli C (1992) Ethanol removal from fermentation broth by gas membrane extraction. *Journal of Membrane Science* 70: 119–127.
[37] Daugulis AJ, Axford DB, and McLellan PJ (1991) The economics of ethanol production by extractive fermentation. *Canadian Journal of Chemical Engineering* 69(2): 488–497.
[38] Hoffmann E, Pfenning DM, Philippsen E, *et al.* (1987) Evaporation of alcohol/water mixtures through hydrophobic porous membranes. *Journal of Membrane Science* 34: 199–206.
[39] Shabtai Y, Chaimovitz S, Freeman A, *et al.* (1991) Continuous ethanol production by immobilized yeast reactor coupled with membrane pervaporation unit. *Biotechnology and Bioengineering* 38(8): 869–876.
[40] Nomura M, Bin T, and Nakao S (2002) Selective ethanol extraction from fermentation broth using a silicalite membrane. *Separation and Purification Technology* 27: 59–66.

5.13 Biofuels from Waste Materials

AA Refaat, Cairo University, Giza, Egypt

© 2012 Elsevier Ltd. All rights reserved.

5.13.1	Introduction	218
5.13.2	Biodiesel Production from WVO	218
5.13.2.1	The Significance of Producing Biodiesel from WVO	218
5.13.2.1.1	Economic	218
5.13.2.1.2	Waste management	218
5.13.2.1.3	Environmental	218
5.13.2.1.4	Social and ethical concerns	219
5.13.2.2	Challenges Facing Biodiesel Production from WVO	219
5.13.2.2.1	Oil collection	219
5.13.2.2.2	Identifying the effect of frying on the characteristics of WVO	219
5.13.2.2.3	Optimization of different techniques for producing biodiesel from WVO	219
5.13.2.3	Quality of WVO-Based Biodiesel	225
5.13.2.3.1	Standard parameters	225
5.13.2.3.2	Engine performance	226
5.13.2.3.3	Emission characteristics	227
5.13.3	**Summary: Biodiesel from Waste**	228
5.13.4	**Bioethanol Production from LCWs**	228
5.13.4.1	Significance of Producing Bioethanol from LCWs	228
5.13.4.2	Sources of LC Biomass	231
5.13.4.3	LC Biomass Recalcitrance	231
5.13.4.4	Factors Limiting LC Biomass Digestibility	232
5.13.4.4.1	Cellulose crystallinity (crystallinity index, CrI)	232
5.13.4.4.2	Cellulose DP (number of glycosyl residues per cellulose chain)	232
5.13.4.4.3	Accessible surface area (pore volume)	232
5.13.4.4.4	Hemicellulose sheathing	232
5.13.4.4.5	Degree of hemicellulose acetylation	232
5.13.4.4.6	Lignin barrier (content and distribution)	232
5.13.4.5	Production of Ethanol from LCWs	233
5.13.4.6	Challenges to Bioethanol Production from Lignocellulose	234
5.13.4.7	Pretreatment Processes	234
5.13.4.7.1	Overview	234
5.13.4.7.2	Different technologies for LC biomass pretreatment	235
5.13.4.7.3	Chemical pretreatment processes	235
5.13.4.7.4	Physical pretreatment processes	240
5.13.4.7.5	Physicochemical pretreatment processes	242
5.13.4.7.6	Biological pretreatment	246
5.13.4.7.7	Comparing different pretreatment methods	248
5.13.4.8	Saccharification and Fermentation	248
5.13.4.8.1	Inhibitors	248
5.13.4.8.2	Cost of enzymes	248
5.13.4.8.3	Enzyme mixture	248
5.13.4.8.4	Enzyme–substrate interaction	249
5.13.4.8.5	Fermentation	249
5.13.4.9	Consolidated Bioprocessing	250
5.13.5	**Summary: Bioethanol from Waste**	250
References		250

Glossary

Biodiesel Fatty acid alkyl esters (methyl/ethyl esters) of short-chain alcohols and long-chain fatty acids derived from natural biological lipid sources like vegetable oils or animal fats, which have had their viscosity reduced using a process called transesterification, and can be used in conventional diesel engines and distributed through existing fuel infrastructure.

Biomass Organic matter which can be used as a renewable energy source in a number of different ways. It includes agricultural crops, crop waste residues, wood, animal waste, animal fat, municipal waste, aquatic plants, fungal growth, etc.

First generation biofuels Conventional biofuels are biofuels made from sugar, starch, and vegetable oil, for example, bioethanol and biodiesel.

Lignocellulose pretreatment The necessary step which should be taken to alter some structural characteristics of lignocellulose, increasing glucan and xylan accessibility to the enzymatic attack.

Second generation biofuels Biofuels produced from cellulose, hemicellulose or lignin, for example, cellulosic ethanol and Fischer–Tropsch fuels.

Transesterification General term used to describe the important class of organic reactions where an ester is transformed into another through interchange of the alkoxy moiety. This reversible reaction is responsible for converting oil to biodiesel.

Waste vegetable oil Vegetable oil which has been used in food production and which is no longer viable for its intended use.

5.13.1 Introduction

Biofuels are normally made from virgin feedstock; however, they can also be made from waste materials without compromising their quality. The production of biofuels from waste materials is motivated by a serious social issue: the 'food versus fuel' debate, as well as the relatively high cost of biofuels, which imposes a major hurdle toward their widespread commercialization. On the other hand, converting waste materials into energy is environmentally beneficial, inasmuch as it provides a cleaner way of disposing of these products and converts waste into a usable commodity.

This chapter is meant to be a perspective of the author rather than an exhaustive review of the topic. It is concerned mainly with the feedstocks that are more commonly abundant and the biofuels that are more widely applicable. Accordingly, the chapter involves two main topics:

- Biodiesel production from waste vegetable oil (WVO)
- Bioethanol production from lignocellulosic wastes (LCWs).

5.13.2 Biodiesel Production from WVO

The overarching goal of this chapter is to demonstrate that waste materials can replace virgin feedstock for the production of biofuels without sacrificing the quality. To verify this statement regarding the production of biodiesel from WVO, the following questions are to be answered: first, what is the significance of producing biodiesel from WVO. Second, what are the challenges facing the production of biodiesel from WVO, and how to overcome such challenges. Finally, whether the produced biodiesel will be comparable in quality to that produced from virgin feedstock or not. This section is an attempt to give an answer to all these inquiries.

5.13.2.1 The Significance of Producing Biodiesel from WVO

5.13.2.1.1 Economic
From an economic point of view, the production of biodiesel has proven to be very feedstock-sensitive. Many studies have shown that feedstock cost represents a very substantial portion of the overall biodiesel cost [1–4]. Estimated cost of the oil feedstock accounted for 80% [5] or even 88% [6] of the total estimated production costs. So, the production of biodiesel from waste oils will have an added attractive advantage of being lower in price.

5.13.2.1.2 Waste management
WVO is a potentially problematic waste stream, which requires to be properly managed. The disposal of WVO can be problematic when disposed, incorrectly, down the kitchen sinks, where it can quickly cause blockages of sewer pipes when the oil solidifies. Properties of degraded used frying oil after it gets into a sewage system are conducive to corrosion of metal and concrete elements. It also affects installations in waste water treatment plants. Thus, it adds to the cost of treating effluent or pollutes waterways [7]. From a waste management standpoint, producing biodiesel from used frying oil provides a cleaner way for disposing of these products.

5.13.2.1.3 Environmental
Producing biodiesel from used frying oil is environmentally beneficial, since it can yield valuable cuts in CO_2 as well as significant tailpipe pollution gains. Relative to the fossil fuels they displace, greenhouse gas (GHG) emissions are reduced by 41% by the production and combustion of biodiesel [8]. Moreover, biodiesel from used frying oil leads to a far better life cycle analysis. It has to be realized that the effect of CO_2 saving is significantly higher when using used frying oil as feedstock, because here the effects of the agricultural production of vegetable oils are not taken into consideration for a second time. In many researches, WVO biodiesel showed a net energy ratio (NER) of 5–6 compared to 2–3 for rapeseed or soybean biodiesel and 0.8 for petrodiesel [9]. The NER

refers to the ratio of the amount of usable energy acquired from a particular energy resource to the amount of energy expended to obtain that energy resource.

5.13.2.1.4 Social and ethical concerns

Any fatty acid source may be used to prepare biodiesel. Thus, any animal or plant lipid should be a ready substrate for the production of biodiesel. The use of edible vegetable oils and animal fats for biodiesel production has recently been of great concern because they compete with food materials – the food versus fuel dispute [10, 11]. There are concerns that biodiesel feedstock may compete with food supply in the long term [12]. The idea of converting food to fuel while millions of people in the world are suffering from malnutrition prompted stern criticisms from nongovernmental organizations (NGOs) [13]. The use of nonedible vegetable oils for biodiesel production is also questionable. Growing crops for fuel squanders land, water, and energy resources vital for the production of food for human consumption [10]. The author therefore concludes that the use of waste oil for the production of biodiesel is the most realistic and effective.

5.13.2.2 Challenges Facing Biodiesel Production from WVO

5.13.2.2.1 Oil collection

The term 'waste vegetable oil' refers to vegetable oil, which has been used in food production and which is no longer viable for its intended use. WVO arises from many different sources, including domestic, commercial, and industrial. A limiting factor is the limited availability of used cooking oil on the market. Oil collection from household, commercial, or industrial sources can be achieved through grease traps [14] or through a holistic policy framework [15]. Formulating a holistic policy framework for vegetable oil waste management tailored for each country or region will serve to clarify the conceptual and procedural constructs within which information can be assimilated and processed to establish a unified scheme complemented by an action plan for implementation of the planned mechanism.

Logistics can be a key factor for determining the feasibility of biodiesel production from waste frying oils (WFOs) because the places that offer this resource are geographically widespread, requiring a planned collection. Nonoptimized collections may lead to inevitable expenses in labor, fuel, and maintenance of vehicles. To determine the logistics cost, a mathematical programming model was proposed by Araujo et al. [16] for the economic assessment of biodiesel production from WFOs. The calculation of the total biodiesel cost incorporated, in addition to the logistics costs, the costs of production, acquisition of inputs, and federal taxes. The results obtained demonstrated the economic viability of biodiesel production from WFO in the urban center studied and the relevance of logistics in the total biodiesel production cost.

5.13.2.2.2 Identifying the effect of frying on the characteristics of WVO

Used frying oils from restaurants and food industries have a wide variety of qualities. During the frying process, the oil is exposed to high temperatures in the presence of air and moisture. Under these conditions, it may undergo important changes due to hydrolytic, oxidative, and thermal reactions. Changes in the main fat constituents are known, although it is not easy to foresee the rate of oil degradation due to the high number of variables involved in the frying process. Some of them are linked to the process itself, such as temperature, duration of heating, heating pattern (continuous or intermittent), turnover rate, and so on, and others to the food subjected to frying, that is, lipid composition, main and minor constituents, and so on, or else to the oil used, for example, degree of unsaturation, initial quality, and additives [17]. Thus, used frying oils can be highly heterogeneous as compared to crude or refined oils.

Some key parameters were selected for determining the viability of the vegetable oil transesterification process. These parameters include acid value and free fatty acid (FFA) content, moisture content, viscosity, and fatty acid profile of the used oil. The usual trend for the oils after frying was found to be an increase in the acid value, an increase in viscosity, and an altered fatty acid profile [18]. The fatty acid profile of the oil is an important determinant for the properties of the biodiesel produced. It was shown that the properties of the various fatty esters are determined by the structural features of the fatty acid and the alcohol moieties that comprise a fatty ester [19]. So, a good knowledge of the aforementioned parameters is essential to identify the right processes that can be performed to achieve best results regarding the yield and purity of the produced biodiesel.

5.13.2.2.3 Optimization of different techniques for producing biodiesel from WVO

Transesterification is the general term used to describe the important class of organic reactions where an ester is transformed into another form through the interchange of the alkoxy moiety [20]. Different techniques can be used in the production of biodiesel from recycled oils; the advantages and limitations of each technique are summarized in **Table 1**.

The details and optimization conditions for these different techniques were described in previous chapters of this volume. In this chapter, we only stress the conditions specifically suiting the use of WVO as a feedstock.

5.13.2.2.3(i) Base-catalyzed transesterification

Base-catalyzed transesterification is the most commonly used technique as it is the most economical process and it requires only low temperatures and pressures; produces over 98% conversion yield (provided the starting oil is low in moisture and FFA) and involves direct conversion to biodiesel with no intermediate compounds; also, no special materials of construction are needed [21].

Table 1 Advantages and limitations of different transesterification techniques for the production of biodiesel from WVO

Process	Advantages	Limitations
Base catalysis	Moderate operation conditions High biodiesel yield No intermediate compounds No special materials of construction	Sensitive to FFA and moisture content of the feedstock oils Energy intensive Difficult recovery of glycerol Catalyst has to be removed from the product Alkaline waste water requires treatment
Acid catalysis	Insensitive to FFA content Catalyze esterification and transesterification simultaneously	Slower reaction rate Higher alcohol to oil ratio is required Acidic effluent and corrosion-related problems No reusable catalyst High cost of equipment
Two-step	Advantages of both base and acid catalysis	Catalyst removal in both stages
Heterogeneous catalysis	Catalyze esterification and transesterification simultaneously Easy separation and reusability of catalyst Very high yields of methyl esters Glycerol with high purity Tolerant to water and FFAs in the feedstock No soap formation	More severe operating conditions Catalyst leaching
Enzymatic catalysis	Efficient Highly selective Less energy consumption Environmentally favorable	Higher production cost Difficulty during manufacturing
Supercritical methanol	High conversion and reaction rates Tolerant to water and FFAs in the feedstock Easy glycerol recovery	Severe operation conditions High alcohol amount and large reactor size Higher energy consumption Higher capital and operation costs
Ultrasonication and microwave-enhanced	Dramatic decrease in reaction rate Better separation Tolerant to water and FFAs in the feedstock	Need to be further investigated for possible scale-up for industrial application

Base-catalyzed transesterification, however, has some limitations, among which are that it is sensitive to FFA content of the feedstock oils. A high FFA content (>1% w/w) will lead to soap formation, which reduces catalyst efficiency, causes an increase in viscosity, leads to gel formation, and makes the separation of glycerol difficult. Also, the oils used in transesterification should be substantially anhydrous (0.06% w/w). The presence of water gives rise to hydrolysis of some of the produced ester, with consequent soap formation [22]. Other drawbacks of the base-catalyzed transesterification are that the process is energy-intensive, recovery of glycerol is difficult, alkaline catalyst has to be removed from the product, and alkaline waste water requires treatment [23].

Before performing the base-catalyzed transesterification for WVO, the negative effects of the undesirable compounds formed during the frying process should be avoided by different types of pretreatment. These processes include filtration for removing suspended solids, maintaining the oil relatively dry, and reducing its high FFA content.

To ensure an anhydrous medium, the filtered oil can be subjected to drying by heating it to 100 °C for at least 15 min with continuous stirring [24]. At industrial scale, moisture removal is usually done by vacuum distillation (0.05 bar) in a temperature range of 30–40 °C [25].

If the FFA content exceeds 1% and if an alkaline catalyst must be used, then a greater amount of catalyst should be added to neutralize the FFA [3]. However, the correct amount of catalyst should be used because both excess as well as insufficient amount of catalyst may cause soap formation. To determine the correct amount of catalyst required, a titration must be performed on the oil being transesterified.

Other pretreatment processes include suitable absorption–adsorption technique, performing film vacuum evaporation [26] or vacuum filtration [27, 28], or applying steam injection [29] or column chromatography technique [30].

The main parameters affecting the base-catalyzed transesterification process are alcohol formulation, alcohol–oil molar ratio, catalyst formulation and concentration, reaction temperature, reaction time, and agitation. The optimum operation conditions for base-catalyzed transesterification of WVO in selected studies are listed in **Table 2**.

The following concluding remarks are important for optimizing the process:

- Methanol is the alcohol more frequently used because methyl esters are the predominant commercial products, methanol is considerably cheaper and more available than ethanol [38], and the downstream recovery of unreacted alcohol is much easier [39].

Table 2 Optimum operation conditions for base-catalyzed transesterification of WVO

Process variables

Alcohol formulation	Alcohol:oil molar ratio	Catalyst formulation	Catalyst concentration (%)	Reaction temperature (°C)	Reaction time (min)	Yield (%)	Reference
Methanol	6:1	KOH	1	65	60	95.8	[31]
Methanol	9:1	NaOH	1	50	90	89.8	[32]
Methanol	6.5:1	KOH	1	48	65	83.3	[33]
Methanol	6:1	KOH	1	65	60	84.3	[34]
Methanol	6:1	KOH	1	65	120	94.0	[35]
Methanol	4.8:1	NaOH	0.6	65	60	92.7	[25]
Ethanol	12:1	KOH	1	78	120	74.2	[36]
Methanol	7.5:1	NaOH	1.1	70	30	85.3	[22]
Methanol	6:1	KOH	1	25	30	94.0	[37]

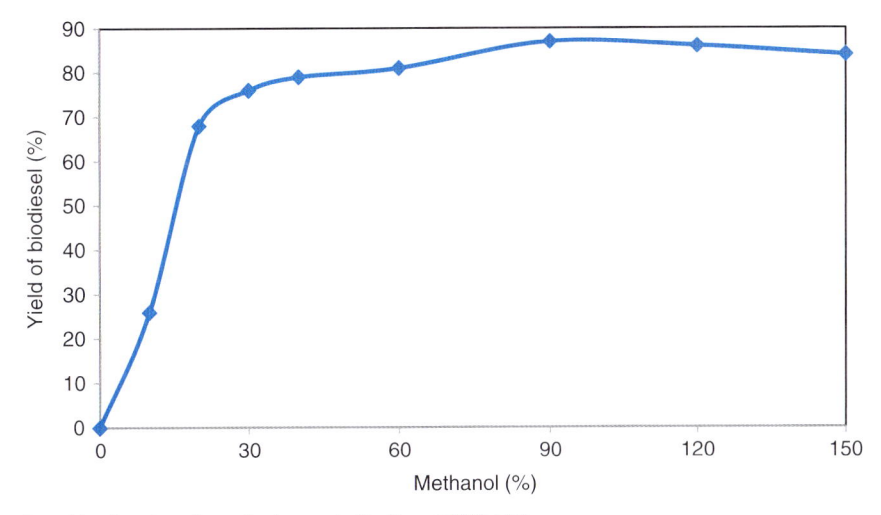

Figure 1 Effect of methanol to oil molar ratio on the transesterification of WVO [40].

- For maximum conversion to the ester, a molar ratio of 6:1 is the most acceptable. With further increase in molar ratio, the conversion efficiency more or less remains the same but the energy required for the recovery of methanol becomes higher [40] (**Figure 1**).
- Among the most commonly used alkaline catalysts in the biodiesel industry are potassium hydroxide (KOH) and sodium hydroxide (NaOH) flakes, which are inexpensive and easy to handle in transportation and storage. They are preferred by small producers. Alkyl oxide solutions of sodium methoxide or potassium methoxide in methanol, which are now commercially available, are the preferred catalysts for large continuous-flow production processes [21].
- Catalyst concentration is closely related to the free acidity of the oil. When there is a large FFA content, the addition of more potassium hydroxide, or any other alkaline catalyst, compensates this acidity and avoids catalyst deactivation [20]. The addition of an excessive amount of catalyst, however, gives rise to the formation of an emulsion, which increases the viscosity and leads to the formation of gels. These hinder the glycerol separation and, hence, reduce the apparent ester yield. The result of these two opposing effects is an optimal catalyst concentration that is about 1.0%. Further increases in catalyst concentration will not increase the conversion and will lead to extra costs because it will be necessary to remove it from the reaction medium at the end [35].
- The usual temperature used during transesterification is 60–65 °C. When the reaction temperature reaches or exceeds the boiling point of methanol (68 °C), the methanol will vaporize and form a large number of bubbles, which may inhibit the reaction [32].
- Most investigators have observed an optimum reaction time around 1 h; however, excess residence time can negatively influence the biodiesel production by favoring the backward reaction (hydrolysis of esters), which results in a reduction of product yield.
- Since the transesterification reaction can only occur in the interfacial region between the liquids and also due to the fact that fats and alcohols are not totally miscible, transesterification is a relatively slow process. As a result, vigorous mixing is required to increase the area of contact between the two immiscible phases [41].
- Under optimum reaction conditions, the percentage yield is not much affected by the quality of the oil used.

5.13.2.2.3(ii) Acid-catalyzed transesterification

As previously stated, one limitation of base-catalyzed transesterification is its sensitivity to the purity of the reactants, especially to moisture and FFA content. Freedman *et al.* [20] have pointed out that acid catalysts are insensitive to FFA and are better than the alkaline catalysts for vegetable oils with FFA >1%. In fact, acid catalysts can simultaneously catalyze both esterification and transesterification. Thus, a great advantage with acid catalysts is that they can directly produce biodiesel from low-cost lipid feedstock generally associated with high FFA concentrations, including WFOs [42]. Although the base-catalyzed process using virgin vegetable oil had the lowest fixed capital cost, the acid-catalyzed process using waste cooking oil was more economically feasible overall, providing a lower total manufacturing cost, a more attractive after-tax rate of return, and a lower biodiesel break-even price [2].

Despite its insensitivity to FFAs in the feedstock, acid-catalyzed transesterification has been largely ignored mainly because of its relatively slower reaction rate [43]. For acid-catalyzed conversion of WVO with high FFA content, higher alcohol to oil ratio is required compared to base-catalyzed operation for better yield of biodiesel. Other disadvantages with this process are acidic effluent, no reusable catalyst, and high cost of equipment [44].

The optimum process parameters for the acid-catalyzed transesterification of WFOs were found to be oil:methanol:acid molar ratios of 1:245:3.8, at 70 °C for 4 h, giving a yield of $99 \pm 1\%$ [45].

5.13.2.2.3(iii) Two-step transesterification

Both the base-catalyzed and the acid-catalyzed transesterification processes have their advantages and disadvantages as previously mentioned. Hence, to avoid the problems associated with the use of these catalysts separately, especially the problems of saponification in base-catalyzed and slow reaction time in acid-catalyzed transesterification, many researchers have adopted the two-stage transesterification. In the first stage, esterification of FFA present in WFO is performed using acid to decrease the FFAs to a level <1%. In the second stage, transesterification of the obtained oil is performed using an alkaline catalyst. Despite its advantages, the two-stage method also faces the problem of catalyst removal in both stages. The problem of catalyst removal in the first stage can be avoided by neutralizing the acid catalyst, using extra alkaline catalyst in the second stage. However, the use of extra catalyst will increase the cost of biodiesel.

A comparison was held between the traditional acid-catalyzed transesterification using sulfuric acid as a catalyst and a two-step method using a ferric sulfate (2.0%)-catalyzed reaction followed by alkali (1.0% potassium hydroxide) transesterification [44]. The feedstock was waste cooking oil with the acid value of 75.92 ± 0.04 mg KOH g^{-1}. In both cases, methanol was used and a reaction temperature of 95 °C was applied. The fatty acid methyl ester (FAME) yield in the two-step method was 97.22% at the reaction time of 4 h, mole ratio of methanol to triglyceride (TG) of 10:1, compared to 90%, 10 h, and 20:1, respectively, in the acid method. The authors argued that the two-step process showed the advantages of no acidic wastewater, high efficiency, low equipment cost, and easy recovery of catalyst compared with the limitations of acidic effluent, no reusable catalyst, and high cost of equipment in the traditional acid process.

Issariyakul *et al.* [28] studied the transesterification of waste fryer grease containing 5–6% (wt%) FFA and showed that >90% ester was obtained when two-stage (acid and alkali catalyzed) method was used compared to ~50% ester in single-stage alkaline catalyst. Similar results were obtained by Encinar *et al.* [36] who showed that the two-stage transesterification of WFO was better than the one-stage process, and the yields of the esters were improved by 30% in relation with the one-stage transesterification.

5.13.2.2.3(iv) Transesterification using heterogeneous catalysts

Heterogeneous (solid) catalysts have the general advantage of easy separation from the reaction medium and reusability. Heterogeneous catalysis is thus considered to be a green process. The process requires neither catalyst recovery nor aqueous treatment steps. The purification steps of products are then much more simplified with very high yields of methyl esters, close to the theoretical value, are obtained [46]. Glycerin is directly produced with high purity levels (at least 98%) and is exempt from any salt contaminants [47, 48]. However, heterogeneously catalyzed transesterification generally requires more severe operating conditions (relatively elevated temperatures and pressures), and the performance of heterogeneous catalysts is generally lower than that of the commonly used homogeneous catalysts [49]. Moreover, one of the main problems with heterogeneous catalysts is their deactivation with time owing to many possible phenomena, such as poisoning, coking, sintering, and leaching [50]. The problem of poisoning is particularly evident when the process involves used oils [51]. More general and dramatic is catalyst leaching, which not only can increase the operational cost as a result of replacing the catalyst but also leads to product contamination.

In general, the best catalysts must have several qualities, that is, catalyzing transesterification and esterification, not being deactivated by water, and being stable, but not give rise to leaching while being active at low temperature with high selectivity [52]. Thus far, the use of solid catalysts to produce biodiesel requires a better understanding of the factors that govern their reactivity. To improve the performance of these catalysts, it is essential to understand the correlations between acid and base strength and catalytic activity. It is clear that the surface of these heterogeneous materials should display some hydrophobic character to promote the preferential adsorption of TGs and to avoid deactivation of catalytic sites by strong adsorption of polar byproducts such as glycerol and water [42].

Heterogeneous catalysis for biodiesel production has been extensively investigated in the past few years. A great variety of materials have been tested as heterogeneous catalysts for the transesterification of vegetable oils; a broad classification of these materials is to categorize them as base or acid heterogeneous catalysts. Compared with solid base catalysts, solid acid catalysts have lower catalytic activity but higher stability, thus, they can be used for feedstock with large amounts of FFAs, such as WVO, without catalyst deactivation [42].

Examples of acid catalysts used successfully for the transesterification of WVO are acid zeolites [53], heteropolyacids (HPAs) [46], and immobilized sulfonic acids [54]. Sulfated zirconia and mixed metal oxides have been studied to catalyze the transesterification of vegetable oils owing to their superacidity. These catalysts have shown good catalytic activities [55–57] and good stability when they are used to catalyze esterification and transesterification simultaneously. However, they have not been generally used in industrial production processes, mainly because of the high catalyst cost and difficulty in filtering the small catalyst particles.

Synthesis of biodiesel from WVO with large amounts of FFAs using a carbon-based solid acid catalyst was reported [58, 59]. Georgogianni *et al.* [60] also reported that the use of ultrasonication significantly accelerated the transesterification reaction compared to the use of mechanical stirring for biodiesel production from soybean frying oil using heterogeneous catalysts.

5.13.2.2.3(v) Enzymatic transesterification
There is a current interest in using enzymatic catalysis to commercially convert vegetable oils and fats to FAME as biodiesel fuel, since it is more efficient, highly selective, involves less energy consumption (reactions can be carried out in mild conditions), and produces less side products or waste (environmentally favorable) [61]. However, the drawbacks of enzymatic catalysts include significantly higher production cost [23] and difficulty during manufacturing due to the need for a careful control of reaction parameters [62].

The enzymatic conversion is based on the use of biocatalysts as lipases that, on one hand, catalyze the hydrolysis of fats and vegetable oils with release of glycerol and, on the other hand, in the presence of short chain alcohols, favor the formation of linear chain esters. Enzymes have several advantages over chemical catalysts such as mild reaction conditions, specificity, and reuse; and enzymes or whole cells can be immobilized, can be genetically engineered to improve their efficiency, accept new substrates, are more thermostable, and are considered natural, and the reactions they catalyze are considered 'green' reactions [61]. The reuse of lipases and the recovery of their stability, both thermal and mechanical, are the most significant issues for making the enzymatic process, whose costs are still too high, more competitive for biodiesel production. A major problem with lipase reaction with methanol is enzyme inactivation by methanol. The stepwise addition of methanol can prevent the inactivation of the lipase and allow its continued usability [63]. Immobilized lipases enable this goal to be achieved [64]. However, they can be maximally exploited only if operating conditions are optimized; a task which requires knowledge of reaction kinetics and, in general, predictions of process performance [65].

Engineering of enzymatic biodiesel synthesis processes requires optimization of such factors as molar ratio of substrates (alcohol:triacylglycerols), temperature, type of organic solvent (if any), and water activity. All of them are correlated with properties of lipase preparation [66]. In addition, knowledge about water content, FFA level, percent conversion, acyl migration, and substrate flow rate in packed bed bioreactors is required to improve the yield of biodiesel [61]. For the use of enzymes, there are some critical factors: there is a minimum water content needed by the lipase, below which it does not work; alcohol has an effect on the reaction, with methanol being the most commonly employed; the effect of temperature is significant because instead of increasing the reaction rate by increasing temperature, enzymes can become denatured at high temperatures; and obviously the raw material is important, because not all oils have the same amount or type of fatty acids, and lipase specificity can become more attractive in some oils than in others [62].

Chen *et al.* [67] have investigated the enzymatic conversion of waste cooking oils into biodiesel. Enzymatic conversion using immobilized lipase based on *Rhizopus oryzae* was considered and the technological process was studied focusing on optimization of several process parameters, including the molar ratio of methanol to waste oils, biocatalyst load, and adding method, reaction temperature, and water content. The results indicated that methanol/oils ratio of 4:1, immobilized lipase/oils of 30 wt%, and 40 °C are suitable for waste oils under 1 atm pressure. The irreversible inactivation of the lipase is presumed, and a stepwise addition of methanol to reduce inactivation of immobilized lipases was proposed. Under the optimum conditions, the yield of methyl esters was around 88–90%.

A more recent study by Maceiras *et al.* [68] was also conducted to investigate the enzymatic conversion of waste cooking oils into biodiesel using immobilized lipase Novozym 435 as catalyst. The effects of methanol to oil molar ratio, dosage of enzyme, and reaction time were investigated. The optimum reaction conditions for fresh enzyme were methanol to oil molar ratio of 25:1, 10% of Novozym 435 based on oil weight, and reaction period of 4 h at 50 °C obtaining a biodiesel yield of 89.1%. Similar results were obtained by Azócar *et al.* [69] by using immobilized lipase Novozym 435 as catalyst for biodiesel production using WFOs as feedstock.

Yagiz *et al.* [70] showed that immobilized lipase on hydrotalcite was found to be able to catalyze the transesterification of waste cooking oil with methanol to produce methyl esters, whereas lipase immobilized on zeolites did not show significant yields at the same reaction conditions.

Li *et al.* [71] presented an inexpensive self-made immobilized lipase from *Penicillium expansum*, which was shown to be an efficient biocatalyst for biodiesel production from waste oil with high acid value in organic solvent. It was revealed that water from the esterification of FFAs and methanol prohibited a high methyl ester yield. The authors showed that adsorbents could effectively control the concentration of water in the reaction system, resulting in an improved methyl ester yield. Silica gel was proved to be the optimal adsorbent, affording a methyl ester yield of 92.8% after 7 h. Moreover, the enzyme preparation displayed a higher stability in waste oil than in corn oil, with 68.4% of the original enzymatic activity retained after being reused for 10 batches.

Abdul Halim *et al.* [72] employed a response surface methodology based on central composite rotatable design for optimization and analysis of transesterification of waste cooking palm oil.

Dizge *et al.* [73] confirmed the successful production of biodiesel from sunflower, soybean, and waste cooking oils by transesterification using lipase immobilized onto a novel microporous polymer. However, biodiesel yield from waste cooking oil was lower (90.2%) compared to biodiesel yields obtained from sunflower oil (97%) and soybean oil (93.9%). This was attributed to the presence of contaminants formed in waste cooking oil affecting the enzyme.

5.13.2.2.3(vi) Noncatalytic transesterification

The noncatalyst options were designed to overcome the reaction initiation lag time caused by poor methanol and oil miscibility. An improved process was investigated for methanolysis of vegetable oil. The process comprises solubilizing oil in methanol by addition of a cosolvent in order to form a one-phase reaction mixture. Tetrahydrofuran (THF) is chosen as a cosolvent because its boiling point is close to that of methanol, so that at the end of the reaction the unreacted methanol and THF can be co-distilled and recycled. At the 6:1 methanol–oil molar ratio, the addition of 1.25 volume of THF per volume of methanol produces an oil-dominant one-phase system in which methanolysis speeds up dramatically to 5–10 min, at ambient temperatures, atmospheric pressure, and without agitation. There are no catalyst residues in either the ester or the glycerol phase [23]. The cosolvent increases the rate of reaction by making the oil soluble in methanol, thus increasing contact of the reactants.

Another noncatalytic approach is the use of methanol at very high temperature and pressure. This is known as supercritical methanol. Under supercritical conditions (350–400 °C and >80 atm) and at high (42:1) alcohol to oil ratio, the reaction is complete in about 4 min [74]. In addition to the high conversion and reaction rates, supercritical transesterification is appealing as it can tolerate feedstock with very high contents of FFAs and water, up to 36 and 30 wt%, respectively [75]. The supercritical method is a catalyst-free approach, which simplifies the recovery of glycerin as a coproduct for biodiesel production and could potentially be a solution to many processing problems. However, the reactor sizes would be larger compared to the normal method for biodiesel production due to the higher amount of alcohol used. Capital and operating costs are higher and so is energy consumption.

Many researchers have focused on how to decrease the severity of the reaction conditions. Co-solvents, such as carbon dioxide, hexane, and calcium oxide, added into the reaction mixture can decrease the operating temperature, pressure, and the amount of alcohol. Examples of the co-solvents used for this purpose are propane [76], calcium oxide [77], and carbon dioxide [78, 79]. Han [78] demonstrated that with an optimal reaction temperature of 280 °C, methanol to oil ratio of 24 and CO_2 to methanol ratio of 0.1, a 98% yield of methyl esters (biodiesel) was observed in 10 min at a reaction pressure of 14.3 MPa, which makes the production of biodiesel using supercritical methanol viable as an industrial process. Whereas Yin [79] showed that with CO_2 or hexane as co-solvent in the reaction system and at an optimal reaction temperature of 160 °C and methanol to oil ratio of 24, a 98% yield of methyl esters was observed in 20 min.

Successful conversion of waste cooking oil to biodiesel using ferric sulfate and supercritical methanol processes was also reported [80]. Demirbas [40], by comparing the effects of base-catalytic and supercritical methanol transesterification of waste cooking oil, reached a similar conclusion and pointed out that the great advantages of supercritical methanol are as follows: (1) no catalyst required; (2) not sensitive to both water and FFA; and (3) FFAs in the waste cooking oil are transesterified simultaneously.

Tan *et al.* [81] showed that both waste palm cooking oil and refined palm oil produced comparable optimum yields by using supercritical methanol for their transesterification, and concluded that the impurities found in waste palm cooking oil did not adversely affect the yield for the supercritical methanol reaction.

5.13.2.2.3(vii) Biodiesel production using ultrasonication

As previously mentioned in discussing the effect of agitation on the base-catalyzed transesterification process, the mass transfer of TGs from the oil phase toward the methanol–oil interface could be a critical step to limit the rate of alcoholysis reaction because the reaction mixture is heterogeneous with two immiscible phases. As a result, a vigorous mixing is required to increase the area of contact between the two immiscible phases, and thus to produce an emulsion. Low-frequency ultrasonic irradiation is a useful tool for emulsification of immiscible liquids [82]. The collapse of the cavitation bubbles disrupts the phase boundary and causes emulsification by ultrasonic jets that impinge one liquid to another [83]. Hence, ultrasonication can provide the mechanical energy for mixing and the required energy for initiating the transesterification reaction.

Refaat and El Sheltawy [84] compared the use of ultrasonication for fast production of biodiesel from WVO with the conventional base-catalyzed transesterification and concluded that transesterification by low-frequency ultrasound (20 kHz) offered a lot of advantages over the conventional classical procedure. It proved to be efficient (biodiesel yield up to 98–99%), as well as saving time and energy (dramatic reduction of reaction time to 5 min, compared to 1 h or more using conventional batch reactor systems, and remarkable reduction in static separation time to 25 min, compared to 8 h).

Hingu *et al.* [85] illustrated the use of a low-frequency ultrasonic reactor (20 kHz) for the synthesis of biodiesel from waste cooking oil under ambient operating conditions. The efficacy of using ultrasound has been compared with the conventional stirring approach. Over a similar time of operation, a 89.5% conversion was achieved by using ultrasonication compared to only 57.5% by the conventional stirring method.

5.13.2.2.3(viii)   Microwave-enhanced transesterification
Thermally driven organic transformations can take place by conventional heating where the reactants are slowly activated by an external heat source. Heat is driven into the substance, passing first through the walls of the vessel in order to reach the solvent and reactants. This is a slow and inefficient method for transferring energy into the reacting system. Alternatively, microwave (MW)-accelerated heating can be employed where MWs couple directly with the molecules of the entire reaction mixture, leading to a rapid rise in temperature. Since the process is not limited by the thermal conductivity of the vessel, the result is an instantaneous localized superheating of any substance that will respond to either dipole rotation or ionic conduction – the two fundamental mechanisms for transferring energy from MWs to the substance(s) being heated [86].

Several examples of MW-irradiated transesterification methods have been reported using adapted domestic ovens to use them as flow systems [87] or batch laboratory ovens [88], but only moderate conversions were obtained. A more recent study used homogeneous catalysis, both in a batch and in a flow system [89]. Leadbeater and Stencel [90] reported the use of MW heating as a fast, simple way to prepare biodiesel in a batch mode. This was followed by a continuous-flow approach allowing for the reaction to be run under atmospheric conditions and performed at flow rates of up to 7.2 l min^{-1} using a 4 l reaction vessel [91].

In a study by Refaat *et al.* [92], the optimum parametric conditions obtained from the conventional technique were applied using MW irradiation in order to compare both systems for the production of biodiesel from neat and WVOs. The results showed that application of radio frequency MW energy offers a fast, easy route to this valuable biofuel with advantages of enhancing the reaction rate and improving the separation process. From these results, it was concluded that using MW irradiation reduces the reaction time by 97% and the separation time by 94%. The methodology allowed for the use of high FFA content feedstock, including used cooking oil without prior pretreatment processes. The authors also proved that MW-enhanced biodiesel is not, at least, inferior to that produced by the conventional technique.

A study was conducted by El Sheltawy and Refaat [93] to compare three options for the production of biodiesel from neat and WVO; the conventional base-catalyzed transesterification, ultrasonication, and MW-enhanced transesterification.

Despite the prominent advantages that ultrasonication and MW technologies offer compared to the conventional base-catalyzed transesterification, these emerging technologies need to be further investigated for possible scale-up for industrial application.

5.13.2.3   Quality of WVO-Based Biodiesel
5.13.2.3.1   Standard parameters
Quality standards are prerequisites for the commercial use of any fuel product. Since the implementation of the European standard specification EN 14214 in 2004, a standardized definition for biodiesel has been agreed as FAMEs from any kind of feedstock, including recycled frying oils, fulfilling the given quality specifications. The standards commonly used as reference for other standards are the European standard specification EN 14214 and the American standard specification ASTM D 6751.

Most studies have shown that biodiesel obtained from low-quality feedstock is comparable in composition and similar in calorific value to biodiesel produced from virgin vegetable oil [49]. The properties of WVO-based biodiesel obtained from selected studies are summarized in **Table 3** and compared to standard parameters.

From the table it is evident that the quality of WVO-based biodiesel, except in few cases, lies within the standard limits. The following remarks can be concluded:

- Biodiesel fuels derived from used frying oils tend to possess higher viscosity than those from most vegetable oils, owing to their higher content of trans fatty acids and saturated, or, more generally speaking, less unsaturated fatty acids. Nevertheless, in most of the studies, the viscosity lies within the standard limits.
- Density limits in the European EN norm are in the range of 860–900 kg m^{-3}. The ASTM norm includes no regulation on this parameter. It is argued that the determination of density is superfluous for biodiesel samples complying with all other prescribed specifications, as these fuels will inevitably have densities in the desired range. Densities of biodiesel fuels are generally higher than those of petro-diesel samples.
- High flash points obtained for most produced samples indicate efficient excess methanol recovery. Such high values indicate that excess methanol was successfully recovered, because otherwise methanol would significantly decrease the flash point. So this parameter is usually unaffected by the type of feedstock.
- Acid number of biodiesel depends on a variety of factors. On the one hand, it is influenced by the type of feedstock used for fuel production and on its respective degree of refinement. On the other hand, acidity can also be generated during the production process, for instance, by mineral acids introduced as catalysts or by FFAs resulting from acid work-up of soaps. Finally, the parameter also mirrors the degree of fuel ageing during storage, as it gradually increases due to hydrolytic cleavage of ester bonds. The respective limit in the European norm is ≤0.5 mg KOH g^{-1} sample, whereas the American standard was allowing slightly higher values. In 2006, the ASTM D 6751 biodiesel acid number limit was harmonized with the European biodiesel value of 0.50 [106].

Table 3 Properties of WVO-based biodiesel compared to standard parameters

Property							
Viscosity (at 40 °C) (mm² s⁻¹)	Density (at 15 °C) (kg m⁻³)	Flash point (°C)	Cetane number	Acid value (mg KOH g⁻¹)	Iodine value (g I₂/100 g)	Ester content % (m/m)	References
Standard parameters							
3.5–5.0	860–900	≥120	≥51	≤0.5	≤120	≥96.5	EN 14214
1.9–6.0	ND	≥130	≥47	≤0.8	ND	ND	ASTM D 6751
WVO-based biodiesel							
4.40	875	**71**	60.4	0.15	62.0	96.5	[94]
4.32	888	156	52.0				[95]
4.23	890	171	54.5	0.48			[32]
3.49	866	192	47.6	0.19	99.7		[36]
4.80	886	177	48.6		99.4		[35]
4.00				0.15		**94.6**	[22]
5.64	886	176					[31]
5.29	882	169	58.7		78.0		[96, 97]
4.92	884			0.64	98.4		[98]
4.68	882		58.3		85.8		[99, 100]
6.32	877	130	62.0				[101]
5.16	887			0.55	97.5		[102]
4.63	882	151		0.23	106.0	97.2	[103]
3.98	880		56.8	0.39	71.0		[104]
4.90	883			0.28	105.0		[105]

Data in boldface are out of the standard parameters limits.

- Whereas the American norm does not contain regulations on this parameter, iodine number is limited to ≤120 (g I₂ per 100 g) in the European specification. The iodine value (IV) of 120 in EN 14214 can serve to restrict certain vegetable oils as biodiesel feedstock, notably soybean oil or sunflower oil [107]. Soybean oil is not an attractive raw material concerning IV (127 g I₂ per 100 g). Sunflower oil showed an IV of 124 g I₂ per 100 g, which is close to the maximum limit. The WFO presented in most studies showed a lower IV figure, because it resulted from the mixture of oils with less unsaturated fatty acid content.

- From the quality parameters, the ones that most depend on the reaction conditions are the kinematic viscosity and the methyl ester content (purity). Low values for pure biodiesel samples may originate from inappropriate reaction conditions or from various minor components within the original fat or oil source.

Dias *et al.* [27] conducted a study to evaluate the quality of the biodiesel synthesized from WFO compared to that produced from sunflower and soybean refined oils by base-catalyzed transesterification. The results obtained showed that the use of virgin oils resulted in higher yields (reaching 97%) as compared to WFOs (reaching 92%). Under optimum operation conditions, a purity of 99.4 (wt%) was obtained in all cases. The quality of the produced biodiesel from all sources, including that from WVO, lay within the standard limits except for the IV. The WFO was the most adequate to be used among the used raw materials, which presented an IV of 117 g I₂ per 100 g.

5.13.2.3.2 Engine performance

Operationally, biodiesel performs very similarly to low sulfur diesel in terms of power, torque, and fuel consumption without major modification of engines or infrastructure [108, 109]. When an engine is fueled with biodiesel, the maximum engine power and torque slightly drops while the brake specific fuel consumption (BSFC) increases with respect to the petro-diesel, whereas the thermal efficiency is practically the same for both fuels [110, 111]. Brake specific energy consumption (BSEC) or brake thermal efficiency (the inverse of BSEC) is a more adequate parameter than the BSFC for comparing fuels and for evaluating the engine capability to be fuelled with biodiesel and biodiesel blends [112].

The brake power depends on the engine design and fuel used. For the same diesel engine, the brake power depends on the type of fuel used. The lower heat of combustion of the biodiesel leads to a decrease of the engine power and torque [113]. The BSFC represents the actual mass of the fuel consumed to produce 1 kW. The engine distributes the fuel on a volumetric basis. As the density of biodiesel is higher, so for the same volume, more biodiesel fuel, based on the mass, is supplied to the engine when compared with diesel, and higher amount of fuel is consumed to achieve the similar maximum brake torque causing an increase in the BSFC [94, 114]. The higher oxygen content, higher cetane number, and shorter autoignition delay promote the combustion process and lead to an improved thermal efficiency [115].

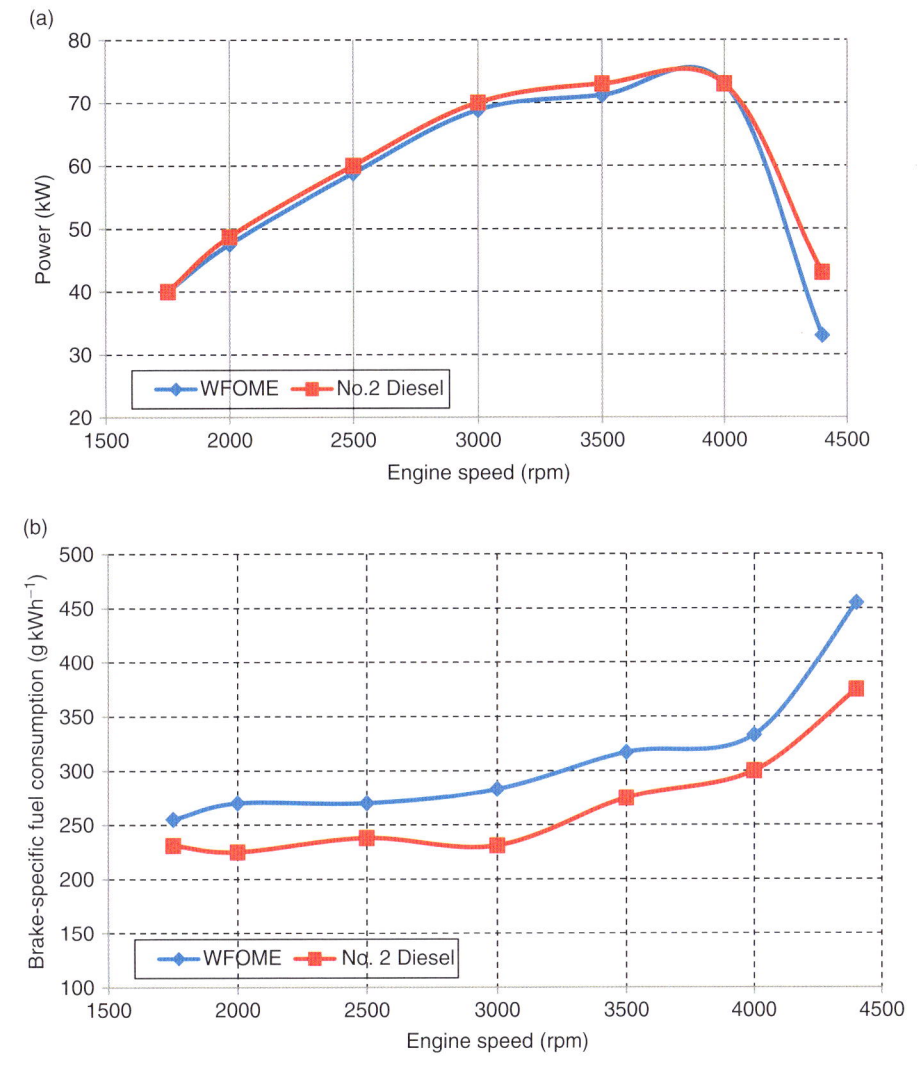

Figure 2 Performance tests for engines fueled by WVO-based biodiesel [95]. (a) Power vs. engine speed. (b) Break-specific fuel consumption vs. engine speed.

The performance of engines fueled with biodiesel produced from WVO was extensively covered in the literature [24, 32, 92, 94–96, 102, 116–119].

Utlu and Kocak [95] evaluated the performance of a direct injection (DI) diesel engine fueled with WFO methyl ester. They noted a slight decrease in the engine torque and output power and an increase in the BSFC as shown in **Figure 2**.

Özsezen *et al.* [94] have compared the performance of a DI diesel engine fueled with petro-diesel (PBDF) and two types of biodiesel; one obtained from virgin canola oil (COME) and the other from waste (frying) palm oil (WPOME). The obtained engine performance values by using the WPOME and COME were almost similar to each other. The maximum brake power and torque for WPOME and COME were lower than that of PBDF by 2.57% and 2.71%, respectively. The BSFC for WPOME and COME was 7.48% and 6.18% higher than that of PBDF, respectively. WPOME and COME, with respect to the PBDF, had a little reduction in brake thermal efficiency of 1.42% and 0.12%, respectively.

5.13.2.3.3 Emission characteristics

Because its physical properties and chemical composition are distinctly different from conventional diesel fuel, biodiesel can alter the fuel injection and ignition processes whether neat or in blends. As a consequence, the emissions of NO_x and the amount, character, and composition of particulate emissions are significantly affected [120]. Biodiesel possesses several distinct advantages over petro-diesel regarding exhaust emissions [110]. Compared to mineral diesel, biodiesel generally causes a decrease of unburned HC, CO, and PM emissions and an increase of NO_x emission [100].

As the ester-based fuel contains some oxygen, it acts as a combustion promoter inside the cylinder, resulting in better combustion than diesel fuel. Hence, carbon monoxide, which is present in the exhaust due to incomplete combustion, reduces drastically [113]. By using biodiesel, the soot and particulate matter emissions, as well as the particle number concentration, decreased sharply, mainly due to the oxygen content of the biodiesel, which improve the oxygen availability in rich zone flames in the combustion chamber [98]. When compared with petroleum diesel fuel, biodiesel emissions contain less soot, and a greater fraction of the particulate is soluble. The analysis and speciation of the soluble organic fraction of biodiesel particulate suggest that the carcinogenic potential of the biodiesel emissions is probably lower than that of petroleum diesel [112, 121].

Advancing injection timing for biodiesel improves the CO, unburned HC emissions and smoke opacity, but it has a reverse effect on NO_x emissions [94]. Szybist [120] showed that retarding injection timing for biodiesel at high load conditions reduce the NO_x emissions. Exhaust emissions, in general, can be reduced to some extent by adjusting the injection pump timing properly [110, 111, 122].

Numerous reports in the literature dealt with the study of exhaust emissions from engines fueled with biodiesel produced from waste vegetable oil [24, 32, 92, 94, 95, 97, 98, 116, 119].

Utlu and Kocak [95] showed that emissions such as CO, CO_2, NO_x, and smoke darkness from WFOs were lower than from No. 2 diesel fuel (**Figure** 3).

Di *et al.* [123] indicated that the combination of ultra-low sulfur diesel and biodiesel from waste cooking oil gave similar results to those in the literature using higher sulfur diesel fuels and biodiesel from other sources. Lapuerta *et al.* [98] tested two different biodiesel fuels obtained from waste cooking oils with different previous uses on diesel particulate emissions. They found no important differences in emissions between the two tested biodiesel fuels.

5.13.3 Summary: Biodiesel from Waste

Although transesterification is well-established and becoming increasingly important, there remains considerable inefficiencies in existing transesterification processes. There is an imperative need to improve the existing biodiesel production methods from both economic and environmental viewpoints, and to investigate alternative and innovative production processes. The identification of some key parameters (acid value and FFA content, moisture content, viscosity, and fatty acid profile of the used oil) is a prerequisite for determining the viability of the vegetable oil transesterification process and therefore is essential for identifying the right processes to perform to achieve best results with respect to yield and purity of the produced biodiesel.

Biodiesels from both used and unused vegetable oils are supposed to have very similar properties and potential in reducing pollutant emission from the engine because both are composed of methyl esters of fatty acids. Furthermore, analyses of used cooking oil showed that the differences between used and unused oils are not very great, and in most cases, a simple pretreatment (removal by filtration of solid particles, esterification process to reduce the content of FFAs) is enough for subsequent transesterification.

Exhaust emissions and performance tests with biodiesel fuels derived from used cooking oils have shown that this kind of biodiesel exhibits properties similar to those of biodiesel derived from 'classical' vegetable oil feedstock. The new process technologies developed during recent years have made it possible to produce biodiesel from recycled frying oils comparable in quality to that of virgin vegetable oil biodiesel with an added attractive advantage of being lower in price. Thus, biodiesel produced from recycled frying oils has the same possibilities to be utilized. These results are expected to encourage the public and private sectors to improve the collecting and recycling of used cooking oil to produce biodiesel.

5.13.4 Bioethanol Production from LCWs

5.13.4.1 Significance of Producing Bioethanol from LCWs

First-generation bioethanol can be derived from renewable sources of virgin feedstock; typically starch and sugar crops such as corn, wheat, or sugarcane. The barriers of first-generation biofuels (e.g., competition with food, high energy inputs, poor energy balances, low yields per hectare, and damage to ecosystem) can be partly overcome by the utilization of lignocellulosic (LC) materials, which are in surplus, relatively cheap, and easily available; use of LC material could allow coproduction of valuable biofuels, chemical compounds, electricity, and heat [124].

The possible competition with food is one of the risks when using agricultural crops for ethanol production. The author considers that this option should be limited to cases where actual and sustainable surplus of crops occurs. Increased ethanol production has prompted a 'food versus fuel' debate over the impacts that the increased demand for corn has on food prices [125]. The use of food and feed crops for energy production will impact their availability for traditional uses. This increased use of corn for ethanol production could result in higher corn prices and could negatively impact the food and feed industries [126].

One potential advantage for cellulosic ethanol technologies is that they can avoid direct competition for crops used in the food supply chain by using dedicated energy crops, crop wastes, or wood wastes as a feedstock. While dedicated energy crops indirectly compete with food production through increased demand for agricultural land, this competition is limited by the fact that these dedicated energy crops can often be grown on marginal lands that may not be suitable for the production of corn or other primary food and/or cash crops [127]. Dedicated energy crops such as switchgrass can often be grown with lower levels of production inputs than corn and, as a deep-rooted perennial, switchgrass generates less erosion than corn [128]. However, switchgrass generally consumes more water than do the traditional crops under all climate conditions and also reduces runoff. Moreover, an intensified cultivation and consequently use of fertilizers and pesticides could put pressure on water resources like declining water availability and/or rising pollution. Scarce land and water resources already impose a major constraint on agricultural production in many parts

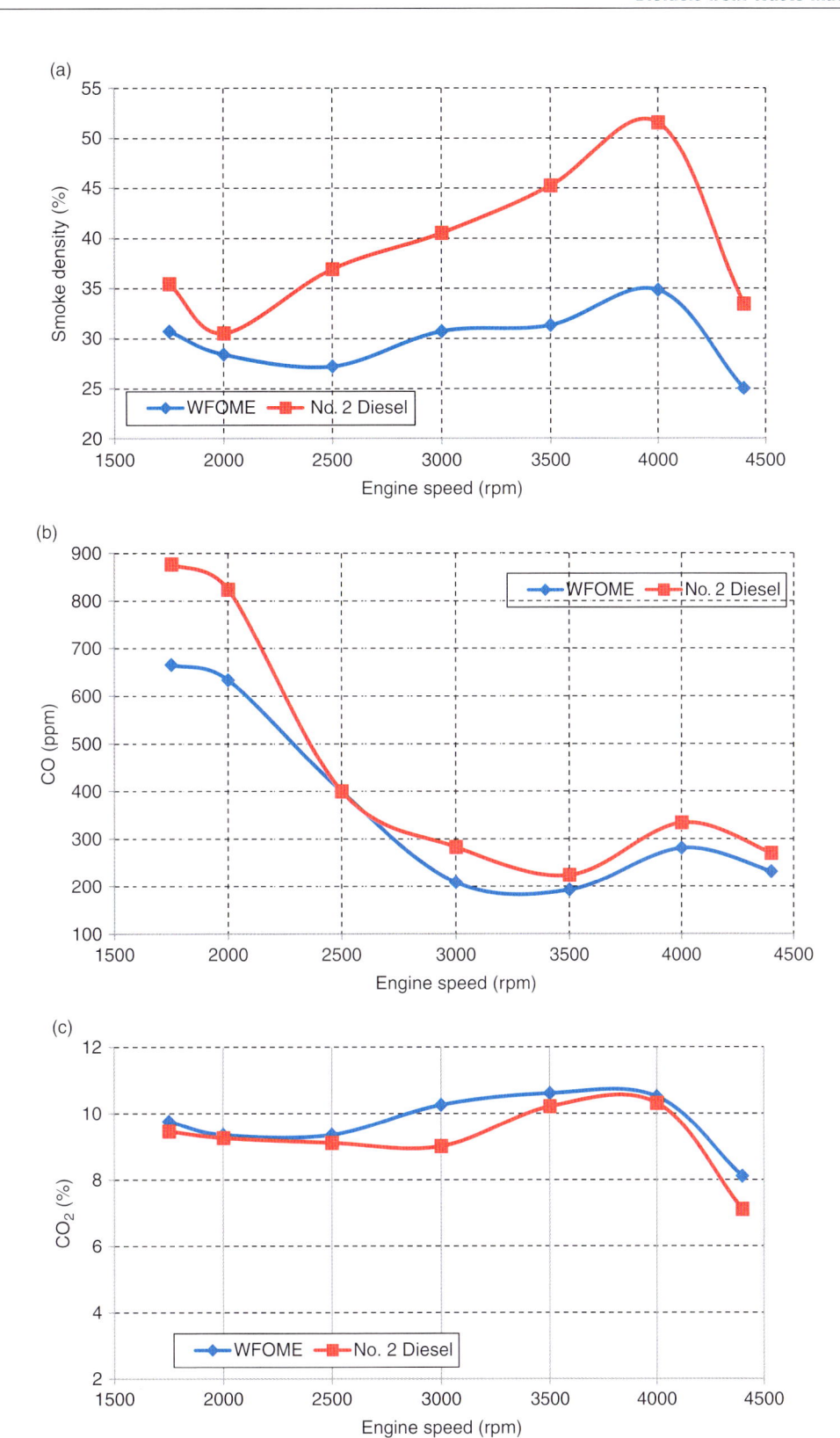

Figure 3 (Continued)

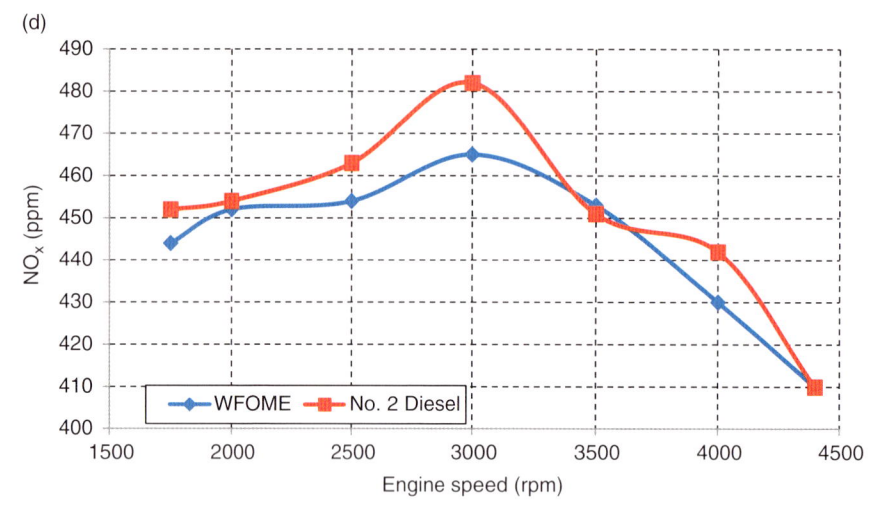

Figure 3 Exhaust emissions from WVO-based biodiesel [95]. (a) Smoke density vs. engine speed. (b) CO emissions vs engine speed. (c) CO_2 emissions versus engine speed. (d) Exchange of NO_x.

of the world [129, 130]. Water resource implications of bioenergy policies should be considered in the rule-making process to ensure that these policies do not drive changes that will put undue stress on water supply [131, 132]. Water is already a limiting resource in many contexts, and increasing human consumption will have a dramatic effect on the earth's ecosystems and biodiversity [133]. Utilizing biomass residues and process by-flows from food and forestry industries may lessen the water intensity of bioenergy production [134].

Due to these impacts, an alternative source from waste materials is attracting interest. A way out is seen in household wastes and wastes from agriculture and forestry, which may be economically converted to bioethanol. This broadening means a far greater source of biomass that can be used for bioethanol production in more areas of the world.

Cellulosic ethanol has a number of potential benefits over corn grain ethanol. Cellulosic ethanol is projected to be much more cost-effective, environmentally beneficial, and have a greater energy output to input ratio than grain ethanol [135]. Cellulosic ethanol production, in particular, can result in a fuel with a net energy yield that is close to CO_2 neutral [136]. Energy analysis studies of ethanol from corn stover [137, 138], switchgrass [139], and woodchip [140] yield a positive net energy value (NEV). When all the coproducts are taken into account, the NEV becomes much higher than the literature covering the corn cases, which shows that ethanol production from cellulosic feedstocks is more energy-efficient than corn-based ethanol. Moreover, cogeneration of electricity from wastes is an important way to increase energy efficiency in the cellulosic ethanol process [138]. The detailed analysis of energy inputs indicates opportunities to optimize the system.

Replacement of fossil gasoline fuel by cellulosic ethanol can be a robust, promising strategy to curb GHG emissions and to reduce the use of fossil fuels [124, 141]. GHG emissions can be reduced by about 50%, and >80% of nonrenewable energy can be saved [142]. Many life cycle assessment (LCA) studies were conducted on ethanol from lignocelluloses including agricultural residues such as corn stover [142–145] and cereal straw [142, 146]; agricultural coproducts such as flax shives [147, 148] and sugarcane bagasse [149, 150]; energy crops such as switchgrass [139, 151], poplar [147], miscanthus, and willow [152]; woodchip and wood wastes [153–155]; and also municipal solid wastes (MSWs) [156]. All these studies, to different extents, showed environmental benefits especially in terms of reduced fossil resource depletion and GHG emissions.

To permit a direct comparison of fuel ethanol from different lignocelluloses in terms of energy use and environmental impact, seven studies conducted by one and the same group were summarized in a paper presented by Luo *et al.* [157]. Where the same technologies were used to convert biomass to ethanol, the same system boundaries were defined, and the same allocation procedures were followed. A complete set of environmental impacts ranging from global warming potential to toxicity aspects was used. The results provided an overview on the energy efficiency and environmental performance of using fuel ethanol derived from different feedstocks in comparison with gasoline. The authors elucidated the potential benefits that cellulosic ethanol possesses over corn grain ethanol. In a previous LCA study on ethanol application, Kim and Dale [158] found that an integrated biorefinery, in which ethanol is produced from both corn stover and corn grain, would have the potential for a better environmental impact profile when utilizing ethanol as liquid fuel compared to a system based on corn grain only. Spatari *et al.* [159], after evaluating the life cycle of emerging LC ethanol conversion technologies, concluded that these technologies offer a positive (fossil) energy gain and a substantial opportunity to reduce GHG emissions relative to gasoline and corn ethanol.

Understanding present and future individual preferences for bioenergy is important for policymakers. Valuing climate protection through public preferences and willingness-to-pay (WTP) for biomass ethanol was reported in many studies around the world [136, 160, 161]. One of these studies was conducted to estimate consumer acceptance or WTP for E85 (automotive fuel blend of 85% ethanol and 15% gasoline) produced from either a corn or a cellulosic (switchgrass or wood wastes) feedstock as compared to E10 (a fuel blend composed of 10% ethanol and 90% unleaded gasoline) produced with corn grain ethanol [160]. Results from the study indicated WTP a premium for E85 from switchgrass compared with E10 from corn. Concerns about land use for 'food versus fuel' had a negative impact on WTP for E85 from corn grain, while greater concerns about fuel security relative to the environment had a positive impact.

5.13.4.2 Sources of LC Biomass

LC biomass includes various agricultural residues (straws, hulls, stems, stalks, e.g., corn stover, wheat straw, and rice straw), agricultural byproducts (e.g., sugarcane bagasse), forestry residues (e.g., sawdust, deciduous, and coniferous woods), cellulosic MSWs (e.g., paper, cardboard, food waste, and yard waste), waste from the pulp and paper industry, and herbaceous energy crops (e.g., switchgrass, sweet sorghum, poplar, and miscanthus).

This chapter focuses on LCWs; however, energy crops are occasionally discussed for illustrative and comparative purposes.

5.13.4.3 LC Biomass Recalcitrance

The LC biomass has a complex structure in which cellulose, hemicellulose, and lignin are the major components. The structure can be described as a skeleton of cellulose chains embedded in a cross-linked matrix of hemicellulose surrounded by a crust of lignin in an intricate structure that is recalcitrant (or resistant) to deconstruction [162].

The amounts of each component vary based on the type of LC biomass. In general, the major component is cellulose (35–50%), followed by hemicellulose (20–35%) and lignin (10–25%) [163]. Table 4 gives the composition of some LCs.

Cellulose is a homopolymer of β-d-glucose units that are linked via β-1-4 glycosidic bonds. The nature of β-1-4 bonds result in the formation of a linear chain of glucose molecules [171]. This linearity results in an ordered packing of cellulose chains that interact via intermolecular and intramolecular hydrogen bonds involving hydroxyl groups and hydrogen atoms of neighboring glucose units. Consequently, cellulose exists as crystalline fibers (microfibrils) with occasional amorphous regions. The amorphous component is digested more easily by enzymes than the crystalline component [172].

Hemicelluloses are heterogeneous polymers of pentoses (β-d-xylose, α-l-arabinose), hexoses (β-d-mannose, β-d-glucose, α-d-galactose), and uronic acids [162]. The most relevant hemicelluloses are xylans and glucomannans, with xylans being the most abundant. Xylans are the main hemicellulose components of secondary cell walls constituting about 20–30% of the biomass of hardwoods and herbaceous plants. In some tissues of grasses and cereals, xylans can account for up to 50% [173]. Xylans are usually available in huge amounts as byproducts of forest, agriculture, agro-industries, wood and pulp, and paper industries. Mannan-type hemicelluloses like glucomannans and galactoglucomannans are the major hemicellulosic components of the secondary wall of softwoods, whereas in hardwoods they occur in minor amounts [162].

While the structure of cellulose is the same for all LC biomass, the structure and composition of hemicelluloses can vary. Grasses such as switchgrass contain two types of hemicelluloses. The major hemicellulose is arabinoxylan, which consists of a xylan backbone made up of β-1,4-linked d-xylose units with frequent arabinose side chains. Although the backbone xylan structure is similar to cellulose, the presence of arabinose side chains minimizes hydrogen bonding. As a result, hemicellulose has low crystallinity. The minor hemicellulose is glucomannan, which is a co-polymeric chain of glucose and mannose units. Occasional branching in glucomannan also contributes to the low crystallinity of hemicellulose. The heteroxylans, which are highly cross-linked by diferulic bridges, constitute a network in which the cellulose microfibrils may be imbedded.

Lignin is a highly complex polymer made up of a mixture of phenylpropanoids linked by way of ester, ether, or carbon–carbon bonds. Lignin is covalently linked to cellulose and xylans in ways that indicate that the orientations of polysaccharides may serve as a template for the lignin patterning. A range of cross-linking possibilities exists including hydrogen bonding, ionic bonding with

Table 4 Composition of lignocellulosic biomass

	Composition (%, dry basis)			
	Cellulose	Hemicellulose	Lignin	References
Corn stover	36–42	22–28	17–22	[163, 168, 169]
Wheat straw	30	50	15–20	[163, 164]
Rice straw	35–37	19–25	12–18	[163, 170]
Sugarcane bagasse	33–40	24–30	19–25	[163, 164]
Switchgrass	45	30	12	[163, 164]
Coastal Bermuda grass	25	36	6	[164]
Hardwood stems (aspen–salix)	40–55	24–40	18–25	[164, 166, 167]
Softwood stems (pine–spruce)	45–50	20–35	25–35	[164–166]
Paper	85–99	0	0–15	[164]
Waste paper from chemical pulps	60–70	10–20	5–10	[164]
Newspaper	40–55	25–40	18–30	[164]

Ca⁺ ions, covalent ester linkages, ether linkages, and van der Waals interactions [169]. The carbon–carbon bonds are the strongest and are primarily responsible for the barrier nature of lignin [174].

The structural and compositional factors believed to contribute to the recalcitrance of LC feedstocks to chemicals or enzymes by affecting liquid penetration and/or enzyme accessibility and activity include the thickness of the epidermal tissue (cuticle and epicuticular waxes) in plants, the degree of lignification, the structural heterogeneity and complexity of its constituents such as microfibrils and matrix polymers, the challenges for enzymes acting on an insoluble substrate, and the inhibitors to subsequent fermentations that exist naturally or are generated during conversion processes [172].

5.13.4.4 Factors Limiting LC Biomass Digestibility

Enzymatic hydrolysis of LC biomass is affected by the structural properties of its components. Several structural and compositional factors affect the enzymatic digestibility of LC materials. Structural features of cellulose commonly considered as rate-impacting factors include crystallinity index, degree of polymerization (DP), and accessible area. Hemicellulose sheathing and degree of hemicellulose acetylation as well as the role of the lignin barrier should be also considered.

5.13.4.4.1 Cellulose crystallinity (crystallinity index, CrI)
The degree of crystallinity of cellulose is expressed in terms of the crystallinity index (CrI); this is determined by the ratio of the crystalline peak to valley (amorphous region) in the diffractogram based on a monoclinic structure of cellulose [175].

The degree of cellulose crystallinity is a major factor affecting enzymatic hydrolysis of the substrate. It has been reported that a decrease in cellulose crystallinity especially influences the initial rate of cellulose hydrolysis by cellulase [169]. The correlation between the CrI and the initial hydrolysis rate shows a continuous decrease in rate as crystallinity increases. At higher degrees of crystallinity, cellulose samples are less amenable to enzymatic hydrolysis, less reactive, and less accessible [176].

It was shown that cellulase readily hydrolyzes the more accessible amorphous portion of cellulose, while the enzyme is not so effective in degrading the less accessible crystalline portion. It is therefore expected that high-crystallinity cellulose will be more resistant to enzymatic hydrolysis, and it is widely accepted that decreasing the crystallinity increases the digestibility of lignocelluloses [177]. However, it is not the only factor in effective enzymatic hydrolysis of these materials, due to the heterogeneous nature of celluloses and the contribution of other components such as lignin and hemicellulose.

5.13.4.4.2 Cellulose DP (number of glycosyl residues per cellulose chain)
Depolymerization depends on the nature of cellulosic substrate. In enzymatic hydrolysis, endoglucanases cut at internal sites of the cellulose chains, which is preferentially less ordered, is primarily responsible for decreasing the DP of cellulosic substrates. However, regardless of the substrate being attacked, there seems to be a 'leveling off' of the cellulose DP, correlated with the increased recalcitrance of the residual crystalline cellulose [178, 179].

5.13.4.4.3 Accessible surface area (pore volume)
The first step of enzymatic hydrolysis consists of (1) adsorption of cellulase enzymes from liquid phase onto the surface of cellulose (solid), (2) biodegradation of cellulose to simple sugars, mainly cellobiose and oligomers, and (3) desorption of cellulase to the liquid phase. Thus, the reaction is a heterogeneous catalytic reaction and direct physical contact between the cellulytic enzymes' molecules and cellulose is a prerequisite for enzymatic hydrolysis. As a result, the accessible surface area in LC material and its interaction with the enzymes can be limiting in enzymatic hydrolysis [177].

In enzymatic hydrolysis of a solid substrate, accessible surface area will present a steric limitation due to the fact that some pores are not large enough to be accessible by enzyme molecules, so only the outer surfaces and large pores are accessible [180]. The smaller sized particles will have a faster hydrolysis rate than the larger sized ones.

5.13.4.4.4 Hemicellulose sheathing
Hemicellulose is known to coat the cellulose microfibrils in the plant cell wall, forming a physical barrier to access by hydrolytic enzymes, and removal of hemicellulose has been reported to increase the enzymatic hydrolysis of cellulose [163].

5.13.4.4.5 Degree of hemicellulose acetylation
Degree of acetylation in the hemicellulose is another important factor because lignin and acetyl groups are attached to the hemicellulose matrix and may hinder polysaccharide breakdown. The bonds between lignin and carbohydrates are predominantly ester-linked to arabinose side chains of arabinoxylans. Xylans are extensively acetylated [169].

5.13.4.4.6 Lignin barrier (content and distribution)
Lignin affects the enzymatic hydrolysis of LC biomass because it forms a physical barrier to attack by enzymes [181]. Lignin is covalently bonded to polysaccharides in the intact plant cell wall, thus reducing accessible surface area of cellulose. The mechanism that explains the protective effect of lignin against polysaccharide hydrolysis remains uncertain although a number of factors, such

as the degree and type of cross-linkage to polysaccharide, the diversity of structures found in the lignin component, and the distribution of phenolic polymers through the cell wall, are important [169].

5.13.4.5 Production of Ethanol from LCWs

Ethanol production from LC materials comprises the following main steps: hydrolysis of cellulose, hydrolysis of hemicellulose, fermentation of all the sugars, separation of lignin residue, recovery and concentration of ethanol, and wastewater handling. In most cases, pretreatment produces water-insoluble solids (WIS) containing cellulose and lignin, and a liquid fraction composed of hemicellulose. The hemicellulose is more or less intact, depending on the pretreatment: when hydrolyzed to monosaccharides, it proceeds to fermentation; when not completely hydrolyzed, that is, composed of oligosaccharides, it requires further hydrolysis before fermentation. Cellulose is hydrolyzed by cellulases and converted to glucose, which is fermented. When hydrolysis of cellulose and fermentation of glucose occur separately, the process is designated to separate hydrolysis and fermentation (SHF). When the pentose fraction is fermented together with the hexose fraction after a separate hydrolysis, it is designated to separate hydrolysis and co-fermentation. When hydrolysis of cellulose is performed simultaneously with fermentation, it is named simultaneous saccharification and fermentation (SSF). When SSF includes the co-fermentation of glucose and xylose, that is, with the whole slurry (WIS and liquid fraction), it is called simultaneous saccharification and co-fermentation (SHCF). Finally, when enzymes are also produced during the process, hydrolysis and fermentation of all sugars are performed in one step, which is denominated consolidated bioprocessing (CBP) [162]. LC ethanol bioprocesses are collectively depicted in **Figure 4**.

Some of the most important factors to reduce the production cost include an efficient utilization of the raw material by having high ethanol yields, high productivity, high ethanol concentration in the distillation feed, and also by employing process integration (at least for the three key steps – pretreatment, hydrolysis, and fermentation) in order to reduce capital cost and energy demand [182, 183]. The microbial conversion of the hemicellulose fraction, either in the monomeric form or in the oligomeric form, is essential for increasing fuel ethanol yields from LC materials. Part of the lignin can be burnt to provide heat and electricity for the process, and the surplus is sold as a coproduct for heat and power applications, which will increase the energy efficiency of the whole system [184].

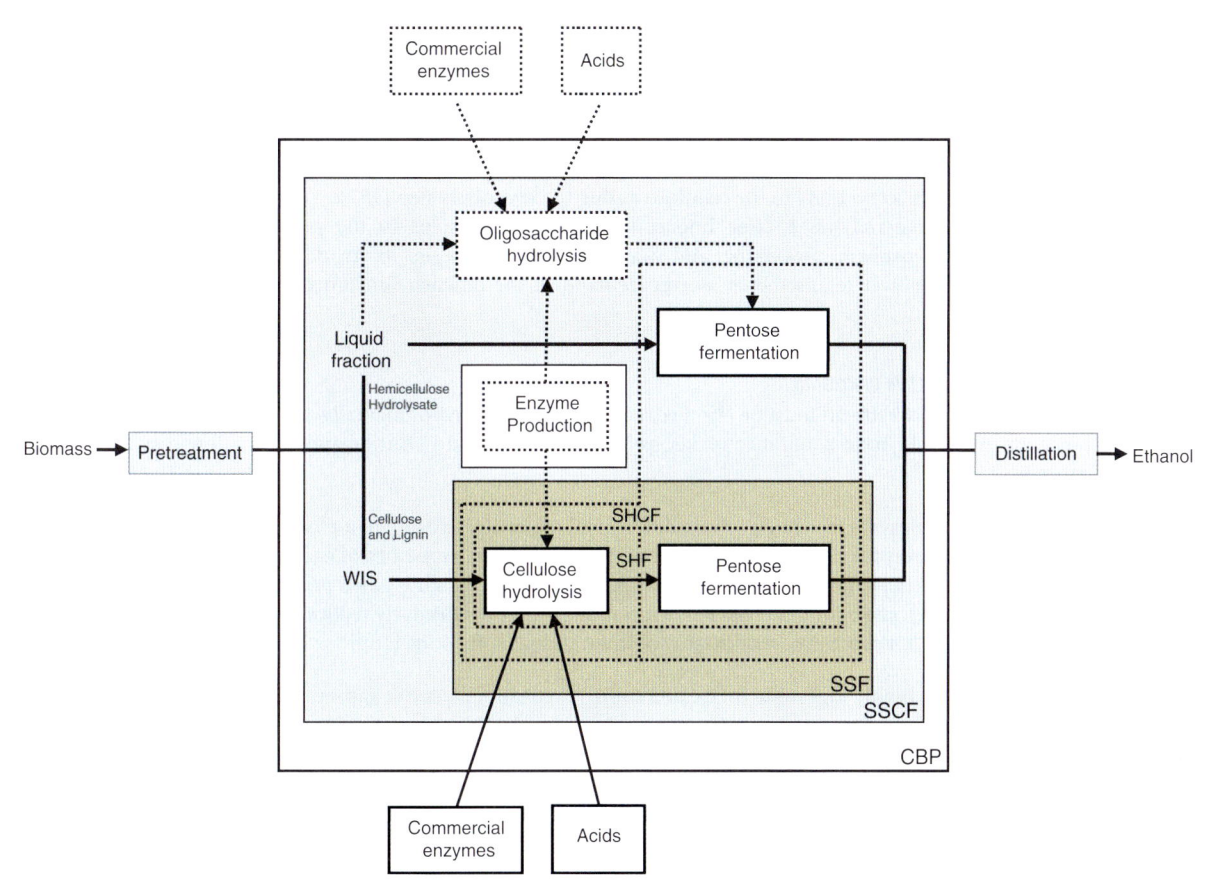

Figure 4 Lignocellulosic ethanol bioprocesses [162].

5.13.4.6 Challenges to Bioethanol Production from Lignocellulose

Although the cost of biomass is low, releasing fermentable sugars from these materials remains challenging. Process optimization solutions for the production of ethanol from LC biomass require a better understanding of the challenges facing the industry. These challenges comprise:

- Overcoming the recalcitrance of LC biomass by developing a feasible pretreatment process.
- Improving the yield and rate of enzymatic hydrolysis by enhancing cellulase activity.
- Improving ethanol yield by effectively converting xylose and arabinose in the hydrolysate into ethanol.

A major challenge is the pretreatment of LC biomass to reduce biomass recalcitrance, in order to improve the yield of fermentable sugars. This recalcitrance is primarily due to the composition of LC biomass and the way specific components interact with each other. Unlike sugar and starch crops, the carbohydrates in lignocelluloses are not easily accessible for enzymatic hydrolysis. Pretreatment can be the most expensive process in biomass-to-fuels conversion but it has great potential for improvements in efficiency and lowering of costs through further research and development.

Bioscientists are focusing on two hurdles that have plagued the technology for decades – the high cost of cellulases, the enzymes that break down cellulose, in comparison to the cost of amylases used in the hydrolysis of starch and sugar crops, and the limited ability of the microbes to ferment the breakdown products [185]. Despite substantial reduction in the cost of cellulolytic enzymes [186], sugar release from biomass still remains an expensive and slow step. Cellulose-consuming bacteria are different to the yeasts that ferment sugar into ethanol. Microorganisms, with unique genotype features, obtained either through recombinant DNA technology and/or through evolutionary engineering techniques, appear to be the best option to overcome the barriers to the commercial exploitation of LC bioethanol [162].

Despite these challenges, an impetus is now provided by scientific and technological advances in biosciences and bioengineering that support increased optimism about realizing the full potential of biomass in the liquid fuels area in the near future. This section will be devoted to an in-depth discussion of the first challenge relating to the pretreatment of LC biomass. The other challenges will be also highlighted.

5.13.4.7 Pretreatment Processes

5.13.4.7.1 Overview

This section provides a review of recent research into techniques for pretreating lignocellulose – an area of extensive activity.

5.13.4.7.1(i) Goals of pretreatment

The pretreatment is a necessary step to alter some structural characteristics of lignocellulose, increasing glucan and xylan accessibility to the enzymatic attack. The aim of the pretreatment is to break down the lignin structure and disrupt the crystalline structure of cellulose for enhancing enzymes accessibility to the cellulose during the hydrolysis step [187].

Pretreatment of the raw material has a large impact on all the other steps in the process, for example, enzymatic hydrolysis, fermentation, downstream processing and wastewater handling, in terms of digestibility of the cellulose, fermentation toxicity, stirring power requirements, energy demand in the downstream processes, and wastewater treatment demands [184].

5.13.4.7.1(ii) Features of an effective pretreatment

For industrial applications, a pretreatment must be effective, economical, safe, environmentally acceptable, and easy to use [188]. An effective pretreatment should have a number of key properties to take into consideration for a low-cost and advanced pretreatment process.

5.13.4.7.1(ii)(a) Appropriateness for feedstock   Since different LC materials have different physico-chemical characteristics, it is necessary to adopt suitable pretreatment technologies based on the LC biomass properties of each raw material. Various pretreatments have been shown to be better suited for specific feedstocks. For example, alkaline-based pretreatment methods such as lime, ammonia fiber explosion (AFEX), and ammonia recycled percolation (ARP) can effectively reduce the lignin content of agricultural residues but are less satisfactory for processing recalcitrant substrate such as softwoods [189].

5.13.4.7.1(ii)(b) Resulting in highly digestible pretreated solid   Pretreatment, under appropriate conditions, retains nearly all of the cellulose present in the original material and allows close to theoretical yields upon enzymatic hydrolysis [175].

5.13.4.7.1(ii)(c) Producing minimum degradation products   No or very limited amounts of sugar and lignin degradation products should be produced in order to render the pretreated liquid ready to ferment without detoxification [190].

5.13.4.7.1(ii)(d) Liberating minimum amount of toxic compounds   Toxic compounds generated and their amounts depend on raw material and harshness of pretreatment.

5.13.4.7.1(ii)(e) **Resulting in high recovery of all carbohydrates** The liquid hydrolysate from pretreatment must be fermentable following a low-cost, high-yield conditioning step.

5.13.4.7.1(ii)(f) **Having minimum heat and power requirements** Heat and power demands for pretreatment should be low and/or compatible with the thermally integrated process.

5.13.4.7.1(ii)(g) **Having a low capital and operational cost** Pretreatment reactors should be low in cost through minimizing their volume, employing appropriate materials of construction for highly corrosive chemical environments, and keeping operating pressures reasonable.

5.13.4.7.1(ii)(h) **Fermentation compatibility** The distribution of sugar recovery between pretreatment and subsequent enzymatic hydrolysis should be compatible with the choice of an organism able to ferment pentoses (arabinose and xylose) in hemicellulose. Obtaining hemicellulose sugars in the liquid as monomer sugars will help to avoid the use of hemicellulases.

5.13.4.7.1(ii)(i) **Lignin recovery** Lignin and other constituents should be recovered, without being oxidized, to simplify downstream processing and for their conversion into valuable coproducts and to alleviate the unproductive binding of cellulases on lignin in the enzymatic hydrolysis step.

5.13.4.7.2 Different technologies for LC biomass pretreatment

Numerous pretreatments have been studied through the years, each having its advantages and disadvantages. **Table 5** summarizes the advantages and disadvantages of the most applicable methods.

Pretreatment methods can be broadly categorized as:

- Chemical (acids, alkalis, organic solvents, ionic liquids (ILs), and oxidizing agents)
- Physical (mechanical comminution, irradiation, and extrusion)
- Physicochemical (steam explosion (SE), liquid hot water (LHW), AFEX, ARP, wet oxidation (WO), and supercritical fluid technology).
- Biological (fungal and enzymatic).

5.13.4.7.3 Chemical pretreatment processes

5.13.4.7.3(i) Acid pretreatment

Acid pretreatment may be carried out at either dilute or concentrated acid conditions. Concentrated acid hydrolysis enables high ethanol yield because of almost quantitative conversion of cellulose into glucose. Strong acids can break glycosidic linkages of polysaccharides, freeing the individual monosaccharide components, but also tend to degrade monomeric sugars [169]. Compared to dilute acid hydrolysis, moderate operation temperature is needed with shorter retention time [191]. However, utilization of concentrated acid is less attractive for ethanol production due to the formation of inhibitory compounds. Furthermore, equipment corrosion problems and acid recovery are important drawbacks when using concentrated acid pretreatments.

The main objective of the dilute acid pretreatments is to solubilize the hemicellulosic fraction of the biomass and to make the cellulose more amenable for a further enzymatic treatment. Diluted acid pretreatment appears as a more favorable method for industrial applications as no acid recovery steps are required and acid losses are not important. On the negative side, the yield on glucose from cellulose is low. Also, depending on the process temperature, some degradation compounds may affect the microorganism metabolism in the fermentation step [192]. Based on their origin, the inhibitors are usually divided into three major groups: weak acids, furan derivatives, and phenolic compounds. These compounds limit efficient utilization of the hydrolyzates for ethanol production by fermentation. If the inhibitors are identified and the mechanisms of inhibition elucidated, fermentation can be improved by developing specific detoxification methods, choosing an adapted microorganism, or optimizing the fermentation strategy [193, 194].

Sulfuric acid is the most commonly used in LC residues hydrolysis [195] although other mineral acids like hydrochloric acid [196], nitric acid [197], or phosphoric acid [198] have also been assayed. Organic acids were also reported as alternatives to enhance cellulose hydrolysis for ethanol production, such as fumaric or maleic acids [199] and also lactic acid and acetic acid [200].

Table 6 shows the operational conditions for dilute acid pretreatment. It is likely that increasing pretreatment time and using low temperature during dilute acid pretreatment have the best effect on pentose yield [201]. Low-temperature dilute acid pretreatment can become useful, when utilization of hemicellulose fraction is also of major importance.

In dilute acid pretreatments, described in the literature, solids loading usually varies from 5% to 15% (w/w) dry LC biomass [213]. Substantially increased lignocellulose solids loading is preferred from an industrial point of view [214], as this reduces the amount of liquid phase per amount of feedstock, leading to lower energy demands and reduced reactor volume. Moreover, a more concentrated product stream would reduce ethanol production costs, as well as water removal costs in the bioethanol separation/purification process.

A comparative study showed that recovery of xylose using H_2SO_4 pretreatment of corn stover was 10–30% greater in comparison with that obtained with H_3PO_4 pretreatment under similar conditions [215]. Hydrochloric acid was found to be less active for the degradation of xylose compared to sulfuric acid [196]. Results showed that organic acids can pretreat wheat straw with high

Table 5 Main effects and advantages and disadvantages of different pretreatment methods

Pretreatment method	Main effects	Advantages	Disadvantages and limitations
Concentrated acid	Hydrolyzes both hemicelluloses and cellulose	High glucose yield Reduction in the operational costs due to moderate operation temperature Low formation of degradation products No enzymes are required	Acid recovery is mandatory Equipment corrosion Generation of inhibitory compounds
Diluted acid	Hydrolyzes hemicelluloses Renders cellulose more amenable for a further enzymatic treatment Alters lignin structure	Less corrosion problems than concentrated acid Low formation of inhibitors	Generation of degradation products due to high temperature Low sugar concentration in exit stream
Alkali	Removes lignin and hemicellulose Increases accessible surface area	High digestibility	Long residence times Irrecoverable salts formation
Organosolv	Hydrolyzes lignin and hemicelluloses	High lignin removal Pure lignin recovery High digestibility	High cost Solvents need to be drained and recycled
Ionic liquids	Reduces cellulose crystallinity Removes lignin	High digestibility Green solvents	Large-scale application still under investigation
Ozonolysis	Reduces lignin content	No formation of inhibitors Mild operational conditions	High cost of large amount of ozone needed
Steam explosion	Causes lignin transformation Causes hemicellulose solubilization	Cost effective Higher yield of glucose and hemicellulose	Generation of inhibitory compounds Partial hemicellulose degradation Incomplete disruption of the lignin–carbohydrate matrix
Liquid hot water	Causes lignin transformation Causes hemicellulose solubilization	Cost effective Low formation of degradation products	High energy consumption Not well developed at industrial scale
AFEX	Increases accessible surface area Removes lignin and hemicellulose to an extent	Low formation of inhibitors	Not efficient for biomass with high lignin content High cost of large amount of ammonia
ARP	Removes lignin	Highly selective delignification	High energy consumption
Wet oxidation	Removes lignin	Low formation of inhibitors	High cost of oxygen and alkaline catalyst
Supercritical fluid technology	Increases accessible surface area	Cost effective No formation of inhibitors	Does not affect lignin and hemicelluloses Very high pressure requirements
Mechanical comminution	Reduces cellulose crystallinity	No formation of inhibitors	High power and energy consumption
Biological pretreatment	Degrades lignin and hemicellulose	Low energy consumption	Low rate of hydrolysis

Table 6 Effect of temperature, reaction time, acid concentration, and substrate loading on pentose recovery

Substrate	Acid	Concentration (%)	Temperature (°C)	Time (min)	Substrate loading (%)	Pentose yield (%)	Reference
Corn stover	H_2SO_4	2	120	90	10	100	[201]
	H_2SO_4	2	95	90		93	[207]
	H_2SO_4	0.5	160	5–10	10	93	[202]
	H_2SO_4	1	180	10	20–30	96	[203]
	H_2SO_4	1.2	180	5	20–30	89	[204]
	H_2SO_4	1.2	180	0.5–1	10	84	[208]
Wheat straw	H_2SO_4	0.75	121	60	7.83	92	[192]
Rice straw	H_2SO_4	1	180	5	10	89	[212]
Rye straw	H_2SO_4	1.2	121	60	10	66	[209]
Cashew apple bagasse	H_2SO_4	0.8	121	15	30		[205]
Herbaceous cardoon	H_2SO_4	0.1	180	10	7.5	90	[211]
Olive tree biomass	H_2SO_4	1	170	10	20	88	[206]
Olive tree pruning	H_3PO_4	8	90	240	10	77	[198]
Sugarcane bagasse	H_3PO_4	6	100	300	10		[210]

efficiency although fumaric acid was less effective than maleic acid. Furthermore, a lower amount of furfural was formed in the maleic and fumaric acid pretreatments than with sulfuric acid [199].

5.13.4.7.3(ii) Alkali pretreatment

Alkaline pretreatment breaks the bonds between lignin and carbohydrates and disrupts the lignin structure, which makes the carbohydrates more accessible to enzymatic attack. Alkali pretreatment is generally more effective than other pretreatments (e.g., dilute acid SE) at solubilizing lignin while leaving much of hemicellulose intact as insoluble polymers [216]. So, it yields highly digestible cellulose and produces liquid streams rich in extracted lignins and polymeric hemicellulose [169]. Retained xylan can usually be hydrolyzed to fermentable pentoses by most commercial cellulase and xylanase mixtures. Nevertheless, possible loss of fermentable sugars and production of inhibitory compounds must be taken into consideration to optimize the pretreatment conditions.

Depending on feedstock and operating conditions, significant increases in glucose recovery are reported (**Table 7**). Since alkali pretreatment can be performed at low temperature and times ranging from seconds to days, it is considered to cause less sugar degradation than acid pretreatment [217]. As it acts mainly by delignification, its effectiveness will depend on the lignin content of the biomass; it is more effective on agricultural residues and herbaceous crops than on wood materials, as these materials in general contain less lignin [187].

Table 7 Alkali pretreatment conditions and results

Substrate	Alkali	Temperature (°C)	Time (h)	Concentration (%)	Solid:liquid ratio	Results	References
Corn stover	NaOH	60	24	1.5	1:10	Glucan digestibility 94%	[219]
Corn stover	NH_4OH	60	12	15	1:6	Digestibility: glucan 85%–xylan 78% Lignin removal 62%	[221]
Wheat straw	NaOH	80	6	0.5	1:20	Sugar recovery increased 3 times	[225]
Rice straw	NH_4OH	69	10	21	1:6	Ethanol yield 83%	[222]
Barley hull	NH_4OH	75	48	15	1:12	Lignin removal 66%	[218]
Sorghum	NH_4OH	160	1	14	1:8	Digestibility: glucan 84%–xylan 73% Lignin removal 44%	[223, 224]
Poplar	$NaOH–H_2O_2$	120	24	5	1:10	Lignin removal 80%	[219]
Softwood (spruce)	NaOH–Urea	−15	24	3/12	1:20	Glucan digestibility over 60%	[220]

Table 8   Lime pretreatment conditions and results

Substrate	Initial lignin (%)	Temperature (°C)	Time (h)	Lime loading[a]	Water loading[b]	Results	Reference
Without oxidative agent							
Corn stover	21.5	120	4	0.075	5	Polysaccharide conversions approaching 100%	[168]
Switchgrass	21.4	50	24	0.1		Reducing sugar yield increased 4 times	[229]
Switchgrass	21.7	120	2	0.1	9	Total sugar yield increased 7 times	[228]
Wheat straw	20.0	50	24	0.1	15	Reducing sugar yield increased 10 times	[230]
Bagasse	22.0	120	1	0.1	10	Reducing sugar yield increased 4 times	[230]
Rice straw	17.6	95	3	0.1	10	Improved digestibility and delignification	[170]
Rice hull	16.0	121	1	0.1	15	No detectable furfural or 5-HMF in hydrolyzate	[231]
With oxidative agent (14.0 bar absolute oxygen)							
Poplar	28.0	150	6	0.1	9	Reducing sugar yield increased 9 times; Lignin removal 82%	[227]
Poplar	29.1	160	2	0.4	15	100% glucan conversion possible	[232]

[a]Lime loading (g Ca(OH)$_2$ g^{-1} dry biomass).
[b]Water loading (ml g^{-1} dry biomass).

NaOH causes swelling, increasing the internal surface of cellulose and decreasing the DP and crystallinity, which provokes lignin structure disruption [177]. Ammonia (NH$_4$OH) as a pretreatment reagent has many advantages for an effective delignification as well as swelling of biomass [218].

Lime (Ca(OH)$_2$) pretreatment removes amorphous substances such as lignin, which increases the crystallinity index. Lignin removal increases enzyme effectiveness by reducing nonproductive adsorption sites for enzymes and by increasing cellulose accessibility [226]. Lime also removes acetyl groups from hemicellulose reducing steric hindrance of enzymes and enhancing cellulose digestibility [217]. Under appropriate pretreatment conditions, lime substantially enhances the digestibility of low- or moderate-lignin biomass (e.g., corn stover, switchgrass, bagasse, and wheat straw) by removing 30–43% of lignin and all acetyl groups (**Table 8**). For high-lignin biomass (e.g., poplar), lime alone does not remove enough lignin to significantly enhance the digestibility, but an oxidant must be added. Lignin removal is the major reason that oxidative lime pretreatment enhances the digestibility [227].

5.13.4.7.3(iii)   Organosolv
In this approach an organic or aqueous–organic solvent mixture is used with addition of an inorganic acid catalyst (H$_2$SO$_4$ or HCl), which is used to break the internal lignin and hemicellulose bonds. The hydrolyzed lignin is thus dissolved and recovered in the organophilic phase. However, this acid addition can be avoided for a satisfactory delignification by increasing process temperature (above 185 °C).

Table 9   Organosolv pretreatment using different solvents and feedstock

Substrate	Solvent	Results	Reference
Wheat straw	Glycerol	Cellulose recovery 95%; lignin removal >70%; digestibility 92%	[237]
	Glycerol	More effective than steam explosion	[238]
	Glycerol (crude)	Digestibility >75% – cost reduction on expense of delignification[a]	[239]
Sugarcane bagasse	Ethanol–H$_2$SO$_4$	Ethanol yield 92.8%	[241]
Lignocellulosic residues	Acetone–H$_3$PO$_4$	Ethanol yield >93%	[242]
Hybrid poplar	Ethanol	Digestibility ~85%	[234]
Beetle-killed lodgepole pine	Ethanol	Digestibility ~97%	[235]
Softwood (Loblolly pine)	Ethanol	Reduced cellulose crystallinity (CrI reduced from 63% to 53%)	[236]
Softwood (*Pinus radiata*)	Acetone–water	Ethanol yield 99.5%	[240]

[a]It was recommended to remove lipophilic compounds from crude glycerol before utilization to overcome decreased delignification.

Solvents that are used are typically methanol, ethanol, acetone, ethylene glycol, triethylene glycol, and phenol. Due to the volatility of organic solvents, some of these substances are explosive and highly inflammable and thus difficult to handle. So, organosolv pretreatment must be performed under extremely tight and efficient control [233]. Examples of different solvents used for organosolv pretreatment are given in **Table 9**.

Compared to other chemical pretreatments the main advantage of organosolv process is the recovery of relatively pure lignin as a byproduct. Most of the hemicellulose and lignin are solubilized, but the cellulose remains as solid [233]. However, solvents need to be separated because they might be inhibitory to enzymatic hydrolysis and fermentative microorganisms [190]. Removal of solvents from the system is necessary using appropriate extraction and separation techniques, for example, evaporation and condensation, and they should be recycled to reduce operational costs.

The high commercial price of solvents is another important factor to consider for industrial applications. For economic reasons, among all possible solvents, the low-molecular weight alcohols with lower boiling points such as ethanol and methanol are favored. Although organosolv pretreatment is more expensive at present than the leading pretreatment processes, it can provide some valuable byproducts. An integral optimization and utilization of byproducts might lead the organosolv pretreatment to be a promising one for biorefining LC feedstock in the future [233].

5.13.4.7.3(iv)   IL's pretreatment

ILs are organic salts, typically composed of large organic cations and small inorganic anions, which exist as liquids at a relatively low temperature (<100 °C). They have many attractive properties, such as chemical and thermal stability, nonflammability, immeasurably low vapor pressure, and a tendency to remain liquid in a wide range of temperatures [243]. Although they are considered green solvents, their toxicity to enzymes and fermentative microorganisms are still under investigation.

Studies have shown that cellulose can be dissolved in some hydrophilic ILs. Chloride containing ILs, incorporating anions, which are strong hydrogen bond acceptors, appear to be the most effective solvents [244]. In particular, 1-butyl-3-methylimidazolium chloride and 1-allyl-3-methylimidazolium chloride are the most commonly used [245]. Hydrogen bonds between the nonhydrated chloride ions of the IL and the sugar hydroxyl protons are formed in a 1:1 stoichiometry. As a result, the intricate network of noncovalent interactions among biomass polymers of cellulose, hemicellulose, and lignin is effectively disrupted while minimizing formation of degradation products. Cellulose can be easily regenerated in the amorphous form from its IL solutions by addition of water, ethanol, or acetone. After its regeneration, the ILs can be recovered and reused [246].

Overall, the ability of ILs to dissolve cellulose depends on the nature of the native cellulose (its DP and its crystallinity) on the operating conditions (temperature, reaction time, initial concentration of cellulose in the IL, and activation with MWs) and presence of impurities, mostly water that can significantly change the result [247].

Most data showing the effectiveness of ILs have been developed by using pure crystalline cellulose [248–252], and its applicability to a more complex combination of constituents in LC biomass requires further studies. Nevertheless, the use of ILs has also already been demonstrated on some LC feedstock such as wheat straw [253, 254], sugarcane bagasse [255], switchgrass [256–258], softwood [259], and wood flour [260].

Comparing the efficiency of two biomass pretreatment technologies, dilute acid hydrolysis and dissolution in an IL, showed that when it is subjected to IL pretreatment, switchgrass exhibited reduced cellulose crystallinity, increased surface area, and decreased lignin content compared to dilute acid pretreatment [256]. IL pretreatment enabled a significant enhancement in the rate of enzyme hydrolysis of the cellulose component of switchgrass, with a rate increase of 16.7-fold, and a glucan yield of 96.0% obtained in 24 h. For the large-scale application of ILs, development of energy-efficient recycling methods for ILs is a prerequisite and should be investigated. In addition, techniques need to be developed to recover hemicellulose and lignin from solutions after extraction of cellulose [261].

5.13.4.7.3(v)   Oxidative pretreatment

5.13.4.7.3(v)(a)   Hydrogen peroxide   Addition of hydrogen peroxide in alkaline pretreatment can improve the performance by favoring oxidative delignification due to breakage of carbon–carbon linkages in lignin along with the cleavage of the aryl ether bonds [262]. Hydrogen peroxide (H_2O_2) under alkaline conditions oxidizes the carbohydrate reducing ends, which are resistant to the carbohydrate peeling reaction [219].

As previously discussed in alkaline pretreatment, hybrid poplar, due to higher lignin content, requires a treatment with higher severity than corn stover in order to achieve an acceptable level of digestibility. The use of H_2O_2 in NaOH treatment seems to increase the selectivity of lignin degradation over hemicellulose degradation. Addition of 5% H_2O_2 with 5% NaOH in the treatment of hybrid poplar at low temperature of 80 °C increased delignification, retention of carbohydrates in solids, and the enzymatic digestibility [219]. Compared with the untreated tobacco wastes, the yield of reducing sugar pretreated by H_2O_2 pretreatment increased by 347.2% [263]. Alkaline peroxide pretreatment proved also to be efficient with wheat straw [264], rice hull [265], and perennial grasses [266].

A mild two-step alkaline/oxidative pretreatment of wheat straw prior to enzymic hydrolysis was reported. It consists of a first alkaline (1% NaOH for 24 h) step, which mainly solubilizes hemicellulose and renders the material more accessible to further chemical attack, and a second alkaline/oxidative step (1% NaOH and 3% H_2O_2 for 24 h), which solubilizes and oxidizes lignin to minor polluting compounds. The entire process was carried out at low temperature (25–40 °C) using a low concentration of chemicals, resulting in a relatively low cost and waste liquors containing only trace amounts of dangerous pollutants derived from lignin. Recovery of cellulose after the double pretreatment reached 90% of that contained in the starting material, with a concomitant 81% degradation of lignin [267]. It is also possible to replace the first alkaline step by the dilute acid pretreatment step [268].

5.13.4.7.3(v)(b) Peracetic acid Peracetic acid (PAA) has been recognized as a powerful oxidizing agent and it is very selective toward the lignin structure. It cleaves aromatic nuclei in lignin generating dicarboxylic acids and their lactones [269]. PAA treatment improved enzymatic digestibility of hybrid poplar and sugarcane bagasse without any need of high temperatures [269]. Compared with H_2SO_4 and NaOH pretreatments under the same mild conditions, PAA pretreatment was the most effective for enhancement of enzymatic digestibility of sugarcane bagasse [270].

5.13.4.7.3(v)(c) Ozone Ozone is a powerful oxidant that shows high delignification efficiency [190]. The pretreatment is usually performed at room temperature and normal pressure and does not lead to the formation of inhibitory compounds that can affect the subsequent hydrolysis and fermentation. However, an important drawback to consider is the large amounts of ozone needed, which can make the process economically unviable.

'Ozonization pretreatment' has been applied on several agricultural residues such as wheat straw and rye straw increasing in both cases the enzymatic hydrolysis yield [271]. Enzymatic hydrolysis yields of up to 88.6% and 57% were obtained compared to 29% and 16% in nonozonated wheat and rye straw, respectively. Ozonization pretreatment has been also applied on other LC materials such as cotton stalks [272], coastal Bermuda grass [273], softwood [274], and waste paper [275].

5.13.4.7.4 Physical pretreatment processes
5.13.4.7.4(i) Mechanical comminution

Comminution of LC materials through a combination of chipping, grinding, and/or milling can be applied to improve their digestibility by reducing their particle size and crystallinity. The reduction in particle size leads to an increase in available specific surface and a reduction in the DP [178]. The process also causes shearing of the biomass. Mechanical pretreatment also results in substantial lignin depolymerization via the cleavage of uncondensed-aryl ether linkages [276]. All these combined factors lead to an increase in the total hydrolysis yield of the lignocellulose in most cases by 5–25% (depending on kind of biomass, kind of milling, and duration of the milling), and also reduces the technical digestion time by 23–59% (thus an increase in hydrolysis rate) [277]. It was shown that, without any pretreatment, corn stover with sizes of 53–75 μm was 1.5 times more productive than larger corn stover particles of 425–710 μm [180].

Milling is considered to be an environmentally friendly pretreatment process. In these pretreatments, no hydrolysis or fermentation inhibitors, such as furfural or hydroxymethyl furfural, are produced [278]. However, size reduction of biomass is an energy-intensive process that warrants improvement to raise the energy efficiency involved in bioethanol production. The National Renewable Energy Laboratory indicated that size reduction required one-third of total energy inputs for biomass to ethanol conversion [279].

The use of mechanical chopping [280], hammer milling [281], grind milling [282], roll milling [283], vibratory milling [284], and ball milling [276] have proved successful as a low-cost pretreatment strategy.

Previously, milling reactors have been used as a means of pretreatment. The milling process has been studied prior to and in combination with enzymatic hydrolysis, where mechanical actions, mass transport, and enzymatic hydrolysis are performed simultaneously in order to improve the hydrolysis process. The attrition mill bioreactor [285] and the intensive mass transfer reactor, including ferromagnetic particles and two ferromagnetic inductors [286, 287], are two examples of these processes. Mais et al. [288] used a ball mill reactor for the pretreatment and hydrolysis of α-cellulose and reported the number of ball beads as an effective parameter to improve enzymatic hydrolysis of α-cellulose.

More recently, studies have shown that energy consumption for grinding biomass depends on initial particle size, moisture content, material properties, mass feed rate, and machine variables [281]. Optimum operating conditions may lead to reduced energy expended for size reduction [289]. Bitra et al. [290] determined the direct mechanical input energy for hammer mill and knife mill [289] size reduction of switchgrass, wheat straw, and corn stover over a range of mill operating speeds, screen sizes, and mass feed rates.

Although milling pretreatments are often described as high-energy requirement techniques, wet disk milling has been recently described as a potential feasible mechanical technique to treat rice straw [291]. Glucose and xylose yields by wet disk milling, ball milling, and hot-compressed water treatment were 78.5% and 41.5%, 89.4% and 54.3%, and 70.3% and 88.6%, respectively. The energy consumption of wet disk milling was lower than that of other pretreatments.

Sugarcane bagasse and straw were treated under comparative conditions by ball milling and wet disk milling techniques and their physical properties and susceptibility toward enzymatic hydrolysis and fermentation were evaluated [278]. Ethanol yields from total fermentable sugars by using a C6-fermenting strain reached 89.8% and 91.8% for bagasse and straw hydrolysates, respectively.

Ball milling pretreatment combined with the addition of dilute acid and alkali proved to be an effective processing to enhance the enzymatic hydrolysis efficiency of corn stover [292]. The results also indicated that the treatment effect of wet milling is better than that of dry milling.

5.13.4.7.4(ii) Irradiation

Irradiation by gamma rays, electron beam, and MWs can improve enzymatic hydrolysis of lignocelluloses [293]. Ionizing irradiation can modify and disrupt the structure of lignocellulose and can be an effective method of pretreatment of LC biomass for sugar production [294]. Irradiation of cellulose by gamma rays cleaves the β-1,4-glycosidic bonds, thus giving a larger surface area and a lower crystallinity. Such ionizing radiation predominantly scissions and degrades or depolymerizes cellulose, thus a reduction of the DP is obtained. This method is, however, far too expensive to be used in a full-scale process [187]. It is also doubtful that it can be used in combination with technologies supposed to be environmentally friendly.

The irradiation degradation of various LC materials for increasing sugar yield has been reported, such as bagasse [295], rice straw, chaff, sawdust [296], corn stalk, peanut husk [297], oil palm empty fruit bunch [298], and wheat straw [294]. Wheat and rice straw, sawdust, and chaff irradiated to 500 kGy showed very high glucose yields when hydrolyzed with cellulase. Bagasse irradiated with 1000 kGy yielded 2 or 4 times as much glucose in enzymatic and acid hydrolysis, respectively, as compared to nonirradiated bagasse. Waste newspaper (predominantly cellulose and residual lignin) irradiated with an electron beam to 100 kGy produced 30% more glucose by acid hydrolysis than samples without electron beam treatment [299]. The best glucose yield was obtained by irradiating the paper to 100 kGy and using maleic acid at 3% for the hydrolysis.

MW, a nonionizing radiation, is an alternative method for conventional heating. Compared with conduction/convection heating, which is based on superficial heat transfer, MW uses the ability of direct interaction between a heated object and an applied electromagnetic field to create heat. Therefore, the heating is volumetric and rapid [300]. When MW is used to treat lignocelluloses, it selectively heats the more polar (lossy) part and creates a 'hot spot' with the inhomogeneous materials. It is hypothesized that this unique heating feature results in an 'explosion' effect among the particles and improves the disruption of the recalcitrant structures of lignocellulose. It disrupts the silicified waxy surface, breaks down lignin–hemicellulose complexes, partially removes silicon and lignin, and exposes more accessible surface area of cellulose to cellulase [301]. In addition, the electromagnetic field used in MW might create nonthermal effects that also accelerate the destruction of the crystal structures [302].

The effect of MW irradiation, in addition to MW-assisted alkali pretreatment of different LC materials has been reported, such as, rice straw [301, 303, 304], wheat [305, 306], and switchgrass [302, 307, 308]. The results demonstrated, though to varying extent, that MW-assisted alkali treatment is an efficient way to improve the enzymatic digestibility of LC biomass. In a comparative study, Zhu *et al.* [304] argued that the MW/chemical pretreatment is a more effective rice-straw pretreatment technique than the conventional heating chemical pretreatment because it accelerates reactions during the pretreatment process.

5.13.4.7.4(iii) Extrusion

Extrusion process is a novel and promising physical pretreatment method for biomass conversion to ethanol production. In extrusion, the materials are subjected to heating, mixing, and shearing, resulting in physical and chemical modifications during their passage through the extruder [309]. Screw speed and barrel temperature are believed to disrupt the lignocellulose structure causing defibrillation, fibrillation, and shortening of the fibers, and, in the end, increasing accessibility of carbohydrates to enzymatic attack.

The extruder has many advantages such as the ability to provide high shear, rapid heat transfer, and effective and rapid mixing. Because of its adaptability to many different process modifications such as the addition of chemicals or removal of materials, and the application of high pressure and expansion treatment (using steam or other solvents) – all in a continuous process, extrusion has the potential to become a viable biomass pretreatment method. Because extrusion is a continuous pretreatment, it would be practicable and easy to adopt at large-scale production [310]. Moreover, no liquid fraction is produced during extrusion; therefore, no effluent disposal/treatment problem arises.

Dale *et al.* [311] reported a 32% increase in enzymatic hydrolysis yield over untreated corn stover when the AFEX process was employed using a twin-screw extruder and a 23% increase over material extruded without ammonia. In recent studies, application of enzymes during an extrusion process is being considered as a promising technology for ethanol production [178]. Lee *et al.* [310] reported cellulose to glucose conversion of 62.4% from Douglas fir fibrillated using a twin screw extruder at 50 rpm and 40 °C when ethylene glycol was added as a cellulose affinity additive.

Table 10 Effect of extrusion bioreactor parameters and biomass moisture content on sugar recovery for different feedstock

Feedstock	Compression ratio	Screw speed (rpm)	Barrel temperature (°C)	Biomass moisture content (%)	Glucose	Xylose	Combined	Reference
Switchgrass	3:1	50	150	15	45.3	43.9	44.5	[313]
Prairie cordgrass	3:1	50	50	25	61.4	84.3	65.8	
Corn stover	ND	75	125	ND	74.6	49.2	60.9	[312]

The different bioreactor parameters must be taken into account to achieve the highest efficiency in the process. Extruder parameters such as compression ratio, screw speed, and barrel temperature are important factors influencing sugar recovery from the biomass [312]. Also the moisture content of the material affects sugar recovery [313] (**Table 10**).

5.13.4.7.5 Physicochemical pretreatment processes

5.13.4.7.5(i) Steam explosion

This is a hydrothermal pretreatment in which the biomass is subjected to pressurized steam for a period of time ranging from several seconds to a few minutes, and then suddenly depressurized. It combines mechanical forces and chemical effects; the mechanical effects are caused by the explosive decompression separating the fibers, whereas the chemical effects are due to the hydrolysis (autohydrolysis) of acetyl groups present in hemicellulose. Autohydrolysis takes place when high temperatures promote the formation of acetic acid from acetyl groups; furthermore, water can also act as an acid at high temperatures [178].

The SE process results in a hydrolysis of glycosidic bonds in the hemicelluloses and, to a lesser extent, in the cellulose. It also leads to a cleavage of hemicellulose–lignin bonds. The reactions result in an increased water solubilization of hemicelluloses and an increased solubility of lignin in alkaline or organic solvents, leaving the cellulose as a solid residue with a reduced DP and exposes the cellulose surface and increases enzyme accessibility to the cellulose microfibrils [314]. The hemicelluloses can be directly recovered from the aqueous fraction after SE. Lignin is removed only to a limited extent during the pretreatment but is redistributed on the fiber surfaces as a result of melting and depolymerization/repolymerization reactions. A subsequent aqueous alkaline or organic solvent step results in an appreciable delignification. A subsequent oxidative treatment can lead to complete delignification [315].

The most important factors affecting the effectiveness of SE are particle size, temperature, residence time, and moisture content. Optimal hemicellulose solubilization and hydrolysis can be achieved by either high temperature with short residence time (270 °C, 1 min) or lower temperature with longer residence time (190 °C, 10 min) [316].

The SE process offers several attractive features when compared to other pretreatment technologies. These include the potential for significantly lower environmental impact, lower capital investment, more potential for energy efficiency, less hazardous process chemicals, and conditions and complete sugar recovery [317]. The conventional mechanical methods require 70% more energy than SE to achieve the same particle size reduction [318]. SE is recognized as one of the most cost-effective pretreatment processes for hardwoods and agricultural residues, but it is less effective for softwoods due to their low content of acetyl groups in the hemicellulosic portion [190].

The main drawbacks of SE include destruction of a portion of the xylan fraction, incomplete disruption of the lignin–carbohydrate matrix [319], and generation of compounds that might be inhibitory to microorganisms used in downstream processes (hydrolysis and fermentation steps) [320].

Addition of H_2SO_4 [321] or SO_2 [322] (typically 0.3–3% (w/w)) in SE can decrease time and temperature, effectively improve hydrolysis, decrease the production of inhibitory compounds, and lead to the complete removal of hemicellulose. SO_2 impregnation was found to be preferable, since it resulted in approximately the same sugar yields, but with better fermentability [323]. Sulfuric acid impregnation led to a threefold increase in the concentration of the fermentation inhibitors furfural and 5-hydroxymethylfurfural (5-HMF) and a twofold increase in the concentration of inhibitory aliphatic acids (formic, acetic, and levulinic acids) [324].

SE technology has proven to be efficient for ethanol production from a wide range of raw materials. **Table 11** shows a summary of the optimum operational conditions for different feedstocks.

Two-step pretreatment has been suggested in several studies as a means of increasing the recovery of hemicellulosic sugars, without reducing the yield of glucose from cellulose [346, 347]. In the first step, pretreatment is performed at low temperature to solubilize the hemicellulosic fraction, and the cellulose fraction is subjected to a second pretreatment step at higher temperatures.

5.13.4.7.5(ii) Liquid hot water

LHW is another hydrothermal treatment, which does not require rapid decompression and does not employ any catalyst or chemicals. Pressure is applied to maintain water in the liquid state at elevated temperatures (160–240 °C) and provoke alterations in the structure of the lignocellulose. The objective of the LHW is to solubilize mainly the hemicellulose, to make the cellulose more accessible, and to avoid the formation of inhibitors. The slurry generated after pretreatment can be filtered to obtain two fractions: one solid cellulose-enriched fraction and one liquid fraction rich in hemicellulose-derived sugars [348].

To avoid the formation of inhibitors, the pH should be kept between 4 and 7 during the pretreatment, because at this pH, hemicellulosic sugars are retained in oligomeric form and monomers formation is minimized. The minimization of complete hydrolysis to monosaccharides minimizes the subsequent degradation of these sugars to various aldehydes. Thus, with an optimized controlled pH, the LHW pretreatment process will reduce the formation of degradation products [348].

The optimal conditions to enhance the enzymatic digestibility of different feedstocks by using LHW are summarized in **Table 12**.

Flow-through (percolation) systems have been reported to remove more hemicellulose and lignin than batch systems from some materials. In cases in which hemicellulose and lignin removal are increased with the acid addition, the addition of external acid during the flow-through process can also be considered [361]. However, percolation or flow-through is

Table 11 Optimum operational conditions for pretreatment of different lignocellulosics by steam explosion

Substrate	Temperature (°C)	Time (min)	Reagent	Concentration (%)	Other conditions	Reference
Corn stover	200	5	H_2SO_4	2		[326]
	190	5	H_2SO_4	3		[327]
	200	10	SO_2	2		[330]
Wheat straw	190	10	H_2SO_4	0.2		[329]
	190	10	H_2SO_4	0.9		[321]
	200	5	H_2SO_4	0.9		
	200	3	None			[331]
	210	10	None			[333]
Barley straw	190	5	H_2SO_4	0.2		[334]
Cereal straw (wheat, barley, oat)	198	2.5	None			[332]
Rice straw	243	2	None			[335]
Sugarcane bagasse	205	10	H_2SO_4	1		[324]
	205	10	SO_2	1.1		
	190	5	SO_2	2		[336]
	190	5	SO_2	2		[337]
Sunflower stalks	220	5	None			[338]
Olive residues	190	5	None			[340]
Citrus peel wastes	160	5	None			[339]
Herbaceous residues (*Brassica*)	210	4–8	None		Larger particle size	[325]
Poplar	214	6	None			[344]
	210	4	None			[345]
	210	4	None			[319]
Softwood	210	5.5	SO_2	3		[322]
	190	12	SO_2	2.5		[328]
	200	5	SO_2	4		[341]
Hardwood	210	10	None			[342]
Household waste	211	3	None			[343]

Table 12 Optimum operational conditions for pretreatment of different lignocellulosics by LHW

Substrate	Temperature (°C)	Time (min)	Flow (ml min^{-1})	Operation	Reference
Corn stover	190	15		Batch	[348]
	190	15		Batch	[180]
	195	15		Batch	[353]
	220	16	10	Flow-through	[359]
	200	24	10	Flow-through	[349]
	190	30	5	Flow-through	[350]
Wheat straw	188	40		Batch	[354]
Rice straw	180	30		Batch	[355]
Sugercane bagasse	220	2		Batch	[351]
	200	10		Batch	[356]
Alfalfa	220	2		Flow-through	[352]
Palm frond	178	11		Batch	[360]
Switchgrass	190	10		Batch	[357]
Poplar biomass	180	48		Batch	[345]
Softwood Hardwood	180–285	60	10	Flow-through	[358]

challenging to implement commercially, and the high amounts of water used result in high-energy requirements for the pretreatment and product recovery.

A two-step pretreatment with hot compressed water was carried out on bamboo, chinquapin (hardwood), and Japan cedar (softwood). The temperature of water was maintained at 180 °C for 20 min, after which it was raised to about 285 °C at a rate of 5 °C min^{-1} and maintained at 285 °C for about 7 min. By these operations, free sugars, some of lignin and most of hemicellulose, were first solubilized in water and flowed out during the initial 20 min and >95% of bamboo and chinquapin were observed to be hydrolyzed [358].

LHW pretreatments are cost-effective due to the reduced cost of the reactor material required in the absence of a catalyst requirement and with low corrosion potential. Compared to SE, higher pentose sugar recovery and lower formation of inhibitors are the most prominent advantages. However, since the water content is much higher than in steam pretreatment, the resulting sugar solution is more diluted and thus causes the downstream processes to be more energy demanding. Moreover, the technique is not well developed at an industrial scale [178].

5.13.4.7.5(iii) Ammonia fiber explosion

In the AFEX process, biomass is treated with liquid anhydrous ammonia at moderate temperatures (between 60 and 100 °C) and high pressure for a variable period of time. The pressure is then instantaneously released, causing the ammonia to flash violently and disrupt the fibrous biomass structure [178]. The ammonia can then be recovered and recycled. The small amount of ammonia that remains in the biomass (<1% by weight of the biomass) might serve as a nitrogen source for the microbes that use the sugars that are enzymatically hydrolyzed from the lignocellulose [169]. Ammonia recovery and recycle is feasible despite of its high volatility [362], though the associated complexity and costs of ammonia recovery may be a significant factor regarding commercial potential of the AFEX pretreatment [363].

The combined chemical effect (cellulose decrystallization, hemicellulose prehydrolysis, and lignin alterations) and physical effect (increased accessible surface area and decreased bulk density) dramatically increase lignocellulose susceptibility to an enzymatic attack [178].

While some other pretreatments such as SE produce a slurry that can be separated into a solid and a liquid fraction, AFEX produces only a pretreated solid material [178]. During the pretreatment, only a small amount of the solid material is solubilized; little hemicellulose or lignin is removed [361]. Deacetylation of hemicellulose is also observed.

The absence of inhibitors to the downstream biological processes is one of the main advantages of the ammonia pretreatment, even though some phenolic fragments of lignin and other cell wall extractives may remain on the cellulosic surface [190]. Development of inexpensive, low thermochemical severity pretreatments that minimize the formation of biological inhibitors while maximizing cell wall deconstruction is an important objective of the nascent cellulosic ethanol industry. It has been shown that the formation of furans was 36-fold lower for AFEX compared to dilute acid treatment, while carboxylic acids (e.g., lactic and succinic acids) yield was 100- to 1000-fold lower during AFEX compared to previous reports using sodium hydroxide as pretreatment reagent [364].

Optimal operational conditions for the pretreatment of corn stover by AFEX were found to be (1) temperature, 90 °C, (2) ammonia loading, 1.0 kg of ammonia:kg of dry corn stover, (3) moisture content of corn stover, 60% (dry weight basis), and (4) residence time (holding at target temperature), 5 min [362].

At optimal conditions, AFEX can achieve >90% conversion of cellulose and hemicellulose to fermentable sugars for a broad variety of LC materials. There are many adjustable parameters in the AFEX process: ammonia loading, water loading, temperature, time, blow-down pressure, and number of treatments [365]. Reduction in substrate particle size was also found to affect the AFEX process and rate of hydrolysis. The corn stover particle size reduction and washing were found to improve effectiveness of AFEX pretreatment and substantially improve the hydrolysis yields [366].

The AFEX pretreatment is more effective on agricultural residues and herbaceous crops, with limited effectiveness demonstrated on woody biomass and other high lignin feedstocks [361]. Nearly, quantitative sugar yields have been produced from bagasse and coastal Bermuda grass [365]. Good results were also achieved with other agricultural residues, for example, corn stalks and barley straw [367], rice straw [368, 369], corn stover [169, 362, 370], and herbaceous crops, for example, forages (namely, timothy grass, alfalfa, and reed canary grass) [367], and switchgrass [371, 372].

Most MSW components have been substantially delignified and pretreated in pulping operations. Therefore, MSW is much more digestible than agricultural residues, as has been previously stated. Whereas AFEX increases agricultural residue digestibilities by 100–1000%, it increases MSW component digestibility by only 15–50%. Since so much of the MSW readily hydrolyzes without pretreatment, only the unreacted residues from saccharification/fermentation should be AFEX-treated, since much of the raw material is already digestible [373].

5.13.4.7.5(iv) Ammonia recycled percolation

The ARP pretreatment employs aqueous ammonia (5–15 wt%) in a flow-through (percolation) reactor packed with biomass at 140–210 °C for a reaction time up to 90 min and percolation rate about 5 ml min^{-1} [184], after which the ammonia is recovered.

As a pretreatment reagent, ammonia has a number of desirable characteristics as follows: swelling of cellulosic materials, highly selective delignification reaction, low interaction with carbohydrates, and high volatility. One of the known reactions of aqueous ammonia with lignin is the cleavage of C-O-C bonding in lignin as well as ether and ester bonding in lignin–carbohydrate complexes [374]. ARP can solubilize hemicellulose but cellulose remains intact. It leads to a short-chained cellulosic material with high glucan content [188]. ARP treatment of corn stover removes 73% of lignin, solubilized 50% of xylan, but retains >92% of cellulose [375].

The use of ammonia not only causes pretreatment effects but also fractionates biomass, especially separating lignin from biomass. Furthermore, the lignin generated in this process is sulfur- and sodium-free, unlike the lignin generated in conventional pulping processes. It is therefore of high quality and may command high byproduct credits [376].

ARP is an efficient delignification method for hardwood and agricultural residues, but is somewhat less effective for softwood. The ARP process has been studied for the pretreatment of various LC biomass feedstocks including hardwood [376], wastepaper and pulp mill sludges [377], waste oak wood [374], herbaceous biomass [378], and corn stover [169, 379, 380].

The primary factors influencing the reactions occurring in the ARP are the reaction time, temperature, ammonia concentrations, and the amount of liquid throughput. For corn stover, the optimum reaction conditions were found to be 15 wt% of ammonia at 170 °C and 3.3 ml min^{-1} of flow rate for 10 min [379].

An important challenge for ARP is to reduce liquid loading or process temperature to lower energy cost. In this context, soaking in aqueous ammonia (SAA) appears as an interesting alternative since it is performed at lower temperature (40–90 °C) and being one of the few pretreatment methods where both glucan and xylan are retained in the solids [218]. The SAA treatment of corn stover removed 55–74% of lignin, but retained 100% of glucan and 85% of xylan under mild conditions (ambient temperature, atmospheric pressure, and 10–60 days treatment time) [380]. In order to reduce the very long reaction time, a slight elevation of the temperature was attempted. SAA operations at 60 °C reduced the reaction time from 10 days of room temperature operation to 12 h [381]. The treated corn stover retained 100% glucan and 85% of xylan, but removed 62% of lignin.

5.13.4.7.5(v) Wet oxidation

WO is an oxidative pretreatment method, which involves the treatment of the biomass with water and air, or oxygen, at temperatures from 170 to 200 °C and pressures of 0.5–2 MPa for 10–15 min. The addition of oxygen at temperatures above 170 °C makes the process exothermic, reducing the total energy demand. Fuel requirements for WO are low since the only thermal energy required for WO is the difference in enthalpy between the incoming and outgoing streams. Though the capital cost for WO is higher than that for other pretreatment techniques, the operating costs are almost entirely for power to compress air [382].

The main reactions in WO are the formation of acids from hydrolytic processes and oxidative reactions [383]. Phenolic compounds are not the end products during WO because they are further degraded to carboxylic acids. However, the production of furfural and 5-HMF is lower during WO when being compared to SE or LHW methods [384].

WO has been reported to be a potentially effective pretreatment technique for fractionating lignocellulose into a solubilized hemicellulose fraction and a solid cellulose-rich fraction with minimum inhibitor formation, thereby facilitating enhanced enzymatic hydrolysis of the pretreated material for subsequent ethanol fermentation with minimum inhibitor formation [383]. The crystalline structure of cellulose is opened during the WO process, the hemicellulose is solubilized, and the lignin is decomposed to CO_2, H_2O, and carboxylic acids. Carboxylic acids are also formed as a result of hemicellulose deacetylation.

WO has successfully been applied to wheat straw [385–388], corn stover [389, 390], sugarcane bagasse [391, 392], rice husk [382], clover–ryegrass mixture [383], other agricultural residues [393], softwood [394], and organic household waste [395].

5.13.4.7.5(vi) Supercritical fluid technology

The utilization of CO_2 as a supercritical fluid significantly reduces corrosive potential while retaining the advantage of an acid-catalyzed process. At the same time, CO_2 is a green process component, which can be easily removed by depressurization and without creating waste products [396].

Supercritical carbon dioxide displays gas-like mass transfer properties, besides a liquid-like solvating power. An increase in pressure facilitates the faster penetration of carbon dioxide molecules into the crystalline structures, thus more glucose is produced from the cellulosic material after the explosion as compared to those without the pretreatment [397]. Carbon dioxide molecules are comparable in size to those of water and ammonia, and thus are able to penetrate small pores accessible to water and ammonia molecules.

Supercritical pretreatment conditions can effectively remove lignin, increasing substrate digestibility. Operation at low temperatures compared to other methods prevents monosaccharides degradation, but in comparison to steam and ammonia explosion sugar yields obtained are lower. Nevertheless, a comparison of different pretreatment methods on several substrates showed that CO_2 explosion was more cost-effective than ammonia explosion and the formation of inhibitors was lower when compared to SE [398].

Supercritical CO_2 has proven to improve enzymatic hydrolysis in many LC materials as in aspen (hardwood) [399], southern yellow pine (softwood) [399], and cellulose-containing wastes from cotton production and reprocessing of crude cotton [400]. An improvement in fermentable hexose production from LCWs, including corn stalks and wheat straw by using combined supercritical and subcritical hydrothermal treatment, has been also reported [401].

Simultaneous pretreatment by CO_2 explosion and enzymatic hydrolysis in one step has also been of interest. The rate of hydrolysis is believed to be enhanced possibly due to the decrease in mass transfer resistance, while the activity and stability of cellulase is sustained during the hydrolysis [402]. Park *et al.* [403] obtained 100% glucose yield, while applying supercritical CO_2 and enzymatic hydrolysis of cellulose simultaneously.

Table 13 Reported fungus pretreatments for different lignocellulosic materials

Substrate	Fungus	References
Corn stover	*Ceriporiopsis subvermispora*	[405, 406]
	Irpex lacteus	[407, 408]
	Echinodontium taxodii	[408]
	Pleurotus ostreatus	[408]
	Cyathus stercoreus	[420]
	Phanerochaete chrysosporium	[420]
Wheat straw	*Phanerochaete chrysosporium*	[414]
	Pycnoporus cinnabarinus	[414]
	Pleurotus ostreatus	[423]
	Ischnoderma benzoinum	[423]
	Fusarium concolor	[424]
Cereal straw	*Pycnoporus sanguineus*	[413]
Rice straw	*Phanerochaete chrysosporium*	[409]
Rice straw	*Pleurotus ostreatus*	[418]
Rice hull	*Pleurotus ostreatus*	[415]
Sugarcane bagasse	*Ceriporiopsis subvermispora*	[421]
	Pleurotus salmoneostramineus	[421]
	Pleurotus eryngii	[421]
	Lentinula edodes	[421]
Sugarcane trash	*Trichoderma reesei*	[410]
	Trichoderma viride	[410]
	Aspergillus terreus	[410]
	Aspergillus awamori	[410]
Cotton stalks	*Phanerochaete chrysosporium*	[411]
Coastal Bermuda grass	*Ceriporiopsis subvermispora*	[419]
	Phanerochaete chrysosporium	[419]
Softwood	*Echinodontium taxodii*	[416]
Hardwood	*Echinodontium taxodii*	[416]
Beech wood	*Ceriporiopsis subvermispora*	[412]
	Pleurotus ostreatus	[412]
	Phanerochaete chrysosporium	[422]
Bamboo residues	*Coriolus versicolor*	[417]

5.13.4.7.6 Biological pretreatment

5.13.4.7.6(i) Fungal pretreatment

In this environmentally friendly approach microorganisms (fungi) that degrade lignin and hemicellulose and very little of cellulose are employed as a pretreatment method for enhancing enzymatic saccharification of LC biomass in ethanol production processes. Lignin degradation by white-rot fungi, the most effective for biological pretreatment of LC materials, occurs through the action of a highly efficient enzymatic system. Fungi have two types of extracellular enzymatic systems; the hydrolytic system, which produces hydrolases that are responsible for polysaccharide degradation, and a unique oxidative and extracellular ligninolytic system, which degrades lignin and opens phenyl rings [404].

In general, such a method offers many advantages such as low capital cost, low energy, no chemicals requirement, and mild environmental conditions. However, the main drawback is that the rate of biological pretreatment processes is far too low for industrial use. Nevertheless, the method could be used as a first step followed by some of the other types of pretreatment methods [190].

Several white-rot fungi have been examined on different LC biomass showing high delignification efficiency. **Table 13** shows reported fungus pretreatments for different LC materials.

5.13.4.7.6(ii) Enzymatic pretreatment

Commercial phenolic acid esterases have been employed to pretreat LC substrates for bioethanol production [425]. Degradability by cellulase was substantially increased by pretreatment with esterases. Corn stover fractions degraded by cellulase, with and without esterase pretreatment, showed that dry weight loss and release of phenolic acids and sugars all improved with esterase pretreatment, but variations occurred with different fractions [426].

Since the phenolic acids are toxic to microbes and enzymes, the separation and collection of phenolic acids released by esterases are necessary to optimize subsequent saccharification and fermentation of the pretreated materials. The use of esterases to release phenolic acids into the filtrate offers the possibility of a value-added coproduct in processes of lignocellulose bioconversion to ethanol. These acids (ferulic and *p*-coumaric acid) may have value, owing to their antioxidant and antimicrobial properties, as

Table 14 Effect of various pretreatment methods on the physicochemical properties of corn stover and respective glucan and xylan conversion after enzymatic hydrolysis

Pretreatment method	CrI	DP	Removal (%)					Yield (%) (after hydrolysis)	
			Cellulose	Hemicellulose		Lignin	Acetyl groups	Glucose	Xylose
Unpretreated	50.30	7000						ND	ND	8.5
Dilute acid	52.51	2700	5–10	70–75	72.8	18	55	92	93	15.7	95.6
LHW (controlled pH)	44.52	5600	5–10	40	ND	ND	55	91	81	85.1	81.8
AFEX	36.29	6600	0	0	0	0	30–35	96	91	90.5	92.7
ARP	25.98	4600	1–5	50–60	51.9	75–85	85–90	90	88	95.9	88.3
Lime	56.17	3200	1–3	30–35	ND	55–60	90–95	94	76	90.1	75.3
Steam explosion –SO$_2$	ND	3000	3–5	40	ND	40–45	55	87	78	92.4	ND
Reference	[169]	[428]	[428]	[428]	[429]	[428]	[428]	[428]	[428]	ND	[363]
								[363]	

[375] 81

natural compounds for pest control, as a substrate for conversion to vanillin used as a flavor constituent and in cosmetic preparations [427].

5.13.4.7.7 Comparing different pretreatment methods

To compare the performance of pretreatment technologies on a consistent basis, a single feedstock, the same cellulase enzyme, shared analytical methods, and common data interpretation approaches should be applied. By comparing five pretreatment processes (dilute acid, LHW, AFEX, ARP, and lime) for the liberation of sugars from corn stover, Eggeman and Elander [363] concluded that all of the designs considered were projected to be capital-intensive. Low-cost pretreatment reactors in some pretreatment processes are often counterbalanced by higher costs associated with pretreatment catalyst recovery or higher costs for ethanol product recovery.

The results from a number of reports are collectively summarized in **Table 14** to facilitate the comparison. The operational conditions, enzyme loadings, and more detailed information can be obtained from these references, if desired.

From the data in the table, the following remarks can be concluded:

- It is evident that dilute acid, neutral pH, and water-only pretreatments solubilized mostly hemicellulose, whereas addition of lime or percolation with ammonia removed mostly lignin.
- Although removal of hemicellulose and lignin differed, high yields of glucose were achieved by enzymatically hydrolyzing the remaining solids for all of these pretreatments.
- The crystallinity index values for the different pretreatments are given at their optimal conditions (highest sugar yield in enzymatic hydrolysis). AFEX and ARP are effective in decrystallizing cellulose. Controlled pH also shows a decreased CrI and lime and dilute acid gives an apparent increase in CrI. These results confirm that crystallinity is not the only factor that affects the enzymatic hydrolysis of corn stover.
- The given results pertain specifically to corn stover. However, they may serve as a guide for the performance of other LC materials in the presence of the relevant additional data.

5.13.4.8 Saccharification and Fermentation

Biomass source, pretreatment, enzyme mixture, and fermentation microbe are interdependent variables.

5.13.4.8.1 Inhibitors

The composition and concentration of degradation compounds resulting from different pretreatment operations vary according to the type of lignocellulose used, the chemistry, and the nature of the pretreatment process such as temperature, time, pressure, pH, redox conditions, and addition of catalysts. These degradation compounds include organic acids such as acetic acid, formic acid, and levulinic acid; sugar degradation products such as furfural from xylose and 5-HMF from glucose; and lignin degradation phenol products such as vanillin, syringaldehyde, and 4-hydroxybenzaldehyde. The order of the inhibition strength by the lignocellulose degradation products to cellulase was found to be lignin derivatives > furan derivatives > organic acids > ethanol [430]. It has been also reported that compounds exhibiting higher hydrophobicity tend to be more inhibitory and that the pH at which fermentation is carried out has a significant effect on the inhibitory actions of many of the listed compounds [431].

Because the resulting degradation products are strong inhibitors to cellulase and fermenting microorganisms, the pretreatment liquor must be detoxified prior to fermentation [193, 194, 432–434].

To avoid the added costs of detoxification steps, attempts have been made to study the mechanisms of stress tolerance, particularly to fermentation inhibitors such as furfural and 5-HMF [435]. By using more inhibitor–tolerant yeast strains for bioethanol fermentation, higher rates were achieved compared to the parental strains.

5.13.4.8.2 Cost of enzymes

The cost of enzymes for converting plant biomass materials to fermentable sugars is a major impediment to the development of a practical LC ethanol industry [436]. Enzymes are intrinsically expensive because they must be produced by living systems and are thermodynamically unstable [437]. The greater the chemical and physical recalcitrance of lignocellulose, the higher will be the enzyme loadings necessary to obtain reasonable degradation rates.

Significant progress has been made in the cost reduction of cellulases [186]. Cost reduction has been achieved by a combination of enzyme engineering and fermentation process development [438]. The way forward for the development of more efficient lignocellulose-degrading enzyme cocktails will require deeper and more precise knowledge about the specific enzymes that are involved in the degradation of lignocellulose. Banerjee et al. [439] presented an assay platform and an optimized 'core' set, which provided a starting point for the rapid testing and optimization of alternate core enzymes from other microbial and recombinant sources as well as for the testing of 'accessory' proteins for development of superior enzyme mixtures for biomass conversion.

5.13.4.8.3 Enzyme mixture

For LC ethanol production, the most desired attributes of cellulases are a composition, which contains the complete hydrolytic machinery, high specific activity, high rate of turnover with native cellulose/biomass as substrate, thermostability, decreased susceptibility to enzyme inhibition (by cellobiose and glucose), selective adsorption on cellulose, and the ability to withstand shear forces.

Efficient cellulose hydrolysis to glucose requires the concerted action of a cellulase system consisting of endo-1,4-β-gluconases (endoglucanases), which randomly attack the internal β-glucosidic bonds within the chain, exo-1,4-β-gluconase (cellobiohydrolases), which remove cellobiose units from the nonreducing ends of the chain, and β-galactosidases, which hydrolyze the soluble oligosaccharides produced by the gluconases to glucose [440]. Active cellulase systems are widespread within the fungi and aerobic and anaerobic bacteria [441].

Several approaches have been utilized to improve cellulase performance and decrease the amount of enzyme needed to saccharify biomass substrates. The primary target for cellulase engineering has been the cellobiohydrolases, as they tend to constitute 60–80% of natural cellulase systems [438]. Several mutants that were expressed from the aerobic fungus *Trichoderma reesei* showed improved thermostability and reversibility [442, 443] as well as suitability for cloning the genes of cellulases [444].

Cellulase enzyme formulations contain enough hemicellulase activity to release about half of the residual hemicellulose, but supplementation with xylanase [429], betaxylobiase, betaglucosidase [445], pectinases [446], and other additives, for example. Bovine serum albumin [447], Tween-20 [448], and polyethylene glycol (PEG-6000) [448] can release more sugars from hemicellulose while reducing total protein levels, and therefore costs.

5.13.4.8.4 Enzyme–substrate interaction

The enzymatic hydrolysis of cellulose encounters various limitations that are both substrate- and enzyme-related. An important criterion related to hydrolysis rate involves the adsorption capacity of cellulases onto cellulose. The rate of hydrolysis was shown to be proportional to the amount of adsorbed enzymes [176].

Because lignin nonproductively ties up and inactivates cellulase enzyme [447], alteration of lignin to reduce its capacity for cellulase or its removal can significantly reduce enzyme costs. Berlin *et al.* [449] proposed a novel approach to improve activity of cellulases for LC hydrolysis based on reduced enzyme–lignin interaction by using weak lignin-binding enzymes. They showed that naturally occurring cellulases with similar catalytic activity on a model cellulosic substrate differed significantly in their affinities for lignin, thereby affecting the performance on native substrates. Palonen [450] found that the location and structure of lignin affected the enzymatic hydrolysis more than the absolute amount of lignin. The study showed that modification of lignin surfaces by oxidative treatments with laccase alone and delignification treatment with a laccase-mediator system led to increased hydrolysis of lignocellulose. Hydrolysis of cellulose was improved by laccase treatment of steam-exploded softwood, and a decrease in the unproductive binding of cellulases to lignin after laccase treatment had been suggested [451]. The fermentability of hydrolysates was greatly improved by the laccase treatment performed on steam-exploded wheat straw [452]. Lu *et al.* [413] presented an efficient system for predelignifying cereal straw *in vitro* using laccase produced by *Pycnoporus sanguineus* H275. Moreover, inhibitory effects caused by furan derivatives, weak acids, and phenolic compounds after lignin breakdown could be reduced by additional laccase.

Recent advent of genomics, proteomics, and associated technologies has enabled researchers to explore various methodologies for controlling and modifying lignins to improve cell wall conversion efficiency (digestibility and pulping) and reduce pretreatment costs [453].

5.13.4.8.5 Fermentation

The ability to use the hemicellulose component in biomass feedstock is critical for any bio-ethanol project. Wild-type *Saccharomyces cerevisiae* (yeast) can ferment glucose but not xylose, whereas xylose and cellooligosaccharides are acceptable to other native or engineered microbes [454]. Organisms that can ferment C5 sugars (e.g., *Pichia stipitis*, *Pachysolen tannophilus*, and *Candida shehatae*) need microaerophilic conditions and are sensitive to inhibitors, higher concentrations of ethanol, and lower pH.

A lot of R&D efforts are being directed to engineer organisms for fermenting both hexose (C6) and pentose (C5) sugars with a considerable amount of success [455–458]. Researchers have basically taken two approaches to increase fermentation yields of ethanol derived from biomass sugars. The first approach has been to add to yeast and other natural ethanologens additional pentose metabolic pathways by genetic engineering. The second approach is to improve ethanol yields by genetic engineering in microorganisms that have the ability to ferment both hexoses and pentoses [459, 460].

Several of the promising results from these studies have also found their way into ethanol production. For example, there are reports on cofermentation using hexose and pentose fermenting yeasts [461], protoplast fusion to impart pentose utilization ability to yeasts [462], and on engineering *Saccharomyces* for C5 utilization [463].

Because the major fermentable sugars in biomass hydrolysate are glucose and xylose (with significantly lower amounts of arabinose, galactose, and mannose), the initial efforts to produce a commercially viable ethanologen have focused on cofermentation of glucose and xylose. In the first approach, xylose-metabolizing genes have been engineered into wild-type ethanologens such as yeast and the bacterium *Zymomonas mobilis* [459, 460]. Recombinant strains of *S. cerevisiae* with the ability to coferment glucose and xylose have been constructed by adding *Pichia stipitis* genes (XYL1, XYL2) for an NADPH-dependent xylose reductase and an NAD$^+$-dependent xylitol dehydrogenase, and by enhancing expression of the endogenous xylulokinase [460].

Functional genomics, including the transcriptome, proteome, metabolome, and fluxome, are powerful tools for targeting metabolic changes to enhance the rate and yield of ethanol production from xylose [464, 465].

5.13.4.9 Consolidated Bioprocessing

CBP of lignocellulose to bioethanol refers to the combining of the four biologically mediated transformations required for this conversion process (production of saccharolytic enzymes, hydrolysis of the polysaccharides present in pretreated biomass, fermentation of hexose sugars, and fermentation of pentose sugars) in one reactor mediated by a microbial consortium [466]. CBP offers the potential for lower biofuel production costs due to simpler feedstock processing, lower energy inputs, and higher conversion efficiencies than SHF processes [467].

Although no natural microorganism exhibits all the features desired for CBP, a number of microorganisms, both bacteria and fungi, possess some of the desirable traits [468]. Cellulolytic fungi, such as *T. reesei*, naturally produce a large repertoire of saccharolytic enzymes to digest lignocellulose efficiently, assimilate all LC sugars, and convert these sugars to ethanol, showing that they naturally possess all pathways for conversion of lignocellulose to bioethanol. For the development of fungi as CBP organisms, the remaining challenges to be met are their low yields and ethanol tolerance, as well as slow rates of fermentation [469].

Biomass-to-ethanol processing mainly focuses on the pure-culture technology that employs recombinant strains to convert the LC biomass into ethanol [470]. One of the challenges in this method is the elevated cost of the external hydrolytic enzymes, which were estimated to account for over 7% of the total production cost [471], thus adding significant operating costs. Furthermore, to prevent contamination, strict aseptic conditions are required [472]; therefore, expensive stainless steel vessels are required, which add significantly to the capital costs.

As an attractive alternative to the traditional pure-culture biotechnology, mixed microbial cultures have evolved to convert biomass into fuels and chemicals. This allows for adaptive microbial diversity, no sterilization requirements, the capacity to use mixed substrates, and the possibility of a continuous process [473]. Mixed-culture fermentation was used successfully with sugarcane bagasse [474], corn stover [475], chicken manure [476], and MSWs [477].

The biomass is chemically pretreated to enhance digestibility and then is fermented anaerobically using a mixed culture of natural acid-forming microorganisms. Enzyme production, substrate hydrolysis, and mixed-acid fermentation are integrated in a single CBP [478]. Traditionally, lime $(Ca(OH)_2)$ treatment is employed as a pretreatment option, because it is robust, effective, inexpensive, and highly recoverable [474]. Furthermore, the calcium cation is common to both the pretreatment agent $(Ca(OH)_2)$ and the fermentation buffer $(CaCO_3)$ [474].

5.13.5 Summary: Bioethanol from Waste

The barriers of first generation biofuels (e.g., competition with food, high energy inputs, poor energy balances, low yields per hectare, damage to ecosystem) can be partly overcome by the utilization of LC materials, which are in surplus, relatively cheap, and easily available. Cellulosic ethanol has a number of potential benefits over corn grain ethanol. Cellulosic ethanol is projected to be much more cost-effective, environmentally beneficial, and have a greater energy output to input ratio than grain ethanol.

Although the cost of biomass is low, releasing fermentable sugars from these materials remains challenging. Process optimization solutions for the production of ethanol from LC biomass require a better understanding of the challenges facing the industry. A major challenge is the pretreatment of LC biomass to reduce biomass recalcitrance, thereby improving the yield of fermentable sugars. This recalcitrance is primarily due to the composition of LC biomass and the way specific components interact with each other. Numerous pretreatments have been presented in this chapter, each having its advantages and disadvantages.

Despite the challenges facing the industry, an impetus is now provided by scientific and technological advances in biosciences and bioengineering that support increased optimism about realizing the full potential of biomass in the liquid fuels area in the near future.

References

[1] Canakci M and van Gerpen JH (2001) A pilot plant to produce biodiesel from high free fatty acid feedstocks, Paper Number 016049, *American Society of Agricultural Engineers, ASAE Annual International Meeting*. Sacramento, CA, USA, 30 July–1 August.

[2] Zhang Y, Dube MA, McLean DD, and Kates M (2003) Biodiesel production from waste cooking oil: 2. Economic assessment and sensitivity analysis. *Bioresource Technology* 90(3): 229–240.

[3] Kulkarni MG and Dalai AK (2006) Waste cooking oil – an economical source for biodiesel: A review. *Industrial and Engineering Chemistry Research* 45(9): 2901–2913.

[4] Dorado MP, Cruz F, Palomar JM, and Lopez FJ (2006) An approach to the economics of two vegetable oil-based biofuels in Spain. *Renewable Energy* 31(8): 1231–1237.

[5] Marchetti JM, Miguel VU, and Errazu AF (2008) Techno-economic study of different alternatives for biodiesel production. *Fuel Processing Technology* 89(8): 740–748.

[6] Haas MJ, McAloon AJ, Yee WC, and Foglia TA (2006) A process model to estimate biodiesel production costs. *Bioresource Technology* 97(4): 671–678.

[7] Szmigielski M, Maniak B, and Piekarski W (2008) Evaluation of chosen quality parameters of used frying rape oil as fuel biocomponent. *International Agrophysics* 22(4): 361–364.

[8] Hill J, Nelson E, Tilman D, *et al.* (2006) Environmental, economic, and energetic costs and benefits of biodiesel and ethanol biofuels. *Proceedings of the National Academy of Science of the United States of America* 103(30): 11206–11210.

[9] Rutz D and Janssen R (2008) *Biofuel Technology Handbook*. Munchen, Germany: WIP Renewable Energies.

[10] Pimentel D, Marklein A, Toth MA, *et al.* (2009) Food versus biofuels: Environmental and economic costs. *Human Ecology* 37(1): 1–12.
[11] Srinivasan S (2009) The food v. fuel debate: A nuanced view of incentive structures. *Renewable Energy* 34(4): 950–954.
[12] Metzger JO (2009) Fats and oils as renewable feedstock for chemistry. *European Journal of Lipid Science and Technology* 111(9): 865–876.
[13] Lam MK, Tan KT, Lee KT, and Mohamed AR (2009) Malaysian palm oil: Surviving the food versus fuel debate for a sustainable future. *Renewable and Sustainable Energy Reviews* 13(6–7): 1456–1464.
[14] Wong NH, Law PL, and Lai SH (2007) Field tests on a grease trap effluent filter. *International Journal of Environmental Science and Technology* 4(3): 345–350.
[15] El Sheltawy ST and Refaat AA (2009) A recommended holistic policy framework for vegetable oil waste management in Egypt. *Proceedings of the 24th International Conference on Solid Waste Technology and Management (ICSW'09)*. Philadelphia, PA, USA, 15–18 March.
[16] Araujo VKWS, Hamacher S, and Scavarda LF (2010) Economic assessment of biodiesel production from waste frying oils. *Bioresource Technology* 101(12): 4415–4422.
[17] Rodrigues Machado E, Marmesat S, Abrantes S, and Dobarganes C (2007) Uncontrolled variables in frying studies: Differences in repeatability between thermoxidation and frying experiments, Grasas Y Aceites. *International Journal of Fats and Oils* 58(3): 283–288.
[18] Knothe G and Steidley KR (2009) A comparison of used cooking oils: A very heterogeneous feedstock for biodiesel. *Bioresource Technology* 100(23): 5796–5801.
[19] Refaat AA (2009) Correlation between the chemical structure of biodiesel and its physical properties. *International Journal of Environmental Science and Technology* 6(4): 677–694.
[20] Freedman B, Butterfield RO, and Pryde EH (1986) Transesterification kinetics of soybean oil. *Journal of American Oil Chemists Society* 63(10): 1375–1380.
[21] Singh A, He B, Thompson J, and van Gerpen J (2006) Process optimization of biodiesel production using different alkaline catalysts. *Applied Engineering in Agriculture* 22(4): 597–600.
[22] Leung DYC and Guo Y (2006) Transesterification of neat and used frying oil: Optimization for biodiesel production. *Fuel Processing Technology* 87(10): 883–890.
[23] Meher LC, Sagar DV, and Naik SN (2006) Technical aspects of biodiesel production by transesterification: A review. *Renewable and Sustainable Energy Reviews* 10(3): 248–268.
[24] Sudhir CV, Sharma NY, and Mohanan P (2007) Potential of waste cooking oil as biodiesel feedstock. *Emirates Journal for Engineering Research* 12(3): 69–75.
[25] Felizardo P, Correia MJ, Raposo I, *et al.* (2006) Production of biodiesel from waste frying oils. *Waste Management* 26(5): 487–494.
[26] Cvengros JJ and Cvengrosová Z (2004) Used frying oils and fats and their utilization in the production of methyl esters of higher fatty acids. *Biomass and Bioenergy* 27(2): 173–181.
[27] Dias JM, Alvim-Ferraz MCM, and Almeida MF (2008) Comparison of different homogeneous alkali catalysts during transesterification of waste and virgin oils and evaluation of biodiesel quality. *Fuel* 87(17–18): 3572–3578.
[28] Issariyakul T, Kulkarni MG, Dalai AK, and Bakhshi NN (2007) Production of biodiesel from waste fryer grease using mixed methanol/ethanol system. *Fuel Processing Technology* 88(5): 429–436.
[29] Supple B, Howard-Hildige R, Gonzalez-Gomez E, and Leahy JJ (2002) The effect of steam treating waste cooking oil on the yield of methyl ester. *Journal of American Oil Chemists Society* 79(2): 175–178.
[30] Lee K, Foglia TA, and Chang K (2002) Production of alkyl ester as biodiesel from fractionated lard and restaurant grease. *Journal of American Oil Chemists Society* 79(2): 191–195.
[31] Refaat AA, Attia NK, Sibak HA, *et al.* (2008) Production optimization and quality assessment of biodiesel from waste vegetable oil. *International Journal of Environmental Science and Technology* 5(1): 75–82.
[32] Meng X, Chen G, and Wang Y (2008) Biodiesel production from waste cooking oil via alkali catalyst and its engine test. *Fuel Processing Technology* 89(9): 851–857.
[33] Yuan X, Liu J, Zeng G, *et al.* (2008) Optimization of conversion of waste rapeseed oil with high FFA to biodiesel using response surface methodology. *Renewable Energy* 33(7): 1678–1684.
[34] Gupta A, Sharma SK, and Toor AP (2007) Production of biodiesel from waste soybean oil. *Journal of Petrotech Society* 4(1): 40–45.
[35] Encinar JM, Gonzalez JF, and Rodriguez-Reinares A (2005) Biodiesel from used frying oil. Variables affecting the yields and characteristics of the biodiesel. *Industrial and Engineering Chemistry Research* 44(15): 5491–5499.
[36] Encinar JM, Juan F, Gonzalez JF, and Rodriguez-Reinares A (2007) Ethanolysis of used frying oils: Biodiesel preparation and characterization. *Fuel Processing Technology* 88(5): 513–522.
[37] Tomasevic AV and Siler-Marinkovic SS (2003) Methanolysis of used frying oil. *Fuel Processing Technology* 81(1): 1–6.
[38] Pinto AC, Guarieiro LN, Rezende MJ, *et al.* (2005) Biodiesel: An overview. *Journal of Brazilian Chemical Society* 16(6B): 1313–1330.
[39] Zhou W and Boocock DGB (2006) Phase behavior of the base-catalyzed transesterification of soybean oil. *Journal of American Oil Chemists Society* 83(12): 1041–1045.
[40] Demirbas A (2009) Biodiesel from waste cooking oil via base-catalytic and supercritical methanol transesterification. *Energy Conversion and Management* 50(4): 923–927.
[41] Singh AK and Fernando SD (2006) Base catalyzed fast-transesterification of soybean oil using ultrasonication, Paper Number 066220. *American Society of Agricultural Engineers, ASAE Annual Meeting*. Portland, OR, USA, 9–12 July.
[42] Lotero E, Liu Y, Lopez DE, *et al.* (2005) Synthesis of biodiesel via acid catalysis. *Industrial and Engineering Chemistry Research* 44(14): 5353–5363.
[43] Zhang Y, Dube MA, McLean DD, and Kates M (2003) Biodiesel production from waste cooking oil: 1. Process design and technological assessment. *Bioresource Technology* 89(1): 1–16.
[44] Wang Y, Ou S, Liu P, *et al.* (2006) Comparison of two different processes to synthesize biodiesel by waste cooking oil. *Journal of Molecular Catalysis A: Chemical* 252(1–2): 107–112.
[45] Zheng S, Kates M, Dube MA, and McLean DD (2006) Acid-catalyzed production of biodiesel from waste frying oil. *Biomass and Bioenergy* 30(3): 267–272.
[46] Cao F, Chen Y, Zhai F, *et al.* (2008) Biodiesel production from high acid value waste frying oil catalyzed by superacid heteropolyacid. *Biotechnology and Bioengineering* 101(1): 93–100.
[47] Bournay L, Casanave D, Delfort B, *et al.* (2005) New heterogeneous process for biodiesel production: A way to improve the quality and the value of the crude glycerin produced by biodiesel plants. *Catalysis Today* 106(1–4): 190–192.
[48] Melero JA, Iglesias J, and Morales G (2009) Heterogeneous acid catalysts for biodiesel production: Current status and future challenges. *Green Chemistry* 11(9): 1285–1308.
[49] Refaat AA (2010) Different techniques for the production of biodiesel from waste vegetable oil. *International Journal of Environmental Science and Technology* 7(1): 183–213.
[50] Sivasamy A, Cheah KY, Fornasiero P, *et al.* (2009) Catalytic applications in the production of biodiesel from vegetable oils. *ChemSusChem* 2(4): 278–300.
[51] Lam MK, Lee KT, and Mohamed AR (2010) Homogeneous, heterogeneous and enzymatic catalysis for transesterification of high free fatty acid oil (waste cooking oil) to biodiesel: A review. *Biotechnology Advances* 28(4): 500–518.
[52] di Serio M, Tesser R, Pengmei L, and Santacesaria E (2008) Heterogeneous catalysts for biodiesel production. *Energy and Fuels* 22(1): 207–217.
[53] Koh T-S and Chung K-H (2008) Production of biodiesel from waste frying oil by transesterification on zeolite catalysts with different acidity. *Journal of the Korean Industrial and Engineering Chemistry* 19(2): 214–221.
[54] Zong M-H, Duan Z-Q, Lou W-Y, *et al.* (2007) Preparation of a sugar catalyst and its use for highly efficient production of biodiesel. *Green Chemistry* 9(5): 434–437.
[55] Furuta S, Matsuhashi H, and Arata K (2004) Biodiesel fuel production with solid superacid catalysis in fixed bed reactor under atmospheric pressure. *Catalysis Communications* 5(12): 721–723.
[56] Jitputti J, Kitiyanan B, Rangsunvigit P, *et al.* (2006) Transesterification of crude palm kernel oil and crude coconut oil by different solid catalysts. *Chemical Engineering Journal* 116(1): 61–66.
[57] Peng B-X, Shu Q, Wang J-F, *et al.* (2008) Biodiesel production from waste oil feedstocks by solid acid catalysis. *Process Safety and Environmental Protection* 86(6): 441–447.

[58] Shu Q, Gao J, Nawar Z, et al. (2010) Synthesis of biodiesel from waste vegetable oil with large amounts of free fatty acids using a carbon-based solid acid catalyst. *Applied Energy* 87(8): 2589–2596.

[59] Shu Q, Nawar Z, Gao J, et al. (2010) Synthesis of biodiesel from a model waste oil feedstock using a carbon-based solid acid catalyst: Reaction and separation. *Bioresource Technology* 101(14): 5374–5384.

[60] Georgogianni KG, Katsoulidis AP, Pomonis PJ, and Kontominas MG (2009) Transesterification of soybean frying oil to biodiesel using heterogeneous catalysts. *Fuel Processing Technology* 90(5): 671–676.

[61] Akoh CC, Chang S-W, Lee G-C, and Shaw J-F (2007) Enzymatic approach to biodiesel production. *Journal of Agricultural and Food Chemistry* 55(22): 8995–9005.

[62] Cerveró JM, Coca J, and Luque S (2008) Production of biodiesel from vegetable oils, Grasas Y Aceites. *International Journal of Fats and Oils* 59(1): 76–83.

[63] Watanabe Y, Shimada Y, Sugihara A, and Tominaga Y (2001) Enzymatic conversion of waste edible oil to biodiesel fuel in a fixed-bed bioreactor. *Journal of American Oil Chemists Society* 78(7): 703–707.

[64] Shimada Y, Watanabe Y, Samukawa T, et al. (1999) Conversion of vegetable oil to biodiesel using immobilized *Candida antarctica* lipase. *Journal of American Oil Chemists Society* 76(7): 789–793.

[65] de Paola MG, Ricca E, Calabro V, et al. (2009) Factor analysis of transesterification reaction of waste oil for biodiesel production. *Bioresource Technology* 100(21): 5126–5131.

[66] Antczak MS, Kubiak A, Antczak T, and Bielecki S (2009) Enzymatic biodiesel synthesis: Key factors affecting efficiency of the process. *Renewable Energy* 34(5): 1185–1194.

[67] Chen G, Ying M, and Li W (2006) Enzymatic conversion of waste cooking oils into alternative fuel – biodiesel. *Applied Biochemistry and Biotechnology* 132(1–3): 911–921.

[68] Maceiras R, Vega M, Costa C, et al. (2009) Effect of methanol content on enzymatic production of biodiesel from waste frying oil. *Fuel* 88(11): 2130–2134.

[69] Azócar L, Ciudad G, Heipieper HJ, et al. (2010) Improving fatty acid methyl ester production yield in a lipase-catalyzed process using waste frying oils as feedstock. *Journal of Bioscience and Bioengineering* 109(6): 609–614.

[70] Yagiz F, Kazan D, and Akin AN (2007) Biodiesel production from waste oils by using lipase immobilized on hydrotalcite and zeolites. *Chemical Engineering Journal* 134(1–3): 262–267.

[71] Li N-W, Zong M-H, and Wu H (2009) Highly efficient transformation of waste oil to biodiesel by immobilized lipase from *Penicillium expansum*. *Process Biochemistry* 44(6): 685–688.

[72] Abdul Halim SF, Kamaruddin AH, and Fernando WJN (2009) Continuous biosynthesis of biodiesel from waste cooking palm oil in a packed bed reactor: Optimization using response surface methodology (RSM) and mass transfer studies. *Bioresource Technology* 100(2): 710–716.

[73] Dizge N, Aydiner C, Imer DY, et al. (2009) Biodiesel production from sunflower, soybean, and waste cooking oils by transesterification using lipase immobilized onto a novel microporous polymer. *Bioresource Technology* 100(6): 1983–1991.

[74] Kusdiana D and Saka S (2001) Kinetics of transesterification in rapeseed oil to biodiesel fuel as treated in supercritical methanol. *Fuel* 80(5): 693–698.

[75] Warabi Y, Kusdiana D, and Saka S (2004) Reactivity of triglycerides and fatty acids of rapeseed oil in supercritical alcohols. *Bioresource Technology* 91(3): 283–287.

[76] Cao WL, Han HW, and Zhang JC (2005) Preparation of biodiesel from soybean oil using supercritical methanol and co-solvent. *Fuel* 84(4): 347–351.

[77] Demirbas A (2007) Biodiesel from sunflower oil in supercritical methanol with calcium oxide. *Energy Conversion and Management* 48(3): 937–941.

[78] Han HW, Cao WL, and Zhang JC (2005) Preparation of biodiesel from soybean oil using supercritical methanol and CO_2 as co-solvent. *Process Biochemistry* 40(9): 3148–3151.

[79] Yin JZ, Xiao M, and Song JB (2008) Biodiesel from soybean oil in supercritical methanol with co-solvent. *Energy Conversion and Management* 49(5): 908–912.

[80] Patil P, Deng S, Rhodes JI, and Lammers PJ (2010) Conversion of waste cooking oil to biodiesel using ferric sulfate and supercritical methanol processes. *Fuel* 89(2): 360–364.

[81] Tan KT, Lee KT, and Mohamed AR (2011) Potential of waste palm cooking oil for catalyst-free biodiesel production. *Energy* 36(4): 2085–2088.

[82] Colucci JA, Borrero EE, and Alape F (2005) Biodiesel from an alkaline transesterification reaction of soybean oil using ultrasonic mixing. *Journal of American Oil Chemists Society* 82(7): 525–530.

[83] Hanh HD, Dong NT, Starvarache C, et al. (2008) Methanolysis of triolein by low frequency ultrasonic irradiation. *Energy Conversion and Management* 49(2): 276–280.

[84] Refaat AA and El Sheltawy ST (2008) Comparing three options for biodiesel production from waste vegetable oil. *WIT Transactions on Ecology and the Environment, Waste Management and the Environment IV*, vol. 109, pp. 133–140. Billerica, MA: WIT Press.

[85] Hingu SM, Gogate PR, and Rathod VK (2010) Synthesis of biodiesel from waste cooking oil using sonochemical reactors. *Ultrasonics Sonochemistry* 17(5): 827–832.

[86] Hayes BL (2004) Recent advances in microwave-assisted synthesis. *Aldrichimica Acta* 37(2): 66–77.

[87] Saifuddin N and Chua KH (2004) Production of ethyl ester (biodiesel) from used frying oil: Optimization of transesterification process using microwave irradiation. *Malaysian Journal of Chemistry* 6(1): 77–82.

[88] Mazzocchia C, Modica G, Nannicini R, and Kaddouri A (2004) Fatty acid methyl esters synthesis from triglycerides over heterogeneous catalysts in the presence of microwaves. *Comptes Rendus Chimie* 7(6–7): 601–605.

[89] Hernando J, Leton P, Matia MP, et al. (2007) Biodiesel and FAME synthesis assisted by microwaves: Homogeneous batch and flow processes. *Fuel* 86(10–11): 1641–1644.

[90] Leadbeater NE and Stencel LM (2006) Fast, easy preparation of biodiesel using microwave heating. *Energy and Fuels* 20(5): 2281–2283.

[91] Barnard TM, Leadbeater NE, Boucher MB, et al. (2007) Continuous-flow preparation of biodiesel using microwave heating. *Energy and Fuels* 21(3): 1777–1781.

[92] Refaat AA, El Sheltawy ST, and Sadek KU (2008) Optimum reaction time, performance and exhaust emissions of biodiesel produced by microwave irradiation. *International Journal of Environmental Science and Technology* 5(3): 315–322.

[93] El Sheltawy ST and Refaat AA (2008) Using ultrasonication for fast production of biodiesel from waste vegetable oil in Egypt. *Proceedings of the 23rd International Conference on Solid Waste Technology and Management*. pp 1288–1297, Philadelphia, PA, USA, 30 March–2 April.

[94] Özsezen AN, Çanakçi M, Turkcan A, and Sayin C (2009) Performance and combustion characteristics of a DI diesel engine fuelled with waste palm oil and canola oil methyl esters. *Fuel* 88(4): 629–636.

[95] Utlu Z and Kocak MS (2008) The effect of biodiesel fuel obtained from waste frying oil on direct injection diesel engine performance and exhaust emissions. *Renewable Energy* 33(8): 1936–1941.

[96] Dorado MP, Ballesteros E, Arnal JM, et al. (2003) Testing waste olive oil methyl ester as a fuel in a diesel engine. *Energy and Fuels* 17(6): 1560–1565.

[97] Dorado MP, Ballesteros E, Arnal JM, et al. (2003) Exhaust emissions from a diesel engine fueled with transesterified waste olive oil. *Fuel* 82(11): 1311–1315.

[98] Lapuerta M, Rodriguez-Fernandez J, and Agudelo JR (2008) Diesel particulate emissions from used cooking oil biodiesel. *Bioresource Technology* 99(4): 731–740.

[99] Tat ME, van Gerpen JH, Wang PS, and Clemente TE (2007) Exhaust emissions from an engine fueled with biodiesel from high-oleic soybeans. *Journal of American Oil Chemists Society* 84(9): 865–869.

[100] Tat ME, van Gerpen JH, and Wang PS (2007) Fuel property effects on injection timing, ignition timing, and oxides of nitrogen emissions from biodiesel-fueled engines. *American Society of Agricultural Engineers* 50(4): 1123–1128.

[101] Lertsathapornsuk V, Pairintra R, Aryusuk K, and Krisnangkura K (2008) Microwave assisted in continuous biodiesel production from waste frying palm oil and its performance in a 100 kW diesel generator. *Fuel Processing Technology* 89(12): 1330–1336.

[102] Lapuerta M, Herreros JM, Lyons LL, et al. (2008) Effect of the alcohol type used in the production of waste cooking oil biodiesel on diesel performance and emissions. *Fuel* 87(15–16): 3161–3169.

[103] Sabudak T and Yildiz M (2010) Biodiesel production from waste frying oils and its quality control. *Waste Management* 30(5): 799–803.

[104] Predojevic ZJ (2008) The production of biodiesel from waste frying oils: A comparison of different purification steps. *Fuel* 87(17–18): 3522–3528.

[105] Frohlich A and Rice B (2005) Evaluation of recovered vegetable oil as a biodiesel feedstock. *Irish Journal of Agricultural and Food Research* 44(1): 129–139.

[106] Mahajan S, Konar SK, and Boocock DGB (2006) Determining the acid number of biodiesel. *Journal of American Oil Chemists Society* 83(6): 567–570.

[107] Knothe G, van Gerpen J, and Krahl J (2005) *The Biodiesel Handbook*. Champaign, IL: AOCS Press.
[108] van Gerpen JH (2005) Biodiesel processing and production. *Fuel Processing Technology* 86(10): 1097–1107.
[109] Sayin C, Özsezen AN, and Çanakçı M (2010) The influence of operating parameters on the performance and emissions of a DI diesel engine using methanol-blended-diesel fuel. *Fuel* 89(7): 1407–1414.
[110] Kegl B (2008) Effects of biodiesel on emissions of a bus diesel engine. *Bioresource Technology* 99(4): 863–873.
[111] Kegl B (2006) Experimental investigation of optimal timing of the diesel engine injection pump using biodiesel fuel. *Energy and Fuels* 20(4): 1460–1470.
[112] Cardone M, Prati MV, Rocco V, *et al.* (2002) *Brassica carinata* as an alternative oil crop for the production of biodiesel in Italy: Engine performance and regulated and unregulated exhaust emissions. *Environmental Science and Technology* 36(21): 4656–4662.
[113] Puhan S and Nagarajan G (2008) NO_x reduction in a DI diesel engine using biodiesel as a renewable fuel. *International Journal of Sustainable Energy* 27(3): 143–154.
[114] Rodriguez-Anton LM, Aparicio C, Guignon B, and Sanz PD (2008) Volumetric properties at high pressure of waste oil methyl ester compared with diesel oil. *Fuel* 87(10–11): 1934–1940.
[115] Radu R, Petru C, Edward R, and Gheorghe M (2009) Fueling an DI agricultural diesel engine with waste oil biodiesel: Effects over injection, combustion and engine characteristics. *Energy Conversion and Management* 50(9): 2158–2166.
[116] Ghobadian B, Rahimi H, Nikbakht AM, *et al.* (2009) Diesel engine performance and exhaust emission analysis using waste cooking biodiesel fuel with an artificial neural network. *Renewable Energy* 34(4): 976–982.
[117] Lin Y, Wu Y-G, and Chang C-T (2007) Combustion characteristics of waste-oil produced biodiesel/diesel fuel blends. *Fuel* 86(12–13): 1772–1780.
[118] Najafi G, Ghobadian B, Yusaf TF, and Rahimi H (2007) Combustion analysis of a CI engine performance using waste cooking biodiesel fuel with an artificial neural network aid. *American Journal of Applied Sciences* 4(10): 756–764.
[119] Tashtoush G, Al-Widyan MI, and Al-Shyoukh AO (2003) Combustion performance and emissions of ethyl ester of a waste vegetable oil in a water-cooled furnace. *Applied Thermal Engineering* 23(3): 285–293.
[120] Szybist JP, Song J, Alam M, and Boehman AL (2007) Biodiesel combustion, emissions and emission control. *Fuel Processing Technology* 88(7): 679–691.
[121] Sendzikiene E, Makareviciene V, and Janulis P (2007) Influence of composition of fatty acid methyl esters on smoke opacity and amount of polycyclic aromatic hydrocarbons in engine emissions. *Polish Journal of Environmental Studies* 16(2): 259–265.
[122] Sun J, Caton JA, and Jacobs TJ (2010) Oxides of nitrogen emissions from biodiesel-fuelled diesel engines. *Progress in Energy and Combustion Science* 36(6): 677–695.
[123] Di Y, Cheung CS, and Huang Z (2009) Experimental investigation on regulated and unregulated emissions of a diesel engine fueled with ultra-low sulfur diesel fuel blended with biodiesel from waste cooking oil. *Science of the Total Environment* 407(2): 835–846.
[124] Singh A, Pant D, Korres NE, *et al.* (2010) Key issues in life cycle assessment of ethanol production from lignocellulosic biomass: Challenges and perspectives. *Bioresource Technology* 101(13): 5003–5012.
[125] Harrison RW (2009) The food versus fuel debate: Implications for consumers. *Journal of Agricultural and Applied Economics* 41(2): 493–500.
[126] Koizumi T and Ohga K (2007) Biofuels policies in Asian countries: Impact of the expanded biofuels programs on world agricultural markets. *Journal of Agricultural and Food Industrial Organization* 5(2): article 8.
[127] McLaughlin SB and Kszos LD (2005) Development of switchgrass (*Panicum virgatum*) as a bioenergy feedstock in the United States. *Biomass and Bioenergy* 28(6): 515–535.
[128] Brown RA, Rosenberg NJ, Hays CJ, *et al.* (2000) Potential production and environmental effects of switchgrass and traditional crops under current and greenhouse-altered climate in the central United States: A simulation study. *Agriculture, Ecosystems and Environment* 78(1): 31–47.
[129] Berndes G (2002) Bioenergy and water: The implications of large-scale bioenergy production for water use and supply. *Global Environmental Change* 12(4): 253–271.
[130] de Fraiture C, Giordano M, and Liao Y (2008) Biofuels and implications for agricultural water use: Blue impacts of green energy. *Water Policy* 10(supplement 1): 67–81.
[131] Dominguez-Faus R, Powers SE, Burken JG, and Alvarez PJ (2009) The water footprint of biofuels: A drink or drive issue? *Environmental Science and Technology* 43(9): 3005–3010.
[132] Fingerman KR, Torn MS, O'Hare MH, and Kammen DM (2010) Accounting for the water impacts of ethanol production. *Environmental Research Letters* 5(1): article 014020.
[133] Alcamo J, van Vuuren D, Ringler C, *et al.* (2005) Changes in nature's balance sheet: Model based estimates of future worldwide ecosystem services. *Ecology and Society* 10(2): 19.
[134] Mulder K, Hagens N, and Fisher B (2010) Burning water: A comparative analysis of the energy return on water invested. *AMBIO: A Journal of the Human Environment* 39(1): 30–39.
[135] Solomon BD, Barnes JR, and Halvorsen KE (2007) Grain and cellulosic ethanol: History, economics, and energy policy. *Biomass and Bioenergy* 31(6): 416–425.
[136] Solomon BD and Johnson NH (2009) Valuing climate protection through willingness to pay for biomass ethanol. *Ecological Economics* 68(7): 2137–2144.
[137] Lavigne A and Powers SE (2007) Evaluating fuel ethanol feedstocks from energy policy perspectives: A comparative energy assessment of corn and corn stover. *Energy Policy* 35(11): 5918–5930.
[138] Luo L, van der Voet E, and Huppes G (2009) An energy analysis of ethanol from cellulosic feedstock: Corn stover. *Renewable and Sustainable Energy Reviews* 13(8): 2003–2011.
[139] Wu M, Wu Y, and Wang M (2006) Energy and emission benefits of alternative transportation liquid fuels derived from switchgrass: A fuel life cycle assessment. *Biotechnology Progress* 22(4): 1012–1024.
[140] Cardona Alzate CA and Sanchez Toro OJ (2006) Energy consumption analysis of integrated flowsheets for production of fuel ethanol from lignocellulosic biomass. *Energy* 31(13): 2447–2459.
[141] Smeets EMW, Lewandowski IM, and Faaij APC (2009) The economical and environmental performance of miscanthus and switchgrass production and supply chains in a European setting. *Renewable and Sustainable Energy Reviews* 13(6–7): 1230–1245.
[142] Cherubini F and Ulgiati S (2010) Crop residues as raw materials for biorefinery systems – a LCA case study. *Applied Energy* 87(1): 47–57.
[143] Kim S, Dale BE, and Jenkins R (2009) Life cycle assessment of corn grain and corn stover in the United States. *International Journal of Life Cycle Assessment* 14(2): 160–174.
[144] Luo L, van der Voet E, Huppes G, and Udo de Haes HA (2009) Allocation issues in LCA methodology: A case study of corn stover-based fuel ethanol. *International Journal of Life Cycle Assessment* 14(6): 529–539.
[145] Sheehan J, Aden A, Paustian K, *et al.* (2004) Energy and environmental aspects of using corn stover for fuel ethanol. *Journal of Industrial Ecology* 7(3–4): 117–146.
[146] Gabrielle B and Gagnaire N (2008) Life-cycle assessment of straw use in bio-ethanol production: A case study based on biophysical modeling. *Biomass and Bioenergy* 32(5): 431–441.
[147] Gonzalez Garcıa S, Moreira MT, and Feijoo G (2010) Comparative environmental performance of lignocellulosic ethanol from different feedstocks. *Renewable and Sustainable Energy Reviews* 14(7): 2077–2085.
[148] Gonzalez Garcıa S, Luo L, Moreira MT, *et al.* (2009) Life cycle assessment of flax shives derived second generation ethanol fueled automobiles in Spain. *Renewable and Sustainable Energy Reviews* 13(8): 1922–1933.
[149] Botha T and von Blottnitz H (2006) A comparison of the environmental benefits of bagasse-derived electricity and fuel ethanol on a life-cycle basis. *Energy Policy* 34(17): 2654–2661.
[150] Luo L, van der Voet E, and Huppes G (2009) Life cycle assessment and life cycle costing of bioethanol from sugarcane in Brazil. *Renewable and Sustainable Energy Reviews* 13(6–7): 1613–1619.
[151] Bai Y, Luo L, and van der Voet E (2010) Life cycle assessment of switchgrass-derived ethanol as transport fuel. *International Journal of Life Cycle Assessment* 15(5): 468–477.
[152] Styles D and Jones MB (2008) Life-cycle environmental and economic impacts of energy-crop fuel-chains: An integrated assessment of potential GHG avoidance in Ireland. *Environmental Science and Policy* 11(4): 294–306.

[153] Beer T and Grant T (2007) Life-cycle analysis of emissions from fuel ethanol and blends in Australian heavy and light vehicles. *Journal of Cleaner Production* 15(8–9): 833–837.
[154] Fu GZ, Chan AW, and Minns DE (2003) Life cycle assessment of bio-ethanol derived from cellulose. *International Journal of Life Cycle Assessment* 8(3): 137–141.
[155] Kemppainen AJ and Shonnard DR (2005) Comparative life-cycle assessments for biomass-to-ethanol production from different regional feedstocks. *Biotechnology Progress* 21(4): 1075–1084.
[156] Stichnothe H and Azapagic A (2009) Bioethanol from waste: Life cycle estimation of the greenhouse gas saving potential. *Resources, Conservation and Recycling* 53(11): 624–630.
[157] Luo L, van der Voet E, and Huppes G (2010) Energy and environmental performance of bioethanol from different lignocelluloses. *International Journal of Chemical Engineering*, 2010: article ID 740962.
[158] Kim S and Dale BE (2005) Life cycle assessment of various cropping systems utilized for producing biofuels: Bioethanol and biodiesel. *Biomass and Bioenergy* 29(6): 426–439.
[159] Spatari S, Bagley DM, and MacLean HL (2010) Life cycle evaluation of emerging lignocellulosic ethanol conversion technologies. *Bioresource Technology* 101(2): 654–667.
[160] Jensen KL, Clark CD, English BC, *et al.* (2010) Willingness to pay for E85 from corn, switchgrass, and wood residues. *Energy Economics* 32(6): 1253–1262.
[161] Susaeta A, Alavalapati J, Lal P, *et al.* (2010) Assessing public preferences for forest biomass based energy in the Southern United States. *Environmental Management* 45(4): 697–710.
[162] Girio FM, Fonseca C, Carvalheiro F, *et al.* (2010) Hemicelluloses for fuel ethanol: A review. *Bioresource Technology* 101(13): 4775–4800.
[163] Saha BC (2003) Hemicellulose bioconversion. *Journal of Industrial Microbiology and Biotechnology* 30(5): 279–291.
[164] Howard RL, Abotsi E, Jansen van Rensburg EL, and Howard S (2003) Lignocellulose biotechnology: Issues of bioconversion and enzyme production. *African Journal of Biotechnology* 12(2): 602–619.
[165] Galbe M and Zacchi G (2002) A review of the production of ethanol from softwood. *Applied Microbiology and Biotechnology* 59(6): 618–628.
[166] Hu G, Heitmann JA, and Rojas OJ (2008) Feedstock pretreatment strategies for producing ethanol from wood, bark, and forest residues. *BioResources* 3(1): 270–294.
[167] Zhu JY and Pan XJ (2010) Woody biomass pretreatment for cellulosic ethanol production: Technology and energy consumption evaluation. *Bioresource Technology* 101(13): 4992–5002.
[168] Kaar WE and Holtzapple MT (2000) Using lime pretreatment to facilitate the enzymic hydrolysis of corn stover. *Biomass and Bioenergy* 18(3): 189–199.
[169] Laureano-Perez L, Teymouri F, Alizadeh H, and Dale BE (2005) Understanding factors that limit enzymatic hydrolysis of biomass: Characterization of pretreated corn stover. *Applied Biochemistry and Biotechnology* 124(1–3): 1081–1099.
[170] Cheng Y-S, Zheng Y, Yu CW, *et al.* (2010) Evaluation of high solids alkaline pretreatment of rice straw. *Applied Biochemistry and Biotechnology* 162(6): 1768–1784.
[171] Rubin EM (2008) Genomics of cellulosic biofuels. *Nature* 454(14): 841–845.
[172] Himmel ME, Ding SY, Johnson DK, *et al.* (2007) Biomass recalcitrance: Engineering plants and enzymes for biofuels production. *Science* 315: 804–807.
[173] Ebringerová A, Hromadkova Z, and Heinze T (2005) Hemicellulose. *Advances in Polymer Science* 186: 1–67.
[174] Vanholme R, Morreel K, Ralph J, and Boerjan W (2008) Lignin engineering. *Current Opinion in Plant Biology* 11(3): 278–285.
[175] Zhang YHP and Lynd LR (2004) Toward an aggregated understanding of enzymatic hydrolysis of cellulose: Noncomplexed cellulase systems. *Biotechnology and Bioengineering* 88(7): 797–824.
[176] Hall M, Bansal P, Lee JH, *et al.* (2010) Cellulose crystallinity: A key predictor of the enzymatic hydrolysis rate. *FEBS Journal* 277(6): 1571–1582.
[177] Taherzadeh MJ and Karimi K (2008) Pretreatment of lignocellulosic wastes to improve ethanol and biogas production: A review. *International Journal of Molecular Sciences* 9(9): 1621–1651.
[178] Alvira P, Tomas-Pejo E, Ballesteros M, and Negro MJ (2010) Pretreatment technologies for an efficient bioethanol production process based on enzymatic hydrolysis: A review. *Bioresource Technology* 101(13): 4851–4861.
[179] Mansfield SD, Mooney C, and Saddler JN (1999) Substrate and enzyme characteristics that limit cellulose hydrolysis. *Biotechnology Progress* 15(5): 804–816.
[180] Zeng M, Mosier NS, Huang C-P, *et al.* (2007) Microscopic examination of changes of plant cell structure in corn stover due to hot water pretreatment and enzymatic hydrolysis. *Biotechnology and Bioengineering* 97(2): 265–278.
[181] Draude KM, Kurniawan CB, and Duff SJB (2001) Effect of oxygen delignification on the rate and extent of enzymatic hydrolysis of lignocellulosic material. *Bioresource Technology* 79(2): 113–120.
[182] Lynd LR, Laser MS, Bransby D, *et al.* (2008) How biotech can transform biofuels. *Nature Biotechnology* 26(2): 169–172.
[183] Margeot A, Hahn-Hagerdal B, Edlund M, *et al.* (2009) New improvements for lignocellulosic ethanol. *Current Opinion in Biotechnology* 20(3): 372–380.
[184] Galbe M and Zacchi G (2007) Pretreatment of lignocellulosic materials for efficient bioethanol production. *Advances in Biochemical Engineering/Biotechnology* 108: 41–65.
[185] Schubert C (2006) Can biofuels finally take center stage? *Nature Biotechnology* 24(7): 777–784.
[186] Stephanopoulos G (2007) Challenges in engineering microbes for biofuels production. *Science* 315: 801–804.
[187] Kumar P, Barrett DM, Delwiche MJ, and Stroeve P (2009) Methods for pretreatment of lignocellulosic biomass for efficient hydrolysis and biofuel production. *Industrial and Engineering Chemistry Research* 48(8): 3713–3729.
[188] Yang B and Wyman CE (2008) Pretreatment: The key to unlocking low-cost cellulosic ethanol. *Biofuels, Bioproducts and Biorefining* 2(1): 26–40.
[189] Chandra RP, Bura R, Mabee WE, *et al.* (2007) Substrate pretreatment: The key to effective enzymatic hydrolysis of lignocellulosics? *Advances in Biochemical Engineering/Biotechnology* 108: 67–93.
[190] Sun Y and Cheng J (2002) Hydrolysis of lignocellulosic materials for ethanol production: A review. *Bioresource Technology* 83(1): 1–11.
[191] Iranmahboob J, Nadim F, and Monemi S (2002) Optimizing acid-hydrolysis: A critical step for production of ethanol from mixed wood chips. *Biomass and Bioenergy* 22(5): 401–404.
[192] Saha BC, Iten LB, Cotta MA, and Wu YV (2005) Dilute acid pretreatment, enzymatic saccharification and fermentation of wheat straw to ethanol. *Process Biochemistry* 40(12): 3693–3700.
[193] Palmqvist E and Hahn-Hagerdal B (2000) Fermentation of lignocellulosic hydrolysates. I: Inhibition and detoxification. *Bioresource Technology* 74(1): 17–24.
[194] Palmqvist E and Hahn-Hagerdal B (2000) Fermentation of lignocellulosic hydrolysates. II: Inhibitors and mechanisms of inhibition. *Bioresource Technology* 74(1): 25–33.
[195] Zhu Z, Sathitsuksanoh N, Vinzant T, *et al.* (2009) Comparative study of corn stover pretreated by dilute acid and cellulose solvent-based lignocellulose fractionation: Enzymatic hydrolysis, supramolecular structure, and substrate accessibility. *Biotechnology and Bioengineering* 103(4): 715–724.
[196] Lavarack BP, Griffin GJ, and Rodman D (2002) The acid hydrolysis of sugarcane bagasse hemicellulose to produce xylose, arabinose, glucose and other products. *Biomass and Bioenergy* 23(5): 367–380.
[197] Rodriguez-Chong A, Ramirez JA, Garrote G, and Vazquez M (2004) Hydrolysis of sugar cane bagasse using nitric acid: A kinetic assessment. *Journal of Food Engineering* 61(2): 143–152.
[198] Romero I, Moya M, Sanchez S, *et al.* (2007) Ethanolic fermentation of phosphoric acid hydrolysates from olive tree pruning. *Industrial Crops and Products* 25(2): 160–168.
[199] Kootstra AMJ, Beeftink HH, Scott EL, and Sanders JPM (2009) Comparison of dilute mineral and organic acid pretreatment for enzymatic hydrolysis of wheat straw. *Biochemical Engineering Journal* 46(2): 126–131.
[200] Xu J, Thomsen MH, and Thomsen AB (2009) Enzymatic hydrolysis and fermentability of corn stover pretreated by lactic acid and/or acetic acid. *Journal of Biotechnology* 139(4): 300–305.
[201] Kálmán G, Varga E, and Réczey K (2002) Dilute sulphuric acid pretreatment of corn stover at long residence times. *Chemical and Biochemical Engineering Quarterly* 16(4): 151–157.

[202] Torget R, Walter P, Himmel M, and Grohmann K (1991) Dilute-acid pretreatment of corn residues and short-rotation woody crops. *Applied Biochemistry and Biotechnology* 28–29(1): 75–86.
[203] Schell DJ, Walter PJ, and Johnson DK (1992) Dilute sulfuric acid pretreatment of corn stover at high solids concentrations. *Applied Biochemistry and Biotechnology* 34–35(1): 659–665.
[204] Fenske JJ, Hashimoto A, and Penner MH (1998) Relative fermentability of lignocellulosic dilute acid prehydrolysates. *Applied Biochemistry and Biotechnology* 73(2–3): 145–157.
[205] Rocha MVP, Rodrigues THS, de Macedo GR, *et al.* (2009) Fermentation of pretreated cashew apple bagasse with alkali and diluted sulfuric acid for bioethanol production. *Applied Biochemistry and Biotechnology* 155(1–3): 104–114.
[206] Cara C, Ruiz E, Oliva JM, *et al.* (2008) Conversion of olive tree biomass into fermentable sugars by dilute acid pretreatment and enzymatic saccharification. *Bioresource Technology* 99(6): 1869–1876.
[207] Yan L, Zhang H, Chen J, *et al.* (2009) Dilute sulfuric acid cycle spray flow-through pretreatment of corn stover for enhancement of sugar recovery. *Bioresource Technology* 100(5): 1803–1808.
[208] Esteghlalian A, Hashimoto AG, Fenske JJ, and Penner MH (1997) Modeling and optimization of the dilute-sulfuric-acid pretreatment of corn stover, poplar and switchgrass. *Bioresource Technology* 59(2–3): 129–136.
[209] Sun Y and Cheng J (2005) Dilute acid pretreatment of rye straw and bermudagrass for ethanol production. *Bioresource Technology* 96(14): 1599–1606.
[210] Gamez S, Ramırez JA, Garrote G, and Vazquez M (2004) Manufacture of fermentable sugar solutions from sugar cane bagasse hydrolyzed with phosphoric acid at atmospheric pressure. *Journal of Agricultural and Food Chemistry* 52(13): 4172–4177.
[211] Ballesteros I, Ballesteros M, Manzanares P, *et al.* (2008) Dilute sulfuric acid pretreatment of cardoon for ethanol production. *Biochemical Engineering Journal* 42(1): 84–91.
[212] Hsu T-C, Guo G-L, Chen W-H, and Hwang W-S (2010) Effect of dilute acid pretreatment of rice straw on structural properties and enzymatic hydrolysis. *Bioresource Technology* 101(13): 4907–4913.
[213] Kabel MA, Bos G, Zeevalking J, *et al.* (2007) Effect of pretreatment severity on xylan solubility and enzymatic breakdown of the remaining cellulose from wheat straw. *Bioresource Technology* 98(10): 2034–2042.
[214] Rosgaard L, Pedersen S, and Meyer AS (2007) Comparison of different pretreatment strategies for enzymatic hydrolysis of wheat and barley straw. *Applied Biochemistry and Biotechnology* 143(3): 284–296.
[215] Um B-H, Karim MN, and Henk LL (2003) Effect of sulfuric and phosphoric acid pretreatments on enzymatic hydrolysis of corn stover. *Applied Biochemistry and Biotechnology* 105(1–3): 115–125.
[216] Wyman CE, Dale BE, Elander RT, *et al.* (2009) Comparative sugar recovery and fermentation data following pretreatment of poplar wood by leading technologies. *Biotechnology Progress* 25(2): 333–339.
[217] Mosier N, Wyman C, Dale B, *et al.* (2005) Features of promising technologies for pretreatment of lignocellulosic biomass. *Bioresource Technology* 96(6): 673–686.
[218] Kim TH, Taylor F, and Hicks KB (2008) Bioethanol production from barley hull using SAA (soaking in aqueous ammonia) pretreatment. *Bioresource Technology* 99(13): 5694–5702.
[219] Gupta R and Lee YY (2010) Pretreatment of corn stover and hybrid poplar by sodium hydroxide and hydrogen peroxide. *Biotechnology Progress* 26(4): 1180–1186.
[220] Zhao Y, Wang Y, Zhu JY, *et al.* (2008) Enhanced enzymatic hydrolysis of spruce by alkaline pretreatment at low temperature. *Biotechnology and Bioengineering* 99(6): 1320–1328.
[221] Kim TH and Lee YY (2007) Pretreatment of corn stover by soaking in aqueous ammonia at moderate temperatures. *Applied Biochemistry and Biotechnology* 137–140(1–12): 81–92.
[222] Ko JK, Bak JS, Jung MW, *et al.* (2009) Ethanol production from rice straw using optimized aqueous-ammonia soaking pretreatment and simultaneous saccharification and fermentation processes. *Bioresource Technology* 100(19): 4374–4380.
[223] Salvi DA, Aita GM, Robert D, and Bazan V (2010) Ethanol production from sorghum by a dilute ammonia pretreatment. *Journal of Industrial Microbiology and Biotechnology* 37(1): 27–34.
[224] Salvi DA, Aita GM, Robert D, and Bazan V (2010) Dilute ammonia pretreatment of sorghum and its effectiveness on enzyme hydrolysis and ethanol fermentation. *Applied Biochemistry and Biotechnology* 161(1–8): 67–74.
[225] Carrillo F, Lis MJ, Colom X, *et al.* (2005) Effect of alkali pretreatment on cellulase hydrolysis of wheat straw: Kinetic study. *Process Biochemistry* 40(10): 3360–3364.
[226] Kim S and Holtzapple MT (2006) Delignification kinetics of corn stover in lime pretreatment. *Bioresource Technology* 97(5): 778–785.
[227] Chang VS, Nagwani M, Kim CH, and Holtzapple MT (2001) Oxidative lime pretreatment of high-lignin biomass: Poplar wood and newspaper. *Applied Biochemistry and Biotechnology* 94(1): 1–28.
[228] Chang VS, Burr B, and Holtzapple MT (1997) Lime pretreatment of switchgrass. *Applied Biochemistry and Biotechnology* 63–65(1): 3–19.
[229] Xu J, Cheng JJ, Sharma-Shivappa RR, and Burns JC (2010) Lime pretreatment of switchgrass at mild temperatures for ethanol production. *Bioresource Technology* 101(8): 2900–2903.
[230] Chang VS, Nagwani M, and Holtzapple MT (1998) Lime pretreatment of crop residues bagasse and wheat straw. *Applied Biochemistry and Biotechnology* 74(3): 135–159.
[231] Saha BC and Cotta MA (2008) Lime pretreatment, enzymatic saccharification and fermentation of rice hulls to ethanol. *Biomass and Bioenergy* 32(10): 971–977.
[232] Sierra R, Granda C, and Holtzapple MT (2009) Short-term lime pretreatment of poplar wood. *Biotechnology Progress* 25(2): 323–332.
[233] Zhao X, Cheng K, and Liu D (2009) Organosolv pretreatment of lignocellulosic biomass for enzymatic hydrolysis. *Applied Microbiology and Biotechnology* 82(5): 815–827.
[234] Pan X, Gilkes N, Kadla J, *et al.* (2006) Bioconversion of hybrid poplar to ethanol and co-products using an organosolv fractionation process: Optimization of process yields. *Biotechnology and Bioengineering* 94(5): 851–861.
[235] Pan X, Xie D, Yu RW, and Saddler JN (2008) The bioconversion of mountain pine beetle-killed lodgepole pine to fuel ethanol using the organosolv process. *Biotechnology and Bioengineering* 101(1): 39–48.
[236] Sannigrahi P, Miller SJ, and Ragauskas AJ (2010) Effects of organosolv pretreatment and enzymatic hydrolysis on cellulose structure and crystallinity in Loblolly pine. *Carbohydrate Research* 345(7): 965–970.
[237] Sun F and Chen H (2007) Evaluation of enzymatic hydrolysis of wheat straw pretreated by atmospheric glycerol autocatalysis. *Journal of Chemical Technology and Biotechnology* 82(11): 1039–1044.
[238] Sun F and Chen H (2008) Comparison of atmospheric aqueous glycerol and steam explosion pretreatments of wheat straw for enhanced enzymatic hydrolysis. *Journal of Chemical Technology and Biotechnology* 83(5): 707–714.
[239] Sun F and Chen H (2008) Organosolv pretreatment by crude glycerol from oleochemicals industry for enzymatic hydrolysis of wheat straw. *Bioresource Technology* 99(13): 5474–5479.
[240] Araque E, Parra C, Freer J, *et al.* (2008) Evaluation of organosolv pretreatment for the conversion of *Pinus radiata* D. Don to ethanol. *Enzyme and Microbial Technology* 43(2): 214–219.
[241] Mesa L, Gonzalez E, Cara C, *et al.* (2010) An approach to optimization of enzymatic hydrolysis from sugarcane bagasse based on organosolv pretreatment. *Journal of Chemical Technology and Biotechnology* 85(8): 1092–1098.
[242] Li H, Kim N-J, Jiang M, *et al.* (2009) Simultaneous saccharification and fermentation of lignocellulosic residues pretreated with phosphoric acid–acetone for bioethanol production. *Bioresource Technology* 100(13): 3245–3251.
[243] Zhu S, Wu Y, Chen Q, *et al.* (2006) Dissolution of cellulose with ionic liquids and its application: A mini-review. *Green Chemistry* 8(4): 325–327.
[244] Swatloski RP, Spear SK, Holbrey JD, and Rogers RD (2002) Dissolution of cellulose with ionic liquids. *Journal of the American Chemical Society* 124(18): 4974–4975.

[245] Vitz J, Erdmenger T, Haensch C, and Schubert US (2009) Extended dissolution studies of cellulose in imidazolium based ionic liquids. *Green Chemistry* 11(3): 417–424.
[246] Datta S, Holmes B, Park JI, et al. (2010) Ionic liquid tolerant hyperthermophilic cellulases for biomass pretreatment and hydrolysis. *Green Chemistry* 12(2): 338–345.
[247] Olivier-Bourbigou H, Magna HL, and Morvan D (2010) Ionic liquids and catalysis: Recent progress from knowledge to applications. *Applied Catalysis A: General* 373(1–2): 1–56.
[248] Dadi AP, Varanasi S, and Schall CA (2006) Enhancement of cellulose saccharification kinetics using an ionic liquid pretreatment step. *Biotechnology and Bioengineering* 95(5): 904–910.
[249] Liebert T and Heinze T (2008) Interactions of ionic liquids with polysaccharides. 5. Solvents and reaction media for the modification of cellulose. *BioResources* 3(2): 576–601.
[250] Yang F, Li L, Li Q, et al. (2010) Enhancement of enzymatic *in situ* saccharification of cellulose in aqueous-ionic liquid media by ultrasonic intensification. *Carbohydrate Polymers* 81(2): 311–316.
[251] Zavrel M, Bross D, Funke M, et al. (2009) High-throughput screening for ionic liquids dissolving (ligno-)cellulose. *Bioresource Technology* 100(9): 2580–2587.
[252] Zhao H, Jones CL, Baker GA, et al. (2009) Regenerating cellulose from ionic liquids for an accelerated enzymatic hydrolysis. *Journal of Biotechnology* 139(1): 47–54.
[253] Li Q, He Y-C, Xian M, et al. (2009) Improving enzymatic hydrolysis of wheat straw using ionic liquid 1-ethyl-3-methyl imidazolium diethyl phosphate pretreatment. *Bioresource Technology* 100(14): 3570–3575.
[254] Liu L and Chen H (2006) Enzymatic hydrolysis of cellulose materials treated with ionic liquid [BMIM] Cl. *Chinese Science Bulletin* 51(20): 2432–2436.
[255] Tan SSY, MacFarlane DR, Upfal J, et al. (2009) Extraction of lignin from lignocellulose at atmospheric pressure using alkylbenzenesulfonate ionic liquid. *Green Chemistry* 11(3): 339–345.
[256] Li C, Knierim B, Manisseri C, et al. (2010) Comparison of dilute acid and ionic liquid pretreatment of switchgrass: Biomass recalcitrance, delignification and enzymatic saccharification. *Bioresource Technology* 101(13): 4900–4906.
[257] Singh S, Simmons BA, and Vogel KP (2009) Visualization of biomass solubilization and cellulose regeneration during ionic liquid pretreatment of switchgrass. *Biotechnology and Bioengineering* 104(1): 68–75.
[258] Zhao H, Baker GA, and Cowins JV (2010) Fast enzymatic saccharification of switchgrass after pretreatment with ionic liquids. *Biotechnology Progress* 26(1): 127–133.
[259] Sun N, Rahman M, Qin Y, et al. (2009) Complete dissolution and partial delignification of wood in the ionic liquid 1-ethyl-3-methylimidazolium acetate. *Green Chemistry* 11(5): 646–655.
[260] Lee SH, Doherty TV, Linhardt RJ, and Dordick JS (2009) Ionic liquid-mediated selective extraction of lignin from wood leading to enhanced enzymatic cellulose hydrolysis. *Biotechnology and Bioengineering* 102(5): 1368–1376.
[261] Zhu S (2008) Use of ionic liquids for the efficient utilization of lignocellulosic materials. *Journal of Chemical Technology and Biotechnology* 83(6): 777–779.
[262] Gould JM and Freer SN (1984) High-efficiency ethanol production from lignocellulosic residues pretreated with alkaline H_2O_2. *Biotechnology and Bioengineering* 26(6): 628–631.
[263] Shen G, Tao H, Zhao M, et al. (2011) Effect of hydrogen peroxide pretreatment on the enzymatic hydrolysis of cellulose. *Journal of Food Process Engineering* 34(2): doi: 10.1111/j.1745-4530.2009.00518.x.
[264] Saha BC and Cotta MA (2006) Ethanol production from alkaline peroxide pretreated enzymatically saccharified wheat straw. *Biotechnology Progress* 22(2): 449–453.
[265] Saha BC and Cotta MA (2007) Enzymatic saccharification and fermentation of alkaline peroxide pretreated rice hulls to ethanol. *Enzyme and Microbial Technology* 41(4): 528–532.
[266] Gould JM (1985) Enhanced polysaccharide recovery from agricultural residues and perennial grasses treated with alkaline hydrogen peroxide. *Biotechnology and Bioengineering* 27(6): 893–896.
[267] Curreli N, Fadda MB, Rescigno A, et al. (1997) Mild alkaline/oxidative pretreatment of wheat straw. *Process Biochemistry* 32(8): 665–670.
[268] Curreli N, Agelli M, Pisu B, et al. (2002) Complete and efficient enzymic hydrolysis of pretreated wheat straw. *Process Biochemistry* 37(9): 937–941.
[269] Teixeira LC, Linden JC, and Schroeder HA (1999) Alkaline and peracetic acid pretreatments of biomass for ethanol production. *Applied Biochemistry and Biotechnology* 77(1–3): 19–34.
[270] Zhao X-B, Wang L, and Liu D-h (2007) Effect of several factors on peracetic acid pretreatment of sugarcane bagasse for enzymatic hydrolysis. *Journal of Chemical Technology and Biotechnology* 82(12): 1115–1121.
[271] García-Cubero MT, González-Benito G, Indacoechea I, et al. (2009) Effect of ozonolysis pretreatment on enzymatic digestibility of wheat and rye straw. *Bioresource Technology* 100(4): 1608–1613.
[272] Silverstein RA, Chen Y, Sharma-Shivappa RR, et al. (2007) A comparison of chemical pretreatment methods for improving saccharification of cotton stalks. *Bioresource Technology* 98(16): 3000–3011.
[273] Lee JM, Jameel H, and Venditti RA (2010) Effect of ozone and autohydrolysis pretreatments on enzymatic digestibility of coastal Bermuda grass. *BioResources* 5(2): 1084–1101.
[274] Sugimoto T, Magara K, Hosoya S, et al. (2009) Ozone pretreatment of lignocellulosic materials for ethanol production: Improvement of enzymatic susceptibility of softwood. *Holzforschung* 63(5): 537–543.
[275] Kojima Y and Yoon S-L (2008) Improved enzymatic hydrolysis of waste paper by ozone pretreatment. *Journal of Material Cycles and Waste Management* 10(2): 134–139.
[276] Inoue H, Yano S, Endo T, et al. (2008) Combining hot-compressed water and ball milling pretreatments to improve the efficiency of the enzymatic hydrolysis of eucalyptus. *Biotechnology for Biofuels* 1(2): 1–9.
[277] Hendriks ATWM and Zeeman G (2009) Pretreatments to enhance the digestibility of lignocellulosic biomass. *Bioresource Technology* 100(1): 10–18.
[278] da Silva AS, Inoue H, Endo T, et al. (2010) Milling pretreatment of sugarcane bagasse and straw for enzymatic hydrolysis and ethanol fermentation. *Bioresource Technology* 101(19): 7402–7409.
[279] Aden A, Ruth M, Ibsen K, et al. (2002) *Lignocellulosic Biomass to Ethanol Process Design and Economics Utilizing Co-Current Dilute Acid Prehydrolysis and Enzymatic Hydrolysis for Corn Stover*, NREL/TP-510-32438, National Renewable Energy Laboratory, CO, USA.
[280] de Sousa MV, Monteiro SN, and d'Almeida JRM (2004) Evaluation of pre-treatment, size and molding pressure on flexural mechanical behavior of chopped bagasse–polyester composites. *Polymer Testing* 23(3): 253–258.
[281] Mani S, Tabil LG, and Sokhansanj S (2004) Grinding performance and physical properties of wheat and barley straws, corn stover and switchgrass. *Biomass and Bioenergy* 27(4): 339–352.
[282] Mtui G and Nakamura Y (2005) Bioconversion of lignocellulosic waste from selected dumping sites in Dar es Salaam, Tanzania. *Biodegradation* 16(6): 493–499.
[283] Qi BC, Aldrich C, Lorenzen L, and Wolfaardt GW (2005) Acidogenic fermentation of lignocellulosic substrate with activated sludge. *Chemical Engineering Communications* 192(9): 1221–1242.
[284] Guerra A, Filpponen I, Lucia LA, et al. (2006) Toward a better understanding of the lignin isolation process from wood. *Journal of Agricultural and Food Chemistry* 54(16): 5939–5947.
[285] Ryu SK and Lee JM (1983) Bioconversion of waste cellulose by using an attrition bioreactor. *Biotechnology and Bioengineering* 25(1): 53–65.
[286] Gusakov AV, Sinitsyn AP, Davydkin IY, et al. (1996) Enhancement of enzymatic cellulose hydrolysis using a novel type of bioreactor with intensive stirring induced by electromagnetic field. *Applied Biochemistry and Biotechnology* 56(2): 141–153.
[287] Sinitsyn AP, Gusakov AV, Davydkin IY, et al. (1993) A hyperefficient process for enzymatic cellulose hydrolysis in the intensive mass transfer reactor. *Biotechnology Letters* 15(3): 283–288.
[288] Mais U, Esteghlalian AR, Saddler JN, and Mansfield SD (2002) Enhancing the enzymatic hydrolysis of cellulosic materials using simultaneous ball milling. *Applied Biochemistry and Biotechnology* 98–100(1–9): 815–832.

[289] Bitra VSP, Womac AR, Igathinathane C, *et al.* (2009) Direct measures of mechanical energy for knife mill size reduction of switchgrass, wheat straw, and corn stover. *Bioresource Technology* 100(24): 6578–6585.
[290] Bitra VSP, Womac AR, Chevanan N, *et al.* (2009) Direct mechanical energy measures of hammer mill comminution of switchgrass, wheat straw, and corn stover and analysis of their particle size distributions. *Powder Technology* 193(1): 32–45.
[291] Hideno A, Inoue H, Tsukahara K, *et al.* (2009) Wet disk milling pretreatment without sulfuric acid for enzymatic hydrolysis of rice straw. *Bioresource Technology* 100(10): 2706–2711.
[292] Lin Z, Huang H, Zhang H, *et al.* (2010) Ball milling pretreatment of corn stover for enhancing the efficiency of enzymatic hydrolysis. *Applied Biochemistry and Biotechnology* 162(7): 1872–1880.
[293] Driscoll M, Stipanovic A, Winter W, *et al.* (2009) Electron beam irradiation of cellulose. *Radiation Physics and Chemistry* 78(7–8): 539–542.
[294] Yang C, Shen Z, Yu G, and Wang J (2008) Effect and aftereffect of γ radiation pretreatment on enzymatic hydrolysis of wheat straw. *Bioresource Technology* 99(14): 6240–6245.
[295] Han YW, Timpa J, Clegler A, *et al.* (1981) γ Ray-induced degradation of lignocellulosic materials. *Biotechnology and Bioengineering* 23(11): 2525–2535.
[296] Kumakura M and Kaetsu I (1984) Effect of electron beam current on radiation pretreatment of cellulosic wastes with electron beam accelerator. *Radiation Physics and Chemistry* 23(5): 523–527.
[297] Chosdu R, Hilmy N, Erizal Erlinda TB, and Abbas B (1993) Radiation and chemical pretreatment of cellulosic waste. *Radiation Physics and Chemistry* 42(4–6): 695–698.
[298] Matsuhashi S, Kume T, Hashimoto S, and Awang MR (1995) Effect of γ-irradiation on enzymatic digestion of oil palm empty fruit bunch. *Journal of the Science of Food and Agriculture* 69(2): 265–267.
[299] Brenner W, Rugg B, Arnon J, *et al.* (1979) Radiation pretreatments for optimizing the sugar yield in the acid hydrolysis of waste cellulose. *Radiation Physics and Chemistry* 14(3–6): 299–308.
[300] de la Hoz A, Diaz-Ortiz A, and Moreno A (2005) Microwaves in organic synthesis: Thermal and non-thermal microwave effects. *Chemical Society Reviews* 34(2): 164–178.
[301] Ma H, Liu W-W, Chen X, *et al.* (2009) Enhanced enzymatic saccharification of rice straw by microwave pretreatment. *Bioresource Technology* 100(3): 1279–1284.
[302] Hu Z and Wen Z (2008) Enhancing enzymatic digestibility of switchgrass by microwave-assisted alkali pretreatment. *Biochemical Engineering Journal* 38(3): 369–378.
[303] Zhu S, Wu Y, Yu Z, *et al.* (2006) Comparison of three microwave/chemical pretreatment processes for enzymatic hydrolysis of rice straw. *Biosystems Engineering* 93(3): 279–283.
[304] Zhu S, Wu Y, Yu Z, *et al.* (2006) The effect of microwave irradiation on enzymatic hydrolysis of rice straw. *Bioresource Technology* 97(15): 1964–1968.
[305] Zhu S, Wu Y, Yu Z, *et al.* (2006) Production of ethanol from microwave-assisted alkali pretreated wheat straw. *Process Biochemistry* 41(4): 869–873.
[306] Zhu SD, Wu YX, Yu ZN, *et al.* (2006) Microwave-assisted alkali pre-treatment of wheat straw and its enzymatic hydrolysis. *Biosystems Engineering* 94(3): 437–442.
[307] Keshwani DR and Cheng JJ (2010) Modeling changes in biomass composition during microwave-based alkali pretreatment of switchgrass. *Biotechnology and Bioengineering* 105(1): 88–97.
[308] Keshwani DR and Cheng JJ (2010) Microwave-based alkali pretreatment of switchgrass and coastal bermudagrass for bioethanol production. *Biotechnology Progress* 26(3): 644–652.
[309] Zhan X, Wang D, Bean SR, *et al.* (2006) Ethanol production from supercritical fluid extrusion cooked sorghum. *Industrial Crops and Products* 23(3): 304–310.
[310] Lee S-H, Teramoto Y, and Endo T (2009) Enzymatic saccharification of woody biomass micro/nanofibrillated by continuous extrusion process I – effect of additives with cellulose affinity. *Bioresource Technology* 100(1): 275–279.
[311] Dale BE, Weaver J, and Byers M (1999) Extrusion processing for ammonia fiber explosion (AFEX). *Applied Biochemistry and Biotechnology* 77(1–3): 35–45.
[312] Karunanithy C and Muthukumarappan K (2010) Influence of extruder temperature and screw speed on pretreatment of corn stover while varying enzymes and their ratios. *Applied Biochemistry and Biotechnology* 162(1): 264–279.
[313] Karunanithy C and Muthukumarappan K (2010) Effect of extruder parameters and moisture content of switchgrass, prairie cord grass on sugar recovery from enzymatic hydrolysis. *Applied Biochemistry and Biotechnology* 162(6): 1785–1803.
[314] Li J, Henriksson G, and Gellerstedt G (2007) Lignin depolymerization/repolymerization and its critical role for delignification of aspen wood by steam explosion. *Bioresource Technology* 98(16): 3061–3068.
[315] Josefsson T, Lennholm H, and Gellerstedt G (2001) Changes in cellulose supramolecular structure and molecular weight distribution during steam explosion of aspen wood. *Cellulose* 8(4): 289–296.
[316] Duff SJB and Murray WD (1996) Bioconversion of forest products industry waste cellulosics to fuel ethanol: A review. *Bioresource Technology* 55(1): 1–33.
[317] Avellar BK and Glasser WG (1998) Steam-assisted biomass fractionation. I. Process considerations and economic evaluation. *Biomass and Bioenergy* 14(3): 205–218.
[318] Holtzapple MT, Humphrey AE, and Taylor JD (1989) Energy requirements for the size reduction of poplar and aspen wood. *Biotechnology and Bioengineering* 33(2): 207–210.
[319] Oliva JM, Sáez F, Ballesteros I, *et al.* (2003) Effect of lignocellulosic degradation compounds from steam explosion pretreatment on ethanol fermentation by thermotolerant yeast *Kluyveromyces marxianus*. *Applied Biochemistry and Biotechnology* 105(1–3): 141–154.
[320] Garcia-Aparicio MA, Ballesteros I, Gónzalez A, *et al.* (2006) Effect of inhibitors released during steam-explosion pretreatment of barley straw on enzymatic hydrolysis. *Applied Biochemistry and Biotechnology* 129(1–3): 278–288.
[321] Ballesteros I, Negro MJ, Oliva JM, *et al.* (2006) Ethanol production from steam-explosion pretreated wheat straw. *Applied Biochemistry and Biotechnology* 130(1–3): 496–508.
[322] Stenberg K, Tengborg C, Galbe M, and Zacchi G (1998) Optimisation of steam pretreatment of SO_2-impregnated mixed softwoods for ethanol production. *Journal of Chemical Technology and Biotechnology* 71(4): 299–308.
[323] Tengborg C, Stenberg K, Galbe M, *et al.* (1998) Comparison of SO_2 and H_2SO_4 impregnation of softwood prior to steam pretreatment on ethanol production. *Applied Biochemistry and Biotechnology* 70–72((1)): 3–15.
[324] Martin C, Galbe M, Nilvebrant N-O, and Jonsson LJ (2002) Comparison of the fermentability of enzymatic hydrolyzates of sugarcane bagasse pretreated by steam explosion using different impregnating agents. *Applied Biochemistry and Biotechnology* 98–100(1–9): 699–716.
[325] Ballesteros I, Oliva JM, Negro MJ, *et al.* (2002) Enzymic hydrolysis of steam exploded herbaceous agricultural waste (*Brassica carinata*) at different particle sizes. *Process Biochemistry* 38(2): 187–192.
[326] Varga E, Réczey K, and Zacchi G (2004) Optimization of steam pretreatment of corn stover to enhance enzymatic digestibility. *Applied Biochemistry and Biotechnology* 114(1–3): 509–523.
[327] Zimbardi F, Viola E, Nanna F, *et al.* (2007) Acid impregnation and steam explosion of corn stover in batch processes. *Industrial Crops and Products* 26(2): 195–206.
[328] Monavari S, Bennato A, Galbe M, and Zacchi G (2010) Improved one-step steam pretreatment of SO_2-impregnated softwood with time-dependent temperature profile for ethanol production. *Biotechnology Progress* 26(4): 1054–1060.
[329] Linde M, Jakobsson E-L, Galbe M, and Zacchi G (2008) Steam pretreatment of dilute H_2SO_4-impregnated wheat straw and SSF with low yeast and enzyme loadings for bioethanol production. *Biomass and Bioenergy* 32(4): 326–332.
[330] Ohgren K, Galbe M, and Zacchi G (2005) Optimization of steam pretreatment of SO_2-impregnated corn stover for fuel ethanol production. *Applied Biochemistry and Biotechnology* 124(1–3): 1055–1067.
[331] Han G, Deng J, Zhang S, *et al.* (2010) Effect of steam explosion treatment on characteristics of wheat straw. *Industrial Crops and Products* 31(1): 28–33.
[332] Viola E, Zimabardi F, Cardinale M, *et al.* (2008) Processing cereal straws by steam explosion in a pilot plant to enhance digestibility in ruminants. *Bioresource Technology* 99(4): 681–689.
[333] Zabihi S, Alinia R, Esmaeilzadeh F, and Kalajahi JF (2010) Pretreatment of wheat straw using steam, steam/acetic acid and steam/ethanol and its enzymatic hydrolysis for sugar production. *Biosystems Engineering* 105(3): 288–297.

[334] Linde M, Galbe M, and Zacchi G (2006) Steam pretreatment of acid-sprayed and acid-soaked barley straw for production of ethanol. *Applied Biochemistry and Biotechnology* 130(1–3): 546–562.

[335] Moniruzzaman M (1996) Effect of steam explosion on the physicochemical properties and enzymatic saccharification of rice straw. *Applied Biochemistry and Biotechnology* 59(3): 283–297.

[336] Carrasco C, Baudel HM, Sendelius J, *et al.* (2010) SO$_2$-catalyzed steam pretreatment and fermentation of enzymatically hydrolyzed sugarcane bagasse. *Enzyme and Microbial Technology* 46(2): 64–73.

[337] Rudolf A, Baudel H, Zacchi G, *et al.* (2008) Simultaneous saccharification and fermentation of steam-pretreated bagasse using *Saccharomyces cerevisiae* TMB3400 and *Pichia stipitis* CBS6054. *Biotechnology and Bioengineering* 99(4): 783–790.

[338] Ruiz E, Cara C, Manzanares P, *et al.* (2008) Evaluation of steam explosion pre-treatment for enzymatic hydrolysis of sunflower stalks. *Enzyme and Microbial Technology* 42(2): 160–166.

[339] Boluda-Aguilar M, Garcia-Vidal L, Gonzalez-Castaneda FP, and Lopez-Gomez A (2010) Mandarin peel wastes pretreatment with steam explosion for bioethanol production. *Bioresource Technology* 101(10): 3506–3513.

[340] Cara C, Ruiz E, Ballesteros I, *et al.* (2006) Enhanced enzymatic hydrolysis of olive tree wood by steam explosion and alkaline peroxide delignification. *Process Biochemistry* 41(2): 423–429.

[341] Ewanick SM, Bura R, and Saddler JN (2007) Acid-catalyzed steam pretreatment of lodgepole pine and subsequent enzymatic hydrolysis and fermentation to ethanol. *Biotechnology and Bioengineering* 98(4): 737–746.

[342] Horn SJ and Eijsink VGH (2010) Enzymatic hydrolysis of steam-exploded hardwood using short processing times. *Bioscience Biotechnology and Biochemistry* 74(6): 1157–1163.

[343] Nakamura Y and Sawada T (2003) Ethanol production from artificial domestic household waste solubilized by steam explosion. *Biotechnology and Bioprocess Engineering* 8(3): 205–209.

[344] Cantarella M, Cantarella L, Gallifuoco A, *et al.* (2004) Effect of inhibitors released during steam-explosion treatment of poplar wood on subsequent enzymatic hydrolysis and SSF. *Biotechnology Progress* 20(1): 200–206.

[345] Negro MJ, Manzanares P, Ballesteros I, *et al.* (2003) Hydrothermal pretreatment conditions to enhance ethanol production from poplar biomass. *Applied Biochemistry and Biotechnology* 105(1–3): 87–100.

[346] Soderstrom J, Galbe M, and Zacchi G (2004) Effect of washing on yield in one- and two-step steam pretreatment of softwood for production of ethanol. *Biotechnology Progress* 20(3): 744–749.

[347] Soderstrom J, Pilcher L, Galbe M, and Zacchi G (2003) Two-step steam pretreatment of softwood by dilute H$_2$SO$_4$ impregnation for ethanol production. *Biomass and Bioenergy* 24(6): 475–486.

[348] Mosier N, Hendrickson R, Ho N, *et al.* (2005) Optimization of pH controlled liquid hot water pretreatment of corn stover. *Bioresource Technology* 96(18): 1986–1993.

[349] Liu C and Wyman CE (2005) Partial flow of compressed-hot water through corn stover to enhance hemicellulose sugar recovery and enzymatic digestibility of cellulose. *Bioresource Technology* 96(18): 1978–1985.

[350] Kim TH and Lee YY (2006) Fractionation of corn stover by hot-water and aqueous ammonia treatment. *Bioresource Technology* 97(2): 224–232.

[351] Laser M, Schulman D, Allen SG, *et al.* (2002) A comparison of liquid hot water and steam pretreatments of sugar cane bagasse for bioconversion to ethanol. *Bioresource Technology* 81(1): 33–44.

[352] Sreenath HK, Koegel RG, Moldes AB, *et al.* (1999) Enzymic saccharification of alfalfa fibre after liquid hot water pretreatment. *Process Biochemistry* 35(1–2): 33–41.

[353] Xu J, Thomsen MH, and Thomsen AB (2010) Ethanol production from hydrothermal pretreated corn stover with a loop reactor. *Biomass and Bioenergy* 34(3): 334–339.

[354] Pérez JA, Ballesteros I, Ballesteros M, *et al.* (2008) Optimizing liquid hot water pretreatment conditions to enhance sugar recovery from wheat straw for fuel-ethanol production. *Fuel* 87(17–18): 3640–3647.

[355] Yu G, Yano S, Inoue H, *et al.* (2010) Pretreatment of rice straw by a hot-compressed water process for enzymatic hydrolysis. *Applied Biochemistry and Biotechnology* 160(2): 539–551.

[356] Jacobsen SE, Wyman CE, and Monomer X (2002) Oligomer yields for uncatalyzed hydrolysis of sugarcane bagasse hemicellulose at varying solids concentration. *Industrial and Engineering Chemistry Research* 41(6): 1454–1461.

[357] Suryawati L, Wilkins MR, Bellmer DD, *et al.* (2009) Effect of hydrothermolysis process conditions on pretreated switchgrass composition and ethanol yield by SSF with *Kluyveromyces marxianus* IMB4. *Process Biochemistry* 44(5): 540–545.

[358] Ando H, Sakaki T, Kokusho T, *et al.* (2000) Decomposition behavior of plant biomass in hot-compressed water. *Industrial and Engineering Chemistry Research* 39(10): 3688–3693.

[359] Liu C and Wyman CE (2003) The effect of flow rate of compressed hot water on xylan, lignin, and total mass removal from corn stover. *Industrial and Engineering Chemistry Research* 42(21): 5409–5416.

[360] Goh CS, Lee KT, and Bhatia S (2010) Hot compressed water pretreatment of oil palm fronds to enhance glucose recovery for production of second generation bio-ethanol. *Bioresource Technology* 101(19): 7362–7367.

[361] Wyman CE, Dale BE, Elander RT, *et al.* (2005) Coordinated development of leading biomass pretreatment technologies. *Bioresource Technology* 96(18): 1959–1966.

[362] Teymouri F, Laureano-Perez L, Alizadeh H, and Dale BE (2005) Optimization of the ammonia fiber explosion (AFEX) treatment parameters for enzymatic hydrolysis of corn stover. *Bioresource Technology* 96(18): 2014–2018.

[363] Eggeman T and Elander RT (2005) Process and economic analysis of pretreatment technologies. *Bioresource Technology* 96(18): 2019–2025.

[364] Chundawat SPS, Vismeh R, Sharma LN, *et al.* (2010) Multifaceted characterization of cell wall decomposition products formed during ammonia fiber expansion (AFEX) and dilute acid based pretreatments. *Bioresource Technology* 101(21): 8429–8438.

[365] Holtzapple MT, Jun J-H, Ashok G, *et al.* (1991) The ammonia freeze explosion (AFEX) process: A practical lignocellulose pretreatment. *Applied Biochemistry and Biotechnology* 28–29(1): 59–74.

[366] Chundawat SPS, Venkatesh B, and Dale BE (2007) Effect of particle size based separation of milled corn stover on AFEX pretreatment and enzymatic digestibility. *Biotechnology and Bioengineering* 96(2): 219–231.

[367] Belkacemi K, Turcotte G, de Halleux D, and Savoie P (1998) Ethanol production from AFEX-treated forages and agricultural residues. *Applied Biochemistry and Biotechnology* 70–72(1): 441–462.

[368] Gollapalli LE, Dale BE, and Rivers DM (2002) Predicting digestibility of ammonia fiber explosion (AFEX)-treated rice straw. *Applied Biochemistry and Biotechnology* 98–100(1–9): 23–35.

[369] Zhong C, Lau MW, Balan V, *et al.* (2009) Optimization of enzymatic hydrolysis and ethanol fermentation from AFEX-treated rice straw. *Applied Microbiology and Biotechnology* 84(4): 667–676.

[370] Lau MW and Dale BE (2009) Cellulosic ethanol production from AFEX-treated corn stover using *Saccharomyces cerevisiae* 424A(LNH-ST). *Proceedings of the National Academy of Sciences of the United States of America* 106(5): 1368–1373.

[371] Alizadeh H, Teymouri F, Gilbert TI, and Dale BE (2005) Pretreatment of switchgrass by ammonia fiber explosion (AFEX). *Applied Biochemistry and Biotechnology* 124(1–3): 1133–1141.

[372] Jin M, Lau MW, Balan V, and Dale BE (2010) Two-step SSCF to convert AFEX-treated switchgrass to ethanol using commercial enzymes and *Saccharomyces cerevisiae* 424A (LNH-ST). *Bioresource Technology* 101(21): 8171–8178.

[373] Holtzapple MT, Lundeen JE, Sturgis R, et al. (1992) Pretreatment of lignocellulosic municipal solid waste by ammonia fiber explosion (AFEX). *Applied Biochemistry and Biotechnology* 34–35(1): 5–21.

[374] Kim JS, Kim H, Lee JS, et al. (2008) Pretreatment characteristics of waste oak wood by ammonia percolation. *Applied Biochemistry and Biotechnology* 148(1–3): 15–22.

[375] Kim TH and Lee YY (2005) Pretreatment and fractionation of corn stover by ammonia recycle percolation process. *Bioresource Technology* 96(18): 2007–2013.

[376] Yoon HH, Wu ZW, and Lee YY (1995) Ammonia-recycled percolation process for pretreatment of biomass feedstock. *Applied Biochemistry and Biotechnology* 51–52(1): 5–19.

[377] Kim JS, Lee YY, and Park SC (2000) Pretreatment of wastepaper and pulp mill sludge by aqueous ammonia and hydrogen peroxide. *Applied Biochemistry and Biotechnology* 84–86(1–9): 129–139.

[378] Kim SB and Lee YY (1996) Fractionation of herbaceous biomass by ammonia-hydrogen peroxide percolation treatment. *Applied Biochemistry and Biotechnology* 57–58(1): 147–156.

[379] Kim TH, Lee YY, Sunwoo C, and Kim JS (2006) Pretreatment of corn stover by low-liquid ammonia recycle percolation process. *Applied Biochemistry and Biotechnology* 133(1): 41–57.

[380] Kim TH and Lee YY (2005) Pretreatment of corn stover by soaking in aqueous ammonia. *Applied Biochemistry and Biotechnology* 124(1–3): 1119–1131.

[381] Kim TH and Lee YY (2007) Pretreatment of corn stover by soaking in aqueous ammonia at moderate temperatures. *Applied Biochemistry and Biotechnology* 137–140(1–12): 81–92.

[382] Banerjee S, Sen R, Pandey RA, et al. (2009) Evaluation of wet air oxidation as a pretreatment strategy for bioethanol production from rice husk and process optimization. *Biomass and Bioenergy* 33(12): 1680–1686.

[383] Martín C, Thomsen MH, Hauggaard H, and Thomsem AB (2008) Wet oxidation pretreatment, enzymatic hydrolysis and simultaneous saccharification and fermentation of clover–ryegrass mixtures. *Bioresource Technology* 99(18): 8777–8782.

[384] Klinke HB, Ahring BK, Schmidt AS, and Thomsen AB (2008) Characterization of degradation products from alkaline wet oxidation of wheat straw. *Bioresource Technology* 82(1): 15–26.

[385] Bjerre AB, Olesen AB, Fernqvist T, et al. (1996) Pretreatment of wheat straw using combined wet oxidation and alkaline hydrolysis resulting in convertible cellulose and hemicellulose. *Biotechnology and Bioengineering* 49(5): 568–577.

[386] Klinke HB, Olsson L, Thomsen AB, and Ahring BK (2003) Potential inhibitors from wet oxidation of wheat straw and their effect on ethanol production of *Saccharomyces cerevisiae*: Wet oxidation and fermentation by yeast. *Biotechnology and Bioengineering* 81(6): 738–747.

[387] Pedersen M and Meyer AS (2009) Influence of substrate particle size and wet oxidation on physical surface structures and enzymatic hydrolysis of wheat straw. *Biotechnology Progress* 25(2): 399–408.

[388] Schmidt AS and Thomsen AB (1998) Optimization of wet oxidation pretreatment of wheat straw. *Bioresource Technology* 64(2): 139–151.

[389] Varga E, Schmidt AS, Réczey K, and Thomsen AB (2003) Pretreatment of corn stover using wet oxidation to enhance enzymatic digestibility. *Applied Biochemistry and Biotechnology* 104(1): 37–50.

[390] Varga E, Klinke HB, Réczey K, and Thomsen AB (2004) High solid simultaneous saccharification and fermentation of wet oxidized corn stover to ethanol. *Biotechnology and Bioengineering* 88(5): 567–574.

[391] Martín C, González Y, Fernández T, and Thomsen AB (2006) Investigation of cellulose convertibility and ethanolic fermentation of sugarcane bagasse pretreated by wet oxidation and steam explosion. *Journal of Chemical Technology and Biotechnology* 81(10): 1669–1677.

[392] Martín C, Klinke HB, and Thomsen AB (2007) Wet oxidation as a pretreatment method for enhancing the enzymatic convertibility of sugarcane bagasse. *Enzyme and Microbial Technology* 40(3): 426–432.

[393] Martin C and Thomsen AB (2007) Wet oxidation pretreatment of lignocellulosic residues of sugarcane, rice, cassava and peanuts for ethanol production. *Journal of Chemical Technology and Biotechnology* 82(2): 174–181.

[394] Palonen H, Thomsen AB, Tenkanen M, et al. (2004) Evaluation of wet oxidation pretreatment for enzymatic hydrolysis of softwood. *Applied Biochemistry and Biotechnology* 117(1): 1–17.

[395] Lissens G, Klinke H, Verstraete W, et al. (2004) Wet oxidation of organic household waste enriched with wheat straw for simultaneous saccharification and fermentation into ethanol. *Environmental Technology* 25(6): 647–655.

[396] Schacht C, Zetzl C, and Brunner G (2008) From plant materials to ethanol by means of supercritical fluid technology. *Journal of Supercritical Fluids* 46(3): 299–321.

[397] Zheng Y, Lin H-M, Wen J, et al. (1995) Supercritical carbon dioxide explosion as a pretreatment for cellulose hydrolysis. *Biotechnology Letters* 17(8): 845–850.

[398] Zheng Y, Lin H-M, and Tsao GT (1998) Pretreatment for cellulose hydrolysis by carbon dioxide explosion. *Biotechnology Progress* 14(6): 890–896.

[399] Kim HK and Hong J (2001) Supercritical CO_2 pretreatment of lignocellulose enhances enzymatic cellulose hydrolysis. *Bioresource Technology* 77(2): 139–144.

[400] Muratov GA (2007) Bioconversion of cotton cellulose to glucose by supercritical CO_2. *Chemistry of Natural Compounds* 43(5): 641–642.

[401] Zhao Y, Lu W-J, Wang H-T, and Yang J-L (2009) Fermentable hexose production from corn stalks and wheat straw with combined supercritical and subcritical hydrothermal technology. *Bioresource Technology* 100(23): 5884–5889.

[402] Zheng Y and Tsao GT (1996) Avicel hydrolysis by cellulase enzyme in supercritical CO_2. *Biotechnology Letters* 18(4): 451–454.

[403] Park CY, Ryu YW, and Kim C (2001) Kinetics and rate of enzymatic hydrolysis of cellulose in supercritical carbon dioxide. *Korean Journal of Chemical Engineering* 18(4): 475–478.

[404] Sanchez C (2009) Lignocellulosic residues: Biodegradation and bioconversion by fungi. *Biotechnology Advances* 27(2): 185–194.

[405] Wan C and Li Y (2010) Microbial pretreatment of corn stover with *Ceriporiopsis subvermispora* for enzymatic hydrolysis and ethanol production. *Bioresource Technology* 101(16): 6398–6403.

[406] Wan C and Li Y (2010) Microbial delignification of corn stover by *Ceriporiopsis subvermispora* for improving cellulose digestibility. *Enzyme and Microbial Technology* 47(1–2): 31–36.

[407] Yang X, Ma F, Zeng Y, et al. (2010) Structure alteration of lignin in corn stover degraded by white-rot fungus *Irpex lacteus* CD2. *International Biodeterioration and Biodegradation* 64(2): 119–123.

[408] Yang X, Zeng Y, Ma F, et al. (2010) Effect of biopretreatment on thermogravimetric and chemical characteristics of corn stover by different white-rot fungi. *Bioresource Technology* 101(14): 5475–5479.

[409] Bak JS, Ko JK, Choi I-G, et al. (2009) Fungal pretreatment of lignocellulose by *Phanerochaete chrysosporium* to produce ethanol from rice straw. *Biotechnology and Bioengineering* 104(3): 471–482.

[410] Singh P, Suman A, Tiwari P, et al. (2008) Biological pretreatment of sugarcane trash for its conversion to fermentable sugars. *World Journal of Microbiology and Biotechnology* 24(5): 667–673.

[411] Shi J, Chinn MS, and Sharma-Shivappa RR (2008) Microbial pretreatment of cotton stalks by solid state cultivation of *Phanerochaete chrysosporium*. *Bioresource Technology* 99(14): 6556–6564.

[412] Itoh H, Wada M, Honda Y, et al. (2003) Bioorganosolve pretreatments for simultaneous saccharification and fermentation of beech wood by ethanolysis and white rot fungi. *Journal of Biotechnology* 103(3): 273–280.

[413] Lu C, Wang H, Luo Y, and Guo L (2010) An efficient system for pre-delignification of gramineous biofuel feedstock *in vitro*: Application of a laccase from *Pycnoporus sanguineus* H275. *Process Biochemistry* 45(7): 1141–1147.

[414] Kuhar S, Nair LM, and Kuhad RC (2008) Pretreatment of lignocellulosic material with fungi capable of higher lignin degradation and lower carbohydrate degradation improves substrate acid hydrolysis and eventual conversion to ethanol. *Canadian Journal of Microbiology* 54(4): 305–313.

[415] Yu J, Zhang J, He J, et al. (2008) Combination of mild physical or chemical pretreatment with biological pretreatment for enzymatic hydrolysis of rice hull. *Bioresource Technology* 100(2): 903–908.

[416] Yu H, Guo G, Zhang X, et al. (2009) The effect of biological pretreatment with the selective white-rot fungus *Echinodontium taxodii* on enzymatic hydrolysis of softwoods and hardwoods. *Bioresource Technology* 100(21): 5170–5175.

[417] Zhang X, Xu C, and Wang H (2007) Pretreatment of bamboo residues with *Coriolus versicolor* for enzymatic hydrolysis. *Journal of Bioscience and Bioengineering* 104(2): 149–151.

[418] Taniguchi M, Suzuki H, Watanabe D, et al. (2005) Evaluation of pretreatment with *Pleurotus ostreatus* for enzymatic hydrolysis of rice straw. *Journal of Bioscience and Bioengineering* 100(6): 637–643.

[419] Akin DE, Sethuraman A, Morrison WH, et al. (1993) Microbial delignification with white-rot fungi improves forage digestibility. *Applied and Environmental Microbiology* 59(12): 4274–4282.

[420] Keller FA, Hamilton JE, and Nguyen QA (2003) Microbial pretreatment of biomass: Potential for reducing severity of thermochemical biomass pretreatment. *Applied Biochemistry and Biotechnology* 105(1–3): 27–41.

[421] Okano K, Iida Y, Samruri M, et al. (2006) Comparison of *in vitro* digestibility and chemical composition among sugarcane bagasses treated by four white-rot fungi. *Animal Science Journal* 77(3): 308–313.

[422] Sawada T, Nakamura Y, and Kobayashi F (1995) Effects of fungal pretreatment and steam explosion pretreatment on enzymatic saccharification of plant biomass. *Biotechnology and Bioengineering* 48(6): 719–724.

[423] Hatakka AI (1983) Pretreatment of wheat straw by white-rot fungi for enzymic saccharification of cellulose. *Applied Microbiology and Biotechnology* 18(6): 350–357.

[424] Li L, Li X-Z, Tang W-Z, et al. (2008) Screening of a fungus capable of powerful and selective delignification on wheat straw. *Letters in Applied Microbiology* 47(5): 415–420.

[425] Anderson WF and Akin DE (2008) Structural and chemical properties of grass lignocelluloses related to conversion for biofuels. *Journal of Industrial Microbiology and Biotechnology* 35(5): 355–366.

[426] Akin DE, Morrison WH, Rigsby LL, et al. (2006) Corn stover fractions and bioenergy: Chemical composition, structure, and response to enzyme pretreatment. *Applied Biochemistry and Biotechnology* 129(1–3): 104–116.

[427] Anderson WF, Peterson J, Akin DE, and Morrison WH (2005) Enzyme pretreatment of grass lignocellulose for potential high-value co-products and an improved fermentable substrate. *Applied Biochemistry and Biotechnology* 121(1–3): 303–310.

[428] da Costa Sousa L, Chundawat SPS, Balan V, and Dale BE (2009) 'Cradle-to-grave' assessment of existing lignocellulose pretreatment technologies. *Current Opinion in Biotechnology* 20(3): 339–347.

[429] Kumar R and Wyman CE (2009) Effect of xylanase supplementation of cellulase on digestion of corn stover solids prepared by leading pretreatment technologies. *Bioresource Technology* 100(18): 4203–4213.

[430] Jing X, Zhang X, and Bao J (2009) Inhibition performance of lignocellulose degradation products on industrial cellulase enzymes during cellulose hydrolysis. *Applied Biochemistry and Biotechnology* 159(3): 696–707.

[431] Du B, Sharma LN, Becker C, et al. (2010) Effect of varying feedstock-pretreatment chemistry combinations on the formation and accumulation of potentially inhibitory degradation products in biomass hydrolysates. *Biotechnology and Bioengineering* 107(3): 430–440.

[432] Klinke HB, Thomsen AB, and Ahring BK (2004) Inhibition of ethanol-producing yeast and bacteria by degradation products produced during pre-treatment of biomass. *Applied Microbiology and Biotechnology* 66(1): 10–26.

[433] Larsson S, Palmqvist E, Hahn-Hagerdal B, et al. (1999) The generation of fermentation inhibitors during dilute acid hydrolysis of softwood. *Enzyme and Microbial Technology* 24(3–4): 151–159.

[434] Weil JR, Dien B, Bothast R, et al. (2002) Removal of fermentation inhibitors formed during pretreatment of biomass by polymeric adsorbents. *Industrial and Engineering Chemistry Research* 41(24): 6132–6138.

[435] Liu ZL, Slininger PJ, and Gorsich SW (2005) Enhanced biotransformation of furfural and hydroxymethylfurfural by newly developed ethanologenic yeast strains. *Applied Biochemistry and Biotechnology* 121(1–3): 451–460.

[436] Merino ST and Cherry J (2007) Progress and challenges in enzyme development for biomass utilization. *Advances in Biochemical Engineering/Biotechnology* 108: 95–120.

[437] Banerjee G, Scott-Craig JS, and Walton JD (2010) Improving enzymes for biomass conversion: A basic research perspective. *Bioenergy Research* 3(1): 82–92.

[438] Gray KA, Zhao L, and Emptage M (2006) Bioethanol. *Current Opinion in Chemical Biology* 10(2): 141–146.

[439] Banerjee G, Car S, Scott-Craig JS, et al. (2010) Synthetic enzyme mixtures for biomass deconstruction: Production and optimization of a core set. *Biotechnology and Bioengineering* 105(5): 707–720.

[440] Wilson DB (2008) Three microbial strategies for plant cell wall degradation. *Annals of the New York Academy of Sciences* 1125(1): 289–297.

[441] Doi RH (2008) Cellulases of mesophilic microorganisms: Cellulosome and noncellulosome producers. *Annals of the New York Academy of Sciences* 1125(1): 267–279.

[442] Adsul MG, Bastawde KB, Varma AJ, and Gokhale DV (2007) Strain improvement of *Penicillium janthinellum* NCIM 1171 for increased cellulase production. *Bioresource Technology* 98(7): 1467–1473.

[443] Chandra M, Kalra A, Sangwan NS, et al. (2009) Development of a mutant of *Trichoderma citrinoviride* for enhanced production of cellulases. *Bioresource Technology* 100(4): 1659–1662.

[444] Nagarajana DR and Krishnan C (2010) Use of a new catabolite repression resistant promoter isolated from *Bacillus subtilis* KCC103 for hyper-production of recombinant enzymes. *Protein Expression and Purification* 70(1): 122–128.

[445] Kumar R and Wyman CE (2009) Effect of enzyme supplementation at moderate cellulase loadings on initial glucose and xylose release from corn stover solids pretreated by leading technologies. *Biotechnology and Bioengineering* 102(2): 457–467.

[446] Berlin A, Maximenko V, Gilkes N, and Saddler J (2007) Optimization of enzyme complexes for lignocellulose hydrolysis. *Biotechnology and Bioengineering* 97(2): 287–296.

[447] Yang B and Wyman CE (2006) BSA treatment to enhance enzymatic hydrolysis of cellulose in lignin containing substrates. *Biotechnology and Bioengineering* 94(4): 611–617.

[448] Kumar R and Wyman CE (2009) Effect of additives on the digestibility of corn stover solids following pretreatment by leading technologies. *Biotechnology and Bioengineering* 102(6): 1544–1557.

[449] Berlin A, Gilkes N, Kurabi A, et al. (2005) Weak lignin-binding enzymes: A novel approach to improve activity of cellulases for hydrolysis of lignocellulosics. *Applied Biochemistry and Biotechnology* 121(1–3): 163–170.

[450] Palonen H (2004) *Role of Lignin in the Enzymatic Hydrolysis of Lignocellulose*. vol. 520, pp. 1–80. Finland: VTT Publications.

[451] Palonen H and Viikari L (2004) Role of oxidative enzymatic treatments on enzymatic hydrolysis of softwood. *Biotechnology and Bioengineering* 86(5): 550–557.

[452] Jurado M, Prieto A, Martínez-Alcalá Á., et al. (2009) Laccase detoxification of steam-exploded wheat straw for second generation bioethanol. *Bioresource Technology* 100(23): 6378–6384.

[453] Simmons BA, Loqué D, and Ralph J (2010) Advances in modifying lignin for enhanced biofuel production. *Current Opinion in Plant Biology* 13(3): 312–319.

[454] Katahira S, Mizuike A, Fukuda H, and Kondo A (2006) Ethanol fermentation from lignocellulosic hydrolysate by a recombinant xylose- and cellooligosaccharide-assimilating yeast strain. *Applied Microbiology and Biotechnology* 72(6): 1136–1143.

[455] Kuyper M, Toirkens MJ, Diderich JA, et al. (2005) Evolutionary engineering of mixed-sugar utilization by a xylose-fermenting *Saccharomyces cerevisiae* strain. *FEMS Yeast Research* 5(10): 925–934.

[456] Lawford HG and Rousseau JD (2002) Performance testing of *Zymomonas mobilis* metabolically engineered for cofermentation of glucose, xylose, and arabinose. *Applied Biochemistry and Biotechnology* 98–100(1–9): 429–448.

[457] Shaw AJ, Podkaminer KK, Desai SG, *et al.* (2008) Metabolic engineering of a thermophilic bacterium to produce ethanol at high yield. *Proceedings of the National Academy of Sciences of the United States of America* 105(37): 13769–13774.
[458] Wisselink HW, Toirkens MJ, Wu Q, *et al.* (2009) Novel evolutionary engineering approach for accelerated utilization of glucose, xylose, and arabinose mixtures by engineered *Saccharomyces cerevisiae* strains. *Applied and Environmental Microbiology* 75(4): 907–914.
[459] Dien BS, Cotta MA, and Jeffries TW (2003) Bacteria engineered for fuel ethanol production: Current status. *Applied Microbiology and Biotechnology* 63(3): 258–266.
[460] Jeffries TW and Jin Y-S (2004) Metabolic engineering for improved fermentation of pentoses by yeasts. *Applied Microbiology and Biotechnology* 63(5): 495–509.
[461] Palnitkar SS and Lachke AH (1990) Efficient simultaneous saccharification and fermentation of agricultural residues by *Saccharomyces cerevisiae* and *Candida shehatae*: The d-xylose fermenting yeast. *Applied Biochemistry and Biotechnology* 26(2): 151–158.
[462] Pasha C, Kuhad RC, and Rao LV (2007) Strain improvement of thermotolerant *Saccharomyces cerevisiae* VS3 strain for better utilization of lignocellulosic substrates. *Journal of Applied Microbiology* 103(5): 1480–1489.
[463] Madhavan A, Tamalampudi S, Ushida K, *et al.* (2009) Xylose isomerase from polycentric fungus Orpinomyces: Gene sequencing, cloning, and expression in *Saccharomyces cerevisiae* for bioconversion of xylose to ethanol. *Applied Microbiology and Biotechnology* 82(6): 1067–1078.
[464] Matsushika A, Inoue H, Kodaki T, and Sawayama S (2009) Ethanol production from xylose in engineered *Saccharomyces cerevisiae* strains: Current state and perspectives. *Applied Microbiology and Biotechnology* 84(1): 37–53.
[465] Otero JM, Panagiotou G, and Olsson L (2007) Fueling industrial biotechnology growth with bioethanol. *Advances in Biochemical Engineering/Biotechnology* 108: 1–40.
[466] van Zyl WH, Lynd LR, Den Haan R, and McBride JE (2007) Consolidated bioprocessing for bioethanol production using *Saccharomyces cerevisiae*. *Advances in Biochemical Engineering/Biotechnology* 108: 205–235.
[467] Carere CR, Sparling R, Cicek N, and Levin DB (2008) Third generation biofuels via direct cellulose fermentation. *International Journal of Molecular Sciences* 9(7): 1342–1360.
[468] Lynd LR, van Zyl WH, McBride JE, and Laser M (2005) Consolidated bioprocessing of cellulosic biomass: An update. *Current Opinion in Biotechnology* 16(5): 577–583.
[469] Xu Q, Singh A, and Himmel ME (2009) Perspectives and new directions for the production of bioethanol using consolidated bioprocessing of lignocellulose. *Current Opinion in Biotechnology* 20(3): 364–371.
[470] Angenent LT (2007) Energy biotechnology: Beyond the general lignocellulose-to-ethanol pathway. *Current Opinion in Biotechnology* 18(3): 191–192.
[471] Aden A and Foust T (2009) Technoeconomic analysis of the dilute sulfuric acid and enzymatic hydrolysis process for the conversion of corn stover to ethanol. *Cellulose* 16(4): 535–545.
[472] Junker B, Lester M, Leporati J, *et al.* (2006) Sustainable reduction of bioreactor contamination in an industrial fermentation pilot plant. *Journal of Bioscience and Bioengineering* 102(4): 251–268.
[473] Kleerebezem R and van Loosdrecht MCM (2007) Mixed culture biotechnology for bioenergy production. *Current Opinion in Biotechnology* 18(3): 207–212.
[474] Fu Z and Holtzapple MT (2010) Anaerobic mixed-culture fermentation of aqueous ammonia-treated sugarcane bagasse in consolidated bioprocessing. *Biotechnology and Bioengineering* 106(2): 216–227.
[475] Thanakoses P, Black AS, and Holtzapple MT (2003) Fermentation of corn stover to carboxylic acids. *Biotechnology and Bioengineering* 83(2): 191–200.
[476] Fu Z and Holtzapple MT (2010) Consolidated bioprocessing of sugarcane bagasse and chicken manure to ammonium carboxylates by a mixed culture of marine microorganisms. *Bioresource Technology* 101(8): 2825–2836.
[477] Chan WN and Holtzapple MT (2003) Conversion of municipal solid wastes to carboxylic acids by thermophilic fermentation. *Applied Biochemistry and Biotechnology* 111(2): 93–112.
[478] Holtzapple MT and Granda CB (2009) Carboxylate platform: The MixAlco process Part 1: Comparison of three biomass conversion platforms. *Applied Biochemistry and Biotechnology* 156(1–3): 95–106.

5.14 Woody Biomass

LL Wright, University of Tennessee, Knoxville, TN, USA
LM Eaton and RD Perlack, Oak Ridge National Laboratory, Oak Ridge, TN, USA
BJ Stokes, CNJV LLC, Washington, DC, USA

© 2012 Elsevier Ltd. All rights reserved.

5.14.1	Introduction	264
5.14.2	Novel Short-Rotation Woody Crops/Short-Rotation Forestry for Bioenergy Applications	264
5.14.2.1	Woody Coppice Production and Harvesting	264
5.14.2.2	Single-Stem Hardwoods	268
5.14.2.3	Single-Stem Softwoods	274
5.14.2.4	Single-Stem Harvest and Handling	276
5.14.2.5	Comparison of Production Inputs and Costs for Poplar, Pine, Eucalypts, and Willow Biomass	277
5.14.2.6	Projections of Energy Crop Supply: A Methodology and US Results	278
5.14.2.7	Sustainability of Short-Rotation Woody Crops/Short-Rotation Forestry	281
5.14.3	Forestland-Derived Resources	282
5.14.3.1	Primary Forest Residues	283
5.14.3.1.1	Background	283
5.14.3.1.2	Environmental sustainability and the collection of primary forest residues	284
5.14.3.1.3	Economics of recovering primary forest residues	284
5.14.3.2	Fuelwood	286
5.14.3.3	Wood Processing Residues	286
5.14.3.3.1	Primary mill residues	286
5.14.3.3.2	Pulping liquors	286
5.14.3.4	Urban Wood Residues	286
5.14.4	Conclusions	287
References		288
Further Reading		291
Relevant Websites		291

Glossary

CAI$_{max}$ (maximum current annual increment) It is the incremental growth of a tree or even-aged tree stand during the year when annual growth is maximized.

Coppice Creation of a multistemmed (bush-like) woody crop by cutting the stems and allowing resprouting to occur.

Fuel treatment thinning This material is classified as standing and downed trees in overstocked stands that, if removed, would leave the forestlands healthier, more productive, and much less susceptible to fire hazard.

Fuelwood Wood that is harvested from forestlands and combusted directly for useable heat in the residential and commercial sectors and power in the electric utility sector.

MAI$_{max}$ (maximum mean annual increment) MAI is the average annual increase in volume or weight of individual trees or stands up to a specified point in time. MAI$_{max}$ identifies the year of the growth cycle in which the MAI is maximized, which is also the optimum biological rotation age.

Primary forest residues, also called logging residues This woody residue material largely consists of tops, branches and limbs, salvable dead trees, rough and rotten trees, noncommercial species, and small trees. This material is often left in the forest.

Primary mill residues Residues such as bark, sawmill slabs, peeler log cores, and sawdust that are generated in the processing of roundwood for lumber, plywood, and pulp.

Rotation age The number of years between planting or resprouting of a tree crop and harvesting of the tree crop. The biologically optimum and economically optimum rotation age may differ slightly.

Short rotation intensive culture (SRIC) is a silvicultural system based on short clear-felling cycles (rotations) generally between 1 and 15 years, employing intensive cultural techniques such as fertilization, irrigation, and weed control utilizing superior planting material. This term was coined early in the development of woody crops and it has been largely replaced in the literature by the terms **Short Rotation Woody Crops (SRWC)** in the United States and **Short Rotation Forestry (SRF)** in many other countries. The definitions are basically the same for SRIC, SRWC, and SRF but the emphasis in the United States is on the production of wood on agricultural land, while in other countries the focus is on the modification of forestry approaches on forest land. **Short Rotation Coppice (SRC)** is a variant of the above approaches (and often included within the scope of the above terms) whereby the single stem trees are cut after the first year of growth to force a bush form that fully occupies the site within 3 or 4 years due to being planted at very high densities. Unfortunately, the acronym SRC has also been associated with (Short Rotation Crops) starting in 2008 when an International Energy Agency/Bioenergy Group included both woody and perennial herbaceous crops as part of the task study.

Single-stem woody crops A term used in this chapter to differentiate woody crops grown as single stem trees from those grown in coppice systems.
Urban wood residues The woody components of municipal solid waste (MSW) and construction and demolition (C&D) waste wood constitute urban wood residues.

5.14.1 Introduction

There are multiple sources of wood for bioenergy applications that include production of heat, electricity, and biofuels. This overview will focus on recent analysis in the United States with brief mention of technology status in other countries. The gathering and use of wood fuels for primary space heating and cooking applications will not be discussed.

The major new or novel emerging sources of wood for bioenergy and also the potentially largest wood energy feedstock sources worldwide are purpose-grown woody crops produced both in coppice and single-stem production systems both of which are encompassed under the terms short-rotation woody crops (SRWCs) and short-rotation forestry (SRF). Willow species are particularly adaptable to high-density coppice management, but other hardwoods can be utilized. In contrast, single-stem woody crop systems are normally planted at densities of 5000 stems per ha^{-1} or less. Most hardwoods managed as single-stem crops in the first rotation will regrow as coppice crops in the following rotations if not replanted. Hybrid poplars, cottonwoods, and eucalypts are all examples of hardwood trees being evaluated for bioenergy applications that also exhibit the ability to coppice. However, coppicing is not a requirement for bioenergy applications as pines also have considerable potential for use as bioenergy feedstocks.

Hardwoods (i.e., poplars and eucalypts) and pines (loblolly pine) will each receive specific attention as primary examples of single-stem woody crops because of the different history of development. A 2006 review of the status of worldwide commercial development of bioenergy using energy crops showed that plantings of SRWC or any type of planted wood for bioenergy were still relatively small in most areas of the world [1]. Exceptions were the countries like Brazil with 30 000 km^2 of eucalyptus plantations largely used to produce charcoal and China with estimates of 70 000–100 000 km^2 of woody crops used primarily for 'fuelwood'. By contrast, Northern Europe, the part of the world with the largest use of willow for bioenergy (primarily district heating), was estimated to have only 180 km^2 planted.

Two potentially large bioenergy wood resources that already exist worldwide are logging residues from commercial harvesting operations and 'thinnings' generated by treatment of forests to reduce fuel loads (also referred to as fuel treatment thinnings). Although these are not 'novel' wood resources *per se*, they are included due to the significant resource potential currently existing and current efforts to reduce extraction and processing costs. Issues surrounding the sustainability of these forest production systems are also addressed comprehensively.

Immediately available (and lower cost) wood resources are already being obtained from primary and secondary processing wood residues from traditional wood products and urban wood wastes. These sources include the bark residuals and black liquors generated by timber processing and paper pulp making and are largely utilized to produce heat and electricity. Efficiency of these resources can be improved, and we provide recommendations on the potential expansion of these feedstocks.

5.14.2 Novel Short-Rotation Woody Crops/Short-Rotation Forestry for Bioenergy Applications

5.14.2.1 Woody Coppice Production and Harvesting

The production of wood in very short rotations for fiber and energy originated in the United States in the 1960s with the testing of sycamore plantations planted at very high density, harvested at an early age, and allowed to sprout multiple stems (or coppice) for several rotations [2]. Most hardwood species have the physiological capability for producing coppice sprouts though differing numbers of sprouts per stump and locations of sprouting buds create differences in form [3]. High-density coppice production techniques have frequently been applied to poplars and eucalypts, but willow has undergone the most genetic selection for clones for high-productivity coppice culture [3]. Willows have been grown as coppice crops since ancient times for basket making, wine trellises, and other uses. Intensive efforts to develop high-yielding willow coppice crops were first initiated by researchers at the Swedish University of Agricultural Sciences, in Uppsala, Sweden, in the 1970s [4]. Willow coppice research quickly spread to several other northern European countries, as well as the University of Toronto in Canada, and the State University of New York (SUNY) by the mid-1980s. Yield trials of willow coppice are now ongoing in 15 states in the United States and six provinces in Canada (**Figure 1**).

Commercial implementation of willow coppice technology for energy occurred first in Sweden, with over 16 000 ha planted by the early 2000s. The majority of the Swedish plantings occurred between 1991 and 1996 as a result of agricultural subsidies that included willow coppice production on surplus arable land, higher fossil fuel taxes, and an established biofuels market already

Figure 1 Resprouting of willow in western New York, USA, following a dormant season coppice. Courtesy of State University of New York – Environmental Sciences & Forestry, SUNY-ESF, Woody Biomass Programs' online images.

using forest fuels [5]. Since the late 1990s, new plantings of willow coppice for bioenergy has slowed; however, plantings for phytoremediation application have improved the economic viability of more recent plantings [6]. By 2005, Poland had approximately 6000 ha of commercial willow coppice plantations [7]. In the United States, the Salix Consortium joined electric utility companies, universities, state and federal agencies, and private companies in the mid-1990s to commercialize willow biomass production. With no subsidies available, only about 280 ha of willow biomass crops had been established in New York by 2000 [8]. Commercial plantings are slowly expanding in the United States with the development of a commercial nursery to provide planting material. Numerous field trials of new willow clones are being tested throughout the northeastern United States and southeastern Canada (**Figure 2**).

Handbooks available on the web provide excellent guidance on the latest advances in production techniques for willow coppice [9, 10] although research on production techniques continues [7]. Willow coppice grown on good agricultural soils will produce greater yields at an earlier age; however, willow coppice can be grown on soils that are marginal for traditional crops. The soils should be imperfectly to moderately well drained, but excessively well-drained (coarse sands) and very poorly drained (heavy clay) soils are considered unsuitable. A soil pH between 5.5 and 8.0 is required. Current site preparation methods usually involve mowing to remove vegetation, application of a total kill herbicide (e.g., glyphosate), and tillage (no-till methods are being investigated). Effective weed control is critical to successful establishment. One advantage to coppice production techniques is that full site occupation is rapidly achieved by the multiple-stem or 'bush-like' tree form, thus minimizing the amount of herbicide applications needed during a rotation.

Willows are mechanically planted as unrooted dormant cuttings in early spring when the site is accessible. Typical machines (e.g., the Salix Maskiner Step Planter® and the Egedal® Willow Planter) cut dormant 1.5–2 m whips of 1-year-old willow into 20 cm sections and insert them vertically into the ground. Future planters may take a 'lay-flat' approach to establishing willow [11]. Commercial willow biomass plantations in Sweden today contain about 12 000 cuttings ha^{-1} arranged in a 'double-row' system where between-row spacing is alternately 1.5 and 0.75 m and within-row spacing is about 0.75 m [12]. The *Willow Producers Handbook* [9] suggests a similar double-row system with tighter within-row spacing, resulting in a somewhat higher density of about 14 760 plants ha^{-1} (**Figure 3**). Recent research has tested production in stands containing up to 40 000 plants ha^{-1} [7]. In all cases, the plants are cut back after the first growing season in order to promote sprouting (coppicing). Productivity is generally higher in the second and later coppice cycles. Harvest of coppiced willows or poplars is conducted every 3–5 years during the period of dormancy with the norm being 3 years. The economic life span of a willow coppice plantation is generally believed to be less than 25 years [12].

Productivity of willow coppice varies greatly depending on soil, climate, management, and all the factors that normally affect yields of agricultural crops, including species, genotype, and rotation. Experimental trials of fertilized and irrigated willows, grown in 3 or 4 years coppice rotations, have occasionally yielded more than 27 oven dry Megagrams (odMg) ha^{-1} yr^{-1} in the northeastern United States [8, 13], 30 odMg ha^{-1} yr^{-1} in southern Sweden [12], and 33 odMg ha^{-1} yr^{-1} in Poland [7]. Numerous experimental trials in North American and Europe have produced willow coppice yields in the range of 7–20 odMg ha^{-1} yr^{-1} [7, 8, 12, 14, 15] (**Table 1**). Unfortunately, average commercial yields of willow coppice have generally been lower. First-rotation yields of the first commercial harvests in the United States (winter of 2001/2002) averaged only 7.5 odMg ha^{-1} yr^{-1} [8], though second-rotation harvests and new clone harvests are reported to average about 11.4 odMg ha^{-1} yr^{-1} [25]. Early commercial production in Sweden averaged as low as 2.6, 4.2, and 4.5 odMg ha^{-1} yr^{-1} for first-, second-, and third-cutting cycles, respectively, though some farmers achieved yields double or triple the average [12]. Proper establishment and tending (including fertilization)

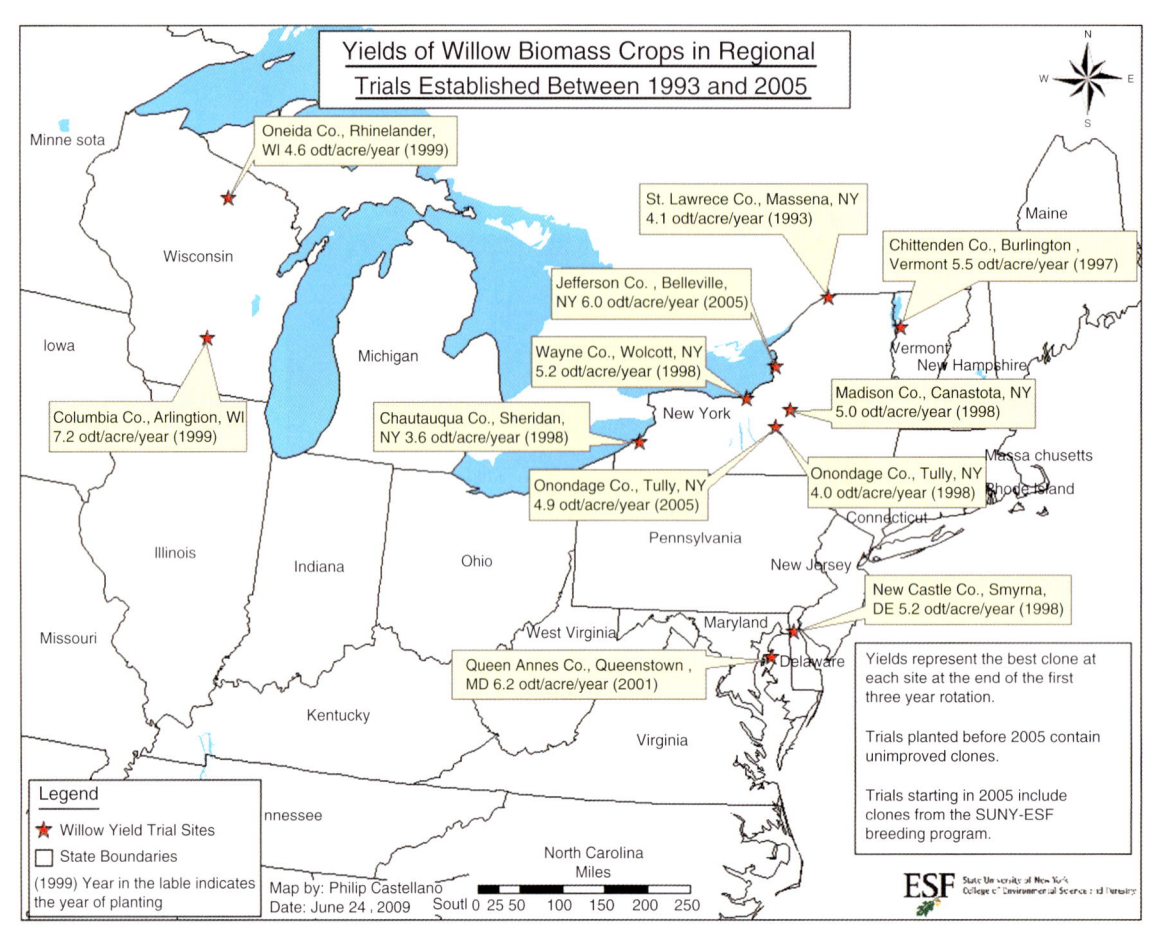

Figure 2 Map of willow test locations in the United States. Courtesy of Tim Volk of SUNY-ESF.

Figure 3 Double-row spacing for coppice willow plantings in the United States. Courtesy of SUNY-ESF Woody Biomass Programs' online images.

and better clones were linked to higher performing farmers. US research has determined that annual fertilization with about 100 kg ha^{-1} annually of commercial fertilizer or addition of manures or biosolids is needed to obtain commercially viable yields [25]. Modeling of yield potential based on oat crops in Sweden suggests that commercial willow coppice yields could easily be doubled in Sweden with appropriate silviculture [12]. Across Europe, yields are estimated to range from 3.5 to 15.1 odMg ha^{-1} yr^{-1} [26].

Poplars are frequently included in high-density coppice production trials [14, 20, 21, 27]. Considering all else equal, the best coppiced willow clones generally outperform the best poplar clones under coppice management [14, 20] (see comparisons in **Table 1**). However, poplars can perform well in high density. For example, a high-density (18 000 trees ha^{-1}) species comparison

Table 1 Selected reports of yields (both observed and modeled) of coppiced willow, poplar, and eucalyptus in experimental and commercial plantings in North America, Europe, and New Zealand (measured at MAI$_{max}$ unless otherwise noted)

Culture intensity[a] location	Genotype[b]	Yield[c] (Mg ha^{-1} yr^{-1})	Stem age[d] (rotation)	Total rotation N,P,K (kg ha^{-1})	Planting density trees (ha^{-1})	Plant year	References
High- to very high-intensity culture – small plot yields							
T, W, I, HF in Tully, NY, USA	*S. viminalis* SV1	23.8	3 (1)[e]	672, 112, 224	36 960	1990	[13, 16][f]
		27.5	3 (1)[e]	672, 112, 224			
T, W, HF in Tully, NY, USA	*S. viminalis* SVI	8.9	3 (1)[g]	672, 112, 224	36 960	1990	[13]
T, W, HF in Tully, NY, USA	*Populus* Hybrid NM5	8.8	1 (3–10)[h]	336, 112, 224		1987	[17]
	S. viminalis SV1	11.6	1 (3–10)[h]	336, 112, 224	107 600		
T in North Island, NZ	*E. viminalis* 10 clones	10.4–23.8	3 (1)	0, 0, 0 (all)	5 000	1990	[18]
		15.5–29.6	3 (2)	Fertile site			
T, W, HF in Kwidzyn Valley, Poland	*S. viminalis* 6 clones	14.3–33.2	4 (1)	450, 88, 330 (all)	40 000	2000	[7]
	S. viminalis × *S. purpurea*, one clone	14.5	1 (1–4 average)	Fertile site	40 000		
T, W, F in Viterbo, Italy	*P. alba* clone	24.5–29.8	3 (2)	792, 22, 45 (all)	10 000	1999	[19]
	P. nigra clone	22.9–29.0	Coppice after first rotation	Fertile site	10 000	1999	
	P. × *euramericana* clone	25.6–29.8			10 000	1999	
Medium-intensity culture – small plot yields							
T, W in Central Scotland	*Populus* hybrid 'Balsam spire'	9.0	3.2 (1)	0, 0, 0	10 000	1989	[20]
	Alnus rubra	8.4	6.2 (1)	0, 0, 0	10 000	1989	[20]
	Willow 'Bowles Hybrid'	14.0	3.2 (1)	0, 0, 0	10 000	1989	[20]
T, W, F in Tully, NY, USA	Average willow clones, first rotation	8.4–11.6	4 (1)	100, 0, 0	14 326	Early 1990s	[8]
T, W, F in Tully, NY, USA	Best five willow clones, second rotation	9.9–18.6	4 (2)	100, 0, 0	14 326	Mid 1990s	[8]
T, W in Montreal, Canada	*Populus* hybrid, two clones	17.2–18.0	4 (1)	0, 0, 0	18 000	1998	[21]
T, W in Montreal, Canada	Willow 10 clones	9.3–14.1	4 (1)	0, 0, 0	18 000	1998	[21]
Modeled commercial coppice yields							
NE in Sweden	Better willow clones	8–9	~4 (1)	Lower water	(12 to 20) × 1000	NA	[22]
E in Sweden	Better willow clones	9–10		Medium water			
S, SW in Sweden	Better willow clones	11–17		Higher water			
Average Swedish grower	Average willow clones assumed	4.4	4.2 (3)	0, 0, 0 to very little N	(12 to 20) × 1000	NA	[12]
Best 25% Swedish growers		5.4–7.1	4.2 (3)	Likely < 100, 0, 0			
Observed commercial coppice yields							
T, W, I, F in Central NY	*S. viminalis* SV1	7.5	4 (1)	100, 0, 0	14 326	~2000	[8]
T, W, I, F in Central NY	*S. viminalis* SV1	11.4	4 (1&2)	100, 0, 0	14 326	~2006	[23]
T, W, F in	All woody crops[i]		Not given	Moderate assumed	Not given	Various	[24]
Germany		4.0–13.4					
France		3.5–15.0					
Italy		3.5–15.1					
Great Britain		3.6–13.2					
Poland		4.1–13.3					

[a] Culture intensity notations are as follows: T, tillage used in site preparation; W, weed control; F, fertilization; I, irrigation; P, pest control; H, high; VH, very high.
[b] NM5, NE388, and NM6 are selected poplar clones used in the United States; SV1 is a selected willow clones developed in Sweden.
[c] Yields are expressed as the mean annual increment of the total aboveground dry weight without foliage for hardwoods.
[d] Stem age represents the growth year in which the stand reached maximum mean annual increment (MAI$_{max}$) based on published growth curves unless footnoted. Stem age for first-rotation coppice does not include the first growth year before the stem is coppiced. Thus, a willow of stem age 3 actually has a 4-year-old root but coppice yield is averaged only over the stem age.
[e] Age of MAI$_{max}$ not verifiable but stand had reached expected harvest age for the planting density and was believed to be close to MAI$_{max}$.
[f] Two separate papers reported data from the same experimental trial, but different subplots may have been measured.
[g] Age of MAI$_{max}$ not verifiable but data were deemed worthy to include for comparison.
[h] Age selected is year of peak average annual yield of annually coppice harvests between years 3–10 (for comparison with age of maximum current annual increment for the stand).
[i] All woody culture approaches and species were included in the estimates for each country, but coppice crops likely predominated.

trial in Canada found two poplar clones that equaled or outperformed the yields of nine willow clones over a 4-year first rotation [21]. Furthermore, recent high-density (10 000 trees ha^{-1}) trials of three poplar species in Italy produced yields as high as 20.9–25.8 odMg ha^{-1} yr^{-1} during a second (coppice) rotation with optimal culture conditions and current climate conditions and up to 28–31 odMg ha^{-1} yr^{-1} in elevated CO_2 conditions [19]. It is likely to be significant that in both high-yield scenarios, poplar trees were not coppiced during the establishment year. Most available poplar and eucalypt clones, while adaptable to coppice techniques, appear to perform better if allowed to grow in the single-stem form for at least 2–3 years after planting even if planted at high density [18, 28]. Some poplar clones only perform well when planted at much wider spacing or when thinned as soon as crown closure occurs.

Harvesting of willow and poplar coppice should only be performed during the dormant season if resprouting is desired. Eucalyptus will resprout during most of the year, but most species tested have shown less vigor when cut in late summer [3]. Harvesting technology for short-rotation coppice is generally the most expensive portion of its production, and the area is developing rapidly. Case New Holland (CNH) has been particularly active in testing and modifying existing harvesting heads for traditional crops. Initial field trials of willow harvesting with a new CNH fb130 header were performed in the United States and United Kingdom in 2008 and 2009. Based on the UK harvest trial, the header was able to harvest and chip willow stems up to 200 mm thick and 12.5 m tall at speeds of 12.5 kph. This rate would allow harvest of as much as 8 ha day^{-1}. The chips were blown directly into a truck following behind or beside the tractor with the harvest header. Other harvesters for woody coppice include sugar cane harvesters made by Austroft, forage harvesters made by Class, various versions of the Bender made by Salix Maskiner, and other harvesters that are adaptations of existing farm equipment. Tests have recently been conducted in Italy on poplar coppice with stems between 2 and 7 cm using several types of Class foragers. Results showed that harvest costs are a function of field stocking and machine power in fields with annual yields ranging from 9 to 15 odMg ha^{-1} yr^{-1} and harvested yields up to 70 green Mg [29]. The current trend in wood coppice harvesting is toward powerful units fitted with a very strong harvest header (**Figure 4**).

The economics of willow biomass crop production in the United States has been analyzed using a publicly available cash flow model, EcoWillow v.1.4 (Beta) [30]. The EcoWillow model incorporates all stages of willow field production: site preparation, planting, maintenance, and harvesting over multiple rotations. The model also includes transportation to an end user. The base case scenario in EcoWillow shows an internal rate of return of 5.5% over seven 3-year cycles (22 years) and payback is reached in the thirteenth year. Harvesting, establishment, and land rent/insurance are the main expenses making up 29%, 25%, and 18%, respectively, of the total undiscounted costs. The remaining costs (undiscounted) including crop removal, transport, administrative costs, and fertilizer applications account for about 28% of the total costs of willow production.

Cost reduction can occur both through genetic selection for high yield and more efficient harvesting technology. Reducing the frequency of harvesting operations can also reduce costs. Additionally, methods to reduce the cost of the planting stock (currently 63% of establishment costs in the EcoWillow baseline) can decrease the overall upfront capital for planting. Another strategy for reducing costs is to combine coppice production for bioenergy with provision of phytoremediation or other environmental services that result in additional income. This is seen as one of the best opportunities for creating win–win scenarios of providing a profit to farmers as well as keeping the feedstock costs to bioenergy facilities low.

5.14.2.2 Single-Stem Hardwoods

Research and commercialization of single-stem hardwood crops (such as hybrid poplars, cottonwoods, eucalypts, and sycamore) on short rotations for fiber and energy began in late 1960s and early 1970s at several locations in the United States with substantial involvement of the US Forest Service [31–33]. However, technology and cultivation practices were developed to a much fuller extent

Figure 4 Picture of Case New Holland coppice harvester and chipper blowing chips into a tractor-pulled transfer bin. Courtesy of Tim Volk, SUNY-ESF.

Figure 5 Very short-rotation eucalyptus in Brazil. Courtesy of Laercio Couto, RENEBIO, www.renebio.org.br.

in the United States as a result of the Short-Rotation Woody Crops Program (SRWCP) initiated in 1981 by the US Department of Energy and managed by scientists at the Oak Ridge National Laboratory (ORNL) in Tennessee [34]. In the United States and Canada, the concept of growing trees as row-crops on short rotations, was originally (and often still is) referred to as short-rotation intensive culture and defined as

> a silvicultural system based upon short clear-felling cycles, generally between one and 15 years, employing intensive cultural techniques such as fertilization, irrigation, and weed control, and utilizing genetically superior planting material [35].

The term SRWC was adopted in the United States around 1989 [36] to focus on the agricultural approach to wood production. In Europe, the term 'short-rotation forestry' is more frequently used to convey the same concept. Although many countries have grown eucalyptus, poplars, cottonwoods, and other hardwoods as row-crops for pulpwood for decades and have, since the 1970s, also considered these hardwoods for energy, there seems to be a recent renewed interest in single-stem short-rotation technology (**Figure 5**). Many other hardwood species have been evaluated for and found to be suitable for both single-stem and coppice production systems such as sweetgum, sycamores, black locust, birches, beeches, silver maple, and others. The short-rotation concept was originally linked to only hardwood culture since most definitions included the concept of relying on coppice regeneration after the first harvest. Coppice regeneration is no longer included as an inherent component of single-stem production of wood, but it remains an option for hardwood species.

The *Populus* genera (including cottonwoods, aspens, balsam poplars, white poplars, and hybrids) contain many species native to Europe, North America, Asia, and North Africa including some of the most studied of all forest tree species. A black cottonwood clone was the first tree species to have its genome sequenced, involving the participation of scientists worldwide [37, 38]. A review of the silviculture and biology of SRWC in 2006 [39] traces the recognition of the value of poplars back to the Roman Empire as well as ancient Asian cultures. The poplars were used in single-stem form for timber, windbreaks, and roadway lining, and as coppiced forms for fuelwood and forage. Early explorers carried poplar trees from the Americas and Asia back to Europe and natural hybrids were first recognized in the mid-1700s. The first controlled crosses of selected hybrid poplar parents was performed in 1912 in London's Kew Garden, but by 1924, wide-scale breeding had been initiated in the United States, and by the 1930s, many countries had poplar breeding programs in place [39]. Many international and national organizations are dedicated to the study and distribution of knowledge about *Populus* species. Poplars have attained such recognition and study due to their rapid growth characteristics, ease of experimental manipulation and clonal propagation, large phenotypic diversity, ease of hybridization, and more recently availability of a nearly complete genomic map [37]. Much research is presently being directed toward using the knowledge gained to develop new clones with special properties that will increase the already high value of poplars for producing fuels and chemicals.

Eucalyptus has been characterized as "an ideal energy crop with certain species and hybrids having excellent biomass productivity, relatively low lignin content, and a short rotation time" [40]. Though more than 700 species of *Eucalyptus* exist, most are native only to Australia and nearby islands and less than 15 species are commercially significant. Eucalypts are claimed to be the 'most valuable and widely planted hardwood in the world', occupying 18 million ha in 90 countries [41]. India has large areas of low-intensity/low-productivity plantings, while Brazil has the largest amount of land dedicated to intensive cultivation of eucalypts. China has the largest commitment to establishing new eucalypt plantations at a rate of 3500–43 000 ha yr^{-1} [41].

Brazil leads the world with experience in selecting improved genotypes and developing short-rotation production techniques for eucalyptus [42]. Four species of eucalyptus and their hybrids account for 80% of plantations worldwide, and of those, *Eucalyptus grandis* is the most widely planted species, showing the fastest growth and widest adaptability of all eucalypt species (**Figure 6**). However, the Brazilian bioenergy eucalyptus plantings are using hybrids of *E. grandis* with combinations of *Eucalyptus urophylla*, *Eucalyptus tereticornis*, and *Eucalyptus camaldulensis* (**Figure 5**). Several eucalyptus species are being planted in Hawaii and the subtropical regions of the US mainland. Eucalyptus genome sequencing is ongoing [43] along with efforts to modify lignin contents

Figure 6 *Eucalyptus grandis* in pastoral forestry systems in Brazil. Courtesy of Laercio Couto, RENEBIO, www.renebio.org.br.

and other wood quality traits [41] of importance to bioenergy/biofuel utilization. Eucalyptus lignin levels are slightly higher than most other fast-growing hardwoods; therefore, the best, immediate bioenergy use may be the production of electricity (thermochemical processes), syngas (which can be transformed to many products), or charcoal for industrial processes, as has been done in Brazil for many years.

Single-stem short-rotation research in the United States in the late 1970s and early 1980s focused on outcomes affecting tree density management and mean annual growth. In particular, when comparing poplar densities in the range of 500–100 000 trees ha^{-1}, an abrupt change in the rotation age–density relationship was observed between 2000 and 4000 trees ha^{-1} such that the age at which maximum mean annual increment was achieved could be reduced by nearly half [34]. This led to recommending planting densities in the range of 2500–4000 trees ha^{-1} (1000–1600 trees per acre) to optimize for rotations of 5–8 years. This density range was initially used in many commercial plantings for short-rotation hardwood pulpwood production in the United States. However, the desire for product flexibility (for both energy and pulp) led to using lower densities (~700 to 800 stems ha^{-1}) and longer rotations (7–12 years) with a resulting increase in individual stem size with lower bark to wood ratios (**Figure 7**). Although the planting densities differ, the same interest in product flexibility was recently given as a rationale for renewed interest in research on hybrid poplars and aspens in Sweden [44]. A negative consequence of lower densities is the increased risk of weed competition for nutrients and water, requiring higher levels of mechanical and chemical weed control in the early years. A possible solution is to plant at higher densities, and then to remove some wood for energy when the stand closes canopy.

Planting strategy depends to a great extent on the planned density. Multiple-row mechanical planters are almost always used for very high-density plantings (such as the willow planters described earlier). The current approach in the United States to planting most poplar or cottonwood cuttings and rooted hardwoods at commercial densities is to use an experienced planting crew that plants the trees by hand using a dibble stick to create the planting hole and a well-placed stomp of the foot to close the dirt around the hole. To facilitate cultivation in two directions for weed control, the field is 'cross-checked' with a tractor prior to planting to establish the desired planting pattern. The alternative for the planting of many hardwood seedlings and cuttings is to use a single- or multiple-row 'planter' pulled by a tractor. This involves individuals sitting on the planter and feeding the cuttings or seedlings into a slot. Time and labor requirements are reduced, but this approach fails to produce evenly spaced plantings suitable for cross-cultivation. The approach is satisfactory for plantings with relatively tight in-row spacing and wide between-row spacing (e.g., 0.5 × 3.0 m spacing), which only require tillage and fertilizer applications in one direction. More efficient planter designs are under development. The author has observed a prototype multiple-row mechanical planter in operation that can simultaneously plant multiple rows (row number is spacing dependent) of hardwood cuttings with greatly improved speed and accuracy [45]. As the demand for novel wood energy crops increases, it is anticipated that multiple new planting equipment designs will become commercially available.

Figure 7 Hybrid poplars near harvest age (~age 7) in the US Pacific Northwest. Courtesy of Lynn Wright, WrightLink Consulting.

Poplar and eucalyptus growth rates and yields at harvest are influenced by water availability, fertility, soil, sunlight levels, genetics, and whether the stand has been allowed to reach its maximum mean annual increment (MAI_{max}). The length of the rotation required to achieve MAI_{max} is heavily influenced by the planting density and the response of the trees to competition and growing-degree days. **Table 2** contains selected representative published data on single-stem hardwood row-crop yields. Selected *Populus* hybrids have achieved highest yields in the United States in the Pacific Northwest where they have access to groundwater or drip irrigation including nutrients (fertigation), long days with plenty of sunshine, and relatively cool nights. The best yields achieved are represented by the *Populus trichocarpa* × *Populus deltoides* ($t \times d$) hybrid (11-11) grown in very small plots on 4 year rotations where the first rotation was estimated to produce 27.5 odMg ha^{-1} yr^{-1} and the second (coppice) rotation produced 43 odMg ha^{-1} yr^{-1} (assuming 100% survival) [46, 47]. Similar first-rotation yields were replicated by similar $t \times d$ hybrids in later small plot studies [48]. The production of $t \times d$ hybrid 11-11 in larger experimental plots produced a maximum of about 18 odMg ha^{-1} yr^{-1} [49], which is more likely to represent the upper yield potential of selected clones grown under optimal conditions on a commercial scale in the US Pacific Northwest. For the North Central, Midwestern, and northeastern portions of the United States, yields of selected single-stem *Populus* hybrid clonal plantings at or near MAI_{max} have ranged from about 9 to 15 odMg ha^{-1} yr^{-1} [50-55] in small experimental plantings and less in first-generation larger-scale plantings [51]. The best *Populus* clones differ considerably with each location. Pure *P. deltoides* (eastern cottonwood) clones are a better choice for most areas of the southern United States that experience frost and heavy infestation by the fungal disease, *Septoria*. Total aboveground yields of *P. deltoides* grown in operational plantations primarily for pulp in the Mississippi Delta region have been estimated to range from 6.7 to 12.5 [56]. But many published results show lower yields for poplars and other hardwoods outside the Mississippi Delta region [57, 58]. Modeling assessments have suggested that fertilized *P. deltoides* stands could yield 20 odMg ha^{-1} yr^{-1} or more on bottom-land sites in latitudes above about 35 degrees North, dropping to as low as 5 odMg ha^{-1} yr^{-1} on sandy soils in southern Georgia (~31 degrees latitude north) [61] (**Figures 8** and **9**). The few recently published yield reports [20, 44, 62, 63] on single-stem poplar and other hardwoods produced in Europe (**Table 3**) appear to fall within the same range as the coppice crop yields summarized in **Table 1**.

Recent US studies are showing very high potential for *Eucalyptus* species at US latitudes below about 31 degrees North. In central Florida, *Eucalyptus* species have been observed to yield 17-32 odMg ha^{-1} yr^{-1} after 3-5 years of growth on a clay settling area [59]

Table 2 Selected hardwood single-stem yields in North America with culture intensity and N levels included

Culture intensity[a] location	Genotype[b]	Yield (dry)[c] (Mg ha^{-1} yr^{-1})	Stem age[d] (rotation)	Total rotation N, P, K (kg ha^{-1})	Planting density trees (ha^{-1})	Plant year	References
Experimental yields							
T, W, F in US Pacific Northwest (WA) (15 tree plots)	*P. trichocarpa* × *deltoides* clones 11-11	27.5 43.0	4 (1)[e] 4 (2)[e]	225, 0, 0 Fertile site	6 944	1979	[46, 47]
T, W, I in US Pacific Northwest (WA) (100 tree plots)	*P. trichocarpa* × *deltoides* clone 11-11	18.4	4 (1)	0, 0, 0 Fertile site	10 000	1986	[49]
T, W (small plots) in US North Central; (WI, MN, IA)	*Populus* hybrids top five clones Best clone	13.5–15.0 20.9	6 (1)[f] 7 (1)[f]	0, 0, 0; 0, 0, 0	1 076	1995	[50]
T, W, I (small plots) in US North Central (WI)	*Populus* hybrids NE386 and NE41	11.4 12.8	7(1) 6(1)	0, 0, 0 0, 0, 0	10 000 10 000	1981	[51]
T, W (small plots) in US North Central (WI)	*Populus* hybrids NE386 and NE41	8.7 9.6	6(1) 7(1)	0, 0, 0 0, 0, 0	10 000 10 000	1981	[51]
T, W (large plantings) in US North Central, six sites (WI, SD, MN)	*Populus* hybrids Average of DN17, DN34, DN182	4.8–9.5	6 (1) to 9 (1)	0, 0, 0	1 682	1988	[55]
T with pest control in US North Central (IA)	*P. deltoides* 91 × 04–03	11.5	8 (1)	0, 0, 0	200	1998	[52]
W, I (first year) in US Midwest (MO) fertile floodplains	*Populus* hybrids 1112, 2059 26C6R51	10.6 11.6 10.6	5 (1)[e] 5 (1)[e] 5 (1)[e]	0, 0, 0 0, 0, 0 0, 0, 0	10 000 10 000 10 000	2000	[53]
T, W, I in US Northeast (PA)	*Populus* hybrid NE388	12.9	3 (2)	0, 0, 0	21 570	1981	[54]
T, W, F in US Mississippi delta	*P. deltoides* multiple clones	6.7–12.5 Fair to best culture	10 (1)	~100, 0, 0	1 537–1 685	1980s	[56]
T, W, I, F in US Southeast (SC)	*P. deltoides* S7C15 Sycamore	3.2 6.3	3 (1)[f] 3 (1)[f]	240, 0, 0 240, 0, 0	1 333	2000	[57]
R, W, I, F in US Southeast (GA)	Sycamore Sweetgum	6.9 8.2	6 (1)[e] 6 (1)[e]	510, 75, 284 510, 75, 284	1 790	1997	[58]
T, B, F (clay settling ponds) in US Southeast (FL)	*E. grandis* *E. amplifolia*	25.2 27.8	3.2 (1) 3.2 (1)	53, 0, 0 53, 0, 0	8 400 8 400	2001	[59]
T, W, F (muck soils) in US Southeast (FL)	*E. grandis*	14.4 23.8	2.5 (1) 1.5 (1)	0, 0. 0 0, 0, 0	1 600 10 000	1980	[60]

[a] Definitions of culture intensity notations are as follows: T, tillage used in site preparation; R, soil ripping used in site preparation; W, chemical weed control; F, fertilization; I, irrigation; P, pest control; VH, very high; H, high.
[b] Specific clone names or numbers were not always available; sweetgum (*Liquidambar styraciflua*) and sycamore (*Plantanus occidentalis*) seedlings were unselected nursery stock.
[c] Yields are expressed as the mean annual increment of the total aboveground dry weight without foliage for hardwoods but with foliage for softwoods. When original data were reported as wet weight, stem dry weight, or stem volume, appropriate conversion factors and expansion factors were used.
[d] Stem age represents the growth year in which the stand reached maximum mean annual increment (MAI$_{max}$) based on published growth curves unless footnoted.
[e] Age of MAI$_{max}$ not verifiable but stand had reached expected harvest age for the planting density and was believed to be close to MAI$_{max}$.
[f] Age of MAI$_{max}$ not verifiable but data were deemed worthy to include for comparison.
[g] Data source is a model calibrated to six cottonwood genotypes grown with fertilization in Sumter, SC.

with yields of 14–24 odMg ha^{-1} yr^{-1} on muck soils [60]. *Eucalyptus grandis* is the highest yielding tree crop in South Florida, while *Eucalyptus amplifolia* has the advantage of being more frost-tolerant. Two new species of interest for United States are *Eucalyptus benthamii* and *Eucalyptus Macarthurii*, which have demonstrated both fast growth potential and sufficient frost tolerance to be considered for most of the Gulf and Atlantic Coastal plains of the Southeastern United States [64]. Intensively managed eucalyptus plantations in Brazil have recently achieved average, stem-only, productivities of about 22.6 odMg ha^{-1} yr^{-1} with current operational rates of fertilization and up to 30.6 odMg ha^{-1} yr^{-1} with irrigated. Total biomass is likely about 30% higher. The study documenting those yields showed that water supply is the limiting factor for plantation productivity in Brazil [65].

Attaining economically viable yields, wherever the location, requires use of clonal material selected for high yield potential, establishment on marginal to good agricultural land, intensive site preparation to minimize weed seeds and break-up hardpans, and weed control until crown closure. Weed control is preferably accomplished with only herbicide applications, but cultivation is often also necessary to achieve adequate control. Except in very high fertility areas, some fertilization with nitrogen (N), phosphorus (P),

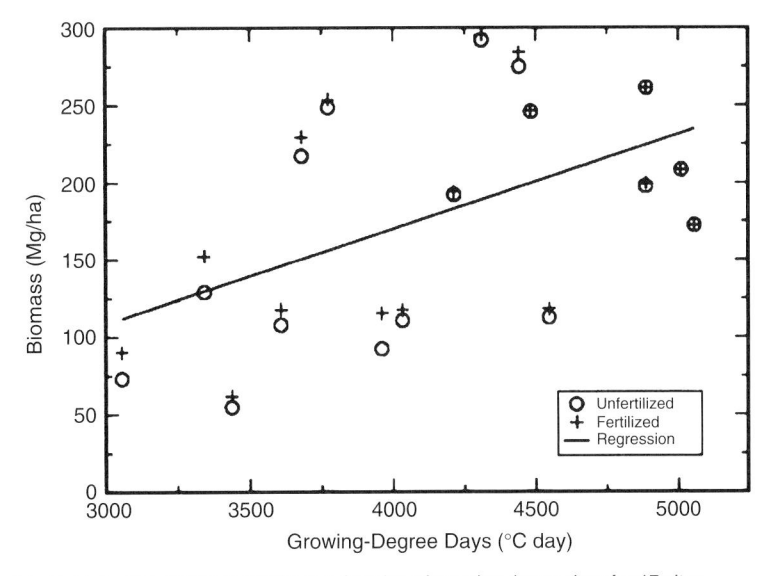

Figures 8 Biomass of simulated loblolly pine stands at age 25 as a function of growing-degree days for 17 sites.

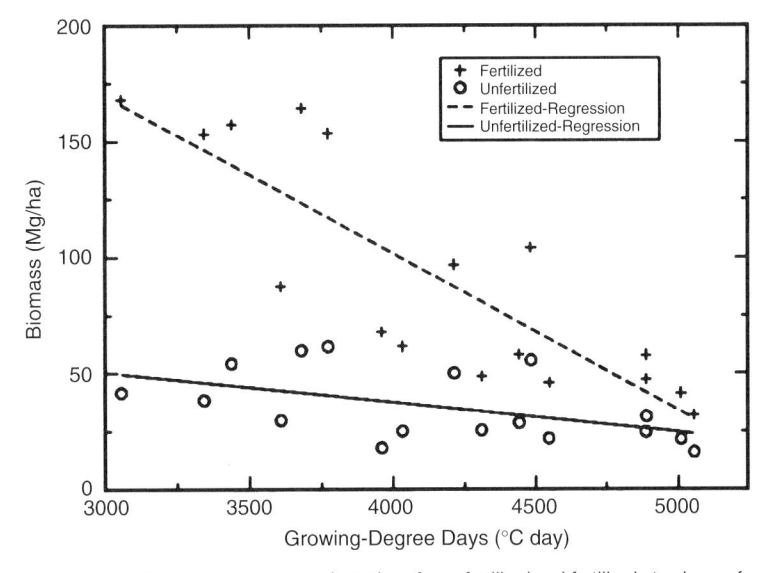

Figure 9 Average simulated biomass from three 7-year cottonwood rotations for unfertilized and fertilized stands as a function of growing-degree days for the same 17 sites. Adapted from Luxmoore RJ, Tharp ML, and Post WM (2008) Simulated biomass and soil carbon of loblolly pine and cottonwood plantations across a thermal gradient in southeastern United States. *Forest Ecology and Management* 254: 291–299.

and potassium (K) will likely be required, but should be applied no sooner than the second year of growth to avoid stimulating weed competition. Additional applications may be needed every other year. Efforts should be made to minimize wasteful fertilizer additions by basing application levels on soil and foliage analysis; small additions of micronutrients may be very helpful in some cases. The best management approaches for single-stem bioenergy production (adjusted to match clones, soils and climate) should be expected to result in reaching crown closure by the end of the second growing season, and produce operational harvest yields in the range of 11–16 odMg ha^{-1} yr^{-1}. Early economic studies suggested that best returns would result from harvesting the stands in the dormant season and allowing coppice regrowth for the second and third rotations [66, 67]. However, harvesting equipment, which can efficiently cut both single-stem trees and multistemmed trees grown on 4–10 year rotations, is not available, and the logistical advantages of year-round harvesting to provide a continuous supply are large. Coppice management of 4–10 years rotation hardwood stands has been used in the southeastern United States but rarely elsewhere [56]. Furthermore, as long as breeding research continues to show the potential for yield improvements of 20–100% within a single rotation, replanting after each rotation remains a viable option [68].

Table 3 Selected hardwood single-stem yields in Europe with culture intensity and N levels included

Culture intensity[a] location	Genotype[b]	Yield (dry)[c] ($Mg\ ha^{-1}\ yr^{-1}$)	Stem age[d] (rotation)	Total rotation N, P, K ($kg\ ha^{-1}$)	Planting density trees (ha^{-1})	Plant year	Reference
Poplar single-stem experimental yields							
T, W in Central Scotland, UK	*Populus* hybrid 'Balsam spire' *Alnus rubra*	11.63 13.13	6.2 (1)	0, 0, 0 0, 0, 0	10 000 10 000	1989 1989	[20] [20]
T, I, thinned 2 × in Karinslund, Sweden Sandy soil	10 best clones of *P. trichocarpa* in trial	9[e]	19 (1)	0, 0, 0	5 000 (625 after thinning)	1990	[44]
T, W, F in Normandy, France Moist grassland soils	*P. trichocarpa × deltoides* 'Beaupre' 'Raspalje'	10.0 9.4	5 (1) 5 (1)	165, 0, 0 165, 0, 0	2 000 2 000	1989 1989	[62] [62]
T, F in Brandenburg, Germany Clayey–Sandy mining soil	*P. trichocarpa × deltoides* 'Beaupre' 'Rap'	6.6 6.25	5 (1) 5 (1)	388, 150, 275 388, 150, 275	8 333 8 333	1995 1995	[63] [63]

[a] Definitions of culture intensity notations are as follows: T, tillage used in site preparation; W, chemical weed control; F, fertilization; I, irrigation; P, pest control; VH, very high; H, high.
[b] Specific clone names or numbers were not always available.
[c] Yields are expressed as the mean annual increment of the total aboveground dry weight without foliage for hardwoods.
[d] Stem age represents the growth year in which the stand reached maximum mean annual increment (MAI_{max}) based on published growth curves unless footnoted.
[e] Age of MAI_{max} not verifiable but stand had reached expected harvest age for the planting density and was believed to be close to MAI_{max}.

5.14.2.3 Single-Stem Softwoods

Pines comprised 32% of the tree species planted for production purposes around the world in 2005 [69] and 83% of tree species planted in the southern United States [70]. Softwoods in the southern United States already contribute 40% of the US total annual industrial wood supply of round wood [71] and 40% of southern softwoods is used for pulpwood and composites. Since the fiber industry has long used both bark and black liquor to produce energy for running the pulp mills, southern pines are already a significant contributor to US biomass energy. Improvements in pine silviculture have resulted in improving southern US pine productivity by a factor of about 6 times since the 1940s, and the number of planted acres of pines increased from zero in the 1940s to 15.243 million ha by 2006 with loblolly pine (*Pinus taeda*) being the most commonly planted species on 12.2 million ha [70]. The shift from natural pine stands to intensively managed pine plantations for fiber production is one of the major success stories in the world for plantation forestry [72]. Loblolly pines are now considered one of the most productive species for bioenergy in the southern United States [73].

Many steps contributed to improving the productivity of loblolly pine in the south [74]. Naturally regenerated low-productivity forests were common practice from the 1920s through the 1950s. Improved nursery and field planting practices begun in the 1950s [72] resulted in whole tree aboveground yields tripling by the 1970s. Seed orchards dedicated to seed improvement were first established in the late 1950s. First-generation improved seeds increased the value of plantation wood by 20% and second-generation improved seeds being used now add another 14–23% yield increase. Nursery production of superior (larger) bare-root seedlings involve planting improved seeds in specialized beds with controlled conditions for 8–12 months, top pruning, lifting, and careful grading (**Figure 10**). Planting into a well-prepared and maintained site is critical to rapid growth. The importance of hardwood competition control was recognized by the early 1970s. First methods of control were entirely mechanical, but by the late 1970s, herbicides were added. By 1990, site preparation was predominately chemical, with limited mechanical site preparation involved. Fertilization of pine plantations was initiated in the late 1960s but was implemented slowly during the 1970s and 1980s [75]. Average productivity increased rapidly from the 1970s to 1990s primarily as a result of implementing the use of improved site preparation, hardwood competition control, and genetically improved seeds. At a national level, average yields in managed plantations increased from 1.1 to 5.6 $odMg\ ha^{-1}\ yr^{-1}$ from 1920 to 1990. (Conversation with John Stanturf verified that reported weights in his 2003 paper and in most other forestry papers are expressed as total aboveground green weights. To be consistent with other biomass literature, all reported green weights are converted to oven dry weights by assuming 50% moisture content.)

Implementation of silviculture and genetic improvements very much accelerated in the 1990s as a result of the nonproprietary research conducted by university–industry cooperatives. During the 1980s and 1990s, cooperative research clearly confirmed the benefits to pine productivity of fertilizing with both N and P, especially in mid-rotation. Further research published since 2000 has shown the need for micronutrients on certain soil types [72, 76, 77]. Several research studies published since 2000 have demonstrated the yield improvement effects of management intensity levels [58, 78–84]. Selected examples are shown in **Table 4**. Third-generation seeds from selected parents were deployed around year 2000 [85].

Figure 10 Southern pine seedlings being lifted. Courtesy of Thomas D. 'Tom' Landis, USDA Forest Service, Bugwood.org.

Table 4 Loblolly pine yields from silvicultural trials in southeastern United States

Culture intensity[a] location	Genotype[b]	Yield (dry)[c] (Mg ha^{-1} yr^{-1})	Stem age[d]	Total rotation N, P, K (kg ha^{-1})	Plant density trees(ha^{-1})	Plant year	Reference
Very high intensity							
W, I, F in Bainbridge, GA	Improved second-generation family 7–56	19.0 (8.5)	11[e]	980, 241, 953	1126 (456)	1995	[78]
W, F (dry site) in Waycross, GA	Improved second-gen family 7–56	16.4 (7.3)	15[e]	1254, 200, 181	1660 (670)	1987	[79]
W, HF in Sanderson, FL	Seven full-sib first-generation family + mix	13.2 (5.9)[d]	5[e]	369, 128, 121	2990 (1210)	2000	[81]
High intensity							
W, I in Bainbridge, GA	Improved second-generation family 7–56	16.0 (7.1)	11[e]	0, 0, 0	1126 (456)	1995	[78]
HF (dry site) in Waycross, GA	Improved second-generation family 7–56	15.2 (6.8)	15[e]	1254, 200, 181	1660 (670)	1987	[79]
T, F, (modeled) in Southwest, GA	Average commercial	8.3 (3.4)[g]	25[h]	300, ?, 0 Site index 100	1682 (681)	1990s	[61]
Medium intensity							
W in Bainbridge, GA	Improved second-generation family 7–56	11.6 (5.2)	11[e]	0, 0, 0	1121 (454)	1995	[78]
W (dry site) in Waycross, GA	Improved second-generation family 7–56	11.2 (5.0)	15[e]	0, 0, 0	1660 (670)	1987	[79]
F at planting, Sanderson, FL	Seven full-sib first-generation family + mix	8.1 (3.6)[d]	5[f]	50, 56, 0	2990 (1210)	2000	[81]
Low-intensity or experimental controls and modeled result							
W in Bainbridge, GA	Four improved second-generation families	8.1 (3.6)[b]	6[f]	0, 0, 0	1126 (456)	1995	[82]
T (dry site) in Waycross, GA	Improved second-generation family 7–56	8.4 (3.8)	15[e]	0, 0, 0	1660 (670)	1987	[79]

[a] Definitions of culture intensity notations are as follows: T, tillage used in site preparation; W, chemical weed control; F, fertilization; I, irrigation; P, pest control; VH, very high; H, high.
[b] Specific family or generation of selection (or both) given if known.
[c] Yields are expressed as the mean annual increment of the total aboveground dry weight including foliage for softwoods. Original data were reported as oven dry Mg of total aboveground biomass, except for Borders et al. [79] who reported stem weights and also provided allometry data, thus facilitating calculation of total aboveground dry weight.
[d] Stem age represents the growth year in which the stand reached maximum mean annual increment (MAI$_{max}$) based on published growth curves unless footnoted.
[e] Age of MAI$_{max}$ not verifiable but stand had reached expected harvest age for the planting density and was believed to be close to MAI$_{max}$.
[f] Age of MAI$_{max}$ not verifiable but data were deemed worthy to include for comparison.
[g] Modeled results for a high site index site in Southwest, GA, may be lower than observed experimental results because based on average commercial conditions with less or incomplete fertilizer and little or no weed management resulting in lower survival (68%) by age 25 than observed in the experimental trial.
[h] Model assumed normal harvest age in commercially managed stands but paper indicates MAI increased from age 7 through age 25.

At present, most loblolly pines stands in the South are currently managed for a combination of pulp and timber so that thinning is incorporated into the management (**Figure 11**). The stands are planted on average at about 1480 trees ha^{-1} for a 25-year rotation, with a thinning at age 15 [73]. An analysis published in 2010 supported this approach, suggesting that production of loblolly pine exclusively for biofuels using intensive site preparation was unprofitable at yields between 5.3 and 7.8 odMg ha^{-1} yr^{-1} [86].

Figure 11 Age 14 loblolly pine planted for pulpwood in the southern United States. Courtesy of David Stephens, Bugwood.org.

However, the study also showed that the most intensive management approaches were optimal for maximizing yields. With many new studies showing the benefits of weed control and fertilization, those practices have become considerably more common [75]. Average operational yields in the southeastern United States were reported in 2003 to be about 9 odMg ha^{-1} yr^{-1} [74]. Companies are predicting future operational yields of 13–18 odMg ha^{-1} yr^{-1} as a result of greater intensity of management [74] and deployment of third-generation seed sources. Field studies comparing intensive silviculture to current less intensive practices have demonstrated that total aboveground yields can be increased 2–4 times with complete control of competing vegetation and yearly fertilization [80, 87]. Analysis of some scenarios has indicated that although the cost of intensive management is higher, yields are also higher and thus returns are also higher [88]. New growth and yield models, not tied to original site index assessments, are needed to more accurately model intensively managed pine plantations and to predict total aboveground biomass yields available for bioenergy (i.e., inclusion of branches and foliage as well as stem and bark).

A likely future scenario for pine management will include markets for both bioenergy, pulp and timber. For this reason, a recent proposal suggests alternating planting densities in each row, a tightly spaced row for bioenergy that would be harvested in 7–8 years and a widely spaced row for lumber production to be harvested at 18–22 years [73, 89]. In addition, future management techniques are predicted to include 'clonal plantations, whole rotation resource management regimes, use of spatially explicit spectral reflectance data as a major information source for management decisions, active management to minimize insect and disease losses, and more attention to growing wood for specific products' [88]. Thus, the economic analysis (discussed below) assumes a future scenario when optimal production of loblolly pine produced for energy is clear-cut at around age 8 and replanted with improved genotypes.

5.14.2.4 Single-Stem Harvest and Handling

The harvest and handling equipment and systems used to collect and transport single-stem woody crops grown for biomass in the United States are essentially the same as those used for logging of pulpwood-sized trees with a feller-buncher (**Figure 12**) [90]. Current pulpwood logging techniques use several different pieces of equipment for felling, extracting, and transporting pulpwood from forests [91]. At a minimum, a feller-buncher fells and stacks whole trees and a second piece of equipment (usually a skidder)

Figure 12 John Deere feller-buncher shown harvesting hybrid poplars is also used for pine harvesting. Courtesy of Lynn Wright, WrightLink Consulting.

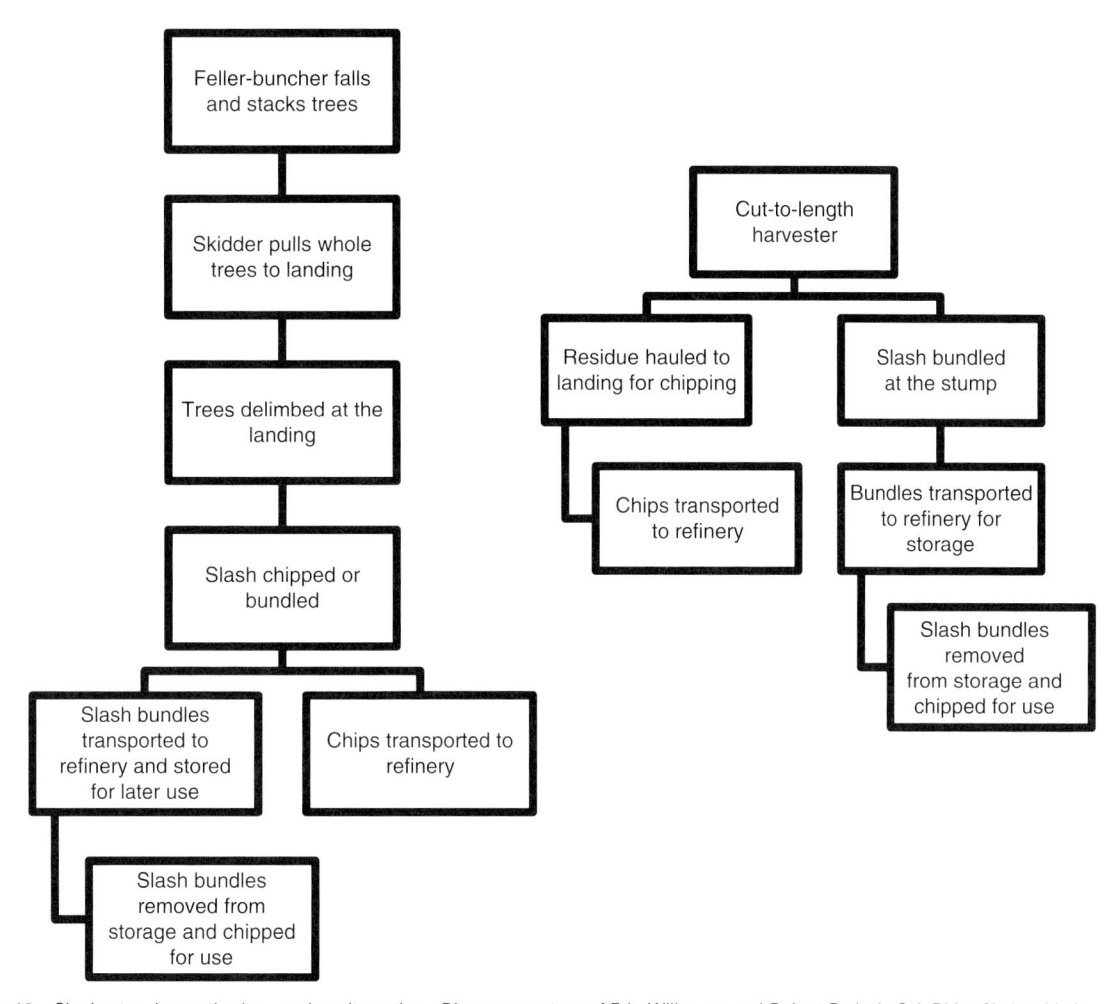

Figure 13 Single-stem harvesting/processing alternatives. Diagram courtesy of Erin Wilkerson and Robert Perlack, Oak Ridge National Laboratory.

conveys the trees to a landing where the trees are delimbed, debarked, and chipped with the chips being transported to the mill [92, 93]. Alternatively, delimbed trees (roundwood) may be loaded onto trucks and transported to the mill where they are chipped for pulpwood. Cut-to-length harvesting is another process used to collect pulpwood. The feller-buncher is replaced by a cut-to-length harvester, which cuts the trees and then removes the tops and limbs while still in the woods. The cut logs are collected by a forwarder, transported to the roadside, and unloaded at the roadside for pick-up by a truck to transport the logs to a mill. The cut-to-length method is preferred in forest areas where there are environmental concerns about the removal of whole trees from the forest. Where trees are managed as row-crops with nutrients inputs as required, whole-tree removal is not an issue [94] and cost models show that whole-tree systems allow cheaper harvesting and transport than cut-to-length systems under a range of conditions [95].

Both harvesting systems described above require modification for dedicated harvesting of row-crop trees for bioenergy or for integrated harvesting of trees for both pulp and bioenergy. **Figure 13** outlines the operations involved when only the residue is collected for bioenergy use. If the trees are harvested entirely for biomass energy, then the whole-tree system would most likely involve a feller-buncher (**Figure 12**) and a front-end loader (**Figure 14**). While both skidders and loaders have been used in conveying single-stem trees to a landing, analysis suggests several advantages of using a loader; less dirt is associated with the wood, more wood is extracted per unit time, and the loader has increased landing capabilities [92, 96]. Efforts are ongoing to develop a Whole-Tree Harvester that combines rapid severance of row-crop single-stem trees with direct loading into road-worthy trailer pulled behind the harvester [97]. Tests have demonstrated that trees with narrow crowns can be loaded directly onto trucks as whole trees, and then transported and processed by the end user or an intermediate wood processor (**Figure 15**).

5.14.2.5 Comparison of Production Inputs and Costs for Poplar, Pine, Eucalypts, and Willow Biomass

Variable costs differ among species and cultivation methods for SRF, specifically those costs related to planting and harvesting (**Table 5**). Planting costs are highest for high-density coppice crops and lowest for pines (assuming use of 1-year-old bare-root seedlings). The machinery costs for establishment of woody crop production are relatively similar for all woody crops (presented in

Figure 14 Front-end loader moving hybrid poplar trees to landing. Courtesy of Raffelle Spinelli, CNR – Timber and Tree Institute, Sesto Fiorentino, Italy.

Figure 15 Loading of whole trees onto transport trucks for delivery to a mill. Photo courtesy of David Ostlie, Energy Performance Systems.

Table 5) for suitable agricultural sites (i.e., NRCS land classification codes 1–4). Willow and poplar cuttings average $0.10–$0.12 each from commercial nurseries. Eucalyptus and pine, both generally planted as bare-root seedlings in the United States, average about $0.10 and $0.06, respectively, once culls and extra seedlings needed for replanting are considered. Containerized seedlings offer several advantages including better survival [98], and though not yet widely used in the United States, they are widely used in Brazil.

When single-stem poplars, pines, and eucalypts are planted on agricultural soils, their management requires very similar levels of site preparation and herbicide and fertilizer applications. However, the costs shown in **Table 5** assume experience with the sites and with best weed competition control measures for local conditions. Inputs (such as lime and fertilizer) are assumed to vary across soil conditions on average for the different tree species. Additionally, different herbicides and pesticides are likely to be required for each species and specific location, which will result in small variations from amounts shown in **Table 5**. Irrigation is not normally recommended for both economic and environmental reasons; however, in some cases, irrigation may be appropriate and necessary for successful stand establishment, thus increasing establishment costs.

5.14.2.6 Projections of Energy Crop Supply: A Methodology and US Results

The spatial range of counties where woody crops can be grown is determined by the level of annual rainfall, soil conditions, land availability, and potential biomass yield (estimated from a combination of field trial measurements, harvest of existing plantings, and expert opinion). Biomass yield (assumed to be MAI_{max}) is estimated at the county level for single-stem crops (poplar, pine, or eucalyptus) grown on an 8-year rotation followed by replanting or for coppice willow grown for five rotations within a 20-year replanting cycle. The resulting woody crop yield patterns currently assumed for the United States are shown in **Figure 16**. For the southeast, pines are the primary woody crop, but pines or eucalyptus may provide highest yields in the southeastern coastal plain and eucalyptus species normally result in highest yields in the extreme southeastern United States (southern Florida). Yield patterns in the Mississippi floodplain, most mid-western crop-producing states, and the Pacific Northwest are based on information from

Table 5 Summary of production inputs for poplar, pine, eucalypts, and willow in the United States

Item	Units	Poplar Northern United States	Pine Southeastern United States	Eucalyptus Southeastern United States	Willow (coppiced) Northeast United States
Rotation	Years	8	8	8	4[a]
Spacing	Square meter	5.6	5.6	5.6	0.7
	trees ha^{-1}	1791	1791	1791	14 126
Productivity	odMg ha^{-1} yr^{-1}	7.8–13.4	11.2–12.3	13.4	11.4
Growing range	Region	Northeast, Lake States, Northwest, Midwest, Plains	Southeast	Sub-tropics	Northeast and Lake States
Establishment, year 1					
Cuttings/seedlings	$ per tree	$0.10	$0.06	$0.25	$0.12
Planting	$ per tree	$0.09	$0.09	$0.09	$0.02
Replants	Percent	5	5	5	5
Moldboard plow		1 time	1 time	1 time	1 time
Disk		1 time	1 time	1 time	1 time
Cultivate		2 times	2 times	2 times	2 times
Total kill herbicide	No. of applications	1 time	1 time	2 times	1 time
	kg a.i. ha^{-1}	1.68	1.68	1.68	1.68
Preemergent herbicide	No. of applications	1	1	2	1
	kg a.i. ha^{-1}	1.68	1.68	1.68	1.68
Phosphorous, year 1	kg ha^{-1}	0	40	40	0
Establishment costs	$ ha^{-1}	$766	$692	$1359	$2766
Maintenance years					
Cultivate, year 2		2 times	2 times	2 times	1 time
Cultivate, year 3		1 time	1 time	1 time	None
Preemergent herbicide, year 2	No. of applications	1	1	1	1
	kg a.i. ha^{-1}	1.68	1.68	1.68	1.68
Lime	Mg ha^{-1}	0	2.24	3.36	0
	Year applied		3	3	
Nitrogen	kg ha^{-1}	100	100	100	112
	Year applied	4 and 6	2, 4, and 6	4 and 6	4
Phosphorous	kg ha^{-1}	22.4	44.8	16.8	0
	Year applied	3	3	3	
Potassium	kg ha^{-1}	49.7	44.8	28	0
	Year applied	3	3	3	
Maintenance costs, year 2	$ ha^{-1}	$148	$247	$247	$74
Maintenance costs, 8 years	$ ha^{-1}	$543	$494	$494	$247[b]
Harvest costs	$ dt^{-1}	$20	$20	$20	$15

[a] Five harvests over 20 years.
[b] Maintenance costs for years 3 and 4.

poplar trials or commercial operations. Yields in the northern Lake States and the northeast are based on trials of either coppiced willow or single-stem poplar production. The most influential parameters that dictate whether woody crops plantings occur and which woody crops are selected are related to the expected net returns in relation to yield and the type of land available for adoption into energy crops (i.e., annual adoption patterns). Costs are estimated per acre for a representative 100-acre farm.

The costs to produce woody crops in a coppice and noncoppice management scheme are presented in **Figure 17**. Both cost curves represent the declining cost per additional mean annual increment per hectare at harvest. The costs include variable production costs (e.g., stand establishment, maintenance, and harvest) assuming at 6.25% annual discount rate at various per hectare yield levels for a representative coppice (willow) and noncoppice (hybrid poplar) system. Mean annual increment is adjusted to account for the increase in yield after the first cut of the coppice (assuming five cuttings in a 20-year rotation) and an 8-year stand life for the noncoppice stand.

Projections of land conversion to woody crops involve detailed land-use models and assumptions beyond those that estimate the cost of producing the woody crop. For example, it is often assumed that landowners adopt crops that produce the highest net

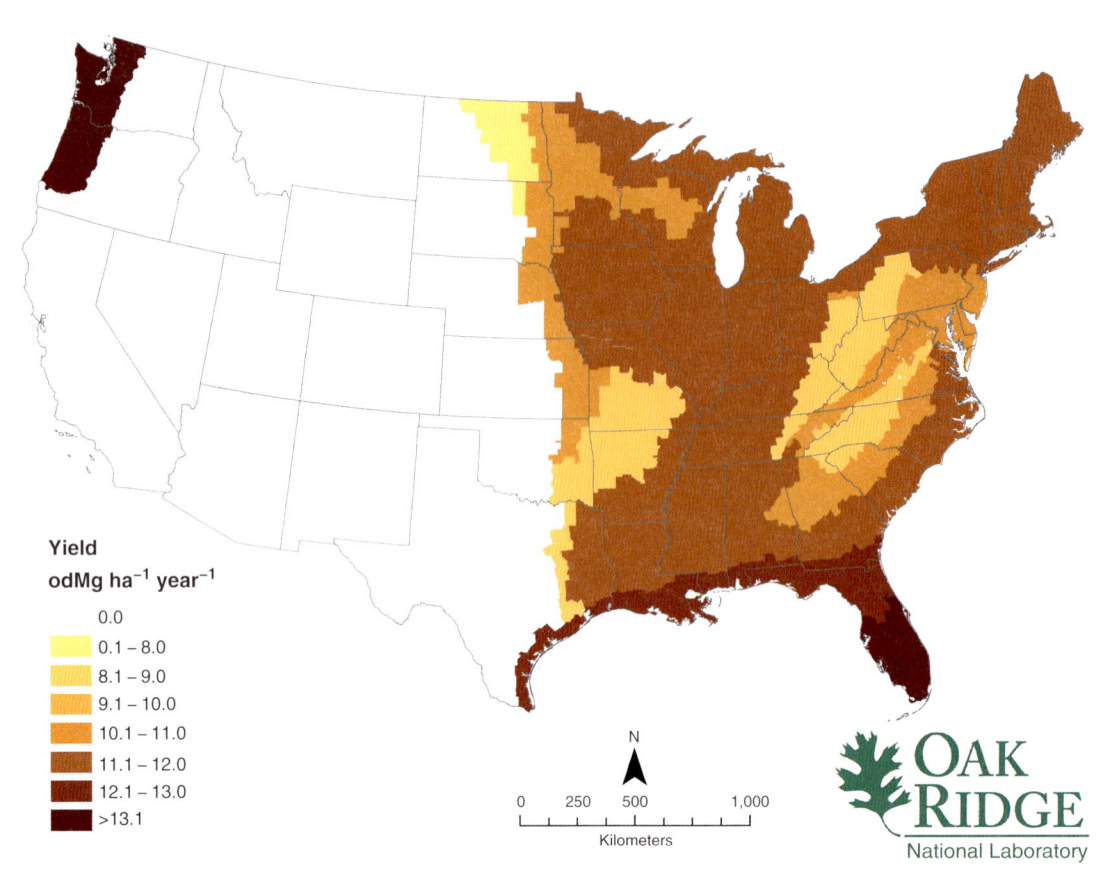

Figure 16 Range of woody crop biomass yields (at maximum mean annual increment) across the United States.

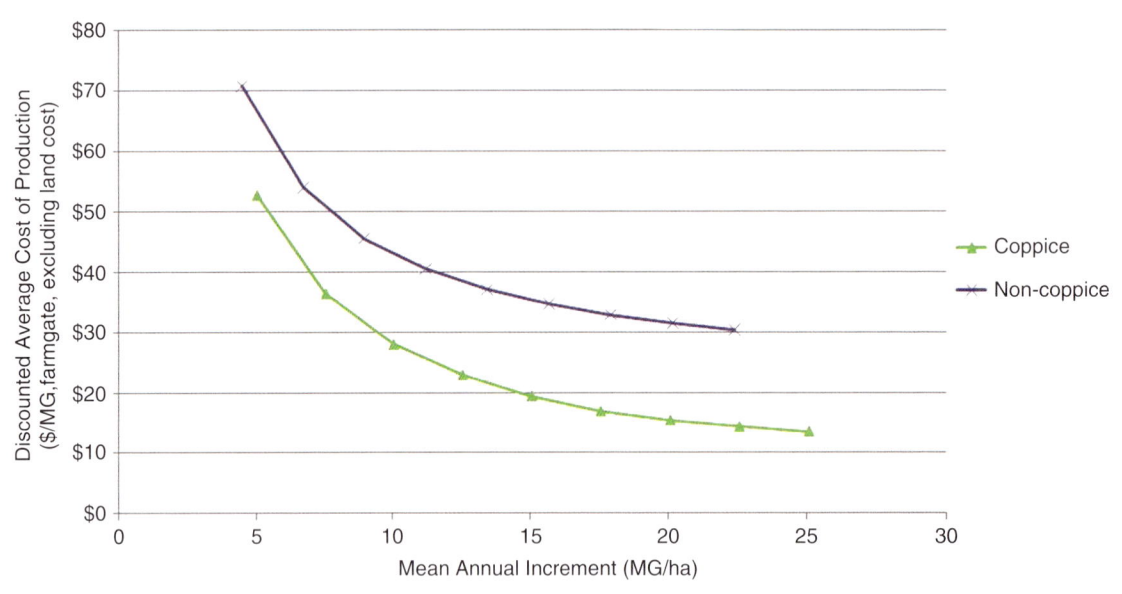

Figure 17 Estimated costs of producing woody crops in coppice and noncoppice management schemes as a function of yield (mean annual increment) at harvest.

returns available to them. In the case that an energy crop market is available and the expected revenue from harvest is higher than a traditional crop or pasture rental rate, energy crop establishment is assumed to occur. Woody crops and perennial herbaceous crops (such as switchgrass or Miscanthus) may compete against each other for land in situations where either may be suitable as feedstocks for the bioenergy technologies being developed. Because woody crops are often perceived to be higher risk than grass crops and require a longer time period before first harvest, the difference between the revenue and costs for woody crops must be higher in order for woody crops to be chosen for adoption by the model. However in reality, several projects are being developed that will utilize both woody and perennial herbaceous crops as a means of minimizing supply risks and storage issues associated with herbaceous crops.

5.14.2.7 Sustainability of Short-Rotation Woody Crops/Short-Rotation Forestry

Sustainability cannot be evaluated in absolute terms, but rather by comparisons across alternative systems. Evaluation is complex as environmental, economic, and social aspects must be integrated and balanced in a sustainable system. As creation of novel wood energy feedstock production systems requires modifying current land uses, the effects on sustainability of those modifications must be evaluated in both local and global contexts of the above three aspects. Protocols have been established by national and international groups to assess sustainable forest management. While these protocols are not specific to woody crops, they do provide an objective framework for assessing widely agreed upon sustainability values. The criteria and indicators established through these protocols were utilized in the sustainability assessment of willow crop production [99]. This assessment of coppice woody crops considered biological diversity, soil and water quality resources, ecosystem services, long-term productivity and health, and maintenance of socioeconomic benefits. The study concluded that production of coppice woody crops in northeastern United States is sustainable in comparison with current agricultural land practices of the region and in comparison with the use of coal to supply electricity. The coppice woody crops support a wide array of species both above- and belowground, and when appropriately located, improve landscape biodiversity. Similar results have been found for single-stem woody crops in other locations [100]. The perennial nature of woody crops, their extensive fine root systems, and ability to coppice protect the soils from erosion and this consequently preserves or enhances water quality. Research and commercial-scale experience shows that woody crop productivity can be maintained over multiple rotations. When grown to supply local facilities, rural development is stimulated and the environmental benefits accrue to the local communities.

Life cycle assessment (LCA) of woody crop production systems suggest that woody crops are energetically efficient and effective at reducing greenhouse gas emissions when substituted for fossil fuels in the production of heat, electricity, or biofuels [101–103]. However, the LCAs also identify possible opportunities for improvement. Inputs of inorganic nitrogen fertilizer in feedstock production account for the largest single source of nonrenewable fossil energy inputs, and contribute to large potential impacts on global climate change, acidification, and eutrophication. Substitution of organic fertilizers, such as sewage sludge biosolids, can substantially improve the net energy ratios. Matching the level and timing of any type of fertilizer addition to the seasonal demand of trees can minimize impacts in other categories. In one study, diesel used in transport vehicles and tractors had significant impacts on 5 of 10 analyzed categories of potential impact [101]. LCA comparisons of total energy systems show that conversion of woody crops to electricity offers more environmental benefits than conversion to biofuels if greenhouse gas reduction is the primary goal [103].

All woody crops have several environmental and logistical advantages over annually harvested crops as a source of sustainable biomass for bioenergy. Multiyear rotations minimize the disturbance of the land and provide more stable habitat for many types of wildlife. Since biomass accumulation occurs at higher per hectare density than herbaceous crops, fewer acres of woody crops must be harvested each year to supply a given facility. Therefore, the majority of the woody crop is retained as habitat year round within the fuel supply shed of a given facility. Additionally, the annual harvesting of a portion of the woody crop supply provides opportunity for more efficient deployment of manpower and equipment and lower transportation costs. A healthy coppice crop can be maintained by limiting harvest to the dormant season, but harvesting of noncoppiced woody crops can be performed at any time of year, reducing some storage losses and infrastructure requirements. Single-stem woody crop harvests can even be advanced or delayed a year or two if warranted by market or climatic conditions without loss of crop value to the landowner or grower, thus minimizing risk.

The strategy of harvesting planted woody crop stands on short rotations sometimes raises concerns about long-term site productivity impacts, particularly for plantations (such as pine plantings) that were originally established on degraded soils and managed at a low level of intensity. Conversion from extensive management of planted trees to more intensive management is needed as the demand for forest products and wood for energy increases. Intensive management should be limited, however, only to soil types with a potential for high growth in order to achieve economic sustainability [94]. Research on intensive pine production in the southeast has shown that good site preparation, chemical control of noncrop vegetation, and fertilizer application at levels and times that optimize utilization by the trees can increases biomass yields in an energy efficient manner while maintaining or even improving soil quality and long-term site productivity [94, 104]. Harvesting and site preparation practices have the greatest potential for directly impacting soil organic matter and soil physical properties. Soil damage during harvesting, especially on fine-textured soil, can decrease long-term productivity unless ameliorative treatments are used. When replanting existing stands, a clear-cut harvest not only improves economic viability but is also a necessary precursor to ameliorative site preparation practices such as subsoiling, disking, and bedding. Such treatments, which must be performed when soils are at proper moisture content, can shatter plow layers and increase available rooting volume to the trees, thereby increasing below- and aboveground growth. Adherence to best management practices (BMPs) during harvesting and site preparation can minimize off-site impacts so that intensive management does not detrimentally impact adjacent systems. Site-specific management is the key to sustaining soil quality, improving long-term site productivity, and minimizing off-site impacts [94].

The long-term sustainability of bioenergy feedstock resources throughout the world depends on land-use practices and landscape dynamics. Land-use decisions about what crops are grown, where they are grown, and how they are managed have global effects on carbon sequestration, native plan diversity, competition with food crops, greenhouse gas emissions, water, and air quality as well as societal effects such as rural development [105]. Some question whether any nonfood crop should be established on arable land. Land and water are the primary limiting resource for supporting both human and wildlife populations worldwide. The availability of even marginal arable land for the sustainable production of biomass feedstocks depends to a great extent on how well agricultural yield increases can meet the need for increased food demand as the global human population continues to expand. Over the past few decades, agricultural yields have grown faster than the world population, so that more food can be produced on existing cropland [106]. However, world population is not only continuing to increase but the demand for animal-based food (which requires a lot of land and water) is also increasing. A recent UN Environment Program analysis suggests that agricultural crop yield increases will not continue to compensate for growing and changing food demand [107].

The likelihood of increased competition for land argues for consideration of an intensive cultural approach to growing SRWC for energy and chemicals and possibly also for using the wood for multiple products. Clearly, some intensive culture approaches (such as irrigation) are not sustainable in water-limited areas and, in general, are not recommended. Some advocates for sustainability and reduction of greenhouse gas emissions reject most of the currently recommended woody crop production approaches (such as the use of monocultures of the highest yielding crop varieties managed under intensive cultural regimes on marginal to good cropland) [108] and argue for double-cropped or mixed cropping systems or use of degraded, abandoned croplands. As for mixed cropping systems, the authors were referring to herbaceous crops, but the development of highly productive, diverse stands of trees is possible and would elevate the sustainability of wood energy crop production systems. Alternatively, researchers in Brazil are leading the way in investigating the production of food crops between rows of woody crops [109]. The solution of using degraded, abandoned croplands to avoid production of bioenergy crops on cropland is discussed in a 2010 review of direct and indirect land-competition issues [110]. Case studies of woody crop production on degraded lands have resulted in low yields. Also degraded land often requires reclamation prior to cropping and is frequently located in areas lacking transportation infrastructure. Thus, while the authors agree that it is one possible solution to avoiding adverse direct or indirect land-use changes, they argue that it will need to be supported by adequate government support schemes. The authors suggest several additional solutions. One is the prioritizing the use of low- or zero-risk feedstocks (such as crop, forest, and urban residues) and algae crops. While the authors did not mention woody crops, we noted that their graphs showed a woody crop/biomass to liquid scenario as having the lowest land-use change effect. The final suggestion by these authors (and many others) was that an emphasis should be placed on increasing the overall efficiency of biomass production, biomass conversion, and also in the use of biomass products. Thus, evaluation of woody crop production sustainability is only a part of the picture, and overall system sustainability must be considered.

5.14.3 Forestland-Derived Resources

Forests comprise about 30% of the land base of the world with slightly higher levels for both the United States (33%) and Europe (36%) [111, 112]. Worldwide forest inventory totals about 384 billion m^3. In the United States, standing volume of growing stock is about 35 billion m^3, while that of Europe is a little less (~ 22 billion m^3) (generally, growing stock is defined as commercially viable trees greater than about 12.7 cm in diameter) [113]. Based on FAO forestry statistics (ForesSTAT) accessed in August 2008 [114], annual wood removals used for the production of fuelwood, industrial roundwood, and sawnwood are relatively similar between the United States and Europe, about 522 and 550 million m^3 for Europe and the United States, respectively. A recent US report [115] indicated total US removals are a little higher (600 million m^3). For both regions, harvests are well below the net annual forest growth and only a very small fraction of total timberland inventory. In the United States, for example, net forest growth exceeds growing-stock removals by 70% nationwide with rates varying by geographic region, species, and ownership (public forest vs. private industrial forests) [115].

Currently used biomass originating from forestlands in the United States comes primarily from three sources – fuelwood used in the residential and commercial sectors for space heating applications and the electric power sector in dedicated biomass plants and co-firing applications, residues generated in the manufacture of forest products for on-site heat and power production, and some municipal or urban wood wastes used for power generation. Current consumption from these combined three sources is estimated at about 108 million m^3 (~ 117 million Mg) [116]. The Energy Information Administration in their reference case projects a rather significant increase in the consumption of fuelwood for meeting renewable portfolio standards as well as from co-firing in which small amounts of biomass are mixed with coal in existing coal-fired plants [117]. Modest growth in industrial consumption of biomass for energy applications is projected with little or no change in the residential and commercial sectors.

In addition, a relatively small amount of forestland biomass is now derived from the removal of a portion of what is called logging residue currently generated during the harvesting of timberlands for conventional forest products and 'thinnings'. This latter component consists of removing merchantable whole trees and excess small trees to roadside based on uneven-aged thinning principles (i.e., removing trees across all diameter classes) in order to reduce risks and losses from catastrophic fires and improve forest health. The tops and branches of the large trees and the excess small trees could be used for bioenergy applications and the main stem for pulpwood and sawlogs.

These resources are largely unused and offer considerable potential to supply additional bioenergy feedstocks beyond what is currently and projected to be consumed. The remainder of this section focuses on this unused potential with discussion of sustainability associated with resource extraction, harvesting and collection, handling and logistics, and economics.

5.14.3.1 Primary Forest Residues

5.14.3.1.1 Background

Slightly more than 70% of current US harvest volume is roundwood with the remainder logging residues and other removals. Total logging residue and other removals in the United States amount to nearly 176 million m^3 annually – 129 m^3 of logging residue and 47 million m^3 of other removal residue [115] (The Forest Inventory Analysis Program of the United States Department of Agriculture (USDA) Forest Service conducts annual surveys and studies of industrial users to determine roundwood harvests for primary wood-using mills. Additional studies are also used to determine nonindustrial (i.e., residential and commercial) uses of roundwood. Taken together, these studies provide a comprehensive description of timber product output for a given year [118].) This residue material largely consists of tops, branches, and limbs; salvable dead trees; rough and rotten trees; noncommercial species; and small trees. Currently, most of this residue is left on-site owing to a variety of sustainability and economic reasons. However, if and when markets for bioenergy feedstocks begin to develop a significant fraction of this logging residue could become economically competitive to remove, most likely in conjunction with conventional harvest operations where the costs of extraction (i.e., felling and skidding) of the pulpwood- and sawlog-sized trees are borne by the conventional forest product.

In addition to forest residues generated as part of timber extraction and land conversion activities, vast areas of forestlands are overstocked with relatively large amounts of excess biomass, which has accumulated as a result of forest growth and alterations in natural cycles through successful suppression of fires. In August 2000, the National Fire Plan was developed to help respond to severe forest fires and their impacts on local communities while ensuring sufficient firefighting capacity for future fires. The National Fire Plan specifically addresses firefighting capabilities, forest rehabilitation, hazardous fuels reduction, community assistance, and accountability. The Healthy Forest Restoration Act (HFRA) of 2003 was then enacted to encourage the removal of hazardous fuels, encourage utilization of the material, and protect, restore, and enhance forest ecosystem components. HFRA is also intended to support R&D to overcome both technical and market barriers to greater utilization of this resource for bioenergy and other commercial uses from both public and private lands. Removing excess woody material has the potential to make relatively large volumes of forest residues and small-diameter trees available for bioenergy and biobased product uses. As part of its healthy forests initiatives, the USDA Forest Service identified timberland and other forestland areas that have tree volumes in excess of prescribed or recommended stocking densities that require some form of treatment or thinning operation to reduce the risks of uncharacteristically severe fires and that are in close proximity to people and infrastructure. This excess biomass is classified as standing and downed trees in overstocked stands that, if removed, would leave the forestlands healthier, more productive, and much less susceptible to fire hazard.

An estimate of the potential supply of this fuel treatment thinning wood was estimated for the 15 US western states [119]. The study identified a large amount of recoverable residue and merchantable wood resource ranging from a low of 520 to a high 1950 million Mg. The low estimate included only 60% of the timberlands in the highest fire-risk class and the high estimate included all timberlands requiring some fuel treatment. About 30% of the total amount is considered residue – tops and limbs of large trees and saplings or trees too small for pulpwood or sawlogs. A web-based tool, the Fuel Treatment Evaluator, was subsequently developed to identify, evaluate, and prioritize fuel treatment opportunities that would remove excess biomass so as to promote a more natural fire regime pattern with recurrence of less severe fire [120, 121]. This tool was used to estimate the potential availability of fuel treatment biomass across the entire continental United States [122]. This study, often referred to as the billion-ton study, estimated the potential at 54 million dry Mg with slightly more than 80% of the biomass on timberland and the remainder on other forestlands. The key assumptions behind this analysis included the exclusion of forestland areas not currently accessible by road and all environmentally sensitive areas, the imposition of equipment recovery limitations, and the merchandizing of thinnings into two utilization groups – conventional forest products and bioenergy products.

In a recent European study (European Environment Agency (EEA) [123]), forestland biomass resources were estimated for three broad categories of bioenergy potential – forest residues associated with commercial harvesting operations, complementary thinnings, and competitive use of wood. Complementary fellings are a potential resource defined as the difference between the maximum sustainable harvest (i.e., net annual forest growth minus requirements needed to ensure sustainability and to provide additional reserved forestlands) and roundwood harvests required to satisfy forest products demand. In some sense, complementary fellings are a broader definition of fuel treatment thinnings, which are defined by stand density index (SDI) and fire-risk potential. The EEA study also provided estimates of how much biomass could shift from current roundwood demand to bioenegy as prices for fossil fuels and carbon credits increase.

Although the demand for roundwood, as well as the extent of land clearing operations, ultimately determines the amount of forest residue generated, environmental and economic considerations set the amount that can be sustainably and economically removed. The next section discusses environmental sustainability related to forest residue extraction.

5.14.3.1.2 Environmental sustainability and the collection of primary forest residues

It is well known that forest residues provide a source of soil nutrients, regulate water flows and curtails soil erosion, and create habitat and increase biodiversity [123, 124]. These considerations are vitally important and must be considered if forest residues are to be removed sustainably. Ensuring the sustainable extraction of forest residues can be achieved through either the application of BMPs that are voluntary or statutory (regulated by States) or through formal forest certification programs [125]. In all cases, these practices are science-based and have the goals of protecting ecological functions and minimizing negative environmental impacts.

Many versions of forest sustainability criteria exist because of the various approaches to applying BMPs or certification [123, 126]. However, most include core ecological and environmental aspects, with additional considerations for economic and social implications. Forestry sustainability criteria usually have these basic elements:

- Conservation of biological diversity,
- Maintenance of productive capacity,
- Maintenance of forest ecosystem health and vitality,
- Conservation and maintenance of soil and water resources,
- Maintenance of forest contribution to global carbon cycles,
- Maintenance and enhancement of long-term multiple socioeconomic benefits, and
- Legal, institutional, and economic framework for forest conservation and sustainable management.

When properly applied under BMPs, regulations, or certification, residue removal does not have significant negative ecological and environmental impacts. In the United States, much effort has gone into educating timber-harvesting operators and designing equipment to minimize ecological impacts. Cautionary actions are taken to minimize soil disturbance, to prevent soil or machine fluids from entering streams and other water bodies, and to meet prescribed biodiversity and habitat requirements, like leaving foliage, roots, and parts of tree crown mass, downed/standing dead trees, avoiding sites with steep slopes and high elevation, protecting sensitive areas, and using retention trees. Logging and site-clearing residues can be removed so as not to accelerate erosion or degrade the site. Studies have shown how to minimize such impacts through use of buffer zones, leaving adequate biomass residue, and nutrient management programs. For example, Belleau *et al.* [127] found that the amount of slash left on the forest floor was the main factor in determining soil nutrient dynamics. They found that slash increased soil acidity and improved cation availability. Slash removal has also been shown to affect forest soil compaction. McDonald and Seixas [128] compared soil compaction caused by a forwarder when the slash density was 0, 10, and 20 kg m^{-2} (0, 0.62, and 1.25 lb ft^{-3}) in dry and wet soils. They found that the presence of slash did reduce soil compaction, particularly in drier soils, but the density of the slash had little to no effect. This seems to indicate that management practices could be developed in which a portion of the slash is left in the forest to improve soil quality, while the rest is recovered for energy. In fuel treatment operations, thinning will enhance forest health and vitality by removing excess biomass provided some stand structure is left to provide continuous cover, erosion control, and habitat [129].

For the United States, Janowiak and Webster [124] offer a set of guiding principles for ensuring the sustainability of harvesting biomass for energy applications. Among these principles are the explicit balancing of the benefits of biomass collection against ecological services provided, using BMPs where collection of biomass is warranted, retaining a portion of organic matter for soil productivity and deadwood for biodiversity, and, where appropriate, using biomass collection as a tool for ecosystem restoration. Further, they recommend increasing the extent of forestland cover including the afforestation of agricultural, abandoned and degraded lands, as well as the establishment of plantations and SRWC.

The Janowiak and Webster [124] guidelines are similar to EEA [123] who offer a set of minimum thresholds for residue extraction based on potential for soil erosion as determined by slope and elevation, soil compaction as influenced by soil moisture, and soil fertility as determined by topsoil and subsoil saturation and soil type. EEA [123] employed a multistage procedure starting with the formulation and use of multiple sustainability criteria to produce a high-resolution map local site suitability map for residue extraction. Their sustainability criteria included the exclusion of protected forest areas, such as nature conservation areas and reserved lands, prohibiting the removal of foliage and root biomass, reducing the area available for potential residue extraction by 5% in order to allow for an increase in protected areas, and setting aside 5% of wood volume as individual and small groups of retention trees after harvesting in order to increase the amount of large diameter trees and deadwood. Operationally, these criteria effectively limit the extraction of residues from stem and branches to 75% on highly suitable sites and to 50% and 15% on moderately and marginally suitable sites, respectively. These rates correspond to 60%, 40%, and 12% of the total aboveground residue biomass.

5.14.3.1.3 Economics of recovering primary forest residues

Forest residues are generated as part of whole-tree operations in which trees are cut mechanically (e.g., feller-buncher) or manually and then skidded or forwarded to a landing area where the trees are delimbed, topped, and bucked [130]. This method results in the accumulation of slash at the forest landing or roadside where it can be chipped and loaded directly into trucks. Because forest residue biomass is a relatively low-value product, it is likely to be collected concurrently with conventional roundwood harvesting operations as opposed to leaving the residue on-site to dry and be removed in a subsequent operation. (In the case of a two-pass system, costs are likely to be higher given the need to move and deploy equipment; however, the biomass will be drier and more attractive for conversion into power.) The costs of this biomass are low and include just stumpage and chipping. Stumpage costs would likely be a nominal amount in initial uses of this material, but could increase as bioenergy markets develop. However, stumpage costs for residue will likely be much less than pulpwood stumpage. **Figure 18** summarizes the total logging residue resource, the sustainable removable quantity, and the available supplies at alternative roadside costs. Thirty percent of logging residue is left on-site for sustainability reasons. These residues include nonmerchantable trees and tree components, as well as standing and dying trees. With stumpage and chipping, about 30% of the logging residue generated in the United States can be had at roadside costs less than $20 dry Mg^{-1} and nearly all of it at less than $30 dry Mg^{-1} [116].

In the case of fuel treatment thinnings, a whole-tree system can be adapted to include small or polewood-sized trees (1–5 inches) that are also cut and moved to the landing for chipping. Since the small trees are a forest residue product, the cost of felling and skidding would be borne by the bioenergy product and not by the primary wood product. To minimize costs of collecting forest fuel treatment thinning biomass, an uneven-aged forest thinning prescription is used in which harvesting operations remove trees across all age classes [98]. This type of harvesting operation provides bioenergy feedstocks at the lowest cost because biomass is removed in combination with removals of larger trees for pulpwood and sawlogs [116].

In the United States, forest thinning biomass costs were estimated based on uneven-aged thinning simulations on Forest Inventory and Analysis (FIA) plots where the plot SDI was greater than 30% of a maximum SDI for that given forest type [116]. The amount of biomass retained for sustainability was determined as function of slope. It was assumed 30% of the residue needed to remain for sustainability where slopes were less than 40%. On intermediate slopes ranging from greater than 40% to less than 80%, 40% of the residue was assumed left on-site. No residue was assumed removed on slopes greater than 80%. In addition to these slope-defined sustainability restrictions, roadless and administratively restricted areas were excluded.

Beginning with 1-inch diameter at breast height (dbh) trees, a treatment successively removes fewer trees from each diameter class where the removals bring the SDI down to 30% of the identified maximum SDI value for that stand type. For the North and South, biomass removals include all wood from trees 1–5 inches dbh and tops and branches of trees greater than 5 inches dbh, except for wood left for sustainability purposes. For the West, biomass removals include all wood from harvested trees 1–7 inches dbh and tops and branches of trees greater than 7 inches dbh. Limbs, tops, and cull components of merchantable trees have a chipping cost (harvest cost, i.e., felling and transport to roadside, are borne by the merchantable bolewood) and stumpage cost. Small, unmerchantable trees and dead trees have harvest, chipping, and stumpage costs. The study results shows a total resource of slightly more than 60 million dry Mg (**Figure 18**). Application of the sustainability criteria reduced the total resource by about 44%. The economically recoverable amounts vary considerably by cost at roadside. Only 7% of the thinnings can be extracted at costs to roadside at $20 per dry Mg or less. Slightly more than 20% and 30% of the resource can be extracted to roadside at $30 and $40 per dry Mg or less, respectively. Less than 50% of the total resource can be extracted at costs less than $80 per dry Mg^{-1}. The higher costs of thinnings relative to logging residue are due to a number of factors. Chief among these are the costs associated with harvesting and skidding large quantities of small trees to roadside where they can be chipped. Stand density and skid distance are also factors.

A potentially low-cost method of harvest and collection of forest residue for biomass is in wood comminution (chipping or bundling of tops and stems) as part of a conventional logging or thinning [130] operation. This type of integrated forest harvesting has occurred for several years in northern European countries such as Finland and Sweden [91] and is beginning to occur in the United States. Communition operations are most effective where logs are extracted by skidding, the site has good road access, and there are large volumes of biomass per hectare. Many sites where biomass could be recovered do not meet these criteria. However, recent technology developments with high potential for reducing collection and handling costs include specialized containers, combined harvester/grinder, and bundling/baling [130]. Specialized containers such as 'roll on/off' containers provide a means of

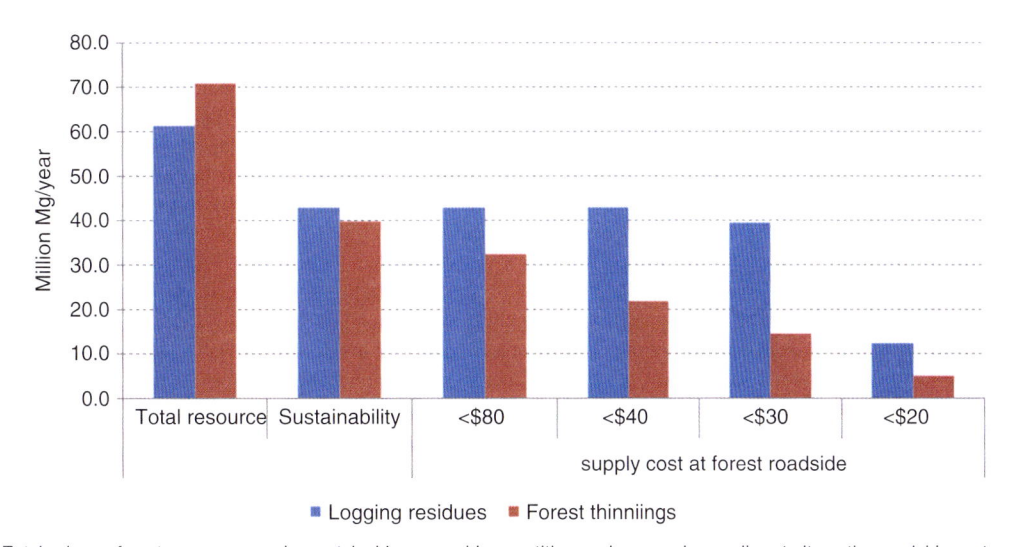

Figure 18 Total primary forest resource supply, sustainably removable quantities, and economic supplies at alternative roadside costs.

collecting slash in the forest and taking it to a grinder at the landing, where the material is size-reduced and deposited directly into trucks. This type of operation would replace using the skidder or front-end loader for the collection of slash. A Finnish company has developed a forwarder/harvester with a grinder and chip container mounted on it. This machine (Valmet 801), which does size reduction at the stump, is best suited for thinning operations. Several forest equipment manufacturing companies, such as John Deere, World Wood Pac, and Pinox Oy, have developed 'bundlers' as a means of hauling loose forests residues to the roadside. Along similar lines, a 'square' baler is being developed by Forest Concepts, Limited Liability Corporation (LLC) in Alabama, United States. The bundles or bales can be compressed so that they are considerably denser than loose residues. The slash bundles or 'composite residue logs' or bales can be stored until needed and suffer little dry matter loss and self-heating, which are common problems with chip piles. Presently, the costs of bundling appear to exceed the cost of collecting loose residues or roadside comminution, but when considered and optimized in the context of the entire supply chain, bundling could become more cost-competitive. Baling has not been fully evaluated, but one advantage is that the square bales can be hauled on a typical flatbed trailer. A small portable baler is especially promising for small logging or forest thinning operations and for urban areas. For both bundling and baling, costs will be lowest in areas with large amounts of logging residues [130].

5.14.3.2 Fuelwood

Fuelwood is wood that is harvested from forestlands and combusted directly for useable heat in the residential and commercial sectors and power in the electric utility sector. In the United States, these sectors account for 30% of current consumption of forestland biomass and about 20% of total biomass energy consumption. The residential sector is about four times as large as the commercial sector and five times as large as the electric power sector. In the most recent year, these three sectors consumed about 0.64 EJ. Most of the fuelwood consumed in the United States is in the Northeast and North Central regions and to a lesser extent in the Southeast and Pacific Coast regions and comes mostly from hardwoods [131]. In the future, large increases in fuelwood consumption for co-firing applications are projected.

5.14.3.3 Wood Processing Residues

The forest products industry worldwide produces two types of processing residues that are used for bioenergy and other uses, primary mill residues and pulping liquors.

5.14.3.3.1 Primary mill residues
Primary mill residues such as bark, sawmill slabs, peeler log cores, and sawdust are generated in the processing of roundwood for lumber, plywood, and pulp. In the United States, about 87 million dry Mg of primary mill residues are generated [132, 133]. About 75% of the bark is used as fuel and 23% is used in low-value products such as mulch. For coarse sawmill residues, about 77% is used in the manufacture of fiber products, 13% used for fuel, and 8% in other uses. About 55% of the fine residues (e.g., sawdust) are used as fuel, 25% in fiber products, and 19% in other uses. Overall, only a small amount goes unused, less than 2 million dry Mg. The large majority of this resource is used at or near the site where it is generated; thus, handling is relatively simple and transportation is generally not an issue. These factors account for the low cost of mill residues. The opportunity for shifting some of the low-value uses into bioenergy applications is available but limited.

5.14.3.3.2 Pulping liquors
In the manufacture of paper products, wood is converted into fiber using a variety of chemical and mechanical pulping process technologies. Kraft (or sulfate) pulping is the most common processing technology. In Kraft pulping, about half the wood is converted into fiber. The other half becomes black liquor, a by-product containing unutilized wood fiber and valuable chemicals. Pulp and paper facilities combust black liquor in recovery boilers to produce energy (i.e., steam), and more importantly, to recover the valuable chemicals present in the liquor. The amount of black liquor generated in the pulp and paper industry in the United States is the equivalent of nearly 53 million dry Mg of biomass [133]. Because the amount of black liquor generated is insufficient to meet all mill needs, recovery boilers are usually supplemented with fossil and wood residue-fired boilers. The US pulp and paper industry utilized enough black liquor, bark, and other wood residues to meet a majority of its energy requirements.

5.14.3.4 Urban Wood Residues

The two major sources of urban wood residues are the woody components of municipal solid waste (MSW) and construction and demolition (C&D) waste wood. MSW consists of a variety of items ranging from organic food scraps to discarded furniture, packaging materials, textiles, batteries, appliances, and other materials including yard trimmings. C&D wood waste is generated during the construction of new buildings and structures, the repair and remodeling of existing buildings and structures, and the demolition of existing buildings and structures [134]. These materials are considered separately from MSW since they come from much different sources.

The United States and the 27 nations now constituting the European Union (EU-27) generate relatively similar amounts of MSW each year with the EU-27 generating a little more in total, but much less per capita. In 2007, the United States generated 230 million

Table 6 Comparison of municipal solid waste generation and use in the United States, EU(27), United Kingdom, and Germany in 2007

Activity	USA[a] Mg × 1000	%	kg yr⁻¹[c]	EU(27)[b] Mg × 1000	%	kg yr⁻¹[c]	UK[b] %	kg yr⁻¹[c]	Germany[b] %	kg yr⁻¹[c]
Generation	230 000	100	765	260 029	100	525	100	572	100	582
Recovery for recycling	57 400	25	190	57 873	22.5	117	22	126	47	274
Recovery for composting	19 600	9	65	42 675	16.4	86	11.5	66	16	94
Combustion with energy recovery[d]	28 900	12	95	49 511	19.0	100	9.3	53	32	188
Discards to landfill, other disposal	124 500	54	414	104 982	40.4	212	57	324	0.8	3.6

[a] EPA, 2008, Municipal Solid Waste in the United States, EPA530-R-08-010 (English units converted to metric).
[b] European Union's Eurostat database: http://epp.eurostat.ec.europa.eu/.
[c] Values are kilogram per year per person in the population.
[d] The Eurostat database provides data on amount incinerated without specifying that energy is recovered; however, a footnote to one of the tables states that the United Kingdom had outlawed incineration without energy recovery, so it is assumed that energy is being recovered by most or all incineration activities across Europe.

Mg of MSW or about 765 kg⁻¹ yr⁻¹ per person [135], whereas the EU-27 generated about 260 million Mg or about 567 kg⁻¹ yr⁻¹ per person (http://epp.eurostat.ec.europa.eu/). Only three of the EU countries generate as much MSW per person as the United States with many countries generating much less. However, management of the MSW can be quite different (Table 6). About 54% and 55% of the total quantity generated in the United States and the United Kingdom was discarded in municipal landfills; however, Germany only sends about 1% of MSW to landfills. In these countries, the remainder was recycled, made into compost, or combusted for energy recovery (Table 6). The currently used forestland-derived component of the MSW is estimated at 12.7 million dry Mg annually for the United States and projected to increase to 18.1 million dry Mg per year by 2030.

In the United States, containers and packaging are the single largest component of MSW totaling some 31% of the total. Durable goods are the second largest portion accounting for 25% of total MSW generated. Yard trimmings are the third largest portion accounting for 13% of the total. Packaging is a much smaller component of the MSW stream in EU-27 countries since recycling and recovery of packaging wastes approaches 60% as of 2007 [136]. The wood component of containers, packaging, and durable goods (e.g., lumber scraps and discarded furniture) currently consumed in the United States is slightly more than 12.7 million Mg [135]. According to [134], about 10% of this material is recycled and 22% is combusted for energy recovery. The remaining material is discarded and landfilled. About one-third of this discarded material is unacceptable for recovery because of contamination, commingling with other wastes, or for other reasons, such as size and distribution of the material [134]. The remainder that is potentially available for bioenergy totals about 5 million dry Mg annually. Yard and tree trimmings are the other woody component of the MSW. Currently, about 29 million dry Mg is generated annually with nearly 19.1 million dry Mg of this amount recovered [135]. An additional 3.9 million dry Mg of wood is assumed recoverable and available for bioenergy applications after accounting for quantities that are likely to be composted, combusted, recycled, or contaminated and unavailable. The fractions composted, combusted, and contaminated are based on technical coefficients developed by McKeever [134].

The other principal source of urban wood residue in the United States is construction and demolition debris. These debris materials are correlated with economic activity (e.g., housing starts), population, demolition activity, and the extent of recycling and reuse programs. Currently, construction and demolition debris wastes in the United States totals nearly 20 million dry Mg with demolition wastes accounting for more than half (11 million dry Mg).

As noted by McKeever [137], many factors affect the availability of urban wood residues, such as size and condition of the material, extent of commingling with other materials, contamination, location and concentration, and, of course, costs associated with acquisition, transport, and processing.

The differing approach of some EU countries to MSW management is related to their efforts to reduce greenhouse gas emissions. EU directives related to waste management began with a packaging directive in 1994 and since then several more directives for specific wastes and general targets have been created. The latest EU directive, issued in December 2008, establishes a legal framework for treatment of waste and encourages protection of the environment and human health through the prevention of the harmful effects of waste generation and waste management. The focus is on prevention, reuse, recycling, and energy recovery (http://europa.eu/legislation_summaries/environment/wastemanagement/ev0010_en.htm). To the extent that countries are successful in prevention, reuse, and recycling, there will be less and less MSW available for energy generation, but the end result will be positive in also reducing the emission of greenhouse gases.

5.14.4 Conclusions

Several types of woody crop production systems are available and suitable for supplying feedstocks to a wide variety of bioenergy applications and bio-products. The multistemmed, high planting density, very short-rotation (1–3 years) 'coppice' systems are currently used to produce feedstocks dedicated to bioenergy utilization. These wood production systems provide earlier financial returns to the growers and investors and are frequently chosen primarily for that reason. The single-stem woody crop production systems vary widely in planting density, rotation length, and intended end-use. These longer rotation single-stem system, have the advantage of allowing the grower greater flexibility in feedstock marketing; the crop can be managed entirely for bioenergy or managed for potentially higher valued end-products when thinned for bioenergy then harvested later for pulpwood or sawtimber production.

Many different hardwood species can be used in either very short or longer rotation management systems with the choice dependent on soil types, climate, management information availability, and commercial availability of planting stock. In most northern temperate areas, willow species and hybrids are predominately chosen for very short coppice management systems. Poplar species and hybrids have become the 'model' hardwood species in northern temperate areas for research on single-stem woody crop production systems of medium to longer rotation ages. In tropical and subtropical areas, eucalyptus species are very widely planted for pulpwood and sawtimber and most likely to also be managed on shorter rotations or in agroforestry systems as bioenergy feedstocks. The large amount of experience available around the world in pine production, especially with loblolly pine, recommends it as an important potential resource for bioenergy production.

Availability of wood resources for bioenergy utilization depends largely on the success of technology innovations to reduce production and harvest costs and on market conditions. Market conditions are heavily affected by the relative prices of biofuels and fossil fuels, environmental drivers, such as international agreements on carbon emissions, international trade in biomass resources, and government policies in the areas of agriculture, forestry, environment, and energy. Analysis in the United States shows that at bioenergy feedstock prices of $50 odMg^{-1}, 36% of the 38 billion gallon Renewable Fuel Standard Mandates established by the United States for the year 2022 are met with herbaceous and woody crop feedstocks. By providing $10 credits to woody feedstocks and including forestland resources at $80 odMg^{-1}, cellulosic feedstocks can supply 65% of the mandate. Woody crop acres planted could be as high as about 60 million hectares.

Numerous studies have shown that woody crop production and harvest and collection of forest residues can be done in a manner that ranks high in meeting sustainability criteria relative to many other bioenergy and fossil fuel feedstock supply options. Such criteria include but are not limited to biological diversity, soil and water quality resources, ecosystem services, long-term productivity and health, and maintenance of socioeconomic benefits. It is critical that BMPs are used and that those are based on the local conditions of soil structure, soil nutrient requirements, climate conditions, and species being managed and harvested. The dominant environmental topic under discussion in 2010 is the effects of land-use change, both direct local effects and indirect global effects. Such discussions have led to recommendations to prioritize use of feedstock resources (e.g., residues) that do not require any land-use change, or to produce both energy and food products on land already under agriculture, or to use only degraded and/or abandoned agricultural lands for woody crop production. Those solutions are either insufficient to meet future demand for nonfossil-based fuels or require substantial government subsidies. A recent overview of the land-use change topic [110] also emphasizes the need for efficiency in all stages of any type of energy production, conversion, and utilization. This includes intensively cultured woody and herbaceous crops selected and managed to optimize yield per hectare, as well as conversion efficiency and overall system financial returns.

References

[1] Wright L (2006) Worldwide commercial development of bioenergy with a focus on energy crop-based projects. *Biomass and Bioenergy* 30: 706–714.
[2] McAlpine RG, Brown CL, Herrick AM, and Ruark HE (1966) 'Silage' sycamore. *Forest Farmer* 26: 6–7, 16.
[3] Ceulemans R, McDonald AJS, and Pereira JS (1996) A comparison among eucalypt, poplar and willow characteristics with particular reference to a coppice, growth-modelling approach. *Biomass and Bioenergy* 11: 215–231.
[4] Siren G, Sennerby-Forsse L, and Ledin S (1987) Energy plantations: Short rotation forestry in Sweden. In: Hall DO and Overend RP, (eds) *Biomass: Regenerable Energy*, pp. 119–143. Chichester, Sweden: Wiley.
[5] Rosenqvist H, Roos A, Ling E, and Hektor B (2000) Willow growers in Sweden. *Biomass and Bioenery* 18: 137–145.
[6] Dimitriou I and Aronsson P (2005) Willows for energy and phytoremediation in Sweden. *Unasylvia* 221: 56.
[7] Stolarski M, Szczukowski S, Tworkowski J, and Klasa A (2008) Productivity of seven clones of willow coppice in annual and quadrennial cutting cycles. *Biomass and Bioenergy* 32: 1227–1234.
[8] Volk TA, Abrahamson LP, Nowak CA, et al. (2006) The development of short-rotation willow in the northeastern United States for bioenergy and bioproducts, agroforestry and phytoremediation. *Biomass and Bioenergy* 30: 715–727.
[9] Abrahamson LP, Volk TA, Kopp RF, et al. (2002) *Willow Biomass Producer's Handbook*. Albany, NY: New York State Energy Research and Development Authority.
[10] Defra (2004) Growing short rotation coppice. Best practice guidelines for applicants to Defra's energy crops scheme. London, UK: Defra Publications. www.naturalengland.org.uk/Images/short-rotation-coppice_tcm6-4262.pdf (last accessed 8 August 2011).
[11] McCracken AR, Moore JP, Walsh LRE, and Lynch M (2010) Effect of planting vertical/horizontal willow (*Salix* spp.) cuttings on establishment and yield. *Biomass and Bioenergy* 34: 1764–1769.
[12] Mola-Yudego B and Aronsson P (2008) Yield models for commercial willow biomass plantations in Sweden. *Biomass and Bioenergy* 32: 829–837.
[13] Adegbidi HG, Volk TA, White EH, et al. (2001) Biomass and nutrient removal by willow clones in experimental bioenergy plantations in New York State. *Biomass and Bioenergy* 20: 399–411.
[14] Aylott MJ, Casella E, Tubby I, et al. (2008) Yield and spatial supply of bioenergy poplar and willow short-rotation coppice in the UK. *New Phytologist* 178: 358–370.
[15] Smart LB (2008) Genetics of yield and biomass composition of shrub willow bioenergy crops bred and selected in North America. In: Zalesny RS, Mitchell, R, and Richardson, J (eds.) *Biofuels, Bioenergy, and Bioproducts from Sustainable Agricultural and Forest Crops*. Proceedings of the Short Rotation Crops International Conference, Bloomington, MN, 19–21 August.
[16] Kopp RF, Abrahamson LP, White EH, et al. (1997) Cutting cycle and spacing effects on biomass production by a willow clone in New York. *Biomass and Bioenergy* 12: 313–319.
[17] Kopp RF, Smart LB, Maynard CA, et al. (2001) The development of improved willow clones for eastern North America. *The Forestry Chronicle* 77: 287–292.
[18] Sims REH, Maiava TG, and Bullock BT (2001) Short rotation coppice tree species selection for woody biomass production in New Zealand. *Biomass and Bioenergy* 20: 329–335.

[19] Liberloo M, Calfapietra C, Lukac M, et al. (2006) Woody biomass production during the second rotation of a bio-energy *Populus* plantation increases in a future high CO_2 world. *Global Change Biology* 12: 1094–1106.
[20] Proe MF, Griffiths JH, and Craig J (2002) Effects of spacing, species and coppicing on leaf area, light interception and photosynthesis in short rotation forestry. *Biomass and Bioenergy* 23: 315–326.
[21] Labrecque M and Teodorescu TI (2005) Field performance and biomass production of 12 willow and poplar clones in short-rotation coppice in southern Quebec (Canada). *Biomass and Bioenergy* 29: 1–9.
[22] Lindroth A and Båth A (1999) Assessment of regional willow coppice yield in Sweden on basis of water availability. *Forest Ecology and Management* 121: 57–65.
[23] Volk TA (2011) Personal Communication with Robert Perlack.
[24] Fischer G, Prieler S, van Velthuizen H, et al. (2010) Biofuel production potentials in Europe: Sustainable use of cultivated land and pastures. Part I: Land productivity potentials. *Biomass and Bioenergy* 34: 159–172.
[25] Volk TA (2011) Personal Communication with Robert Perlack.
[26] Fischer G, Prieler S, van Velthuizen H, et al (2010) Biofuel production potentials in Europe: Sustainable use of cultivated land and pastures. Part I: Land productivity potentials. *Biomass and Bioenergy* 34: 159–172.
[27] Afas NA, Marron N, Van Dongen S, et al. (2008) Dynamics of biomass production in a poplar coppice culture over three rotations (11 years). *Forest Ecology and Management* 255: 1883–1891.
[28] Herve C and Ceulemans R (1996) Short-rotation coppiced vs non-coppiced poplar: A comparative study at two different field sites. *Biomass and Bioenergy* 11: 139–150.
[29] Spinelli R, Nati C, and Magagnotti N (2009) Using modified foragers to harvest short-rotation poplar plantations. *Biomass and Bioenergy* 33: 817–821.
[30] Buchholz T, Volk TA, Abrahamson LP, and Smart LB (2008) The EcoWillow v. 1.4 (Beta) – An economic analysis tool for willow short-rotation coppice for wood chip production. State University of New York, College of Environmental Sciences and Forestry (SUNY-ESF). http://www.esf.edu/willow (last accessed 10 August 2011).
[31] Dawson DH (1976) History and organization of the maximum wood yield program. In: Ohman JH, (ed.) *Intensive Plantation Culture*. U.S. Department of Agriculture, Forest Service, North Central Forest Experiment Station, St. Paul, Minnesota.
[32] Johnson RL (1972) *Genetically improved cottonwood: A research and development success*. Proceedings of the 1972 National Convention, Society of American Foresters. pp. 113–119.
[33] Debell DS, Heilman PE, and Peabody DV, Jr. (1972) Potential production of black cottonwood and red alder at dense spacings in the Pacific Northwest. *Abstracts: Sixth Forest Biology Conference*. pp. 2. Appleton, WI: Institute of Paper Chemistry.
[34] Ranney JW, Wright LL, and Layton PA (1987) Hardwood energy crops: The technology of intensive culture. *Journal of Forestry* 85: 17–28.
[35] Drew AP, Zsuffa L, and Mitchell CP (1987) Terminology relating to woody plant biomass and its production. *Biomass and Bioenergy* 12: 79–82.
[36] Wright LL, Cushman JH, and Layton PA (1989) Dedicated energy crops: Expanding the market by improving the resource. *Biologue* 6: 12–19.
[37] Tuskan GA, DiFazio S, Jansson S, et al. (2006) The genome of black cottonwood, *Populus trichocarpa* (Torr. & Gray). *Science* 313: 1596–1604.
[38] Forestry Commission England (FCE) (2010) Short rotation forestry trial in England: Overview and update June 2010. UK: FCE. http://www.forestry.gov.uk/srf#background (last accessed 10 August 2011).
[39] Dickman DI (2006) Silviculture and biology of short-rotation woody crops in temperate regions: Then and now. *Biomass and Bioenergy* 30: 696–705.
[40] Hinchee M and Rottmann W (2009) Short-rotation woody crops for bioenergy and biofuels applications. *In Vitro Cellular and Developmental Biology Plant* 45: 619–629.
[41] Rockwood DL, Rudie AW, Ralph S, et al. (2008) Energy product options for *Eucalyptus* species grown as short rotation woody crops. *International Journal of Molecular Sciences* 9: 1361–1378.
[42] Anonymous (2010) Entrevista com Laércio Couto – Florestas de Curta Rotacao. Radar Silviconsult. pp. 18–20. Curitiba, Brazil: Silviconsult Engenharia. http://www.silviconsult.com.br(accessed 5 December 2010).
[43] Myburg A, Tuskan GA, Grattapaglia D, and Hinchee M (2007) South Africa: Eucalyptus genome sequencing for bioenergy. *Industrial Bioprocessing* 29: 10.
[44] Christersson L (2010) Wood production potential in poplar plantations in Sweden. *Biomass and Bioenergy* 34: 1289–1299.
[45] Ostlie D (2011) Personal communication with Lynn Wright regarding performance of Energy Performance Systems' mechanical planter.
[46] Heilman PE and Stettler RF (1985) Genetic variation and productivity of *Populus trichocarpa* and its hybrids. II, Biomass Production in a 4-year plantation. *Canadian Journal of Forest Research* 15: 384–388.
[47] Heilman PE and Stettler RF (1990) Genetic variation and productivity of *Populus trichocarpa* and its hybrids. IV. Performance in short-rotation coppice. *Canadian Journal of Forest Research* 20: 1257–1264.
[48] Heilman PE, Ekuan G, and Fogle DB (1994) Above- and below-ground biomass and fine roots of four-year-old hybrids of *Populus trichocarpa* x *P. deltoides* and parental species in short rotation culture. *Canadian Journal of Forest Research* 24: 1186–1192.
[49] DeBell DS, Clendenen GW, Harrington CA, and Zasada JC (1996) Tree growth and stand development in short-rotation Populus plantings: 7-year results for two clones at three spacings. *Biomass and Bioenergy* 11: 253–269.
[50] Riemenschneider DE, Berguson WE, Dickman DI, et al. (2001) Poplar breeding and testing strategies in the north-central U.S.: Demonstration of potential yield and consideration of future research needs. *The Forestry Chronicle* 77: 246–253.
[51] Strong TF and Hansen EA (1993) Hybrid poplar spacing/productivity relations in short rotation intensive culture plantations. *Biomass and Bioenergy* 4: 255–261.
[52] Coyle DR, Hart ER, McMillin JD, et al. (2008) Effects of repeated cottonwood leaf beetle defoliation on Populus growth and economic value over an 8-year harvest rotation. *Forest Ecology and Management* 255: 3365–3373.
[53] Dowell RC, Gibbins D, Rhoads JL, and Pallardy SG (2009) Biomass production physiology and soil carbon dynamics in short-rotation-grown *Populus deltoides* and *P. deltoides* x *P. nigra* hybrids. *Forest Ecology and Management* 257: 134–142.
[54] Strauss CH, Grado SC, Blankenhorn PR, and Bowersox TW (1990) Cost parameters affecting multiple rotation SRIC biomass systems. *Applied Biochemistry and Biotechnology* 24–25: 721–733.
[55] Netzer DA, Tolsted DN, Ostry ME, et al. (2002) *Growth, Yield, and Disease Resistance of 7–12 Year Old Poplar Clones in the North Central United States*. General Technical Report GTR-NC-229. pp. 33. St. Paul, MN: USDA Forest Service, North Central Experiment Station.
[56] Stanturf JA, van Oosten C, Netzer DA. et al. (2001) Ecology and silviculture of poplar plantations. In: Dickman DI, Isebrands JG, Eckenwalder JE, and Richardson J (eds) *Poplar Culture in North America*, ch. 5, p. 397. Ottawa, CA: NRC Research Press.
[57] Coyle DR and Coleman MD (2005) Forest production responses to irrigation and fertilization are not explained by shifts in allocation. *Forest Ecology and Management* 208: 137–152.
[58] Cobb WR, Will RE, Daniels RF, and Jacobson MA (2008) Aboveground biomass and nitrogen in four short-rotation woody crop species growing with different water and nutrient availabilities. *Forest Ecology and Management* 255: 4032–4039.
[59] Langholtz M, Carter DR, Rockwood DL, and Alavalapati JRR (2007) The economic feasibility of reclaiming phosphate mined lands with short-rotation woody crops in Florida. *Journal of Forest Economics* 12: 237–249.
[60] Rockwood DL, Comer CW, Dippon DR, and Huffman JB (1985) Woody biomass production options for Florida. Bulletin 865. Agricultural Experiment Station Institute of Food and Agriculture Sciences (IFAS), University of Florida Gainesville, Florida.
[61] Luxmoore RJ, Tharp ML, and Post WM (2008) Simulated biomass and soil carbon of loblolly pine and cottonwood plantations across a thermal gradient in southeastern United States. *Forest Ecology and Management* 254: 291–299.
[62] Berthelot A, Ranger J, and Gelhaye D (2000) Nutrient uptake and immobilization in a short-rotation coppice stand of hybrid poplars in north-west France. *Forest Ecology and Management* 128: 167–179.

[63] Bungart R and Reinhard FH (2004) Growth dynamics and biomass accumulation of 8-year-old hybrid poplar clones in a short-rotation plantation on a clayey-sandy mining substrate with respect to plant nutrition and water budget. *European Journal of Forest Research* 123: 105–115.

[64] Wright J (2010) Personal communication about ArborGen research with Lynn Wright.

[65] Stape JL, Binkley D, Ryan MG, et al. (2010) The Brazil eucalyptus potential productivity project: Influence of water, nutrients, and stand uniformity on wood production. *Forest Ecology and Management* 259: 1684–1694.

[66] Strauss CH and Grado SC (1992) Input-output analysis of energy requirements for short rotation, intensive culture, woody biomass. *Solar Energy* 1: 45–51.

[67] Perlack RD and Wright LL (1995) Technical and economic status of wood energy feedstock production. *Energy* 20: 279–284.

[68] Riemenschneider DE, Stanton BJ, Vallee G, and Perinet P (2001) Poplar breeding strategy. In: Dickman DI, Isebrands JG, Eckenwalder JE, and Richardson J (eds.) *Poplar Culture in North America*, ch 2. Ottawa, CA: National Research Council of Canada.

[69] Food and Agricultural Organization (FAO) (2007) State of the World's Forests, 2007. p. 157. Rome, Italy: FAO United Nations.

[70] Smith WB, Miles PD, Perry CH, and Pugh SA (2009) Forest resources of the United States, 2007 – Table 8. General Technical Report WO-78. Washington, DC: U.S. Department of Agriculture, Forest Service, Washington Office.

[71] Smith WB, Miles PD, Perry CH, and Pugh SA (2009) Forest resources of the United States, 2007 – Table 41. General Technical Report WO-78. Washington, DC: U.S. Department of Agriculture, Forest Service, Washington Office.

[72] Fox TR, Jokela EJ, and Allen HL (2007) The development of pine plantation silviculture in the Southern United States. *Journal of Forestry* 105: 337–347.

[73] Gonzalez R, Wright J, and Saloni E (2009) Filling a need: Forest plantations for bioenergy in the Southern US. *Biomass Magazine* 8: 44–47.

[74] Stanturf JA, Kellison RC, Broerman FS, and Jones SB (2003) Productivity of southern pine plantations: Where are we and how did we get here? *Journal of Forestry* 101: 26–31.

[75] Albaugh TJ, Allen HL, and Fox TR (2007) Historical patterns of forest fertilization in the Southeastern United States from 1969 to 2004. *Southern Journal of Applied Forestry* 31: 129–137.

[76] Fox TR, Allen HL, Albaugh TJ, et al. (2007) Tree nutrition and forest fertilization of pine plantations in the Southern United States. *Southern Journal of Applied Forestry* 31: 5–11.

[77] Kyle KH, Andrews LJ, Fox TR, et al. (2005) Long-term effects of drainage, bedding, and fertilization on growth of loblolly pine (*Pinus taeda* L.) in the coastal plain of Virginia. *Southern Journal of Applied Forestry* 29: 205–214.

[78] Samuelson LJ, Butnor J, Maier C, et al. (2008) Growth and physiology of loblolly pine in response to long-term resource management: Defining growth potential in the southern United States. *Canadian Journal of Forest Research* 38: 721–732.

[79] Borders BE, Will RE, Markewitz D, et al. (2004) Effect of complete competition control and annual fertilization on stem growth and canopy relations for a chronosequence of loblolly pine plantations in the lower coastal plain of Georgia. *Forest Ecology and Management* 192: 21–37.

[80] Will RE, Markewitz D, Hendrick RL, et al. (2006) Nitrogen and phosphorus dynamics for 13-year-old loblolly pine stands receiving complete competition control and annual N fertilizer. *Forest Ecology and Management* 227: 155–168.

[81] Roth BE, Jokela EJ, Martin TA, et al. (2007) Genotype × environment interactions in selected loblolly and slash pine plantations in the Southeastern United States. *Forest Ecology and Management* 238: 175–188.

[82] Williams TM and Gresham CA (2006) Biomass accumulation in rapidly growing loblolly pine and sweetgum. *Biomass and Bioenergy* 30: 370–377.

[83] Jokela JJ (1984) Status of poplar breeding in the United States. *17th Session of the International Poplar Commission*, 1–4 October. p. 3. Ottawa, Canada: International Union of Forestry Research Organization.

[84] Jokela EJ and Martin TA (2000) Effects of ontogeny and soil nutrient supply on production, allocation, and leaf area efficiency in loblolly and slash pine stands. *Canadian Journal of Forest Research* 30: 1511–1524.

[85] McKeand S, Mullin T, Byram T, and White T (2003) Deployment of genetically improved loblolly and slash pines in the South. *Journal of Forestry* 101: 32–37.

[86] Guo Z, Grebner DL, Sun C, and Grado SC (2010) Evaluation of loblolly pine management regimes in Mississippi for biomass supplies: A simulation approach. *Southern Journal of Applied Forestry* 34: 65–71.

[87] Borders BE and Bailey RL (2001) Loblolly pine: pushing the limits of growth. *Southern Journal of Applied Forestry* 25: 69–74.

[88] Allen HL, Fox TR, and Campbell RG (2005) What is ahead for intensive Pine plantation silviculture in the South? *Southern Journal of Applied Forestry* 29: 62–69.

[89] Scott DA and Tiarks A (2008) Dual-cropping loblolly pine for biomass energy and conventional wood products. *Southern Journal of Applied Forestry* 32: 33–37.

[90] Wilkerson EG and Perlack RD (2009) Resource assessment, economics and technology for collection and harvesting. In: Solomon BD and Luzadis VA (eds.) *Renewable Energy from Forest Resources in the United States*, New York: Routledge.

[91] Leinonen A (2004) *Harvesting Technology of Forest Residues for Fuel in the USA and Finland*. Finland: VTT, JYVASKYLA.

[92] Spinelli R and Hartsough B (2001) Extracting whole short rotation trees with skidder and a front-end loader. *Biomass and Bioenergy* 21: 425–431.

[93] Hartsough BR, Spinelli R, and Pottle SJ (2002) Delimbing hybrid poplar prior to processing with a flail/chipper. *Forest Products Journal* 52: 85–94.

[94] Fox TR (2000) Sustained productivity in intensively managed forest plantations. *Forest Ecology and Management* 138: 187–202.

[95] Spinelli R, Ward SM, and Owende PM (2009) A harvest and transport cost model for *Eucalyptus* spp. fast-growing short rotation plantations. *Biomass and Bioenergy* 33: 1265–1270.

[96] Baker SA, Westbrook MD, Jr., and Greene WD (2010) Evaluation of integrated harvesting systems in pine stands of the southern United States. *Biomass and Bioenergy* 34: 720–727.

[97] Ostlie DL (2010) Personal communication with Lynn Wright regarding whole-tree woody crop harvester development; April 2010.

[98] Taylor EL, Holley AG, and Blazier M (2006) New pine planting strategies for the Western Gulf States. Southern Regional Extension Forestry Technology Bulletin, SREF-FM-003. pp. 8, 805–126. College Station, Texas: Texas A&M Publications.

[99] Volk TA, Verwijst T, Tharakan PJ, et al. (2004) Growing fuel: A sustainability assessment of willow biomass crops. *Frontiers in Ecology and the Environment* 2: 411–418.

[100] Tolbert VR (1998) Guest editorial. *Biomass and Bioenergy* 14: 301–306.

[101] Gasol CM, Gabarrell X, Anton A, et al.(2009) LCA of poplar bioenergy system compared with *Brassica carinata* energy crop and natural gas in regional scenario. *Biomass and Bioenergy* 33: 119–129.

[102] Heller MC, Keoleian GA, and Volk TA (2003) Life cycle assessment of a willow bioenergy cropping system. *Biomass and Bioenergy* 25: 147–165.

[103] Adler PR, Del Grosso SJ, and Parton WJ (2007) Life-cycle assessment of net greenhouse-gas flux for bioenergy cropping systems. *Ecological Applications* 7: 675–691.

[104] Scott AD and Dean TJ (2006) Energy trade-offs between intensive biomass utilization, site productivity loss, and ameliorative treatments in loblolly pine plantations. *Biomass and Bioenergy* 30: 1001–1010.

[105] Dale VH, Kline KL, Wright LD, et al. (2010) Interactions between bioenergy feedstock choices, landscape dynamics, and land use. *Ecological Applications* 24: 1039–1054.

[106] Lotze-Campen H, Müller C, Bondeau A, et al.(2008) Global food demand, productivity growth, and the scarcity of land and water resources: A spatially explicit mathematical programming approach. *Agricultural Economics* 39: 325–338.

[107] Bringezu S, Schutz S, O'Brien M, et al. (2009) Towards sustainable production and use of resources: Assessing biofuels. Paris, France: International Panel for Sustainable Resource Management. p. 120. United Nations Environment Program.

[108] Tilman D, Socolow R, Foley J, et al. (2009) Beneficial biofuels: The food, energy, and environmental trilemma. *Science* 325: 270–271.

[109] Couto L, Graca LR, Betters DR, and Passos CAM (1993) Agroforestry as an alternative to reduce establishment costs of short-rotation eucalypt plantations in southeastern Brazil. *The Third North American Agroforestry Conference – Opportunities for Agroforestry in the Temperate Zone Worldwide*. pp. 23–24. Ames, IA: Iowa State University Press. Contractor file.

[110] Fritsche UR, Sims REH, and Monti A (2010) Direct and indirect land-use competition issues for energy crops and their sustainable production: An overview. *Biofuels, Bioproducts and Biorefining* 4: 692–704.

[111] Food and Agricultural Organization (FAO) (2009) State of the World's Forests 2009. Annex Table 2, forest area and area change. p. 7. Rome, Italy: FAO of the United Nations. http://www.fao.org/docrep/011/i0350e/i350e00.htm (last accessed 10 August 2011).
[112] Food and Agricultural Organization (FAO) (2009) State of the World's Forests 2009. Annex Table 1, basic data on countries and areas. p. 8. Rome, Italy: FAO of the United Nations. http://www.fao.org/docrep/011/i0350e/i0350e00.htm (accessed 10 August 2011).
[113] FAO. State of the World's Forests 2009. Annex Table 3, forest growing stock, biomass and carbon. Food and Agricultural Organization of the United Nations, Rome, 2009. http://www.fao.org/docrep/011/i0350e/i0350e00.htm (accessed 10 August 2011).
[114] FAO (2006) State of the World's Forests 2009. Annex Table 4, production, trade, and consumption of woodfuel, roundwood and sawnwood. Rome, Italy: Food and Agricultural Organization of the United Nations, 2009.
[115] Smith JE, Miles PD, Perry CH, and Pugh SA (2009) Forest resources of the United States, 2007, Chapter 6. General Technical Report WO-78. Washington, DC: U.S. Department of Agriculture, Forest Service.
[116] US Department of Energy (2011) US Billion-Ton Update: Biomass Supply for a Bioenergy and Bioproducts Industry. RD Perlack and BJ Stokes (Leads), ORNL/TM-2011/224. Oak Ridge National Laboratory, Oak Ridge, TN. 227pp. http://www1.eere.energy.gov/biomass/pdfs/billion_ton_update.pdf (last accessed 9 August 2011).
[117] Energy Information Administration (2010) Annual Energy Outlook 2010. Report DOE/EIA-0383(2010). US Department of Energy. Energy Information Administration. Washington DC.
[118] United States Department of Agriculture (USDA) Forest Service (2010). The forest inventory and database: database description and user's manual version 4.0 for phase 2. US Department of Agriculture, Forest Service, Washington DC.
[119] USDA Forest Service (2005) A Strategic Assessment of Forest Biomass and Fuel Reduction Treatments in Western States. Gen. Tech. Rep. RMRS-GTR-149. Fort Collins, Co: US Department of Agriculture, Forest Service, Rocky Mountain Research Station. Fort Collins, CO. 17pp.
[120] Skog KE, Barbour RJ, Abt KL, et al. (2006) Evaluation of silvicultural treatments and biomass use for reducing fire hazard in western states. FPL-RP-634. USDA Forest Service, Forest Products Laboratory. Madison, WI. 29pp.
[121] Miles PD, Skog KE, Shepperd WD, Reinhardt ED, and Fight RD (2006) Broad-Scale Assessment of Fuel Treatment Opportunities. Proceedings of the Sixth Forest Inventory and Analysis Symposium, 2004 September 21–24, Denver, CO. Gen. Tech. Rep. WO-70. US Department of Agricultural Forest Service. Washington, DC. 126pp.
[122] Perlack RD, Wright LL, Turhollow AF, et al. (2005) Biomass as feedstock for a bioenergy and bioprocucts industry: The technical feasibility of a billion-ton annual supply. DOE/GO102995-2135 or ORNL/TM-2005/66. Oak Ridge National Laboratory, Oak Ridge, TN. 60pp.
[123] European Environment Agency (EEA) (2006) How much bioenergy can Europe produce without harming the environment? – 67 pp. EEA Report No. 7/Copenhagen.
[124] Janowiak MK and Webster CR (2010) Promoting ecological sustainability in woody biomass harvesting. *Journal of Forestry* 108: 16–23.
[125] Biomass Research and Development Initiative (BRDI) (2008) Increasing feedstock production for biofuels: economic drivers, environmental implications, and the role of research. Washington, DC. 146pp.
[126] Evans AM and Perschel RT (2009) An assessment of biomass harvesting guidelines. Forest Guild, Santa Fe, NM.
[127] Belleau A, Brais S, and Pare, D (2006) Soil nutrient dynamics after harvesting and slash treatments in boreal aspen stands. Soil Science Society of America Journal 70: 1189-1199.
[128] McDonald and Seixas F (1997) Effect of slash on forwarder soil compaction. *Journal of Forest Engineering* 8: 15–26.
[129] Graham RT McCaffrey S, and Jain TB (technical editors) (2004) Science Basis for Changing Forest Structure to Modify Wildfire Behavior and Severity. Gen. Tech. Rep. RMRS-GTR-120. US Department of Agriculture, Forest Service, Rocky Mountain Research Station, Fort Collins, CO.
[130] Wilkerson EG, Blackwelder DB, Perlack RD, *et al.* (2008) A preliminary assessment of the state of harvest and collection technology for forest residues. Oak Ridge, TN: Oak Ridge National Laboratory. http://www.osti.gov/bridge (accessed 10 August 2011).
[131] Smith WB, Miles PD, Perry CH, and Pugh SA (2009) Forest Resources of the United States, 2007 (Chapter 6). Gen. Tech. Rep. WO-78. Washington, DC: US Department of Agriculture, Forest Service, Washington Office, 336pp.
[132] Smith WB, Miles PD, Perry CH, and Pugh SA (2009) Forest Resources of the United States, 2007 (Table 42). Gen. Tech. Rep. WO-78. Washington, DC: US Department of Agriculture, Forest Service, Washington Office. 336pp.
[133] Energy Information Administration (EIA) (2009) *Renewable Energy Annual*, 2007 edn. Washington, DC: U.S. EIA. http://www.eia.gov/cneaf/solar.renewables/page/rea_data/rea_sum.html (accessed 10 August 2011).
[134] McKeever D (2004) Inventories of woody residues and solid wood waste in the United States, 2002. *Ninth International Conference, Inorganic-Bonded Composite Materials*, 10–13 October. British Columbia, Canada: Vancouver.
[135] Environmental Protection Agency (EPA) (2008) *Municipal Solid Waste in the United States: 2007 Facts and Figures*. U.S. EPA. http://www.epa.gov/wastes/nonhaz/muncipal/pubs/msw07-rpt.pdf (accessed 10 August 2011).
[136] European Union (2008) Flash report on recycling results in the EU. http://ec.europa.eu/environment/waste/reporting/pdf/flash_report.pdf (last accessed 8 September 2011).
[137] McKeever D (1998) Wood residual quantities in the United States, Biocycle January.

Further Reading

[1] Karp A and Shield I (2008) Bioenergy from plants and the sustainable yield challenge. *New Pytologist* 179: 15–32.
[2] Rowe RL, Street NR, and Taylor I (2009) Identifying potential environmental impacts of large-scale deployment of dedicated energy crops in the UK.
[3] United Nations Environment Program (UNEP) (2009) Towards sustainable production and use of resources: Assessing biofuels. Produced by the International Panel for Sustainable Resource Management. Paris: UNEP. http://www.unep.r/scp/rpanel/Biofuels.htm (accessed 14 September 2010).
[4] Solomon, BD and Kyzadism VA (eds.) (2010) *Renewable Energy from Forest Resources in the United States*, New York: Routledge.
[5] Faaij A and Londo M (2010) A roadmap for biofuels (Guest Editorial), and all other articles in *Biomass and Bioenergy* 34.
[6] US Department of Energy (2011) US Billion Update: Biomass Supply for a Bioenergy and Bioproducts Industry. RD Perlack and BJ Stokes (Leads), ORNL/TM-2011/224. Oak Ridge National Laboratory, Oak Ridge, TN. 227pp. http://www1.eere.energy.gov/biomass/pdfs/billion_ton_update.pdf (last accessed 9 August 2011).

Relevant Websites

http://www.bioenergy.ornl.gov – Biomass Feedstock Information Network, created by Oak Ridge National Laboratory, Oak Ridge, Tennessee.
http://www.esf.edu/willow – Willow/Woody Biomass at ESF
http://bioenergykdf.net – Bioenergy Knowledge Discovery Framework website of the US Department of Energy.

5.15 Potential for Yield Improvement

J Spink and E Mullins, Teagasc, Oak Park Crops Research Centre, Carlow, Republic of Ireland
P Berry, ADAS High Mowthorpe, Malton, UK

© 2012 Elsevier Ltd. All rights reserved.

5.15.1	Introduction	293
5.15.2	History of Oilseed Rape Production	293
5.15.3	Yield Potential	296
5.15.4	Genetic Constraint to Yield Improvement	299
5.15.5	Crop Management Constraint to Yield Improvement	299
5.15.6	Genetic Approaches	300
5.15.7	Conclusions	301
References		302
Further Reading		303

5.15.1 Introduction

In its simplest terms, the yield potential of a crop is determined by its ability to capture resources and the efficiency with which it can convert those resources into harvestable biomass. The yield potential in any given environment will then be determined by which ever of, light, water, nutrients or CO_2, is most limiting.

The degree to which a crop complies with this simple explanation is determined by the definition of the word 'harvestable'. Arguably, all crop biomass is harvestable, and our definition would perhaps be more usefully defined as usable biomass. Crops grown for energy production for which all of the above-ground biomass can be utilized, such as *Miscanthus* for combustion or lingo-cellulosic digestion or grass for anaerobic digestion, most easily fit with this simple understanding. However, for the majority of crops the total biomass is partitioned into high-value (often reproductive) and low-value (structural) materials. In such cases, a more sophisticated consideration of yield potential must be employed. One such approach has been to consider the 'harvest index' of the crop [1]. This assumes that a given proportion of the total biomass production will be partitioned into usable biomass. However, this seems an oversimplification, as the structural and reproductive parts of a crop are produced at different stages in its life cycle. The duration of the stages of the life cycle and availability of resources through the growing season are affected by the environment and the acquisition and conversion of those resources by the physiology of the crop.

If we are to consider the technological solutions to increasing crop yield as fully as possible, and accepting that due to limitations on space this is best achieved by concentrating on one crop, then it seems sensible to choose a crop in which biomass production and partitioning are both important.

Oilseed rape, otherwise known as 'rapeseed' or 'canola', has been of interest in biofuel production in recent years because of the high suitability of its oil to biodiesel production [2]. As a crop, it is also widely grown being produced in all the major populated continents. Oilseed rape yield potential also requires consideration not just of total biomass production but of the partitioning of biomass into vegetative materials and seeds and further into the partitioning of seed biomass into oil and other constituents. Its ability to acquire and utilize resources is also known to change as it progresses through its life cycle [3]. One of the key technical areas for consideration over recent years has been genetic improvement, and oilseed rape is closely related to *Arabidopsis*, one of the key model species used in the development of genetic techniques in plant science. It is also a genetically diverse crop with four species of Brassica widely cultivated as oilseed crops in different parts of the world: *Brassica napus* (Swede rape), *Brassica rapa* (Turnip rape), *Brassica juncea* (Indian mustard), and *Brassica carinata* (Ethiopian mustard). The genomic relationships between the *Brassica* species are well understood [4]. *Brassica rapa* ($n = 10$; A), *Brassica nigra* ($n = 8$; B), and *Brassica oleracea* ($n = 9$; C) are the primary species. Amphidiploid crosses between corresponding pairs of the primary species have produced *B. juncea* ($n = 18$; AB), *B. napus* ($n = 19$; AC), and *B. carinata* ($n = 17$; BC). Autumn-sown *B. napus* is the most common rapeseed grown in Europe and China. In cooler areas of northern Europe and in Canada, spring-sown *B. napus* and autumn- and spring-sown *B. rapa* are grown. In Australia, spring-sown *B. napus* is now the most frequently grown rapeseed. In India and parts of China, *B. juncea* is commonly grown, whereas *B. carinata* is grown in North East Africa.

Oilseed rape therefore seems an ideal exemplar crop, in which to consider the technological approaches that may be taken in order to increase productivity for energy production.

5.15.2 History of Oilseed Rape Production

Before considering the potential for future yield improvement, we should look at what progress has been made to-date in terms of oilseeds production and yield.

An analysis of FAOStat data shows that globally the area of oilseed rape grown has increased from 6.3 million ha in 1961 to nearly 31 million ha in 2007, close to a fivefold increase. Over the same period, global oilseed rape production has increased from 3.6 to 50.6 million tons, a 14-fold increase (**Figure 1(a)**). In order to achieve this rate of productivity increase, yields have been increasing at the rate of 26 kg ha^{-1} yr^{-1}, roughly a threefold increase from about 0.6 to 1.8 t ha^{-1} (**Figure 1(b)**).

This global picture can be considered in more detail by looking at the major production areas to examine if the global trends are generally applicable. There are eight countries that can be considered as major production areas (defined as producing an average of more than 1 million tons per annum in the 5 years from 2003 to 2007): Australia, Canada, China, France, Germany, India, Poland, and the United Kingdom (**Table 1**). It can be seen that the fastest rates of the expansion in area produced have generally occurred in nontraditional production areas, for example, Australia, Canada, France, Germany, and the United Kingdom. The exception to this is China, which in the early 1960s was the second largest producer, producing about half as much as India, but by the mid-2000s was by far the largest producer with nearly a quarter of global production.

While the yields in all major producing countries have increased significantly (**Table 1**), we need to look in more detail at trends through time to examine if the steady global progress in yield improvement applies in all production regions (**Figure 2**). Using a linear regression of yield through time shows that the rate of yield increase has varied from 15 kg ha^{-1} yr^{-1} in Canada to 40 kg ha^{-1} yr^{-1} in Germany (**Table 2**). In order to investigate if there has been a change in the rate of yield progress, quadratic, linear plus exponential, and two straight line regressions were fitted using Genstat v10. There was no improvement in fit using a curvilinear rather than straight line regression in four of the eight countries (e.g., Canada, China, Germany, and Poland), indicating that yields have been increasing steadily over the period tested. The Australian yield data were significantly better described by both the quadratic and linear plus exponential curves, the r^2 increasing from 26.3% to 44.5%, and both curves predicting an asymptote in 1994. The French data were also better described by all three nonlinear regressions, and neither the quadratic nor the linear plus exponential curve predicted an asymptote but rather a decline in the rate of yield increase (**Figure 2**). The two straight line regressions did predict a decline in yield, but only since 2005, which as it is based on only the last 2 years, data must be treated with skepticism. There was a small improvement in fit for the Indian yields from both the quadratic and the

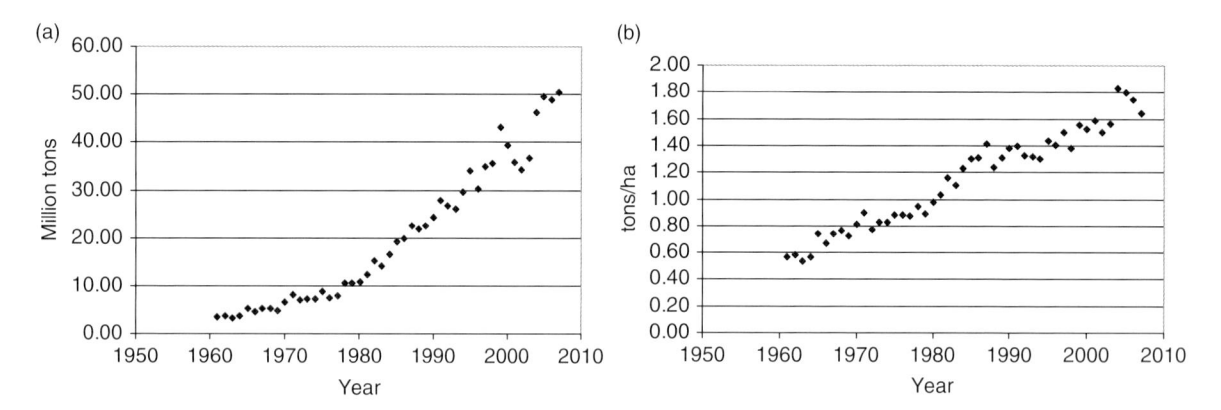

Figure 1 Global oilseed rape (a) production and (b) yield.
Source: FAOStat (2009) www.faostat.fao.org [5].

Table 1 Production area (ha), yield (t ha^{-1}), and average annual production for the major oilseed rape-producing areas of the world for 1961–65 and 2003–07

	Annual production (t)		Yield (t ha^{-1})[a]		Average area grown (ha)	
	1961–65	2003–07	1961–65	2003–07	1961–65	2003–07
Australia	0	1 263 864		1.11	0	1 136 012
Canada	277 962	8 491 380	0.91	1.62	306 383	5 249 360
China	699 064	12 045 860	0.43	1.69	1 588 990	7 112 229
France	196 450	4 117 208	1.78	3.23	107 399	1 284 273
Germany	268 225	4 923 849	1.72	3.58	155 935	1 374 008
India	1 277 000	6 666 700	0.42	1.05	3 026 800	6 271 000
Poland	323 200	1 531 409	1.43	2.57	223 440	587 059
UK	2 500	1 855 940	Na	3.15	1 000	589 660

[a] Only yields calculated on areas over 5000 ha have been quoted.
Source: FAOStat (2009) www.faostat.fao.org [5].

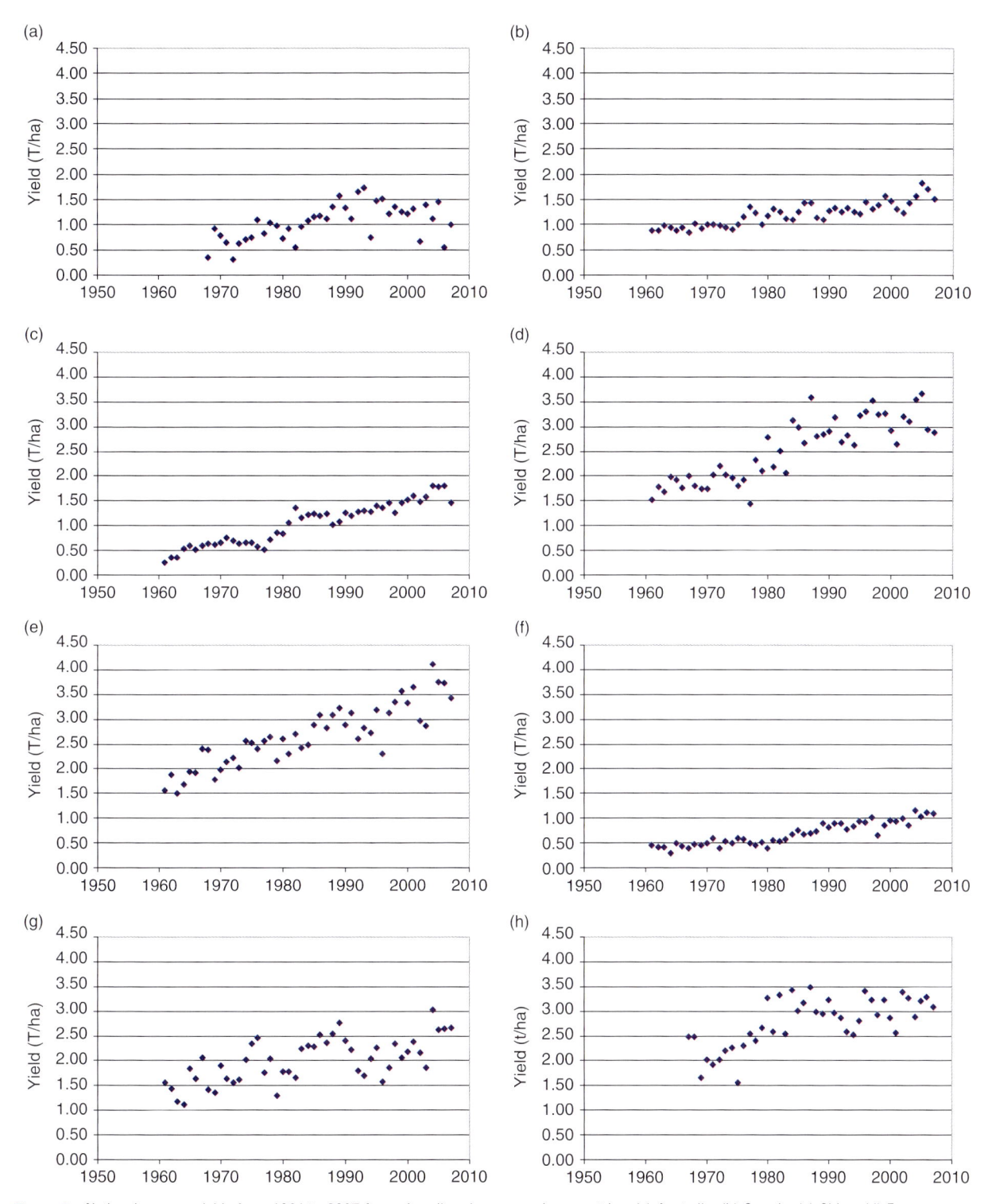

Figure 2 National average yields from 1961 to 2007 for major oilseed rape growing countries: (a) Australia, (b) Canada, (c) China, (d) France, (e) Germany, (f) India, (g) Poland, and (h) United Kingdom.
Source: FAOStat (2009) www.faostat.fao.org [5].

linear plus exponential curves; this was due to accounting for a small apparent drop in yields over the period 1961–64, followed by a steady rate of yield increase. The UK data were again better predicted by nonlinear regressions; the best fit being with the two straight line regressions, this predicted that the rate of yield improvement had changed in 1984 (99% confidence interval, 1979–90). The predicted rate of yield improvement prior to this was 65.9 kg ha^{-1} yr^{-1} and since then only 2.9 kg ha^{-1} yr^{-1}.

Table 2 Rate of yield progress (1961–2007) fitted as a single straight line and improvement in fit using a quadratic, linear plus exponential (Lexp) or two straight line regressions

Country	Straight line r^2 (%)	Slope (kg ha^{-1} yr^{-1})	Quadratic r^2 (%)	Lexp r^2 (%)	Two straight lines r^2 (%)
Australia	26.3	16.1	44.5	44.3	No fit
Canada	75.8	15.2	75.4	75.8	No fit
China	90.8	29.7	90.6	90.4	No fit
France	73.2	39.8	73.4	76.0	75.4
Germany	78.5	40.0	78.0	78.2	No fit
India	84.3	15.6	85.8	85.9	No fit
Poland	41.2	21.3	40.9	40.3	41.1
UK	44.0	28.1	51.3	50.0	55.6

Given that the change in the rate of yield improvement is most marked in the United Kingdom, this seems an obvious test case to investigate the cause of the yield stagnation and the prospects for technology to reinstate or improve the previous rate of yield improvement.

There are three possible explanations for the yield stagnation: the environmental potential in terms of resource availability has been reached, genetic improvement has ceased, or crop management has been suboptimal to exploit the yield potential.

5.15.3 Yield Potential

A recent review by Berry and Spink [3] on the yield potential of oilseed rape in the UK environment calculated two potential yields, a conservative estimate and the ultimate yield potential. The review used the average environmental conditions for the United Kingdom in terms of solar radiation, temperature, and rainfall, and assumed a deep soil (>1.5 m) and a high level of management inputs to remove biotic limits to crop growth. The conservative estimate was based on a crop with characteristics already observed in field crops but not necessarily combined into one variety. The ultimate yield potential assumed some genetic improvement outside of currently observed ranges, but only of traits considered to have a reasonable prospect for genetic improvement. In order to assess whether yields have reached their environmental potential, it seems most appropriate here to use the conservative estimate.

The two components of yield potential, seed number per square meter which determines sink size and seed size which is a measure of source capacity, were considered separately, and their potential optimization was based on resource availability and resource-use efficiency.

Seed number has frequently been demonstrated to be the most important yield component. Mendham *et al.* [6] reported that it accounted for 85% of yield variation. It has also been shown that there is a critical phase for pod and seed abortion lasting about 300 °Cd after mid-flowering during which the number of seeds per square meter is determined [6, 7]. Under UK conditions, this equates to about 19–25 days. The survival of pods and seeds has been shown to be related to the amount of radiation intercepted by photosynthetic tissue per flower and per pod, respectively, during this critical period [6, 7]. The radiation intercepted by photosynthetic tissues at this time can be severely reduced by the flower layer, which absorbs and reflects radiation. Flower cover has been measured at 50% during mid-flowering across several varieties [8]. Mendham *et al.* [6] measured a similar sized flower cover of 60%. In a crop with a flower cover of 62% at mid-flowering, the flowers absorbed and reflected 58% of photosynthetically active radiation [8].

The review showed that the components of seed number per square meter, namely, pod number per square meter and seed number/pod, were negatively related. This relationship resulted in an optimum fertile pod number of between 6000 and 8000 pods per square meter to maximize seed number per square meter. It was hypothesized that the canopy size of crops with fewer than 6000 pods per square meter would be too small to trap all of the incident radiation, resulting in fewer seeds set per square meter. Conversely, for crops with more than 8000 pods per square meter, it was hypothesized that the thickness of the flower layer would reduce the amount of radiation reaching the photosynthetic tissues, thus reducing the number of seeds per pod and seeds per square meter.

Clearly, in order to maximize the key determinant of yield, seed number per square meter, the amount of photoassimilate produced during the period of seed determination must be maximized. The review identified a number of methods of achieving this, including advancing flowering date, reducing the amount of light reflected by the flowering layer, and increasing the leaf area.

Advancing flowering into cooler days would increase the number of days required to achieve the 300 °Cd period over which seed number is determined resulting in an increase in the radiation received during the period. Anecdotal evidence indicated that yield losses from frost damage are rare in the United Kingdom and so there appears to be scope to bring flowering forward by about 1 week without significantly increasing the risk of frost damage. It was calculated that if the date of mid-flowering was advanced from 1 May to 23 April, radiation received by the crop during the seed determination period would be increased by about 2%. It was suggested that advancing flowering could be achieved by choosing early developing varieties and/or earlier sowing.

Reducing the amount of light reflected by the flowering layer without reducing the potential pod number could be achieved by reducing the area of individual petals. Apetalous lines have been shown to increase yield in Australia [9], conversely, no yield increase was found under UK conditions [10]. More recent work has indicated that apetalous traits could be advantageous in UK conditions [11]. Flower cover at mid-flowering has been shown to vary by 50% between varieties [8]. This variation was due to both variation in petal size of more than 50% and variation in flower number. In Yates and Stevens [8], the varieties with moderate flower covers of 38–50% had a greater seed yield than varieties with a flower cover of greater than 50%. It was hypothesized that varieties with flower covers of below 38% did not follow this trend because they had insufficient pods. Reducing flower cover from 50% to 38% has been calculated to increase the amount of radiation received by the green tissue by 25%.

Excessive flower cover can also be reduced through agronomic means, for example, by avoiding very early sowing, using lower seed rates, and applying plant growth regulators [12]. Berry and Spink [13] also demonstrated that yield responses due to the application of metconazole as a growth regulator were consistently associated with an increase in seed number per square meter.

During flowering, crops with the optimum pod number have about 2.5 units of leaf area and 1.5 units of stem area [14]. The radiation-use efficiency (RUE) of leaf material is about 3 times greater than that of stem tissue (Major 1977). Therefore, if leaf area can be increased by half a unit by increasing the size and duration of the leaf canopy and the stem area can be reduced by half a unit through stem shortening, the overall RUE of the canopy would increase by about 12%.

Berry and Spink [3] calculated that if flowering could be brought forward by 1 week, flower cover reduced by 25% and leaf area increased by half a unit, then photoassimilate estimated during the period of seed determination could be increased by 39%. Applying this to crops with the optimum number of pods would increase the number of seeds from 93 000 to 130 000 m^{-2}. This seems a realistic target as crops with 130 000 seeds per square meter have been reported in the United Kingdom [10] and Australia [9]. In order to achieve this, each pod would have to contain on average 19 seeds, which is well below the maximum of 30, observed by Mendham and Salisbury [15].

Once the maximum number of seeds has been determined in order to maximize yield, there needs to be an adequate supply of photoassimilate for them to reach their maximum potential size. The seed-filling period from mid-flowering to physiological maturity has been shown to last for 715 °Cd above 4.2 °C in cultivar Victor grown in the United Kingdom [6]. If mid-flowering occurs on 23 April, then using this relationship, physiological maturity will occur on the 1 July in average UK temperatures. The end of seed number determination has been estimated to occur on 18 May. This gives a seed growth period of 43 days. Results from the UK national variety testing system show that scores for the earliness to flowering and earliness to maturity are not well correlated. Moderate–late maturing varieties can either be early or late flowering. Some of this variation may be caused by variation in the duration of flowering, but it seems likely that there must be some genetic variation in the duration of seed filling. Therefore, the review by Berry and Spink [3] predicted that a seed-filling period of 46 days seemed realistic.

Solar RUE during seed filling has been measured at between $0.4\,g\,MJ^{-1}$ (Habekotte 1997) and $0.75\,g\,MJ^{-1}$ [16]. This compares with RUEs before flowering of between $1.2\,g\,MJ^{-1}$ [6] and $1.7\,g\,MJ^{-1}$ [9]. RUE is less during seed filling, because 45% more assimilate is needed to produce each gram of oil-rich seed compared with lingo-cellulosic material [17], and pods have a photosynthetic capacity that is estimated at between 50% and 70% of that of leaves (Major 1977) [18].

Berry and Spink [3] suggested that attaining this RUE target could be further facilitated by using erectophile pods [10] and by avoiding lodging. Lodged crops have been shown to reduce yield by between 16% and 50% (Baylis and Wright 1990) [19]. Lodging compresses the oilseed rape canopy and forces the photosynthetic tissues to adopt a horizontal posture. This reduces the efficiency with which the crop is able to use the available light because the upper pods easily become light-saturated due to their modest photosynthetic capacity and the lower pods experience low levels of light. In oilseed rape, lodging can occur either by anchorage failure or stem buckling/breakage [20]. Lodging risk can be effectively reduced with shorter crops, stiffer stems, and stiffer, longer tap roots [20]. Breeders could exploit semi-dwarfs to reduce lodging risk. There may also be genetic variation in stem stiffness and root properties, as found in wheat by Berry et al. (2003).

The photosynthetic efficiency of stems and pods has been estimated at 37% and 67%, respectively, of that of leaves (Major 1977). Therefore, maximizing the proportion of leaves within the canopy will increase the overall photosynthesis. At early flowering, the optimum canopy structure has been estimated to have a green area index (GAI) of about four 4 [12], of which three units are leaf and one unit is stem. During flowering and seed determination, the leaf area decreases and the pod area increases, resulting in little change in the overall GAI. In less dense canopies at the beginning of seed filling, leaves can make up 30% of the total green area and can persist throughout most of the seed-filling period [21, 22]. Norton et al. [23] reported that there is little change in the green area of the stems and pods during seed filling. Berry and Spink [3] therefore assumed a GAI of an optimum canopy at the start of seed fill of four units and that the leaf area would decline linearly from 30% (1.2 units) to zero at the end of seed filling. Stem and pod areas would remain constant at 1 unit and 1.8 units, respectively. Averaged over the whole seed-filling period, leaves would represent 18% of the total green area, stems 29%, and pods 53%. This compares with pre-flowering when the canopy is made up of 75% leaf area and 25% stem. It was assumed that if the amount of light intercepted was proportional to the area of each tissue component and photosynthetic capacity was as estimated by Major (1977), then the RUE during seed filling was estimated to be 76% of the RUE before flowering. Accounting for the extra energy costs of forming oil-rich seed, reduced this to 53%. The maximum pre-flowering RUE has been measured at $1.7\,g\,MJ^{-1}$ [9], so it was assumed that the postflowering RUE measured by Dreccer et al. [16] of $0.75\,g\,MJ^{-1}$ was a realistic target.

The proportion of incident radiation intercepted at the beginning of seed filling by a crop with a GAI of 4 and extinction coefficient of 0.6 is 0.91. This is expected to decrease to 0.81 at the end of seed filling due to senescence of the leaf canopy. This results in an average proportion of light intercepted during grain filling of 0.86. Given the average amount of incident radiation in the United Kingdom during the proposed 46-day seed-filling period as 868 MJ m^{-2}. If 0.86 of the incident radiation is intercepted by the crop and if an RUE of 0.75 g MJ^{-1} can be achieved, then the amount of pod and seed dry matter accumulated during the seed-filling period will be 560 g m^{-2}. At the start of seed filling, the pods have reached their final length, but pods still accumulate some biomass during seed filling. Pod wall growth accounts for between 5% and 25% of the biomass accumulated during seed filling (Hocking and Mason 1993) [24]. Assuming 5% gives a biomass available for seed growth of 532 g m^{-2}.

Water-soluble carbohydrates, accumulated before flowering and predominantly stored in the stem, can contribute as much as 30% to seed filling in cereals [25]. In oilseed rape however, estimates vary between a negligible amount [22] and 12% [24] of final yield. Stem reserves have been measured at between 40 and 110 g m^{-2} [24]. If stem reserves are assumed to contribute 10% of final yield, then they would have to contribute 532/9 or 59 g m^{-2} of seed yield; however, due to the increased energy content of the seed, 85 g m^{-2} of stem reserves must be relocated to achieve this resulting in a seed biomass of 591 g m^{-2}. A crop yielding 591 g m^{-2} with 130 000 seeds per square meter would have a mean seed dry weight of 4.55 mg, which is well within the normal range of seed weight [15]. At 91% DM, the theoretical potential yield of oilseed rape was therefore calculated in the United Kingdom as 6.49 t ha^{-1} based on genetic variation found in existing germplasm.

This conservative estimate of yield potential of 6.5 t ha^{-1} should be achievable given that all of the characteristics have been reported in the peer-reviewed literature or are realistic for current varieties. The challenge lies with the breeders to combine these traits in the same crop and with agronomists to ensure that crop management is optimal for achieving the characteristics. A comparison of the characteristics of a crop yielding 6.5 t ha^{-1} with characteristics of a crop yielding the UK farm average yield of 3 t ha^{-1} illustrates that several traits must undergo a significant amount of improvement. However, farm yields above 5 t ha^{-1} have been observed and this suggests that parts of farms/fields could be yielding significantly more. Therefore, the estimated potential yield with current germplasm of 6.5 t ha^{-1} does not seem unrealistic.

Thus far, we have considered only solar radiation as a limiting resource. While water supply can be manipulated by the grower, given predictions of reduced water availability and the large financial and environmental costs of irrigation, we will assume the crop should survive on rainfed water supply. Water-use efficiency (WUE) is commonly observed to be about 5 g of carbohydrate dry matter per square meter per liter of water [26]. Given the lower RUE for the production of oil than for lingo-cellulosic material, it seems reasonable to assume a similarly reduced WUE of 3.4 g m^{-2} per liter for the seed [27]. We have assumed that the stem and leaf biomass of a high-yielding crop remain the same as a current average crop at 700 g m^{-2} and the pod biomass is 50% of the seed weight [24]; for a crop yielding 591 g m^{-2}, the total amount of non-seed biomass will be 996 g m^{-2}. This will require 355 mm of rainfall or soil water storage, after accounting for the contribution of stem reserves. The majority of this water will be required between the onset of stem extension in mid-March and canopy senescence on the 1 July. A survey of commercial crops in the United Kingdom in 2006 (unpublished data) showed that the average canopy size in mid-March was 1.52 GAI. Using the relationship between GAI and biomass from Lunn et al. [14] (biomass (g) = GAI × 147.06 − 0.6979), it can be calculated that the average crop biomass in mid-March is 222 g m^{-2}. Then the crop will require 311 mm during the following 3.5 months to produce the remaining 1305 g of biomass. Assuming that the soil is at field capacity in mid-March, the available water capacity of the soil to a depth of 1.5 m would be between 210 and 330 mm, depending on soil type. Using information about the root length density of oilseed rape [28], assuming a similar relationship between root length density and water extraction for cereals [29], it is estimated that oilseed rape roots may extract about 68% of available water to a depth of 1.5 m. This means that oilseed rape crops could extract between 143 and 224 mm of water from the soil. This leaves a shortfall of between 87 and 168 mm that must be supplied by rainfall between mid-March and 2 July. The average monthly rainfall varies between 45 mm in the east of the United Kingdom and 83 mm in the south and west. On light soils such as sandy loams in the east of England, given average rainfall, total water availability would be (143 + 3.5 × 45) 300.5 mm, insufficient to achieve maximum yield from being attained. The maximum yield would be limited to 6.1 t ha^{-1} (91% DM). However, it must be recognized that oilseed rape is mainly grown on heavier, moisture-retentive soils, where even in the east, soil water storage would make up the deficit in water supply.

In addition to estimating the conservative yield potential, Berry and Spink [3] also calculated an 'ultimate' or environmental yield potential, which assumed that plant breeders could improve some plant characteristics outside the range that had been observed. Key characteristics for which improvement would have a large effect on yield include the seed number per square meter, duration of seed filling, RUE during seed filling, and the proportion of pre-flowering assimilate transferred to the seeds.

Reducing the amount of light reflected by the flower canopy was assumed to increase the number of seeds set to at least 150 000 m^{-2}. Seed filling was assumed to increases to 50 days. The RUE of stems and pods was assumed to increase 0.88 g MJ^{-1}. The pre-flowering assimilate contribution to grain yield was assumed to increase to 15% (half of that achieved in wheat). Using these characteristics with the calculations described previously gives an ultimate light-limited yield potential of 9.2 t ha^{-1}.

Using the same WUE as previously, we can calculate that to achieve this yield level would require 393 mm of water supply either from that stored in soil or from rainfall after mid-March. Given this level of light-limited yield potential, it is clear that water availability would become the limiting resource in many areas, with yield potential determined by the water-holding capacity of the soil and thus rainfall. In the east, where rainfall is low, the yield potential would be limited on a greater range of soils, decreasing to 8.65 t ha^{-1} on sandy clay loams, 7.4 t ha^{-1} on clays and silt clays, and to 6.73 t ha^{-1} on sandy loams. Thus, improving water capture or WUE should become crop improvement targets. Oilseed rape is known to have a poorer rooting system at depth than wheat [28, 30]. Low summer rainfall has also been associated with lower oilseed rape yields [31]. Recent work has shown that the application of triazole growth regulators can enhance root length density at depth [13], and genetic differences in the root length density of oilseed rape have been observed between oilseed rape cultivars Apex and Capitol [32]. Cultivar differences in root biomass have been observed in pot experiments [33], further illustrating that differences exist for rooting traits between oilseed rape cultivars and that both cultural and genetic approaches could reduce this limitation to yield potential.

Given that even the conservative yield potential, which uses currently known genetic variation, is twice more than that currently being achieved on farm in the United Kingdom, we must assume that the environmental potential in terms of resource availability has not been reached. This therefore leaves two possibilities: either genetic improvement has ceased or crop management has been suboptimal to exploit the yield potential or possibly a combination of both. We will now examine these two possibilities in turn.

5.15.4 Genetic Constraint to Yield Improvement

There has been a formal variety testing system for new oilseed rape varieties running in the United Kingdom since the 1970s. These official trials have always been run with high levels of inputs, in order that the genetic potential of varieties is fully expressed. The data from these trials can therefore be used to track the rate of genetic improvement. Surveys of commercial farmers show that there is rapid uptake of new varieties [34], so the yield potential of varieties grown on farm should reflect those that are grown in the testing system, albeit with a lag of a couple of years, for varieties to achieve recommendation and widespread seed availability.

The data for all of the individual varieties were analyzed and best described by a linear plus exponential curve fit ($p < 0.001$, $r^2 = 84.9\%$), which showed that the yield potential of new varieties has increased steadily; however, the rate of improvement has slowed from 139 kg ha^{-1} yr^{-1} in the late 1970s to 17 kg ha^{-1} yr^{-1} in the mid-2000s (**Figure 3**). Despite this decline in the apparent rate of genetic improvement, it is still much greater than the apparent rate of yield improvement of the commercial crop at 2.9 kg ha^{-1} yr^{-1}.

This analysis shows that the rate of genetic improvement is slowing, and that even if grown in the well-managed conditions of an official testing system, the yield of the best varieties (which does not get above 5 t ha^{-1}) is still well below the environmental potential calculated previously. Reinstating or improving on the previous rate of genetic improvement is a definite target for technological intervention to increase crop productivity, and possible techniques to achieve this will be discussed later. However, what is obvious from this analysis is that there is a growing gap between the yields achieved in the official variety testing system and on-farm crop yields, whereas in the late 1970s and early 1980s, the yields were comparable. This possibly indicates that there is a growing deficit in the husbandry of commercial crops that is limiting the realization of the yield potential of existing varieties.

5.15.5 Crop Management Constraint to Yield Improvement

Given the difference in yield between commercial crops and the variety testing system, comparing the husbandry used should provide an indication of any crop management constraints to yield improvement. The differences in agronomy between the UK recommended list testing system and farm crops were identified by Spink and Berry [35] as shorter rotations, less-intensive cultivation, earlier drilling, higher seed rate, fewer fungicide applications, less sulfur, and possibly less nitrogen fertilizer.

Shorter rotations have been shown to increase disease pressure and yield loss due to disease. In a comparison of oilseed rape grown 1 year in 2 compared with 1 year in 3, Sieling and Christen [36] reported an average yield loss of about 0.5 t ha^{-1}. Recently, closer rotations of oilseed rape have become more common with a number of growers moving to a rotation, which alternates wheat and oilseed rape due to the relative decline in profitability of other combinable crop options, whereas in 1990, only 8% of the crop was grown 1 in 3 [37]. In contrast, the official testing system trials are grown on fields with longer rotations to reduce the risk of 'volunteer' plants of varieties growing from seeds shed by previous crops.

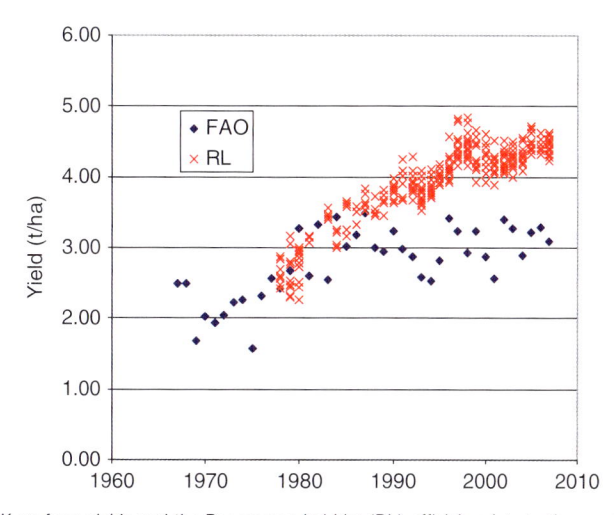

Figure 3 Comparison of FAOStat UK on-farm yields and the Recommended List (RL) official variety testing system.

The vast majority of official variety trials are established following plow-based cultivations as trial drills do not perform well in the presence of residues of the previous crop. In contrast, over recent years an increasing proportion of the commercial crop in the United Kingdom has been established following noninversion shallow cultivations or no cultivation, for example, 'Autocast'. Although many authors [38, 39] report yields from minimum cultivations to be similar to plow-based cultivations, it is likely that when used commercially, minimal cultivations may result in more variable crops, or be used in less than ideal conditions, thus limiting yield potential.

Commercially, crops tend to be drilled earlier, and in some cases, at higher seed rates than the variety testing system, due to the time delay in collating all of the varieties for the trials. Early drilling and high seed rates can result in over-large crops with too high flower number and consequent yield reductions unless subsequent agronomy is adjusted accordingly.

The protocol for the variety trials is designed to limit disease levels to less than 5% in even the most susceptible varieties. For example, the protocol for the 2008/09 trials specified five compulsory fungicide applications applying a total of 5.75 full label rates of product with an option for a further two applications. In contrast, Garthwaite et al. [40] reported that in 2006, commercial crops received on average 2.3 fungicide applications with rates of the main products being between half and a full label rate. Disease-induced yield loss may therefore account for some of the yield deficit in commercial crops.

Nitrogen fertilizer application to oilseed rape have declined dramatically over the recent years with average application rate in 2008 being 194 kg ha^{-1} compared to about 275 kg ha^{-1} in the early 1980s [41]. These much lower nitrogen fertilizer inputs may be restricting the expression of the higher yield potential of more modern varieties; however, this does not necessarily explain the difference between commercial and variety testing yields, as the variety trials receive nitrogen applications according to standard recommendation systems [42].

5.15.6 Genetic Approaches

Recent advancements in plant breeding and biotechnology provide plant breeders with the ability to expand the genetic base of oilseed rape through either large-scale mutagenesis programs or through the transfer of specific homo/heterologous gene(s) into the *Brassica* genome, affording them the opportunity to rectify the loss of genetic improvement as illustrated in **Figure 3**.

The transfer of heterologous genes using *Agrobacterium tumefaciens*-mediated transformation (ATMT) has seen the production of transgenic oilseed rape with enhanced resistance to *Sclerotinia sclerotiorum* via overexpression of the mitogen-activated protein kinase 4 gene [43] or the barley-derived oxalate oxidase gene [44], transgenic *B. rapa* with increased tolerance to soft rot disease via overexpression of the *Bacillus* spp. N-acyl-homoserine lactonase gene [45], and transgenic *B. juncea* modified to arrest Alternaria leaf spot infection [46]. Separately, the fatty acid composition of *B. napus* has been significantly modified following transgene insertion via ATMT [47], with reports detailing reductions in total saturated fatty acid content [48], increased oleic acid (C18:1) levels from 53% to 73% [49], and the possibility that super HEAR oilseed rape could eventually be produced [47]. Additional efforts have been focussed on the transformation of *B. napus* with improved nitrogen-use efficiency (NUE). Yet, to be commercialized, the NUE phenotype was generated through the overexpression of barley alanine aminotransferase [50]. Requiring up to 40% less nitrogen to achieve yields equivalent to non-GM conventional varieties, a life-cycle assessment of the potential environmental impact of growing NUE oilseed rape compared to a conventional variety predicted energy savings of up to 22% (Strange *et al.* 2008).

The significance of seed number per square meter has already been detailed. Efforts to exert strong genetic control over oilseed's propensity for premature pod shatter and subsequent seed loss have benefited from the common ancestry of *Brassica* spp. and the model plant species *Arabidopsis thaliana*. The genetic processes underlying pod maturation have been dissected, and a model of the pathway describing the responsibility and interactions of the SHATTERPROOF [51], FRUITFULL [52], and INDEHISCENT genes has been detailed [53]. Subsequent knowledge transfer to *Brassica* has delivered a seed-loss-proof phenotype in transgenic *B. juncea* [54].

Capitalizing on the high-sequence conservation within the protein-coding regions of the genomes of *Brassica* species with those of *A. thaliana*, Li *et al.* have reported on candidate genes of agronomic importance (e.g., flowering time and leaf morphological traits) within the *B. rapa* genome, which can be inferred from a mapped region of *A. thaliana* [55]. Similarly, the importance of *B. napus* WRI1 on oil content and seed mass was demonstrated through an overexpression of the WRL1 sequence in *Arabidopsis* [56]. In contrast, molecular mechanisms governing the adaptability of root systems to changing environmental conditions are poorly understood. Although oilseed rape roots descend to 120–180 cm (Gabrielle *et al.* 1998) [28], the crop has been shown to have a lower root length density than wheat particularly at depth (Kjellstrom 1991) [28]. Genetic differences in the root length density of oilseed rape have been observed between cultivars [32] and similarly for root biomass [33], further illustrating that differences exist for rooting traits between oilseed rape cultivars. Also looking at *Arabidopsis*, recent reports highlight the significance of the chitinase-like protein CTL1, which plays a role in altering root system architecture in response to multiple environmental conditions [57].

For *Brassica* breeders, the sequencing and mapping of the nuclear genome of *Arabidopsis* was a defining moment due to the high level of relatedness between *Brassica* and *Arabidopsis*. Although *Arabidopsis* has a small genome (~146 Mb) with relatively little repetitive DNA and a high gene density [58], the diploid *Brassica* genome is significantly larger with a lower gene density (*B. rapa*, 717 Mb) [59]. Physical mapping and microsynteny analysis by nucleotide sequencing has identified 33 large syntenic regions on a comparative map of the *B. rapa* and *Arabidopsis* genomes [60]. Also, the availability of genome sequences from several plant models enables the identification and cloning of specific sequences based on a comparative genomics approach. Mun *et al.* [61] identified 92 nonredundant nucleotide-binding site (NBS)-encoding resistance genes within the *B. rapa* euchromatic genome sequence, representing a novel suite of disease resistance with potential application across the *Brassica* family. A comprehensive resource base is available to *Arabidopsis* researchers (http://www.tair.org), with similar initiatives having been established (albeit on a much smaller scale) for *Brassica* spp; for example, the *Brassica* database (http://brassica.bbsrc.ac.uk/BrassicaDB/) and the *B. rapa* genome sequencing project (http://www.brassica-rapa.org/BRGP/status.jsp), which is ongoing.

Increasing genetic variation can also be achieved through the chemical-based mutagenic treatment of oilseed rape seed. Using alkylating agents such as ethyl methanesulfonate (EMS) and diethyl sulfate (DES) to produce libraries of mutant individuals, lines with improved disease resistance [62, 63] and herbicide tolerance (described in Tan *et al.* 2005) have been isolated. Imidazolinone (IMI) herbicides control weed populations through inhibition of amino acid synthesis. The imposition of two amino acid changes as a result of chemical mutagenesis to acetohydroxyacid synthase, a critical enzyme for the biosynthesis of branched-chain amino acids in plants, precipitated the development of herbicide-tolerant oilseed rape under the trade name Clearfield™ Canola. Now accounting for over 20% of the oilseed acreage sown in Canada, the next generation of Clearfield material has been developed via the patented Rapid Trait Development System (RTDS™). RTDS (or direct mutagenesis) capitalizes on the cell's natural process of gene repair to correct coding mistakes in gene sequences specific for a desired trait. Developed as a result of large-scale genome mapping initiatives, RTDS has facilitated the production of IMI-tolerant winter oilseed rape, which is anticipated for release in 2012 for the European market.

The identification of natural spontaneous mutations within the oilseed rape genome is also possible, but owing to the narrow genetic base of oilseed rape, it can be logistically challenging and time-consuming to successfully identify required phenotypes. That said, natural variation within an old German oilseed rape cultivar (cv. Liho) led to the identification of low erucic acid mutants, which provided a foundation for the development of the first low C22:1 oilseed rape variety (cv. Oro) in 1968 [64]. Conversely, industrial usage of rapeseed oil as a lubricant is reliant on a high erucic acid content within the seed oil (termed HEAR oilseed rape) in order to reduce the cost of postharvest purification. This was achieved through the characterization of high C22:1 germplasm in Swedish rape, which was introduced into breeding programs to develop HEAR material with low glucosinolate levels but strong agronomic performance. Oilseed rape cultivar Mercury (54% C22:1) was registered in 1992 [65], and further to that cultivars Castor [66] and MilleniUM01 [67] with improved performance and 55% C22:1 content have been bred.

Going forward, the necessity to improve the field performance of oilseed rape cannot be overstated. Advancements in biotechnology can assist in achieving these goals, be it through the provision of marker-assisted selection (MAS) strategies in breeding through to the direct transfer of gene(s) into a target genome via transgenesis. Both processes will afford the early and efficient selection of traits of interest, thereby allowing the 'stacking' of genetically distinct components of the same trait and potentially shortening the breeding process by several years. While the transformation of spring *B. rapa* and *B. napus* using the soil-borne pathogen *A. tumefaciens* was first reported in 1989 [68], multiple variants of the protocol have expanded its remit into winter varieties [69], which improved transformation efficiencies and decreased the influence of genotype dependency [70]. But the process of ATMT as utilized by the community for complementation analysis is tightly controlled through a myriad of patents [71]. In an attempt to bypass the challenge of having to negotiate with patent holders, Broothaerts *et al.* [72] described the functionality and availability of their TransBacter technology through the BiOS licensing system of CAMBIA [73]. Although they did not specifically include *Brassica* spp. in their research, they showed that non-*Agrobacterium* strains from the Rhizobia family (*Sinorhizobium meliloti*, *Rhizobium* spp. NGR234, *Mesorhizobium loti*) have the ability to transform tobacco (*Nicotiana tabaccum*), rice (*Oryza sativa*), and significantly *A. thaliana*, while bypassing all existing patent claims [71, 72].

5.15.7 Conclusions

The data presented in this chapter demonstrate that for oilseed rape grown in the United Kingdom, a yield of 6.5 t ha^{-1} should be achievable compared with the average actual farm yield of 3 ha^{-1}. The ultimate yield potential could be as high as 9.2 ha^{-1} if water capture or WUE can be improved. Interestingly, a threefold increase in global oilseed rape yield was achieved between 1961 and 2007. Looking still more broadly, this review of the prospects and techniques for the improvement of yield in oilseed rape demonstrates the approach that must be applied for any crop species in any environment.

First, an understanding of the resource availability in the region in question must be well understood. An understanding of the actual and potential temporal resource capture and conversion efficiency of the crop species in question is then needed to identify the resource most likely to be limiting yield formation. Based on this analysis, physiological approaches can then be identified to overcome limitations to growth and/or partitioning of growth into usable biomass. The complexity of this analysis will of course be dependent on the crop species in question, but in most cases will be less convoluted than that required for oilseed rape.

The most immediate solutions to overcoming growth restrictions will undoubtedly be the changes to the agronomy or husbandry of the crop; however, the most effective solutions are likely to arise through genetic improvement. It is clear that over recent years, the range of genetic approaches and the rate of progress that can be made in crop improvement have increased significantly compared with the conventional breeding approaches available only 20 years ago. Whereas the potential for the application of these techniques is arguably most advanced in *Brassica* species due to their close relationship with *A. thaliana*, similar advances are rapidly being made in other crop species.

Given the large potential for yield improvement in oilseed rape in the UK environment, which is predominantly light-limited, it seems reasonable to assume that similar increases in yield potential could be realized in other crops in similar environments if appropriate technology were brought to bear. The prospects for yield improvement in water-limited environments are, however, likely to be less rewarding without the large-scale manipulation of water supply.

References

[1] Hay RKM (1995) Harvest index: A review of its use in plant-breeding and crop physiology. *Annals of Applied Biology* 126: 197–216.
[2] Mittelbach M and Remschmidt C (2004) Biodiesel the comprehensive handbook. *Am Blumenhang* 27: A-8010. Graz, Austria: Martin Mittelbach.
[3] Berry PM and Spink JH (2006) A physiological analysis of oilseed rape yields: Past and future. *Journal of Agricultural Science, Cambridge* 144: 381–392.
[4] Downey RK and Rimmer SR (1993) Agronomic improvement on oilseed *Brassicas*. *Advances in Agronomy* 50: 1–65.
[5] FAOStat (2009) www.faostat.fao.org
[6] Mendham NJ, Shipway PA, and Scott RK (1981) The effects of delayed sowing and weather on growth, development and yield of winter oilseed rape (*Brassica napus*). *Journal of Agricultural Science, Cambridge* 96: 389–416.
[7] Leterme P (1988) Modelisation du fonctionnement du peuplement de colza d'hiver en fin de cycle: Elaboration des composantes finales du rendement. *Colza: Physiologie et Elaboaration du Rendement CETIOM*. pp. 124–129. Paris, France.
[8] Yates DJ and Steven MD (1987) Reflection and absorption of solar radiation by flowering canopies of oilseed rape (*Brassica napus* L.). *Journal of Agricultural Science, Cambridge* 109: 495–502.
[9] Rao MSS, Mendham NJ, and Buzza GC (1991) Effect of apetalous flower character on radiation distribution in the crop canopy, yield and its components of oilseed rape (*Brassica napus*). *Journal of Agricultural Science, Cambridge* 117: 189–196.
[10] Fray MJ, Evans EJ, Lydiate DJ, and Arthur AE (1996) Physiological assessment of apetalous flowers and erectophile pods in oilseed rape (*Brassica napus*). *Journal of Agricultural Science, Cambridge* 127: 193–200.
[11] Evans EJ, Gemmill JM, Werner CP, and Willimas E (2003) Physiological factors contributing to yield enhancement in winter apetalous oilseed rape (*Brassic napus*). In: Sprensen H (ed.) *Proceedings of the 11th International Rapeseed Congress*, vol. 3, p. 804. Copenhagen, Denmark.
[12] Lunn GD, Spink JH, Wade A, and Clare RW (2003) Spring remedial treatments to improve canopy structure and yield in oilseed rape. HGCA Project Report No. OS64. London, UK: Home-Grown Cereals Authority.
[13] Berry PM and Spink JH (2009) Understanding the effect of a triazole with anti-gibberellin activity on the growth and yield of oilseed rape (*Brassica napus*). *Journal of Agricultural Science* 147: 273–285.
[14] Lunn GD, Spink JH, Stokes DT, *et al.* (2001) Canopy management in winter oilseed rape. HGCA Project Report No. OS49. London, UK: Home-Grown Cereals Authority.
[15] Mendham NJ and Salisbury PA (1995) Physiology: Crop development, growth and yield. In: Kimber DS and McGregor DI (eds.) *Brassica Oilseeds*, pp. 11–63. Oxford, UK: CAB International.
[16] Dreccer MF, Schapendonk AHCM, Slafer GA, and Rabbinge R (2000) Comparative response of wheat and oilseed rape to nitrogen supply: Absorption and utilisation efficiency of radiation and nitrogen during the reproductive stages determining yield. *Plant and Soil* 220: 189–205.
[17] Sinclair TR and de Witt CT (1975) Photosynthate and nitrogen requirements for seed production by various crops. *Science* 189: 565–567.
[18] Gammelvind LH, Schjoerring JK, Mogensen CR, *et al.* (1996) Photosynthesis in leaves and siliques of winter oilseed rape (*Brassica napus* L.). *Plant and Soil* 186: 227–236.
[19] Armstrong EL and Nicol HI (1991) Reducing height and lodging in rapeseed with growth regulators. *Australian Journal of Experimental Agriculture* 31: 245–250.
[20] Goodman AM, Crook MJ, and Ennos AR (2001) Anchorage mechanics of the tap root system of winter sown oilseed rape (*Brassica napus* L.). *Annals of Botany* 87: 397–404.
[21] McWilliam SC, Stafford JA, Scott RK, *et al.* (1995) The relationship between canopy structure and yield in oilseed rape. In: Murphy D (ed.) *Proceedings of the 9th International Rapeseed Congress*, vol. 2, pp. 485–490. Cambridge, UK.
[22] Stafford JA (1996) The Effects of Prochloraz on the Growth and Yield of Oil Seed Rape. PhD Thesis, University of Nottingham.
[23] Norton G, Bilsborrow PE, and Shipway PA (1991) Comparative physiology of divergent types of winter rapeseed. In: McGregor DI (ed.) *Proceedings of the 8th International Rapeseed Congress*, pp. 578–582. Saskatoon, Canada.
[24] Habekotté B (1993) Quantitative analysis of pod formation, seed set and seed filling in winter oilseed rape (*Brassica napus* L.) under field conditions. *Field Crops Research* 35: 21–33.
[25] Foulkes MJ, Scott RK, and Sylvester-Bradley R (2002) The ability of wheat cultivars to withstand drought in UK conditions: Formation of grain yield. *Journal of Agricultural Science* 138: 153–169.
[26] Green CF, Vaidyanathan LV, and Hough MN (1983) An analysis of the relationship between potential evapotranspiration and dry matter accumulation for winter wheat. *Journal of Agricultural Science, Cambridge* 100: 351–358.
[27] Penning de Vries FWT, Jansen DM, ten Berge HFM, and Bakema A (1989) Simulation of Ecophysiological Processes of Growth in Several Annual Crops. In *Simulation Monographs 29*. Wageningen, The Netherlands: Pudoc.
[28] Barraclough PB (1989) Root growth, macro-nutrient uptake dynamics and soil fertility requirements of a high-yielding winter oilseed rape crop. *Plant and Soil* 119: 59–70.
[29] King J, Gay A, Sylvester-Bradley R, *et al.* (2004) Modelling cereal root systems for water and nitrogen capture: Towards and economic optimum. *Annals of Botany* 91: 383–390.
[30] Barraclough PB and Leigh RA (1984) The growth and activity of winter wheat roots in the field: The effect of sowing date and soil type on root growth of high yielding crops. *Journal of Agricultural Science, Cambridge* 103: 59–74.
[31] Blake JJ and Spink JH (2005) Variability of rooting in oilseed rape. *Aspects of Applied Biology* 73: 195–198.
[32] Kamh M, Wiesler F, Ulas A, and Horst WJ (2005) Root growth and N-uptake activity of oilseed rape (*Brassica napus* L.) cultivars differing in nitrogen efficiency. *Journal of Plant Nutrition and Soil Science* 168: 130–137.
[33] Lou YS, Liang Y, Yang Y, and Bell RW (2003) Effect of fertilization on plant growth and nutrient uptake in oilseed rape under varying boron supply. *Communications in Soil Science and Plant Analysis* 34: 1059–1075.
[34] Sylvester-Bradley R, Lunn G, Foulkes J, *et al.* (2002) Management strategies for high yields of cereals and oilseed rape. *Proceedings of HGCA Conference 'Agronomic Intelligence: The Basis for Profitable Production'*. pp. 9.1–8.17. Home-Grown Cereals Authority, Coventry.
[35] Spink JH and Berry PM (2005) Yield of UK oilseed rape: Physiological and technological constraints, and expectations of progress to 2010. *Proceedings of the 61st Easter School*. pp. 311–334. Nottingham University, UK: University of Nottingham Press.
[36] Sieling K and Christen O (1997) Effect of preceding crop combination and N fertilization on yield of six oilseed rape cultivars (*Brassica napus* L.). *European Journal of Agronomy* 7: 301–306.
[37] Turner JA and Hardwick NV (1995) The rise and fall of *Sclerotinia sclerotiorum*, the cause of stem rot of oilseed rape in the UK. In: Murphy D (ed.) *Proceedings of the 9th International Rapeseed Congress*, vol. 2, pp. 640–642. Cambridge, UK.
[38] Bowerman P, Chambers BJ, and Jones AE (1995) Winter oilseed rape establishment methods on clay soils. In: Murphy D (ed.) *Proceedings of the 9th International Rapeseed Congress*, vol. 2, pp. 220–222. Cambridge, UK.
[39] Sauzet G, Reau R, and Palleau J (2003) Evaluation of oilseed rape crop managements with minimum tillage. In: Sprensen H (ed.) *Proceedings of the 11th International Rapeseed Congress*, vol. 3, pp. 863–864. Copenhagen, Denmark.
[40] Garthwaite DG, Thomas MR, Anderson H, and Stoddart H (2006) Pesticide usage survey. DEFRA Report No. 2002. London, UK: Department for the Environment Food and Rural Affairs.
[41] Thomas M (2009) *British Survey of Fertiliser Practice, Fertiliser Used on Farm Crops in 2008*. London, UK: Defra.
[42] Anon (2000) *Fertiliser Recommendations for Agricultural and Horticultural Crops*, 7th edn., MAFF (now DEFRA) Reference Book 209. London, UK: HMSO.
[43] Wang Z,, Mao H,, Dong C,, *et al.* (2009) Overexpression of *Brassica napus* MPK4 enhances resistance to *Sclerotinia sclerotiorum* in oilseed rape. *Molecular Plant-Microbe Interactions* 22: 235–244.

[44] Dong X, Ji R, Guo X, *et al.* (2008) Expressing a gene encoding wheat oxalate oxidase enhances resistance to *Sclerotinia sclerotiorum* in oilseed rape (*Brassica napus*) *Planta* 228: 331–340.
[45] Vanjildorj E, Song SY, Yang ZH, *et al.* (2009) Enhancement of tolerance to soft rot disease in the transgenic Chinese cabbage (*Brassica rapa* L. ssp. pekinensis) inbred line, Kenshin. *Plant Cell Reports* 28: 1581–1591.
[46] Mondal KK, Bhattacharya RC, Koundal KR, and Chatterjee SC (2007) Transgenic Indian mustard (*Brassica juncea*) expressing tomato glucanase leads to arrested growth of Alternaria brassicae. *Plant Cell Reports* 26: 247–252.
[47] Scarth R and Tang J (2006) Modification of *Brassica* oil using conventional and transgenic approaches. *Crop Science* 46: 1225–1236.
[48] Dehesh K (2004) Nucleic Acid Sequences Encoding Beta-Ketoacyl ACp Synthase and Uses Thereof. US Patent 20,040,132,189.
[49] Sivaraman I, Arumugam N, Sodhi YS, and Gupta A (2004) Development of high oleic acid and low linoleic acid transgenics in a zero erucic acid *Brassica juncea* L. line by antisense suppression of the fad2 gene. *Molecular Breeding* 13: 365–375.
[50] Good AG, Johnson SJ, De Pauw M, *et al.* (2007) Engineering nitrogen use efficiency with alanine aminotransferase. *Canadian Journal of Botany* 85: 252–262.
[51] Liljegren SJ, Ditta GS, Eshed Y, *et al.* (2000) SHATTERPROOF MADS-box genes control seed dispersal in *Arabidopsis*. *Nature* 404: 766–770.
[52] Ferrándiz C, Liljegren SJ, and Yanofsky MF (2000) Negative regulation of the SHATTERPROOF genes by FRUITFULL during *Arabidopsis* fruit development. *Science* 289: 436–438.
[53] Liljegren SJ, Roeder AHK, Kempin SA, *et al.*(2004) Control of fruit patterning in *Arabidopsis* by INDEHISCENT. *Cell* 116: 843–853.
[54] Østergaard L, Kempin SA, Bies D, *et al.* (2006) Pod shatter-resistant *Brassica* fruit produced by ectopic expression of the FRUITFULL gene. *Plant Biotechnology Journal* 4: 45–51.
[55] Li F, Kitashiba H, Inaba K, and Nishio T (2009) A *Brassica rapa* linkage map of EST-based SNP markers for identification of candidate genes controlling flowering time and leaf morphological traits. *DNA Research* 16: 311–323.
[56] Liu J, Hua W, Zhan G, et al. (In press) Increasing seed mass and oil content in transgenic *Arabidopsis* by the overexpression of wri1-like gene from *Brassica napus*. *Plant Physiology and Biochemistry.*
[57] Hermans C, Porco S, Verbruggen N, and Bush DR (2009) Chitinase-like protein CTL1 plays a role in altering root system architecture in response to multiple environmental conditions. *Plant Physiology* 109149849.
[58] Bevan M and Walsh S (2005) The *Arabidopsis* genome: A foundation for plant research. *Genome Research* 15: 1632–1642.
[59] Qiu D, Gao M, Li G, and Quiros C (2009) Comparative sequence analysis for *Brassica oleracea* with similar sequences in *B. rapa* and *Arabidopsis thaliana*. *Plant Cell Reports* 28: 649–661.
[60] Choi SR, Teakle GR, and Plaha P (2007) The reference genetic linkage map for the multinational *Brassica rapa* genome sequencing project. *Theoretical and Applied Genetics* 115: 777–792.
[61] Mun JH, Yu HJ, Park S, and Park BS (2009) Genome-wide identification of NBS-encoding resistance genes in *Brassica rapa*. *Molecular Genetics and Genomics* October 17 [Epub ahead of print].
[62] Liu S, Wang W, Zhang J, *et al.* (2005) In vitro mutation and selection of doubled-haploid *Brassica napus* lines with improved resistance to *Sclerotinia sclerotiorum*. *Plant Cell Reports* 24: 133–144.
[63] Mullins E, Quinlan C, and Jones P (1999) Isolation of mutants exhibiting altered resistance to *Sclerotinia sclerotiorum* from small M2 populations of an oilseed rape (*Brassica napus*) variety. *European Journal of Plant Pathology* 105: 465–475.
[64] Stefansson BR and Downey RK (1995) Harvest of gold: The history of field crop breeding in Canada. In: Slinkard AE and Knott DR (eds.) *Rapeseed.* 140–152 pp. Saskatchewan, Canada: University Extension Press.
[65] Scarth R, McVetty PBE, and Rimmer SR (1995) Mercury high erucic acid, low glucosinolate summer rape. *Canadian Journal of Plant Science* 75: 205–206.
[66] McVetty PBE, Rimmer SR, and Scarth R (1998) Castor high erucic acid, low glucosinolate summer rape. *Canadian Journal of Plant Science* 78: 305–306.
[67] McVetty PBE, Scarth R, and Rimmer SR (1999) MillenniUM01 summer rape. *Canadian Journal of Plant Science* 79: 251–252.
[68] De Block M, De Brouwer D, and Tenning P (1989) Transformation of *Brassica napus* and *Brassica oleracea* using *Agrobacterium tumefaciens* and the expression of the bar and neo genes in the transgenic plants. *Plant Physiology* 91: 694–701.
[69] Thomzik JE (1995) *Agrobacterium*-mediated transformation of stem disks from oilseed rape (*Brassica napus* L.). *Methods in Molecular Biology.* vol. 44, pp. 79–85.
[70] Bhalla PL and Singh MB (2008) *Agrobacterium*-mediated transformation of *Brassica napus* and *Brassica oleracea*. *Nature Protocols* 3: 181–189.
[71] Nottenburg C and Rodriguez CR (eds.) (2007) *Agrobacterium-Mediated Gene Transfer: A Lawyer's Perspective.* 750 pp. New York: Springer.
[72] Broothaerts W, Mitchell HJ, Weir B, *et al.* (2005) Gene transfer to plants by diverse species of bacteria. *Nature* 433: 629–632.
[73] Cambia (2009) http://www.cambia.org/daisy/cambia/home.html (accessed 7 December 2009).

Further Reading

Flanagan P, Meade C, and Mullins E (2008) Evaluating management strategies to mitigate the impact of seed-mediated gene flow. Presented at Implications of GM-Crop Cultivation at Large Spatial Scales. *Proceedings of the GMLS Conference 2008.* Bremen, Germany.
Lutman PJW (1993) The occurrence and persistence of volunteer oilseed rape (*Brassica napus*). *Aspects of Applied Biology* 35: 29–36.
Major DJ (1975). Influence of seed size on yield and yield components of rape. *Agronomy Journal* 69: 541–543.
Pekrun C, Lutman PJW, and Lopez-Granados F (1996) Population dynamics of volunteer rape and possible means of control. *Proceedings of the Second International Weed Control Congress.* Copenhagen, Denmark.

5.16 Renewable Fuels: An Automotive Perspective

RJ Pearson and JWG Turner, Lotus Engineering, Norwich, UK

© 2010 Lotus Cars Limited. Published by Elsevier Ltd. All rights reserved.

5.16.1	Introduction	305
5.16.1.1	Causes for Concern	305
5.16.1.2	What Are the Options?	307
5.16.2	Competing Transport Energy Carriers	308
5.16.2.1	Electrification of the Vehicle Fleet	308
5.16.2.2	Hydrogen	310
5.16.2.3	Biofuels	313
5.16.2.3.1	Vehicle manufacturers' perspective	313
5.16.2.3.2	Overview of production methods	314
5.16.3	Alcohol as Fuels for ICEs	316
5.16.3.1	Physicochemical Properties	317
5.16.3.2	Low-Carbon-Number Alcohols as Fuels for SI Engines	319
5.16.3.3	Low-Carbon-Number Alcohols as Fuels for Compression-Ignition Engines	322
5.16.3.4	Safety Aspects of Alcohol Fuels	323
5.16.3.4.1	General safety aspects of methanol as a fuel	323
5.16.3.4.2	Ingestion	324
5.16.3.4.3	Skin/eye contact	324
5.16.3.4.4	Inhalation	325
5.16.3.4.5	Toxic emissions when burned	325
5.16.3.4.6	Fire safety	325
5.16.3.4.7	Groundwater leakage	326
5.16.3.4.8	Concluding remarks on safety	326
5.16.4	The Biomass Limit and Beyond	327
5.16.4.1	The Biomass Limit	327
5.16.4.2	Beyond the Biomass Limit – Electrofuels	328
5.16.4.2.1	Concentrating CO_2 directly from the atmosphere	330
5.16.4.2.2	Renewable liquid electrofuels from atmospheric CO_2	331
5.16.5	Technologies to Increase the Use of Alcohols in the Vehicle Fleet	332
5.16.5.1	Tri-Flex-Fuel Vehicles	332
5.16.5.2	Ternary Blends to Extend the Displacement of Gasoline by Alcohols	333
5.16.6	Sustainable Organic Fuels for Transport	335
5.16.7	Conclusions	338
References		338
Further Reading		342

5.16.1 Introduction

5.16.1.1 Causes for Concern

Concerns regarding the effects of anthropogenic CO_2 emissions on the Earth's climate and security of supply are the principal factors motivating the adoption of alternatives to fossil fuels. With almost 1.5 billion mobile emitters globally, including motorcycles and mopeds [1], over 95% dependency on oil [2] and even greater dependency on fossil fuels in general, transport is perhaps the most troublesome sector to decarbonize. It is responsible for 23% of greenhouse gas (GHG) emissions, of which 73% is generated by road transport, and its contribution is projected to increase faster than any other, with a projected growth of 80% by 2030 [3]. The increasing dependence of many developed nations on external oil together with concomitant price instability gives rise to anxiety over security of supply but resorting to unconventional feedstocks such as oil sands or coal exacerbates the CO_2 problem.

Figure 1 illustrates the origin of the concern over security of feedstock supply. It shows that although the United States is responsible for nearly 25% of the global consumption of petroleum (i.e., crude oil and oil-based products including crude oil, lease condensate, unfinished oil, refined petroleum products, natural gas plant liquids, and non-hydrocarbon compounds blended into finished petroleum products), it contributes only 8% of production and has less than 2% of global oil reserves. The consumption levels of China and India, standing at 9% and 3%, respectively, in 2006 [1] and rapidly growing thereafter, are supported by indigenous oil reserves of less than 2% and 1%, respectively, of the global total. Conversely, the Organization of Petroleum Exporting Countries (OPEC) consumes only 9% of petroleum, produces 41%, and holds 69% of the oil reserves. At an oil price of

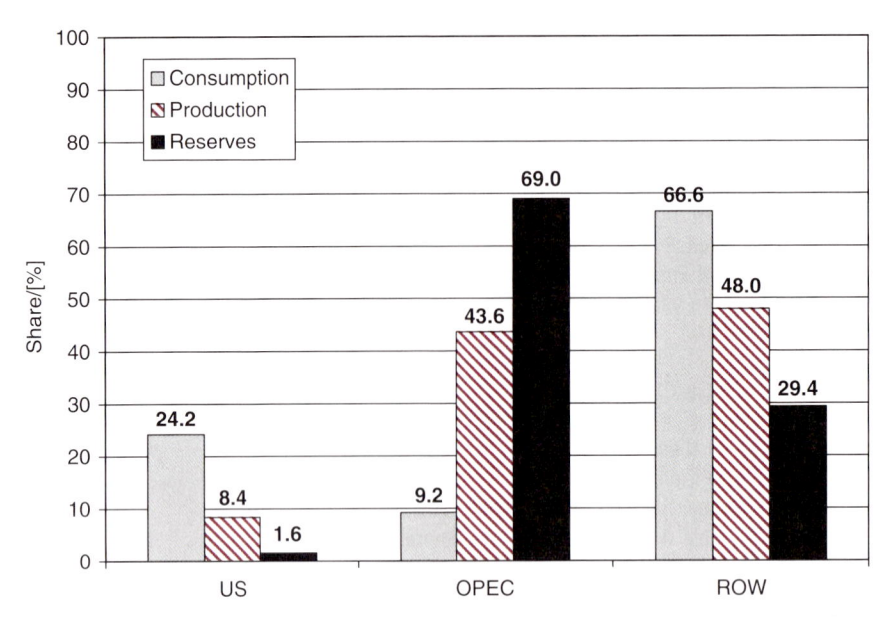

Figure 1 Proportion of petroleum consumption, production, and oil reserves for United States, OPEC, and Rest of World (ROW) – 2007. Based on Davis SC, Diegel SW, and Boundy RG (2009) *Transportation Energy Data Book: Edition 28.* ORNL-6984. Center for Transportation Analysis, Energy and Transportation Science Division, Oak Ridge National Laboratory, Tennessee, USA. Prepared for the Office of Energy Efficiency and Renewable Energy, US Department of Energy [2].

$100 per barrel over the year, the 11 million barrels of oil per day imported by the United States in 2008 [2] resulted in an external transfer of wealth amounting to over $400 billion; OPEC's revenues from oil exceeded $1 trillion in the same year.

Up to the early 1970s, Western investor-owned oil companies controlled directly or indirectly almost all of the world's oil production and reserves, but despite their already existing vast revenues (over $1.6 trillion for the top six companies in 2007), they now control less than 10% of reserves. ExxonMobil, the largest investor-owned company in the world, is only the fourteenth largest oil company defined in terms of oil reserves [1]. In 2006, companies owned or claimed by their national governments controlled 80% of global oil reserves, with a further 14% controlled by Russian companies and joint ventures between Western and national oil companies. Western investor-owned companies controlled only the remaining 6% outright [1]. This lack of control over feedstock supply and prices has led to legislation such as the recent US Energy Independence and Security Act, mandating increased supply of alcohol fuels [4].

Growth in national demand for transportation is closely correlated with growth in gross domestic product (GDP) per capita, as shown in **Figure 2**. China has sustained growth in GDP of almost 10% since the beginning of economic reforms in 1978. With a population growth rate of only about 0.5%, this growth rate doubles GDP per capita approximately every 8 years. While China still

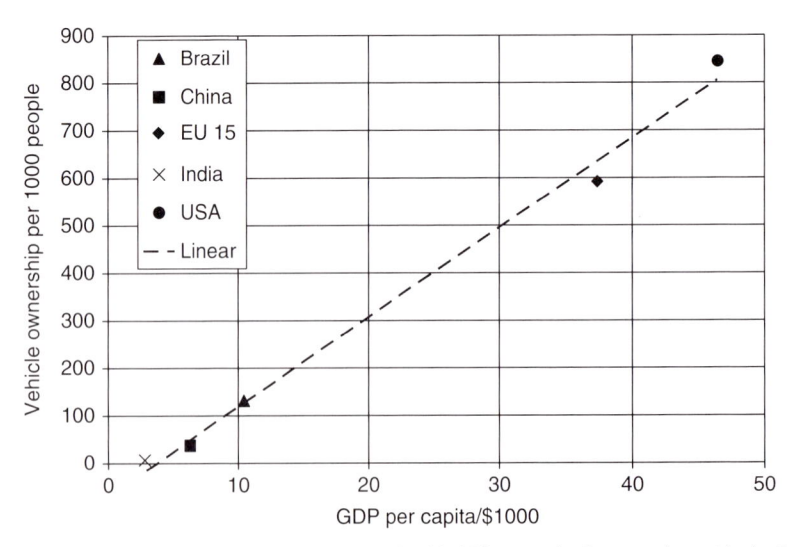

Figure 2 Variation of number of vehicles (cars and trucks) per 1000 people with GDP per capita for several countries/regions.

has some way to go to match the vehicle ownership level in the United States, if it does eventually do so, it would have 1 billion vehicles on its roads!

Between 2005 and 2030, the projected growth in the total distance travelled by automobiles is 37% in countries within the Organization for Economic Co-operation and Development (OECD) but 241% in non-OECD countries, giving a remarkable world growth of 92% [5]. The demand for personal mobility in developing countries will be accelerated by the production of ultra-low-cost cars such as the Tata Nano, which with a retail price of $2000, is 10 times cheaper than the adjusted initial price of the Ford Model-T (Refinements in the production process of the Model-T reduced the vehicle price by a factor of 6 over the following 10–15 years. This was possible because the vehicle and its powertrain and fuel system were made from abundant low-cost materials with low processing energies and simple construction techniques.) and 5 times cheaper than the VW Beetle and Austin Mini [6]. It is vital that approaches to decarbonizing transport are based on technology that is compatible with the production costs of such vehicles since without draconian legislation they will continue to be offered in the market. The huge pressure increasing levels of demand placed on fuel supply will lead to significant price escalation and instability, providing its own direct financial incentive, in addition to those from climate change and security of supply, to consider alternatives.

5.16.1.2 What Are the Options?

In order to address the concerns of both climate change and security of supply, only long-term solutions that are effectively carbon-neutral can be considered. The three most frequently advocated routes to address these issues in the transport sector are as follows:

- electrification of the vehicle fleet
- conversion to a 'hydrogen economy'
- adoption of biofuels.

Of these, only the use of biofuels offers the prospect of an evolutionary transition in technology, which results in vehicles of equivalent range and cost to those to which the user is accustomed to. Electrification and adoption of hydrogen require significant infrastructure changes, with concomitant costs – these are huge in the case of hydrogen and frequently underestimated in the case of electricity. The incorporation of batteries or hydrogen storage systems and fuel cells results, and will continue to result, in vehicles that are much more expensive than the current products, in terms of both energy and capital. Production of such vehicles will require quantum changes in manufacturing facilities. This also leads to the stranding of the vast assets that inhere in engine production lines and will require massive investment in, and validation of, new technologies. Thus, the most basic requirement of vehicle manufacturers from a new fuel or energy carrier – that it should facilitate its continued survival – may be in doubt for these options.

Biofuels, in the form of ethanol and biodiesel, are miscible with current gasoline and diesel formulations, respectively, and can be used even in high concentration levels with minimum engine and fuel system modification. They can therefore be introduced incrementally, with a fuel supply infrastructure which is broadly similar to the current distribution network. This close compatibility is responsible for the presence of more than 6 million E85/gasoline flex-fuel vehicles (FFVs) in the global fleet [7]. The emergence of these vehicles, which can run on any blended combination of ethanol and gasoline up to 85% ethanol, and legislation, such as the US Energy Independence and Security Act [4] and the EU Renewable Energy Directive [8], has lead to the growth of many commercial ventures that produce or plan to produce such fuels. The requirement to reduce the carbon intensity of automotive fuels in Europe has also led to biofuels being the only near-term option available to oil companies.

However, the high-profile market presence of biofuels has attracted the scrutiny of political and environmental lobby groups who have raised concerns over their sustainability credentials. The land area requirements to produce biofuels and the GHG emissions associated with the direct or indirect conversion of previously uncultivated land have led to a belief that there is a global 'biomass limit', which confines the properly sustainable supply to approximately 30% of the current transport energy requirement. Biofuels are, therefore, vulnerable to the accusation that they are a dead end and this is clearly of concern to the automobile manufacturers looking to embrace them. This chapter aims to show that biofuels are not limited to providing an ephemeral palliative but can be part of a more universal solution in the long term where similar fuels can be synthesized using recycled feedstocks from the ocean and the atmosphere. In this way, carbon-neutral liquid fuels can be supplied in full amounts for transport when sufficient renewable energy is made available. The chapter will make brief assessments of electrification and the use of hydrogen in transport in order to show that they lead to high vehicle capital costs and that they are not suitable for aircraft, ships, and trucks, where the need for high onboard energy density is paramount so that range and payload are not compromised.

The automotive industry and the downstream sector of the fuel business operate much more smoothly when the fuel around which their businesses are based is of consistent, tightly controlled composition. From this perspective, alcohol fuels are highly desirable, whereas biodiesel produced by esterification of vegetable or animal fats can be problematic since the fuel properties vary enormously with the feedstock composition. The latter issues can be addressed by using biomass gasification to produce synthesis (or syn) gas from which high-quality diesel and aviation fuel can be synthesized using the Fischer–Tropsch (FT), or a similar, process. These so-called biomass-to-liquids (BTLs) (gas-to-liquids (GTLs) and coal-to-liquids (CTLs) are the equivalent fossil-based synthetic fuels produced from natural gas and coal, respectively) fuels can be designed to specific formulations with very high quality and consistency. In principle, gasification with its eclectic feedstock appetite obviates some of the issues raised by the specter of agricultural monocultures where, notwithstanding aesthetic considerations, vulnerability to pests threatens security of supply.

This chapter will focus on alcohol fuels since, if BTL diesel fuels are made, their characteristics are essentially similar to GTL and CTL diesel fuel. In addition, ethanol is currently present in the market in much larger volumes than biodiesel. The characteristics of alcohols as fuels for spark-ignition (SI) and compression-ignition engines will be described and it will be shown that, in the form of the low carbon-number alcohols, these fuels are synergistic with the technology trend toward pressure-charged downsized internal combustion engines (ICEs). The desirability of methanol as a fuel will be asserted, both due to its performance in engines and the diverse feedstocks and methods that can be used to manufacture it. A simple low-cost vehicle technology will be described that enables an SI engine to run on any combination of gasoline, ethanol, and methanol using a single-fuel system. Fuel blending concepts, which enable methanol to substitute for ethanol in mixes maintaining the same properties, will also be covered and a route to produce alcohol engines with peak fuel conversion efficiencies which match or exceed those of diesel engines will be described.

A concept for a fully renewable endgame will be posited that emancipates renewable alcohol, diesel, and kerosene fuels from the production constraints of biofuels by utilizing renewable energy, carbon in the atmosphere, and hydrogen in the oceans. In the long term, this route enables carbon-neutral liquid fuels to be supplied to the transport sector in full amounts, fueling all vehicles via an infrastructure which is broadly compatible with the current state of the art in terms of technology and capital cost. Thus, biofuels avoid being regarded as a dead-end solution or a mere palliative. In addition, it is possible to avoid the strategic vulnerability of addressing a threat from excessive variation in the world's climate by employing a solution, which is itself dependent on the climate.

Finally, an alternative vehicle and fuel legislation and taxation system will be discussed that resolves well-to-tank (WTT) and tank-to-wheels' (TTW) contributions. The development of a system that recognizes reduced WTT fossil carbon content of fuels and also the rating of vehicles in terms of the energy they require to propel themselves is viewed as a key instrument in incentivizing the development of closed-carbon-cycle fuels and their adoption by the automotive industry and its customers. This provides a mechanism for governments to levy taxation fairly on the stakeholders in the transport sector in accordance with the degree of control they have over the various factors, which comprise the CO_2 emissions from the transport sector.

5.16.2 Competing Transport Energy Carriers

This section starts by examining the two main competitors to biofuels as a route to addressing climate change and energy security in the context of the transport sector. It then offers a vehicle manufacturers' perspective on biofuels in general. It concludes by reviewing key features of the production process for a wide range of biofuels, some of which are covered in more detail in other chapters within the volume. Road transport is difficult to decarbonize due to its high reliance on fossil-based fuels and the large number of mobile emitters. Burning 1 l of gasoline creates 2.33 kg of CO_2; hence, every 50 l tank refill signifies the release of 116.5 kg of CO_2 into the atmosphere. After 11 refueling stops of this type, a 1250 kg vehicle will emit more than its own mass in CO_2 emissions, and a vehicle with a fuel consumption of 7 l per 100 km (about 40 miles per UK gallon) will emit almost 400 tons of CO_2 in its lifetime. The quantity of all gases emitted from the exhaust tailpipe of a vehicle powered by a gasoline engine is about 550 kg per 50 l tank. This high rate of mass accumulation makes it implausible to capture and store exhaust gas onboard a vehicle for subsequent separation and sequestration of the CO_2.

The difficulty of preventing CO_2 emission from vehicles with ICEs burning fossil fuels immediately suggests the option of using a fuel or energy carrier that does not release CO_2. Clearly, the use of fuels that recycle CO_2 aims to achieve a similar effect. The success of either approach is dependent on the degree to which the creation of the energy carrier/manufacture of the fuel can be decarbonized. The focus of fiscal measures in Europe on TTW CO_2 provides a strong incentive for manufacturers to promote vehicles that have zero tailpipe CO_2 regardless of the WTT carbon intensity of the energy carrier.

5.16.2.1 Electrification of the Vehicle Fleet

There is no doubt that vehicle powertrain systems will become increasingly 'electrified' via the hybridization of ICEs, supplied by energy stored in the form of the chemical availability of the fuel, with electric motors supplied by energy stored in the form of the electrochemical potential of the cells comprising the battery. The so-called 'stop-at-idle systems' are beginning to appear on higher-specification vehicles, where enhanced capacity batteries enable combined starter–alternator units to cut fuel to the engine when the vehicle is stationary and restart the engine when required. Mild- and full-parallel hybrid powertrains are currently offered, notably in the Toyota Prius, where electric motors of increasing power levels are able to replace or supplement (in parallel) drive from the engine. Stop-at-idle systems provide about a 5% improvement in fuel economy over the New European Drive Cycle (NEDC) at relatively low cost, while full-parallel hybrids can give between 20% and 45% benefit at higher cost levels, depending on the specific hybrid architecture employed and the battery capacity, for a SI engine. These benefits of hybridization are clearly available to all vehicles using ICE as the primary source of motive power, including those using biofuels.

The 'electric-only' range of parallel hybrid vehicles is usually less than about 4 km and the electrical energy stored in their batteries has all been generated onboard the vehicle during parts of its usage cycle where there is excess power capacity of the ICE. In this way, the engine is forced to operate at higher efficiency point and the excess energy is stored in electrical form for use in the electric motor when engine operation would be particularly inefficient, that is, at very low loads. Plug-in hybrid electric vehicles

(PHEVs) have significantly higher electric-only range, around 50–70 km, and can store mains-generated electricity that is taken onboard while the vehicle is not in use. These vehicles may use ICEs and, usually, liquid fuel systems to extend their range to a level close to that of a conventional vehicle. In this way, the use of a liquid fuel with its high energy density allows the development of a vehicle that has a practical electric-only range and a high total range capability without the cost implications of a full electric vehicle discussed later in this chapter. This avoids the so-called range anxiety experienced by users of more affordable electric vehicles due to their cheaper, smaller capacity batteries and the consequent limited autonomy and utility of such vehicles.

In the long term, electrification of transport aims at the use of at least dedicated electric automotive vehicles with batteries capable of providing a range close to that of a conventional vehicle. The TTW efficiency of a vehicle operating in electric drive mode is between 2.5 and 4 times higher than that of a vehicle powered by a nonhybridized ICE over a drive cycle such as the NEDC. This gives electrification the ostensible appeal of minimizing the investment in the upstream energy generation capacity. However, in order to convert this apparent advantage into a significant reduction in carbon dioxide emissions, it is essential to decarbonize the upstream energy supply or implement widespread carbon capture and storage technology on fossil-fueled power stations.

Using a grid carbon intensity of 119.4 $gCO_2 MJ^{-1}$, representing the Department of Environment, Food, and Rural Affairs (DEFRA) long-term marginal factor for the UK National Grid [9], and an electric vehicle TTW energy efficiency of 0.55 $MJ km^{-1}$ over the NEDC gives a well-to-wheel (WTW) emission rate of 66 $gCO_2 km^{-1}$. A more appropriate value for the United Kingdom in 2010 might be the incremental intensity, calculated by Hitchin and Pout [10], of 153 $gCO_2 MJ^{-1}$ or the 164 $gCO_2 MJ^{-1}$, recommended by Pout [11], giving 84 and 90 $gCO_2 km^{-1}$, respectively, although a value equivalent to 100 $gCO_2 km^{-1}$ for the vehicle energy efficiency considered here has also been suggested [9]. The same vehicle energy efficiency gives 92 $gCO_2 km^{-1}$ for a battery electric vehicles (BEVs) using marginal electricity generated in California with a carbon intensity of 166.7 $gCO_2 MJ^{-1}$ [12]. At the more extreme end of the range, a BEV operating on electricity generated in a typical coal-fired power station will generate about 153 $gCO_2 km^{-1}$. A similar-sized (B/C class) vehicle with 'stop-at-idle' technology operating on fossil diesel fuel with a TTW emission rate of 99 $gCO_2 km^{-1}$ (equivalent to a TTW energy efficiency of 1.35 $MJ km^{-1}$) gives a WTW emission rate of about 117 $gCO_2 km^{-1}$. These examples (some of which are compared in **Figure 3**) illustrate the sensitivity of the WTW savings in GHG emissions achieved by the electrification of road transport to the carbon intensity of the electricity supplied to the vehicles. Clearly, the GHG benefit of vehicle electrification is limited by the rate at which the supply network can be decarbonized.

Electrification of the vehicle fleet has the additional theoretical attraction that most of the various forms of renewable energy are conveniently converted to electricity, and utilizing this in the grid to power electric vehicles removes the conversion losses involved in manufacturing a chemical energy carrier. An infrastructure for supplying end-user vehicles at low rates of charge is available to those with access to electricity supplies, which are close to where their vehicles are parked. However, transmission lines required to convey the renewable electricity from the remote locations in which it may be generated to the regions in which it is required are often not readily available and would be extremely expensive to install.

As energy carriers, batteries are fundamentally limited by the electrical potential available from the elements used in the construction of the cells and the general requirement to carry the oxidant in addition to the reductant (analogous to oxygen in the air and the fuel, respectively, in a combustion reaction). At the upper levels available using lithium-ion chemistries, cell

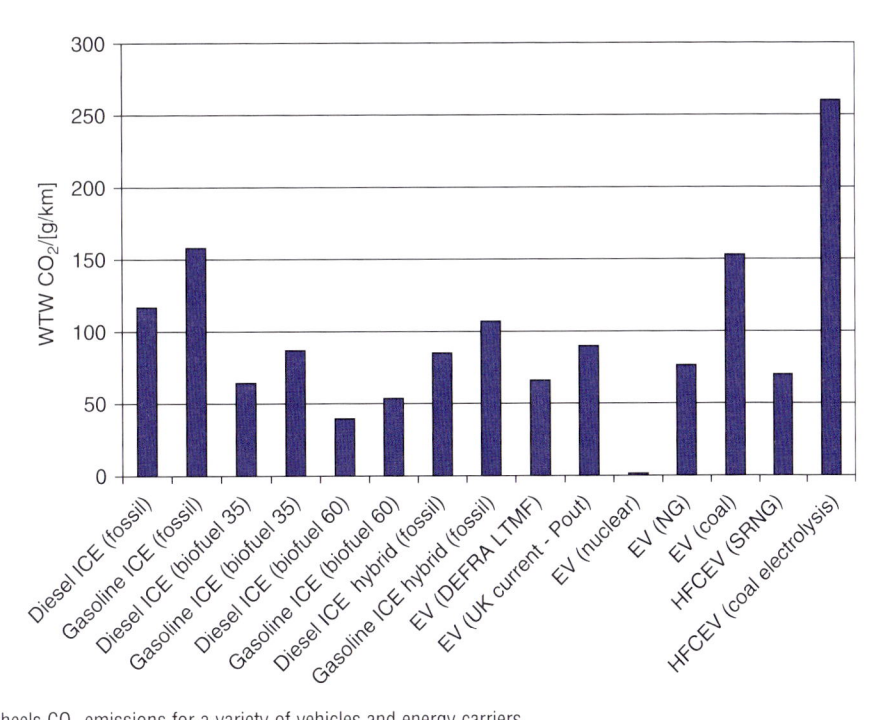

Figure 3 Well-to-wheels CO_2 emissions for a variety of vehicles and energy carriers.

potentials for stable batteries appear to be close to their limit. While advances in metal–air batteries, where oxygen from the ambient air is drawn through a porous cathode, have recently been made using ionic liquid electrolytes [13], these developments are presently only at the laboratory stage.

The very low net gravimetric and volumetric energy densities of batteries are shown for lead–acid, nickel–metal hydride, and lithium-ion chemistries in **Figure 4**. To match the range of a conventional gasoline, vehicle with a 50 l fuel tank would require a useable battery capacity of approximately 100 kWh, thus accounting for the greater TTW efficiency of an electric vehicle. A fuel tank containing 50 l of gasoline would weigh about 46 kg; a 100 kWh battery would weigh 600–800 kg, depending on the technology and the permissible depth of discharge.

Cost estimates for batteries of a given capacity vary enormously depending on the number of cells used; the choice of the cathode material; the cost of materials used for the anode, separators, electrolyte, and packaging; the details of the production process; and the maximum permissible depth of discharge (which dictates the degree of overspecification of the battery necessary to achieve the durability required). These separate costs are often crudely lumped together to give a cost per kilowatt hour of storage.

The most optimistic medium-term estimates for a lithium-ion battery at 100 000 units per annum production levels are in the region of $250 kWh^{-1}. This puts the cost of a 100 kWh battery at about $25 000 (represented by the €16 000 value shown in **Figure 5**). More common price estimates are in the range $800–$1000 kWh^{-1} [9], putting a 100 kWh battery at over $80 000 (represented by the €50 000 value shown in **Figure 5**). Cell durability is a major concern for electric vehicles and failure of the battery to last the life of the vehicle will compound the high initial cost. Durability can generally be increased by reducing the maximum permissible depth of discharge but this has the effect of overspecifying the battery size, thus increasing the cost further. A maximum depth of discharge of 80% (i.e., 20% capacity redundancy) is generally taken as necessary to ensure a 10-year life for the battery of a dedicated electric vehicle.

Even without the costs of battery replacement, the purchase price of electric vehicles that are not range-compromised is such that the total cost of ownership over the vehicle lifetime would be substantially higher than those of current vehicles. In this context, it is clear why many pure electric vehicles currently on offer have ranges of the order of 200 km, or even substantially lower for so-called city cars. Marketing them as premium vehicles is a way of justifying the high purchase prices.

Figure 6 shows the large cost increments of even range-compromised BEVs (with 50 kWh batteries) above vehicles with ICEs and liquid fuel systems based on the energy costs shown in **Figure 5**. Vehicle costs at both $250 kWh^{-1} and $800 kWh^{-1} for the battery are given. The rationale for range-extended electric vehicles is clear from **Figure 6**, where a low-cost ICE and liquid fuel tank (see **Figure 5**) may be used to provide range back up so that the electric-only range can be reduced to about 50 km using a battery of say 8 kWh usable energy storage capacity (this would equate to a total capacity of 16 kWh at the 50% maximum depth of discharge levels necessary for 10-year durability in such vehicles with their high battery charge cycling frequencies). The ICE is used only at high-efficiency operating points to drive the vehicle via the generator or recharge the battery and extends the total vehicle range to between 300 and 400 km via the high energy density of the liquid fuel.

5.16.2.2 Hydrogen

For mobile emitters, hydrogen is an appealing energy carrier from the perspective that it can be burnt in an engine or oxidized at relatively high efficiency in a fuel cell with no release of CO_2 from the vehicle into the atmosphere. Reciprocating ICEs (as distinct from their fuel systems) and gas turbines require relatively little modification to run on hydrogen. The gas can also be used to fuel proton exchange membrane fuel cells. Currently, these low-temperature fuel cells are the most suitable for transport applications

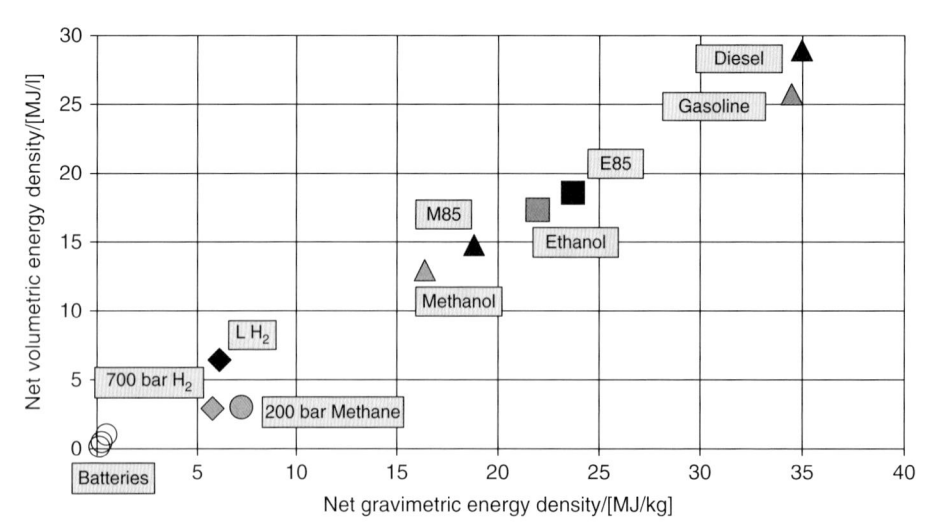

Figure 4 Net system volumetric and gravimetric energy densities for various onboard energy carriers (based on lower heating values).

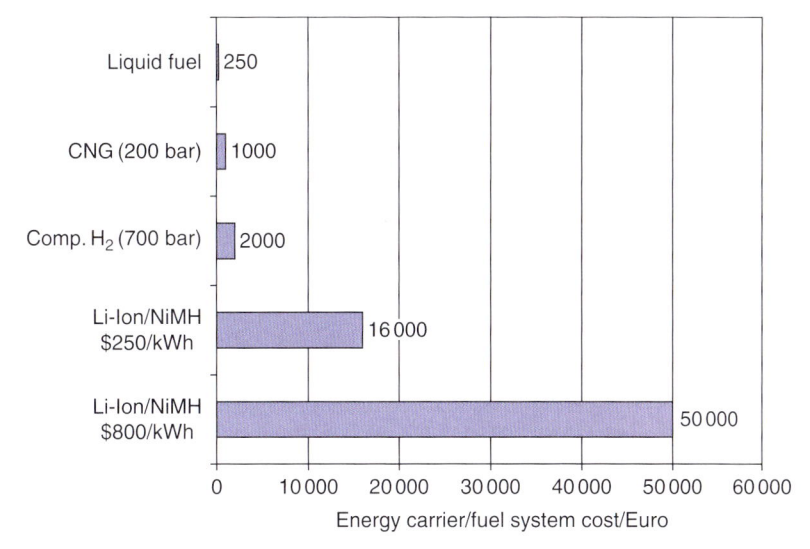

Figure 5 Fuel/energy carrier system costs for volume production (100 000 units per annum) at 2010 costs – based on vehicle range of 50 l of gasoline. Data derived partly from Jackson N (2006) Low carbon vehicle strategies: Options and potential benefits. *Cost-Effective Low Carbon Engines Conference*, Institution of Mechanical Engineers, London, UK, November [14] and Eberle U (2006) GM's research strategy: Towards a hydrogen-based transportation system. *FuncHy Workshop*, Hamburg, Germany, September [15].

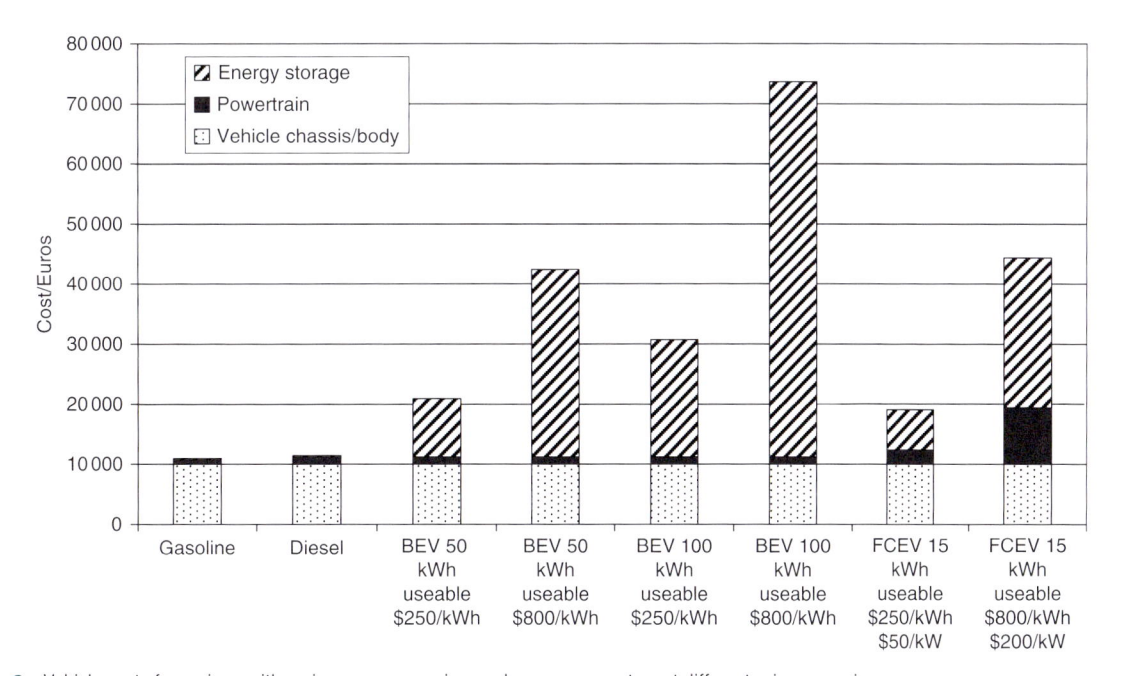

Figure 6 Vehicle costs for various with various energy carriers and energy converters at different price scenarios.

but require precious metal catalysts and other expensive components such as precisely manufactured polymer membranes and bipolar plates.

The fuel cell is an energy converter, not an engine, converting chemical energy into electrical energy that sits between the energy storage medium and the electric motor that provides the actual force propelling the vehicle. As such, it is an additional component in the powertrain system compared with a BEV or ICE-powered vehicle. Hydrogen fuel cell vehicles (HFCEVs) are usually hybridized by using batteries of significant storage capacity, in order to maintain high operating efficiencies.

As is the case with electrification, the WTW GHG emissions of HFCEVs in the short to medium terms are strongly dependent on the specific hydrogen production pathways. The WTT carbon intensity of hydrogen ranges from 100–130 $gCO_2\,MJ^{-1}$ for production via steam reformation of natural gas (currently the largest industrial source) to about 425 $gCO_2\,MJ^{-1}$ for production via electrolysis of water using electricity generated by coal [16]. When suitably hybridized, a vehicle energy efficiency of about twice that of a nonhybrid diesel engine vehicle is possible over the NEDC, giving a WTW CO_2 emission in the range of 70 to 260 $gCO_2\,km^{-1}$.

Figure 4 shows that while the net onboard energy density of hydrogen comfortably exceeds that of batteries, it is still very low compared with liquid fuels. The net volumetric energy densities shown in **Figure 4** include system package volumes and show the deficiency of even liquid hydrogen as an energy storage medium. Because of the extreme physical conditions required to package hydrogen, the bulky system volume becomes a high percentage of the net volumetric energy content. The packaging problems are exacerbated by the constraints on the tank shapes imposed by pressure vessel design considerations and the requirement to minimize heat ingress in cryogenic systems.

Although hydrogen itself has a very high energy per unit mass (gravimetric energy density), its net packaged value, including the storage system mass, suffers in an even more marked way than the volumetric energy density, as shown in **Figure 4**. Pressure vessels and cryogenic tanks are extremely heavy: a 700 bar system for automotive use holding 4.6 kg of hydrogen (the energy equivalent to 17.5 l of gasoline) is quoted by Eberle [15] as weighing 95 kg, while cryogenic systems can weigh around 170 kg and contain only 9 kg of hydrogen (the energy equivalent of about 34 l of gasoline). In contrast, a tank for a liquid hydrocarbon fuel system may weigh around 10 kg. While physical metal hydride storage systems for hydrogen [17, 18] achieve similar volumetric energy density to a 700 bar gaseous system, the gravimetric energy content is comparable with lithium-ion batteries. Chemical metal hydrides can achieve superior volumetric hydrogen storage density to 700 bar gas storage or liquid hydrogen, but their gravimetric energy density is significantly worse, being in the region of 1–3 MJ kg^{-1} [19, 20]. Many of the metals used in hydride systems (e.g., lanthanum, titanium, manganese, nickel, zirconium) are expensive, and while some lower-cost materials (e.g., magnesium-based compounds) also offer higher gravimetric densities, they may have high heats of formation and require high temperatures (>200 °C) to release the hydrogen [20].

If mechanical and electrical losses are also considered, the total energy used for compression of hydrogen to an 800 bar supply pressure may reach around 15% of the higher heating value (HHV) of the hydrogen undergoing the process [17, 18]. The energy efficiency of liquefaction plants is strongly dependent on size. For a large-scale plant, about 40% of the HHV is consumed in liquefaction. For small-scale systems, the energy consumed in liquefaction can approach or exceed the energy content of the fuel [17, 18]. The high degree of purity required by current hydrogen fuel cells compounds the upstream fuel energy loss. The purification process can involve a 'distillation' process in which the hydrogen is evaporated. The effect of boil-off losses during distribution and refueling can lead to an unacceptable loss of hydrogen [21].

Hydrogen storage systems are expensive. Eberle [15] quotes €2000 as a target for a 700 bar hydrogen tank capable of storing 6 kg of hydrogen, but a cost of €10 000 was deemed more realistic by Jackson for such a system [14]. The system cost is also considerably increased by the fuel cell. Fuel cell cost estimates for volume production vary enormously from the US Department of Energy (DOE) target of $50 kW^{-1} and the fuel cell industry estimates of $60–$80 kW^{-1} [22] (at 500 000 units yr^{-1}) to those of Jackson [14] at $500–$1000 kW^{-1}. Compared with the $15 kW^{-1} and $25 kW^{-1} for gasoline and diesel engines, respectively, even the lower end of these estimates leaves a significant differential over current vehicle costs. Additional bills of material costs are also incurred by the requirement to hybridize the powertrain in order for the fuel cell to operate in its high efficiency region. (It should be noted that in many instances, quoted fuel cell efficiencies are based on the lower heating value (LHV) of hydrogen. When calculating the amount of upstream renewable energy required for a given application, the HHV energy carrier is the correct parameter to be considered. For hydrogen, using an LHV produces an efficiency overestimate of about 18% compared with an overestimate of only 6% if efficiencies are based on gasoline LHV. Using HHV-based efficiencies brings the peak efficiencies of ICEs and fuel cells closer together than is often claimed. Additionally, care must be taken to compare efficiencies of hybridized vehicles with those of other hybridized vehicles.) Battery capacities in the range of 10–15 kWh may be required, with costs in line with those quoted in the discussion of BEVs. As noted by Jackson [14], the fuel economy potential of ICE/hybrid systems may improve significantly at US$50 kW^{-1}. The manufacture of ICEs and their fuel systems places low demands on scarce materials – they are made from cheap, abundant raw materials at concomitantly low costs and contain low-embedded energy levels.

Figure 6 shows HFCEVs at the extreme low end of the cost spectrum and at a less ambitious cost reduction level. The low-cost estimate is based on the following assumptions: $50 kW^{-1} (assumed to be 75 kW in all cases) for the fuel cell, €2000 for the hydrogen storage tank, and $250 (kWh)$^{-1}$ for the battery (assumed to be $15 kWh total capacity). The more conservative cost reduction estimate is based on the following assumptions: $200 kW^{-1} for the fuel cell, €10 000 for the hydrogen storage tank, and $800 kWh^{-1} for the battery. If the lower estimates of fuel cell costs are realistic, the implications on the full vehicle cost are less severe than those produced by electric vehicles with high levels of autonomy (range) but are very significant to the customer.

Clearly, the provision of hydrogen production, distribution, and refueling facilities will require large investment since a completely new infrastructure capable of dealing safely with a highly explosive gas is needed. Being the smallest molecule, hydrogen has a higher propensity to leak through imperfect seals than other fuels. It may even diffuse through metals and can cause embrittlement in some high-strength steels. Hydrogen has much wider flammability limits in air than methane, propane, or gasoline, and its minimum ignition energy is about an order of magnitude lower than for these fuels [23]. In addition to danger of static electricity generation causing ignition in venting situations, a diffusion–ignition mechanism is thought to exist where local autoignition is caused by a shock wave resulting from the expansion of high-pressure gas into air [23]. In the event of a spill, hydrogen would form a flammable mixture more readily than other fuels due to its higher buoyancy and large flammable range. Liquid fuels such as gasoline and, by inference, ethanol and methanol are several orders of magnitude slower at forming a flammable mixture. Although the rapid mixing property of hydrogen gas leads to its ready dispersal, this is not the case for liquid hydrogen that, as it boils, creates a vapor with a similar density to air and this can lead to the propagation of transiently nonbuoyant flammable mixtures to considerable distances from the spill [23].

Mintz et al. [24] have estimated the cost of providing a hydrogen infrastructure in the United States capable of refueling 100 million fuel cell vehicles (40% of the light-duty vehicle fleet) at up to $650 billion. Moreover, in the transition period to a hydrogen-based energy economy, a dual infrastructure must be maintained and vehicles with two incompatible fuel storage systems must be produced, thereby escalating costs of both appreciably.

It is clear that there are huge hurdles restricting the penetration of HFCEVs into the market. Their high cost, due to the use of precious metal catalysts, requirement for high-energy density batteries, and the expense of the hydrogen storage system, render them generally unaffordable as a mass-market vehicle. Their use of scarce materials is likely to limit production numbers so that they could only provide a partial solution; this presents great difficulty in justifying the enormous cost of installing a completely new fuel production and distribution infrastructure. Finally, the potential GHG benefit of HFCEVs is not sufficiently high to justify their introduction without decarbonizing the fuel supply chain.

5.16.2.3 Biofuels

5.16.2.3.1 Vehicle manufacturers' perspective

For manufacturers in the road transport sector, one of the alluring features of producing BEVs and HFCEVs is the fact that because only TTW emissions are accounted for, the manufacturers are credited with producing a vehicle that emits zero CO_2 when their fleet-averaged levels are evaluated. In the EU, manufacturers of vehicles capable of being operated on high-concentration biofuels do not receive a credit, which is directly linked to the WTT GHG savings commensurate with the use of the fuel. Hence, to date, only Sweden has a significant number of E85/gasoline FFVs in service and pumps to supply them, due to large financial incentives put in place by the Swedish government. There is a legislative commitment by vehicle manufacturers to achieve the 2015 EU target of reducing fleet-average CO_2 emissions to a level of $130 \, gCO_2 \, km^{-1}$ by 2015, which requires that an additional $10 \, gCO_2 \, km^{-1}$ reduction be achieved through 'complementary measures' such as alternative fuels, along with technologies like tyre pressure monitoring systems. This produces little incentive for the production of vehicles capable of being operated on high levels of biofuel concentration.

However, in the United States there are a large number of FFVs, but only very few operate regularly on E85. This situation is a result of the relatively small number of E85 dispensing pumps available (about 2100 in February 2010 [25]) and, more significantly, the favorable dispensation given to FFVs in the Corporate Average Fuel Economy (CAFE) standards [26]. CAFE regulations, which mandate average fuel consumption targets for US vehicles, assume that an E85/gasoline FFV uses ethanol 50% of the time, despite evidence that the actual number is much lower than this (see below), and only count the nominal 15% gasoline component in E85 as consumed fuel. A harmonic mean is used to calculate the resulting fuel consumption so that an FFV giving, say, 25 miles per gallon on gasoline and 15 miles per gallon on E85 will be credited with a fuel consumption of 40 miles per gallon. (The harmonic mean calculates the fuel consumption of a trip using each fuel on different halves of the trip, as opposed to simply averaging the respective fuel consumption values expressed in miles per gallon (which assumes different distances are driven). In this example, the respective amounts of gasoline consumed operating on gasoline and E85 are $(1/25)$ and $(0.15/15)$ gallons on each half of a 2 mile trip, respectively. The fuel consumption for the total journey is then $(1+1)/((1/25)+(0.15/15)) = 40$ miles per gallon.). Despite limits on the credits generated in this way by FFVs, the legislation effectively created a loophole allowing manufacturers to avoid reducing the energy consumption of their vehicles to meet stricter targets by instead taking the relatively low-cost option of making them flex-fuel compatible. The additional cost of an FFV is in the range €100–€200, which in the context of the alternatives shown in **Figure 6**, is a minimal addition to the cost of the conventional vehicles.

The WTT CO_2 emissions of biofuels vary enormously depending on the input energy source to the plant, the feedstock, the type of fuel produced, and credits attributed to any coproducts. For example, the production of ethanol from Brazilian sugarcane, where the bagasse is used as fuel for the plant and produces waste heat, requires an energy input of 1.79 MJ per MJ of fuel energy produced, with the emission of $10.4 \, gCO_2 eq \, MJ^{-1}$ (without credits for the renewable combustion CO_2) [27]. On the other hand, production of ethanol from wheat using input energy from lignite-fueled CHP and using some of the by-products as animal feed requires a similar level of energy at 1.74 MJ per MJ of fuel produces $92.6 \, gCO_2 eq \, MJ^{-1}$. These carbon intensities produce WTW values of between about 20 and $170 \, gCO_2 \, km^{-1}$ in an FFV. In order to avoid listing the multifarious pathways for biofuel production, **Figure 3** uses the 35% and 60% GHG saving targets for biofuels set by the EU for the end of 2010 and 2018, respectively [28], and assumes vehicles running on the high-concentration forms of the biofuels. Clearly, the values quoted above for Brazilian sugarcane ethanol are such that it can surpass even the 2018 target, demonstrating that biofuels which meet the required GHG standards can make immediate and significant contributions to reducing WTW transport emissions if there is sufficient supply.

Biomass-based fuels are being produced today in the form of ethanol from a variety of feedstocks and biodiesel from vegetable oil methyl esters. In 2007, the global ethanol and biodiesel production was 40 million tons (50 billion liters) and 8 million tons (10 billion liters), respectively [29], together equating to about 1.5% of global transport energy. The EU has mandated that the transport sector should source 10% of its energy needs from renewable energy, including biofuels, by 2020 [28]. The US Energy Independence and Security Act of 2007 [30] has mandated the supply of 36 billion gallons (136 billion liters) of renewable fuel by 2022, representing about 20% of the total US highway fuel use in 2007, of which 21 billion gallons (79 billion liters) is to be obtained from advanced biofuels (specifically not corn starch). Biofuel use in the United States in 2006 was about 5 billion gallons.

Figures 7(a) and **7(b)** show that for the United States in 2006, ethanol blended into gasoline in low concentrations (typically at E10 level, producing the so-called gasohol) was responsible for 77% of all alternative fuel usage by energy content, with E85 comprising 0.9%. For comparison, electricity and hydrogen provided 0.1% and 0.0009% of transport energy, respectively.

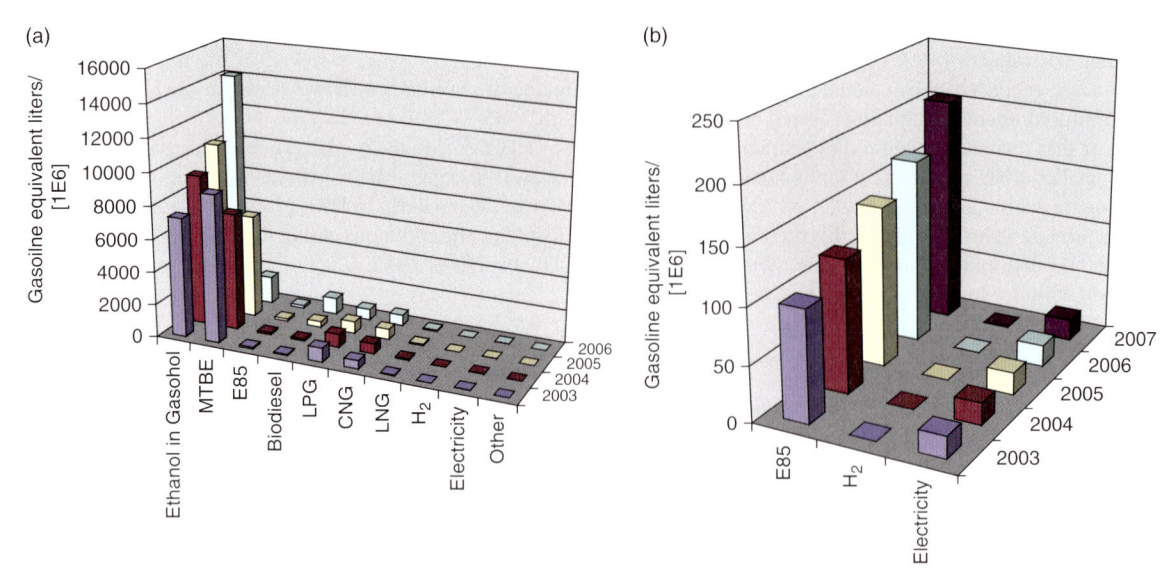

Figure 7 (a) Alternative fuel consumption in the United States (millions of liters gasoline equivalent), 2003–06. Based on Davis SC, Diegel SW, and Boundy RG (2009) *Transportation Energy Data Book: Edition 28.* ORNL-6984. Center for Transportation Analysis, Energy and Transportation Science Division, Oak Ridge National Laboratory, Tennessee, USA. Prepared for the Office of Energy Efficiency and Renewable Energy, US Department of Energy [2]. (b) Alternative fuel consumption in the United States (millions of liters gasoline equivalent), 2003–07 – detail of **Figure 7**(**a**). Based on Davis SC, Diegel SW, and Boundy RG (2009) *Transportation Energy Data Book: Edition 28.* ORNL-6984. Center for Transportation Analysis, Energy and Transportation Science Division, Oak Ridge National Laboratory, Tennessee, USA. Prepared for the Office of Energy Efficiency and Renewable Energy, US Department of Energy [2].

Of the 4.1 million 'alternative energy' automotive vehicles produced in 2007, 66% were FFVs, 16% hybrids (excluding micro hybrids), 10% compressed natural gas-fueled vehicles, and 8% liquified petroleum gas (LPG)-fueled vehicles [29]. Despite the manifold motivations, it is argued that the key parameters enabling the propagation of alcohol fuels and the vehicles capable of using them are the low additional cost requirements due to the broad compatibility with systems that currently exist. This requires only evolution rather than revolution of the fuel infrastructure and vehicle technology, avoiding stranding the vast assets which vehicle manufacturers have invested in their existing production facilities. Thus, if properly regulated, biofuels have the potential to make an immediate contribution to decarbonizing transport, as evidenced by examples such as the use of sugarcane ethanol in Brazil. This potential for immediate impact should not be underestimated in view of the slow rate of implementation of the alternative options for decarbonizing transport described above. Since the power generation sector has wider options for decarbonizing than the transport sector, there is a motivation for converting as much biomass as possible to a versatile liquid fuel. There is a further rationale for producing biofuel for export in countries with surplus requirements, as opposed to shipping biomass of much lower energy density and value.

Alcohol fuels have the great benefit of being pure substances so that the fuel blender and additive supplier know precisely what they are dealing with and the vehicle manufacturer is presented with a tightly defined fuel with consistent properties (to within the variation of the base gasoline in the blend). In the same way that the chemical composition of petroleum-derived diesel is dependent on the composition of the crude oil from which it is derived and the refining process used, the chemical composition of biodiesel formed by transesterification of seed-oils or animal fats to form fatty acid methyl esters (FAMEs) is dependent on the original feedstock source and the esterification process. Thus, the effect of blending FAME into diesel fuel is very difficult to predict. The wide variations in the FAME composition and its interaction with the base diesel in a blend can have markedly different effects on low-temperature vehicle operability, with the fuel pour point and cold filter plugging point changing significantly with FAME composition [31]. The fuel's oxidation stability [32–34], its compatibility with the vehicle fuel injection equipment, and its propensity to form deposits [35, 36] and cause oil dilution [37] are also affected by the FAME composition. Bespoke additives are required for specific blend compositions, making the task of ensuring fuel compliance with the vehicle fleet a complex task. The issues are well summarized by Richards *et al.* [38]. In contrast, BTL fuels produced from gasification and subsequent carefully controlled synthesis can have 'designer compositions' that are very close or identical to the equivalent GTL or CTL fuels, giving properties which are more closely controlled than, and often superior to, their fossil-based counterparts.

5.16.2.3.2 Overview of production methods

Biomass is usually defined as material that is directly or indirectly derived from plant life and that is renewable in time periods of less than about 100 years [39]. Biomass is produced from combining 'feedstocks', which essentially are often the products of combustion (CO_2 and H_2O) and effectively have zero chemical availability (exergy), via the process of photosynthesis, to form oxidizable organic matter of higher chemical availability. The oxidizable materials of relevance to biomass energy conversion are carbohydrates and lignin. The photosynthesis process for the production of carbohydrates can be represented by the overall reaction:

$$nCO_2 + mH_2O \xrightarrow[\text{chlorophyll}]{\text{sunlight}} C_n(H_2O)_m + nO_2; \quad \Delta H^0_{298} = +470 \text{ kJ mol}^{-1} \quad [1]$$

A plant typically contains between 0.1% and 3.0% of the original solar energy, which is incident upon it during its growth [39]. The CO_2 that is taken from the biosphere by the plant may be formed by respiration, biological degradation, or combustion, and is reprocessed by photosynthesis into biomass. The regrowth of an equivalent amount of vegetation ensures renewability and that theoretically there is no net accumulation of CO_2. Clearly, the concern over the climatic impact of burning fossil-based fuels is the return to the atmosphere within a few decades, and the accumulation of a large amount of CO_2 which was converted to biomass or animal matter and accumulated in a hydrocarbon store over a period of millions of years.

The production methods for biofuels can be broadly classified as extractive, fermentative (biochemical), and thermochemical (mainly gasification). The main biofuels currently in the market are bioethanol and biodiesel, made by fermentative and extractive processes, respectively. Biodiesel can be made by transesterification (using methanol) of plant oils, animal fats, and recycled cooking oils and fats and is classed as FAME. Rapeseed methyl ester (RME) is a widely used form of biodiesel in Europe, with palm oil, and soybean oil being widely used feedstocks in other regions. Biodiesel can also be made by hydroprocessing in which hydrogen is used to convert bio-oils into a product that can be refined in a conventional refinery [40].

The carbohydrates are either mono- or disaccharides (sugars), or polysaccharides (polymers of sugars). The monosaccharides ($C_6H_{12}O_6/C_5H_{10}O_5$) such as glucose, found in corn and grapes, and fructose, found in other fruits, are fermentable to ethanol. Butanol can also be fermented directly from sugars but its production is threefold less efficient than for ethanol production [41].

The disaccharide ($C_{12}H_{22}O_{11}$) such as sucrose, which is the primary sugar in the sap of plants and is abundant in sugarcane and sugar beet, can be hydrolyzed by an enzyme (catalyst) present in yeast to form fermentable monosaccharides. The polysaccharides include starch, hemicellulose, and cellulose, together with the noncarbohydrate lignin. Starch is readily turned into fermentable sugars via enzymatic hydrolysis. An example of the saccharification of starch (maltose) and the subsequent fermentation process to form ethanol can be summarized by the following reactions [39]:

$$(C_6H_{10})_n + \frac{n}{2}H_2O \rightarrow \frac{n}{2}C_{12}H_{22}O_{11} \quad [2]$$

$$C_{12}H_{22}O_{11} + H_2O \rightarrow 2\ C_6H_{12}O_6 \rightarrow 4\ C_2H_5OH + 4CO_2 \quad [3]$$

It can be seen that for every 12 atoms of carbon contained in the original biomass, 4 atoms are converted back to CO_2 during the fermentation process; indeed, CO_2 is produced at a molar rate equivalent to that of the ethanol. This is a consequence of the oxygen ratio in the original biomass being higher than that required for the intended alcoholic product. The fermented liquid contains up to 18% ethanol and is fractionated (distilled) in order to concentrate the alcohol up to the required level. Separation of the ethanol is an energy-intensive step. Increasing the concentration of ethanol before distillation improves the process efficiency but is constrained by the maximum level at which the microorganisms can tolerate the alcohol.

First-generation biofuels are made from fermentation of plant sugars (bioethanol) or transesterification of plant oil (biodiesel). There are significant concerns regarding the production of these first-generation fuels on a large scale (as discussed in Section 5.16.4), which have led to the considerable recent efforts to develop second-generation biofuels which employ advanced pretreatment techniques in order to break down lignocellulosic biomass into fermentable sugars.

Hemicellulose is more resistant than starch to being hydrolyzed into fermentable sugars, traditionally requiring the use of dilute alkaline solutions [39], and new approaches to fermenting the pentoses (C_5-sugars) derived from hemicellulose are under development [41]. Cellulose, being the main constituent of the cell walls of land plants, is the most abundant naturally occurring organic substance on earth. As it is a major component of wood, hemp, and straw, it has the potential to supply significant quantities of biomass that does not cause conflict with food requirements, but it is extremely resistant to traditional enzymatic hydrolysis. Cellulose can be processed by acid hydrolysis but this is expensive, due to the costly wastewater recovery and treatment, and reduces the yield of sugar. Lignin, which is a polymer of single benzene rings (often phenolic (a phenolic compound is one in which a hydroxyl group is attached to the benzene ring)) linked by aliphatic chains, is also formed as a constituent of the walls of woody cells but totally resists hydrolysis and is resistant to microbial degradation [39]. Lignin and its by-products need to be removed before fermentation as they can be toxic to the microorganisms and enzymes used for hydrolysis. It can be burnt, however, to provide part of the process heat requirements.

The vegetation providing the main source of sugars and lignocellulosic compounds useful for biomass energy includes trees, grasses, legumes, grain and sugar crops, and aquatic plants. Wood provides perhaps the greatest potential source of biomass but it contains about two-thirds cellulose and hemicellulose (together known as holocellulose) and one-quarter lignin (the remainder being extraneous materials such as resins, gums, tannins, and waxes [39]). Since only the hemicellulose and about one-quarter of the cellulose can be readily hydrolyzed to fermentable sugars, biochemical processes are of limited application in the utilization of woody biomass.

There has been considerable effort recently to develop the so-called 'second-generation' biofuels that employ steam explosion, high-pressure hot water treatments, and advanced enzymatic hydrolysis techniques in order to break down lingocellulosic biomass into fermentable sugars, but the optimal pretreatment will be feedstock-specific [41]. However, biomass materials can be gasified and the resulting gas may be used for the synthesis of liquid fuels – this is sometimes referred to as thermochemical conversion, as opposed to biochemical conversion. Most biomass materials can be gasified, including wood, municipal solid waste, gases, and crop residues. Gasified biomass materials produce little by-product and many of the chars and oils that are evolved may be recycled until they are eliminated [39]. A large portion of the calorific value of the original biomass material leaves the gasifier in the chemical energy of the resulting carbon monoxide (CO) and hydrogen syngas mixture. With the provision of additional hydrogen, gasification allows the utilization of all the biomass, that is, total plant use, and permits the use of a wide variety of biogenic resources, conserving ecological diversity [42, 43]. Gasification processes tolerate a wide range of biomass feedstocks. The avoidance of propagating monocultures, since specific enzymes do not have to be tailored to particular crops, enhances security of supply as the feedstock is not then vulnerable to the propagation of a single crop disease.

Fuel production via biomass gasification also enables a wide range of fuels to be produced, if required – these are generically categorized as BTL fuels. Among the fuels that can be produced from the syngas are methanol, ethanol, dimethyl ether (DME), synthetic natural gas (SNG), hydrogen, and synthetic gasoline and diesel. Methanol and DME are most easily produced by this process. The production of the higher alcohols and longer-chain hydrocarbons, such as the components of synthetic gasoline, diesel, and kerosene, requires FT or methanol-to-gasoline (MTG)/methanol-to-synfuels (MtSynfuels) [43, 44] technology. In these processes, the small molecules of the syngas are reassembled into more complex molecules. The processing plants required are large and complex with significantly higher capital costs. They give a mixture of products and there is a reduction in the resulting fuel energy supplied (of about 10% points).

In the primary thermochemical conversion step, the biomass is ideally decomposed into a gas with hydrogen and carbon monoxide as the main components. Air, oxygen, water vapor, and hydrogen in any partial mixture usually form the gasification components, with the main challenge being the production of syngas of the desired composition which is free of tar, particles, and catalytic poisons, having a low concentration of inert gas and a high concentration of hydrogen [43]. The composition of the syngas is often characterized by the stoichiometry factor, S, which is defined as

$$S = \frac{(p_{H_2} - p_{CO_2})}{(p_{CO} + p_{CO_2})} \quad [4]$$

where p represents the partial pressure of the species identified by their subscripts.

The simplest reaction involving the syngas, resulting from gasification, leads to the production of methanol via combination of 1 mole of carbon monoxide with 2 moles of hydrogen via the path:

$$CO + 2H_2 \Leftrightarrow CH_3OH(l) \quad \Delta H^0_{298} = -128.2 \text{ kJ mol}^{-1} \quad [5]$$

Clearly, this reaction requires syngas with composition such that $S = 2$, as does the production of FT fuels via the reaction:

$$n(CO + 2H_2) \rightarrow n(-CH_2-) + nH_2O \quad \Delta H^0_{298} = -162 \text{ kJ mol}^{-1} \quad [6]$$

In fact, because part of the biomass carbon is converted to CO_2 in the gasification step, and its subsequent hydrogenation to methanol requires 3 moles of hydrogen according to

$$CO_2 + 3H_2 \Leftrightarrow CH_3OH + H_2O \quad \Delta H^0_{298} = -49.9 \text{ kJ mol}^{-1} \quad [7]$$

the stoichiometry factor, S, defined in eqn [4] needs to be greater than 2 in order avoid the use of a shift reactor in the plant with a concomitant increase in cost [45]. This can be achieved either by adding hydrogen or removing CO_2 or both. By using renewable energy to electrolyze water, oxygen and steam can be added to the gasifier and the hydrogen can be added to the product from the gasifier to produce methanol with a biomass carbon conversion efficiency of over 80% for the entire crop [45]. Achieving a high level of carbon conversion efficiency is an important aspect of biofuel production due to the limitations imposed on its production (as discussed in Section 5.16.4).

The synthesis of methanol or other fuels via biomass conversion using renewable hydrogen addition requires high investment costs for the electrolysis unit but provides high production rates, together with high energy (over 50%) and carbon conversion efficiency. The cost estimates made by Specht *et al.* [45] are clearly dependent on the costs of the energy and biomass inputs and the capital costs of the production plant at the time of the study, but simple analysis indicates that methanol made in this way would be about 50% more expensive than $65 per barrel gasoline on an equivalent energy basis.

Currently, there is no commercial biomethanol plant using gasification of biomass, but some use mixed biomass and fossil-based feedstocks [42]. The gasification and gas cleaning processes involved in the approaches described above still require large-scale demonstration, but the methanol synthesis and MTG processes are commercially available [43]. BioMCN have started production of biomethanol using the glycerin by-product from the biodiesel manufacturing process [46]. Some processes developed recently for ethanol production use a combination of thermochemical (gasification) and biochemical processes to avoid the total reliance on catalysts, which are sensitive to poisoning, or expensive enzymes, while being able to process a wide range of carbon-based feedstocks [47, 48].

5.16.3 Alcohol as Fuels for ICEs

The potential of alcohols as fuels for the ICE was noted as early as 1907 in the literature [49], and ethanol was initially a competitor to tetraethyl lead as a knock inhibitor. Because it can be synthesized from a wide range of renewable and alternative fossil-based feedstocks, methanol was the subject of many studies during the oil crises of the 1970s and 1980s [50–52]. More recently, the focus has shifted to ethanol made from biomass. Both alcohols are liquid fuels that can be stored in low-cost fuel systems. They also have the enormous advantage of being miscible with gasoline so that a single vehicle fuel system can be used and an infrastructure relatively similar to that which exists currently can be used to distribute them. The miscibility of methanol with ethanol and with gasoline means that it may be considered initially as an ethanol 'extender'; it will be shown in later sections that methanol itself could form the basis of an alternative transport fuel which, in the long-term, is carbon-neutral.

5.16.3.1 Physicochemical Properties

The presence of the hydroxyl (OH) group in alcohol molecules gives rise to local polarity, endowing them with various desirable physicochemical properties which are much more pronounced in the smaller, low-carbon-number alcohols such as methanol (CH_3OH) and ethanol (C_2H_5OH) than the higher alcohols such as butanol (C_4H_9OH) and pentanol ($C_5H_{11}OH$). The two 'lone pairs' of electrons on the oxygen atom, shown in **Figure 8**, give rise to a net negative charge around it and this produces a net positive charge on the rest of the molecule, which is particularly concentrated around the oxygen-attached hydrogen atom of the hydroxyl group. The molecular polarity generates strong intermolecular forces, known as hydrogen bonds, and these forces give rise to high boiling points (for their molecular mass), high heats of vaporization, and good miscibility with nominally dissimilar substances having strong molecular polarity (e.g., water). This polarity is also the reason for the greater corrosiveness of these fuels toward some materials compared with gasoline. Methanol and ethanol also have much higher octane indices than the higher normal (straight-chain) alcohols.

Table 1 lists several properties of a typical 95 research octane number (RON) unleaded gasoline, methanol, ethanol, and 1-butanol. It can be seen that the RON of methanol and ethanol are 106 and 108, respectively, whereas that of 1-butanol (the straight-chain isomer with its OH group on the first carbon atom) is 94.

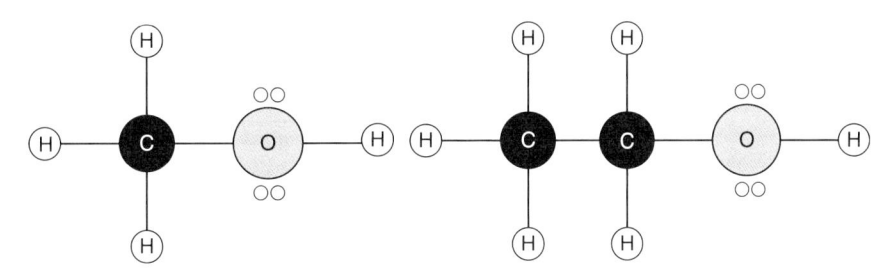

Figure 8 Schematic of methanol (left) and ethanol (right) molecules.

Table 1 Properties of gasoline, methanol, ethanol, and 1-butanol

Property	Gasoline[a]	Methanol	Ethanol	1-Butanol
Chemical formula	Various	CH_3OH	C_2H_5OH	C_4H_9OH
Oxygen content by mass (%)	0	50	34.8	21.6
Density at atmospheric 1 bar and 293K (kg l^{-1})	0.74	0.79	0.79	0.81
Lower heating value (MJ kg^{-1})	42.9	20.09	26.95	33.08
Volumetric energy content (MJ l^{-1})	31.7	15.9	21.3	26.8
Stoichiometric AFR (kg kg^{-1})	14.6	6.5	9	11.1
Energy per unit mass of air (MJ kg^{-1})	2.952	3.121	3.009	2.971
Energy per unit mass of air relative to gasoline	1	1.057	1.019	1.006
Research octane number (RON)	95	106	108	94
Motor octane number (MON)	85	92	98	81
Sensitivity (RON - MON)	10	14	11	13
Boiling point at 1 bar (°C)	25–215	65	79	118
Heat of vaporization (kJ kg^{-1})	180–350	1100	838	585
Heat of vaporization per unit mass of air (kJ kg^{-1})	24.1	170.9	93.6	52.5
Relative evaporation energy[b]	1	7.09	3.88	2.18
Mole ratio of products to reactants[c]	0.937	1.061	1.065	1.067
Ratio of triatomic to diatomic products[c]	0.351	0.532	0.443	0.399
Triatomic/diatomic products relative to gasoline	1	1.517	1.264	1.138
Specific CO_2 emissions (g MJ^{-1})	73.95	68.44	70.99	71.90
Specific CO_2 emissions relative to gasoline	1	0.926	0.960	0.972

[a] Typical.
[b] Relative to gasoline.
[c] Includes atmospheric nitrogen.

The presence of the oxygen atom in the alcohol molecule acts to reduce its heating value below that of the corresponding alkane (paraffin). This is due to the lower enthalpy of the carbon–oxygen bond relative to the carbon–hydrogen bond and leads to the alcohols, sometimes being referred to as 'partially oxidized'. **Figure** 9 shows that as the number of carbon atoms in the alcohol molecule increases, the reduction in the LHV of the alcohol decreases relative to the value of the corresponding alkane. **Figures** 10 and 11 show that the presence of the hydroxyl group in the lower-carbon-number alcohols has a much greater effect on the heat of

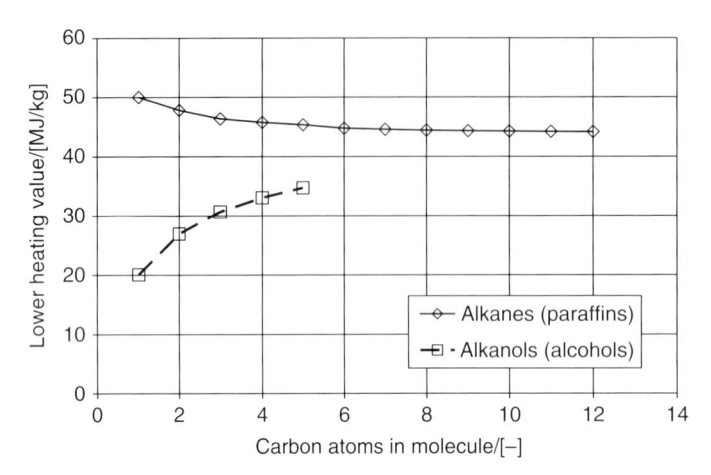

Figure 9 Variation of lower heating value with number of carbon atoms for alkanes and alcohols.

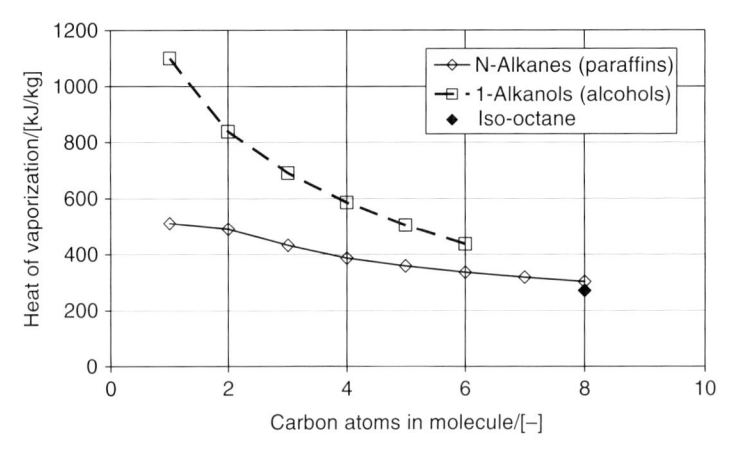

Figure 10 Variation of heat of vaporization with number of carbon atoms for alkanes and alcohols.

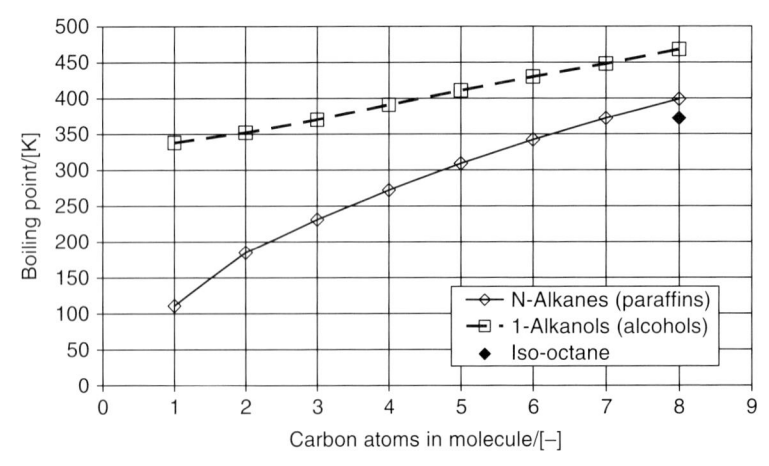

Figure 11 Variation of boiling point with number of carbon atoms for alkanes and alcohols.

vaporization and the boiling point, respectively, than in the higher-carbon-number alcohols relative to their corresponding alkanes. In the case of the heat of vaporization, the low stoichiometric air–fuel ratio (AFR) of the fuels means that the effect is accentuated beyond that indicated in **Figure 10** (see values per unit mass of air in **Table 1**) but is limited in practice by the saturation point of the mixture being reached.

The high polarity of the methanol and ethanol molecules, which endows them with their desirable properties as fuels, also differentiates them from gasoline in ways which require additional care to be taken in their handling and storage. These effects account for their aggressive behavior toward some of the materials to which gasoline is benign. However, their superiority in the combustion chamber and the wide range of feedstocks from which they can be manufactured leads them, in the authors' opinion, to be preferable to higher-carbon-number alcohols. Butanol is preferred as a blending agent by some fossil fuel producers as the OH group does not dominate the characteristic of the molecule to the same degree so that it does not phase-separate in the presence of water and causes less deviation from the properties of the base gasoline.

5.16.3.2 Low-Carbon-Number Alcohols as Fuels for SI Engines

Unusually for 'alternative' fuels, ethanol and methanol have the potential to increase engine performance and efficiency over that achievable with gasoline. This is due to a variety of factors, including their higher octane rating, heat of vaporization, flame speed, energy per unit mass of air, molar ratio of products to reactants, and heat capacity of combustion products due to a high ratio of triatomic to diatomic molecules. It should be noted here that the familiar increase in volumetric fuel consumption of about 25% when operating an unmodified gasoline engine on high-concentration ethanol (E85) is simply due to the lower volumetric energy content of the fuel. The thermal efficiency of the engine, defined as work produced per unit of fuel energy supplied, is usually slightly higher when operating on the alcohol fuel.

Figure 12 shows that the RON of ethanol in 95 RON gasoline increases nonlinearly with alcohol concentration, with much of the benefit being available at 50% ethanol by volume in the blend. (The octane number of a fuel is a measure of its resistance to abnormal combustion known as knock. Knock originates with the autoignition of regions of the end gas (the fuel, air, and residual gas mixture) ahead of the propagating flame front in an SI engine. Low octane number fuels readily cause knocking in engines with high compression ratios or high cylinder pressures, such as turbocharged engines. Knocking thus limits engine efficiency and performance through limiting allowable compression ratio or delaying the phase of the combustion event.) Brinkman *et al.* [53] studied low-level blends of methanol and ethanol in production gasoline engines of the time and concluded that the behavior of the two alcohols in these blends was similar. Brinkman [54] found a 3–4% improvement in thermal efficiency using ethanol (E100) relative to operation on a control gasoline fuel using a single-cylinder engine with a low compression ratio. Using methanol (M100), Koenig *et al.* [55] found improvements of around 8% in thermal efficiency over gasoline operating at full load at 2000 rpm with a compression ratio of 8.2:1; a power increase of about 12% was achieved. A thermal efficiency of over 40% was reported when a compression ratio of 12:1 was used.

Recent work on modern multicylinder engines has demonstrated significant opportunities for both increasing efficiency and performance. Nakata *et al.* [56] used a high compression ratio (13:1) naturally aspirated port fuel-injected SI and found that engine torque increased by 5% and 20% using E100 compared with the operation on 100 RON and 92 RON gasoline, respectively. The full improvements in torque due to being able to run MBT ignition timing were apparent for E50. This may have been due to a combined effect of the maximum charge cooling (which enhances knock resistance) occurring with blends between 30% and 50% ethanol concentration and the increasing RON level [57]. Using E100, a full-load thermal efficiency at 2800 rpm of 39.6% was reported by Nakata *et al.* [56], compared with 37.9% and 31.7% using the high- and low-octane gasoline, respectively. A thermal

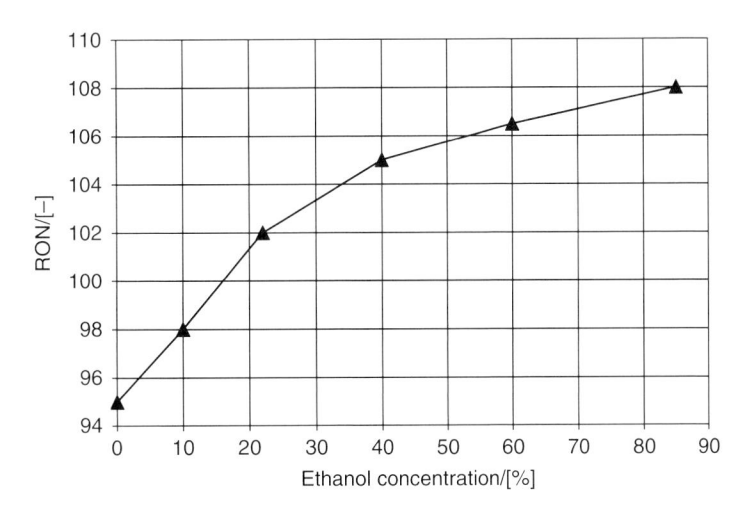

Figure 12 Variation of research octane number with ethanol concentration in 95 RON gasoline.

efficiency improvement of 3% was achieved using E100 over the 100 RON gasoline at the 2000 rpm at 2 bar BMEP operating point, where the engine was far from the area where knock becomes a limiting factor – this is indicative of the benefits of faster flame speed, higher product specific heat capacity, and lower combustion temperatures (lowering heat losses) of the alcohol fuel. Similar results were reported by Marriott et al. [58] at this operating point; the improvements were attributed to the reduced heat losses when running on E85, established by heat release analysis. Up to 6% benefit was found at other low-speed/load points, with CO_2 emissions being reduced by up to 11%, with the additional benefit above the efficiency gain being due to the low CO_2 emissions per unit energy released by combustion of the alcohol fuel.

The high potential to cool the cylinder charge as the fuel evaporates has an appreciable effect on reducing the propensity of the engine to knock, which is a supplementary effect to that of the high octane numbers of the fuels. This enhanced knock resistance of methanol and ethanol and the potential to increase intake charge density makes these fuels well suited to pressure-charged engines [59] where improvements in fuel economy achieved by 'downsizing' may be compromised when using gasoline by the requirement to use a relatively low compression ratio to avoid excessive knock at high loads. The lower exhaust temperatures obtained using alcohol fuels also reduce the requirement for component protection overfueling. The engine used in the tri-FFV (as described in Section 5.16.6) was modified to realize the benefit of the charge cooling effect at full load by introducing a portion of the fuel load upstream of the supercharger. The thermal efficiency and performance benefits using E85 fuel in this engine have been described in detail elsewhere [60, 61].

Peak torque and power increases of 15% and 10%, respectively, were obtained by Bergstrom et al. [62, 63] using a production turbocharged ethanol–gasoline flex-fuel engine with port fuel injection. The lower exhaust gas temperatures experienced when running on E85 allowed the fuel enrichment level at full load to be reduced to the extent that, for the same limiting peak pressures as those tolerated using gasoline fuel, stoichiometric operation across the engine speed range is possible [63]. Kapus et al. [64] found that for identical engine performance, the more favorable combustion phasing when operating on E85 at full load leads to less requirement for fuel enrichment giving a 24% improvement in efficiency compared with operation on 95 RON gasoline. Thermal efficiency improvements at full load of over 35% relative to 95 RON gasoline have been found using E100 in a direct-injection, turbocharged SI engine [65] operating at high BMEP levels.

Direct injection of the fuel into the cylinder increases the possibility to exploit the heat of vaporization of E85 to good effect in order to increase the effective octane benefit. Weinowski et al. [66] found that they were able to increase spark timing by as much as 16 degrees crank angle using E85 compared with operation on 95 RON gasoline. Marriott et al. [58] quote a 13% increase in maximum power when running on E85 fuel relative to 91 RON gasoline in a naturally aspirated engine and show that, of the 11.3% increase in peak torque, 3.1% was due to improved volumetric efficiency, with 3.7% and 4.5% being attributed to improved combustion phasing and reduced heat losses, respectively. When the fueling on E85 was limited to stoichiometric across the speed range, peak torque and power were still improved by 8.2% and 10.7%, respectively, above the results obtained with enriched operation on the baseline 91 RON gasoline. Compared with 104 RON gasoline fuel, which was not knock limited at maximum torque, the improvement in peak torque was about 7%, which is indicative of the improved volumetric efficiency and combustion phasing obtained using E85 and the reduced heat loss from lower combustion temperatures.

Recent work by Malcolm et al. [67] has shown faster burn rates than iso-octane using commercial E85 fuel at stoichiometric and lean AFRs but a splash-blended E85/iso-octane mixture gave slightly slower burn rates at lean operation conditions. Several studies have identified that the faster combustion rate experienced using methanol extends the dilution limit relative to gasoline [51, 55, 68], and Pannone and Johnson [69] employed these characteristics in a lean-burn turbocharged engine.

The greater dilution limit of methanol and ethanol was exploited by Brusstar et al. [70] who converted a base 1.9 l direct-injection, turbocharged diesel engine to run on M100 and E100 by replacing the diesel injectors with spark plugs and fitting a low-pressure alcohol fuel injection system in the intake manifold. Running at the 19.5:1 compression ratio of the base diesel engine, the PFI methanol variant increased the peak brake thermal efficiency from 40% to 42%, while parity with the diesel was achieved using ethanol. Cooled exhaust gas recirculation (EGR) enabled the engine to achieve close-to-MBT ignition timing at high loads, while high levels of EGR dilution were used to spread the high-efficiency regions to extensive areas of the part-load operating map. Emissions of NO_x, CO, and HC were extremely low operating on methanol using a conventional 'three-way' aftertreatment system. Particulate and aldehyde emissions were not measured due to earlier work [71], which had established the ability to control these to very low levels using a conventional oxidation catalyst. Low-carbon-number alcohols can, with good mixture preparation, also give low particulate emissions, particularly methanol that has no carbon–carbon bonds. Similar results were found by Brusstar and Gray [72] using a 4.5 l V6 diesel as a base engine. The dilution limits for methanol and ethanol were established for throttleless operation, and these also increase with the proportion of alcohol in the fuel so that for M100, throttleless operation from a BMEP of 16 bars down to 4 bars is possible. This was possible due to the higher flame speeds of the fuels providing higher combustion tolerance to cooled EGR.

While the high heat of vaporization and low stoichiometric AFR are beneficial from the perspective of engine performance, they are also responsible, together with their relatively high boiling points (65 °C for methanol and 78 °C for ethanol, at 1 bar), for the additional attention required in order to achieve acceptable cold-start performance using low-carbon-number alcohols. **Figure 13**, based on the approach used by Nakata et al. [56], shows the theoretical [73] variation of the vapor pressure of methanol, ethanol, and iso-octane with temperature. Iso-octane, having molecular mass of 114, clearly has none of the light fractions that are present in gasoline and so has a low vapor pressure. **Figure 14** compares the saturated vapor pressure of the three fuels at 0 °C with the vapor pressure required to form a stoichiometric air–fuel mixture ($\lambda = 1$) at an ambient pressure of 1.01 bar. With its combination of low vapor pressure and relatively low stoichiometric AFR, ethanol is the furthest from forming a stoichiometric mixture at this

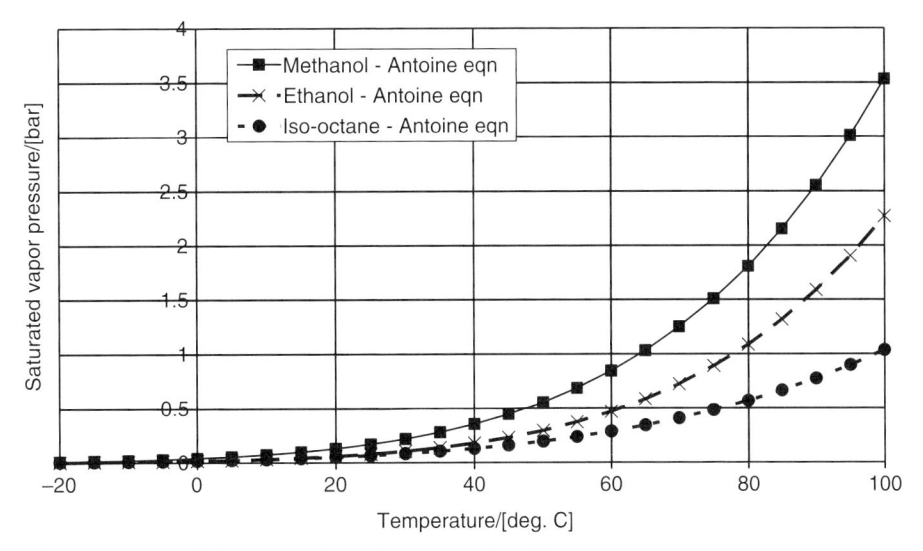

Figure 13 Variation of vapor pressure with temperature for methanol, ethanol, and iso-octane.

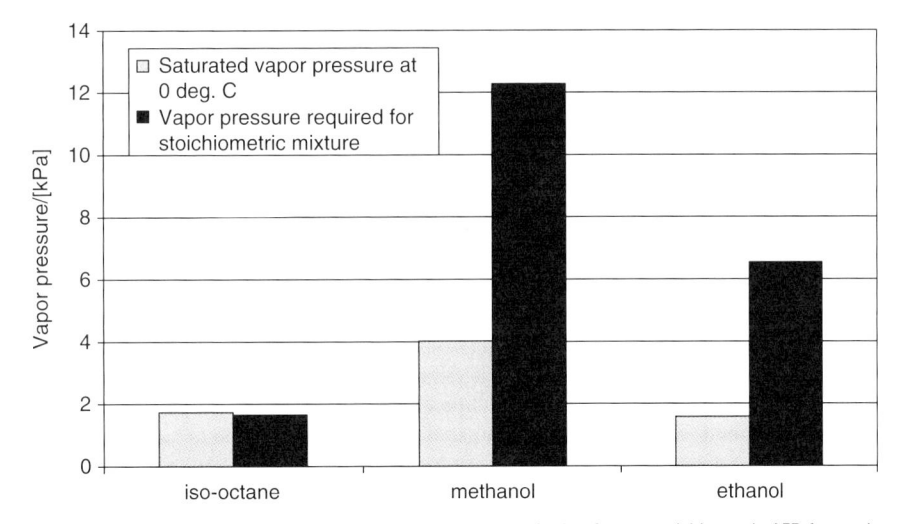

Figure 14 Comparison of saturated vapor pressure at 0 °C and vapor pressure required to form a stoichiometric AFR for methanol, ethanol, and iso-octane.

temperature (defined by the ratio of the saturated vapor pressure at the temperature concerned to the vapor pressure require to form a stoichiometric mixture). A similar behavior is illustrated in **Figure 15** where the excess air ratio (λ = actual AFR/stoichiometric AFR) formed by a saturated mixture is shown at various temperatures. Even without its light fractions, the saturated vapor pressure of iso-octane is sufficient to form a stoichiometric air–fuel mixture at 0 °C.

Mixtures of alcohol and gasoline are nonideal solutions in that partial vapor pressure of a component (gasoline itself is a mixture of components) is not proportional to its concentration (mole fraction) and its vapor pressure when pure, that is, they do not obey Raoult's law. Not only is the variation of the vapor pressure nonlinear with alcohol concentration, but it is also not monotonic. This irregular behavior is thought to be caused by hydrogen bonding where, for example, methanol forms a 'quasi-super-molecule' known as a cyclic tetramer in which four methanol molecules form a superstructure via hydrogen bonds between the individual molecules. These cyclic tetramers have an effective molecular mass of 128 (4 times that of an individual molecule) rendering the vapor pressure of the pure methanol relatively low [74]. The hydrogen bonds are progressively weakened and become less extensive when the alcohol is mixed with increasing quantities of a nonpolar solvent such as gasoline, making them behave as low-molecular-mass components (32 in the case of methanol) which increase the vapor pressure of the mixture. Fuel volatility is also increased because alcohols form low boiling point azeotropes with some hydrocarbons. Compared with a typical gasoline, the Reid vapor pressures of methanol and ethanol blends with the same gasoline are higher up to concentrations of about 80% and 45%, respectively, before dropping steeply [52, 57, 73]. In addition to affecting the cold-start performance of an engine, this behavior illustrates how evaporative emissions using methanol and ethanol at high concentration levels can be lower than those of gasoline while they can be higher using low-concentration blends.

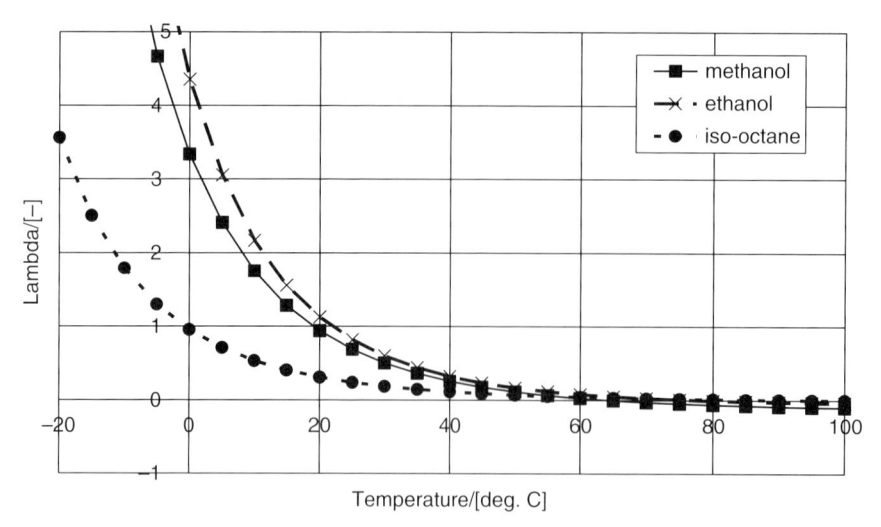

Figure 15 Variation of excess air ratio (lambda) produced by saturated vapor with temperature for methanol, ethanol, and iso-octane.

In addition to the performance benefits resulting from the adoption of direct fuel injection, Siewart and Groff [75] have achieved cold start at −29 °C using charge stratification and late fuel injection. Kapus *et al.* [64] and Marriott *et al.* [58] have proposed high-pressure late injections, using several split injections to further augment the quality of the start. For port fuel-injected engines measures such as heating the fuel rail can enable acceptable cold-start performance down to −25 °C. Bergström *et al.* [62] report acceptable cold starts down to −25 °C in the absence of additional technology with a PFI engine using Swedish winter standard bioethanol (E75 with Reid vapor pressure = 50).

It should be noted that while ethanol and methanol offer some significant advantages over gasoline as fuels for SI engines, the normal-configuration higher alcohols, which have the hydroxyl group on the end of a straight chain of carbon atoms, exhibit progressively degraded knock resistance such that propanol could be considered only slightly better than gasoline, and *n*-butanol and *n*-pentanol significantly worse. Yacoub *et al.* [76] and Gautum and Martins [77] have shown that whether a binary mixture of gasoline and alcohols or multiple blends are considered (all with controlled oxygen content), methanol and ethanol clearly produce superior fuels to the normal forms of the higher alcohols. The gasoline they used, UTG-96 (i.e., unleaded test gasoline-96 (also known as indolene) is supplied by Chevron Phillips; it has a RON of 96.1 and a MON of 87.0 and is the certification test gasoline in the United States) [78], had an RON of 96 and so can be considered representative of a premium US gasoline or a regular European one. More recently, Cairns *et al.* [79] have also tested blends of different alcohols in a more modern engine configuration with direct injection and turbocharging, and their full-load results indicate that matched oxygen content blends of ethanol or *n*-butanol with gasoline provide better and worse knock resistance than the base 95 RON fuel, respectively.

Thus, the normal alcohol molecules considered to be beneficial in blends with gasoline are those with up to only two carbon atoms. In general, however, the alcohols display similar characteristics to the paraffins (alkanes) as the molecule is branched. Popuri and Bata [80] suggest that the branched molecules of isobutanol make it the equal of ethanol and methanol as a blending component but at the expense of considerable extra complication in the manufacturing process over *n*-butanol, the fuel most readily manufactured and generally used by other researchers (note that Popuri and Bata were using a Co-operative Fuels Research (CFR) engine with a carburetor and did not test all of the fuels at exactly the same equivalence ratio [80]).

In summary, for SI combustion, when blending alcohols with gasoline or considering the alcohols as fuels in their own right, the lower alcohols methanol and ethanol are superior to gasoline, with monotonic degradation in performance from propanol onwards. *n*-Butanol (1-butanol) is quantifiably worse than gasoline. In a future transport energy economy where WTW energy efficiency is a key criterion, the clear benefit of only synthesizing C1 and C2 alcohols is plainly apparent: they will require less energy to create and will provide higher thermal efficiency in use.

5.16.3.3 Low-Carbon-Number Alcohols as Fuels for Compression-Ignition Engines

As a corollary of the low-carbon-number alcohols having high octane numbers, they have very low cetane numbers (CNs). For methanol, the number is so low that it cannot be measured directly. Extrapolation of test data using additives gives a CN of 3 for pure methanol and a CN of 2 for methanol with 10% water [51]. Since CN is a measure of a fuel's autoignitibility, pure methanol and ethanol are unsuitable for use in conventional compression-ignition engines; however, they can be used in conjunction with another fuel which is more autoignitable, or with an 'ignition improver'. In the 1980s, the Detroit Diesel Company (DDC) and MAN [81] produced modified versions of their compression-ignition engines that ran on 'ignition-improved' methanol fuel (the ignition improver constituted about 5% by volume of the fuel). The MAN engine was a four-stroke engine using spark-assisted ignition, while the DDC engines operated on the two-stroke cycle, controlling the scavenge ratio and using glow plugs to assist ignition [82, 83]. Urban [83] showed that the diesel base DDC engine was easily modified to run on ignition-improved methanol and could develop more power at the same level of particulate emissions. These engines ran in service in heavy-duty applications [81, 84].

Hikino and Suzuki [85] modified a 9.9 l six-cylinder direct-injection diesel engine to run on pure methanol in compression-ignition mode. The engine ran in naturally aspirated form with its compression ratio increased from 17.9:1 to 27:1 in order to achieve autoignition and using EGR to increase the intake temperature at low loads. Significant improvement in NOx was achieved as a result of the combustion system employed. Additionally, both ethanol and methanol produce low levels of particulate emissions when used in compression-ignition engines due to smaller, or in the case of methanol, lack of, carbon–carbon chains in the fuel. These characteristics show the potential of methanol as a heavy-duty engine fuel against the necessity of reducing pollutant emissions while maintaining high thermal efficiency operation.

5.16.3.4 Safety Aspects of Alcohol Fuels

The safety of all fuels and energy carriers has to be reviewed with respect to their suitability for use in the mass market by vehicle operators who at present require no special training to handle apparatus that dispenses the fuel. The incumbent fuels for light-duty vehicles – gasoline and, to a lesser extent on a global scale, diesel – are easily dispensed by self-service and the equipment used to vend them has been developed such that unintended ignition at point of dispensation is an extremely rare occurrence. However, it is true that while familiarity breeds contempt, it also leads to a *status quo* in which these commonplace fuels are seen as inherently safe. Thus, a situation exists where all other fuels proposed as alternatives are scrutinized with regards to their safety, and if any issues are found with them in an absolute sense, then they are criticized severely, despite their being significant safety issues with the incumbents. It is argued that either this approach of intense scrutiny should also be applied to gasoline and diesel (in which case both would probably be withdrawn from service) or alternative fuels should be fairly compared with the incumbents. If this is done, it is posited here that the alcohols present themselves as far more attractive fuels from a safety viewpoint, be it on grounds of death, injury, or property damage.

Gasoline, in particular, is highly dangerous. It is poisonous and can readily be ignited unintentionally. When it burns, it releases a huge amount of heat that is effectively radiated due to the high carbon intensity of the fuel. Diesel is safer only with regard to unintended ignition from which perspective it is a very safe fuel. These issues must be borne in mind when comparing alternatives, and will be discussed in the following sections, which will primarily address them from the perspective of methanol safety.

This approach has been adopted in this section not just because of the later discussion of methanol as potentially providing the bulk of transport fuel in the long-term but because methanol shares many of its characteristics with ethanol, the other low-carbon-number alcohol which is used as an alternative light-duty transport fuel, except that methanol exhibits an increased level of acute toxicity in humans. Thus, it is argued that if it can be demonstrated that methanol is a viable and preferable alternative to gasoline and diesel as an energy carrier, then the same will also apply to ethanol. It should be noted, however, that ethanol is also toxic despite its widespread use as a social drink: the relative toxicity of ethanol, methanol, and gasoline will be quantified below.

5.16.3.4.1 *General safety aspects of methanol as a fuel*

The issue of safety has plagued every attempt to introduce methanol as a widespread transport fuel, possibly as a result of it being a genuine, non-feedstock-limited, practically implementable alternative to the *status quo* of fossil fuels. As a consequence of this, there has been much debate and misunderstanding about issues such as acute and chronic toxicity and fire safety, almost all of it without declaring the true baseline for comparison. It seems that any alternative fuel must be 100% safe in an absolute sense before it will even be considered for use on the forecourt, while the current fuels, that is, fossil-based gasoline and diesel, continue to benefit from a 'grandfather clause' when in fact they are easily shown to be at best only as safe as methanol (and, in many of their characteristics, significantly less so) [86–88].

Unlike some of the compounds found in gasoline, such as benzene, methanol is not presently classed as a carcinogen [87], although it and many other chemicals are currently being assessed by the US Environmental Protection Agency (EPA) with regard to their carcinogenity (note that conversely ethanol 'can' increase the risks of developing certain cancers when it is ingested in large quantities [89]). Instead, the major issue with safety that methanol, or indeed any alternative fuel choice, has to face is toxicity, both in terms of ingestion, skin or eye contact, or inhalation (in either acute or chronic poisoning scenarios) or increased levels of formaldehyde emission when it is burned. In the following, it is intended to discuss these issues first and then to present a case in which the inherent safety of methanol, in terms of unintended ignition, outweighs the likely death and injury rate associated with physical contact with the neat fuel. Much of the data referred to come from US EPA sources, since they have been instrumental in calling for the widespread use of methanol as a transport fuel due to its improved emissions upon combustion and its being a potential solution to help massively reduce transport-related CO_2 emission. It is hoped that the conclusions reached and the provenance of these data will serve to strengthen the case for methanol as a transport fuel, even on the basis of a balanced assessment of its safety versus gasoline and diesel alone and without considering its GHG reduction potential.

Methanol is one of the most widely used industrial chemicals and is readily metabolized in small amounts by the human body on account of its being found naturally in fruit and vegetables, in background amounts within the human body and formed readily through the hydrolysis of aspartame in the digestive system (this being one of the most widely used food sweeteners) [86]. This leads to the fact that methanol is a natural chemical for the human body to ingest and consequently that there is no mechanism to vomit it should it be ingested in any amount. The pure hydrocarbons found in gasoline and diesel, conversely, are completely alien compounds for the human body, and so are readily vomited if swallowed. While in some respects this could be considered advantageous, in itself it can lead to fatal consequences as we shall see later. The issue of toxicity of methanol actually arises solely as a result of overloading the digestive system with the chemical. To a large extent, this is because of the general metabolic pathway followed:

$$CH_3OH \rightarrow \quad HCHO \rightarrow \quad HCOOH \rightarrow \quad CO_2 + H_2O$$
$$\text{(methanol)} \quad \text{(formaldehyde)} \quad \text{(formic acid)} \quad \text{(carbon dioxide + water)}$$

The crucial step is that involving the final metabolism of formic acid (formate) to carbon dioxide and water. This occurs via pathways dependent on folic acid (folate) and gives rise to a variability in the fatal dose depending on the mass of the victim and on whether they belong to a group commonly deficient in folic acid, for example, pregnant women or elderly people [86]. As a consequence of this variability, Fishbein and Henry [90] quote the fatal dose when untreated to be considered to be between 0.3 and 1.3 g kg^{-1} body weight. Machiele reports a normally fatal dose range of 60–240 ml, although this can go as low as 26 ml depending on the individual; he also points out that the fatal dose range for gasoline is only twice as much (at 115–470 ml) [86, 87], and yet its toxicity is not considered bad by most individuals, due to the fact that it is such an everyday commodity. A final point indicating that methanol is not generally as toxic in relation to other compounds as many believe is that in some test animals lethal doses of methanol have been found to be greater than for ethanol [89, 91].

5.16.3.4.2 Ingestion

Progressive symptoms of acute methanol poisoning from direct ingestion include dizziness, nausea, respiratory problems, coma, and finally death. However, this process can take between 10 and 48 h after ingestion and the cure is well understood, in the form of the intravenous administration of ethanol (which the body preferentially metabolizes while the methanol is ejected) together with sodium bicarbonate to control blood acidity [92]. As mentioned above, ingestion of gasoline or diesel, conversely, can be fatal in amounts only a factor of 2 higher, and if the victim survives this, the only cure is a lengthy period of rest and recuperation, versus a very short recuperation period following survival of methanol poisoning. While methanol is tasteless and odorless and thus could readily be ingested accidentally, it is, however, difficult to ignore the swallowing of pure hydrocarbons because of their taste and the fact that the body has a strong desire to vomit them; this latter point has been promoted as a distinct advantage by the anti-methanol lobby, and would be so were it not for the fact that the direct communication of esophagus and trachea at the epiglottis can mean that any vomited hydrocarbons can directly enter the lungs, in turn causing severe damage and, in extremis, death by suffocation (since the hydrocarbon molecules can form an impervious membrane on the lungs). Machiele [86] states that if gasoline is aspirated into the lungs in this manner, the fatal dose is much smaller than that if swallowed and not vomited.

While it is often cited that methanol is extremely toxic and so should be avoided at all costs, it is salutary to reflect that a widely found application of methanol is in the denitrification of drinking water, which in turn leads to some of the background levels found in the human body. This shows that if its concentration and deployment is closely controlled, there is no danger to human health from its application [91]. It should also be noted that ethanol is also considered acutely toxic in doses only approximately 2 times that of methanol (276–455 g, or 350–577 ml, according to Gable [93]), and yet as noted, ethanol is widely enjoyed by society at large in alcoholic beverages. From the foregoing, one can make the observation that ethanol is as dangerous to drink as gasoline or diesel.

Since, as mentioned above, the main problem with regard to methanol poisoning is overload of the metabolic system (whether intentional or not), steps can readily be taken to render void the disadvantages of its lack of odor and taste; the use of a compound such as denatonium (which is sold under the trade name Bitrex), can make it completely unpalatable to human taste in concentrations well below that at which its desirable characteristics as a fuel would be affected (concentrations of Bitrex as low as 10 ppm are unbearable to humans [91, 94]). Similar approaches are possible for odor and this approach is successfully employed with natural gas, which is similarly odorless.

A final point concerning the swallowing of methanol is that most gasoline or diesel ingestion has historically been as a result of siphoning of fuel tanks. It has been pointed out that it would be relatively easy to put barriers in fuel tank filler necks to make this extremely difficult, and such steps have been suggested as part of the insertion of flame arrestors [86], the level of requirement for which will be discussed later. Since methanol was investigated in this manner in the 1980s, however, fuel filler systems have become more complex in order to avoid vapor release into the atmosphere and consequently it has become more difficult to siphon fuel tank contents anyway. Machiele [86] suggests that one of the prime reasons for siphoning fuel from vehicle tanks is to transfer it to lawn mowers, and so on; if these were left as gasoline-fueled, there would be little or no reason to siphon methanol. This, coupled with the ability to make fuel methanol unpalatable through the adoption of specific additives as discussed above, makes the likelihood of unintentional ingestion of lethal amounts still more unlikely.

5.16.3.4.3 Skin/eye contact

Methanol can enter the body through the skin or the eyes; its effect is different to gasoline which is similarly to be avoided, since it is especially likely to dry the skin through solvent action. Machiele [86] states that infrequent splashes of methanol will be of little concern, but issues start to arise with continual or frequent exposure, where the accumulation of methanol in the body can reach dangerous levels such that acute poisoning is possible; this is stated to be equivalent to total immersion of a hand for 4 h for death to be possible. This scenario is considered to be unlikely and to be addressable via a conventional health and safety approach (which is the case at present for industrial uses of methanol). Generally, the bioaccumulation danger of methanol is negligible [91].

5.16.3.4.4 Inhalation

As is the case for skin and eye contact, the effects of inhalation of methanol are not severe until the acute toxic limit is approached; in other respects, methanol fumes are less harmful than gasoline ones. In terms of the accumulation of methanol emissions in the atmosphere along the roadside, EPA's analysis in the 1980s showed that the concentration of methanol would be at a rate significantly below the minimum lethal dose, even assuming all vehicles adopt M100 and 25% have serious malfunctions of the emissions control system; it has been pointed out that since that time emissions regulations have become much stricter and so this means of transferring methanol into the human body would be even less of a risk [87].

In terms of significant fume buildup in confined spaces, Fishbein and Henry [90] discuss some work with laboratory animals which showed that extremely long-term continual exposure to methanol fumes below the lethal dose did not affect the reproductive system, while some effects on growth rates were seen in rat pups. Conversely, Brusstar *et al.* [87] state that acute methanol exposure is suspected to have an effect on the human reproductive system and to be capable of promoting some birth defects; they do, however, point out that such exposure is typically of very short duration and, since the adoption of severe evaporative emissions regulation is only likely to be found in closed rooms (such as personal garages) with poor ventilation where there is a large, open methanol container. This scenario is unlikely and probably made more so because methanol is not as good a solvent as gasoline for cleaning grease: it would not be the first choice for this role, whereas gasoline is often left open to the atmosphere for this purpose. This observation also removes one secondary reason to siphon fuels from tanks (as discussed above). One challenge here would be to give fuel methanol an odor that is immediately recognizable (as mentioned above), so that if a storage vessel were open, the fact would be readily apparent.

The situation in car parks and filling stations is estimated to be less serious than for private garages, since these are usually open or force-ventilated; Brusstar *et al.* [87] do state that some legislation dependent on filling station configuration may be required in order to protect attendants who are present in the region for long periods of time, but for most, this is not expected to be a significant issue.

In terms of air quality, methanol is approximately 20% as photochemically reactive as gasoline, and its ozone-producing potential is concomitantly reduced. In this respect, it is seen as being of great benefit in terms of local air quality, and indeed this can outweigh the roadside accumulation issues stated above [87].

5.16.3.4.5 Toxic emissions when burned

Methanol, like all combustion engine fuels, causes airborne emissions of various species, some of which are more of a health concern than others. The main concern for methanol is the emission of formaldehyde, which is a major intermediate species in its oxidation and the absorption of which into the body is harmful for reasons discussed previously. However, for vehicle use, formaldehyde emissions can be dealt with by catalysts [95], and conventional formulations for catalytic converters have for some time been known to reduce formaldehyde emissions in methanol-fueled engines to a similar level as gasoline-fueled ones [96], although earlier work suggested that some changes may be necessary to ensure long-term catalyst durability [97]. This is not expected to be an issue with present-day technology: FFVs have been shown to be capable of meeting limits for formaldehyde when operated on E85 [98] and are expected to be able to do so for other alcohols such as *n*-butanol [99]. Gasoline may actually yield greater challenges on drive cycles in the future: some technologies such as cooled EGR increase its aldehyde emissions [99], and in one study, E85 actually had lower aldehyde emissions on the US06 drive cycle which requires higher driving loads at the wheel than is typically the case for others [98].

All other criteria toxic emissions – hydrocarbons, carbon monoxide, oxides of nitrogen, and particulate matter – are generally expected to be lower with methanol than with gasoline, and all (except particulate matter) are further reduced with catalytic converters. Overall, EPA estimated that emissions of air toxins with methanol would be 7% those of gasoline, and these would to a great extent be offset by the lower photoreactivity causing better air quality as discussed in Section 5.16.3.4.4 [87]. It should also be remembered that many species found in gasoline emissions are also carcinogens, although the widespread use of catalytic converters likewise reduces their concentration in the atmosphere to very low levels. Overall, with current emissions technology, it is possible to produce versions of existing FFVs that use the same catalyst formulation as dedicated gasoline ones that can readily comply with hydrocarbon, carbon monoxide, and oxides of nitrogen emissions levels when operating on any combination of methanol, ethanol, and gasoline [100].

5.16.3.4.6 Fire safety

It is in the area of fire safety that methanol shows a clear and overwhelming advantage over gasoline. The flammability index of methanol is akin to that of diesel [101, 102]; in open spaces it is not readily ignitable at all below 10 °C (50 °F). When compared with gasoline, it has much lower volatility and heat release rate, has a lower vapor density, and requires a greater concentration of vapor to form a combustible mixture in air. The low volatility combined with the high lower ignition limit means an ignitable mixture is unlikely to form before being dispersed, significantly reducing the likelihood of fire breaking out. If fire does occur, then the rate of heat release is only approximately 11% that of gasoline; this is because methanol has a very high heat of vaporization and a low stoichiometric AFR, which together mean that a lot of the fire's energy is itself absorbed in vaporizing its feedstock and the absence of carbon–carbon bonds in the molecule means that soot cannot form to radiate heat.

This last point is important because it also means that methanol flames are practically invisible, especially in sunlight. This is a major potential issue for fire fighters, who may not realize that there is a methanol fire underway and could consequently step into it, but as is the case for the lack of taste and smell, additives have been investigated to improve this issue. It has also been pointed out that in a fire onboard a vehicle, there is usually something with carbon-containing molecules which will ignite shortly after the fuel to give a visual indication of a fire taking place, although, of course, it would be preferable if the flames of the methanol fuel were visible in their own right.

The addition of 15% gasoline to methanol to form M85 has historically been one route to addressing taste, smell, and flame visibility, while at the same time improving the low-temperature startability of methanol-fueled vehicles. However, it is sobering to note that this alone indicates the sheer fire hazard of gasoline versus diesel: just 15% gasoline in methanol raises its flammability index from near-diesel levels to 50% that of straight gasoline [101].

In order to ignite a pool of methanol, a similar approach is needed to igniting a pool of diesel, that is, a source of ignition has to be placed in or in close proximity to the surface of the fuel and energy continually supplied to vaporize it and form an ignitable mixture in air. Once ignition has occurred, however, methanol is significantly safer than diesel or gasoline because the pure hydrocarbon fuels release more energy per unit mass of fuel and also radiate the heat much further. As a consequence, for any given distance from a pool fire's edge, the chances of fatality can be expected to be approximately 90% less with methanol [101, 102].

Both methanol and ethanol do have the potential to form ignitable mixtures in closed vessels such as fuel tanks under some conditions of air-to-liquid volume ratio and ambient temperature; note that this can also theoretically happen for gasoline as well as for alcohol [103]. However, this concern can be addressed by the inclusion of a flame arrestor in the tank filler neck (which can also readily function as an anti-siphoning device, further enhancing active safety with regard to accidental ingestion of methanol).

A final observation on the relative safety of methanol as a fuel is that it is extinguishable with water (because of its miscibility). This and all of the fire safety factors outlined above were the primary reasons why Indianapolis-style racing in the United States adopted pure methanol (M100) as its only fuel for many years; the serious crash involving seven cars fueled with gasoline at the 1964 Indianapolis 500 persuaded the US Auto Club to move to ban the use of gasoline on safety grounds from 1965 [104]. Even the clear flame of methanol, and its consequent effect in improving visibility, was one of the attractions of moving to this fuel.

5.16.3.4.7 Groundwater leakage

If methanol leaks into the ground, it is rapidly metabolized by microorganisms and biodegrades in a very short timescale [51, 91]. In this respect, its reputation has been somewhat damaged by its association with methyl *tert*-butyl ether (MTBE), which is formed by the chemical reaction of methanol and isobutylene and is often used as an octane-enhancing additive in gasoline. In the United States, MTBE is now banned as an additive to gasoline because of groundwater adulteration from leaking gasoline storage tanks (MTBE is not as readily biodegradable, requiring specialized bacteria to do so and consequently tends to travel widely from the leakage source, thus forming a path for the carcinogenic compounds in gasoline to follow) [105]. While methanol also readily dissolves in subsurface water, it degrades quickly and so does not form long pathways for other compounds to follow, although it is reported that methanol can act to extend gasoline leakage plumes, primarily because it is preferentially metabolized by many organisms. Unfortunately, methanol appears to sit in a similar place in the public consciousness with regard to groundwater issues, whereas this is not the case (witness its use to denitrify drinking water already referred to). The MTBE groundwater issue can also be firmly addressed by improved storage tanks, as is the case in Europe where it is still permitted as an additive to gasoline up to 5% by volume.

Overall, methanol leakages will readily biodegrade and as a consequence methanol spills mostly self-clean. It is safer and more environmentally benign than gasoline and certainly more so than many common gasoline components such as aromatic compounds [91]. The same is true for ethanol [89]. Even large spills of either alcohol into open water present little issue since the infinite solubility of both means they quickly disperse to safe levels and then biodegrade rapidly. This in itself offers passive environmental benefits compared with fuels derived from crude oil, since any methanol or ethanol tanker breakup at sea would not be expected to damage the environment.

5.16.3.4.8 Concluding remarks on safety

As a consequence of the foregoing, widespread methanol usage would be expected to lead to an improvement in local and national air quality and a reduction in deaths, fires, and property loss in the region of 90–95% versus gasoline [101, 102]. The fact that it can be made renewably from fully sustainable feedstocks also means that methanol can contribute disproportionately to the global reduction of GHG emissions in a way which cannot be done cost-effectively with either battery electric or fuel cell vehicles. With various blending strategies, it can also be introduced more rapidly and more widely than any competing GHG mitigation technology (see Section 5.16.5).

Finally, it should be noted that in the Californian M85 trial of the late 1980s to early 1990s, there were approximately 15 000 cars, trucks, and buses in use being fueled with M85 by ordinary citizens with no special training. During this trial, extensive information gathering was conducted on the use of M85 as a transport fuel. Despite the fact that M85 was pumped from fundamentally standard gasoline-type dispensing nozzles by untrained users, there were no issues of toxicity associated with the use of methanol, despite minor issues such as fuel hose degradation being extensively reported [106]. This practical trial, brought to an end not because of any shortcoming of methanol but because of a shift of emphasis to bioethanol, provides empirical proof that methanol is not in itself the deadly substance it has been widely made out to be, and can be used quite safely at high blend rates provided similar safety precautions to those in place for gasoline and diesel are followed.

Therefore, while methanol is likely to continue to be labeled as 'extremely toxic and dangerous', it is very important to remember that gasoline is 'extremely toxic and dangerous' too. Realistically, in terms of potential fire hazard, gasoline is an even more dangerous substance that has equivalent toxicity issues; the US DOE is reported to consider gasoline to be overall more hazardous to health than is methanol [91]. Accepting this fact, a balanced view of the safety implications of methanol – including fire danger and atmospheric impact when burned, both from a regulated pollutant and CO_2 emission standpoint – is likely to lead to the conclusion that it is a far safer and more preferable liquid energy carrier to fossil gasoline and diesel. From a safety perspective, it is reasonable to conjecture that neither of those two hydrocarbon fuels would now be accepted if subjected to the same level of scrutiny as any alternative, and that they only persist in the modern world because of the grandfather clause they have benefited from for so long.

5.16.4 The Biomass Limit and Beyond

5.16.4.1 The Biomass Limit

The presence of biofuels in the market now is driven by their potential to improve energy security and to contribute toward climate change mitigation. Their use has been mandated in the EU and the United States. In the EU, 10% of transport energy must be from renewable sources by 2020 [8], and the latter at a level of 36 billion gallons by 2022 (from 4.7 billion gallons in 2007), 21 billion gallons of which should be produced from non-corn starch feedstock [30]. In the EU and California, minimum GHG savings from biofuels are also proposed.

Assessments of reductions in GHG emissions compared with gasoline for biofuels, based on life-cycle analysis, range from about 80% for Brazilian sugarcane ethanol to less than 10% for some US maize-based ethanol [41]. Life-cycle analyses of fuels can produce extremely varied results depending on the assumptions made regarding factors such as feedstock types and yields, management practices, how to account for coproduct credits, nitrous oxide emissions from soil arising from the application of nitrogen-based fertilizer, and land-use changes. For example, ethanol produced from wheat in the United Kingdom has been assessed as providing between 10% and 80% reductions in GHG emissions [41]. Most analyses continue to indicate that first-generation biofuels (based on conventional fermentative and extractive methods) show a net benefit in terms of GHG emissions reduction and energy balance [107], but recent studies have concluded that in some instances they are significantly overestimated [108]. Other concerns expressed about biofuels include as follows:

- With the exception of sugarcane ethanol, they provide only limited GHG reduction benefits at a relatively high cost ($ per ton CO_2 avoided).
- They compete with food crops and may contribute to increasing food prices.
- They compete for scarce water resources in some regions.
- They may struggle to meet their claimed environmental benefits as the biomass feedstock may not be produced sustainably.
- They may promote monocultures that have a negative impact on biodiversity.
- There is insufficient land area to provide substantial security of energy supply in most countries.
- Security of supply may be vulnerable to disease or insect plagues, particularly when monocultures are used as feedstocks.

The cost of reducing GHG emissions using maize-based ethanol and biodiesel from palm oil or soya is mostly in the region of $150–$250 ton^{-1} CO_2 [41] (compared with $40–$150 ton^{-1} for sugarcane ethanol) and this is not expected to reduce in the short term.

Second-generation biofuels that use lignocellulosic feedstocks made from agricultural and forest residues and non-food crops, as described above, ameliorate many of the concerns of first-generation biofuels. On the whole, lignocellulosic feedstock produced from specialist energy crops will give higher energy yields per unit area of land because of their greater carbon utilization. These crops may also be grown on poorer quality marginal land. With the exception of sugarcane ethanol, this will lead to gradual replacement of first-generation biofuels by their second-generation counterparts, but this is not likely to occur to a significant degree until around 2020. Policies that mandate sustainability and environmental criteria for biofuels, in addition to setting targets for substitution levels, are beginning to materialize and these will incentivize the development of second-generation biofuels.

The issue of land utilization is key to the future development of biofuels due to pressures that will be brought about by the projected growth in world population whose food consumption patterns are increasingly land-intensive, and the increasing demand for land to cultivate industrial feedstock [109]. In countries with high population densities, biofuels are not likely to achieve substantial energy security by exploiting indigenous biomass resources. For example, wheat straw ethanol and rapeseed biodiesel would require approximately 45% and 40%, respectively, of the UK arable land area to supply 5% of the UK energy demand by transport in 2001 [110]. These figures reduce to between 10% and 15% of the arable land area for sugar beet ethanol and wood methanol, respectively, but they remain unviable.

In order to quantify the potential of the global biomass resource, it has also become increasingly clear that assessment of the fuel production process must consider any effects of land-use change. These may be direct or indirect effects where if the land was previously uncultivated or if there is a usage change, a large one-off release of carbon from the soil into the atmosphere may occur [111, 112]. **Table 2**, based on the data of Fargione *et al.* [111], shows the impact of these emissions, quantified in terms of 'carbon payback' time, that is, the time required for the production and use of the biofuels to produce a net positive saving in GHG emissions. It can be seen that the time required to produce a net benefit from some biofuel production chains is claimed to be

Table 2 GHG release from land clearing and time required to repay the carbon debt

Fuel chain	Assumed country of origin	Converted eco-system	GHG release (tons ha^{-1})	Time to repay carbon debt (years)
Palm to biodiesel	Indonesia	Peat forest	3003	423
Soya to biodiesel	Brazil	Rain forest	287	319
Corn bioethanol	United States	Grassland	111	93
Palm to biodiesel	Indonesia	Rain forest	611	86
Corn to bioethanol	United States	Abandoned cropland	57	48
Soy to biodiesel	Brazil	Grassland	33	37
Sugarcane to bioethanol	Brazil	Cerrado woodland	165	17
Prairie grass to ethanol	United States	Abandoned cropland	6	1

Based on Fargione J, Hill J, Tilman D, *et al.* (2008) Land clearing and the biofuel carbon debt. *Science Express* 319: 1235–1238 [111].

hundreds of years. While there is considerable controversy around the numbers quoted in such studies, it is clear that some biofuels have significantly greater environmental benefits than others.

A recent German Advisory Council on Global Climate Change (WBGU) study [109] estimates the sustainable potential of biogenic wastes and residues worldwide at approximately 50 EJ yr^{-1} (1 EJ = 1 × 10^{18} J). The estimate of the global sustainable potential of energy crops has a huge spread: between 30 and 120 EJ yr^{-1}, depending mainly on the assumptions made regarding food security and biodiversity. The total sustainable technical potential of bioenergy in 2050 is thus projected to be between 80 and 170 EJ yr^{-1}. This quantity of energy is around one-quarter of the current global energy use (about 450–500 EJ yr^{-1}) and less than one-tenth of the projected global energy use in 2050 [109]. The economically/politically realizable quantity may amount to around one-half of the technically sustainable potential, and the amount of this quantity available for transport use a fraction of this number, as the use of biomass for electricity production leads to significantly lower cost and greater yield (ton of CO_2 avoided per hectare) than its use as a transport fuel.

Currently, biofuels for transport amount to only about 2.2% of all bioenergy; the vast majority (almost 90%), amounting to 47 EJ yr^{-1} (around one-tenth of global primary energy use) is accounted for by traditional use, burning wood, charcoal, biogenic residues, or dung on basic open-hearth fires [109]. On top of this, a well-, or field-to-tank energy conversion efficiency of about 50% applies for biomass-to-synfuel conversion [43]. Assuming that ultimately around half of the biomass energy was available for use as transport fuel gives a substitution potential of about 15 EJ yr^{-1}. With the current global transport energy requirement at between 85 and 90 EJ yr^{-1}, this represents a global substitution of less than 20%. Bandi and Specht [43] arrived at a level of 27% substitution globally, and 18% for the EU-27, based on transport energy consumptions (for 1999) of 70.2 and 12.0 EJ yr^{-1}, respectively. For Germany, around 7% substitution was deemed to be possible.

It is clear that biofuels cannot substitute fossil fuels completely in the transport sector. A biomass limit exists that globally is between 20% and 30% by energy at current usage levels, and is much lower for developed countries with high population densities. Improvements in vehicle fuel efficiency (due to downsizing of powertrains, their optimization to operate on the biofuel, and low mass, low drag/rolling resistance vehicle technology) and behavioral mode switching have the potential to extend the biomass limit in developed countries in which the population and automotive transport fuel demand might be in decline. However, increased efficiency and even improved crop yields due to advances in biotechnology will not be sufficient to offset the burgeoning demand for personal mobility in developing countries. There is also an implicit risk with high dependency on biofuels associated with attempting to solve the climate change problem using a technology which is itself dependent on the climate. Nevertheless, with appropriate sustainability criteria in place which limits the amount of fuel supplied, biofuels are capable of delivering reductions in GHG emissions immediately in a sector in which the emissions are growing and which is extremely difficult to decarbonize by other means.

5.16.4.2 Beyond the Biomass Limit – Electrofuels

Section 5.16.2 has described how ethanol and, in particular, methanol can be made renewably from a wide variety of biomass feedstocks but are constrained in the extent to which they can supply the transport fleet, at the level imposed by the biomass limit established in the above section. In this section, approaches to synthesizing alcohol and hydrocarbon fuels that are theoretically capable of supplying them in sufficient quantities to meet the entire global transport fuel demand are described.

Biofuels result from producing oxidizable organic matter by combining carbon dioxide and water in a biogenic cycle involving photosynthesis according to eqn [1]. Equation [7] shows that it is possible to synthesize methanol directly from hydrogen and carbon dioxide: this can be viewed as a mechanism for liquefying chemically the hydrogen using carbon dioxide. The product is the simplest organic hydrogen carrier that is liquid at ambient conditions. In the same way that biofuels recycle carbon biologically, a cycle where the carbon in the methanol is recycled artificially by extracting CO_2 from the atmosphere is shown in **Figure 16** (based on Olah *et al.* [113]). In order for the production and use of methanol in this cycle to be a carbon-neutral process, all of the energy inputs to the cycle must also be carbon-neutral. Thus, the energy used to produce hydrogen by the electrolysis of water and that used for the capture and release of the CO_2 should be carbon-neutral. The basic cycle shown in **Figure 16** has been proposed by a number of previous workers over a period of 30 years [18, 113–119]. The production of fuel in this way can be viewed as an energy vector or storage buffer for renewable electricity, giving rise to the term electrofuels.

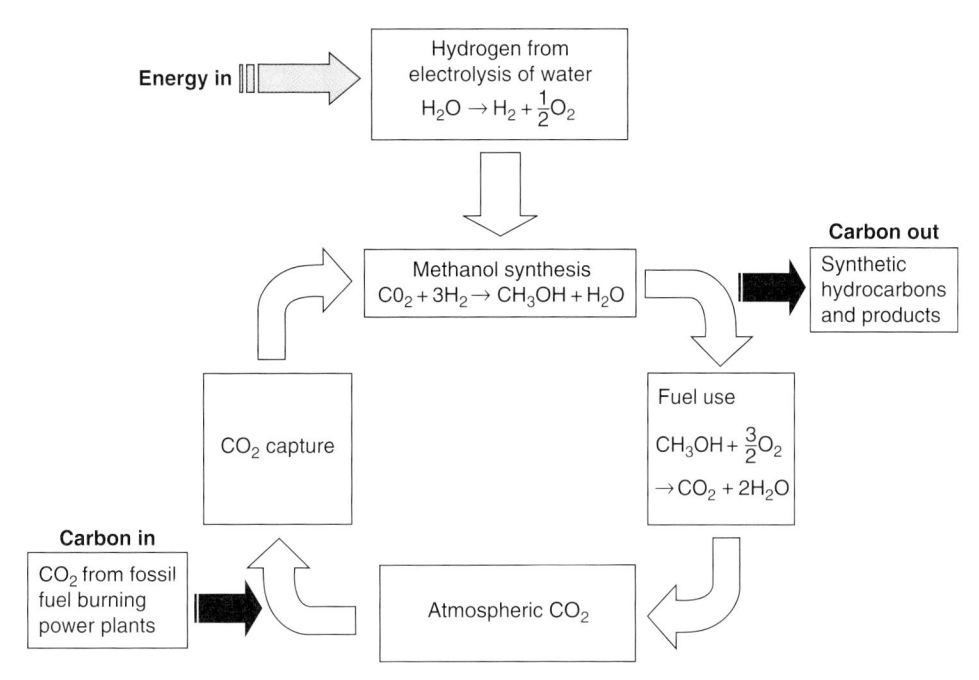

Figure 16 Cycle for sustainable methanol production and use. Adapted from Olah GA, Goeppert A, and Prakash GKS (2009) *Beyond Oil and Gas: The Methanol Economy*, 2nd edn. Weinheim, Germany: Wiley-VCH Verlag GmbH & Co. KGaA. ISBN: 98-3-527-32422-4 [113].

An additional feature of the cycle is that by synthesizing chemical feedstocks for the manufacture of plastics and paints, carbon is effectively sequestered such as to allow the continued exploitation of remaining fossil fuel reserves without causing a net accumulation of CO_2 in the atmosphere. This is facilitated by the ready manufacture of olefins from methanol – the so-called methanol-to-olefins (MTOs) process [113, 119]. The viability of the cycle is predicated on (1) investment in upstream renewable energy and (2) investment in a CO_2 extraction and regeneration infrastructure. The provision of large quantities of renewable energy is a prerequisite for any sustainable decarbonized transport economy. The separation of CO_2 at higher concentrations is routine in some large industrial plants such as natural gas processing and ammonia production facilities and the future challenges and costs of flue gas capture are well understood [120]. The extraction of CO_2 from the atmosphere is ostensibly a future technology, but there has already been a significant body of work in the area. References dating back to the 1940s exist [121] but significant interest has arisen in the last 10–15 years [115, 116, 122–133].

Figure 17 shows the variation of theoretical CO_2 separation energy with concentration, where the free energy for separation is given by

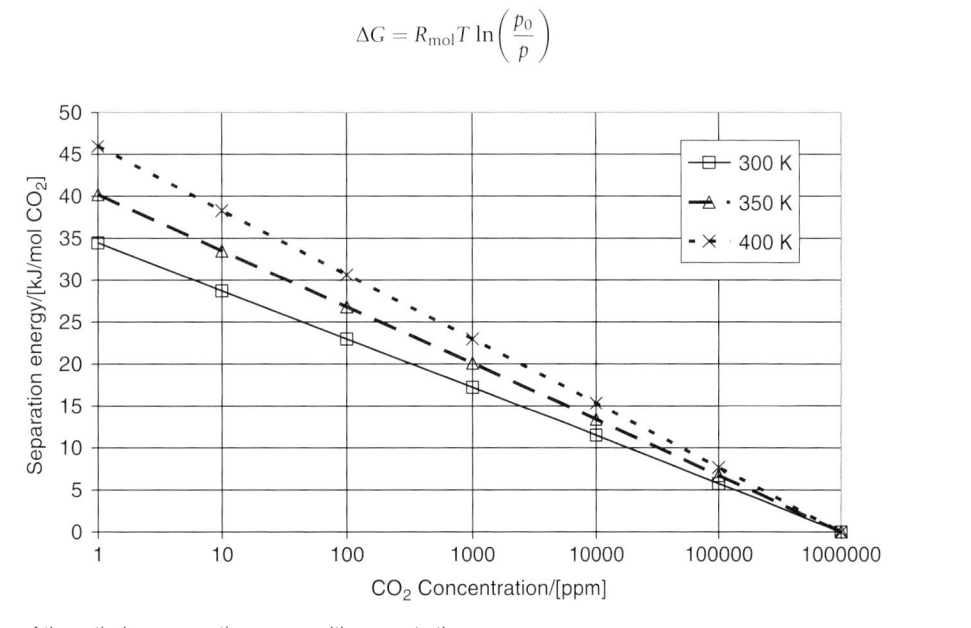

$$\Delta G = R_{\mathrm{mol}} T \ln\left(\frac{p_0}{p}\right) \qquad [8]$$

Figure 17 Variation of theoretical gas separation energy with concentration.

In eqn [8], p is the partial pressure of ambient CO_2 and p_0 the desired pressure in the output stream. At the current atmospheric CO_2 concentration of 387 ppm, the theoretical separation energy is in the region of 20 kJ per mole CO_2. The logarithmic nature of eqn [8] means that the energy to separate atmospheric CO_2 is only 4 times higher than that required for flue gas separation, even though the concentration level is a factor of about 300 times lower. In fact, the difference between the energy for flue gas capture and atmospheric capture is lower than the factor of 4 described above due to the requirement for flue gas capture to extract a large percentage of the CO_2 in a single pass so that the energy to capture the marginal concentrations is higher than that for the initial concentrations. Keith et al. [127] put the figure for the theoretical ratio of atmospheric capture to flue gas capture at 1.8.

Although the minimum energy of separation is less than 3% of the HHV for methanol (1 mole of CO_2 makes 1 mole of methanol with HHV = 726 kJ mol^{-1}), many of the actual values achieved in practice have been an order of magnitude higher, as described in the following section. Despite this, it is believed that fuel can be produced using CO_2 extracted from the atmosphere at overall efficiency levels which will make it attractive in the medium to long term.

5.16.4.2.1 Concentrating CO₂ directly from the atmosphere

References can be found from the 1940s that describe research into capturing CO_2 directly from the air [121], and NASA developed devices in the 1970s and 1980s capable of removing CO_2 from enclosed cabin air [134–140]. The prospect of climate change due to increased atmospheric CO_2 concentrations has caused increased interest over the last decade into cost-effective, energy-efficient, and high-rate direct air capture technologies [115, 116, 122–133].

Concentrating CO_2 from atmospheric concentrations to a stream of pure CO_2 typically involves two steps: capture and extraction. First, the atmosphere (containing CO_2 at about 387 ppm) is contacted with either a solution or treated surface that selectively captures (absorbs or adsorbs) the CO_2 from the air. Next, the captured CO_2 is extracted from the solution or surface to produce a pure stream of CO_2. This second step may use thermal [141, 142], chemical and thermal [141, 143–145], or electrochemical methods [115, 132, 133, 142], among others [142]. This pure stream of CO_2 can then be optionally treated (e.g., dehumidified or pressurized) before sending it to a chemical reactor where it can be combined with, for example, hydrogen produced using renewable electricity to produce an electrofuel.

Most approaches to CO_2 concentration that are currently being pursued accomplish the first step of CO_2 capture by contacting air with a caustic liquid capture solution in a 'wet scrubbing' technique that has been known for several decades [121, 146, 147]. In the specific case of a sodium hydroxide capture solution, the mechanism is initiated by the absorption of CO_2 in the sodium hydroxide in the reaction [134]

$$2\,NaOH_{(aq)} + CO_{2(g)} \rightarrow Na_2CO_{3(aq)} + H_2O_{(l)} \quad \Delta H^0 = -109.4 \text{ kJ mol}^{-1} \qquad [9]$$

While many research groups propose spray tower capture for the first step, they differ in their approach to the subsequent extraction. Keith et al. [127] and Lackner [142] have both investigated capture via a sodium hydroxide solution, followed by regeneration of the sodium hydroxide via the causticization reaction

$$Na_2CO_{3(aq)} + Ca(OH)_{2(s)} \rightarrow 2\,NaOH_{(aq)} + CaCO_{3(s)}, \quad \Delta H^0 = -5.3 \text{ kJ mol}^{-1} \qquad [10]$$

which readily transfers 94% of the carbonate ions from the sodium to the calcium cation to produce an emulsion of calcium hydroxide. The calcium carbonate precipitate is filtered from solution and thermally decomposed to release the CO_2 according to the following reaction:

$$CaCO_{3(s)} \rightarrow CaO_{(s)} + CO_{2(g)}, \quad \Delta H^0 = 179.2 \text{ kJ mol}^{-1} \qquad [11]$$

Finally, the calcium hydroxide is regenerated by hydration of the lime according to

$$CaO_{(s)} + H_2O \rightarrow Ca(OH)_{2(s)}, \quad \Delta H^0 = -64.5 \text{ kJ mol}^{-1} \qquad [12]$$

The sodium and calcium hydroxides are recycled in two separate loops and there are CO_2 emissions associated with their initial production. Nikulshina et al. [143, 144] have also investigated air capture using both Ca-based and Na-based [145] capture solutions. Keith et al. [127] and Zeman [128] give the net energy requirement for the above processes as about 350 kJ per mole CO_2, and indicate that there is scope for significant further improvements on this figure [141]. Lackner [142] gives a figure of '< 250 kJ per mole CO_2'.

Lackner is also pursuing the commercialization of atmospheric CO_2 capture technology through the company Global Research Technologies, LLC [142]. This proprietary technology captures CO_2 by binding it to the surface of an ion-exchange sorbent material. Lackner lists a variety of possible regeneration techniques, including pressure swing, temperature swing, water swing (liquid or vapor), or carbonate wash plus electrodialysis [142].

Steinberg [114] and Stucki [115] have proposed combined electrolysis/electrodialysis units for the production of methanol. Stucki [115] constructed an electrochemical membrane cell that can be used for the regeneration of the potassium (in this case rather than sodium) hydroxide and for simultaneous production of hydrogen at the cathode, obviating the requirement for a second loop for the ion-exchange process described above. The overall reaction can be summarized by the equation

$$2H_2O + K_2CO_3 \rightarrow H_2 + \frac{1}{2}O_2 + 2KOH + CO_2 \qquad [13]$$

which has identical stoichiometry when sodium is used instead of potassium.

In order to demonstrate energy-efficient and scalable technology for atmospheric CO_2 capture that will enable the generation of carbon-neutral liquid fuels, Littau and co-workers [132, 133] at PARC have developed an approach based on the use of a KOH capture solution, followed by regeneration of the CO_2 via high-pressure electrodialysis. The capture solution, once loaded with CO_2, is pressurized and passed into a bipolar membrane electrodialysis (BPMED) unit. Bicarbonate ions are transferred across an ion-exchange membrane to a CO_2-rich acid stream which is held at a pH of 3–4 by acidic buffers and flow rate control. The capture solution is regenerated by the hydroxyl ion flux from the bipolar membrane and by partially depleting it of bicarbonate via electrodialysis. The high-pressure acid stream is transferred to a gas evolution/separation tank where the pressure is reduced resulting in the release of pure CO_2. The CO_2 is removed and fed to a reactor for the production of fuel. The now CO_2-depleted acid stream is returned to the electrodialysis unit via a repressurization pump while the regenerated capture solution is returned to the capture apparatus, for example, a spray tower. Crucially, in concentrating the CO_2, both the acid and base solutions are regenerated, resulting in two closed, continuous process loops – this minimizes the amount of solvent required for operation.

The BPMED device and initial results are described by Pearson *et al.* [148, 149]. In parallel to the CO_2 capture, H_2 for fuel production can be produced via electrolysis of water. The separation of the electrodialysis for CO_2 regeneration and electrolysis for H_2 production is in contrast to the approach of Stucki *et al.* [115], which combines both processes into one unit. Separating the electrodialysis and electrolysis provides more flexibility to optimize the two processes independently. Assuming a typical BPMED current efficiency of 85% and effective pH control, it is estimated that this system will extract CO_2 gas from the capture solution with an energy consumption of approximately 100–150 kJ per mole CO_2. This estimate does not include the energy required for spray tower operation, pumping of fluid, or compression and dehumidification of the extracted CO_2. The energy requirements for spray tower operation have been measured at about 5 kJ per mole CO_2 [150].

5.16.4.2.2 Renewable liquid electrofuels from atmospheric CO_2

In order to produce a stoichiometric mixture for methanol synthesis (eqn [7]), the hydrogen must be supplied using a separate water electrolyzer. **Figure 18** shows that by far the largest component of the process energy requirements for synthesizing methanol, or any other potential electrofuel, is that to produce the hydrogen. An 80% electrolyzer efficiency has been assumed together with a conservative CO_2 extraction energy of 250 kJ per mole CO_2. This gives a HHV 'wind-to-tank' (WTT) efficiency of 46%, including multipass synthesis and recompression. **Figure 19** shows the estimated sensitivity of the process efficiency to the CO_2 extraction energy requirement. An electricity-to-tank efficiency about 50% may be possible when the CO_2 extraction energy is 125 kJ per mole CO_2. In the calculation of these efficiencies, it has also been assumed that the heat of reaction generated in forming the methanol can be used elsewhere in the process, for example, to offset the distillation energy. These figures compare well with the number measured by Specht *et al.* [116, 151], using an electrodialysis process to recover the absorbed CO_2.

An increase of about 8% points in the fuel synthesis efficiency is likely using CO_2 extracted from flue gas [151], and overall efficiencies that are well over 50% are thought to be possible with high-temperature electrolysis. Indeed, recent improvements in solid oxide electrolyzer cell technology have given electricity-to-hydrogen efficiencies of 95% [152] – improvements of this magnitude on a commercial scale will offer significant reductions in the upstream energy requirement for synthesizing fuel.

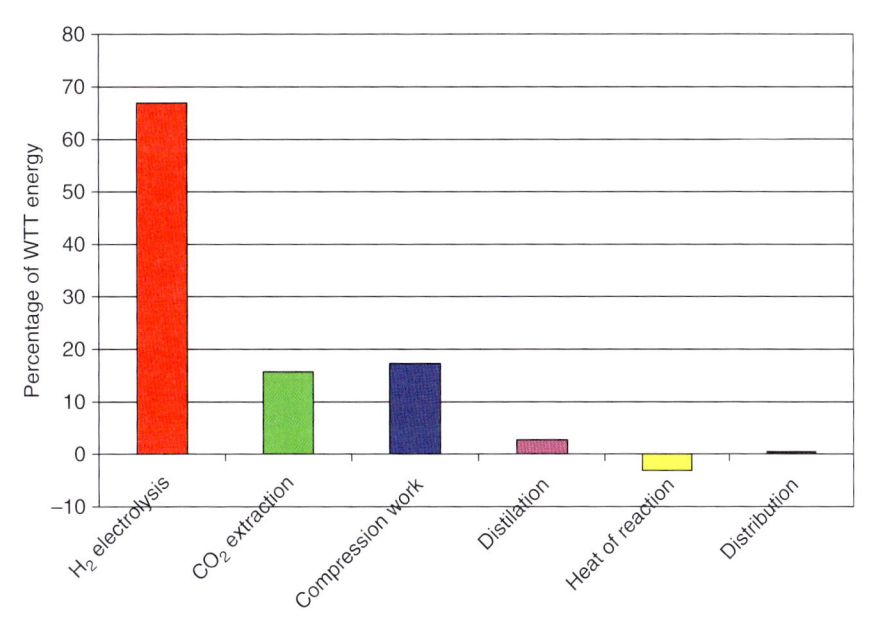

Figure 18 Breakdown of process energy requirements for synthesis of methanol from atmospheric CO_2 and renewable hydrogen.

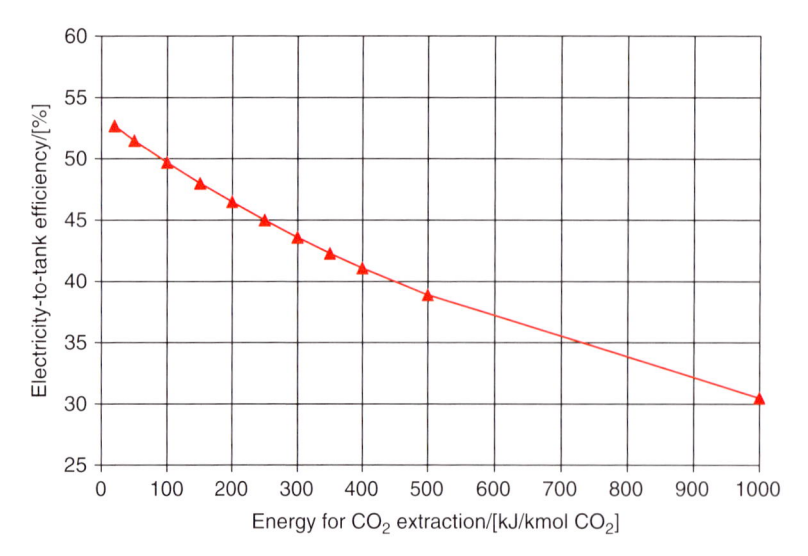

Figure 19 Sensitivity of methanol electrofuel synthesis to energy required for CO_2 extraction and concentration.

Lackner [142] claims that large extractors of 60 m × 50 m dimensions would extract 3 kg of $CO_2\,s^{-1}$ (90 000 tons yr^{-1}), which copes with the emissions rate from 15 000 cars; 250 000 such units could deal with all annual anthropogenic CO_2 emissions if sequestration were possible. The use of CO_2 in a closed cycle to produce carbon-neutral liquid fuels obviates the requirement to sequestrate the component of emissions from the transport sector, and since the mixing time in the atmosphere is rapid, there is no geographical concentration of feedstock, ensuring security of supply for the carbon ingredient. Note further that for a plant manufacturing electrofuels from atmospheric CO_2 and sea water, the chemical feedstocks are essentially free.

It has been established that a renewable means of synthesizing a low-carbon-number alcohol fuel, namely, methanol, is feasible, which with the provision of sufficient upstream renewable energy enables the continued use of liquid fuels. This synthesized methanol would ultimately form the basis of the bulk of the transport fuel requirement, significantly exceeding the availability of properly sustainable biofuels without the supply constraints implied by the impacts of land-use change and other issues discussed earlier. The miscibility of methanol with ethanol and gasoline supports the gradual transition toward the use of carbon-neutral liquid fuels as the provision of renewable energy is increased, with the only feedstock constraints being access to the atmosphere and water.

5.16.5 Technologies to Increase the Use of Alcohols in the Vehicle Fleet

FFVs capable of operating on any mixture between 100% gasoline and 15% gasoline, 85% methanol (M85) were introduced during fleet trials in California in the 1980s and early 1990s [153]. With the advent of farming subsidies for ethanol production and the formulation of the CAFE regulations to boost fuel economy accreditations (as described in Section 5.16.2.3), E85 gasoline FFVs have now sold in the millions in the United States. In Brazil, E85 FFVs have also been common since the mid-1990s. The development of electronic engine control systems over the past 30 years has now enabled practical realization of highly developed FFVs that can operate seamlessly on a variety of fuel mixtures and acceptable cold start down to very low (−25 °C) ambient temperatures [62]. Saab, Ford, and Renault have shown how the approach can work beneficially within a European architecture and General Motors (GM) has led the major manufacturers in the United States; there are many similar vehicles in other markets around the world.

5.16.5.1 Tri-Flex-Fuel Vehicles

Synthesized methanol would ultimately form the basis of the bulk of the transport fuel requirement, significantly exceeding the availability of properly sustainable biofuels. However, ethanol from biomass is present in the fuel market today in significant quantities and has been mandated to increase in its share in the United States and Europe. The miscibility of methanol with ethanol and gasoline supports the gradual transition toward the use of carbon-neutral liquid fuels to replace fossil fuels. In an attempt to illustrate the ease with which vehicles capable of supporting the transition can be provided, a production vehicle was taken and modified to operate on standard 95 RON gasoline (its normal fuel), ethanol, methanol, or any combination of these fuels. Vehicles capable of this degree of flexibility are mentioned by Nichols [153], but no technical details were given. The tri-FFV described here was a continuation of a previous project that sought to identify the necessary engine and vehicle modifications required to operate on E85 [60, 61, 154]. The vehicle was a Lotus Exige S, which uses a Toyota 2ZZ-GE engine fitted with a supercharger system engineered by Lotus and which uses Lotus's own production engine management system.

The fuel system of the vehicle was modified to accept alcohol fuel through the application of alcohol-resistant fuel lines and the fitment of an alcohol sensor (manufactured by Continental Automotive Systems). A fuel pump with increased flow rate was also fitted to account for the lower volumetric energy content of the alcohol fuels. The additional software required was developed within the environment of the production Lotus T4e engine management system using the spare inputs and outputs for the alcohol sensor and the precompressor injectors that are specific to this application [60]. Starting with the existing E85/gasoline flex-fuel system already developed [154], the calibration was evolved to deduce the possible range of AFRs for 100% ethanol or 100% methanol in the fuel. Hence, no new sensor input was required for the tri-flex-fuel conversion and the standard AFR sensor was retained. Only injector pulse width and precompressor-injection duty factor were influenced by the software and the signal from the AFR sensor; ignition timing was found to be dependent on alcohol content only.

While identical spark advance was used with methanol and ethanol, some preignition was noticed using the former fuel. Small amounts of preignition can be compensated for in the ignition timing table and this is the route taken by Saab for their BioPower engines [62], but methanol shows a greater propensity toward this phenomenon due to the lower temperature at which it decomposes, advancing the phenomenon into the compression stroke. Fortunately, a significant reduction in the propensity to preignite can be achieved by adopting spark plugs with electrodes made from nonprecious (noncatalytic) metals. Replacing the standard iridium electrodes with copper-cored versions was shown to eliminate the preignition issue up to 100% methanol concentration in the fuel. There were no further hardware modifications necessary over those required for E85 use.

The aim of the calibration process was to comply with Euro 4 emissions limits on any combination of the three fuels and this was achieved while using the standard vehicle catalyst, which was formulated primarily for operation on gasoline [100]. The tailpipe CO_2 emissions are shown in **Figure 20** – in general, as the alcohol concentration increases, so the CO_2 emissions reduce. The figure of 210 (gCO_2) km^{-1} represents a total energetic requirement by the vehicle of 2.84 MJ km^{-1} to complete the drive cycle. Both ethanol and methanol generate less CO_2 per unit of energy released than gasoline (4.0% and 7.5%, respectively). The fuel concentration used in test 3, 88% by volume methanol, should produce 69.61 (gCO_2) MJ^{-1}, 94% of the CO_2 emissions when operating on gasoline. The measured results of 199 (gCO_2) km^{-1} correlate well with this expectation. In a more optimized heavily downsized engine or when applied to a heavier vehicle, the octane rating of the alcohol component and its reduced need for component protection fueling could be more beneficially exploited in the drive cycle. The tailpipe CO_2 benefit of the alcohol blend over straight gasoline would then be expected to be even greater.

Using modern control technology, the conversion of existing production vehicles to tri-flex-fuel operation on gasoline, ethanol, and methanol is therefore straightforward and can be achieved with very low on-cost. The demonstrator vehicle is shown in **Figure 21**. A more complete description is given by Pearson *et al.* [100]. The ability to continue to produce low-cost, globally compatible vehicles with very low WTW GHG emissions for the mass market, helps ensure the survival of the vehicle manufacturers and secures fuel demand from the fuel/energy providers. From the customer's perspective, the low vehicle cost ensures continued access to personal mobility, which is financed by the high-cost capital available to the individual to purchase an asset which sits idle for 95% of its life.

5.16.5.2 Ternary Blends to Extend the Displacement of Gasoline by Alcohols

In addition to the concept of introducing a tri-FFV as a means of operating vehicles on any combination of the two alcohols and gasoline, it may be possible to introduce methanol in a far more pragmatic manner more quickly and thus accelerate the

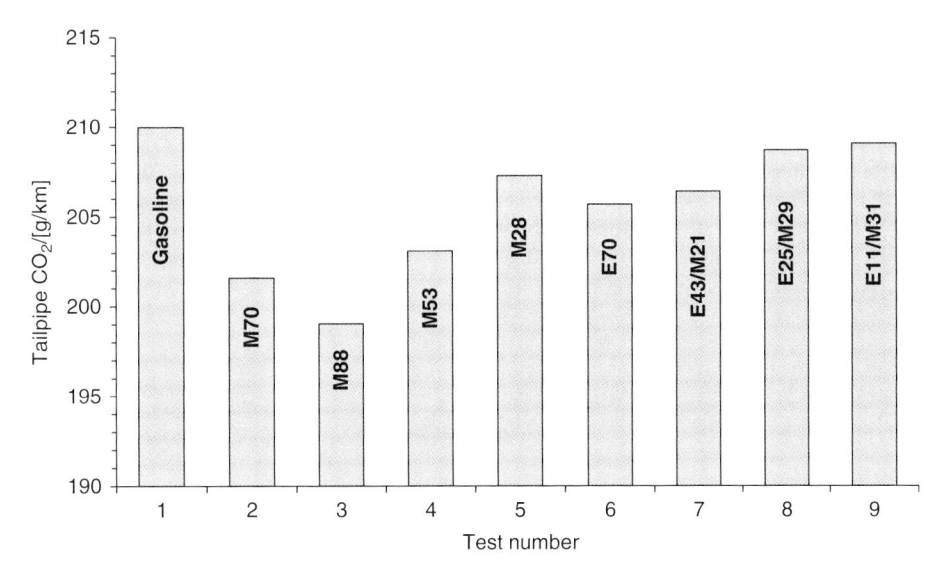

Figure 20 Tailpipe CO_2 emissions of tri-flex-fuel demonstrator vehicle when operating on various mixtures of gasoline, methanol, and ethanol on the NEDC.

Figure 21 Lotus Exige 270E tri-flex-fuel demonstrator vehicle.

displacement of fossil energy. The aim of the concept outlined below is to exploit the physicochemical similarities of ethanol and methanol to produce ternary mixtures of the two alcohols with gasoline in a preblended form that can be used seamlessly by any existing E85/gasoline FFV.

Methanol can be introduced into gasoline now. In the EU, 3% by volume is permissible. In the United States, the DuPont Waiver [76, 155] permits blends of up to 5% by volume methanol with a minimum of 2.5% by volume co-solvent alcohols having a carbon number of 4 or lower (ethanol, propanol, butanol, and/or gasoline-grade *tert*-butyl alcohol) as long as the total oxygen content does not exceed 3.7% by mass. However, the resulting mixtures are still predominantly a gasoline-based fuel and would thus be suitable for gasoline cars operating at a normal gasoline stoichiometric AFR in the region of 14.7:1.

As discussed above, over recent years, the United States has, through CAFE regulations, encouraged manufacturers in the production of so-called FFVs capable of operating on gasoline or E85 or any mixture of the two. There are issues of fuel availability for these cars, which the US Energy Independence and Security Act has mandated [4, 30]. In view of the aggressive level of the target stipulated by the latter legislation and due to the concerns over the sustainability of fuels from some biomass sources and the issues of land-use change, it is desirable to find means of extending the amount of renewable fuel that can be introduced in the short term. Many vehicles are in the field at the moment, which can utilize alcohol fuels and the number is increasing continuously: about 2.7 million of these vehicles were sold worldwide in 2007. Since these FFVs are capable of running on any binary fuel blend with a stoichiometric AFR between that of gasoline (14.7:1) and E85 (9.7:1), methanol could be introduced into the 'E85' to produce an equivalent ternary blend of ethanol, methanol, and gasoline with similar properties to the binary ethanol and gasoline mixtures by readjusting the amount of gasoline in the mix. This can extend the utilization of a given quantity of ethanol in the market to the benefit of security of fuel supply and, depending on the source of the methanol, GHG emissions.

The fuel properties used in this analysis are listed in **Table 3**. From the data, different blend proportions to achieve the same AFR can be calculated. Three examples of ternary blends are given in **Table 4**.

The second blend in **Table 4** is termed E42.5 G28.8 M28.7, which corresponds to the volume fraction of the major blend components. It spreads the available ethanol across twice the volume of blended fuel supplied to the market at the same energy level per unit volume. In terms of equivalent energy of gasoline, 1 l of ethanol displaces 0.673 l of gasoline, while for this ternary blend, the extra 0.675 l of methanol supplied enables 1 l of ethanol to displace 1.011 l of gasoline – an increase of about 50%. It is interesting to note in this mixture that the gasoline content, nearly 30%, is almost the same as winter-grade E85 (typically E70 G30 M0), and thus it might be expected that this blend would be suitable for year-round use, particularly since methanol is more readily started under cold conditions than ethanol (see above). This implies a greater potential use of ethanol all year round.

Table 3 Values used in the AFR calculations

Fuel component	Stoichiometric AFR (:1)	Gravimetric LHV (MJ kg^{-1})	Density (kg l^{-1})	Molecular mass (–)
Gasoline	14.53	42.7	0.736	114.6
Ethanol	8.60	26.8	0.789	46
Methanol	6.44	19.9	0.791	32

Table 4 Ternary mixtures of ethanol, gasoline, and methanol to yield the same stoichiometric AFR as E85

Ethanol (vol. %)	Gasoline (vol. %)	Methanol (vol. %)
85	15	0
42.5	28.8	28.7
0	42.6	57.3

5.16.6 Sustainable Organic Fuels for Transport

In the near term, security of energy supply and climate change are driving consideration of alternatives to fossil-based fuels, while in the longer term, sustainability is the motivation. A lack of global consensus for fueling transport may lead to the development of vehicle technologies that are peculiar to local geographic regions. This will limit export markets and may create practical difficulties when vehicles are driven between regions. Some suggested alternatives, for example, electrification, might suit a portion of the light-duty transport fleet but cannot realistically form the basis for heavy-duty land transport (with the obvious exception of vehicles with predefined paths, e.g., trains, trams, and trolleybuses, to which electricity can be supplied externally), marine, or air transport. It is extremely unlikely that the latter transport mode will be fueled by molecular hydrogen and clear that electric vehicles are not feasible for use in remote regions with no grid infrastructure.

While biofuels are currently part of the transport fuel mix and under the correct conditions can make positive contributions to reducing GHG emissions and improving security of supply, they are limited in the extent to which they can achieve these goals. Biofuels can thus be part of a complete solution, but they cannot supply transport energy in full amounts. Beyond the limit of the quantity of fuel that can be made in a sustainable manner from biomass, renewable energy can be used to generate hydrogen which can then be chemically liquefied by combining it with a CO_2 molecule to produce a carbon-neutral liquid fuel. Methanol, the simplest hydrogen carrier which is liquid over a wide temperature range, can be efficiently produced in this way and is suitable, together with ethanol, for light- and heavy-duty automotive applications. For applications where vehicle range is of paramount importance, further processing to kerosene and diesel can produce high-energy density drop-in fuels at a drop in overall process efficiency and with a significant increase in plant costs.

Bandi and Specht [43] and Biedermann et al. [44] describe processes for the FT synthesis of gasoline and diesel from both CO and CO_2 with hydrogen; they also give details of the MTG and MtSynfuels processes. In the MTG process, the methanol is first converted to DME from which light olefins are produced, which eventually gets convert to heavier olefins, paraffins, and aromatics. A 14 000 barrel day^{-1} MTG plant, using technology developed by ExxonMobil, was built in New Zealand in the early 1980s. The MtSynfuels process was developed by Lurgi and has the advantage over the conventional FT route that it is easier to downscale and thus may be better suited to the decentralized availability of biomass and small plants synthesizing methanol from atmospheric CO_2 and renewable hydrogen. The mechanism operates in a similar way to the MTG process where DME and olefins are created as intermediate products before hydrogen addition to yield diesel, kerosene, gasoline, or LPG. It is estimated that the MtSynfuels process is 10% more efficient and requires 10% lower investment costs than a conventional FT plant. Both processes produce fuel of very high quality and provide high versatility for a future transport energy economy underpinned by the synthesis of methanol from atmospheric CO_2. Steinberg [114], Martin and Kubic [156], and Zeman and Keith [118] all propose synthesis of hydrocarbon fuels in this way. In view of the desirable properties of alcohol fuels and the relatively small vehicle modifications required to incorporate their use, it is proposed here that the additional synthesis step, with its concomitant energy penalty, should be reserved to supply the applications requiring the highest onboard energy storage densities possible.

Methanol can be phased in for automotive and light-duty transport applications with SI engine powertrains via the technology described in Section 5.16.5. Eventually, optimized engines with high compression ratios would be adopted, achieving considerable efficiency improvements over existing gasoline engines. Methanol and ethanol can be phased in as fuels for compression-ignition engines using the technology described in Section 5.16.3.3, where relatively small engine modifications are required. Depending on how high the thermal efficiency of SI engines using methanol with high EGR rates can be raised, it may be expedient to transition toward gradual replacement of CI engines with high-efficiency methanol SI engines.

The combination of bio-alcohols, and methanol, diesel, and kerosene, made as electrofuels, constitute a potentially carbon-neutral system for the provision of fuel for all types of transport in full amounts. Collectively, they are 'sustainable organic fuels for transportation' (organic meaning 'carbon-containing'). **Figure 18** shows that the energy requirements for the production of these fuels are dominated by the renewable hydrogen requirements and the fuel costs would likewise be dominated by the costs of making the hydrogen.

Biedermann et al. [44], Aldewereld et al. [157], and Olah et al. [113, 119] all point out the synergies possible from the adoption of methanol as the basis of the transport energy economy and its diverse applicability as a base feedstock for the petrochemical industry.

Figure 22 shows how the transition to sustainable organic fuels might occur; the dynamics will clearly differ between countries depending on various factors, such as their state of development, geographical location, and population density. In developed

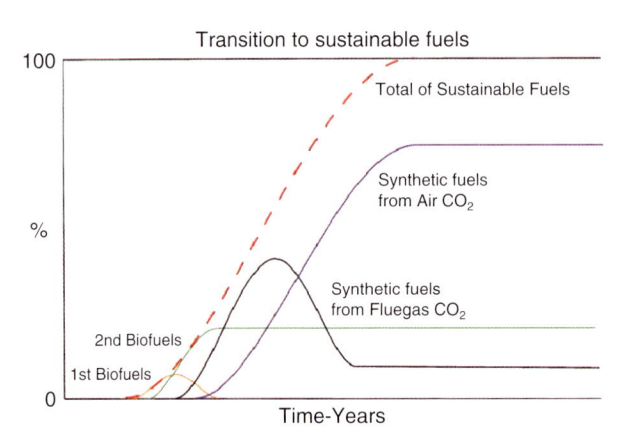

Figure 22 Schematic of possible fuel transition. Courtesy: Gordon Taylor.

countries, first-generation biofuels, with the exception of sugarcane ethanol, would be phased out with second-generation biofuels replacing them and supplying the fleet up to the biomass limit of between, say, 10% and 30%. The remaining fuel demand would be provided by electrofuel production from atmospheric CO_2 capture and flue gas capture of CO_2 from power plants burning a mixture of fossil fuel and biomass in combined heat, power, and fuel plants (CHP + F). Developing countries with sufficient land area could adopt or continue with first-generation biofuels, the production facilities for which can be developed at relatively low cost to diversify the use of their produce and, where local fuel demand is exceeded, may provide opportunities for export. It is likely to be more profitable to export high-energy density liquid fuels than 'raw' biomass, providing a low-carbon solution to the transport sector which has limited options for reducing its dependency on oil.

A schematic of a CHP + F plant is shown in **Figure 23**, where the ratio of coal to biomass is dictated by the desired overall CO_2 saving and feedstock availability. The process integration could provide low-temperature reject heat for district heating networks in buildings and industrial processes. In addition to the CO_2 capture apparatus, such a plant would house the electrolyzers producing hydrogen from low-cost 'surplus' wind electricity. The electricity input and fuel production could be distributed between CHP + F plants to suit their local heat loads.

It is interesting to note that pilot plants producing methanol from CO_2 via industrial/geothermal processes are currently in operation by Mitsui Chemicals in Japan [158] and Carbon Recycling International in Iceland [159].

The current global transport fuel demand is between 85EJ and 90EJ per annum. The upper bound figure represents an average power consumption of 2.85 TW. As a first (worst case) approximation, if it is assumed that the TTW efficiency of vehicles using sustainable organic fuels is equal to their fossil fuel replacements and the WTT efficiency of the fuel is taken as 0.5, the ultimate renewable energy demand for powering the transport fleet with such fuels is in the region of 6 TW. This is clearly a huge requirement – world electricity generation in 2006 averaged 2.06 TW [160] – however, to take just one form of renewable energy, the available global wind resource of 78 TW [161] is more than capable of providing the power to produce fuel and electricity in the long term. There are also synergies that can reduce the overall energy requirements via process integration such as the CHP + F plant with district heating, as shown in **Figure 23**. Additionally, fuel synthesis plants using electrolyzers may be a practical way to store 'stranded' wind energy in remote locations where installation of an electricity grid is not economic. Such plants would provide ideal interruptible loads for wind turbines, obviating the problem of the intermittent nature of wind energy.

Reductions in upstream energy demand due to the higher TTW efficiencies of BEVs or, to a lesser extent, hybridized fuel cell vehicles, are possible at large on-cost to vehicles (as described in Section 5.16.2). Additionally, full life-cycle analyses of energy

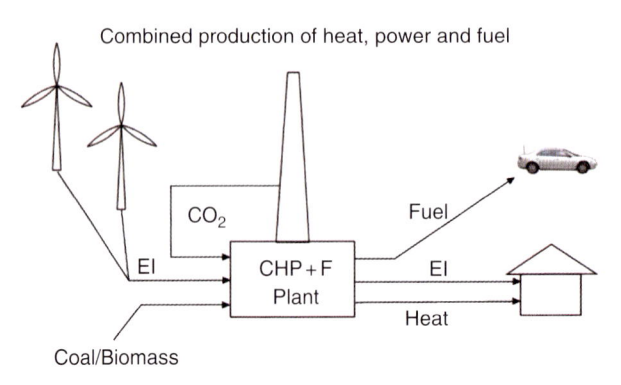

Figure 23 Schematic of combined heat, power, and fuel plant. Courtesy: Gordon Taylor.

requirements have shown that the life-cycle CO_2 emissions for BEVs and HFCEVs can be higher, under some operating conditions, than even vehicles powered by gasoline-fueled ICEs due to the higher emissions in the vehicle production process [162, 163]. Initial work by the authors indicated that these high embedded GHG emissions for BEVs and HFCEVs translate into high embedded energy costs, which give a substantial overhead to accommodate the construction of the upstream energy supply of carbon-neutral liquid fuels.

The precedents of the large-scale fleet trials conducted in the California and Canada in the 1970s, 1980s, and 1990s [51, 106, 153, 164, 165] show that the implementation of methanol as an automotive fuel is feasible. From the mid-1980s to the late 1990s, over 15 000 methanol FFVs were used in California, along with hundreds of methanol-fueled transit and school buses. Over 12 million gallons of methanol were used as transport fuel in the state at the height of the program in 1993, dispensed at 105 fuel stations which were converted at low cost [164]. A series of initiatives led to the demonstration of 18 different models of methanol-fueled cars from a dozen of US, European, and Asian manufacturers, four of which were produced commercially, including the Ford Taurus which was produced between 1993 and 1998 [166] in both methanol (M85) and ethanol (E85)/gasoline flex-fuel versions. Methanol-fueled heavy-duty vehicles were demonstrated by many major OEMs for applications such as refuse trucks, dump trucks, school and transit buses, and haulage and delivery trucks, using ignition-improved fuel or spark-assisted ignition [165] described in Section 5.16.3.3.

Since 1975, with its National Alcohol Program, Brazil has promoted ethanol made from sugarcane as a fuel. After some severe fluctuations in penetration following those of the oil price, the fuel is now well established, to the extent that 'pure' gasoline is no longer available as a fuel, the base blend varying between 20% and 25%, depending on the sugarcane harvest. The development of FFVs in the early 1990s has allowed the expansion of ethanol use so that it provided over 50% by volume of the market share of fuel for the national gasoline-powered fleet. In 2008–09, over 90% of new car sales were E85/gasoline FFVs.

Outside Brazil, several other countries, notably the United States and Sweden, have built up substantial ethanol–gasoline FFV fleets, and fuel production is set to grow, supported by legislation and initiatives. Many FFVs have been recently developed [167, 168], some of which offer substantial performance improvements over the equivalent gasoline-fueled model, particularly in turbocharged form [34, 62, 142, 169]. The benefits of low-carbon-number alcohol fuels in SI engines are described in Section 5.16.3.

In the heavy-duty field, SEKAB is supplying renewable ethanol-based fuel designated E95 for use in compression-ignition engines [170]. In this case, instead of being mixed with 5% gasoline, the 95% ethanol is mixed with 5% ignition (cetane) improver which is a polyethylene glycol derivative. Since 1989, Scania has built around 600 ethanol-fueled city buses that operate in Swedish cities. The latest engines give 43% peak thermal efficiency compared with 44% for their diesel-fueled counterparts and meet Euro 5 emissions legislation. Such engines have been demonstrated in fleet trials in Brazil [171], and the technology has been extended to passenger cars with CI engines [172].

The presence of ethanol-fueled vehicles in the market in significant numbers (in the case of vehicles with SI engines), and the miscibility of ethanol, methanol, and gasoline, together with the ability to synthesize gasoline, diesel, and kerosene from biomass, methanol, or renewable hydrogen and CO_2 feedstock, allows a soft start to the introduction of sustainable organic fuels for transport with renewable methanol as its basis. It could be expedited by the mandating of flex-fuel (or tri-flex-fuel) capability for all new vehicles with SI engine powertrains. With the correct materials selection in the design of the next generation of gasoline/ethanol FFVs, methanol operation could be implemented by software changes when the fuel becomes available. The on-cost to the customer, whose investment drives the economics of vehicle manufacture, would be minimal, especially in comparison to BEV and HFCEV technology.

Methanol is currently made in quantities of around $50 \times 10^9 \, l \, yr^{-1}$ (compared with gasoline and diesel at about 1.25×10^{12} and $1.1 \times 10^{12} \, l \, yr^{-1}$, respectively) as a chemical feedstock, mainly from natural gas and coal, with considerable potential to increase production in the near term. China is now exploiting its abundant coal deposits (it is the world's largest producer and consumer of coal) and is now the world's largest producer of methanol [173]. In 2007, China imported 47% of its oil; it is keen to reduce this external dependency but has banned the use of grain for ethanol production in order to ensure food supplies and so has declared coal-based methanol to be a strategic transportation fuel [173]. The wholesale price of methanol in China is about one-third that of gasoline making it cheaper per unit energy contained in the fuel. About $3.4 \times 10^9 \, l$ of methanol was blended in gasoline in 2007 [173, 174], and many indigenous manufacturers are developing methanol FFVs. National standards for high-proportion and low-proportion methanol fuels are being put in place and local standards are proliferating [175]. In Shanxi province, there are over 2000 M100 taxis and around 400 city buses; already 770 methanol fuel stations have been set up [175]. A $100\,000 \, \text{ton} \, yr^{-1}$ MTG demonstrator plant is being built in this province, which will be in service in 2009. The methanol derivative, DME, is also being considered as a diesel substitute; the city of Shanghai had 90 DME buses in operation in 2008 and plans to have 1000 such vehicles running in the city by 2010.

The rapid implementation of methanol as a transport fuel in China demonstrates the ease with which the technology can be applied, the low cost of the vehicles in which the fuel is used, and the low cost of the fuel distribution infrastructure. Unfortunately, methanol produced from coal can generate over twice as much WTW GHG emissions as gasoline, emphasizing the desirability of flue gas capture if this feedstock is to be used for fuel production.

Finally, an alternative vehicle and fuel legislation and taxation system is proposed that resolves WTT and TTWs contributions. Development of a system that recognizes reduced WTT fossil carbon content of fuels and the rating of vehicles in terms of the energy they require to travel a unit distance is viewed as a key instrument in incentivizing the development of closed-carbon-cycle fuels and their adoption by the automotive industry and its customers. This provides a mechanism for governments to levy taxation fairly on the stakeholders in the transport sector in accordance with the degree of control they have over the various factors that comprise gross vehicle CO_2 emissions. With the advent of new fuels on the market with different energy densities, fuel taxation based on the energy content of the fuel with tax relief based on the audited WTW GHG savings afforded by the use of the fuel is a rational direction to remove inconsistencies in current taxation policies and incentivize the uptake of carbon-neutral liquid fuels.

5.16.7 Conclusions

Fundamental physical and chemical principles dictate that the energy density of batteries and molecular hydrogen is unlikely ever to be competitive with liquid fuels for transport applications. The cost of personal transport incorporating these technologies, which sits idle for 95% of its lifetime, is and will continue to be excessive for a high proportion of the market in developed economies. In Europe, over 70% of automobile sales are of C-segment vehicles or smaller where cost is the most sensitive purchase parameter. For countries with developing economies, where the majority of the medium- to long-term growth in transport is projected, the cost is prohibitively high. The production of sustainable organic liquid fuels is proposed as a route to the continued provision of compatible, affordable, and sustainable transport to the market. This approach retains the use of low-cost ICEs and liquid fuel systems. These powertrain systems have high power and energy storage densities, and low embedded manufacturing and materials extraction energies; there is considerable potential for further efficiency improvements, especially combined with mild electrification.

Replacement of fossil fuels with carbon-neutral liquid fuels would not compromise current levels of mobility and would enable transport to remain globally compatible. Low-carbon-number alcohols can be used for personal mobility and light-duty applications, and synthetic higher hydrocarbons for applications where maximum energy density is crucial. The technology to enable the evolution, not revolution, from the current vehicle fleet to equivalent-cost vehicles capable of using sustainable methanol has been described in the form of either tri-FFVs capable of running on any combination of gasoline, ethanol, or methanol or current FFVs that can run on specific preblended mixtures of these three fuels. All transport energy can be supplied using biofuels up to the biomass limit, and beyond it using carbon-neutral liquid electrofuels made using renewable energy and CO_2 from the atmosphere. The role of biofuels in this transitional route and end-game prevents them from being regarded as a dead-end by vehicle manufacturers.

Populations in countries with developing economies have the right to increased mobility as their wealth grows. The current tendency to focus on vehicle CO_2 emissions results in rapid escalation in the large capital commitment required for vehicle purchase. Setting targets for vehicles in terms of energy usage per unit distance travelled (e.g., $MJ\,km^{-1}$) and targets for fuels/energy carriers in terms of nonrenewable carbon (dioxide) per unit energy generated in production/use (e.g., $gCO_2\,MJ^{-1}$) resolves the TTW and WTT emissions in a way in which the parties responsible for their respective contributions are able to take the appropriate responsibilities. It is posited that such a system would accelerate the development of all forms of carbon-neutral fuels.

References

[1] Sperling D and Gordon D (2009) *Two Billion Cars*. Oxford, UK: Oxford University Press. ISBN: 978-0-19-537664-7.
[2] Davis SC, Diegel SW, and Boundy RG (2009) *Transportation Energy Data Book: Edition 28*. ORNL-6984. Center for Transportation Analysis, Energy and Transportation Science Division, Oak Ridge National Laboratory, Tennessee, USA. Prepared for the Office of Energy Efficiency and Renewable Energy, US Department of Energy.
[3] (2007) Climate change 2007: Mitigation of climate change. In: Metz B, Davidson OR, Bosch PR (eds.) *Contribution of Working Group III to the Fourth Assessment Report of the Intergovernmental Panel on Climate Change*. Cambridge, UK; New York: Cambridge University Press.
[4] Sissine F (2007) Energy independence and security act of 2007: A summary of major provisions. CRS Report for Congress, Oorder Code RL34294, 21 December. Washington DC: Congressional Research Service.
[5] Reducing CO_2 emissions in the global road transport sector. Tokyo, Japan: Japan Automobile Manufacturers Association, Inc. 2008. www.jama-english.jp (accessed August 2008).
[6] The next people's car. *Forbes Magazine* 16 April 2007.
[7] Jones C (2008) Biofuels and vehicle performance. *SAE BioFuels: Specification and Performance Symposium*. Paris, France, 7–9 July.
[8] COM (2006) 845, Communication of the European Commission to the Council and the European Parliament: Biofuels Progress Report. Commission of European Communities, Brussels, 10th January 2007.
[9] Department for Bussiness, Enterprise and Regulatory Reform (BERR), Department of Transport (2008) Investigation into the scope for the transport sector to switch to electric vehicles and plug-in hybrid vehicles. UK, October 2008. BERR & DfT. http://www.bis.gov.uk/files/file48653.pdf (accessed 15 December 2011).
[10] Hitchin ER and Pout CH (2002) The carbon intensity of electricity: How many kgC per kWh_e? *Building Service Engineering Research and Technology* 23(4): 215–222.
[11] Pout C (2009) Revised emissions factors for the national calculation methodologies. Technical Papers Supporting SAP 2009, STP 09/CO201, March. Watford, UK: BRE.
[12] McCarthy RW and Yang C (2010) Determining marginal electricity for near-term plug-in and fuel cell vehicle demands in California: Impacts on vehicle greenhouse gas emissions. *Journal of Power Sources* 195(7): 2099–2109, doi: 10.1016/j.jpowersour. 2009.10.024.
[13] Rodgers RD and Voth GA (2007) Ionic liquids. *Accounts of Chemical Research* 40: 1077–1078.
[14] Jackson N (2006) Low carbon vehicle strategies: Options and potential benefits. *Cost-Effective Low Carbon Engines Conference*, Institution of Mechanical Engineers, London, UK, 6–7 November.
[15] Eberle U (2006) GM's research strategy: Towards a hydrogen-based transportation system. *FuncHy Workshop*, Geesthacht Research Centre, Geesthacht, Germany, 20–22 September.
[16] Well-to-wheels analysis of future automotive fuels and powertrains in the European context. Well-to-tank Report, Version 2b, EUCAR, CONCAWE, and the Joint Research Centre of the European Commission Directorate-General. http://ies.jrc.ec.europa.eu/WTW (accessed May 2006).
[17] Bossel U (2006) Does a hydrogen economy make sense? *Proceedings of IEEE* 84(10): 1826–1837.
[18] Bossel U, Eliasson B, and Taylor G (2003) The future of the hydrogen economy: Bright or bleak? *Proceedings of European Fuel Cell Forum*. With revised foreword 26 February 2005. www.efcf.com/reports/E08.pdf (accessed 15 December 2011).

[19] Eberle U, Arnold G, and von Helmolt R (2006) Hydrogen storage in metal-hydrogen systems and their derivatives. *Journal of Power Sources* 154: 456–460.
[20] Casten S, Teagan P, and Stobart R (2000) Fuels for fuel cell-powered vehicles. SAE Paper No. 2000-01-0001. Warrendale, PA: Society of Automotive Engineers.
[21] von Helmolt R and Eberle U (2007) Fuel cell vehicles: Status 2007. *Journal of Power Sources* 165: 833–843.
[22] Fuel cell system cost for trnasportation – 2008 cost estimate. NREL/BK-6 A1-45457, May 2009. US Department of Commerce National Technical Information Service, Springfield, VA, USA. http://hydrogendoedev.nrel.gov/pdfs/45457.pdf (accessed 15 December 2011).
[23] Cracknell RF, Alcock JL, Rowson JJ, *et al.* (2002) Safety considerations in retailing hydrogen. SAE Paper No. 2002-01-1928. Warrendale, PA: Society of Automotive Engineers.
[24] Mintz M, Folga S, Molburg J, and Gillette J (2002) Cost of some hydrogen fuel infrastructure options. Argonne National Laboratory Transportation Technology R&D Center, Transportation Research Board, 16 January.
[25] www.e85refueling.com (accessed 5 February 2010).
[26] Laws and Regulations, CAFE – Fuel economy, National Highway Traffic Safety Administration. http://www.nhtsa.gov/staticfiles/rulemaking/pdf/cafe/CAFE-GHG_MY_2012-2106_Final_Rule_FR.pdf (accessed 15 December 2011).
[27] Well-to-wheels analysis of future automotive fuels and powertrains in the European context. Well-to-tank Report, Version 2b, WTT Appendix 2: Description and detailed energy and GHG balance of individual pathways, EUCAR, CONCAWE, and the Joint Research Centre of the European Commission Directorate-General. http://ies.jrc.ec.europa.eu/WTW (accessed May 2006).
[28] Directive 2009/30/ec of the European Parliament (2009) Official Journal of the European Union, 5th June. http://eur-lex.europa.eu/LexUriServ/LexUriServ.do?uri=OJ:L2009:140:0088:0113:EN:PDF (accessed 15 December 2011).
[29] Piraccini M (2008) Marketing perspectives for biofuel vehicles. *International Conference on Automotive Biofuels*. IQPC, Berlin, Germany, 9–12 September.
[30] The US Energy Independence and Security Act of 2007. Public Law 110–140. *110th Congress*, DOCID: f:publ140. 110, 2007. Washington, DC: Congressional Research Service.
[31] Saito K, Kobayashi S, and Tanaka S (2008) Storage stability of FAME blended diesel fuels. SAE Paper No. 2008-01-2805. Warrendale, PA: Society of Automotive Engineers.
[32] McCormick RL, Alleman TL, Waynick JA, *et al.* (2006) Stability of biodiesel and biodiesel blends: Interim report. Technical Report NREL/TP-540-39721, National Renewable Energy Laboratory, April 2006. Washington DC, USA.
[33] Miyata I, Takei Y, Tsurutani K, and Okada M (2004) Effects of bio-fuels on vehicle performance – Degradation mechanism analysis of bio-fuels. SAE Paper No. 2004-01-3031. Warrendale, PA: Society of Automotive Engineers.
[34] Ogawa T, Kajiya S, Kosaka S, *et al.* (2008) Analysis of oxidative deterioration of biodiesel fuel. SAE Paper No. 2008-01-2502. Warrendale, PA: Society of Automotive Engineers.
[35] Caprotti R, Breakspear A, Klaua T, *et al.* (2007) RME behaviour in current and future diesel fuel FIEs. SAE Paper No. 2007-01-3982. SAE Paper No. 2007-01-3982. Warrendale, PA: Society of Automotive Engineers.
[36] Hawthorne M, Roos JW, and Openshaw MJ (2008) Use of fuel additives to maintain modern diesel engine performance with severe test conditions. SAE Paper No. 2008-01-1806. Warrendale, PA: Society of Automotive Engineers.
[37] Thornton MJ (2009) Impacts of biodiesel fuel blends oil dilution on light-duty diesel engine operation. SAE Paper No. 2009-01-1790. Warrendale, PA: Society of Automotive Engineers.
[38] Richards P, Ried J, Tok L-H, and MacMillan I (2007) The emerging market for biodiesel and the role of fuel additives. SAE Paper No. 2007-01-2033 (JSAE Paper No. 20077232). Warrendale, PA: Society of Automotive Engineers.
[39] Probstein RF and Hicks RE (2006) *Synthetic Fuels*. Dover Publications, Mineola, NY, USA. ISBN: 978-0486449777.
[40] Global watch mission report: Second generation transport biofuels – A mission to the Netherlands, Germany and Finland. London, UK: UK Government Department of Trade and Industry, 2006.
[41] *Sustainable Biofuels: Prospects and Challenges*. The Royal Society, 2008. ISBN: 978 0 85403 662 2.
[42] Specht M, Zuberbuhler U, and Bandi A (2005) Why biofuels? – An introduction into the topic. *RENEW – 1st European Summer School on Renewable Motor Fuels*. Uwelt-Campus-Birkenfeld, 29–31 August.
[43] Bandi A and Specht M (2006) Renewable carbon-based transportation fuels. In: Bornstein L (ed.) *Energy Technologies, Subvolume C: Renewable Energy, VIII/3C*, pp. 441–482. Berlin, Germany: Springer. ISBN 978-3-540-42962-3.
[44] Biedermann P, Grube T, and Hohlein B (2006) Methanol as an energy carrier. *Schrifen des Forschungszentrums Julich Reihe Energietechnik/Energy Technology*, vol. 55. Forschungszentrum Julich GmbH. Julich, Germany. ISBN-13: 978-3-89336-446-6.
[45] Specht M, Bandi A, Baumgart F, *et al.* (1999) Synthesis of methanol from biomass/CO$_2$ resources. In: Eliasson B, Riener PWF, and Wokaun A (eds.) *Greenhouse Gas Control Technologies*. Amsterdam, The Netherlands: Pergamon.
[46] Dekker E (2008) Bio-methanol, the versatile biofuel. *CMAI World Methanol Conference*. Lisbon, Portugal, 8–10 December.
[47] Lippert AM and Smyth G (2009) Global energy systems in transportation: Next steps in energy diversity for transport. *30th International Vienna Motor Symposium*. Vienna, Austria, 7–8 May.
[48] Clark G (2008) Coskata unveils ethanol technology and strategic partnership. *Biofuel Review*, 14 January. www.biofuelreview.com/content/view/1406/
[49] White TL (1907) Alcohol as a fuel for the automotive motor. SAE Paper No. 070002. Society of Automotive Engineers, Warrendale, PA, USA.
[50] Paul JK (ed.) (1978) Methanol technology and application in motor fuels. Chemical Technology Review No. 114, Energy Technology Review No. 31, Noyes Data Corporation, Park Ridge, NJ, USA. ISBN0-8155-07 19-4.
[51] Hagen DL (1977) Methanol as a fuel: A review with bibliography. SAE Paper No. 770792. Society of Automotive Engineers, Warrendale, PA, USA.
[52] Black F (1991) An overview of the technical implications of methanol and ethanol as highway motor vehicle fuels. SAE Paper No. 912413. Society of Automotive Engineers, Warrendale, PA, USA.
[53] Brinkman ND, Gallopoulos NE, and Jackson MW (1975) Exhaust emissions, fuel economy, and driveability of vehicles fuelled with alcohol-gasoline blends. SAE Paper No. 750120. Society of Automotive Engineers, Warrendale, PA, USA.
[54] Brinkman ND (1981) Ethanol fuel: A single-cylinder engine study of efficiency and exhaust emissions. SAE Paper No. 810345 and SAE Transactions. vol. 90, sec. 2, pp. 1410–1424.
[55] Koenig A, Lee W, and Bernhardt W (1976) Technical and economical aspects of methanol as an automotive fuel. SAE Paper No. 760545. Society of Automotive Engineers, Warrendale, PA, USA.
[56] Nakata K, Utsumi S, Ota A, *et al.* (2006) The effect of ethanol fuel on a spark ignition engine. SAE Paper No. 2006-01-3380. Warrendale, PA: Society of Automotive Engineers.
[57] Kar K, Last T, Haywood R, and Raine R (2008) Measurement of vapor pressures and enthalpies of vaporization of gasoline and ethanol blends and their effects on mixture preparation in an SI engine. SAE Paper No. 2008-01-0317. Warrendale, PA: Society of Automotive Engineers.
[58] Marriott CD, Wiles MA, Gwidt JM, and Parrish SE (2008) Development of a naturally aspirated spark ignition direct-injection flex-fuel engine. SAE Paper No. 2008-01-0319. Warrendale, PA: Society of Automotive Engineers.
[59] Takagi Y, Nakajima Y, Muranaka S, and Ohkawa K (1983) Characteristics of fuel economy and output in methanol fueled turbocharged SI engine. SAE Paper No. 830123. Warrendale, PA: Society of Automotive Engineers.
[60] Turner JWG, Pearson RJ, Holland B, and Peck R (2007) Alcohol-based fuels in high performance engines. SAE Paper No. 2007-01-0056. *SAE Fuels and Emissions Conference*. Cape Town, South Africa, 23–25 January.
[61] Turner JWG, Peck A, and Pearson RJ (2007) Flex-fuel vehicle development to promote synthetic alcohols as the basis for a potential negative-CO$_2$ energy economy. SAE Paper No. 2007-01-3618. Warrendale, PA: Society of Automotive Engineers.
[62] Bergström K, Melin S-A, and Jones CC (2007) The new ECOTEC turbo BioPower engine from GM powertrain: Utilizing the power of nature's resources. *28th International Vienna Motor Symposium*. Vienna, Austria, 26–27 April.
[63] Bergström K, Nordin H, Konigstein A, *et al.* (2007) ABC, alcohol based combustion engines: Challenges and opportunities. *16th Aachener Kolloquium Fahrzeug-und Motorentechnik*. Aachen, Germany, 8–10 October.

[64] Kapus PE, Fuerhapter A, Fuchs H, and Fraidl GK (2007) Ethanol direct injection on turbocharged SI engines: Potential and challenges. SAE Paper No. 2007-01-1408. Society of Automotive Engineers, Warrendale, PA, USA.

[65] Brewster S (2007) Initial development of a turbo-charged direct injection E100 combustion system. SAE Paper No. 2007-01-3625. Warrendale, PA: Society of Automotive Engineers.

[66] Weinowski R, Sehr A, Rutten O, et al. (2008) Impact of the ethanol fuel content on operation parameters of passenger car gasoline engines. *17th Aachener Kolloquium Fahrzeug-und Motorentechnik.* Aachen, Germany, 6–8 October.

[67] Malcolm JS, Aleiferis PG, Todd AR, et al. (2007) A study of alcohol blended fuels in a new optical spark-ignition engine. *Institution of Mechanical Engineers Performance, Fuel Economy and Emissions Conference.* London, UK, 11–12 December.

[68] Most WJ and Longwell JP (1975) Single-cylinder engine evaluation of methanol: Improved energy economy and reduced NO_x. SAE Paper No. 750119. Society of Automotive Engineers, Warrendale, PA, USA.

[69] Pannone GM and Johnson RT (1985) Methanol as a fuel for a lean turbocharged spark ignition engine. SAE Paper No. 890435. Society of Automotive Engineers, Warrendale, PA, USA.

[70] Brusstar M, Stuhldreher M, Swain D, and Pidgeon W (2002) High efficiency and low emissions from a port-injected engine with neat alcohol fuels. SAE Paper No. 2002-01-2743. Warrendale, PA: Society of Automotive Engineers.

[71] Bruetsch RI and Hellman KH (1992) Evaluation of a passenger car equipped with a direct injection neat methanol engine. SAE Paper No. 920196. Warrendale, PA: Society of Automotive Engineers.

[72] Brusstar MJ and Gray CL (2007) High efficiency with future alcohol fuels in a stoichiometric medium duty spark ignition engine. SAE Paper No. 2007-01-3993. Warrendale, PA: Society of Automotive Engineers.

[73] Poling BE, Prausnitz JM, and O'Connell JP (2001) *The Properties of Gases and Liquids*, 5th edn. New York: McGraw-Hill. ISBN: 0-07-011682-2.

[74] Furey RL (1985) Volatility characteristics of gasoline-alcohol and gasoline-ether blends. SAE Paper No. 852116. Warrendale, PA: Society of Automotive Engineers.

[75] Siewart RM and Groff EG (1987) Unassisted cold starts to –29 °C and steady-state tests of a direct-injection, stratified-charge (DISC) engine operated on neat alcohols. SAE Paper No. 872066. Warrendale, PA: Society of Automotive Engineers.

[76] Yacoub Y, Bata R, and Gautam M (1998) The performance and emission characteristics of C_1-C_5 alcohol-gasoline blends with matched oxygen content in a single-cylinder spark ignition engine. *Journal of Automotive Engineering* 212(Pt. A): 363–379, *Proceedings of Institution of Mechanical Engineers.*

[77] Gautam M and Martin DW (2000) Combustion characteristics of higher-alcohol/gasoline blends. *Journal of Automotive Engineering* 214(Pt. A): 497–511, *Proceedings of Institution of Mechanical Engineers.*

[78] Chevron Philips Chemical Company (2008) Sales Specification UTG 96. http://www.cpchem.com/bl/specchem/en-us/Pages/UTG96unleadedtestgasoline.aspx (accessed 15 December 2011).

[79] Cairns A, Stansfield P, Fraser N, et al. (2009) A study of gasoline-alcohol blended fuels in an advanced turbocharged DISI engine. *SAE 2009 World Congress.* Detroit, MI, USA, 20–23 April. SAE Paper No. 2009-0-0038.

[80] Popuri SSS and Bata RM (1993) A performance study of iso-butanol-, methanol-, and ethanol-gasoline blends using a single cylinder engine. SAE Paper No. 932953 and SAE Transactions. vol. 102, sec. 2, pp. 576–595. Warrendale, PA: Society of Automotive Engineers.

[81] Jackson MD, Unnasch S, Sullivan C, and Renner RA (1985) Transit bus operation with methanol fuel. SAE Paper No. 850216. Warrendale, PA: Society of Automotive Engineers.

[82] Toepel RR, Bennethum JE, and Heruth RE (1983) Development of detroit diesel allison 6V-92TA methanol fueled coach engine. SAE Paper No. 831744. Warrendale, PA: Society of Automotive Engineers.

[83] Urban CM, Timbario TJ, and Bechtold RL (1989) Performance and emissions of a DDC 8V-71 engine fueled with cetane improved methanol. SAE Paper No. 892064. Warrendale, PA: Society of Automotive Engineers.

[84] Wuebben P, Unnasch S, Pellegrin V, et al. (1990) Transit bus operation with a DDC 6V-92TAC engine operating on ignition-improved methanol. SAE Paper No. 902161. Warrendale, PA: Society of Automotive Engineers.

[85] Hikino K and Suzuki T (1989) Development of methanol engine with autoignition for low NO_x and better fuel economy. *SAE International Off-Highway & Powerplant Congress and Exposition.* Milwaukee, WI, 11–14 September. SAE Paper No. 891842.

[86] Machiele PA (1990) A health and safety assessment of methanol as an alternative fuel. In: Kohl WL (ed.) *Methanol as An Alternative Fuel Choice: An Assessment*, pp. 217–239. Washington, DC: Johns Hopkins Foreign Policy Institute. ISBN: 094170064X.

[87] Brusstar M, Haugen D, and Gray C (2008) Environmental and human ealth considerations for methanol as a transportation fuel. *17th International Symposium on Alternative Fuels.* Taiyuan, China, 14 October.

[88] Machiele PA (1987) Flammability and toxicity tradeoffs with methanol fuels. SAE Paper No. 872064 and SAE 1987 Transactions, vol. 96, sec. 7, pp. 344–356.

[89] Malcolm Pirnie, Inc. (1998) Evaluation of the fate and transport of methanol in the environment. http://www.methanol.org/Environment/Resources/Environment/MP-Methanol-Fate.aspx (accessed 15 December 2011).

[90] Fishbein L and Henry CJ (1990) Health effects of methanol: An overview. In: Kohl WL (ed.) *Methanol as An Alternative Fuel Choice: An Assessment*, pp. 241–249. Washington, DC: Johns Hopkins Foreign Policy Institute. ISBN: 094170064X.

[91] Malcolm Pirnie, Inc. (1999) Evaluation of the fate and transport of methanol in the environment. http://www.methanol.org/Environment/Resources/Environment/MP-Methanol-Fate.aspx (accessed 15 December 2011).

[92] Methanol Toxicology, University of Cambridge. http://www-clinpharm.medschl.cam.ac.uk/pages/teaching/topics/poison/poison9.html (accessed 15 April 2010).

[93] Gable RS (2004) Comparison of acute lethal toxicity of commonly abused psychoactive substances. *Addiction* 99: 686–696.

[94] Denatonium. Wikipedia article. http://en.wikipedia.org/wiki/Denatonium (accessed 15 December 2011).

[95] Menrad H, Bernhardt W, and Decker G (1988) Methanol vehicles of Volkswagen – A contribution to better air quality. SAE Paper No. 881196 and SAE 1988 Transactions, vol. 97, sec. 3, pp. 373–384. Warrendale, PA: Society of Automotive Engineers.

[96] Wagner T and Wyszyński ML (1996) Aldehydes and ketones in engine exhaust emissions: A review. *Journal of Automotive Engineering* 210(Pt. D): 109–122, *Proceedings of Institution Mechanical Engineers.*

[97] Nichols RJ, Clinton EL, King ET, et al. (1988) A view of flexible fuel vehicle aldehyde emissions. SAE Paper No. 881200 and SAE 1988 Transactions. vol. 97, sec. 3, pp. 422–429. Warrendale, PA: Society of Automotive Engineers.

[98] West BH, López AJ, Theiss TJ, et al. (2007) Fuel economy and emissions of the ethanol-optimized Saab 9-5Biopower. *SAE Powertrain & Fluid Systems Conference and Exhibition*, Chicago, IL, USA, October, SAE Paper No. 2007-01-3994.

[99] Gingrich J, Khalek I, Alger T, and Mangold B (2009) Consideration of emissions standards for a dilute spark-ignited engine operating on gasoline, butanol, and E85. *SIA International Conference: The Spark-Ignition Engine of the Future*, Strasbourg, France, 2–3 December.

[100] Pearson RJ, Turner JWG, and Peck AJ (2009) Gasoline-ethanol-methanol tri-fuel vehicle development and its role in expediting sustainable organic fuels for transport. *Institution of Mechanical Engineers Conference: Low Carbon Vehicles*, London, UK, 20–21 May.

[101] Machiele PA (1990) Summary of the fire safety impacts of methanol as a transportation fuel. SAE Paper No. 901113. Warrendale, PA: Society of Automotive Engineers.

[102] Environmental Protection Agency (1994) Office of mobile sources, methanol fuels and fire safety, fact sheet OMS-8/EPA 400-F-92-010. http://www.epa.gov/oms/consumer/08-fire.pdf (accessed August 1994).

[103] Bardon MF, Rao VK, and Battista V (1989) Volatility and flammability of methanol/gasoline blends. SAE Paper No. 892062 and SAE 1989 Transactions, vol. 98, sec. 4, pp. 803–809. Warrendale, PA: Society of Automotive Engineers.

[104] Methanol fuel. Wikipedia article. http://en.wikipedia.org/wiki/Methanol_fuel (accessed 15 December 2011).

[105] Methyl *tert*-butyl ether. Wikipedia. http://en.wikipedia.org/wiki/MTBE (accessed 15 December 2011).
[106] Ward PF and Teague JM (1996) Fifteen years of fuel methanol distribution. *11th International Symposium on Alcohol Fuels*. Sun City, South Africa, 14–17 April.
[107] Hammerschlag R (2006) Ethanol's energy return on investment: A survey of the literature 1990-present. *Environmental Science & Technology* 40(6): 1744–1750.
[108] The Gallagher review of the indirect effects of biofuels production, Renewable Fuels Agency, St-Leonards-on-Sea, UK, July 2008. http://webarchive.nationalarchives.gov.uk/20110131070443/, http://www.renewablefuelsagency.gov.uk/sites/renewablefuelsagency.gov.uk/files/_documents/Report_of_the_Gallagher_review.pdf (accessed 15 December 2011).
[109] World in transition: Future bioenergy and sustainable land use: Summary for policy makers, WBGU, October 2008. ISBN: 978-3-936191-24-0. http://www.cbd.int/doc/biofuel/wbgu-bioenergy-SDM-en-20090603.pdf (accessed 15 December 2011).
[110] Woods J and Bauen A Technology status review and carbon abatement potential of renewable transport fuels (RTF) in the UK. DTI; AEAT. B/U2/00785/REP URN 03/982:1-150. London: Department of Trade and Industry.
[111] Fargione J, Hill J, Tilman D, *et al.* (2008) Land clearing and the biofuel carbon debt. *Science Express* 319: 1235–1238.
[112] Searchinger T, Heimlich R, Houghton RA, *et al.* (2008) Use of US croplands for biofuels increases greenhouse gases through emissions from land-use change. *Science Express* 319: 1238–1240.
[113] Olah GA, Goeppert A, and Prakash GKS (2009) *Beyond Oil and Gas: The Methanol Economy*, 2nd edn. Weinheim, Germany: Wiley-VCH Verlag GmbH & Co. KGaA, ISBN 98-3-527-32422-4.
[114] Steinberg M (1977) Synthetic carbonaceous fuels and feedstocks from oxides of carbon and nuclear power. *12th Intersociety Energy Conversion Engineering Conference*. Washington, DC, USA, 28 August–2 September.
[115] Stucki S, Schuler A, and Constantinescu M (1995) Coupled CO_2 recovery from the atmosphere and water electrolysis: Feasibility of a new process for hydrogen storage. *International Journal of Hydrogen Energy* 20(8): 653–663.
[116] Specht M, Staiss F, Bandi A, and Weimer (1998) Comparison of the renewable transport fuels, liquid hydrogen and methanol, with gasoline: Energetic and economic aspects. *International Journal of Hydrogen Energy* 23(5): 387–396.
[117] Pearson RJ and Turner JWG (2007) Exploitation of energy resources and future automotive fuels. *SAE Fuels and Emissions Conference*, Cape Town, South Africa, January 2007. SAE Paper No. 2007-01-0034.
[118] Zeman FS and Keith DW (2008) Carbon neutral hydrocarbons. *Philosophical Transactions of the Royal Society A* 366: 3901–3918.
[119] Olah G, Goeppert A, and Prakash GKS (2009) Chemical recycling of carbon dioxide to methanol and dimethyl ether: From greenhouse gas to renewable, environmentally carbon neutral fuels and synthetic hydrocarbons. *Journal of Organic Chemistry* 74(2): 487–498.
[120] Thambimuthu K, Soltanieh M, and Abanades JC (2005) Capture of CO_2, in IPCC special report on carbon dioxide capture and storage, prepared by working group III of the intergovernmental panel on climate change. Metz B, Davidson O, de Conink H, *et al.* (eds.) Cambridge, UK; New York: Cambridge University Press.
[121] Spector NA and Dodge BF (1946) Removal of carbon dioxide from atmospheric air. *Transactions of American Institute of Chemical Engineers* 42: 827–848.
[122] Lackner K, Ziock H-J, and Grimes P (1999) Carbon dioxide extraction from air: Is it an option? *Proceedings of the 24th International Conference on Coal Utilization and Fuel Systems*, Clearwater, Florida, USA, March 8–11.
[123] Lackner KS, Ziock H-J, and Grimes P (1999) The case for carbon dioxide extraction from air. *Source Book* 57: 6–10.
[124] Zeman FS (2003) An investigation into the feasibility of capturing carbon dioxide directly from the atmosphere. *Second Annual Conference on Carbon Sequestration*, Paper No. 235. 5–8 May. Alexandria, VA, USA.
[125] Zeman FS and Lackner KS (2004) Capturing carbon dioxide directly from the atmosphere. *World Resource Review* 16(2): 157–172.
[126] Stolaroff JK (2006) Capturing CO_2 from Ambient Air: A Feasibility Assessment. PhD Thesis, Carnegie Mellon University.
[127] Keith D, Ha-Duong M, and Stolaroff K (2006) Climate strategy with CO_2 capture from the air. *Climate Change* 74: 17–45.
[128] Zeman F (2007) Energy and material balance of CO_2 capture from ambient air. *Environmental Science and Technology* 41: 7558–7563.
[129] Stolaroff JK, Keith DW, and Lowry GV (2008) Carbon dioxide capture from atmospheric air using sodium hydroxide spray. *Environmental Science and Technology* 42: 2728–2735.
[130] Zeman F (2008) Experimental results for capturing CO_2 from the atmosphere. *AIChE Journal* 54: 1396–1399.
[131] Littau K (2008) An 'atmospherically healthy' recipe for carbon-neutral fuels: A synthetic fuel made from sunlight, CO_2, and water. *CTSI Clean Technology & Sustainable Industries Conference & Trade Show*, Boston, MA, USA, 1–5 June.
[132] Eisaman MD, Schwartz DE, Amic S, *et al.* (2009) Energy-efficient electrochemical CO_2 capture from the atmosphere. *Technical Proceedings of the 2009 Clean Technology Conference and Trade Show*. Houston, TX, USA. May 3–7.
[133] Littau K (2010) System and Method for Recovery of CO_2 by Aqueous Carbonate Flue Gas Capture and High Efficiency Bipolar Membrane Electrodialysis. Patent application number: 20100059377, 03/11/2010.
[134] Winnick J, Marshall RD, and Schubert FH (1974) An electrochemical device for carbon dioxide concentration. I. System design and performance. *Industrial and Engineering Chemistry, Process Design and Development* 13: 59–63.
[135] Lin CH and Winnick J (1974) An electrochemical device for carbon dioxide concentration. II. Steady-state analysis: CO_2 transfer. *Industrial and Engineering Chemistry, Process Design and Development* 13: 63–70.
[136] Lin CH, Heinemann ML, and Angus RM (1974) An electrochemical device for carbon dioxide concentration. III. Steady-state analysis: Energy and water transfer. *Industrial and Engineering Chemistry, Process Design and Development* 13: 261–265.
[137] Abdel-Salam OE and Winnick J (1976) Simulation of an electrochemical carbon dioxide concentrator. *AIChE Journal* 22: 1042–1050.
[138] Koszenski EP, Heppner DB, and Bunnell CT (1986) Electrochemical carbon dioxide concentrator subsystem development, NASA-CR-177411. Moffett Field, CA: National Aeronautical and Space Administration.
[139] Powell FT (1989) Refurbishment of one-person regenerative air revitalization system, NASA-CR-183757. Moffett Field, CA: National Aeronautical and Space Administration.
[140] Xiao SQ and Li K (1997) On the use of an electrochemical membrane for removal of CO_2 from a breathing gas mixture. *Transactions Institution of Chemical Engineers* 75: 438–446.
[141] Keith D (2008) CO_2 capture from air. *MIT Carbon Sequestration Forum*, Cambridge, MA, USA, 16 September.
[142] Lackner KS (2008) Options for capturing carbon dioxide from the air. *2nd US-China Symposium on CO_2 Emissions Control Science and Technology*, Hangzhou, China, 28–30 May 2008.
[143] Nikulshina V, Hirsch D, Mazzotti M, and Steinfeld A (2006) CO_2 capture from air and co-production of H_2 via the $Ca(OH)_2$–$CaCO_3$ cycle using concentrated solar power–thermodynamic analysis. *Energy* 31: 1379–1389.
[144] Nikulshina V, Galvez ME, and Steinfeld A (2007) Kinetic analysis of the carbonation reactions for the capture of CO_2 from air via the $Ca(OH)_2$–$CaCO_3$–CaO solar thermochemical cycle. *Chemical Engineering Journal* 129: 75–83.
[145] Nikulshina V, Ayesa N, Galvez ME, and Steinfeld A (2008) Feasibility of Na-based thermochemical cycles for the capture of CO_2 from air: Thermodynamic and thermogravimetric analyses. *Chemical Engineering Journal* 140: 62–70.
[146] Greenwood K and Pearce M (1953) The removal of carbon dioxide from atmospheric air by scrubbing with caustic soda in packed towers. *Transactions Institution of Chemical Engineers* 31: 201–207.
[147] Hoftyzer PJ and van Krevelen DW (1954) Applicability of the results of small-scale experiments to the design of technical apparatus for gas absorption. *Transactions Institution of Chemical Engineers* 32: S60–S67, *Proceedings of the Symposium on Gas Absorption*.
[148] Pearson RJ, Turner JWG, Eisaman MD, and Littau KA (2009) Extending the supply of alcohol fuels for energy security and carbon reduction. *SAE Powertrains, Fuels, and Lubricants Conference*, San Antonio, TX, 2–4 November 2009, SAE Paper No. 2009-01-2764.

[149] Pearson RJ, Turner JWG, Eisaman MD, *et al.* (2009) Sustainable organic fuels for transport. *SIA International Conference: The Spark-Ignition Engine of the Future*, Strasbourg, France, 2–3 December.
[150] Mahmoudkhani M, Heidel KR, Ferreira JC, *et al.* (2009) Low energy packed tower and caustic recovery for direct capture of CO_2 from air. *Energy Procedia* 1: 1535–1542.
[151] Specht M, Bandi A, Elser M, and Staiss F (1998) Comparison of CO_2 sources for the synthesis of renewable methanol. In: Inui T, Anpo M, Izui K, *et al.* (eds.) *Advances in Chemical Conversion for Mitigating Carbon Dioxide*, Studies in Surface Science, vol. 114, pp. 363–367. Elsevier Science, BV.
[152] Jensen SH, Larsen PH, and Mogensen M (2007) Hydrogen and synthetic fuel production from renewable energy sources. *International Journal of Hydrogen Energy* 32: 3253–3257.
[153] Nichols RJ (2003) The methanol story: A sustainable fuel for the future. *Journal of Scientific & Industrial Research* 62: 97–105.
[154] Turner JWG, Peck R, and Pearson RJ (2007) Development of a high performance sports car for operation on a high-alcohol blend fuel. *JSAE Annual Congress*, Pacifico Yokohama, Japan, 23–25 May, JSAE Paper No. 20075038.
[155] US Department of Energy, Washington D.C. USA. http://tonto.eia.doe.gov/dnav/pet/tbldefs/pet_pnp_inpt3_tbldef2.asp (accessed 15 December 2011).
[156] Martin FJ and Kubic WL (2007) Green freedom: A concept for producing carbon-neutral synthetic fuels and chemicals, Los Alamos National Laboratory Report No.LA-UR-07-7897. Moffett Field, CA: National Aeronautical and Space Administration.
[157] Aldewereld C, Dautzenberg B, Guldemond M, and Wijers J (2006) Back from the future: The petrochemical industry in the Rhine-Scheldt delta in 2030. *Chemagine*, April.
[158] Mitsui Chemicals Inc. http://www.mitsuichem.com.techno/lab_06.htm (accessed 15 December 2011).
[159] Carbon Recycling International. http://www.carbonrecycling.is/index.php?option=com_content&view=article&id=13&Itemid=26&lang=en (accessed 15 December 2011).
[160] International Energy Annual (2006) Energy information administration. www.eia.doe.gov/iea/elect.html (accessed 12 August 2008).
[161] Lu X, McElroy MB, and Kiviluoma J (2009) Global potential for wind-generated electricity. www.pnas.org/cgi/doi/10.1073/pnas.0904101106 (accessed 15 December 2011).
[162] Pehnt M (2002) Life cycle assessment of fuel cells in mobile and stationary applications. Institut fur Technische Thermodynamik Deutsches Zentrum fur Luft- und Raumfahrt (DLR). ISBN: 3-18-347606-1. http://www.ifeu.de/energie/pdf/dissertation_pehnt.pdf (accessed May 2002).
[163] Kudoh Y, Nansai K, Kondo Y, and Tahara K (2007) Life cycle CO_2 emissions of FCEV, BEV and GV in actual use. *23rd International Battery, Hybrid, and Fuel Cell Electric Vehicle Symposium and Exposition*, Anaheim, CA, 2–5 December.
[164] Dolan G (2005) Methanol transportation fuels: A look back and a look forward. *International Symposium on Alcohol Fuels*, San Diego, CA, 27 September.
[165] McCoy GA, Kerstetter J, Lyons JK, and Downey P (1993) Alcohol-fueled vehicles: An alternative fuels vehicle, emissions, and refueling infrastructure technology assessment. Washington State Department of Ecology and the Department of Transportation, WSEO-93-125, June. Olympia, WA: DOE Scientific and Technical Information.
[166] Cowart JS, Boruta WE, Dalton JD, *et al.* (1995) Powertrain development of the 1996 Ford flexible fuel Taurus. *Alternative Fuels Conference and Exposition*, San Diego, CA, 6–8 December, SAE Paper No. 952751.
[167] Giroldo MB, Werninghaus E, Coelho E, and Makant W (2005) Development of 1.6 l flex fuel engine for Brazilian market. SAE Paper No. 2005-01-4130. Warrendale, PA: Society of Automotive Engineers.
[168] Nakajima S, Saiki R, and Goryozono Y (2007) Development of an engine for flexible fuel vehicles (FFV). SAE Paper No. 2007-01-3616. Warrendale, PA: Society of Automotive Engineers.
[169] Nilsson M (2007) The new ECOTEC turbo BioPower engine from GM Powertrain. *Institution of Mechanical Engineers Seminar: Biofuels for Future Transport and Mobility*, Hethel, Norwich, UK, 20 September.
[170] Ethanol also for lorries, SEKAB press information. www.sekab.com (accessed 17 March 2008).
[171] Moreira JR, Coelho ST, Velazquez SMSG, *et al.* (2008) BEST project – Contribution of ethanol usage in public urban transport. www.aea.org.br/twiki/pub/AEA/PAPERS/PAP0018-17.09-13h30-AnditriolPE.pdf (accessed November 2008).
[172] Bioethanol for Sustainable Transport (2008) World's first ethanol powered diesel car. www.best-europe.org/Pages/ContentPage.aspx%3Fid=488 (accessed December 2008).
[173] Dolan G (2008) Methanol transportation fuels: From U.S. to China, IAGS Briefing, U.S. House of Representatives, 16 April. http://www.setamericafree.org/Dolan041608.pdf (accessed 15 December 2011).
[174] Sutton M (2008) China: New methanol capacity, new applications, new technology, new methanol world order. *CMAI World Methanol Conference*, Lisbon, Portugal, 8–10 December.
[175] Li W, Zhong L, and Xie K (2008) The development of methanol industry and methanol fuel in China. *6th Annual Methanol Forum*, Dubai, 3–5 November.

Further Reading

[1] Stone R (1999) *Introduction to Internal Combustion Engines*. London, UK: MacMillan Press Ltd. ISBN: 0-333-74013-0.
[2] Heywood JB (1989) *Internal Combustion Engine Fundamentals*. Maidenhead, UK: McGraw-Hill Education Europe. ISBN10: 0071004998, ISBN13: 9780071004992.
[3] Bandi A and Specht M (2006) Renewable carbon-based transportation fuels. *'Landolt-Bornstein', Energy Technologies, Subvolume C: Renewable Energy, VIII/3C*, pp. 441–482. Berlin, Germany: Springer. ISBN: 978-3-540-42962-3.
[4] Olah GA, Goeppert A, and Prakash GKS (2009) *Beyond Oil and Gas: The Methanol Economy*, 2nd edn. Weinheim, Germany: Wiley-VCH Verlag GmbH & Co. KGaA. ISBN: 98-3-527-32422-4.
[5] Kohl WL (ed.) (1990) *Methanol as an Alternative Fuel Choice: An Assessment*. Washington, DC: Johns Hopkins Foreign Policy Institute. ISBN: 094170064X.
[6] Roddy D (2009) Biofuels: Environmental friend or foe? *Energy* 162: 121–130, Proceeding Institution of Civil Engineers.

5.17 Use of Biofuels in a Range of Engine Configurations

A Roskilly, Y Wang, R Mikalsen, and H Yu, Newcastle University, Newcastle upon Tyne, UK

© 2012 Elsevier Ltd. All rights reserved.

5.17.1	Introduction	343
5.17.2	Biofuel Blends with Fossil Fuels for Transport Use	343
5.17.2.1	Ethanol–Diesel Blends	343
5.17.3	Engine Modifications for Biofuel Operation	346
5.17.3.1	Petrol (Gasoline) Engines	346
5.17.3.2	Diesel Engines	347
5.17.4	Biofuels and Bio-Oils in Stationary Engines	348
5.17.4.1	Biodiesel/Fossil Diesel Blends	348
5.17.4.2	Straight Vegetable Oils	349
5.17.5	Dual Fuel Operation	349
5.17.5.1	Fuels and Fuel Properties	350
5.17.5.2	The Dual Fuel Combustion Process	350
5.17.5.3	Reported Operational Experience on Dual Fuel Stationary Engines	350
5.17.5.4	Combustion Improvement in Dual Fuel Engines Running on Straight Vegetable Oil	351
5.17.5.5	Utilization of Biomass-Derived Gaseous Fuels in Stationary Engines	351
5.17.6	Conclusions	354
References		354

Glossary

Biodiesel A fuel made by processing bio-oil (e.g., straight vegetable oil) via transesterification and subsequent purification.
Bm A blended fuel containing $m\%$ biodiesel, the remainder being either bioethanol or fossil diesel depending on the context (e.g., B45 contains 45% biodiesel).
BSFC Brake specific fuel consumption.
Cetane number A measure of a fuel's ignition delay, which is the time period between the start of fuel injection and the start of combustion (ignition) of the fuel.
En A blended fuel containing $n\%$ ethanol, the remainder being either biodiesel or gasoline depending on the context (e.g., E20 contains 20% ethanol).
PAH Polycyclic aromatic hydrocarbon.
PM Particulate matter.

5.17.1 Introduction

The rate of deployment of biofuels depends on whether they are used for transport only or also for power generation and combined heat and power; whether they are used as liquids, gases, or both; and the balance between fuel refining and engine development in setting out to meet emission performance standards. This chapter explores all these aspects in the context of internal combustion engines.

Section 5.17.2 looks at blends of liquid biofuels for transport applications with particular emphasis on bioethanol/biodiesel emulsions as a relatively novel approach. Section 5.17.3 discusses the subject of engine modifications to support the use of pure biofuels and strong blends. The potential for using biofuels in stationary engines is explored in Section 5.17.4 with particular emphasis on strong biodiesel/fossil diesel blends and on the use of straight vegetable oils. Finally, Section 5.17.5 looks at dual-fueling opportunities in stationary engines where there is the potential to approach zero-carbon operation by deployment of both liquid and gaseous biofuels.

5.17.2 Biofuel Blends with Fossil Fuels for Transport Use

A very attractive option for utilizing biofuels is to blend them with fossil fuels. With very simple implementation, the quality of the mixture can be controlled through the fraction of biofuel used. This is, in fact, already used in many countries, albeit to a limited degree. Norway, for example, has a legal requirement that 2.5% (increasing to 5%) of fuel sold for transport should be biofuels, which is achieved by blending biodiesel with automotive diesel. Use of blended biofuels features prominently in the plans of most EU countries to achieve the mandated 10% renewable fuel content (by energy value) by 2020 in the transport fuel pool. Low blend ratios allow consumers to use the fuel without implications for engine warranty or reliability. For higher blends, engine modifications are required (as described in Section 5.17.3). For petrol engines, high-ethanol blends are unproblematic to use and are readily available in many countries such as Sweden, Brazil, and the United States for use in engines that have been developed for use with such fuels.

5.17.2.1 Ethanol–Diesel Blends

A more unconventional method, which has been studied by some authors, is to use a blend of ethanol and diesel for compression-ignition engines. Ethanol is different from diesel in chemical structure and properties. Ethanol has a polar and hydrophilic hydroxyl group, while diesel consists mainly of alkanes and some alkenes, which are nonpolar and hydrophobic in nature. It is therefore difficult to form a composite fuel from ethanol and diesel that will satisfy requirements over a wide temperature range.

To blend ethanol with diesel, two methods are generally used: one is mechanical agitation to produce low blending ratios (usually lower than 5% w/w) and blends that tend to be unstable; and the other is by adding an emulsifier or cosolvent to provide high blending ratios and stable blends.

Common emulsifiers or cosolvents include higher alcohols, esters, vegetable oils, and amines [1–4]. C4–C11 alcohols are usually recommended for reducing the solution's surface tension and critical micelle concentration. The higher the carbon atomic number, the more similar will be the distillation curves for the ethanol–diesel blend and the diesel. Esters can be dissolved in either diesel or ethanol, and are thus good for preventing phase separation. Suitable esters include methyl oleate, fatty acid methyl ester (biodiesel), and acetic ester dimethylcarbonate. The purpose of adding vegetable oils is to improve the viscosity and density of blends, while amines are advocated for improving cetane number and to some extent for improving solubility [2].

Early studies in the 1980s have shown that 10–15% ethanol–diesel blending is technically feasible, with the blended fuel usually being referred to as E-diesel [5, 6]. Nevertheless, temperature and water content have significant influence on the stability of E-diesel. As an example, **Figures 1** and **2** illustrate these influences using ternary liquid–liquid phase diagrams [3, 7]. It was concluded that to maintain fuel stability at 0 °C, the ratio of ethyl acetate to ethanol should be 1:2. Li [4] chose n-butyl ethanol as a cosolvent for E-diesel. Test results showed that for higher additive proportions, better fuel stability was achieved. The E10 and E20 blends remained stable for 2 months at room temperature when the additive level relative to ethanol was 50%. Moses *et al.* [8] also pointed out that the ratio of surfactant to aqueous ethanol (5% water) in the blend was about 1:2.5. Some of the commercial additives for E-diesel are listed in **Table 1**.

Ethanol–diesel blending has proved to be corrosive to engine components, the extent being mostly determined by ethanol quality. The corrosion due to ethanol can be divided into three categories: (1) general corrosion caused by ionic impurities; (2) dry corrosion which is attributed to its polar molecules; and (3) wet corrosion due to the water content in ethanol. Ten to twenty percent dry ethanol blended with diesel shows no corrosion or negligible corrosion of metallic fuel system components, although pure ethanol has been reported as having the potential for chemical attack of certain metals like magnesium, lead, and aluminum. Experiments have also revealed that new elastomeric and plastic parts present reasonable resistance to corrosion by E10, while old components such as o-rings and seals tend to be attacked. In addition, ethanol–diesel blends held in long-term storage absorb water and become more corrosive.

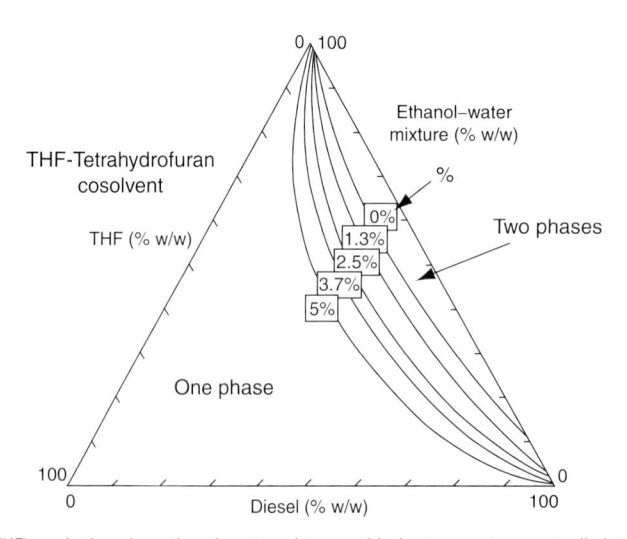

Figure 1 Diesel, tetrahydrofuran (THF), and ethanol or ethanol–water mixtures with the temperature controlled at 0 °C. Reproduced from Letcher TM (1980) Ternary liquid–liquid phase diagrams for diesel fuel blends. *South African Journal of Science* 76(2): 130–132 [7].

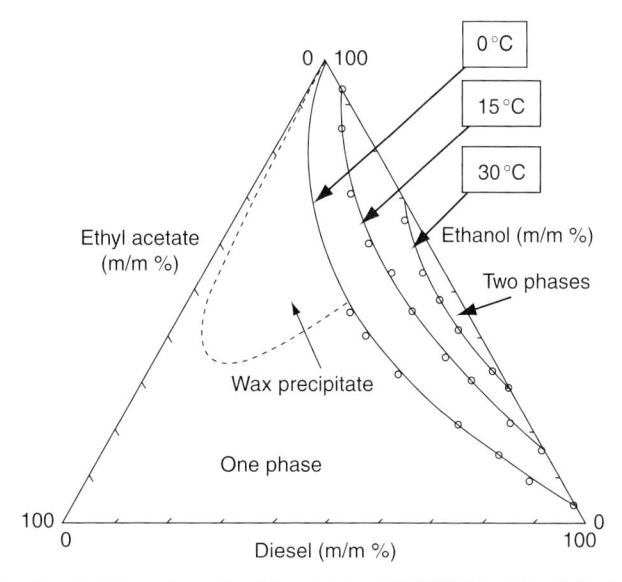

Figure 2 Diesel, ethyl acetate, and dry ethanol mixtures. Reproduced from Letcher TM (1983) Diesel blends for diesel engines. *South African Journal of Science* 79(1): 4–7 [3].

Table 1 Commercial additives for E-diesel

Name of additives	Company	Vol.% of fuel	Remark
Puranol	Pure Energy Corporation (PEC), USA	82–94% No. 2 diesel + 5–15% ethanol + 1–3% additive + 0.33% cetane improver	Additives contain only elements of C, H, and O
AAE-05	AAE, UK	91.3% diesel + 7.7% ethanol + 1% AAE additive	The properties of E-diesel (ethanol less than 8%) are similar to those of diesel
Lubrizol	Lubrizol, USA	89% diesel + 10% ethanol + 1% additive	Fuels include E-diesel with and without cetane improver
Dalco Beraiol ED10	AKZO Surface Chemistry, Sweden	0.5–5% additive for E10–E15, for example, 80% diesel + 15% ethanol + 5% Dalco additive	E10 with 2% additive had been tested on vehicle for 124 000 km till October 2001
SOA	Shell Chemicals Inc., the Netherlands	4%, 8%, and 12% additives for E10, E20, and E30, respectively	

Reproduced from Corkwell K (2002) The development of diesel/ethanol (diesehol) fuel blends for diesel vehicles: Fuel formulation and properties. *The 14th International Symposium on Alcohol Fuels.* Thailand [9].

Generally, no modification is needed for using ethanol–diesel blends in conventional diesel engines. Compared with straight diesel, power reduction is observed in engines fueled by ethanol–diesel blends, and the extent is proportional to ethanol content in the blend. This is mainly due to ethanol's low cetane number of 5–15 [10]. Wrage and Goering [11] tested E0–E50 and depicted the linearly decreasing relationship between ethanol fraction and cetane number (see **Figure 3**). The other reason for the power reduction lies in fuel pump leakage caused by the low viscosity of ethanol. Li *et al.* [12] measured a steady decrease in kinematic viscosity, in accordance with increasing ethanol content in E-diesel. They claimed that the viscosity of E10–E20 cannot meet the lowest requirement for diesel fuels. Meiring *et al.* [13] observed a 5% decline in maximum fuel delivery when a 30% ethanol–diesel blend was pumped by a rotary distributor pump.

In recent studies, Satgé de Caro *et al.* [14] measured a power decrease of 5% and a fuel consumption increase of 3% with E10 fueled on a DI Hatz engine. When E20 was adopted on another IDI Renault engine, these figures increased to 11% and 7%, respectively. Kass *et al.* [15] announced roughly 8% torque reduction for E10 and E15 with 2% GE Betz additive. Hansen *et al.* [16] evaluated an E15 blend (15% dry ethanol, 2.35% PEC additive, and 82.65% No. 2 diesel fuel) in a Cummins engine and reported a 7–10% power decrease.

On the other hand, ethanol is regarded as an environmentally friendly oxygenated fuel which possesses the advantage of emission reduction, although specific emissions may be affected by engine running conditions, engine type, test procedures, and base fuels. Oxygen content and local oxygen concentration in the fuel plume (rather than ratio of oxygenates in blends or their type) have been verified to be the key factors for improving exhaust emissions, especially particulate matter (PM) [17–19]. Some examples of emission tests on engines fueled by E10 and E15 are summarized in **Table 2**. It can be seen that PM dropped

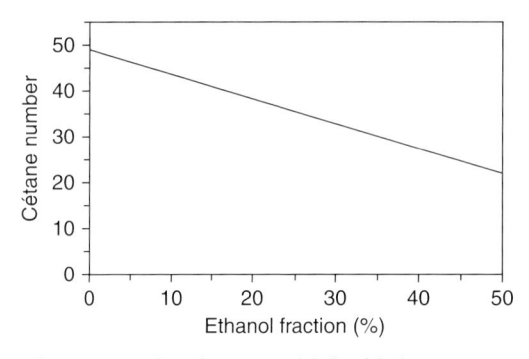

Figure 3 Effect of the addition of ethanol on the cetane number of a commercial diesel fuel.

Table 2 E-diesel emissions compared to conventional diesel

References	Spreen [20]		Li et al. [12]		Lofvenbeng [21]
Engine	1991 DDC series 60 12.7 l turbo-charging intercooling engine		ZS1100 single-cylinder DI engine		Scania 380HP diesel engine
Fuel	E10	E15	E10	E15	E10
PM (%)	↓ 27	↓ 41			↓ 31
NO$_x$ (%)	↓ 4	↓ 5	↓ 2.3	↓ 4.2	↓ 5
CO (%)	↓ 20	↓ 27	↓ 16.7	↓ 5.8	↓ 29
HC (%)	↑ 71	↑ 120	↑ 45.4	↑ 41.2	↓ 13

HC, hydrocarbon; PM, particulate matter.

dramatically by between 27% and 31%. Another index related closely to PM emission is smoke. He et al. [22] reported a reduction in smoke of 6.3% and 43.8% by introducing E10 and E30 (with additive and cetane improver), respectively.

A slight improvement in NO$_x$ emissions is, as expected, achieved. As shown in **Table 2**, these figures are between 2.3% and 5%. He et al. [22] observed a less distinct tendency at high load.

Although a substantial reduction in CO emissions is depicted in **Table 2**, other studies have reported contradictory trends. Kass et al. [15] reported a 40% and a 60% increase in CO by E10 and E15, respectively. He et al. [22] also claimed notably high CO emissions from E10. Similar trends occurred for unburnt hydrocarbon (HC) emissions as well. Most of the tests have reported high HC emissions compared to diesel [12, 14, 20], while Lofvenbeng [21] reported a 13% decrease on a Scania 380HP (horsepower) diesel engine. Lower emissions at high/full loads were also found by He et al. [22] and Li [4]. Although Kass et al. [15] announced the influence on NO$_x$, CO and HC were still indistinct. Factors such as the high latent heat and low heating value of ethanol may help to explain the low in-cylinder temperature as well as combustion delay, especially at low load and low engine speed, which have large effects on exhaust formation.

5.17.3 Engine Modifications for Biofuel Operation

5.17.3.1 Petrol (Gasoline) Engines

Ethanol and methanol are the biofuels most commonly used as alternatives to petrol. There is a long history of ethanol being used as a fuel for engines. In 1826, Samuel Morey used ethanol and turpentine as the fuel to run an engine that he had developed. Nicolaus Otto, inventor of the Otto cycle, used ethanol as the fuel for one of his engines. In 1896, Henry Ford built his first automobile which ran on pure ethanol. The most recent return to using ethanol occurred in 1970s, due to the oil crisis. The history of bioethanol use is covered in more detail elsewhere in the volume (see Chapter 5.02).

Brazil and the United States are two countries that have used blends of alcohol with petrol since the 1970s. A detailed account of bioethanol development and deployment in Brazil appears elsewhere in the volume (see Chapter 5.04). According to their experience, if the blends contain 10% or less of ethanol, they can be used in any car with no need for modification. For blends of over 10% alcohol, some modifications are required.

Ethanol and methanol (which are the lightest members of the alcohols family) have similar properties to petrol and can be used in low-percentage blends in unmodified petrol engines. Some specially developed cars, called flex fuel vehicles, can use blends containing up to 85% alcohol.

Using ethanol and methanol as the fuel for spark-ignition engines may increase the engine performance and efficiency and reduce emissions. This is because ethanol and methanol contain chemically bound oxygen, which gives them a higher octane number, heat of vaporization, flame speed, and heat capacity of combustion products. But alcohol has also some different properties compared to petrol because of that same oxygen content. It may degrade some rubber and plastic parts in engines, necessitating modifications to the engine or the fuel train. There are two main areas where modifications are required: the engine's air and fuel supply system and the engine's combustion system.

Starting with the air and fuel supply system, due to the lower calorific value (CV) of bioethanol and biomethanol, more fuel is required for the engines. To preserve the same power output and the same vehicle range, a larger fuel tank is required. Another problem is that the bioethanol and biomethanol degrade the rubber, elastomer, and plastic parts in the fuel delivery system and accelerate the corrosion of some metal parts in the petrol engine. These components therefore have to be replaced or made from different materials. It is also necessary to change or service the fuel filters more often, as ethanol blends can loosen solid deposits that are present in vehicle fuel tanks and fuel lines, which then accumulate in the filters.

Because the fuel consumption for high-alcohol blends is higher than for pure petrol, the fuel injectors need to be adjusted to a higher flow rate in order to make up for the lower energy content per unit mass of fuel, due to the lower heating value of alcohol compared with pure petrol.

When using blends with a high percentage of ethanol, the airflow into the engine needs to be adjusted due to the lower air:fuel ratio required for the alcohol (because of its oxygen content). Typically, the air:fuel ratio required for pure petrol to support complete combustion is around 14.6. This means that 14.6 kg of air is needed for the complete combustion of 1 kg of petrol. For ethanol, the air:fuel ratio required for complete combustion is 9; for methanol, the required air:fuel ratio is 6.5.

Turning now to the engine combustion system, the key considerations are ignition timing, compression ratio, and cold-start performance. Due to the higher octane number for bioethanol and biomethanol, the combustion characteristics of these fuels are different from those of petrol, so the ignition timing requires some changes or adjustment. The higher octane number also leads to better antiknock qualities, which means that the engine compression ratio may be increased up to 13, leading to a higher thermal efficiency for the engine. Both ethanol and methanol have higher latent heats of evaporation than petrol. Slower rates of evaporation can lead to problems with cold starting. For example, pure methanol will have starting problems at 10 °C and lower. To solve this problem, a small amount of petrol may be used for cold starting in cold weather, or a blended fuel such as E85 can be used.

Ethanol blends of 14–24% have been used for many years in Brazil (*see* Chapter 5.04). To enable older cars made before 1980 to run on high-bioethanol blends, it is common to make changes to cylinder walls, cylinder heads, valves and valve seats, pistons, piston rings, intake manifolds, and carburetors. Nickel plating of steel fuel lines and fuel tanks is often employed to prevent ethanol corrosion. Higher fuel flow rate injectors are used to support the higher volumetric flow rates required as a result of the oxygenate qualities of ethanol.

Further details of the practical implications of using bioethanol and biomethanol as fuels and the development of flex fuel vehicles can be found elsewhere in the volume (*see* Chapter 5.22).

5.17.3.2 Diesel Engines

One important consideration is engine emissions. Diesel engines running on biodiesel/bio-oils will emit carbon dioxide (CO_2), carbon monoxide (CO), oxides of nitrogen (NO_x), and particulates. Basha *et al.* [23] have conducted an extensive review of work on biodiesel production, combustion, emissions, and performance carried out by 130 scientists between 1980 and 2008 from which a number of conclusions can be drawn. NO_x emissions are reduced when using biodiesel/bio-oils in most of the cases studied [24–26]. Smoke and PMs are reduced when using biodiesel/bio-oils in most of the cases studied [27–29]. Unburnt HCs are reduced when using biodiesel/bio-oils in most of the cases studied [28–30]. Carbon monoxide is reduced when using biodiesel/bio-oils in most of the cases studied, especially at engine high loads [27, 31–34].

Another potential problem area is carbon deposition. Carbon deposits tend to accumulate more on the fuel injector tip when using biodiesel/bio-oils as the fuel than that when running on diesel. The same is true in respect of the piston crown, piston rings, and the combustion chamber. To solve the problem, blending the biodiesel/bio-oils with diesel is one option; another is to clean and service the injector and the other parts more frequently.

For fuels used in diesel engines, the most important parameter is cetane number. Cetane number is a measure of a fuel's ignition delay, which is the time period between the start of fuel injection and the start of combustion (ignition) of the fuel. Fuels with a high cetane number have a short ignition delay, leaving time for full combustion to be achieved within the cycle. The normal range for cetane numbers is between 40 and 55.

The original diesel engine was reportedly designed to run on bio-oils (a detailed account of historical developments appears elsewhere in the volume (*see* Chapter 5.02)). As a consequence, most modern diesel engines can be run on biodiesel or other bio-oils; however, they may need some modifications since modern diesel engines are designed to run on high-quality diesel fuel. However, diesel engines to be run on biodiesel or other bio-oils need less extensive engine modification than do petrol engines to be run on bioethanol. The modifications required for diesel engines are outlined below.

The first consideration is engine timing. A characteristic of biodiesels/bio-oils is that their cetane number is higher than that of diesel fuel, which means they have a shorter ignition delay. Therefore, when using blends of diesel with biodiesel/bio-oils, it is recommended that the engine timing should be advanced by between 2 and 3 degrees, especially for a 100% biodiesel or bio-oil, in order to improve the engine performance. NO_x emissions are reduced when using these advanced injection timings along with an increased injection pressure.

The second consideration is cold-start performance. Cold starting is one of the main problems for diesel engines when using biodiesel/bio-oils or their blends with diesel. This is due to the higher viscosity of biodiesel/bio-oils in cold weather compared with fossil diesel. To solve this problem, a fuel heating unit can be used to reduce the viscosity of biodiesel/bio-oils and assist cold starting. Another solution is to use biodegradable additives that reduce the viscosity.

The third consideration is fuel system seals. Some diesel engines use rubber seals in the fuel lines. Since biodiesel/bio-oils may react with these rubber parts, they are required to be replaced with nonrubber parts.

The fourth consideration concerns the lubrication system. Diesel engines running on biodiesel/bio-oils need to change lubrication oil more often than those running on conventional fossil diesel. This is because the biodiesel/bio-oils contain chemically bound oxygen within the structure of the fatty acid or methyl ester. If biodiesel or bio-oil leaks into the lubrication system, the oxygen is liable to react with the lubrication oil, shortening its life.

Finally, there is the subject of biodiesel-induced corrosion, which has been investigated by a number of people. Kaul *et al.* [35] studied corrosive behaviors of four nonedible biodiesels (derived from mahua, karanja, *Jatropha*, and *Salvadora oleoides*). They found that the first two fuels had 'no corrosion on piston metal and piston liner', Jatropha biodiesel produced mild corrosion, whereas Salvadora biodiesel presented a remarkable corrosion effect due to its high sulfur compounds, and thus may be more suitable as a lubricity improvement additive. Kinast [36] reported that the lubricity of biodiesel is about 2 times greater than that of diesel, and that in blend concentrations of 3% or less it may enhance the lubricity of a biodiesel–diesel blend significantly with consequential benefit to engine durability. Pehan *et al.* [37] announced that rapeseed biodiesel may cause a deterioration in pump plunger surface roughness, but make no difference to sliding. Pehan *et al.* also showed that carbon deposition in the combustion chambers and the injector nozzles maintained the normal level, and thus would not affect engine durability.

5.17.4 Biofuels and Bio-Oils in Stationary Engines

Stationary engines for power generation or for combined heat and power can run on a range of fuels including biodiesel and some bio-oils. The performance of biofuels and raw bio-oils depends on their source and on the extent to which they have been processed. Biodiesel can be made from vegetable oils, waste oil, animal fats, and grease. Edible oils are the major feedstocks in Europe and America, while inedible oils are used mainly in Asia. Compared to animal fat and waste grease, vegetable oils are cleaner and well suited for producing high-quality biodiesel, as additional after-treatments are usually needed with lower-grade feedstocks in order to meet the ASTM D 6751-02 specification [36].

As a result of transesterification, biodiesels have physicochemical properties that are substantially improved relative to vegetable oils. Biodiesel has a typical viscosity ranging from 2.35 to 5.62, only 1–2 times higher than that of fossil diesel. It also has a similar density to diesel, typically between 860 and $900 \, g \, l^{-1}$. Moreover, biodiesel has typical higher heating values (HHVs) of $41-42 \, MJ \, kg^{-1}$, only roughly 10% lower than diesel. As for cetane number, typical figures of 50–60 are between 9% and 42% higher than the cetane number of fossil diesel. These properties make it possible to use biodiesel in unmodified diesel engines without causing durability problems. Other characteristics of biodiesel include its oxygen content, its sulfur-free composition, and its high flash point (over 100 °C) [36, 38, 39].

5.17.4.1 Biodiesel/Fossil Diesel Blends

Lot of research has been carried out in recent years, mostly centered on performance and emissions of engines fueled by biodiesels and biodiesel–diesel blends. Diesel engines are compatible with biodiesels and their blends. When run on biodiesel they show almost the same power output as when run on diesel, but thermal efficiency may drop slightly and result in higher fuel consumption [40–42]. Lin *et al.* [41] tested palm biodiesel–diesel blends ranging from B0 to B100 in a 40 kW diesel generator and found that the brake specific fuel consumption (BSFC) of B100 increased by only 5.35% relative to diesel. It was concluded that palm biodiesel 'seems to be the most feasible biodiesel' compared with other feedstock types.

As for emissions, due to the natural oxygen content and sulfur-free composition of biodiesels, lower smoke, HC, CO, and SO_2 emissions are expected to be achieved. Nabi *et al.* [43] reported reductions of 14% smoke and 24% CO on a single-cylinder 4.476 kW diesel engine fueled by B10 and B30, respectively. Lertsathapornsuk *et al.* [44] report decreases in CO and HC emissions both in volume concentration and in brake specific emissions. Park *et al.* [45] tested two biodiesel–diesel blends in a 28 kW diesel generator and found that the CO and SO_2 emissions of the blends fell. Pereira *et al.* [46] investigated the performance and emissions of soybean biodiesel and its blends in a 1.8 kW/3600 rpm stationary engine. The generator delivered almost the same brake power, while lower HC, CO, and SO_2 emissions were observed. Durbin *et al.* [42] also recorded a decrease in HC emissions from two diesel generators running on B20 biodiesel.

Most NO_x emissions of biodiesel and biodiesel–diesel mixtures increase relative to diesel, apart from a few biofuels made from inedible oils, which present the reverse tendency [46, 47]. Park *et al.* [45] reported a very close match in NO_2 emissions by a B45 palm oil biodiesel–diesel blend and a rapeseed oil biodiesel–diesel blend compared to diesel, while their NO_x content increased by about 10%. Lertsathapornsuk *et al.* [44] and Durbin *et al.* [42] claimed a slight increase in NO_x emissions by B20 and B50. All of these effects are mainly due to the so-called 'biodiesel NO_x effect' [48]. That is, biodiesel has a higher bulk modulus of compressibility, which transfers a pressure wave faster from fuel injection pump to injector, hence resulting in advancing of the injection timing and earlier initiation of combustion. Other factors, such as high cetane number and poor spray and atomization properties, may retard the combustion process and extend reaction time, thereby increasing NO_x formation.

A variation in PM emissions has been observed in engines fueled by different biodiesels. Generally, blends with less than 30 vol.% biodiesel tend to lead to increased PM emissions, or maintain the same level as diesel, while reduced emissions are observed for higher biodiesel blends. Sahoo *et al.* [49] reported a remarkable reduction in HC and PM by biodiesels made from three inedible oils and their mixtures. Nabi *et al.* [43] reported a 24% decrease in PM emissions by B10. Durbin *et al.* [42] observed a slight increase in PM emissions on a 250 kW generator run on B20 and B100, and on a 60 kW generator run on B20. Lin *et al.* [41] reported an increase in PM emissions ranging from 4.6% to 51% by running on B10–B30 fuels and a decrease of 10.9–29.3% on B50–B100 fuels, respectively.

Moreover, Lin *et al.* [41] also observed a dramatic reduction in polycyclic aromatic hydrocarbons (PAHs) and other potentially carcinogenic emissions using pure palm biodiesel, with reductions of 98.8% and 58.2% on average, respectively.

5.17.4.2 Straight Vegetable Oils

From the very beginning of biofuel research, efforts have been made to burn vegetable oils directly as an engine fuel with limited success. Vegetable oil is mainly a saturated HC with a triglyceride backbone along with some free fatty acids and other nongrease substances. It has a similar cetane number to diesel, but differs from diesel by exhibiting high viscosity, low volatility, low air to fuel ratio, and low CV. Viscosity is a key measure of a fuel's internal frictional resistance to flow. The viscosities of vegetable oils mostly fall in the 30–50 cSt range (at 40 °C), which is 9–17 times higher than that of diesel [38]. These figures will sharply decrease to 5–10 cSt when the oil is heated to over 85 °C, bringing them close to the viscosity of fossil diesel.

Due to the high viscosity, direct use of vegetable oils in an engine may lead to poor fuel atomization and rough burning, thus resulting in many problems such as carbon deposition in the combustion chamber, piston ring and injector obstruction, and lube oil dilution [50, 51].

Diesel engines fueled by vegetable oil deliver almost the same power as those fueled by diesel. Nevertheless, because of the low CV of vegetable oils, low thermal efficiency and high fuel consumption are also observed [52–55]. Masjuki *et al.* [55] compared 10–50% palm oil–diesel to fossil diesel in an indirect injection diesel engine. The brake power of the engine fell by less than 5%, and specific fuel consumption increased in accordance with the blending proportions. Hemmeriein *et al.* [56] investigated the physicochemical properties of rapeseed oil and reported that the heating value of the fuel was 7% lower compared to diesel. Accordingly, the engine power decreased and the effective thermal efficiency was about 2% lower. Lower combustion noise and NO_x emissions were observed, due to the lower cetane number and combustion speed, whereas CO and HC emissions increased sharply.

High viscosity of vegetable oil will degrade engine performance and durability. Bari *et al.* [57] tested crude palm oil in a diesel engine and found that the engine ran normally in the short term but the performance deteriorated after 500 h, manifested as a power loss of 20% and an increase in minimum BSFC of 26%. After overhaul inspection, some problems were observed: (1) severe combustion chamber carbon deposits; (2) piston rings and injection pump wear; (3) mild scoring on the cylinder liner; and (4) improper injecting of the nozzles. Tests identified that gas leakage through the intake and exhaust valves caused by the sticking of carbon and colloidal particles was the major reason for the poor performance and fuel economy.

Preheating of vegetable oil is an effective way of not only reducing its viscosity but also improving engine performance and endurance [58–60]. De Almeida *et al.* [60] and Agarwal and Agarwal [58] heated pure palm oil and Jatropha–diesel blends to 100 °C before supplying them to diesel engines. They reported a 5–10% increase in fuel consumption for maintaining the same power output as diesel, and the emissions of CO, CO_2, and HC increased. A reverse emission tendency was found when using crude sunflower oil preheated to 75 °C [59], with a particularly dramatic reduction of 34% in HC emissions. Canakci *et al.* [59] and Agarwal and Agarwal [58] also declared that sunflower oil and Jatropha can be directly used in diesel engines in the short term without causing any problem. However, combustion of palm oil that had been preheated to 50 °C resulted in heavy carbon deposition on the cylinder head. In order to improve engine performance, emissions, stability, and reliability, De Almeida *et al.* [60] offered some constructive proposals, including increasing fuel injection pressure, turbo-charging, and improving the lube oil and fuel injection system.

The emissions of diesel engines can be improved when fueled by vegetable oil–diesel blends compared with straight diesel [53, 55, 61]. Masjuki *et al.* [55] announced that engine emissions were improved when fueled by 10–50% palm oil–diesel blends, especially for HC and PAH emissions, and that 10–30% coconut oil-based fuels were comparable with diesel in terms of lubricity. Wang *et al.* [61] also claimed a similar engine performance and lower emissions of HC, CO, and NO_x on a diesel generator fueled by vegetable oil–diesel blends. Haldar *et al.* [62] investigated the degumming of karanja, Jatropha, and Putranjiva oil on a single-cylinder variable compression engine. Compared to diesel, the engine performed best at an injection timing of 45° before top dead center when fueled by 20–30% blends, 5° ahead of the diesel injection timing.

5.17.5 Dual Fuel Operation

An increasingly studied option for the direct use of liquid or gaseous biofuels is to use both of them simultaneously in a dual fuel engine. This is most commonly done by converting a direct injection (diesel) engine to allow additional induction of gaseous fuel in the intake air. Using dual fuel operation of internal combustion engines can give more flexibility in the fuel supply, but also a potential for operational optimization of the engine, improvements in the combustion process, and reductions in exhaust gas emissions by controlling the energy distribution between the fuels as well as other operational parameters.

When converting a diesel engine to dual fuel operation, engine operational characteristics can remain largely unchanged, with the majority of the energy being provided by the diesel fuel. Alternatively, if the gaseous fuel is to provide the larger energy fraction, the liquid fuel then acts only as a pilot fuel to ignite the cylinder charge. In the latter case, the quantity of pilot fuel must, as a minimum, be sufficient to provide the ignition energy required to ignite the gaseous fuel. Due to the use of a premixed charge, problems of preignition and detonating combustion (knock) may, however, occur, and the use of an appropriate engine control system is therefore essential.

The additional complexity associated with storing and supplying two fuels means that dual fuel operation is best suited to stationary and/or large-scale applications in power generation or combined heat and power. However, there is no fundamental barrier in principle to its use in transport applications such as automotive engines.

5.17.5.1 Fuels and Fuel Properties

Gas fuels used in dual fuel engines range from natural gas, synthesis gas, and landfill gas to hydrogen and biogas. Liquid fuels may include standard diesel, biodiesel, bio-oils, petrol, etc.

In order to provide near-zero carbon emissions, a combination of a 'renewable' gaseous and liquid fuel must be found. However, even if only the main fuel is renewable, substantial reductions in CO_2 emissions may be possible. For example, one can use fossil diesel, which has high quality and good ignition properties, as the pilot fuel and synthesis gas (from gasifying biomass) as the main fuel. In such a system, the synthesis gas could provide in the order of 90% of the energy, giving significant carbon reductions compared with conventional, fossil fuel operation. Similarly, a small amount of natural gas or hydrogen can be used as a combustion improver for vegetable oil operation. If the addition of, for example, 20% nonrenewable fuels provides operational benefits (e.g., particulate emission reductions), it may be worthwhile.

The inducted fuel is added by means of electronic fuel injectors controlling gas injection valves in the intake system (usually at the intake manifold). As the gas displaces a part of the intake air, a power reduction may occur, particularly for high gas fuel fractions. Throttling, as practiced with conventional spark-ignition engines, is never used, as this would lead to an unacceptable reduction in the airflow and power output.

The optimum balance between gaseous and liquid fuels at any operating condition will depend on a number of factors, most importantly the cost of the different fuels and the fuel efficiency and emission characteristics of the engine for the different fuel balance ratios. For example, with a configuration based on standard diesel and natural gas, one would seek to maximize the use of natural gas as this is usually considerably cheaper than diesel fuel. For biofuels, other factors, in addition to fuel cost, may be important, such as the need to meet emission limits or ensure stable combustion for low-quality fuels.

5.17.5.2 The Dual Fuel Combustion Process

The combustion process in dual fuel engines is somewhat more complicated than that of conventional engines since a combination of premixed and diffusion combustion occurs in this mode of engine operation. The contribution and characteristics of each type of combustion depend on several parameters, including fuel properties, injector characteristics, and combustion chamber design, as well as operational variables such as the engine load, speed, manifold air pressure and temperature, and the amount of each fuel present in the combustion chamber.

The combustion process in a dual fuel engine can be divided into three distinct subprocesses:

- ignition of the pilot fuel;
- combustion of the liquid fuel and the gaseous fuel in the vicinity of the pilot fuel cores; and
- combustion of the gaseous fuel due to flame propagation into the premixed lean charge.

The conditions of the combustion chamber charge will depend on the types of fuel used, the balance between liquid and gaseous fuels, and other parameters such as load and injection timing. Furthermore, the equivalence ratio of the cylinder charge varies spatially from point to point within the combustion chamber, depending on the same factors. The in-cylinder processes of a dual fuel engine are therefore extremely complex and difficult to predict.

5.17.5.3 Reported Operational Experience on Dual Fuel Stationary Engines

Numerous reports have discussed dual fuel operation with diesel and natural gas, commonly discussing the conversion of standard diesel engines to use natural gas as the main fuel and diesel as a pilot fuel (providing 10–20% of the energy) [63]. These reports provide a good starting point for work on engines running on liquid or gaseous biofuels in a dual fuel configuration. In general, it is reported that conversion to dual fuel operation can result in reductions in NO_x and particulate emissions, but increases in emissions of carbon monoxide (CO) and unburnt HCs (which are emissions commonly associated with premixed fuel, but not diesel, engines). Results relating to fuel consumption are somewhat conflicting, but some reports indicate a slight reduction in fuel efficiency when operating in dual fuel mode with high gas fuel energy fractions compared to standard

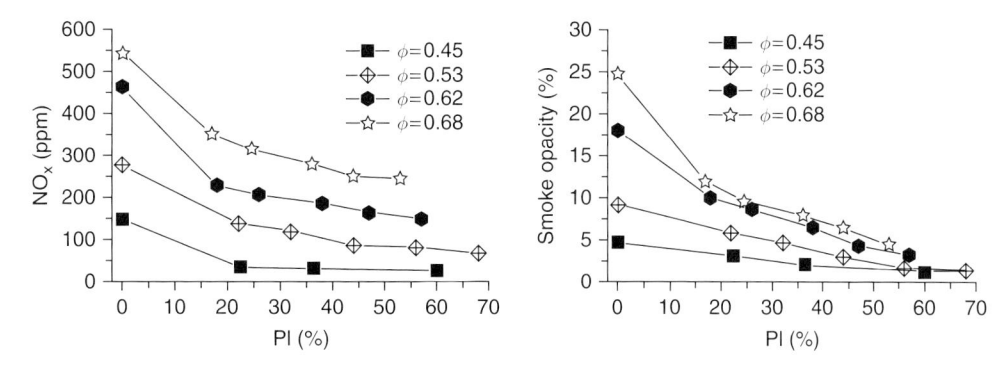

Figure 4 NO$_x$ and smoke emissions from biodiesel-fueled dual fuel engine with port injection (PI) of ethanol. Reproduced from Lu X, Ma J, Ji L, and Huang Z (2008) Simultaneous reduction of NO$_x$ emissions and smoke opacity of biodiesel-fuelled engines by port injection of ethanol. *Fuel* 87: 189–1296 [66].

diesel operation, whereas others show that substituting a small amount (20–30%) of diesel fuel with natural gas can improve fuel efficiency.

One comprehensive study was carried out by Papagiannakis and Hountalas [64, 65], who investigated the performance of a dual fuel diesel–natural gas engine, using approximately 20% diesel and 80% natural gas, and compared this to standard diesel operation. The authors demonstrated reductions in NO$_x$ of between 25% and 50% at full load, as well as a near-complete elimination of soot emissions. However, increases in CO and HC emissions were reported as well as an increase in fuel consumption.

Returning to biofuels, Lu *et al.* [66] showed how simultaneous reductions in NO$_x$ and smoke could be achieved in a biodiesel-fueled diesel engine using port injection of ethanol. **Figure 4** shows the results for varying ethanol energy ratios (quoted as % port injection or % PI) at different equivalence ratios. As in most other reports, the introduction of a premixed fuel increases HC and CO emissions. The induction of ethanol led to a slight increase in fuel efficiency up to a premixed ratio (PI) of approximately 40%; for higher ethanol fractions, the efficiency dropped.

5.17.5.4 Combustion Improvement in Dual Fuel Engines Running on Straight Vegetable Oil

The use of inducted hydrogen to improve the performance of diesel engines fueled with vegetable oils was studied by Geo *et al.* [67] and Senthil Kumar *et al.* [26]. These studies utilized unprocessed vegetable oils, which are normally not suitable as a fuel for diesel engines due to their low volatility, high viscosity, and poor injection properties, leading to reduced engine efficiency and high exhaust emissions.

Geo *et al.* [67] studied the use of rubber seed oil (RSO), rubber seed oil methyl ester (RSOME), and diesel fuel, with varying levels of hydrogen induction in a single-cylinder 4.4 kW diesel engine. **Figure 5** shows the results. It can be seen that the induction of hydrogen can improve fuel efficiency for all fuels studied, but that an efficiency equal to that of conventional diesel operation cannot be achieved using vegetable oils and hydrogen.

Figure 5(b) shows that a substantial reduction in smoke emissions can be achieved in all cases with only a very small amount of hydrogen fuel, indicating that the inducted fuel benefits the combustion process and oxidation of soot. However, the RSO- and RSOME-fueled engines do not achieve the low soot emissions of the diesel-fueled engine for any hydrogen induction rate.

Figure 5(c) shows nitrogen oxide emissions under the same operating conditions, and a clear advantage can be seen for the vegetable oil-fueled engines. This is probably due to a slower heat release rate, reducing peak in-cylinder temperatures. Since there is a trade-off between NO$_x$ emissions, soot, and efficiency, it is likely that the efficiency and soot emissions when using vegetable oil can be improved somewhat by advancing the injection, if an increase in NO$_x$ can be tolerated.

Comparing RSO operation with hydrogen induction to pure RSOME operation, it can be seen that the use of dual fueling with hydrogen mitigates the performance drawbacks of RSO compared with RSOME. At 8–10% hydrogen energy share, RSO provides comparable efficiency and NO$_x$ emissions to pure RSOME operation and significantly lower soot emissions. Therefore, dual fuel operation provides a real alternative to the processing of RSO into RSOME for use in a standard diesel engine.

Figure 6 shows the results of a similar study by Senthil Kumar *et al.* [26], using diesel and Jatropha oil fuels. It can be seen that hydrogen induction provides only minor advantages at part load, but that at full load induction of 5–10% hydrogen provides marked emission improvements. A similar trend is seen for the soot emissions; however, in this case, a vegetable oil + hydrogen dual fuel engine is able to provide lower emissions than a standard diesel engine (without hydrogen injection).

5.17.5.5 Utilization of Biomass-Derived Gaseous Fuels in Stationary Engines

Gaseous fuels are available from a variety of sources, with large differences in quality, energy content, and composition. Natural gas is widely available, with efficient distribution networks existing in many countries, and can readily be utilized in heat engines. Recently, other types of gaseous fuels, such as gasified biomass or waste, landfill gas, and by-products from industrial processes,

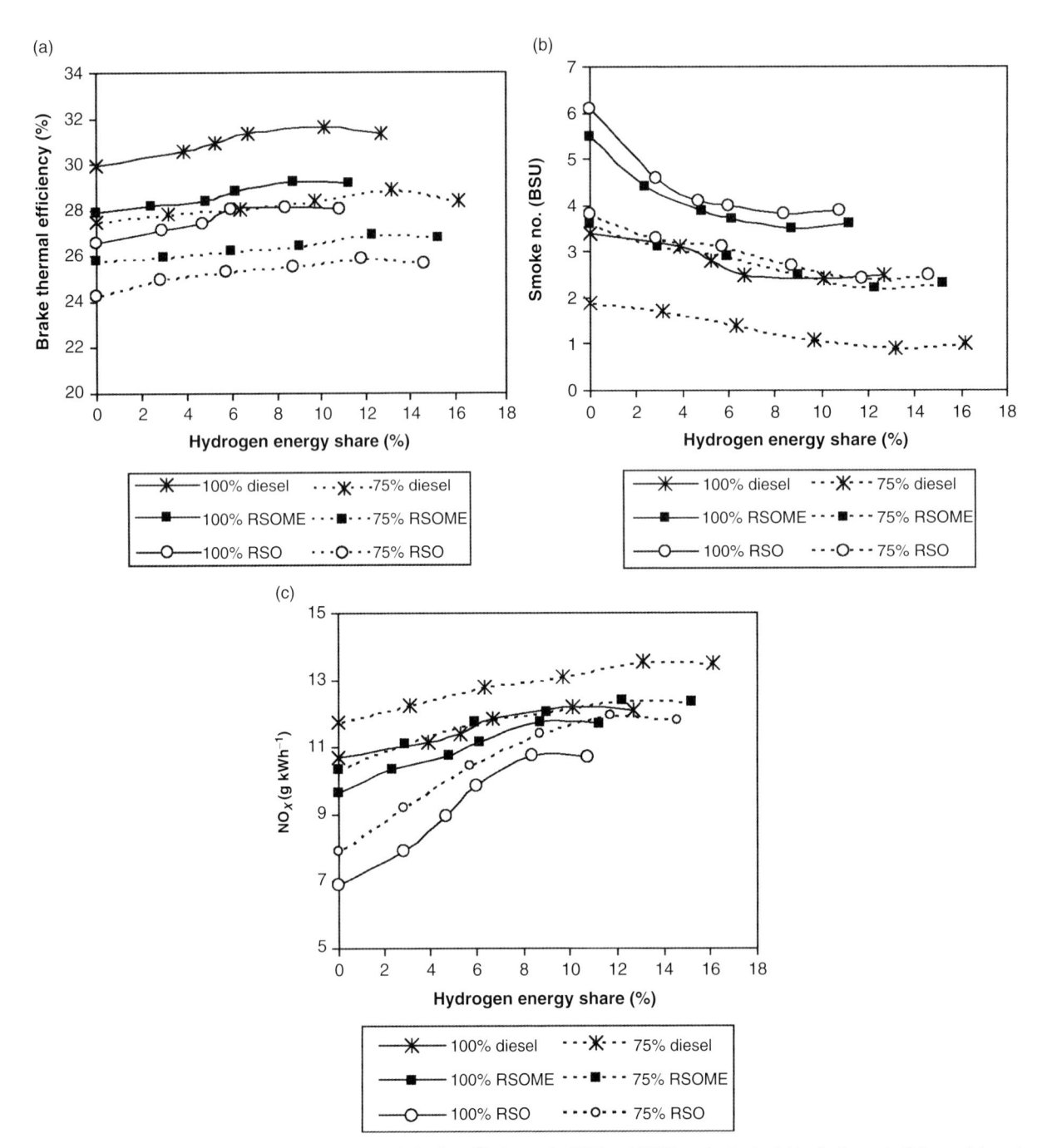

Figure 5 Performance of diesel engine with intake port induction of hydrogen for 75% and 100% engine loads: (a) brake thermal efficiency; (b) smoke emissions; (c) NO_x emissions. RSO, rubber seed oil; RSOME, rubber seed oil methyl ester. Reproduced from Geo EV, Nagarajan G, and Nagalingam B (2008) Studies on dual fuel operation of rubber seed oil and its bio-diesel with hydrogen as the inducted fuel. *International Journal of Hydrogen Energy* 33: 6357–6367 [67].

have received increasing interest for use in electrical power generation. However, most of these fuels have a lower energy content than processed natural gas due to, among other things, high levels of inert gas. Furthermore, these fuels commonly vary in composition depending on, for example, biomass quality or waste composition (in gasification plants) and life cycle stage in landfills. These characteristics present barriers to their efficient utilization for power generation purposes.

Typically, biomass-derived gaseous fuels have an energy content which is 30–70% that of natural gas. Landfill gas, a product of anaerobic digestion, consists of methane, but with significant levels of CO_2 (typically 30–50%). Hence, the energy content of such gas is around half that of natural gas. If synthesis gas is produced from gasification of biomass or waste using air (as opposed to oxygen) as the oxidant, it will consist of a mixture of carbon monoxide (typically around 20%), hydrogen (10–20%), carbon

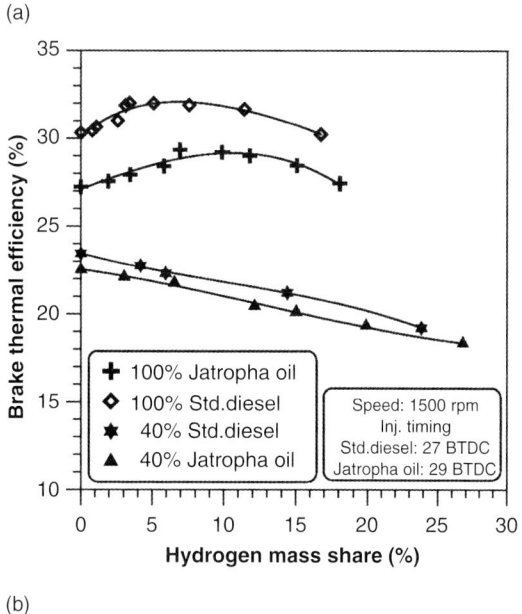

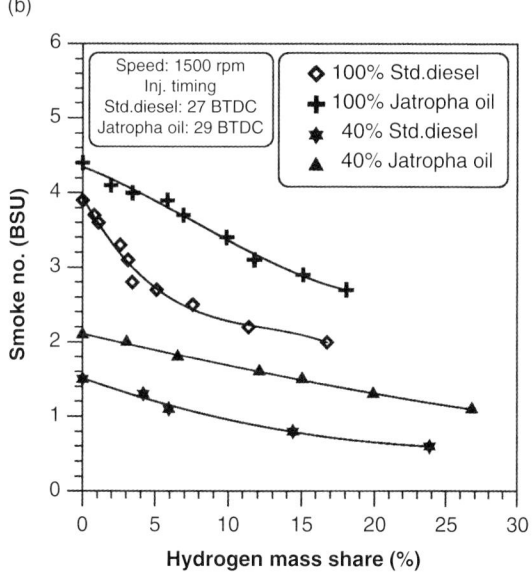

Figure 6 Performance of diesel engine with inducted hydrogen at 100% and 40% loads: (a) thermal efficiency; (b) smoke emissions. Reproduced from Senthil Kumar M, Ramesh A, and Nagalingam B (2003) Use of hydrogen to enhance the performance of a vegetable oil fuelled compression ignition engine. *International Journal of Hydrogen Energy* 28: 1143–1154 [26].

dioxide (10%), and the rest nitrogen (N_2), although the composition depends heavily on the input fuel properties and gasifier efficiency. In a full combustion process, a stoichiometric mixture of synthesis gas and air typically has an energy content 20–40% lower than that of a natural gas–air mixture.

Although internal combustion engines operating on gaseous fuels (natural gas being most common) are widely used, some challenges exist and these are particularly prominent at small scale. The main problem is power derating of the engine since a gaseous fuel in a premixed engine displaces a significant amount of intake air. This reduces the work output of the cycle, which makes the mechanical losses more influential. One option that has been investigated by some authors is the use of low-CV gaseous fuels in dual fuel engines.

Mohammadi *et al.* [68] described the testing of a standard diesel engine in which a low-CV mixture of N_2 and H_2 was added to the intake air. **Figure 7** shows the results for varying loads (shown as mean effective pressure, p_e), with the intake air comprising 15%$_{vol}$ low-CV gas ($r_{LCG} = 0.15$) and the low-CV gas consisting of 0–30%$_{vol}$ H_2 ($r_H = 0$–0.3). It can be seen that the addition of low-CV gas to the intake air does not lead to major reductions in the fuel efficiency, but that it can result in notable reductions in diesel fuel consumption, be_{DF}. This indicates that the low-CV fuel is well utilized, even at such lean concentrations.

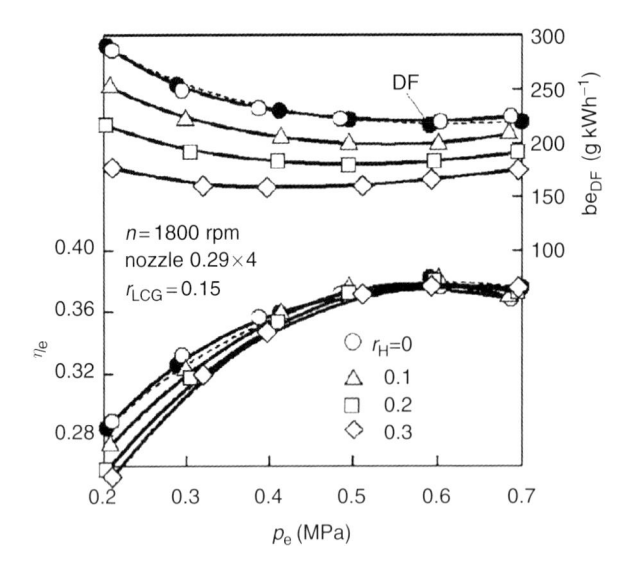

Figure 7 Effect of the addition of low-calorific-value gas to diesel engine intake air. Reproduced from Mohammadi A, Shioji M, Ishiyama T, and Kitazaki M (2006) Utilization of low-calorific gaseous fuel in a direct-injection diesel engine. *Journal of Engineering for Gas Turbines and Power* 128: 915–920 [68].

5.17.6 Conclusions

Looking beyond current activity which deploys liquid biofuels in weak blends across a wide network of filling stations, and in stronger blends in car and truck engines that have been modified for the purpose, this chapter starts by summarizing work on developing biodiesel/bioethanol emulsions for use in compression-ignition engines. Data for a variety of commercially available emulsifier additives point to changes in a range of emissions (relative to conventional diesel) which are mainly beneficial.

One approach to increasing deployment of liquid biofuels is to modify conventional spark-ignition and compression-ignition vehicle engines so that they can run on pure biofuels or even raw vegetable oils in some cases. Guidance on the required modifications is provided along with some summary data on resulting engine performance and emissions, which, though mixed, are mainly positive.

Another approach to increasing the deployment of liquid biofuels and bio-oils in the pursuit of CO_2 reductions and reducing reliance on finite fossil fuel reserves is to use them in stationary engines for power generation or combined heat and power. Data on the performance of stationary engines running on pure biodiesel or strong biodiesel blends show that while there is a variation with feedstock type, in most cases there is a small fuel consumption penalty and a small increase in NO_x emissions combined with beneficial reductions in SO_2, smoke, unburnt HCs, and carbon monoxide. Particulate emissions can increase or reduce depending on blend strength and feedstock material. Data on the performance of straight vegetable oils as an engine fuel – with and without preheating to reduce viscosity – show a wide range of behaviors (positive and negative with respect to diesel) in terms of emissions, short-term engine performance, and long-term engine performance. There is considerable variation between vegetable oil types.

The final approach is dual fueling with a liquid biofuel and a gaseous biofuel, where the latter is being injected via the air intake. This is of particular interest in stationary engines for power generation or combined heat and power where an optimum balance can be struck between liquid energy and gaseous energy supply. Data are presented for a range of biodiesels and straight vegetable oils (on the liquid side) and for synthesis gas and hydrogen (on the gaseous side). From these data, some trade-offs can be identified with respect to cost, fuel efficiency, and emission profile.

References

[1] Chotwichien A, Luengnaruemitchai A, and Jai-In S (2009) Utilization of palm oil alkyl esters as an additive in ethanol–diesel and butanol–diesel blends. *Fuel* 88(9): 1618–1624.
[2] Cui X (2007) *Substitute Fuel and Biomass Energy for Vehicle*. Beijing, China: China Petrochemical Press.
[3] Letcher TM (1983) Diesel blends for diesel engines. *South African Journal of Science* 79(1): 4–7.
[4] Li S-D (2008) The Experimental Study on Ethanol–Diesel Engine. MSc Thesis, Guangxi University.
[5] Hansen AC, Zhang Q, and Lyne PWL (2005) Ethanol–diesel fuel blends – A review. *Bioresource Technology* 96(3): 277–285.
[6] Minteer S (2006) *Alcoholic Fuels*. New York: CRC Press.
[7] Letcher TM (1980) Ternary liquid–liquid phase diagrams for diesel fuel blends. *South African Journal of Science* 76(2): 130–132.
[8] Moses CA, Ryan TW, and Likos WE (1980) Experiments with alcohol/diesel fuel blends in compression-ignition engines. *Proceedings of the VI International Symposium on Alcohol Fuels Technology*, volume 2, p. 493, Instituto de Pesquisas Technologicas do Estada de Sao Paulo-IPT, 1981.
[9] Corkwell K (2002) The development of diesel/ethanol (diesehol) fuel blends for diesel vehicles: Fuel formulation and properties. *The 14th International Symposium on Alcohol Fuels*. November 12–15, Phuket, Thailand.
[10] Hardenberg HO and Ehnert ER (1981) Ignition quality determination problems with alternative fuels for compression ignition engines. SAE Technical Paper 811212.

[11] Wrage KE and Goering CE (1980) Technical feasibility of diesohol. *Transactions of the American Society of Agricultural Engineers*, vol. 23, pp. 1338–1343.
[12] Li D-G, Zhen H, Lu X, Zhang W-G, and Yang J-G (2005) Physico-chemical properties of ethanol–diesel blend fuel and its effect on performance and emissions of diesel engines. *Renewable Energy* 30(6): 967–976.
[13] Meiring P, Hansen AC, Vosloo AP, and Lyne PWL (1983) High concentration ethanol–diesel blends for compression-ignition engines. SAE Technical Paper No. 831360. Warrendale, PA: Society of Automotive Engineers.
[14] Satgé de Caro P, Mouloungui Z, Vaitilingom G, and Berge JC (2001) Interest of combining an additive with diesel–ethanol blends for use in diesel engines. *Fuel* 80(4): 565–574.
[15] Kass MD, Thomas JF, Storey JM, et al. (2001) Emissions from a 5.9 liter diesel engine fueled with ethanol diesel blends. SAE Technical Paper 2001-01-2018 (SP-1632).
[16] Hansen AC, Mendoza M, Zhang Q, and Reid JF (2000) Evaluation of oxydiesel as a fuel for direct-injection compression-ignition engines. *Final Report for Illinois Department of Commerce and Community Affairs*, Contract IDCCA 96-32434.
[17] Donahue RJ and Foster DE (2000) Effects of oxygen enhancement on the emissions from a DI diesel via manipulation of fuels and combustion chamber gas composition. SAE Technical Paper 2000-01-0512.
[18] Kitamura T, Ito T, Senda J, and Fujimoto H (2001) Extraction of the suppression effects of oxygenated fuels on soot formation using a detailed chemical kinetic model. *The Japan Society of Automotive Engineers Review* 22(2001): 139–145.
[19] Miyamoto N, Ogawa H, Nurun N, et al. (1998) Smokeless, low NO_x, high thermal efficiency, and low noise diesel combustion with oxygenated agents as main fuel. SAE Technical Paper 980506.
[20] Spreen K (1999) Evaluation of oxygenated diesel fuels. *Final Report for Pure Energy Corporation Prepared at Southwest Research Institute*, San Antonio, TX.
[21] Lofvenbeng D (2002) E-diesel in Europe: A new available fuel technology. *The 14th International Symposium on Alcohol Fuels*. Thailand.
[22] He B-Q, Shuai S-J, Wang J-X, and He H (2003) The effect of ethanol blended diesel fuels on emissions from a diesel engine. *Atmospheric Environment* 37(35): 4965–4971.
[23] Basha SA, Raja GK, and Jebaraj S (2009) A review on biodiesel production, combustion, emissions and performance. *Renewable and Sustainable Energy Reviews* 13: 1628–1634.
[24] Hess MA, Haas MJ, and Foglia TA (2007) Attempts to reduce NO_x exhaust emissions by using reformulated biodiesel. *Fuel Processing Technology* 88: 693–699.
[25] Ladommatos N, Abdelhalim SM, Zhao H, and Hu Z (1998) The effects of carbon dioxide in exhaust gas recirculation on diesel engine emissions. *Journal of Automobile Engineering* 212: 25–42.
[26] Senthil Kumar M, Ramesh A, and Nagalingam B (2003) Use of hydrogen to enhance the performance of a vegetable oil fuelled compression ignition engine. *International Journal of Hydrogen Energy* 28: 1143–1154.
[27] Arregle J, Ruis S, Desantes JM, and Delage A (1999) Characterisation of the injection-combustion process in a D.I. diesel engine running with rape oil methyl ester. SAE Paper 1999-01-1497.
[28] Kalligeros S, Zannikos F, Stournas S, et al. (2003) An investigation of using biodiesel/marine diesel blends on the performance of a stationary diesel engine. *Biomass and Bioenergy* 24: 141–149.
[29] Labeckas G and Slavinskas S (2006) The effect of rapeseed oil methyl ester on direct injection diesel engine performance and exhaust emissions. *Energy Conversion and Management* 47: 1954–1967.
[30] Nwafor OMI and Rice G (1995) Performance of rapeseed methyl ester in diesel engine. *Renewable Energy* 6: 335–342.
[31] Yusuf A, Hanna MA, and Borg JE (1995) Methyl tallowate and ethanol blend for reducing emissions from diesel engine. *Bioresource and Technology* 52: 237–243.
[32] Dorado MP, Ballesteros E, Arnal JM, et al. (2003) Exhaust emissions from a diesel engine fueled with transesterified waste olive oil. *Fuel* 82: 1311–1315.
[33] Niemi SA, Murtonen TT, Lauren MJ, and Vaino OK (2002) Exhaust particulate emissions of a mustard seed oil driven tractor engine. SAE Paper 2002-01-0866.
[34] Usta N (2005) An experimental study on performance and exhaust emissions of a diesel engine fuelled with tobacco seed oil methyl ester. *Energy Conversion and Management* 46: 2373–2386.
[35] Kaul S, Saxena RC, Kumar A, et al. (2007) Corrosion behavior of biodiesel from seed oils of Indian origin on diesel engine parts. *Fuel Processing Technology* 88(3): 303–307.
[36] Kinast JA (2003) *Production of Biodiesels from Multiple Feedstocks and Properties of Biodiesels and Biodiesel/Diesel Blends*. National Renewable Energy Laboratory, Golden, CO.
[37] Pehan S, Jerman MS, Kegl M, and Kegl B (2009) Biodiesel influence on tribology characteristics of a diesel engine. *Fuel* 88(6): 970–979.
[38] Demirbas A (2008) Relationships derived from physical properties of vegetable oil and biodiesel fuels. *Fuel* 87: 1743–1748.
[39] Patil PD and Deng S (2009) Optimization of biodiesel production from edible and non-edible vegetable oils. *Fuel* 88(7): 1302–1306.
[40] Baiju B, Naik MK, and Das LM (2009) A comparative evaluation of compression ignition engine characteristics using methyl and ethyl esters of Karanja oil. *Renewable Energy* 34(6): 1616–1621.
[41] Lin Y-C, Lee W-J, and Hou H-C (2006) PAH emissions and energy efficiency of palm–biodiesel blends fueled on diesel generator. *Atmospheric Environment* 40(21): 3930–3940.
[42] Durbin TD, Cocker DR, Sawant AA, et al. (2007) Regulated emissions from biodiesel fuels from on/off-road applications. *Atmospheric Environment* 41(27): 5647–5658.
[43] Nabi MN, Rahman MM, and Akhter S (2009) Biodiesel from cotton seed oil and its effect on engine performance and exhaust emissions. *Applied Thermal Engineering* 29 (11–22): 2265–2270.
[44] Lertsathapornsuk V, Pairintra R, Aryusuk K and Krisnangkura K (2008) Microwave assisted in continuous biodiesel production from waste frying palm oil and its performance in a 100 kW diesel generator. *Fuel Processing Technology* 89(12): 1330–1336.
[45] Park EY, Sato M, and Kojima S (2008) Lipase-catalyzed biodiesel production from waste activated bleaching earth as raw material in a pilot plant. *Bioresource Technology* 99(8): 3130–3135.
[46] Pereira RG, Oliveira CD, Oliveira JL, et al. (2007) Exhaust emissions and electric energy generation in a stationary engine using blends of diesel and soybean biodiesel. *Renewable Energy* 32(14): 2453–2460.
[47] Raheman H and Phadatare AG (2004) Diesel engine emissions and performance from blends of karanja methyl ester and diesel. *Biomass and Bioenergy* 27(4): 393–397.
[48] Szybist JP, Song J, Alam M, and Boehman A (2007) Biodiesel combustion, emissions and emission control. *Fuel Processing Technology* 88(7): 679–691.
[49] Sahoo PK, Das LM, Babu MKG, et al. (2009) Comparative evaluation of performance and emission characteristics of jatropha, karanja and polanga based biodiesel as fuel in a tractor engine. *Fuel* 88(9): 1698–1707.
[50] Ye-jian Q and Cheng-ji Z (2006) Review of researches on biofuel as fuels for diesel engines. *Tractor & Farm Transport* 33: 12–16.
[51] Sharma YC, Singh B, and Upadhyay S (2008) Advancements in development and characterization of biodiesel: A review. *Fuel* 87(12): 2355–2373.
[52] Cetin M and Yuksel F (2007) The use of hazelnut oil as a fuel in pre-chamber diesel engine. *Applied Thermal Engineering* 27(1): 63–67.
[53] Devan PK and Mahalakshmi NV (2009) Performance, emission and combustion characteristics of poon oil and its diesel blends in a DI diesel engine. *Fuel* 88(5): 861–867.
[54] Hebbal OD, Reddy KV, and Rajagopal K (2006) Performance characteristics of a diesel engine with deccan hemp oil. *Fuel* 85(14–15): 2187–2194.
[55] Masjuki H, Kalam M, Maleque MA, et al. (2001) Performance, emissions and wear characteristics of an indirect injection diesel engine using coconut oil blended fuel. *Proceedings of the Institution of Mechanical Engineers, Part D: Journal of Automobile Engineering* 215(3): 393–404.
[56] Hemmeriein N, Korte V, Richter H, and Schroder D (1991) Performance exhaust emissions and durability of modern diesel engines running on rapeseed oil. SAE 910848.
[57] Bari S, Yu W, and Lim TH (2002) Performance deterioration and durability issues while running a diesel engine with crude palm oil. *Automobile Engineering* 216(D1): 785–792.
[58] Agarwal D and Agarwal AK (2007) Performance and emissions characteristics of Jatropha oil (preheated and blends) in a direct injection compression ignition engine. *Applied Thermal Engineering* 27(13): 2314–2323.
[59] Canakci M, Ozsezen AN, and Turkcan A (2009) Combustion analysis of preheated crude sunflower oil in an IDI diesel engine. *Biomass and Bioenergy* 33(5): 760–767.

[60] De Almeida SCA, Belchior CR, Nascimento MVG, *et al.* (2002) Performance of a diesel generator fuelled with palm oil. *Fuel* 81(16): 2097–2102.
[61] Wang YD, Al-Shemmeri T, Eames P, *et al.* (2006) An experimental investigation of the performance and gaseous exhaust emissions of a diesel engine using blends of a vegetable oil. *Applied Thermal Engineering* 26(14–15): 1684–1691.
[62] Haldar SK, Ghosh BB, and Naga A (2009) Studies on the comparison of performance and emission characteristics of a diesel engine using three degummed non-edible vegetable oils. *Biomass and Bioenergy* 33(8): 1013–1018.
[63] Sahoo BB, Sahoo N, and Saha UK (2009) Effect of engine parameters and type of gaseous fuel on the performance of dual-fuel gas diesel engines – A critical review. *Renewable and Sustainable Energy Reviews* 13: 1151–1184.
[64] Papagiannakis RG and Hountalas DT (2003) Experimental investigation concerning the effect of natural gas percentage on performance and emissions of a DI dual fuel diesel engine. *Applied Thermal Engineering* 23(3): 353–365.
[65] Papagiannakis RG and Hountalas DT (2004) Combustion and exhaust emission characteristics of a dual fuel compression ignition engine operated with pilot diesel fuel and natural gas. *Energy Conversion and Management* 45(18/19): 2971–2987.
[66] Lu X, Ma J, Ji L, and Huang Z (2008) Simultaneous reduction of NO_x emissions and smoke opacity of biodiesel-fuelled engines by port injection of ethanol. *Fuel* 87: 1289–1296.
[67] Geo EV, Nagarajan G, and Nagalingam B (2008) Studies on dual fuel operation of rubber seed oil and its bio-diesel with hydrogen as the inducted fuel. *International Journal of Hydrogen Energy* 33: 6357–6367.
[68] Mohammadi A, Shioji M, Ishiyama T, and Kitazaki M (2006) Utilization of low-calorific gaseous fuel in a direct-injection diesel engine. *Journal of Engineering for Gas Turbines and Power* 128: 915–920.

5.18 Biochar

CE Brewer and RC Brown, Iowa State University, Ames, IA, USA

© 2012 Elsevier Ltd. All rights reserved.

5.18.1	Introduction	357
5.18.2	Archaeology and Soil Fertility Beginnings	358
5.18.2.1	Soil Organic Matter	358
5.18.2.2	Terra Preta	359
5.18.3	A New Focus: Carbon Sequestration	360
5.18.3.1	The Global Carbon Cycle	362
5.18.3.2	Black Carbons	362
5.18.3.3	Carbon Sequestration Potential of Biochar	364
5.18.3.4	Half-Life of Biochar in Soils	364
5.18.3.5	Efforts to Encourage the Adoption of Biochar into Agricultural Practices	365
5.18.4	Biochar Sources	366
5.18.4.1	Slow Pyrolysis and Traditional Charcoal Making	366
5.18.4.2	Torrefaction and Feedstock Pretreatment	368
5.18.4.3	Fast Pyrolysis and Bio-Oil	368
5.18.4.4	Flash Pyrolysis and the Effects of Pressure	370
5.18.4.5	Gasification and Syngas	371
5.18.4.6	Biochar as a Coproduct	371
5.18.5	Biochar Properties	372
5.18.5.1	Biochar Composition	372
5.18.5.2	Physical Properties	373
5.18.5.3	Chemical Properties	374
5.18.5.4	Biochar Engineering	377
5.18.6	Promising Biochar Scenarios and Synergies	378
5.18.6.1	Bioenergy and Biochar Coproduction	379
5.18.6.2	Farming Impacts	379
5.18.6.3	Site Remediation	380
5.18.6.4	Developing Countries	380
5.18.7	Challenges to Applying Biochar	382
5.18.7.1	Economics of Alternative Uses	382
5.18.7.2	Handling	382
5.18.7.3	Potential Soil/Crop Drawbacks	383
5.18.8	Future Progress and Development	384
References		384
Further Reading		384

Glossary

Aromaticity Fraction of carbons in an organic molecule that are involved in at least one aromatic bond; frequently used to represent degree of carbonization reaction and carbon recalcitrance.
Biochar Sustainably produced carbonaceous solid from the pyrolysis of biomass used as a soil amendment and/or a carbon sequestration agent.
Black carbon Pyrogenic, recalcitrant carbonaceous solid found in the environment as char or soot.

Cation exchange capacity Amount of positively charged ions that a soil or other material can adsorb and exchange.
Charcoal Carbonaceous solid obtained from the pyrolysis of biomass used as a fuel for cooking, heating, or energy production.
Soil organic matter Organic fraction of the soil including microbial biomass, plant and animal residues, black carbon, and humic substances (fulvic acid, humic acid, and humin).

5.18.1 Introduction

Biochar is the carbonaceous solid residue obtained upon heating biomass under oxygen-deficient conditions. It has potential as a nutrient recycler, soil conditioner, income generator, waste management system, and agent for long-term, safe and economical carbon sequestration. The goal of this chapter is to introduce some of these topics and highlight future research directions.

5.18.2 Archaeology and Soil Fertility Beginnings

Original interest in biochar did not stem from concerns over burning fossil fuels or anthropogenic global warming. Rather, research into biochar began from trying to understand the secrets of dark, permanently fertile soils in the central Amazon called terra preta or, more generally, Amazonian dark earths. In 1542, a Spanish explorer named Francisco de Orellana returned home from a voyage down the Rio Negro tributary of the Amazon River (near the modern-day city of Manaus, Brazil – see map in **Figure 1**) and described the presence of large, well-established networks of agricultural settlements and cities along the river banks. These were not the legendary city of gold he had been looking for, but he considered them worth reporting to the Spanish court, nonetheless. In years to come, other gold seekers, explorers, and missionaries would scour the region but would find no evidence to support Orellana's claims. There were no walled cities or extensive farming; there were only solitary groups of hunter-gatherers moving from place to place.

Anthropologists studying the possibility of large, densely populated, permanent settlements in the central Amazon also expressed doubt in Orellana's claims of advanced civilizations based on the area's infertile soils. Large permanent settlements require access to intensive and sustainable agriculture, which, even today, is nearly impossible on the yellow jungle soils. These soils present several serious problems for agricultural farming: low soil organic matter (SOM) content, acidic conditions, low nutrient retention, high temperatures, and high rainfalls.

5.18.2.1 Soil Organic Matter

SOM is the overall name for three groups of organic materials in soils: living biomass such as microorganisms, plant and animal residues, and humic substances. Humic substances are defined as plant or animal residues that are degraded to the point that the original biomass can no longer be identified. Humic substances are further divided into fractions based on their solubility in strong alkali and/or strong acid: humin (insoluble in base), humic acid (soluble in base but not in acid), and fulvic acid (soluble in base and acid). SOM, especially the humic fraction, gives soil a slightly darker color and is composed of approximately 50% carbon (referred to as soil organic carbon) and 5% nitrogen. SOM is also a source of slow-release macronutrients such as phosphorus and sulfur, microbial food, and micronutrients such as trace metals.

SOM is critical to several aspects of soil quality (**Table 1**). It promotes good soil structure by serving as the 'glue' of soil aggregates, adds water retention capacity to fast-draining sandy soils, increases infiltration and drainage in clayey soils, and

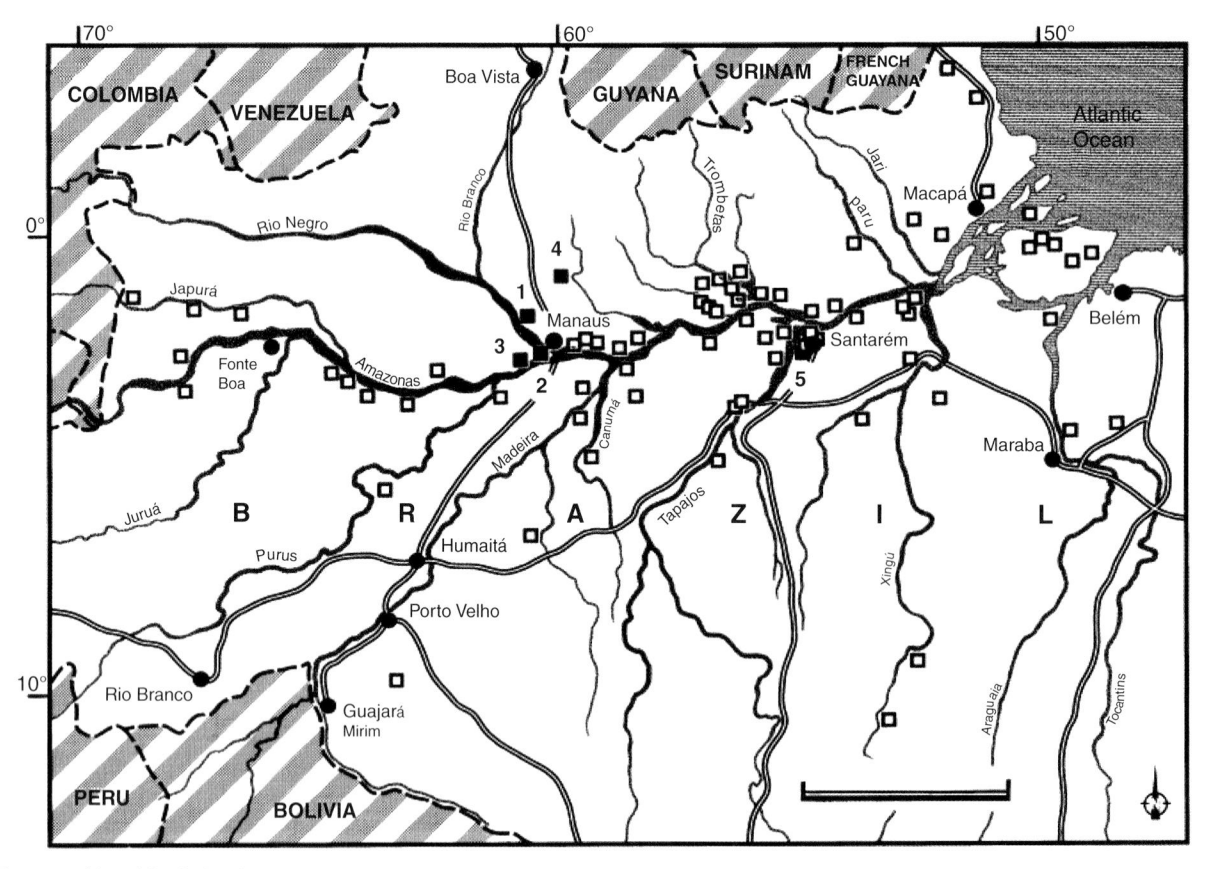

Figure 1 Map of Brazil showing some of the known (open shapes) and investigated (closed shapes) terra preta sites along the Amazon River in Brazil (scale = 500 km). Reprinted from Glaser B, Balashov E, Haumaier L, *et al*. (2000) Black carbon density fractions of anthropogenic soils of the Brazilian Amazon region. *Organic Geochemistry* 31: 669–678, Copyright (2000), with permission of Elsevier.

Table 1 Effects and benefits of soil organic matter

Effects of soil organic matter on soil	Associated benefit
Increases soil aggregate stability	Improved soil structure
	Less erosion
Increases macroporosity	Improved aeration
Decreases soil bulk density	Improved water infiltration
	Improved root penetration
Provides energy source	Increased microbial activity and diversity
	Increased nutrient cycling
Provides nutrient source	Increased N, P, S, and micronutrient availability
	Increased plant productivity
Increases water-holding capacity	Increased plant-available water
	Less runoff, flooding, and water pollution
Increases cation exchange capacity	Increased Ca, Mg, K, and micronutrient availability
	Improved pH stability
Forms organic complexes with trace metals	Increased micronutrient availability
	Adsorption of heavy metal pollutants
Sorbs hydrophobic compounds	Immobilization of toxic organic compounds
	Less water pollution
Buffers pH	Less risk of aluminum and other trace metal toxicity due to low pH
	Less risk of micronutrient deficiency due to high pH
	Increased microbial activity and diversity

decreases soil bulk density, thus improving aeration and root penetration. Negatively charged functional groups on the SOM surface substantially increase the soil's cation exchange capacity (CEC). CEC is the ability to adhere and exchange positively charged cations such as important nutrients like potassium (K^+), calcium (Ca^{2+}), and magnesium (Mg^{2+}). Clays with a large degree of isomorphic substitution and SOM make up the majority of a soil's CEC. SOM, especially the fulvic acid and humic acid fractions, can form organic complexes with otherwise insoluble trace metal micronutrients such as copper, zinc, iron, and manganese, making them plant-available. The hydrophobic nature of some SOM makes it an excellent sorbent for other hydrophobic molecules such as pesticides, aromatic compounds, and oily substances. The available carbon in the SOM provides energy and biomass building material for microorganisms, which among other things fix nitrogen, form symbiotic relationships with plants, and cycle soil nutrients. For all of these reasons, crop residues are left in fields, and compost, peat, and manure are applied to fields and incorporated into soils. Like other organic materials, however, SOM is eventually mineralized to carbon dioxide by abiotic chemical oxidation or microbial respiration, or can be lost to erosion.

Maintaining SOM in tropical soils can be particularly difficult. High temperatures increase the rate of abiotic and biotic organic matter decomposition, meaning that added crop residues, manure, and composts are mineralized to CO_2 very quickly. In addition, high rainfall increases soil erosion. The loss of SOM quickly depletes the weathered soil's CEC, which then allows chemical fertilizers to leach from the soil and into the water cycle. The loss of SOM and the leaching of basic cations that normally buffer soil pH cause the soil to become very acidic. As the pH decreases, the solubility of plant-toxic metals such as aluminum and cadmium increases. All of these factors make growing agricultural crops in the central Amazon very difficult. Techniques such as slash and burn improve the soil fertility for a few crop cycles, but soon the mineral ash nutrients are leached away and the deposited carbon is mineralized, and the farmer must allow the land a long (10–20 years) fallow period and clear a new area of land. Liming the soils can increase soil pH, and adding chemical fertilizers can improve the crop yield, but these techniques are expensive and the effects are relatively short-lived.

If intensive, expensive, modern soil technology cannot achieve a sustainable crop yield in the central Amazon, anthropologists argued, how could natives grow enough food year after year to support a large permanent population at Orellana's time 500 years ago?

The answer to that question took several decades of discovery and rediscovery to formulate into a cohesive hypothesis. Over the course of nearly a century and a half, numerous researchers in several locations would make the connection between dark soils, the abundance of ancient artifacts from previous settlements, high amounts of SOM, and the possibility of sustainable agriculture on poor jungle soil; unfortunately, much of their work failed to gain the attention of the wider community and was forgotten until someone else made similar discoveries.

5.18.2.2 Terra Preta

From Orellana's time until the middle of the nineteenth century, explorers passing through the central Amazon region did not make reference to the dark soils or the soil management practices of the natives in their writings. In the 1870s, several English-speaking geologists began making comments about fertile dark soils on sites of previous native villages as they surveyed areas around 'Confederado' farms. 'Confederados' were landowners from the Confederate States who had moved to South America after the end of the American Civil War. In 1875, explorer James Orton commented that areas around Santarém with black soil were more fertile for growing rice than South Carolina. Briton C. Barrington Brown is believed to be the first to record the term terra preta or dark earth; he and coauthor William Lidstone described the native farmers' preference for cultivating black soils at ancient village sites in Guyana and near Óbidos that had obvious 'artificial' origin. In 1879, Charles Hartt and Herbert Smith, who had surveyed the lower Tapajós earlier that decade, referred to dark soil areas as 'kitchen middens' due to the amount of pottery found and the assumption that the fertility was caused by high organic residue deposition. It is speculated that the displaced Confederate farmers had learned about the value of the dark soils from local farmers and had chosen the locations for their farms accordingly. **Figure** 2 shows sample soil profiles of terra preta soils and a typical jungle Oxisol soil. Dark soil layers can be up to several meters thick, and cover patches from a few square meters to several square kilometers in size.

The next significant mention of dark earths in the Amazon came in 1903 when Friedlich Katzer [1] published a book in Leipzig, Germany, on Amazon geology. Katzer, who had previously worked on naturally occurring black soils in central Europe called Chernozems, was one of the first to report extensive analytical data based on his fieldwork in the lower Amazon, south of Santarém. He described the Amazonian dark soils as containing decomposed organic matter, mineral residues, and charred plant material. Nearly a century ahead of his time, Katzer concluded that the high organic matter content of the dark earths showed that the soils were different from the surrounding jungle soils, but at the same time, they were made by human activity and therefore were also not the same as Chernozems. A phrase often quoted from his writing that summarizes his insightful observations about these dark soils is that the Amazon's 'more distinguished wealth lies in its soils'.

Following Katzer, a handful of other geologists, anthropologists, and archaeologists would also make note of the Amazonian dark earths and their apparently anthropogenic origins in the 1920s and 1930s. Most notable was Curt Unkel Nimuendaju, a German-nationalized Brazilian anthropologist, who worked in the lower Tapajós and posthumously contributed significant notes and maps on the dark earths in that area. The next three decades of Amazonian dark earth research focused on formulating other, nonanthropogenic origin theories for the fertile soils. Among the theories were that terra preta came from volcanic ash; that the fertile sites were locations of former lakes and ponds that had accumulated organic matter and therefore attracted artifact-leaving native farmers; or that the dark soils were the results of repetitive short-term settlements.

The work that really began to draw international attention to Amazonian dark earths and their potential was that of the Dutch soil scientist Wim Sombroek. In his 1966 book, *Amazon Soils*, he described and provided laboratory analysis results for the dark soils of the Belterra Plateau [2]. (Ironically, Belterra Plateau was the same place where rubber tree plantations were relocated in 1934 for reasons unrelated to soil fertility following the infamous Fordlandia failure.) Sombroek also mapped the distribution of dark soils along the bluffs of the Tapajós River. He introduced the term terra mulata or brown soil to describe the high-organic-matter soils often surrounding terra preta soils and likely the sites of field agriculture of ancient natives. Unlike terra preta soils, which were more likely waste disposal zones, terra mulatas are slightly lighter in color, contain few artifacts, have lower concentrations of plant nutrients, and appear to be the result of semi-intensive cultivation over long periods of time, containing material from low-temperature field burning. **Figure** 3 shows an example of the difference in the appearance of a terra preta, a terra mulata, and an adjacent jungle soil. For the next four decades up until his death in 2003, Sombroek was responsible for enormous amounts of dark earth research and advocated the creation of terra preta nova, or new dark earth, to improve soil carbon stores and intensive agriculture.

'Modern' scientific study of Amazonian dark earths began in the late 1970s with publications in Japanese and German soil science journals by Renzo Kondo [3] and Wolfgang Zech *et al.* [4]. Since then and especially since 2000, numerous journal articles, review papers, and two books have been published describing terra preta sites and soil management practices throughout South America, anthropogenic dark earths found in some central African communities, traditional Japanese horticulture practices incorporating charcoal, and improved soil fertility around former charcoal production sites throughout the world. A short study by Bruno Glaser *et al.* [5], published in *Naturwissenschaften* in 2001, is often cited as demonstrating that black carbon (BC) in soils is the key to terra preta's long organic matter residence times and continuing fertility.

Several researchers have investigated the effects of charcoal addition on jungle soils, in combination with mineral fertilizers and other organic amendments, to try to identify which factors and interactions contributed to terra preta's success. In his 2006 dissertation and related publications with colleagues, Christoph Steiner described the results of several such field studies and the potential for a 'slash and char' system of agriculture to replace 'slash and burn' [6]. In general, it was found that charcoal additions alone were not nearly as effective as combinations of charcoal and mineral fertilizer or charcoal and organic amendments (chicken manure, compost, kitchen scraps) applied to the soil. The effect of charcoal was more in that it helped soils retain the added fertilizers and organic matter, so that fewer inputs needed to be added less often, even with the tropical heat and high rainfall. The benefit of 'slash and char' over 'slash and burn' is that there is more of the beneficial carbon left (~50%) after pyrolysis than the few percent typically left after a high-temperature burn that is mineralized or washed away in 2 or 3 years. Overall, the secret to sustainable agriculture in the tropics, according to field study results and supported by local wisdom passed down for generations, appeared to be a 'fire and organic matter' combination.

5.18.3 A New Focus: Carbon Sequestration

Researchers carbon-dating charcoals found in terra preta soils found that they were hundreds to thousands of years old, meaning that carbon removed from the atmosphere by plants long ago had been effectively sequestered as a stable solid. During a time when vast amounts of research funding are being channeled into developing carbon capture and storage (CCS) technologies, carbon stability in soil has enormous significance and has brought anthropogenic soils like terra preta into the international limelight for a new reason: a way to sequester carbon and thus combat global warming.

Figure 2 Examples of Amazonian dark earths in comparison to a typical jungle soil profile. (a) A terra preta containing numerous artifacts at the Hatahara site. (b) A deep terra preta. (c) A close-up of terra preta from the Laranjal Coast. (d) A soil profile from the Laranjal Coast. (e) A soil profile from the Açutuba Coast. (f) A typical jungle Oxisol soil profile. Source: Newton Falcão, Instituto Nacional de Pesquisas da Amazônia, Manaus, Brazil.

Figure 3 Terra preta, terra mulata, and the adjacent Latassol soil from a site in the central Amazon. All three soils have similar soil texture. Source: Newton Falcão, Instituto Nacional de Pesquisas da Amazônia, Manaus, Brazil.

5.18.3.1 The Global Carbon Cycle

The concerns about carbon dioxide emissions stem from the concern about imbalances in the global carbon cycle. This cycle consists of three main carbon locations: the atmosphere, the biosphere, and the lithosphere, also sometimes called the geosphere. In the atmosphere, carbon exists as gases (carbon dioxide, carbon monoxide, methane, etc.) as well as some fine particulates such as soot. The biosphere includes carbon held in living organisms such as plants, animals, and microorganisms. Carbon stored in the lithosphere includes fossil fuels such as crude oil, natural gas, and coal, mineral formations such as carbonates, and soil and sediment carbons such as residues, organic matter, humus, and BC. Significant carbon is also stored in the hydrosphere, as carbon dioxide in the air is in equilibrium with carbonic acid in the world's oceans, rivers, and lakes. When the carbon cycle is balanced, carbon removed from the atmosphere by photosynthesis exists in the biosphere until the organism dies, at which point the carbon is returned to the atmosphere by mineralization or stored in the lithosphere in a more stable form.

By burning fossil fuels, excessively tilling agricultural fields, and cutting down forests, humans move carbon from the lithosphere and biosphere to the atmosphere faster than photosynthesis can remove it; such processes are therefore carbon positive. **Figure 4** shows the major sources, sinks, and fluxes of the global carbon cycle. Overall, there is a net annual increase in atmospheric carbon on the order of 5 gigatons (10^{15} g) of carbon per year ($GtC\ yr^{-1}$). Many of today's bioenergy systems and environmentally conscious consumer products strive to be carbon neutral, where the rate of carbon dioxide production throughout the process is equal to the rate of carbon removal from the atmosphere. The carbon neutrality of a product or process is heavily dependent on where 'start' and 'end' are defined in the life cycle analysis and what aspects of the process are included in the accounting. In the case of fossil fuel use, CCS technologies currently under development hope to collect, pressurize, and permanently store carbon dioxide flue gases in geological formations such as former natural gas reservoirs, deep underground saline aquifers, or active oil wells to increase the amount of recovered oil. As long as that carbon dioxide stays out of the atmosphere and no additional carbon dioxide is released in the transportation, upgrading, storage, and other processes of these fuels, these processes could be considered carbon neutral. Biochar has the potential to be carbon negative, that is, its production and application have the potential to turn the carbon dioxide removed from the atmosphere by plants into a solid carbon that will stay solid (and out of the atmosphere) for a sufficiently long time. Carbon-dating evidence from terra preta soils and existing studies of BCs in the environment demonstrate how this can be possible.

5.18.3.2 Black Carbons

BCs are found nearly everywhere in the environment: terrestrial soils, sediments under bodies of water, and the atmosphere as small particulates (referred as 'elemental carbon' in atmospheric sciences). BC tends to be the oldest and most stable form of organic carbon in soils, especially when soil aggregates form around BC particles and protect them from microbial and chemical oxidation. BCs are most frequently found in areas prone to vegetation fires such as forests and open prairies. The incredible fertility and dark color of midwestern US soils are often attributed to thousands of years of prairie fires building up organic carbon, and especially BC.

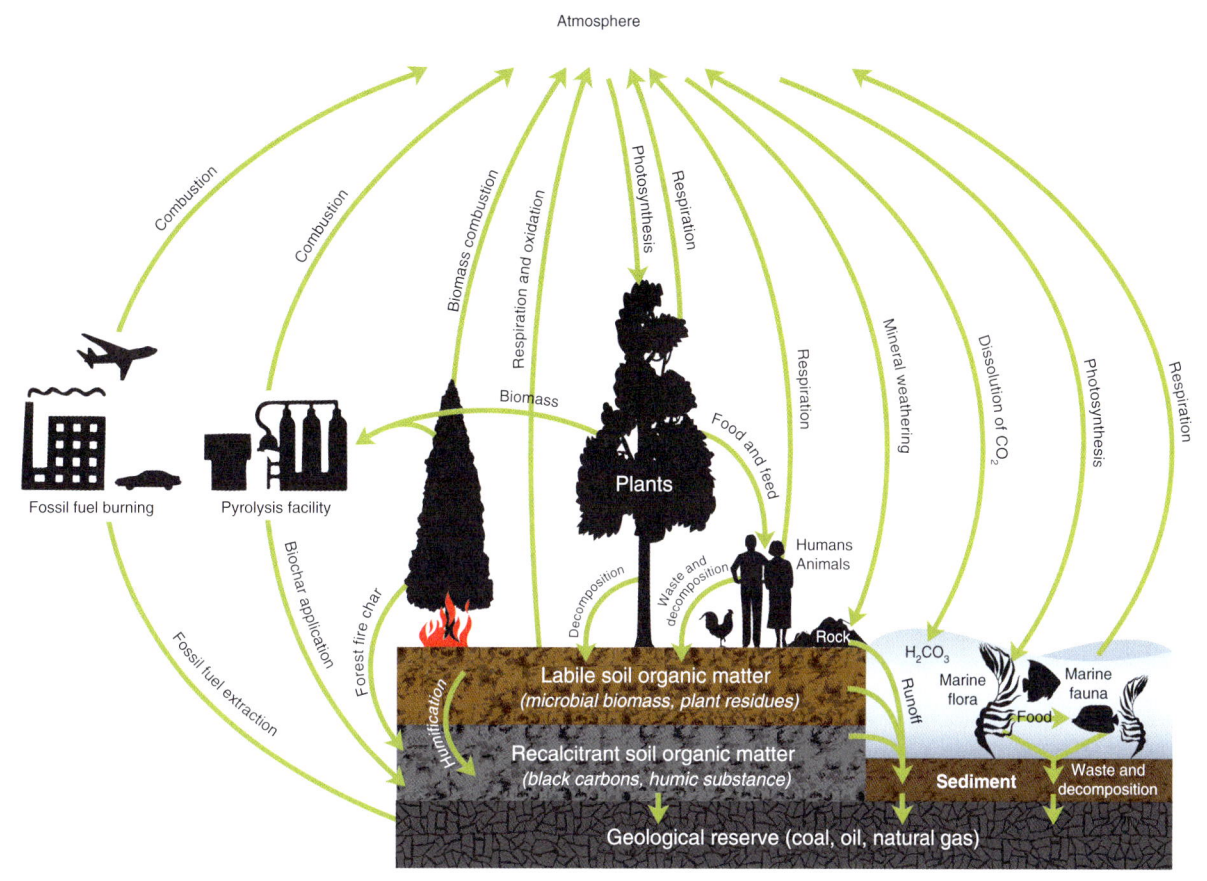

Figure 4 The global carbon cycle representing natural and anthropogenic contributions.

(The relatively young age of the soils, the organic matter from perennial grass roots, and sufficient rainfall are also factors.) Even in areas with few vegetation fires, BC can still be deposited in soils as small particulates in the atmosphere from distant fires fall to the ground. BCs in river and ocean beds are deposited through erosion of soils and burial in the sediments. Overall, the long-term existence of BC in so many of the world's soils and sediments gives credibility to the possibility of using biochar as a way to stably sequester large amounts of carbon.

As important as BCs are in the global carbon cycle, the exact amount of carbon sequestered as BC is very difficult to quantify and has long been the subject of analytical methodology discussions. By definition, BC is a carbonaceous material that is pyrogenic (fire-derived) and recalcitrant (resistant to biotic or abiotic degradation). Char, the product of solid-phase thermochemical reactions, and soot, the gas-phase condensation product of combustion, are both considered BCs. The analytical difficulty is that pyrogenic carbons exhibit different degrees of recalcitrance. Table 2 lists some different types of thermochemically produced

Table 2 A black carbon continuum

	Black carbon type				
	Slightly charred biomass	*Charred biomass*	*Activated carbon*	*Soot*	*Graphitic black carbon*
Representative formation process	Torrefaction	Pyrolysis/ gasification	Gasification/ activation	Combustion gas-phase reactions	High-temperature carbonization
Formation temperature	200–50 °C	400–800 °C	>800 °C	High	High
Relative reactivity	High	←	→	Low	Very low
Relative size	>mm	μm–mm	μm–mm	<μm	<μm
Plant structures	Abundant	Significant	Few	None	None

Arrangement of table based on Figure 1 from Masiello CA (2004) New directions in black carbon organic geochemistry. *Marine Chemistry* 92: 201–213.

carbons from brown-colored, barely burned biomass to graphite-like soot, as well as their relative reactivities, formation temperatures, and representative thermochemical properties. Each of these materials has slightly different chemical and physical properties, meaning that, for a given analytical technique, some will be identified as BC and some will not. Adding to the confusion, there are several other carbon forms in the environment, such as coal, shale, and some humic substances that are recalcitrant but are not pyrogenic. The presence of these materials in a sample can result in an overestimation of BC content based on false positive results. (Note that the analysis for BC should not be confused with the analysis for humic substances. The former is based on recalcitrance, the latter on solubility. In theory, BC in soil would be included in all three of the humic substances based on the alkali/acid separation, especially the humin fraction for the more condensed BCs and the humic acid fraction for the less condensed BC.)

To address this BC quantification issue, a round-robin study was organized by Hammes *et al.* [7] in the early 2000s to compare how much 'black carbon' was present in different reference materials according to methods found in the literature or methods frequently employed in a given laboratory. Seventeen laboratories from several countries and across several disciplines (environmental science, atmospheric science, civil engineering, etc.) were sent samples of the same 12 materials: some different types of BC, some matrix samples like soil or air particulates containing BC, and some non-BC materials known to interfere in BC analyses. Each laboratory analyzed the samples using the techniques they had available and shared their results with the other laboratories. The most common kind of method used was some sort of oxidation in which chemicals (acids, dichromate, hypochlorite (bleach)) and/or heat would oxidize and remove different fractions of the carbon present. Another method was a derivitization or 'molecular marker' method called benzene polycarboxylic acid (BPCA) method; the aromatic carbons in BC are hydrolyzed and partially oxidized to form specific aromatic carboxylic acids that can be analyzed by gas chromatography. From the atmospheric science methodologies, a thermal/optical transmittance and reflectance (TOT/R) method was also used. Researchers involved in the study quickly learned that different methods yielded very different results and even laboratories using the same method could not achieve good intralaboratory reproducibility due to small differences in the method protocol. The problems encountered in BC analysis demonstrate some of the difficulties facing biochar today. Different methods were designed to provide information specific to a given kind of carbon used in a given application and this information may not be useful in a different setting. The challenge with BC is to decide which methods provide the most meaning for BC in global carbon accounting.

5.18.3.3 Carbon Sequestration Potential of Biochar

The potential of biochar as a carbon sequestration agent depends upon both the amount of carbon dioxide in the atmosphere and the rate at which it could be removed from the atmosphere and stored as carbonaceous solid in soils. The amount that could be removed is enormous. To reduce CO_2 levels in the atmosphere to preindustrial levels, every hectare of arable land (about 6% of the Earth's surface) would have to incorporate about 90 t (metric tons) of biochar, a large but not inconceivable quantity. (For comparison, biochar for agronomic purposes is often applied at rates of $50\,t\,ha^{-1}$.)

More daunting is the time it would take to remove this excess carbon from the atmosphere. Assuming that $4\,t\,ha^{-1}$ of biomass residue could be removed annually from the arable lands of the world, then it would take 93 years to return to preindustrial levels of atmospheric carbon dioxide. Even with the most efficient and inexpensive pyrolysis process, the supply of available biomass will always be a limiting factor on the rate at which biochar can be produced and applied.

5.18.3.4 Half-Life of Biochar in Soils

One aspect of biochar that is critical to its inclusion in future policymaking is the ability to quantify biochar's expected residence time in the soil. For example, if a given amount of biochar with certain properties is applied to soil, how much carbon will remain in 10 years? 100 years? 1000 years? How does one verify that biochar added to the soil stays there and is not lost to mineralization, erosion, and other processes? How many carbon credits would biochar be worth?

To answer the first question, one must consider kinetic models. Researchers measure the rate of degradation by tracking the amount of material remaining over time. A typical decay curve is shaped like a hyperbola: the curve declines sharply early and then gradually levels off. In terms of chemical reactions, the rate of decay is very fast at the beginning and then slows until the line eventually flattens and the rate no longer changes. Nuclear scientists use these types of kinetic models on a regular basis to measure the half-life of radioactive isotopes. If it were possible to measure the 'half-life' of biochar in soil and know how much carbon had been added at time zero, one could predict the amount of carbon remaining in the soil after a given amount of time. The rate of biochar mineralization (i.e., oxidation to carbon dioxide and loss from the soil) depends on how resistant the biochar is to biological digestion or abiotic (nonbiological) oxidation. Fresh biochar is a mixture of more and less resistant forms of carbon. The less resistant forms are oxidized quickly, causing a steep initial drop in mass and leaving evermore resistant forms of carbon behind. The more resistant forms of carbon break down more slowly, so that it takes longer each time per drop in mass. Eventually, the carbon forms remaining are so recalcitrant that the mass of biochar does not appear to change at all, suggesting a degradation rate of zero. In truth, the rate of degradation never actually stops (otherwise, the earth would be covered in a very thick layer of char), it simply is so slow that it cannot be measured within a reasonable timescale.

The degradation of biochar in soil is different from the degradation of fresh biomass in two ways: the initial loss of carbon in the thermochemical processing and the amount of carbon remaining at the 'steady-state' point. With biomass, 100% of the biomass is initially applied to soil; with char, about 50% of the carbon is removed in the pyrolysis process meaning that only about 50% of the carbon in the original biomass is actually applied to the soil. The carbon in the untreated biomass is degraded in the soil relatively

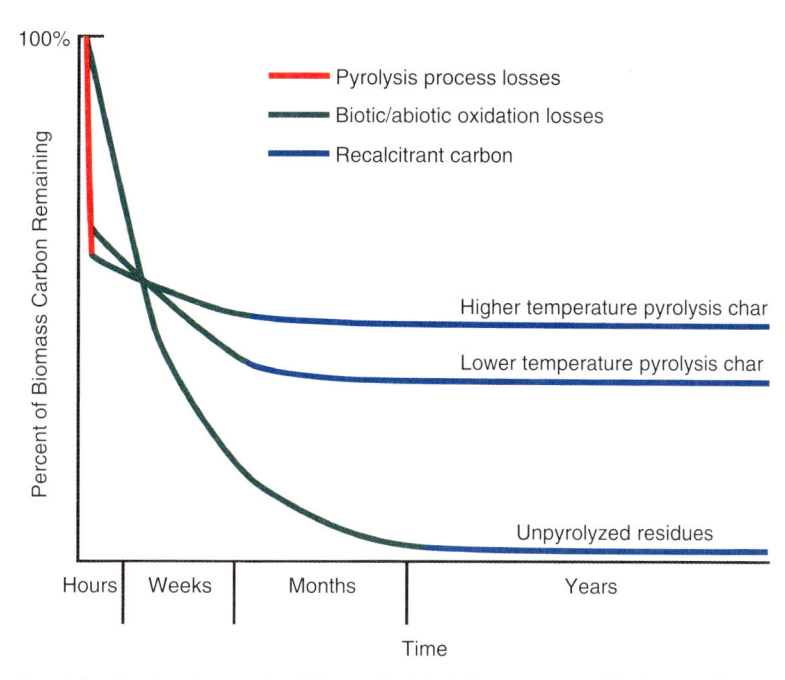

Figure 5 Schematic of the degradation kinetics of unpyrolyzed biomass feedstock, low-temperature biochar, and high-temperature biochar in the environment.

rapidly by microorganisms (much of the available carbon is gone in a few weeks); by the time the rate of decay has stabilized, there is very little of the biomass carbon remaining in the soil. In contrast, the carbon in the biochar is much more resistant to decay, the rate of loss levels off much faster and more carbon remains in the soil over the long term. **Figure 5** shows what a graph of mass remaining in relation to soil residence time might look like. In general, the higher the temperature of the pyrolysis process, the less carbon there is in the biochar but the more stable that carbon is.

Several scientists have attempted to measure the residence time of biochars (and BCs) in soils, both at ambient conditions as would occur in nature or using elevated temperatures to accelerate the process, and have encountered difficulties. First, the slow rate of oxidation pushes the limits of analytical detection. This is especially true in soil incubation situations where the signal from the degradation of microbial biomass or SOM is so much larger than the signal from the biochar degradation. Isotope labeling techniques, such as creating biochars from ^{14}C-enriched biomass and applying it to unlabeled soil, show promise in addressing this problem since the sources of evolved CO_2 can be identified and the detection limits in ^{14}C isotope analytical methods are much lower. The second problem is that measuring the degradation of biochar over a few months or years may overestimate the rate of 'steady-state' degradation and thereby underestimate the residence time of biochar in soils. One way to address this problem is to study the rate of decomposition of much older chars such as those from around old charcoal kilns that were in operation during a known time period; in this way, the measured rate of decomposition would better represent the 'steady-state' rate. Unfortunately, this approach means that not much can be known about the original sample or how much carbon was initially applied. In another approach, increasing the incubation temperature accelerates chemical reactions, allowing the results from many years worth of reactions to be observed in days or weeks. However, these methods are effective only if there is a reliable way to correlate the accelerated reaction rates with the 'real-life' reaction rates. Also, elevated temperatures could potentially cause chemical reactions to occur that would not normally happen at ambient temperatures.

On the basis of the results of studies so far, scientists are confident that the residence time of biochars in soil is on the magnitude of hundreds, if not thousands, of years depending on the conditions under which the biochar was made and the soil environment in which it is applied. For the purposes of carbon credits and accounting, evidence that a biochar with certain properties will remain sequestered in a certain soil environment for a minimum amount of time (such as >1000 years) will probably be sufficient. As with BCs, however, defining what these quantities are and determining exactly how to measure them will be anything but straightforward.

5.18.3.5 Efforts to Encourage the Adoption of Biochar into Agricultural Practices

The idea of combined carbon sequestration and soil fertility improvement is understandably attracting much international attention. Several organizations have been formed with the goals of promoting biochar research and implementation as part of a sustainable economy. The International Biochar Initiative (IBI), a nonprofit organization formed in 2006, is by far the largest, though numerous states, countries, and regions have also formed their own initiatives. Among its activities, IBI organizes regional and international conferences; coordinates communication between biochar researchers, businesses, and users; and works to promote the incorporation of biochar into legislation, such as including biochar research and development into the 2008 United States Farm Bill. More recently, IBI has been working with the United Nations Convention to Combat Desertification (UNCCD) and several member nations and parties to promote biochar as part of the mitigation strategies in post-Kyoto climate agreements under the UN Framework Convention on Climate Change (UNFCCC), including the December 2009 meeting in Copenhagen. While specific mention of biochar was not retained in the language of the negotiation document consolidated by the Ad Hoc Working Group on Long-Term Cooperative Action (AWGLCA) leading up to Copenhagen, language on mitigation options that could include biochar was retained in an appendix, suggesting biochar has the potential to be specifically identified as a strategy in future international treaties on greenhouse gas emissions and climate change.

5.18.4 Biochar Sources

In theory, potential biochars could come from just about any thermochemical processing of a carbonaceous material. Feedstocks could include agricultural wastes, forestry residues, used tires, old building materials, municipal solid wastes, and others. Those feedstocks and processes suitable for the sustainable production of biochar are, in reality, limited by feedstock material safety and availability, market conditions for biochar and its process coproducts, local soil properties, and the combined environmental impacts. The five processes explored in this section and summarized in Table 3 – slow pyrolysis, torrefaction, fast pyrolysis, flash pyrolysis, and gasification – represent the processes receiving the most attention across the thermochemical platform for production of biochar as well as heat, power, fuels, and chemicals. All of these processes create some amount of three products: solid (char and/or ash), liquid (bio-oil or tar), and gas (syngas or producer gas). Depending on the product quantity and quality goals, each process uses different reaction conditions (temperature, pressure, heating rate, residence time, reactive or inert atmosphere, purge gas flow rate, etc.) to optimize the production of one or more specific products.

A key to analyzing a thermochemical process is to understand what occurs during combustion, that is, burning in the presence of sufficient or excess oxygen. Some or all of these steps occur in the other thermochemical processes, but often to a lesser extent. The first step in combustion is drying since most biomass contains at least some moisture. As water boils at a relatively low temperature, steam is the first to be removed. Fires are more difficult to get started than to maintain because water evaporation is an endothermic (energy-requiring) process. Energy must be added to start a fire before any energy can be extracted from the fire. The second combustion step is volatilization or pyrolysis (no oxygen needed yet). As heat breaks the chemical bonds within the biomass, smaller molecules vaporize and escape from the biomass particle. It is not until the third step, gas-phase oxidation, however, that one sees a flame. As hot, volatile molecules leave the biomass particle, they come in contact with oxygen and are oxidized, releasing heat and light. If there is enough oxygen present, the only products are carbon dioxide and water. If there is not enough oxygen, however, these volatiles do not burn completely and can result in heavy smoke/tar or gas-phase polymerization to soot. When all of the volatile parts of the biomass have been oxidized and removed, only a very hot, slow-burning solid shell is left to undergo the final step of combustion: solid-phase oxidation. These solid glowing 'coals' are still reacting with oxygen, but because the oxygen has to diffuse to the surface of the solid rather than react with gas-phase volatiles, the process is much slower and does not give off a visible flame. Eventually, all of the carbon is oxidized to carbon dioxide and only the noncombustible mineral material, the ash, is left. The extent to which each combustion process occurs depends on the amount of energy available (i.e., the temperature), the amount of oxygen, and the residence time of the biomass particle and product fractions in the oxidizing atmosphere. In combustion chambers and boilers, for example, high temperatures and excess oxygen are used to drive all reactions to completion.

5.18.4.1 Slow Pyrolysis and Traditional Charcoal Making

Charcoal for heating and other purposes is traditionally made by slow pyrolysis: heating in the absence of oxygen to moderate or high temperatures. The process is characterized by slow heating rates and long residence times. Necessary heat to start and drive the reaction is usually provided internally by combusting a portion of the feedstock. In research and situations where greater control is needed, heat is often produced externally and transferred to the biomass by a heat carrier or through the reaction container walls (i.e., placing a sealed reaction vessel inside a furnace). The goal of slow pyrolysis is a high-carbon, energy-dense solid char product. The coproducts are a watery, low-molecular-weight acidic liquid called pyroligneous acid or wood tar, and a low-energy, combustible gas.

Table 3   Thermochemical processes, their representative reaction conditions, particle residence times, and primary products

Thermochemical process	Temperature range (°C)	Heating rate	Pressure	Residence time	Primary product
Slow pyrolysis	350–800	Slow (<10 °C min^{-1})	Atmospheric	Hours–days	Char
Torrefaction	200–300	Slow (<10 °C min^{-1})	Atmospheric	Minutes–hours	Stabilized, friable biomass
Fast pyrolysis	400–600	Very fast (~1000 °C s^{-1})	Vacuum–atmospheric	Seconds	Bio-oil
Flash pyrolysis	300–800	Fast	Elevated	Minutes	Biocarbon/char
Gasification	700–1500	Moderate–very fast	Atmospheric–elevated	Seconds–minutes	Syngas/producer gas

Charcoal production has existed in the repertoire of human technologies for thousands of years, most likely since humans learned how to control fire. In early fire pits, bits of charcoal would have been left over after a fire, especially if the center of larger pieces did not burn completely. Humans gradually learned that they could produce more of this black, light, and friable material if they covered burning wood or debris. Some of the first techniques to produce charcoal, such as in pit kilns or mound kilns, were used through the early twentieth century, and are still practiced in developing countries around the world.

To build a pit kiln, workers would dig a hole, pack it with dry material (mostly wood) leaving room at each end for an air inlet and outlet, and ignite the material at one end. Once a strong fire was going, less dense material (branches, leaves, etc.) was piled on top, followed by a layer of soil thick enough to keep out the air (~20 cm). Air would be allowed to enter on one side of the pit and exit on the other, causing the combustion region to gradually move across the pit. Workers would tend the kiln constantly over the next 2 or 3 days, opening and closing holes in the soil layer to control the amount of air. Once the carbonization process was complete, the pit would be uncovered and the newly made charcoal allowed to cool. The advantages of a pit kiln are that they are inexpensive and can be constructed just about anywhere that has a supply of biomass and workable, dry soil. On the downside, these kilns must be monitored constantly during the entire burn, and even then, the operators still have limited control over the reaction conditions. The resulting yields of charcoal are generally very low (~10–30%), there are wide variations in the quality of the product due to inhomogeneous conditions within the pit, and the product may contain significant amounts of contaminants such as the soil used to cover the pile. Pit kilns tend to be energy inefficient and create large amounts of air pollution from the venting of the volatiles (smoke), noncondensable gases (carbon monoxide, methane, low-molecular-weight hydrocarbons, etc.), and particulate matter. For this reason, pit kilns are typically located outside of populated areas, and charcoal makers often suffer from the health issues associated with breathing this polluted air.

Mound kilns are essentially aboveground pit kilns, using similar burn-and-cover methods and being susceptible to many of the same problems. One advantage of using a mound kiln instead of a pit kiln is that a mound kiln can be constructed in areas where the water table is high or the soil is difficult to work. Maintaining the mound shape and preventing too much airspace requires careful stacking of the feedstock (wood). First, a large, tall piece of wood is set vertically in the center surrounded by small, easily ignited wood pieces. Around the center post is stacked progressively shorter and smaller logs, all vertically arranged with small pieces packed in between. As was done with the pit kiln, the mound is then covered with a layer of branches and leaves, followed by soil. The center log is removed to serve as a flue and the fire is ignited by dropping burning material into the center opening. The burn/carbonization process is controlled by opening or sealing holes in the soil layer along the bottom edges of the mound. A model of a mound kiln is shown in **Figure 6**.

Building kilns from brick, concrete, or metal was the next step in improving charcoal-making technology. Not only are these kilns more permanent in nature, they also allowed for greater heat insulation and control of conditions, thus increasing char yield, consistency, and quality. Brick kilns are made of bricks sealed together with mortar or mud set on top of a brick base, are shaped like mounds or beehives, and tend to be larger than the mound kilns. One opening is used to load in wood, while another on the opposite side is used to unload the finished charcoal. Vents along the bottom of the kiln can be opened or closed depending on the color of the smoke leaving the 'eye' hole in the top center of the kiln (where white smoke indicates drying, yellow/brown indicates volatilization, and bluish/clear indicates carbonization is complete). Carbonization generally takes close to a week of adding air

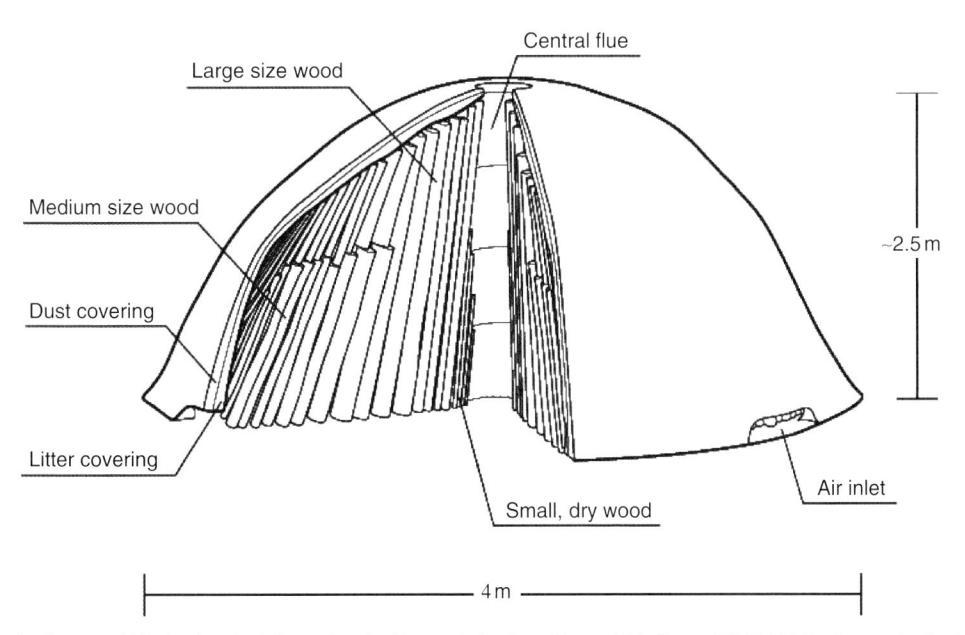

Figure 6 Example of a mound kiln (scale = 4 m). Reproduced with permission from Figure 8.2 in Brown RC (2009) Biochar production technologies. In: Lehmann J and Joseph S (eds.) *Biochar for Environmental Management: Science and Technology*. London: Earthscan.

through the vents, followed by a couple of days leaving just the 'eye' hole open to vent volatiles, and finally, a cooling period with the kiln completely sealed. This method allows for a slower, more even burn, which means less carbon is lost during the combustion phase. Also, with the use of bricks instead of loose soil, the charcoal coming out is less likely to be contaminated with mineral matter.

Rectangular, reinforced concrete kilns with steel doors and clay pipe stacks, also called Missouri kilns, were very common in regions where a lot of charcoal was produced for the steel industry, and several are still commercially operational today, especially for the production of grill charcoal briquettes. The rectangular shape and large doors make mechanized loading of feedstock and removal of finished charcoal much easier. Missouri kilns tend to be much larger than brick kilns (they produce around 12 metric tons of charcoal about every 3 weeks) yet still have good heat insulation properties. Air inlet pipes that can be easily closed and thermocouples located throughout the kiln give operators much more control over hot and cold spots in the kiln. Since all of the emissions leave through a few pipe stacks, it is possible to collect the gases as they leave the kiln for potential recovery of liquid products or passage through an afterburner to control air pollution. With all of the additional controls, Missouri kilns can consistently achieve yields of about 33% relatively high-quality charcoal.

Metal kilns can also be used; they provide the same level of control as a brick or a concrete kiln but are much more easily moved. These types of kilns originated in Europe in the 1930s and are frequently found in developing countries. With steel, one can create a kiln that can be manufactured in one place and reassembled near the biomass source. One of the best known designs is that of a transportable metal kiln by Tropical Products Institute for use in rural, high-rainfall areas.

The future design of kilns for clean and efficient large-scale char production will likely focus on continuous process kilns, instead of the kiln types already mentioned, which all run as batch processes. The advantage of a continuous process is greater consistency and control as operations are run at a steady state and thus can avoid the hassles and inefficiencies inherent with repeated start-up and shutdown cycles. One common design for a continuous process kiln is the rotary kiln. Feedstock in the form of ground wood or other biomass is added to the top of what looks like a winding staircase or slide. Paddles or brushes move the feedstock around in a circle, pushing it gradually down the reactor through three different zones. In the top zone, the biomass is dried by hot combustion gases from the lower zones. In the middle zone, a limited amount of outside air is added to keep a combustion front going. Below the combustion front is the cooling zone, where the charcoal made in the combustion zone is cooled with recycled combustion gases. Charcoal exits from the bottom, while the unrecycled combustion gases containing the tars and vapors exit from the top to an afterburner. From a gas perspective, air enters in the middle zone where all the oxygen reacts with the vapors coming off the biomass, creating heat and combustion products. Then, the now-hot and oxygen-depleted air goes through the drying zone, transferring heat from the combustion to the incoming fresh biomass. Finally, the cool, oxygen-free gas is recycled to the bottom of the reactor to cool the hot charcoal or let out from the top to the afterburner. An example of such a kiln is shown in **Figure 7**. The advantages of this system are increased control of reaction conditions and very low emissions. Operators can adjust the reaction temperature by controlling the rate of biomass being fed in the top and the rate at which air is allowed into the middle combustion zone. Since the process is continuous, parameters can be tweaked over a long period of time until a desired steady state is reached. Recycling the spent combustion gases provides a way to cool the finished charcoal without the risk of starting a fire (due to the presence of oxygen) and without needing an external inert coolant such as nitrogen or water. The use of an afterburner means that any unburned particle matter, hydrocarbons, or carbon monoxide gases can be completely oxidized before they are released to the environment. The emissions from such a kiln are thus very clean, consisting of water, carbon dioxide, and almost no NO_x, SO_x, or mercury.

5.18.4.2 Torrefaction and Feedstock Pretreatment

Torrefaction can be thought of as low-temperature (200–300 °C), slow pyrolysis. One example of a torrefaction process is the roasting of coffee beans. Torrefaction removes water and some volatiles from biomass, making the biomass easier to grind, transport, and store. Wet, untreated biomass presents several logistical problems. It requires a lot of energy to cut or grind because it is flexible and does not readily crumble. It has a low bulk energy density, so a large volume has to be transported to move relatively little energy. Finally, its high moisture content makes it more susceptible to microbial decay, meaning that a significant amount can be lost to fermentation during storage. By heating the biomass to 200–300 °C, the moisture and some of the more readily available carbon structures can be driven off. The resulting products are much the same as those from regular slow pyrolysis except that the solid char product is browner in color than black. This brown 'char' is easy to grind, has a higher energy density, and is slightly hydrophobic, making it less likely to absorb water and less likely to decay in storage. While this torrefaction char may not be as suitable for direct use as a biochar, the ability to transform raw biomass into a more easily managed feedstock that is available year-round is potentially critical to the economical implementation of other thermochemical processes.

5.18.4.3 Fast Pyrolysis and Bio-Oil

Fast pyrolysis, like slow pyrolysis, is the heating of biomass in the absence of oxygen. Unlike slow pyrolysis, however, fast pyrolysis uses very high heating rates (~1000 °C s^{-1}), short residence times, and rapid quenching of vapors to maximize the production of the liquid product, bio-oil. The theory behind fast pyrolysis design highlights the difference between a thermodynamically controlled process and a kinetically controlled process. In a thermodynamically controlled process, reactants and products are allowed sufficient contact time to reach thermodynamic equilibrium. The final distribution of products depends on process conditions

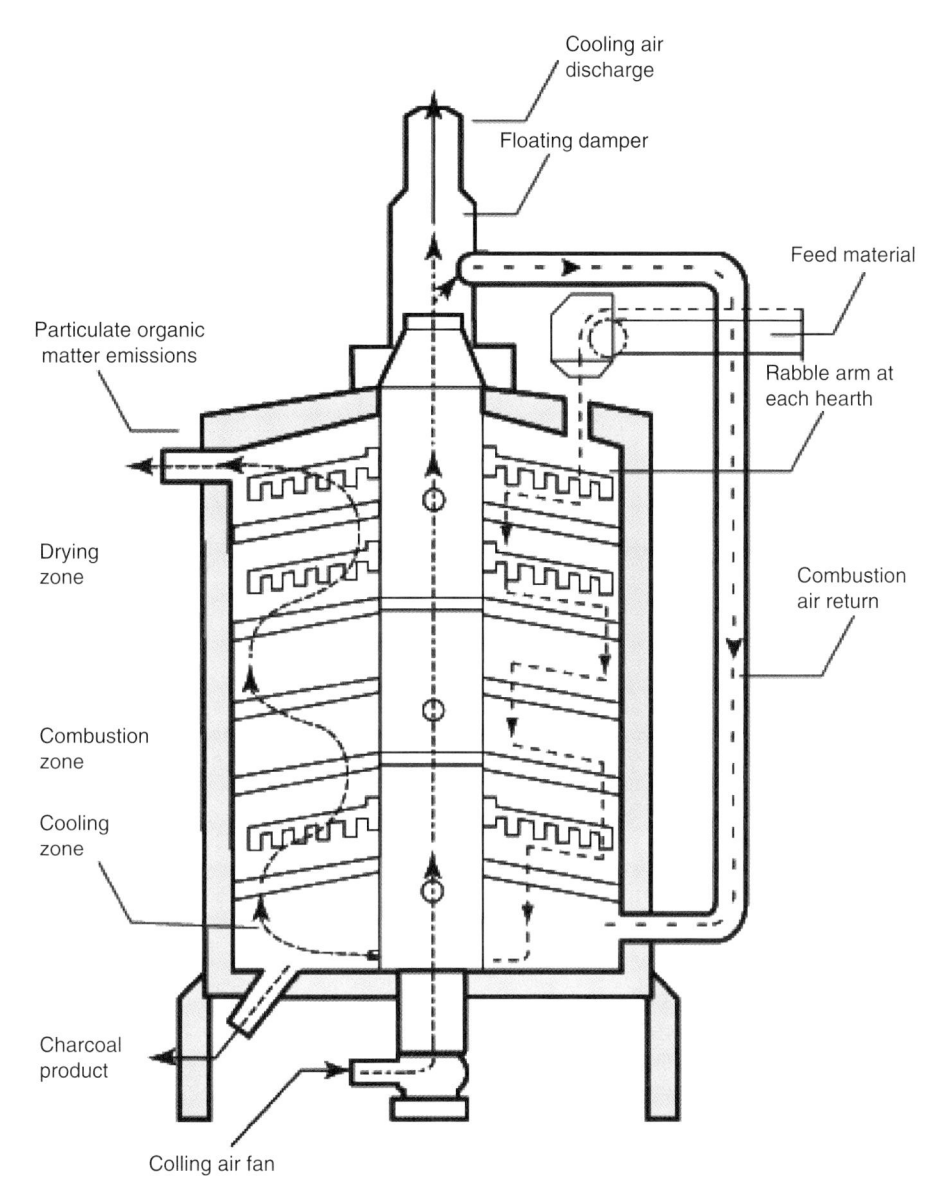

Figure 7 Example of a continuous process kiln. Reproduced with permission from Figure 8.7 in Brown RC (2009) Biochar production technologies. In: Lehmann J and Joseph S (eds.) *Biochar for Environmental Management: Science and Technology.* London: Earthscan.

such as temperature and pressure, but not on reaction rate. In thermochemical processing, slow pyrolysis represents a thermodynamically controlled process; the amount of char or gas products varies with temperature, pressure, and feedstock composition, but would be the same regardless of whether the reaction lasted for a few hours or a few days. In fast pyrolysis, a kinetically controlled reaction, the goal is to create and separate vapors as quickly as possible before they can condense and carbonize as secondary chars or crack into low-molecular-weight noncondensable gases. In other words, one wants to avoid thermodynamic equilibrium. This is accomplished through a high rate of heat transfer to the biomass, causing the drying and volatilization steps to occur almost instantaneously. Methods to achieve such high heat transfer rates include reducing the particle size, selecting an effective heat carrier (such as sand or steel shot), and using a fluidized bed, heated blade (ablative pyrolysis), or screw mixer (auger pyrolysis) reactor design. Once heated, the large amount of created volatile molecules and aerosols quickly expand out of the biomass particles (sometimes causing the particles to fracture apart) and are removed from the reaction zone by a vacuum (vacuum pyrolysis) or high flow rates of an inert sweep gas. Outside of the reaction zone, the hot vapors are quickly separated from the solid char (which can catalyze secondary carbonization or cracking reactions) by cyclones or other kinds of filters. Finally, the vapors and aerosols are condensed out of the gas phase by cooling, scrubbing, electrostatic precipitation, and other treatments, while the noncondensable gases are sent on to an afterburner for energy or heat recovery. To achieve a maximum yield of oil (~70% by weight), fast pyrolysis reactors are designed to achieve a vapor residence time of no more than a few seconds and moderate temperatures (400–600 °C).

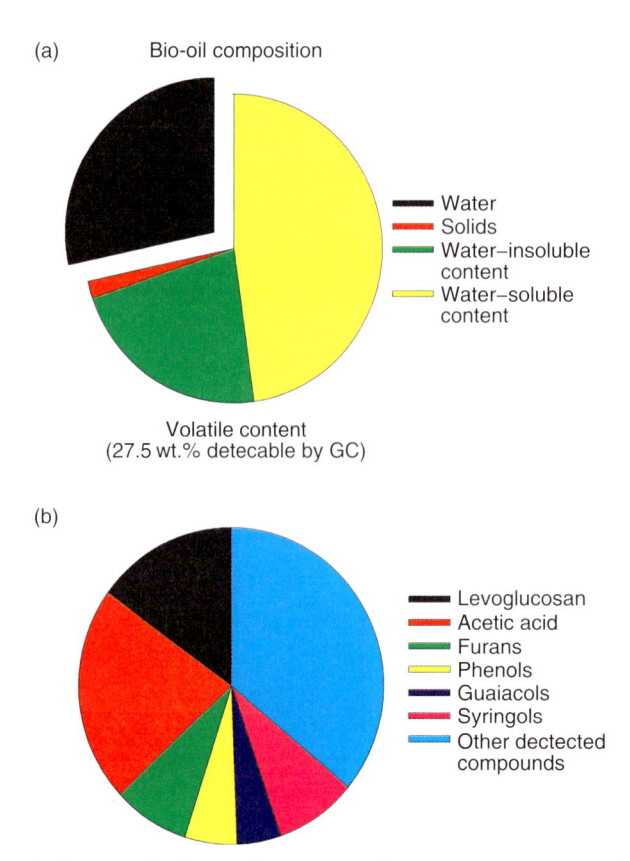

Figure 8 Composition of bio-oil from the fast pyrolysis of red oak based on solubility (a) and gas chromatography (GC)-detectable volatile compounds (b). Percents are weight percent of the whole bio-oil on a wet basis. Source: Pollard AJS, Center for Sustainable Environmental Technologies, Iowa State University.

Bio-oil from fast pyrolysis is a complicated mixture of water and oxygenated organic compounds including organic acids, aldehydes, alcohols, furans, pyrans, anhydrosugars, and aromatic compounds (see **Figure 8**). Approximately 300 different compounds have been identified in bio-oil from the decomposition of hemicellulose, cellulose, and lignin. As a feedstock for the production of organic chemicals and transportation fuels, bio-oil has been compared to crude petroleum in that it can provide a wide variety of products but requires fractionation and upgrading. There are three key differences between crude oil and bio-oil that pose a significant problem for its direct use in existing refineries, namely, water content, oxygen content, and high acidity. Bio-oil is also unstable, especially when stored at high temperatures. It tends to separate into aqueous and hydrophobic phases, and the high acidity and oxygen content catalyze polymerization reactions, which dramatically increase oil viscosity. Research aimed at improving bio-oil properties has included bio-oil collection system designs that separate the oil into fractions, catalytic reforming of aqueous bio-oil to produce hydrogen, and bio-oil upgrading through hydrogenation to remove carboxylic acids and oxygen. Currently, bio-oil can be used as a heavy oil replacement in commercial boilers and some steam turbines for heat and electricity, as an energy-dense and pumpable biorenewable feedstock for gasification, and as a petroleum replacement in the production of asphalt (i.e., 'bioasphalt').

5.18.4.4 Flash Pyrolysis and the Effects of Pressure

Flash Pyrolysis™ is a batch pyrolysis process that uses moderate pressures (2–25 atm) to minimize reaction time and maximize biocarbon yield. The research and commercial technology is based on the work of Michael J. Antal Jr.'s group at the Hawaii National Energy Institute, University of Hawaii at Manoa [8]. The flash pyrolysis process uses pressure to promote volatile condensation and secondary char formation (exactly opposite of the vapor removal goals of fast pyrolysis). In this process, biomass is packed into canisters, which are loaded into a high-pressure chamber. Compressed air is pumped into the chamber and the combustion/pyrolysis reaction is initiated by electric heaters on the bottom of the reactor. The biomass at the bottom of the reactor begins to burn, heating the biomass above it. After about 30–45 min, the oxygen in the chamber gets depleted and all of the biomass is transformed into biocarbon. Vented gases are sent to an afterburner that can potentially produce heat and/or electricity. The increased pressure shifts the thermodynamic equilibrium of the reaction to strongly favor char formation and also increases the rate of reaction, making the overall throughput rate only slightly slower than that of continuous fast pyrolysis process. Current marketing of the process is focused on more traditional uses of charcoal (coal replacements and activated carbons) but has strong potential in the areas of waste management (waste-to-carbon) and application of biochar in horticulture and agriculture.

5.18.4.5 Gasification and Syngas

As the name implies, the primary product of gasification is the noncondensable gas fraction. The process is characterized by higher temperatures (750–1800 °C) and the presence of some oxygen, measured in equivalence ratio or the fraction of the amount of oxygen needed for stoichiometric combustion (typically around 0.25 or 25%). The product gas, called syn gas ('synthesis gas') or producer gas if it contains nitrogen, consists mostly of carbon monoxide (CO) and hydrogen (H_2) with smaller amounts of carbon dioxide, methane, and other low-molecular-weight hydrocarbons. Overall, gasification is very similar to combustion, but due to the limited oxygen, it is not able to complete the gas-phase and solid-phase oxidation steps which would yield carbon dioxide (CO_2) and water (H_2O). In an ideal gasification situation, the reaction is thermodynamically controlled. The gas composition and carbon conversion can be predicted based on temperature and pressure, and the only coproduct is char. In reality, there is not sufficient time for the reaction to reach equilibrium, resulting in the creation of sticky, viscous tars that can clog reactor plumbing and cause significant problems in downstream gas applications. Much research has been devoted to the development of methods to address this problem, such as the use of steam and/or catalysts to promote tar cracking, tar filtering or scrubbing systems for downstream gas cleaning, and raising the reaction temperature and/or residence time.

There are numerous gasification reactor configurations such as bubbling fluidized beds, circulating fluidized beds (indirectly heated gasification), downdraft reactors, and updraft reactors, as well as several reaction modes. For example, a 'slagging' gasifier is run at very high temperatures (> 1000 °C) such that the mineral components in the feedstock vitrify during the reaction and form a very stable slag. This vitrification may be advantageous in cases when toxic or heavy metal components of a feedstock need to be stabilized, such as with the gasification of some municipal wastes. Slagging reactors would not be conducive to the production of biochar or the recycling of plant nutrients. A 'nonslagging' reactor (i.e., at 750–900 °C) yields a small amount of high-ash char (~10 wt.%) and tends to produce more tars (up to 10 wt.%). Indirectly heated gasifiers consist of two reactors with a heat carrier circulating between them: a combustion chamber where tars, chars, or other carbon sources are burned to provide energy to the heat carrier, and a gasification chamber where heat from the heat carrier and some added oxygen are used to drive the gasification reactions.

The oxygen needed for gasification can come from air (air-blown gasification) or from a mixture of steam and oxygen (steam/oxygen-blown gasification). Steam/oxygen-blown gasification has three advantages over air-blown gasification. First, the product gas stream is not diluted with nitrogen. Second, steam can easily be separated from the gas stream by condensation. Finally, steam in the reaction can be used to accomplish an *in situ* water–gas shift (WGS) reaction to increase the hydrogen content of the product gas. The WGS reaction is based on the equilibrium between water, carbon monoxide, carbon dioxide, and hydrogen:

$$CO + H_2O \leftrightarrow CO_2 + H_2$$

One downside of steam/oxygen-blown gasification is that it requires the use of expensive gas separation equipment to produce pure oxygen from air.

There are several uses for syngas and producer gas. The most direct use is as an alternative to natural gas (i.e., methane). Prior to the widespread use of natural gas, 'town gas' from the gasification of coal was commonly used in heaters, stoves, and light fixtures. Syngas, which contains carbon that has already been mostly oxidized, is much less energy dense than natural gas, especially where the product gases were diluted with nitrogen from air. Transportation fuels and chemicals can be synthesized from syngas. One important reaction is the production of methanol from 1 mol of carbon monoxide and 2 mol of hydrogen:

$$CO + 2H_2 \leftrightarrow CH_3OH$$

Hydrocarbons can even be produced from syngas through the catalytic Fisher–Tropsch process, which uses low–moderate temperatures, high pressures, and cobalt, iron, ruthenium, or nickel transition metal catalysts to produce a distribution of alkanes and paraffin waxes. Depending on the reaction conditions, the alkanes can range from the shorter-chain gasoline fraction to the medium-length jet fuels to the longer diesel fuels and waxes:

$$(2n+1)H_2 + nCO \leftrightarrow C_nH_{(2n+2)} + nH_2O$$

One challenge with the Fisher–Tropsch synthesis is that its optimal hydrogen-to-carbon monoxide ratio is around 2, while the ratio in the syngas from the gasifier is lower (generally closer to 1), meaning that significant amounts of CO must be converted to CO_2 by the WGS reaction to provide the necessary hydrogen. Another challenge to this and other catalytic processes is the coking or fouling of the catalyst. Even tiny amounts (on the parts per billion scale) of some species that foul catalysts can be enough to ruin a process. Therefore, compounds containing sulfur, nitrogen, halides (fluoride, bromide, chloride, and iodide), and tars or particulate matter that can form coke on catalysts must be meticulously removed from the product gas stream prior to the catalysis reactor. For this reason, the gas cleaning/conditioning segment of a gasification process is often one of the most complicated and expensive system components.

5.18.4.6 Biochar as a Coproduct

As seen from the five thermochemical processes described above, biochar can be a primary or an auxiliary coproduct. The key to designing an efficient and sustainable process for a given feedstock, region, and economic environment is to consider the potential uses of every coproduct. Just because a process may be optimized for a product other than biochar does not mean that biochar cannot significantly contribute to the overall scheme. For example, a fast pyrolysis process designed for maximum high-quality oil yields might still produce 10–15% weight of biochar and 15–20% combustible gases. The biochar can be applied to the soils from which the biomass was harvested to recycle plant nutrients (concentrated in the solid fraction) and sequester some carbon. The noncondensable gases can be combusted to produce process heat. One problem with traditional charcoal-making technologies, and a key difference in comparison with modern processes, is the lack of utilization of the gas and liquid fractions, causing a low overall process efficiency and significant pollution. Future thermochemical processes that can carefully control and take advantage of each product fraction, and possibly alternate between primary product fractions based on feedstock availability, market demand, and local conditions, are the most likely to be successful.

5.18.5 Biochar Properties

Biochar properties are easiest to describe if char is treated as having two fractions: the 'carbon' fraction and the inorganic ash fraction. The 'carbon' fraction includes hydrogen, oxygen, and other elements bonded to carbon and is the fraction most affected by reaction conditions. Reaction time, temperature, heating rate, and other parameters convert – to some degree – the mostly carbohydrate organic components into the condensed aromatic structures characteristic of char. The inorganic ash fraction is the fraction most affected by feedstock properties; the reaction conditions have some effect on the ash properties and ash-to-carbon ratio of the char, but overall, whatever mineral constituents are in the biomass become concentrated in the ash.

5.18.5.1 Biochar Composition

Quantifying the amount of ash and the amount of (mostly carbon) organic material is done by proximate analysis, a thermogravimetric method traditionally considered the most basic for determining char quality. According to the ASTM standard for wood charcoals (D1762–84), mass lost at 110 °C is moisture, mass lost in an inert atmosphere at 950 °C constitutes 'volatile matter', mass lost at 750 °C in an oxic atmosphere (normally air) is 'fixed carbon', and the remainder is 'ash'. This analysis and the selected temperatures were designed for chars used as combustion fuels in high-temperature boilers. For such an application, moisture and ash represent fractions of the char that do not contribute to the energy content. A 'good' charcoal is one that is mostly fixed carbon, with some volatiles to ease the ignition process and low moisture and ash. Use of some form of proximate analysis (temperatures and heating times vary slightly) is prevalent in biochar literature, though numerous researchers have questioned the relevance of proximate analysis data for soil applications. For example, the connection between a char compound's 'volatility' and its recalcitrance in soil is not clear. It is true that dense aromatic carbons that are recalcitrant in soil also tend to have low 'volatile matter content', and that 'high volatile matter' chars have appeared to cause nitrogen immobilization problems in some soil studies (see Section 5.18.7.3), but much more work is needed to make this analysis more useful for determining char quality in relation to soil application.

The second most common analysis and one that is critical to further characterizations is the measurement of carbon, hydrogen, and nitrogen content, also known as elemental or CHN analysis. In this technique, a sample (liquid or solid) is combusted at very high temperatures with excess oxygen and the produced carbon, hydrogen, and nitrogen species (CO_2, H_2O, and nitric oxide (NO), respectively) are trapped and quantified. Results from this analysis are typically reported in terms of percent weight of a dry sample. Elemental analysis can also include the separate trapping and measurement of sulfur (CHNS) and oxygen content (CHNOS). The total or 'ultimate' analysis of a char includes information from both the elemental and the proximate analyses, in addition to the chlorine content. The composition of a given char, therefore, will often be reported as a certain amount of moisture, carbon, hydrogen, nitrogen, sulfur, chlorine, and ash, with the difference in total dry weight assumed to be oxygen. The practice of determining oxygen 'by difference' stems from the difficulty in obtaining a consistent direct oxygen measurement due to the decomposition of mineral oxides in the ash.

The composition of potential biochars varies greatly with the feedstock and the pyrolysis process. For example, biochars from the slow pyrolysis of hardwoods might have over 90% carbon with very little of anything else; on the other hand, biochars from the fast pyrolysis of switchgrass might have only 35% carbon, some oxygen, and over 60% ash from the high silica content in the feedstock and the low solid carbon yield of the process. In general, the higher the temperatures and residence time, the less carbon, oxygen, and hydrogen remain in the solid product. One way to represent the extent of a thermochemical reaction is through a Van Krevelen diagram, which plots the molar oxygen-to-carbon (O/C) ratio in relation to the molar hydrogen-to-carbon (H/C) ratio. An example of a Van Krevelen plot of chars from torrefaction, slow pyrolysis, fast pyrolysis, and gasification is shown in **Figure 9**. Lignocellulosic feedstocks, which consist mostly of carbohydrates, have O/C ratios close to 1 and H/C ratios close to 2. As these feedstocks are heated, both ratios decrease as oxygen and hydrogen are removed as CO, CO_2, H_2O, and other O- and H-containing volatiles, thus 'concentrating' the carbon. Later, as fresh chars oxidize in the environment and gain oxygen-containing surface functional groups, the O/C ratio increases again, fast at first, then more gradually over time until it approaches a steady state.

The composition of the ash fraction of biochar is mostly dependent on the minerals found in the feedstock since most inorganic elements do not volatilize at typical pyrolysis temperatures. There are several ways of determining which elements are present and in what relative quantity. One of the easier techniques is X-ray fluorescence (XRF) spectroscopy. Fluorescence occurs when an atom absorbs energy from an electromagnetic photon, raising the energy level of an electron; as the electron relaxes, it emits a lower energy electromagnetic photon. Each element has characteristic wavelength or set of wavelengths that it emits when bombarded

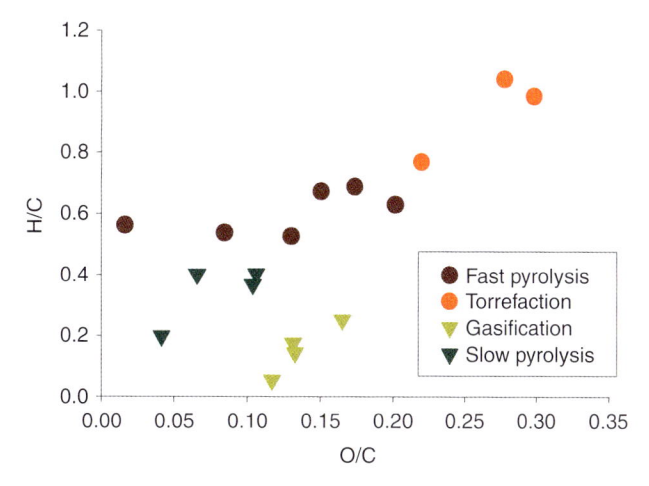

Figure 9 Van Krevelen plot of biochars from torrefaction, slow pyrolysis, fast pyrolysis, and gasification. O/C and H/C ratios are molar ratios. In general, both ratios decrease with increasing reaction temperature.

with X-ray radiation, and the intensity of the emission is relative to the amount of that element present in the sample. XRF spectroscopy uses this phenomenon to measure the amounts of nearly all the elements larger than sodium present in a sample. Data from XRF analysis are often reported as weight percents of the most common elemental oxide. For example, the instrument would measure the number of calcium atoms but the results would report the weight percent of calcium oxide (CaO) in the sample. If samples such as char or feedstock contain the element in a different form, such as calcium hydroxide (Ca(OH)$_2$), the mass balances may not match exactly. The relative amounts of one element to another, however, will be accurately reflected. Another way in which the ash composition of a char sample might be measured is digesting or leaching the sample, and then measuring the concentration of given ions in the resulting solution. For example, to determine the amount of potassium in a char sample, one might combust the sample, dissolve the resulting ash in acid, and then measure the potassium concentration of the solution by atomic absorption spectroscopy (AAS) or inductively coupled plasma atomic emission spectroscopy (ICP-AES).

The elemental composition of char closely resembles that of its feedstock. The elements found in biomass chars, therefore, include plant macro- and micronutrients (in ratios similar to that of the plant material) such as calcium, copper, iron, potassium, magnesium, manganese, molybdenum, nickel, phosphorus, sulfur, and zinc. As plants occasionally take up other elements even though they are not essential, char can also contain sodium, chlorine, silicon, and traces of other elements. If the feedstock sample was contaminated with soil or other chemicals, these will also appear in the ash analysis. For this reason, crop and forestry residues may contain soil minerals such as aluminum and silicon, which may affect the thermochemical process and certain analytical techniques.

5.18.5.2 Physical Properties

The particle size of chars produced at lower heating rates is similar to the particle size of the feedstock before pyrolysis. If the feedstock was ground to 1 mm particles, one would expect the majority of the char produced to be also in the 1 mm range. As volatile matter is slowly removed during the pyrolysis process, the char becomes more porous but still holds its overall shape and size. The fines generated during pyrolysis, such as those one would find at the bottom of charcoal kilns, are the result of the partial feedstock combustion (high-ash chars) and the generation of dust from rubbing the now-friable char particles together. At higher heating rates, the rapid escape of volatiles is believed to play an additional role in fines generation as particles fracture (explode) from the generated internal pressure. The typical preprocess grinding of feedstock to improve heat transfer for fast pyrolysis and gasification also means that chars from these processes tend to be very fine (1–100 μm). Overall, particle size decreases and the risk of problems from dust increases. The majority of char particles are larger than the PM$_{10}$ (<10 μm) and PM$_2$ (<2 μm) air pollution cutoffs for particulate matter that can cause respiratory health problems; even so, measures for controlling dust and particulate matter exposure during handling are still strongly recommended. Particle size down to approximately 50 μm is most easily measured by sieve methods. Laser particle counting techniques can be useful for the smaller particle sizes. Settling techniques, such as the techniques used to classify soil texture, however, are difficult to use on chars due to their low density (char floats instead of sinking in water).

The density of char can be measured in two ways: in terms of either bulk density, which includes structural and pore space volume, or particle density (also known as skeletal or true density), which includes only the volume occupied by solid molecules. Bulk density is measured by adding a known amount of sample mass into a container of known volume. Compaction has a significant effect on pore volumes, so measurement standards frequently have specific protocols for sample packing or settling. Biochar bulk density is low, around 0.2–0.5 g cm^{-3} (specific gravity of 0.2–0.5), but this can vary with feedstock and process. For example, chars from high-ash feedstocks or processes that result in low char carbon contents will have significantly higher densities due to the mineral material contribution. Particle density is measured using a pycnometer and since pore volume is no longer included, it is higher than the bulk

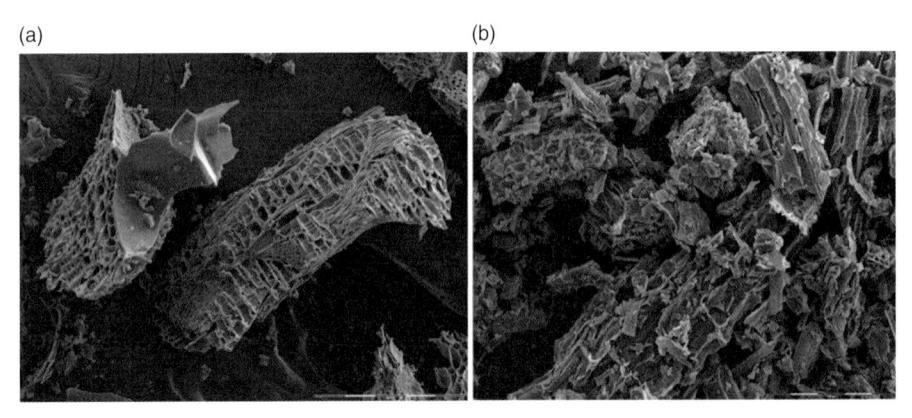

Figure 10 Scanning electron micrographs of biochar particles showing porosity. (a) Hardwood slow pyrolysis biochar from a commercial kiln (scale = 200 μm). (b) Biochar from the fast pyrolysis of corn stover (scale = 100 μm). Source: Laird D, USDA ARS, National Laboratory for Agriculture and the Environment, Ames, IA. Images taken by Tracy Pepper.

density for a given solid. Particle density is not affected by compaction. Biochar particle density is usually between 1.5 and 1.7 g cm^{-3} and generally increases with pyrolysis temperature as the solid carbon condenses into dense aromatic ring structures. Some high-temperature chars can even have particle densities approaching that of solid graphite (2.25 g cm^{-3}). As with bulk density, particle density also increases with mineral ash content and can exceed 2.0 g cm^{-3} for high-ash chars.

There are three kinds of porosity in biochars based on pore size. According to material scientists, pores can be divided into micropores, mesopores, and macropores, which have internal diameters of <2, 2–50, and >200 nm, respectively. (Note that soil scientists may use different systems of classifications such as calling all pores with diameters <200 nm micropores.) Each size range of pores contributes to a different property of the sample. In the activated carbon industry, micropores (<2 nm) contribute the vast majority of the surface area and are considered important for adsorption applications. For soil applications, macropores in biochar affect the soil's hydrology and microbial environment. The larger the pores, the easier water, plant roots, and fungal hyphae can penetrate the particle. For smaller microorganisms, pores provide shelter from larger, predatory organisms. Biochars will frequently have specific pore size distributions and arrangements due to maintenance of the plant structure. This regularly sized and extensive porosity can be seen in the scanning electron micrographs of biochar shown in **Figure 10**. Pore size distribution in solid materials can be measured in several ways. One method is gas sorptometry. Two examples of this method applied to chars are micropore analysis by carbon dioxide and mesopore analysis by nitrogen. Another method is mercury porosimetry, which calculates the pore size based on the pressure required to push mercury into the pore (the smaller the pore, the higher the pressure needed). Mercury porosimetry is typically used to measure pores in the macro- and mesopore range. One limitation of mercury porosimetry is that pores between particles (interparticle porosity) and pores within particles (intraparticle porosity) are measured simultaneously. Porosity, when reported as a single sample property, is simply defined as the amount of total pore volume relative to the total bulk sample volume.

The surface area of biochar is another important physical property of biochar that has a significant impact on the magnitude of interactions between biochar and the soil environment; the higher its surface area, the more chemical interactions char can participate in per gram. Selecting a method for measuring biochar surface area that provides meaning for soil applications has been an area of contention. The most common type of analysis is a gas sorption isotherm measurement. Different analysis gases and isotherm temperatures can give different values of surface area. In the activated carbon field, surface area is traditionally measured by the Brunauer–Emmett–Teller (BET) nitrogen gas physisorption method at 77 K over the relative pressure range $P/P_0 = 0.05$–0.30. BET surface areas for lower temperature biochars are often around 1 m^2 g^{-1}, which is only slightly higher than that of lignocellulosic biomass and is due to the majority of pores being macropores. High BET surface areas are the result of long residence times, higher temperatures, and/or the use of activation processes such as heating with steam; all of these processes promote the formation of micropores in the carbon structure. Depending on the feedstock and pyrolysis process, some biochars can have surface areas of hundreds and even thousands of meters squared per gram, potentially making them suitable for activated carbon applications. Achievable surface area does reach a maximum, however, as micropore structure eventually collapses into macropores and surface area is lost. Among other methods suggested for measuring surface area are the ethylene glycol monoethyl ether (EGME) specific surface area method (typically used for soils) and gas sorption methods using larger and/or more hydrophobic molecules to imitate the organic matter that would adsorb to biochar in soil. Most biochar literature reports surface area values in terms of the BET method, but more work is needed to demonstrate how this or other measurements relate to the quantity of reactive surface sites.

5.18.5.3 Chemical Properties

Part of the decision to use char as a charcoal or as a biochar is the char's higher heating value (HHV); the higher the energy content of the char, the higher its value as a fuel. HHV is measured by bomb calorimetry and represents the energy that can be extracted from the char by combustion if all of the combustion products are allowed to cool back to 25 °C. The other way of quantifying energy content, based on the lower heating value, also measures the energy of combustion but assumes that water put into the vapor phase stays as steam. In general, HHV increases with increasing carbon and hydrogen content and decreases with increasing moisture, oxygen, and ash content. As char composition varies significantly with feedstock and process, the HHV of chars also varies. Low-ash slow pyrolysis chars can have HHVs above 30 MJ kg^{-1} (higher than that of several coals); char coproducts from processes have much lower HHVs (in the teens and lower twenties of megajoules per kilogram).

Most of the chemical properties of biochars are related to two 'carbon fraction' concepts, aromaticity and surface functionality. Aromaticity is defined as the fraction of carbons in char that participate in aromatic bonds. Lignocellulosic feedstocks, which consist of sugar polymers (all aliphatic carbons) and lignin (some aromatic rings), have relatively low aromaticity. As the pyrolysis reaction progresses, oxygen and hydrogen are removed, leaving the remaining carbons to form new aromatic carbon–carbon bonds. The 'orderliness' of the aromatic structures also increases with increasing temperature, forming gradually larger sheets of interconnected aromatic rings. Eventually, the arrangement of these aromatic carbon sheets changes from random to aligned, stacked sheets resembling graphite at the highest temperatures. The degree of aromatic condensation in biochars is believed to be related to recalcitrance in the environment; carbons in dense aromatic structures are more resistant to oxidation and few microorganisms have enzymes capable of breaking down such bonds. This stability comes from the fact that electrons are shared over more than one bond in aromatic molecules. By 'spreading out' electrons over the molecule, aromatic molecules can exist at lower energy (i.e., more thermodynamically favored) states than nonaromatic molecules. Such sharing of electrons is so efficient in graphite and some highly condensed chars that these materials can even conduct electricity. Most of the techniques used to measure the degree of aromatic condensation in char are the same as those used to analyze surface functionality and will be discussed later in this section. Two other techniques being explored are particle density (the closer the density is to graphite, the more aromatic the char) and electrical conductance/resistivity (the lower the resistance to electron movement, the greater the aromatic condensation).

Many chemical interactions between biochar and the environment are directly related to its surface chemistry. In lignocellulosic feedstocks, the surface functional groups present are mostly hydroxyls (–OH), carboxylic acids (COOH), and small alkyl chains such as methyl groups (–CH$_3$). With this kind of surface chemistry, feedstocks tend to be polar, hydrophilic, and relatively reactive. Chars coming out of the pyrolysis reaction have very different surface chemistry. Most of the functional groups (containing oxygen, hydrogen, and nitrogen) have volatilized off, leaving aromatic carbon surfaces behind. These surfaces are reduced (i.e., the carbon is in the C^0 oxidation state), nonpolar, and hydrophobic. As the surface is exposed to air over time, the carbon oxidizes, creating new oxygen-containing aromatic functional groups such as hydroxyls (–OH), carbonyls (–C=O), and carboxylic acids (–COOH), and making the surface polar again. These oxygen-containing functional groups are the same as those found on SOM and are critical for biochar–soil interactions in similar ways. First, these functional groups have variable charge, meaning that they can receive or donate a proton (H$^+$) depending on the pH. At a higher pH, the carboxylic acids (–COOH) and some of the hydroxyls (–OH) give up protons and become negatively charged (–COO$^-$ and –O$^-$, respectively). In low-pH environments, these same groups can accept a proton. In this way, the carbon fraction of the biochar acts as a weak acid and partially buffers the pH of the system. (The ash fraction of the feedstock affects pH separately and may override any effect of the carbon fraction, especially with high-ash, alkaline chars.) Second, the negatively charged surface functional groups can attract positively charged cations and thus contribute significantly to the soil's CEC. In cases of metal toxicity due to low soil pH, biochar can help in two ways: raising the pH, which makes plant-toxic metals like aluminum (Al^{3+}) less soluble, and adsorbing the positively charged metal ions, which removes them from the solution. Finally, the hydrophobic and hydrophilic regions of the biochar surface can serve as adsorbents for nonpolar and polar organic molecules in the environment. This adsorptive power can be good, such as when char adsorbs organic matter or environmental contaminants. On the downside, these same surfaces might also adsorb a pesticide and reduce its effectiveness.

There are several ways to analyze the surface functionality of biochar to get information about its potential chemical interactions. In all of these methods, it is important to keep in mind that biochar surfaces change with exposure to the environment, especially at first. Fresh char just out of the pyrolyzer will have surface characteristics that are much different from those of biochar that has been lying in the open air for several weeks or that has been in the soil for several years.

Since pH affects so many physical, chemical, and biological properties of soil, being able to predict the pH effects of a biochar is critical to choosing the right char for the right application. The simplest way to measure pH is to make a char and water slurry and use a standard laboratory pH meter. As with soils, pH is sometimes also measured in a solution of potassium chloride (KCl) or a buffer to quantify the exchangeable acidity (i.e., the protons on the CEC that can be readily released in the presence of other cations). Another way to measure a char's acidity is a Boehm titration. In this method, char is titrated with gradually increasing strengths of base to quantify the types of acidic functional groups present. A char's alkalinity can be measured in a similar fashion using acids of differing strengths. The total acid-neutralizing ability of a biochar is especially important for high-ash chars that can act as liming agents in soils.

Fourier transform infrared spectroscopy (FTIR) is frequently used to identify and qualitatively track changes in functional groups in biochar and soil samples. Since biochars are opaque solids, an FTIR analysis requires special sample preparation and/or detection method. Some common methods include conventional transmission FTIR using potassium bromide (KBr) pressed pellets, diffuse reflectance infrared Fourier transform (DRIFT) spectroscopy, and Fourier transform infrared photoacoustic spectroscopy (FTIR-PAS). A sample set of FTIR-PAS feedstock and char spectra are shown in **Figure 11**. Important peaks in the feedstock and biochar spectra are the O–H stretch (3400 cm^{-1}), the aliphatic C–H stretch (3000–2860 cm^{-1}), the aromatic C–H stretch (3060 cm^{-1}), the carboxyl (C=O) stretch (1700 cm^{-1}), and the various aromatic ring modes at 1590 and 1515 cm^{-1}. The feedstock spectrum is dominated by the O–H stretch, aliphatic C–H stretch, and carboxyl C=O stretch. As the pyrolysis reaction progresses, certain peaks (O–H stretch and carboxyl C=O stretch) disappear, the C–H peaks shift from being more aliphatic to more aromatic (and eventually disappear altogether), and peaks representing aromatic carbon compounds begin to appear. In biochar aging studies, such as those presented

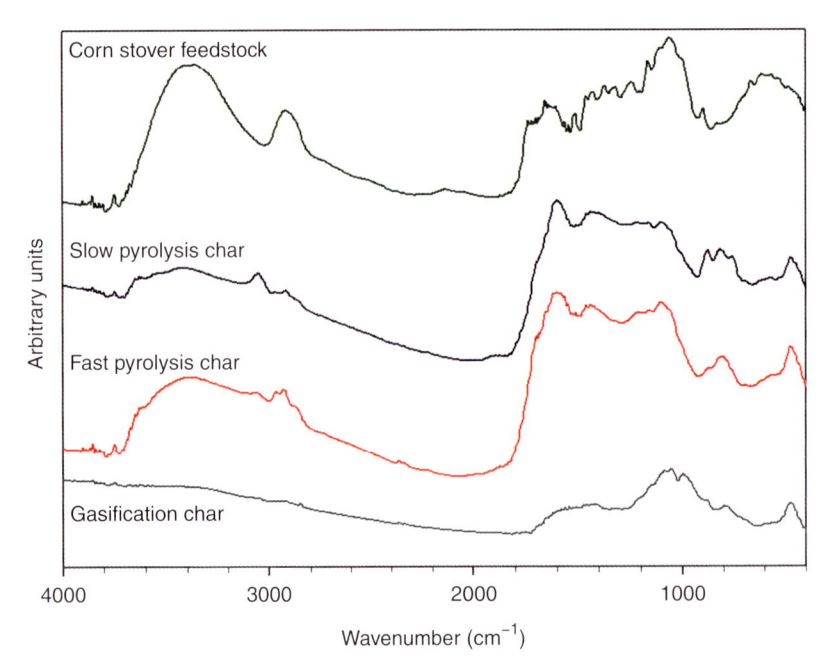

Figure 11 Fourier-transform infrared photoacoustic spectroscopy (FTIR-PAS) spectra of corn stover feedstock and biochars.

by Cheng et al. [9], FTIR spectra can be used to demonstrate the degree of biochar oxidation (appearance of C–O and O–H peaks), albeit only qualitatively.

One complicated yet informative technique used to characterize the carbon fraction of biochars is ^{13}C solid-state nuclear magnetic resonance spectroscopy (NMR). NMR uses a very strong magnetic field and radio frequency (RF) pulses to study the structure of molecules using the resonance frequencies of nuclei with specific spins. For biochars, ^{13}C and ^{1}H (proton) nuclei can be used to determine the relative quantity of carbon functional groups, the approximate degree of condensation of the aromatic rings, and the overall structure of the char molecules. **Figures 12** and **13** show some of the kinds of information that can be obtained using NMR techniques. In **Figure 12**, the ^{1}H–^{13}C cross-polarization with total suppression of spinning sidebands (CP/TOSS) spectrum of a typical lignocellulosic material is compared to that of corn stover chars, including some that were only partially pyrolyzed. Unlike FTIR spectra, where pyrolyzed and partially pyrolyzed samples may be difficult to distinguish, the difference is very apparent in the NMR spectra as the aliphatic oxygen-containing functional groups in the feedstock are gradually replaced by the dominating aromatic carbon signal of the pyrolyzed chars. In **Figure 13**, information from direct polarization (DP) spectral analysis and the results from dipolar dephasing and recoupling experiments have been combined to create chemical models of what 'average' slow pyrolysis, fast pyrolysis, and gasification char from switchgrass might look like. In spite of the chemically detailed and quantitative information that NMR can provide, its expense, complexity, and analysis time requirements make it unlikely to be an 'everyday' biochar characterization technique. Rather, NMR is more likely to serve as a verification tool in the development of other characterization techniques.

One of the several soil analysis techniques that researchers have tried to apply to biochars alone is the measurement of CEC. Like many soil chemical analyses, CEC measurement involves mixing the solid with an extracting solution, allowing the system time to equilibrate, separating the liquid phase from the solid phase, and measuring a change in the chemical composition of the liquid. Three properties of biochars make them difficult to analyze with these kinds of methods. First, the low bulk density of biochars creates a problem for liquid–solid separation. Mineral-rich soil solids are typically removed from solution by centrifuging or settling. These separation techniques, however, are not efficient for biochars, which tend to split into three fractions upon centrifugation: some fraction that floats, some that sinks, and some that stays suspended. Filtering of samples does provide a workable alternative if the filter is fine enough but can add time and difficulty to the analysis. Second, the high pH of some chars interferes with pH control during the analysis. Many of the chemical properties of soil and biochar, such as CEC, are heavily dependent on pH, and biochars that are high in ash, especially in low-solubility basic metal oxides, continuously push the pH up outside of the analysis range, even in buffered methods such as CEC by ammonium acetate. To obtain meaningful data on pH-dependent properties, these chars may need to be rinsed and the alkalinity neutralized prior to analysis. Finally, biochars can contain elements that are not in the form being tested by the analysis and therefore give erroneously high results. For example, a CEC analysis that considers all base cations extracted from a sample by ammonium acetate to be 'exchangeable' would overestimate the CEC of a high-ash biochar that contained significant amounts of alkali metal oxide or hydroxide crystals. Researchers developing methods to measure such properties in biochar may need to consider rinse or digestion steps in their protocols. Overall, the use of existing soil chemistry methods to characterize the soil-relevant properties of biochar has many potential advantages, but there are key differences between biochars and soils that require consideration in method development and caution in data interpretation. In some cases, it may be necessary to obtain biochar characteristics by comparing changes in soil properties on amended and control soils, rather than by direct measurement.

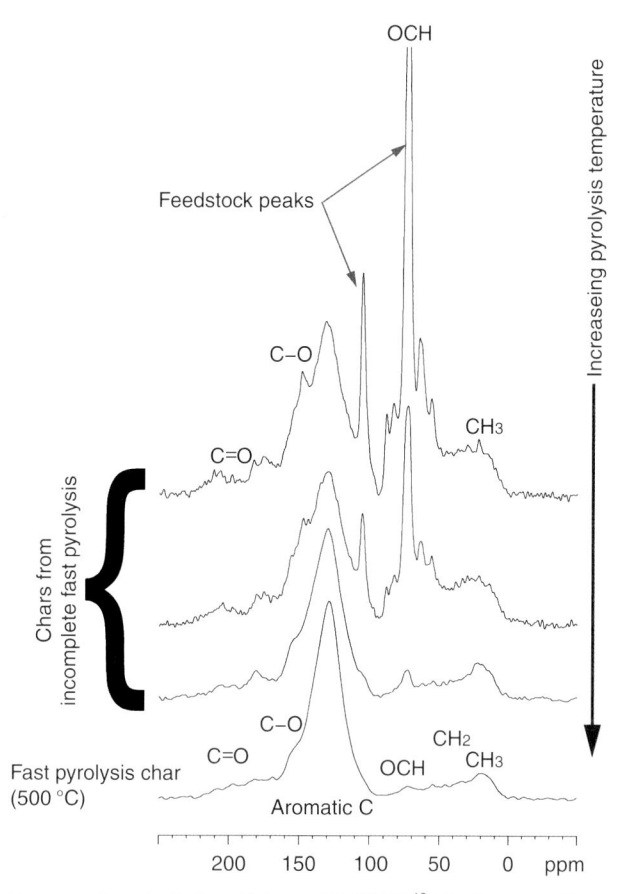

Figure 12 Cross-polarization with total suppression of spinning sidebands (CP/TOSS) ^{13}C NMR spectra of incompletely and completely pyrolyzed biochars from the fast pyrolysis of corn stover. Note that as the pyrolysis temperature increases, the peaks from the lignocellulosic feedstock gradually shift to the aromatic carbon peaks characteristic of char.

Several other analytical methods have been used to investigate the chemical properties of biochars and can be found in the literature. Among these are X-ray photoelectron spectroscopy (XPS) of biochar surfaces, stable isotope analysis, water-holding capacity and other adsorption measurements, stability measurements using chemical or radiation-catalyzed oxidations, and characterization of compounds obtained by leaching or pyrolyzing biochar. The challenge with any biochar chemical analysis technique is the correlation of measured biochar properties with desired soil responses such that researchers can make predictions about the performance of biochar based on its properties.

5.18.5.4 Biochar Engineering

The idea of biochar engineering is based on the assumption that knowledge of pyrolysis reaction conditions, biochar properties, and soil responses to biochar amendments can be used to design an optimum biochar for a given region depending on its feedstock availability and soil needs. Research in this area involves an iterative process of producing biochars under known conditions, characterizing the biochars, measuring soil responses to biochar amendments, and finally formulating biochars with favorable properties. Work similar to this has been done in the past to estimate char production conditions based on its properties. For example, spectra of char made at known pyrolysis temperatures have been used to estimate the temperature of forest fires based on the spectra of chars from the fire. As would be expected from the wide variety of feedstocks, production systems, and soils, data from biochar engineering research are very location-specific. A few trends, however, have started to emerge: in general, the higher the temperature of the pyrolysis process, the less carbon in the feedstock is converted to char but that the carbon is more condensed with fewer remaining functional groups. These biochars will likely cause higher pH conditions, be more hydrophobic, and take longer to oxidize in the soil. Biochars like this are likely to be well matched with acidic soils in more tropical regions that will benefit from the higher pH and whose warmer climate will speed up the otherwise slow oxidation process. For soils such as calcareous, saline soils in drier, more temperate regions, a lower temperature biochar made from low-ash feedstocks may be more beneficial. Such biochars are likely to have retained more oxygen-containing hydrophilic and slightly acidic functional groups that will help bring the pH closer to neutral and improve water-holding capacity without adding too much more mineral matter to the soil. Evidence to support or challenge these trends is expected in the near future, especially as more field trials using a wider variety of soils and biochars are conducted.

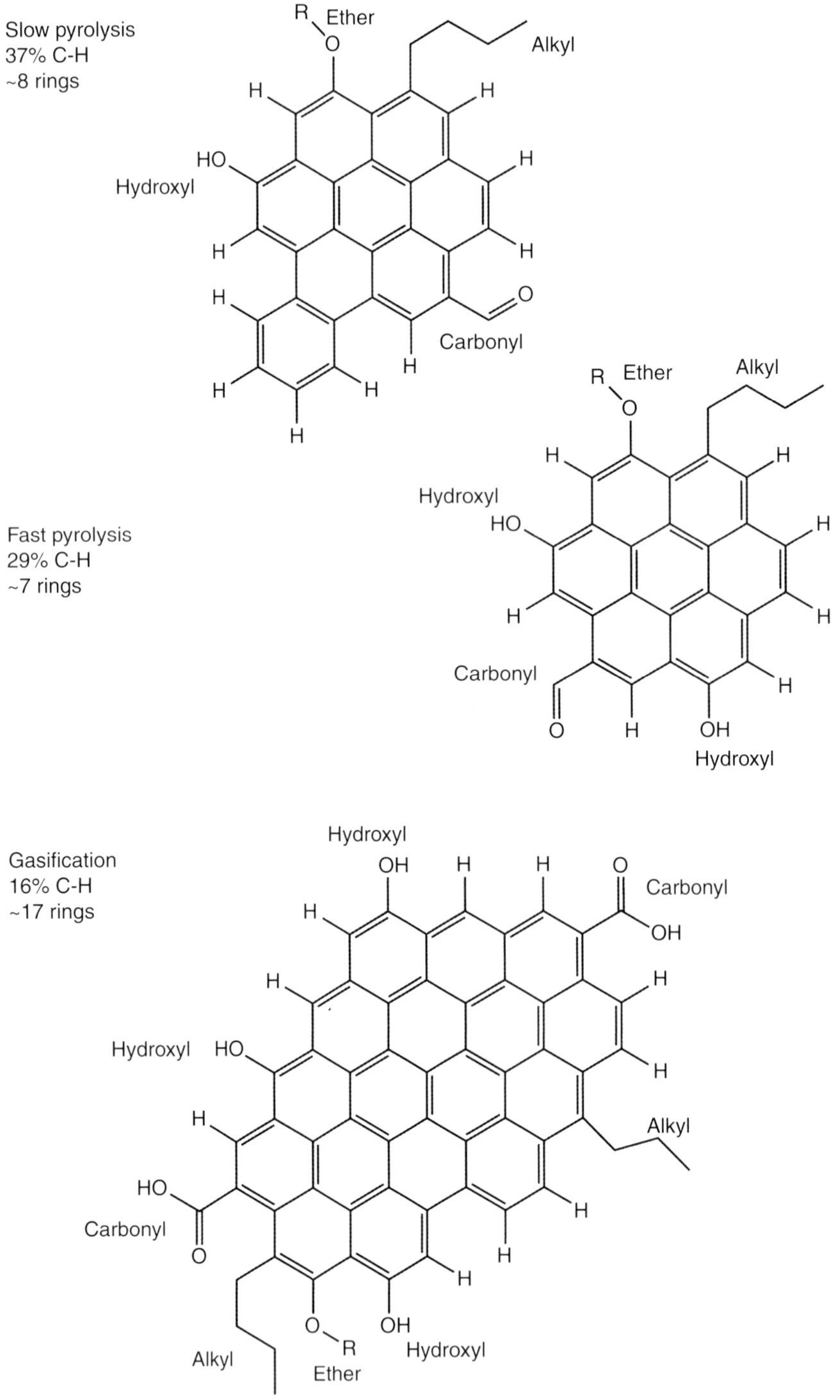

Figure 13 Model compounds of char from slow pyrolysis, fast pyrolysis, and gasification of switchgrass. Redrawn and modified from Brewer CE, Schmidt-Rohr K, Satrio JA, and Brown RC (2009) Characterization of biochar from fast pyrolysis and gasification systems. *Environmental Progress & Sustainable Energy* 28(3): 386–396.

5.18.6 Promising Biochar Scenarios and Synergies

Biochar is unique among biorenewable resource technologies in that it provides the potential to address several problems at once: soil quality, water quality, crop yield, carbon sequestration, energy production, and greenhouse gas emissions. How to get the most out of any biochar system will require the creativity and cooperation of multiple players across agriculture, government, and industry. What follows is a description of what some future biochar utilization scenarios and synergisms might look like.

5.18.6.1 Bioenergy and Biochar Coproduction

The three products from the thermochemical processing of biomass, that is, char, bio-oil/tar, and syngas, are essentially energy products, providing a way to obtain renewable energy from the sun through plant photosynthesis. One can expect, therefore, that energy production will be a key part of any biochar system, whether that energy is used immediately, such as combusting the syngas on-site for heat and electricity, or transformed into another form for later use, such as the production of liquid transportation fuels through bio-oil reforming and upgrading. Energy and biochar coproduction can occur across several scales, from small on-farm gasifiers for electricity generation to city or co-op size flash pyrolyzers for waste management, all the way up to several-hundred-ton-per-day industrial biorefineries making transportation fuels and chemicals and using biomass from two or three counties.

Consider one example of a distributed fast pyrolysis bio-oil and biochar system: farmers collect about half of their plant residues and transport them a few kilometers to the cooperative's fast pyrolyzer. The pyrolyzer turns about 60% of the biomass into bio-oil, which is trucked 150 km to the bio-oil refinery. At the refinery, the aqueous fraction of the bio-oil is steam reformed into hydrogen, which is used to catalytically upgrade the lignin-derived bio-oil fraction into hydrocarbons, which are then sold as transportation and farm equipment fuel. Twenty percent of the biomass fed into the co-op pyrolyzer is turned into syngas, which is combusted to heat the pyrolyzer and supply energy to the on-site biomass drying and grinding systems. The 20% remaining from the original biomass exits as a fine, medium-ash biochar, which the farmers take back to the fields, where they slurry the biochar with the liquid manure that they use as a fertilizer supplement and spread this mixture on the fields.

In another scenario, a city uses a combination of a composting system and a flash pyrolyzer to manage its yard and municipal wastes. Weekly collections of grass clipping, leaves, tree and garden residues, food scraps, and nonrecyclable paper and plastic wastes are delivered to the waste management site. The more nitrogen-rich wastes are composted, while the higher carbon and less compost-friendly wastes are pyrolyzed in 1 ton batches, which produce biocarbon yields of about 50%. The syngas product from the process is combusted and used in a steam turbine for electricity that supplies power to the pyrolyzer, several public buildings, and a few local manufacturing facilities. The biocarbon products are blended with the finished compost and used as topsoil in parks and public areas or sold to local nurseries and gardeners.

For all of the potential bioenergy and biochar scenarios, carbon market benefits from fossil fuel displacement and carbon sequestration will be critical to creating a favorable economic situation that will drive implementation. Without monetary incentives to sequester carbon, power companies utilizing biomass may not see the advantage of saving the char for soil application rather than combusting it for substantial additional energy. Likewise, a farmer might not feel that the long-term benefits of biochar application justify the short-term time, effort, and expense required to purchase/produce and apply biochar. One advantage biochar has over other carbon sequestration schemes is the ease in carbon accounting; the amount of biochar applied to a field and the carbon content of the biochar can be verified in a relatively straightforward manner. If the pyrolyzer is properly designed and operated, one can also assume that nearly all (>95%) of the carbon in the biochar will remain sequestered in the soil for millennia and the only emissions from the process are carbon-neutral carbon dioxide and water. The coproduction of electricity, heat, and/or fuels offers additional opportunities for carbon credits from displacing fossil fuels, especially coal and natural gas.

5.18.6.2 Farming Impacts

Less visible but just as important as the direct impacts of biochar carbon sequestration and energy coproduction on mitigating climate change are the indirect impacts biochar application has on soil input requirements, nutrient leaching, water usage, and greenhouse gas emissions. While such benefits are expected to some extent from biochar application in nearly all soils and climates, the greatest improvements in yield and soil quality are most likely in regions with poor soil quality or adverse growing conditions. For example, crop yields in already fertile soils may not improve significantly with biochar application during good growing seasons; the effects of biochar might only be observed under some kind of environmental stress such as a drought, a decrease in applied nutrients, or a heavy rain storm. Either way, biochar's recalcitrance means it will be present for many growing seasons to have an impact and any decision to apply biochar should be made with the short- and long-term impacts in mind.

In several studies of biochar application to soils, biochar has been shown to decrease nutrient leaching and other losses such as ammonia volatilization and denitrification, meaning that nutrient inputs are less likely to end up in the water supply or the atmosphere. The increase in CEC from the biochar application holds more beneficial base cations such as potassium and calcium in locations that plants can use them. The change in pH, especially the neutralization of acidic soils, improves the environment for microorganisms that regulate nutrient cycling and immobilizes plant-toxic elements such as aluminum. As overall nutrient use efficiency increases, higher yields can be achieved with fewer fertilizer inputs, meaning that less energy and natural gas are needed in fertilizer production, fewer chemicals have to be mined (i.e., rock phosphate and limestone), less fertilizer and lime need to be transported to farms, and the farmer has to make fewer passes across a given field (all reducing the amount of fossil fuels being used). The avoided water contamination represents another saving in the energy and chemicals (used to treat the water), as well as prevents the negative environmental impacts of nutrient-enriched runoff such as eutrophication (i.e., the cause of hypoxic dead zones in bodies of water).

Biochar application has also been shown to improve the soil's ability to retain water and make it available to plants. Two properties of biochar are believed to contribute to this ability: its pore size distribution and its surface chemistry. Pore size is critical to water availability in that it determines how tightly water is held within pores. If a pore is too big, the force of gravity will be greater than water's surface tension and water will drain out of the pore. Sandy soils, which have mostly big pore spaces, tend to have good drainage properties for this reason, but can dry out easily. If a pore is too small, capillary forces holding the water inside the pore are so strong that plant roots cannot extract the water. This is why a clayey soil might contain significant amounts of water but plants may still start to wilt. The pore sizes in biochar are typically in the intermediate range where water no longer drains freely but plants can still extract it. The hydrophilic chemical functional groups on biochar surfaces may further enhance this physical water retention through hydrogen bonding and electrostatic attraction. The hydrophobic regions of biochar may also help in water retention by adsorbing other kinds of SOM, which in turn may contain pores or hydrophilic surfaces that attract water. In these ways, biochar can increase soil's water use efficiency, meaning that drier areas or areas with intermittent rainfall may benefit from biochar application through increased resistance to drought and decreased need for irrigation. Such a benefit has drawn the attention of the UNCCD since many regions of the world are facing increasing water shortages from population increases and changing weather patterns caused by climate change.

Carbon dioxide is only one of several greenhouse gases emitted from soils; two others of significant importance, methane and nitrous oxide (N_2O), cause even stronger heat trapping effects, having approximately 20 and 300 times the radiative forcing as carbon dioxide, respectively. These gases are generally produced by soil microorganisms under anaerobic conditions. In the case of nitrous oxide, lack of oxygen stimulates the denitrification process by which nitrate (NO_3^-) in the soil solution is used as a terminal electron receptor and reduced to nitrous oxide and nitrogen (N_2) gas. Studies of greenhouse gas emissions from biochar-amended soils have shown that biochar may decrease both methane and nitrous oxide emissions, in some cases up to 70% of the N_2O compared to the control soils. While the reasons for these observed decreases are not understood, it is believed that the decrease in soil bulk density from biochar addition may help prevent anaerobic conditions by improving air penetration into the soil. Agricultural soil management is by far the greatest source of nitrous oxide emissions in the United States (contributing about two-thirds of the total), indicating that the potential benefit of emission reductions from soil through biochar addition is very significant.

5.18.6.3 Site Remediation

One challenge of cleaning up areas devastated by natural disasters, such as hurricanes, or pests, such as the mountain pine bark beetle, is deciding what to do with all of the dead biomass. Left alone, this biomass gradually decomposes, emitting significant amounts of previously sequestered carbon dioxide, as well as methane and nitrous oxide. Pyrolyzing these residues offers several advantages. First, the high temperatures of the pyrolysis process sterilize the material, preventing the continued spread of a biological pest, including invasive plant species. Second, some of the carbon that would have been lost to the atmosphere as carbon dioxide can be sequestered in a manner that is also beneficial to the soil environment and may help the recovery process. Finally, some energy and other coproducts may be recovered from the process which could provide an economical benefit to the affected region.

Biochar's adsorptive properties, as well as its promotion of plant and microbial activity, have also attracted the attention of those interested in the remediation of soils contaminated by organic chemicals. Similar to activated carbons (albeit perhaps not as effective on a mass basis), biochars have been shown to adsorb a wide variety of organic compounds, especially polycyclic aromatic hydrocarbons (PAHs) and phenolic compounds. Other studies focusing on char's ability to remove metal ions from aqueous solutions have demonstrated some success. These adsorptive properties suggest that biochar may be especially beneficial in the containment step of the remediation process, perhaps not as effective as purpose-made activated carbons but potentially more cost effective. Bioremediation processes, that is, those using microorganisms, plants, or their enzymes to decompose organic contaminants, utilize predominantly aerobic processes. Biochar applications which lower soil bulk density may improve soil aeration and thus may accelerate these processes. At the same time, the strong adsorbing ability of biochar might also make the sorbed contaminants less susceptible to enzymatic attack.

5.18.6.4 Developing Countries

In addition to the potentially dramatic improvements in soil quality and crop yields, biochar implementation provides several other opportunities for people living in developing countries. Not least of these opportunities is improving the efficiency and safety of energy production for cooking and heating. Many households obtain their energy from open fires or crude stoves and spend significant time collecting fuel. The burning process in open fires and many of these stoves is very inefficient and results in significant air pollution, which contributes to numerous health problems and premature deaths in those working around these fires. One branch of biochar research is devoted to addressing these problems through the design of efficient stoves made from simple materials that produce heat and biochar simultaneously. Two representative designs of such stoves include the top-lit updraft (TLUD) gasifier and the Lucia Stove from WorldStove. The basic TLUD gasifier uses two airstreams, a restricted one entering at the bottom of the heating chamber (the primary air) to gasify the biomass, and another going around the sides of the container (the secondary air) to supply oxygen to the top part of the stove where the flammable vapors are combusted as they exit (a schematic is shown in **Figure 14**). The Lucia Stove also uses gasification to produce vapors that are combusted as they exit, but uses only one airstream. Once a fire has been started in the stove, a fan is used to pull the pyrolysis vapors out from the bottom of the heating chamber, up the sides between the inner and outer metal cylinders, and in toward the center at the top of the stove. New air is pulled into the stove through the flame front at the top so that there is little oxygen left in the heated gas when it reaches the biomass fuel (see **Figure 15**). The scale of these stoves can range from the very small single-household stoves to much larger stoves that can serve

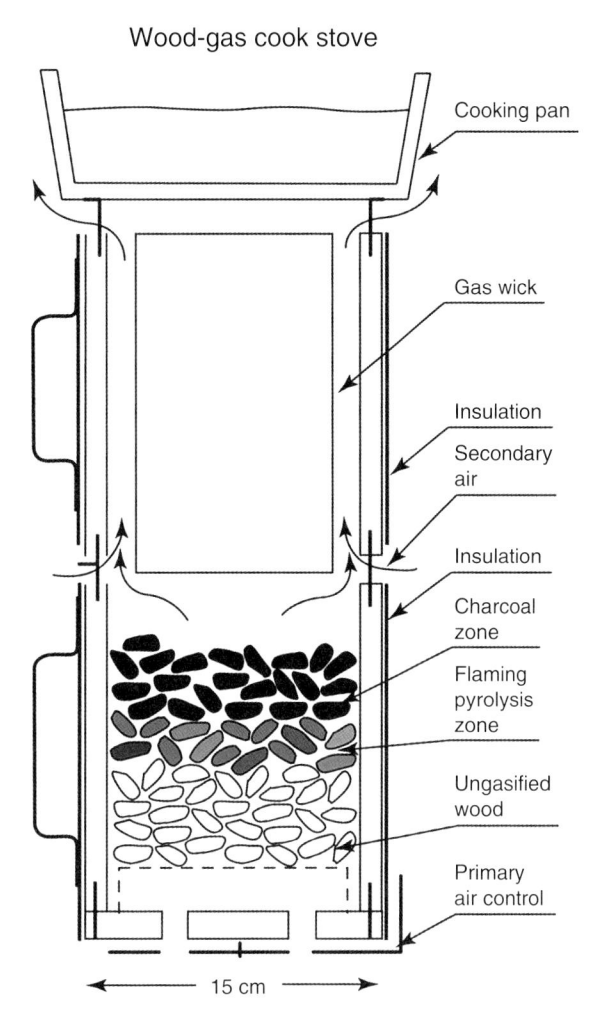

Figure 14 Schematic of a top-lit updraft (TLUD) gasifier wood cook stove (scale = 15 cm). Reproduced with permission from Figure 8.20 in Brown RC (2009) Biochar production technologies. In: Lehmann J and Joseph S (eds.) *Biochar for Environmental Management: Science and Technology.* London: Earthscan.

public buildings such as schools or hospitals; some run only in a batch mode while others can be refilled throughout the process. Both kinds of stoves produce a small amount of char (10–20% of the initial biomass) that remains after the gasification has stopped and that can be applied to nearby fields or gardens. Like other biochars, the amount and properties of this char depend on the feedstock and the reaction conditions such as the temperature reached inside the stove and the length of time the stove was running. These kinds of stoves are very clean-burning (most of the emissions are carbon dioxide and water only) and they are much more efficient (some have > 90% carbon conversion), producing more heat using less fuel and lower quality fuels such as crop residues. The advantages of being able to use crop residues are that less forest has to be cut down and there would be an incentive to collect and pyrolyze crop residues rather than burn them in the fields.

The implementation of biochar production and application systems in developing countries also creates an opportunity for income generation. This income would likely come from carbon credits for avoided emissions (from reforestation or preventing deforestation/in-field crop residue burning) and sequestering biochar. One such program existing today that could be implemented for a biochar or stove–biochar combination project is the clean development mechanism (CDM) program, a program stemming from the Kyoto Protocol that allows developed nations to gain emission reduction credits by funding emission reduction projects in developing countries that would otherwise not have happened. Small biochar producers might organize larger cooperatives and sell carbon credits on the world carbon markets, in addition to selling biochar to local farmers to improve their soils. With efficient stoves, those responsible for collecting fuel and cooking (mainly women) could devote more time and resources to other income-increasing activities such as producing handicrafts to sell or furthering their education.

One criticism of biochar is that its production might encourage deforestation. Another is that production of biochar in inefficient kilns would create air pollution, especially in developing countries where pollution is less regulated. To be sustainable (a key defining quality of biochar), biochars need to be produced from materials that would otherwise decompose (such as forestry slash, dead biomass, crop residues, and urban yard wastes) and that do not compete with food production (i.e., energy crops grown on

Figure 15 Diagram of gas flows in a Lucia Stove from WorldStove. Source: Nathanial Mulcahy, WorldStove, Tortona, Italy.

prime agricultural land). Biochar must be produced in efficient reactors that produce very few or no emissions aside from carbon dioxide and water. For many kiln designs, this can be achieved with proper heat insulation, effective inlet air control and process monitoring, and a type of afterburner system to crack tars and completely combust any remaining carbon monoxide, hydrocarbons, and other gases.

5.18.7 Challenges to Applying Biochar

5.18.7.1 Economics of Alternative Uses

Reaping the many potential benefits from biochar and its coproducts will not happen without overcoming certain challenges. Perhaps the most daunting of these challenges is economic. To be sustainable in a market-driven society, biochar utilization (and the whole thermochemical biorenewable platform) must provide valuable benefits to consumers that can compete with multiple alternatives. As can be seen from the charcoal and activated carbon industries today, there are other and sometimes very high-value alternative uses for chars. For example, future high costs of emissions from coal-burning power plants and metal smelters may drive these industries to obtain their power and heat from charcoal instead, thus diverting chars that might have been applied to soils. Likewise, producers of certain low-ash chars may decide to make more profit by selling the chars as activated carbons for water treatment rather than to farmers or gardeners. Prior to the accumulation of much more biochar field trial data and research regarding biochar mechanisms, demonstrating the economical value of biochar soil application to consumers or making any kind of performance guarantees will be very difficult. Business plans for the large-scale production and sale of biochar, therefore, may need to focus on coproducts such as heat or electricity with more developed markets until such biochar quality and performance information becomes available.

5.18.7.2 Handling

Biochar, like charcoal, is a flammable solid and as such, requires careful handling. According to the UN Hazardous Goods classification system (used to regulate the shipping and handling of potentially dangerous materials), chars are Class 4.2 Spontaneously Combustible Materials, meaning that they can self-heat and even ignite when exposed to air. This classification likely stems from the testing of freshly pyrolyzed materials that have not yet surface oxidized. When such chars are first exposed to the oxygen in the air, the relatively fast surface oxidations that occur release small amounts of heat that catalyze further oxidations (and more heat), which can cause the char to ignite. Some ways to mitigate this risk include making sure that fresh, cooled biochar has been carefully and completely exposed to air prior to shipping, packing biochar in airtight containers or under an inert gas like nitrogen to limit oxygen exposure, and/or mixing char with sufficient water to absorb any produced heat. For storage, biochars should be kept in cool, dry places – preferably in airtight containers – away from heat and ignition sources, sparks, or strong oxidizing chemicals.

The greatest health danger of biochar and the greatest challenge to field application is dust. When inhaled, small char particles can cause respiratory irritation and lung damage. Some biochars, especially those high in alkali ash content, can be irritating to the skin. For this reason, those handling biochar are recommended to use personal protective equipment such as safety glasses, dust masks, and protective clothing. In general, the finer the biochar, the greater the risk of dust. Extra care must be taken around char dust to avoid sparks, which, under certain conditions, could pose an explosion hazard. With regard to biochar field application strategies, several engineering solutions have been suggested, though many have yet to be tested. Among the proposed solutions are mixing biochars with liquids such as manure, fertilizers, or water and using liquid spreading techniques, co-applying biochar with a semi-moist solid such as compost, pelletizing biochar alone or with biodegradable binders, and applying solid biochars using agricultural lime application techniques plus some kind of water spraying mechanism. One potential use for biochar that would include an application component but that has been little explored is the addition of biochar to animal feed, with subsequent soil application of the biochar-rich manure.

Methodology for the soil incorporation of biochar is another area of uncertainty, especially for reduced tillage or no-till management systems. In many cases, biochar is surface applied and then plowed or disked into the soil. For reduced tillage systems, it has been suggested that biochar be applied one time at a relatively high rate and tilled in, after which the field could be returned to its original tillage scheme.

5.18.7.3 Potential Soil/Crop Drawbacks

For most soils, the application of biochar will be beneficial for soil quality and crop yields, with the worst-case scenario being no effect at all. There are three cases, however, where char may produce a negative effect. The first case involves the pH effects of biochar application, especially when very alkaline (pH values around 10), high-ash biochars are used. If adding biochar raises the soil pH too high, certain microbial populations involved in nutrient cycling and the plant availability of certain micronutrients like iron would be adversely affected. The second case is contamination of the soil with heavy metals or other toxins from applying biochar made from inappropriate feedstocks such as municipal wastes containing arsenic, cadmium, lead, and other toxic metals. An example of this would be the pyrolysis of certain treated wood products used in fences or decks. To avoid this problem, questionable feedstocks should be tested prior to use or avoided.

The third case is nitrogen immobilization due to the high ratio of available carbon to available nitrogen in the biochar amendment. When microorganisms are actively growing (i.e., producing more biomass), they need about 1 mol of nitrogen for every 5–10 mol of carbon that they consume. If a source of carbon is added to the soil without sufficient nitrogen, microorganisms must scavenge nitrogen from the soil environment, which can result in little nitrogen being available for plants, which can greatly limit crop growth. In general, an amendment needs to have a C:N ratio that is no higher than about 30 to avoid nitrogen immobilization (the additional C is used for maintenance respiration). Biochars, which are mostly carbon, usually have very high C:N ratios on an elemental composition basis; fortunately, nearly all of this carbon will not be available to microorganisms, meaning that the effective C:N ratio is much lower. If a biochar is not pyrolyzed sufficiently, however, some of the carbon may still be bioavailable and may cause nitrogen immobilization, resulting in short-term negative effects on crop yield. Depending on the magnitude of the carbon overloading, the nitrogen in the microbial biomass will eventually become plant-available again as

Figure 16 An example of nitrogen immobilization by microorganisms: the effect of soil amendment C:N ratio on corn growth in a greenhouse study. Soils used in the study were amended with either corn stover (CS), which had a high available C:N ratio, or carbonized corn stover (CCS), which had a much lower available C:N ratio due to the carbonization process, at application rates of 0.5, 1.0, or 2.0 wt.% of soil. The corn grown on soils amended with the higher amounts of corn stover (total C:N = 71) did worse than that grown on soils amended with the carbonized crop residue (total C:N = 49). Source: Christoph Steiner, Biorefining and Carbon Cycling Center, University of Georgia, USA.

microorganisms die off and the nitrogen is recycled, but by then (a few weeks to a few months later), the plants may not be able to recover. An example of nitrogen immobilization is shown in **Figure 16**. In this study, corn stover and carbonized corn stover (i.e., corn stover biochar) were used as soil amendments in pots growing corn. Both amendments had high C:N ratios but only the corn in the pots with the highest rates of uncarbonized amendment showed signs of nitrogen immobilization (the stunted plant growth in pots with 1.0% and 2.0% by weight of corn stover added).

5.18.8 Future Progress and Development

Future progress in biochar implementation will likely center around addressing the issue of biochar quality standards and performance expectations for development of the market for biochars. As previously mentioned, most companies selling biochar today produce energy as their primary project as they wait for agronomic research data to quantify the value of a given biochar application. As biochar quality varies significantly depending on feedstock and process conditions, the development of some kind of rating system is critical. The IBI currently has an interdisciplinary task force from multiple countries working to draft standards regarding production process sustainability (i.e., a biochar life cycle assessment), characterization methodology, and product labeling. Once this kind of developmental framework is in place, biochar producers, consumers, and policymakers will be able to make more meaningful comparisons between biochars and biochar systems that will influence decisions about what kind of biochar to make, which biochar product to buy, and which biochar systems to support in new legislation. Other critical research areas in the near future will be developing economic models to evaluate and predict the effects of biochar implementation, as well as more fundamental approaches to understand how biochar production conditions and properties are related and the mechanisms influencing biochar's effects on the soil environment.

References

[1] Katzer F (1903) *Grundzüge der Geologie des unteren Amazonasgebietes (das Saates Pará in Brasilien)*. Leipzig: Verlag von Max Weg.
[2] Sombroek WG (1966) *Amazon Soils: A Reconnaissance of the Soils of the Brazilian Amazon Region*. Wageningen: Center for Agricultural Publications and Documentation.
[3] Kondo R (1978) Opal phytoliths, inorganic, biogenic particles in plants and soils. *Japan Agricultural Research Quarterly* 11: 198–203.
[4] Zech W, Pabst E, and Bechtold G (1979) Analytische Kennzeichnung von Terra Preta do Indio. *Mitteilungen der Deutschen Bodenkundlichen Gesellschaft* 29: 709–716.
[5] Glaser B, Haumaier L, Guggenberger G, and Zech W (2001) The 'Terra Preta' phenomenon: A model for sustainable agriculture in the humid tropics. *Naturwissenschaften* 88(1):37–41.
[6] Steiner C, Teixeira W, Lehmann J, *et al.* (2007) Long term effects of manure, charcoal and mineral fertilization on crop production and fertility on a highly weathered Central Amazonian upland soil. *Plant Soil* 291(1): 275–290.
[7] Hammes K, Schmidt MWI, Smernik R, *et al.* (2007) Comparison of quantification methods to measure fire-derived (black/elemental) carbon in soils and sediments using reference materials from soil, water, sediment and the atmosphere. *Global Biogeochemical Cycles* 21: 1–18.
[8] Antal MJ, Allen SG, Dai X, *et al.* (2000) Attainment of the theoretical yield of carbon from biomass. *Industrial & Engineering Chemistry Research* 39(11): 4024–4031.
[9] Cheng C-H, Lehmann J, Thies JE, *et al.* (2006) Oxidation of black carbon by biotic and abiotic processes. *Organic Geochemistry* 37(11): 1477–1488.

Further Reading

[1] Antal MJ and Gronli M (2003) The art, science, and technology of charcoal production. *Industrial & Engineering Chemistry Research* 42(8): 1619–1640.
[2] Gaunt JL and Lehmann J (2008) Energy balance and emissions associated with biochar sequestration and pyrolysis bioenergy production. *Environmental Science & Technology* 42: 4152–4158.
[3] Laird DA, Brown RC, Amonette JE, and Lehmann J (2009) Review of the pyrolysis platform for coproducing bio-oil and biochar. *Biofuels, Bioproducts and Biorefining* 3(5): 547–562.
[4] Lehmann J, Gaunt J, and Rondon M (2006) Bio-char sequestration in terrestrial ecosystems – a review. *Mitigation and Adaptation Strategies for Global Change* 11(2): 395–419.
[5] Lehmann J and Joseph S (eds.) (2009) *Biochar for Environmental Management: Science and Technology*. London: Earthscan.
[6] Masiello CA (2004) New directions in black carbon organic geochemistry. *Marine Chemistry* 92(1–4): 201–213.
[7] Woods WI, Teixeira WG, Lehmann J, *et al.* (2009) *Amazonian Dark Earths: Wim Sombroek's Vision*. London: Springer.

Relevant Websites

http://biocharfund.org – Biochar Fund.
http://www.biochar.org – Biochar.org.
wwww.biochar-international.org – International Biochar Initiative.

5.19 Extracting Additional Value from Biomass

MF Askew, Wolverhampton, UK

© 2012 Elsevier Ltd. All rights reserved.

5.19.1	Introduction	385
5.19.2	The Current Position	387
5.19.3	Future Development – Background	389
5.19.4	The Future: Extending the Envelope by Exploiting Higher Value Metabolites	390
5.19.5	Conclusion	392
References		393
Further Reading		393

5.19.1 Introduction

The concept of using biomass as a feedstock for a wide range of molecules has hardly been exploited at all in the land-based sector of agriculture and only marginally more so in the forestry sector. However, for a number of reasons, it is clear that the same approach could be taken with surplus or processed biomass materials (including outputs from processed foods) as is taken with crude oil whereby a wide range of products are developed from that oil, and according to anecdote, about 80% of the incoming revenue stream is produced by approximately 20% of the fractionated crude oil.

Many years of experience and development have led to general agreement throughout the oil-refining industry that basic crude oil can be split into a small number of major components, and that they in turn can be processed to produce at least 12 other secondary chemical groupings, which in turn produce a wide range of intermediates including biofuels and additives for biofuels, and many nonfuel feedstocks. The latter in turn are used to produce an even wider range of crude oil-derived finished products for the marketplace. This process does pose the basic question as to what is the primary target output, that is, is the primary target of processing a fuel or an added-value product or a range of products and should the production of a fuel or biofuel be the driver for all decision making in the processing chain? In reality, the answer to this fundamental question is probably 'no', which in turn raises the question of rethinking of current processing in the biomass sector, particularly in the manufacture of first-generation biofuels such as rapeseed methyl ester or grain-derived bioethanol, if higher value coproducts are to be developed and marketed. Hence the 'traditional' biorefining process may have energy as the final rather than the primary output (see **Figure 1**).

The experience in land-based industry to date has been that coproducts, or rather vegetable wastes as they are called by many primary manufacturers, have been fed to livestock predominantly. This has occurred in the production of sucrose from sugar beet where wet or dry extracted pulp has been fed directly to livestock or in the dry state incorporated into livestock rations, while stones and soil from the harvested crop have been marketed separately. Some of the products produced from processing of the sugar beet and its extracted sucrose (e.g., factory lime) are sold as ameliorators for soils on-farm. The sale of distillers grains (sometimes called draff) or brewers grains from the production of whisky or beer and pomace from the production of perry or cider has in reality been a way of finding a cheap feed for animals that would use up the 'wastes' from the primary food or industrial production in a way that does not involve significant investment or reprocessing of these so-called wastes. This chapter in no way decries the exploitation of these materials but perhaps highlights the traditional linkages between agricultural produce and the utilization of coproducts from those primary feedstocks on-farm. However, and conversely, in the production of cane sugar, the primary product has been sucrose while the waste has been bagasse, and this has until recently been used almost exclusively as a biomass feedstock for cane refineries, being used as a primary fuel for boilers. With the advent of improved boiler systems and enhanced yields and factory throughput, these uses are declining and new uses for some bagasse are being sought. In this way, opportunities to extract additional value products are emerging.

In forestry, the primary uses of wood have been as a structural material, a fuel, or a feedstock for paper pulp. In the first two cases much of the primary material (e.g., leaves and small branches from trees) has not been exploited to the full extent. However, in the case of paper pulp, then black liquor, for example, has been and is being developed further as a feedstock for further products. Similarly, wood chips from knots and larger pieces of wood in the pulp mill have been used in the production of composites or elsewhere, and in the amenity horticulture sector bark these chips have become a major market.

So to develop further and maximize the economic potential of biomass, the biomass sector has to learn lessons from the crude oil industry and integrate the lessons with existing ways of utilizing 'waste' biomass while introducing additional novelty. It has to be recognized that the key element in developing sustainable products is that there is no waste, only wasted opportunity, and that interestingly, many of the developments of new molecules from biomass do not need new chemistry, but rather application of existing technologies to new scenarios.

Clearly, when sustainability is recognized as a three-component issue, being a function of economic cost, environmental cost, and acceptability and cultural/social factors, the potential benefits of development of additional molecules from an existing feedstock become self-evident.

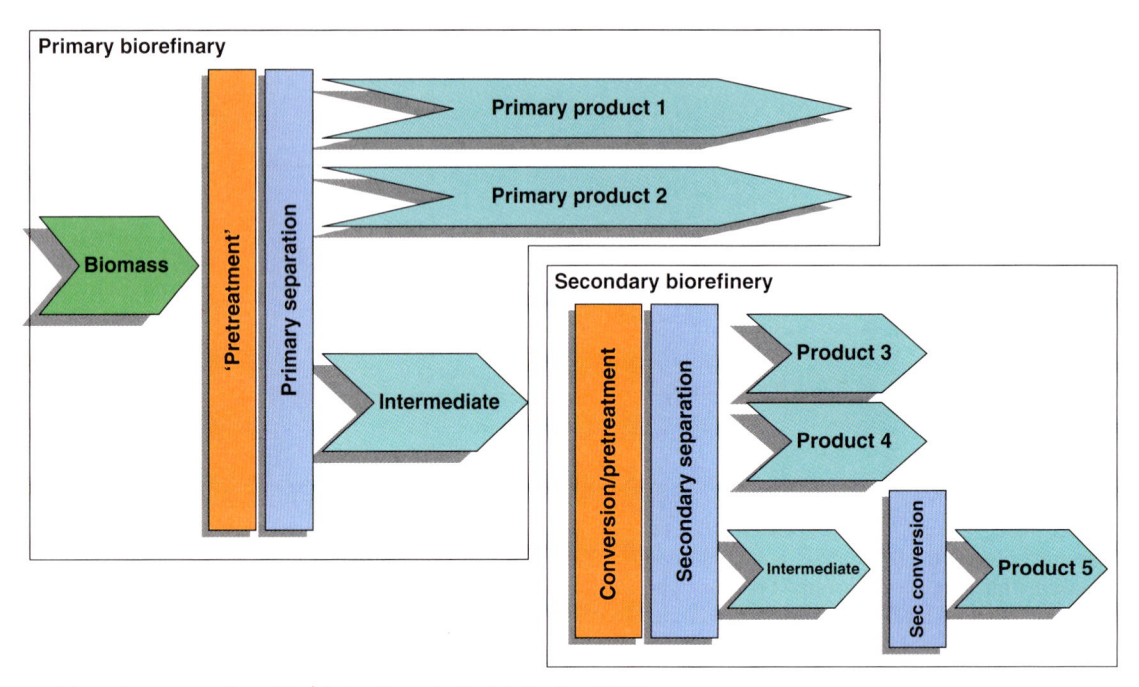

Figure 1 Schematic representation of biorefining. Drawn by Prof. J. Sanders (2006).

Some efforts have been made to identify pathways for total utilization of some crop plants, even though these are not fully operational at present, for instance in wheat, as an example of a major cereal, and in hemp (*Cannabis sativa*), as an example of a primary fiber-producing plant. These are shown in **Figures 2** and **3**.

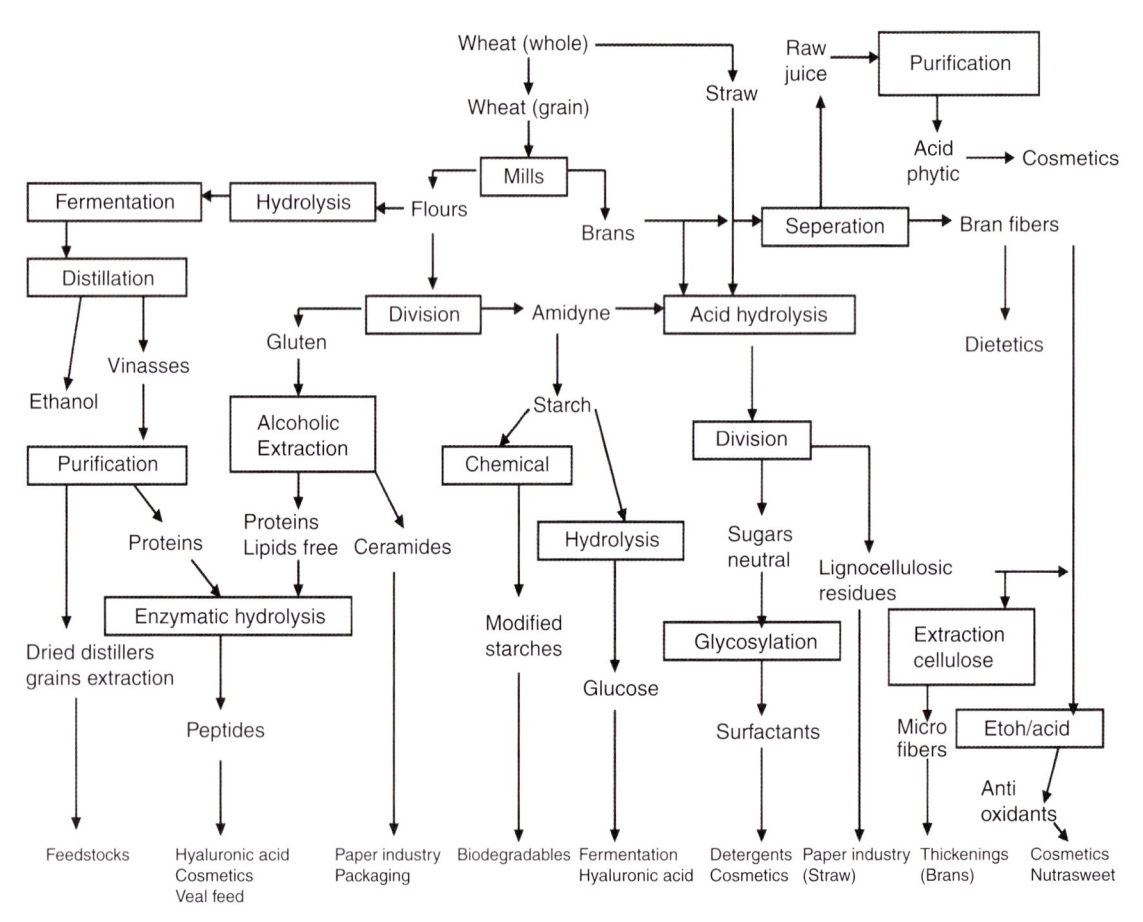

Figure 2 The potential to exploit metabolites of wheat (*Triticum aestivum*). Reproduced from IENICA website (http://www.ienica.net).

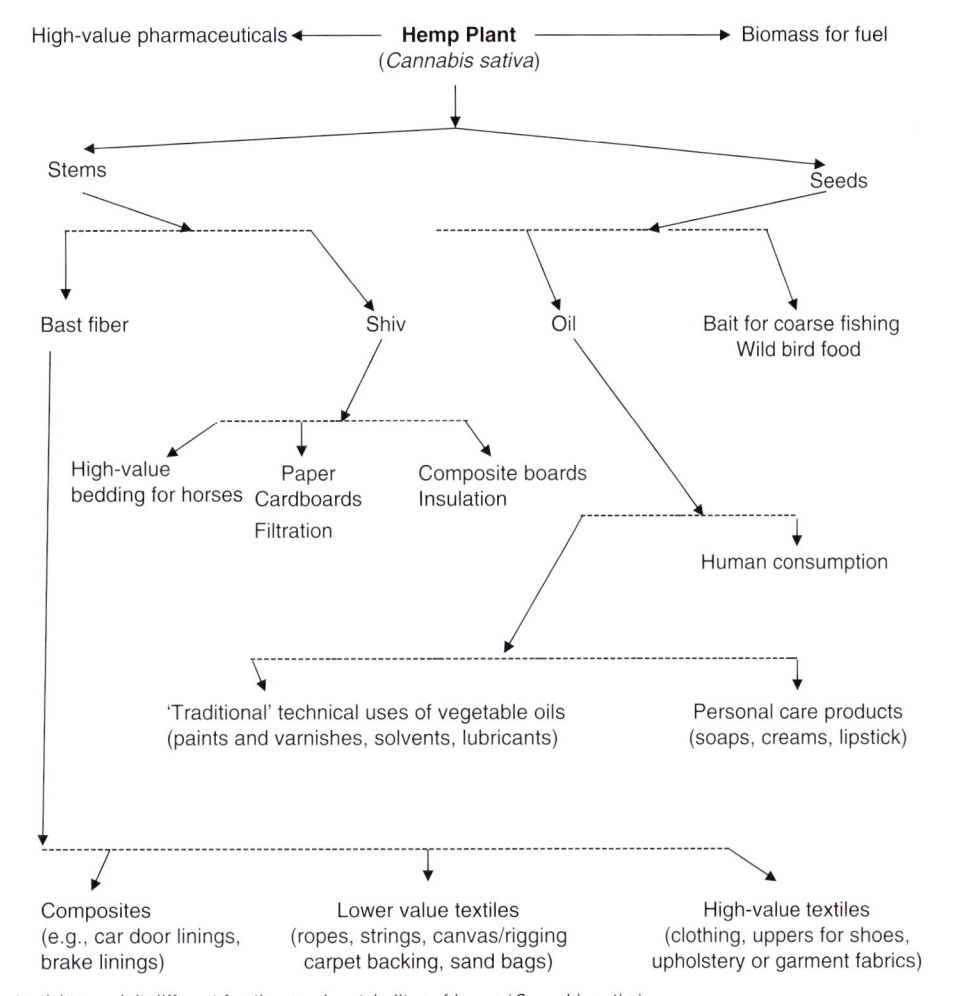

Figure 3 The potential to exploit different fractions and metabolites of hemp (*Cannabis sativa*).

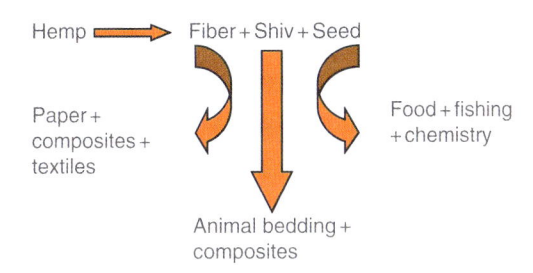

Figure 4 Diagrammatic representation of biofractionation.

Interestingly, the components of hemp are separated as physical entities rather than by chemical fractionation or separation. So this process, physical fractionation, is fundamentally different though equally important as biorefining (**Figure 4**).

5.19.2 The Current Position

Not surprisingly, the marketplace has been the primary driver for exploitation of many plant-based materials. The exploitation has been based hitherto on the need for a primary product from that plant rather than the fully integrated exploitation of that plant's potential. However, research in EU15 and EU27 has confirmed massive markets for sustainable nonenergy bioproducts (IENICA, 2000 and 2003).

Wheat remains as one of the world's major crops (see **Table 1**). It is used both as animal feed and as a basis for bakery products, in particular in the human food sector. In addition, some wheat starch has nonfood or nonfeed uses. Yet the grain component of

Table 1 Production of mainstream cereal crops on a world basis

Crop	Harvest 2005	Harvest 2006	Harvest 2007
Wheat: area (in million hectares)	220	212	214
Wheat: production (in million tonnes)	627.7	605.1	606.0
Maize: area (in million hectares)	147	148	158
Maize: production of grain (in million tonnes)	713.9	706.3	788.1
Paddy rice: area (in million hectares)	155	156	156
Paddy rice: production (in million tonnes)	634.5	641.1	657.4

Note: All data are rounded from more detailed FAO estimates.
Reproduced from FAOstat website.

wheat as expressed by its weight as a proportion of aboveground biomass (termed the harvest index) is approximately 50%. Hence, a significant proportion of the wheat plant remains after harvest. Traditional uses of wheat straw include thatching (specialty thatching wheat cultivars only), animal bedding, packaging for delicate items, and paper production. Inevitably, a proportion of the wheat straw is not harvestable because of practical harvesting difficulties and a proportion must remain in the field and be reintroduced into the field soils to maintain soil nutrient status, friability, stability, and so forth. Hence, only a proportion of the massive wheat straw tonnage is available for novel uses. Biofuel, as second-generation bioethanol, has been suggested as one and clearly that technology is developing at an advanced rate. However, thought should be given to the molecular components of wheat straw, rather than just targeting the lignocelluloses and associated celluloses present there.

Evidence has shown that winter wheat straw in the United Kingdom has the potential to supply a number of high-value products [1]. Initial analyses of wheat straw in the United Kingdom by HTGC-MS (high-temperature gas chromatography-mass spectrometry) reported free fatty acids, fatty alcohols, alkanes, wax esters, sterols, and β-diketones. The melting point of the wheat straw wax identified falls between that of animal-derived lanolin and currently available vegetable waxes, providing a potentially high added value but relatively low tonnage market for some wheat straw. Further developments in extraction procedures have identified the potential for polycosanols, sterols, and long-chain odd-numbered alkanes, which could be extracted in a single-stage extraction process from wheat straw.

Clearly, high-value coproducts can be obtained from an erstwhile waste or at best low-grade biomass. Other evidence suggests that silicon compounds could be extracted from wheat straw and that these would have uses in the water-processing industry. However, the question arises as to whether these procedures to extract high-value molecules should perhaps precede those of bioethanol production from wheat straw. And further, if lignocellulosics are to be a major feedstock for second-generation biofuels to replace gasoline, then thought needs to be given to the method by which lignin is removed from the lignocellulosic molecules and how value is added to it, rather than using it as a heating fuel as occurs frequently at present. Early evidence from Sweden indicates the view held by many chemists that at least in terms of technology, lignin, a complex cyclic molecule, could form the basis for future aromatic chemistry [2].

Oil rapeseed is the third major vegetable oil in the world after soy and palm oil, although its production does not reach anywhere near their levels (see Table 2).

In Europe in particular rapeseed oil has become a key feedstock for the production of biodiesel, a first-generation biofuel. The chemical processes involved are very straightforward and new uses for the large tonnage of low-grade glycerol formed as a coproduct are being examined. However, there is growing evidence that rapeseed oil has significant beneficial effects on human health, especially when ingested as cold-pressed oil rapeseed. Cold pressing should take place at not more than 40 °C. The author's own estimates suggest it to be the best vegetable oil in terms of human health, being on a par with extra virgin, cold-pressed olive oil, but potentially cheaper and in much greater supply.

In the manufacture of biodiesel from rapeseed at present, oil extraction begins with extrusion followed by hexane extraction of the residual oily meal. The final residual hexane-extracted meal has a very low oil content and is fed to livestock as a proteinaceous

Table 2 Area and production of major oilseed crops on a world basis

Crop	Harvest 2005	Harvest 2006	Harvest 2007
Soybean: area (in million hectares)	92.5	95.2	90.1
Soybean: production (in million tonnes)	214.3	218.4	219.5
Oil palm (as oil palm fruit): area (in million hectares)	12.9	13.2	13.9
Oil palm (as oil palm fruit): production (in million tonnes)	181.9	195.0	192.6
Rapeseed: area (in million hectares)	27.7	27.4	29.7
Rapeseed: production (in million tonnes)	50.0	48.0	51.4

Note: All data are rounded from more detailed FAO statistics.
Reproduced from FAOstat website.

food, partially substituting for soybean meal. Unfortunately, the processes used for current oilseed extraction are not at all conducive to the development of virgin cold-pressed oil rapeseed for human consumption or for the extraction of high-value molecules from the residual rapeseed meal. Hence a number of questions arise, namely, is it prudent to use an oil with proven human health benefits primarily as a feedstock for a lower value biofuel to replace diesel oil? Also, if the development of cold-pressed oil rapeseed is to continue, and the marketplace in a number of European Union (EU) member states suggests it will, then current processing of bulk rapeseed may need to be revised and this in turn would lead to the potential to exploit more high-value molecules from the meal, such as albumins and associated feedstocks for adhesives [3, 4] and even plant or health protection products such as derivatives of glucosinolates.

While the first example cited above emanated from the extended use of wheat straw, its concepts could have enormous impact on the forestry and woodland biomass sectors and assist in their continued economic development especially in nontropical areas. Evidence to support this view was confirmed in studies on 12 main tree species in the United Kingdom undertaken for UK Forestry Commission by Central Science Laboratory, York, UK (now FERA) [5]. Fundamentally this study indicated that large numbers of molecules had been identified in the tree species concerned and that few had been extracted commercially.

While the current major broad-acre crops have been used as examples above, over time and especially because of climate change and the need to adapt cropping to environmental protection and avoidance of erosion, while trying to conserve water, grassland will become a major land user of the future on a worldwide scale. Potential yield from grassland is not well exploited, with estimates suggesting only 33% of the yield potential being achieved [6]. However, with improved technology and application to production, up to 50 million tonnes of grain currently being used as animal feed could be released for new uses (Riveros). This would offer excellent opportunities for industrial use and at the same time, the grassland itself, where not grazed (e.g., in areas suffering from seasonal inundation), would offer a feedstock for high-value metabolites as well as fibers for anaerobic digestion or biofuel use.

5.19.3 Future Development – Background

While the opportunities for exploiting high-value metabolites from plant materials are many, little progress has been made to date except in a few cases like starch production or the extraction of anticancer drugs from Californian yew.

First there is the issue of the marketplace itself and the use to which the primary biomass may be put. As an example, in EU countries, *Miscanthus* species are grown, initially as a feedstock for heat or electricity generation. However, from the growers' perspective, these bulk uses are not the most profitable. Evidence accrued informally by Turley showed that most alternative uses of *Miscanthus* provided a much higher return at the farm gate than did power generation (see **Table 3**).

Hence the issue in this instance is not one of adding value to biomass for fuel, but substituting a more profitable market *in toto*. Fortunately, this is an exception rather than a normal opportunity. Nonetheless, other constraints to exploitation of secondary or high-value primary metabolites exist in industry and in the investor's mind.

The IENICA project (2000) identified major markets for many plant products, yet few have been developed as already reported. One key reason for lack of development has been that many primary products from land-based industry are bulky and relatively expensive to transport. Furthermore, they occur in relatively small lots and, being biological products, have a degree of variability in terms of yield and composition. Interestingly though, the IENICA project identified a number of nontechnical/scientific issues that contribute to slow development.

These included

- lack of awareness of opportunities by both the general public and industrial users,
- a reluctance to change from proven processing technologies from other feedstocks, frequently nonsustainable feedstocks,
- concerns over the costs of retooling to utilize new feedstocks,
- concerns that investors would be exposed to higher risks than with proven technologies, and
- absence of any coherent or robust supply chain for much biomass.

Table 3 An example of conflict between markets for one crop, *Miscanthus*

Use	Value[a] (£ sterling per tonne)
Power generation	20–40
Equine bedding	45–70
Bagged equine bedding	160–200
Organic straw	70
Industrial use/composites	70

[a]Approximate values for different uses of the same crop.
Reproduced from Askew MF (2005) Quoting unpublished data from Turley. In: McGilloway DA (ed.) *Grassland: A Global Resource*. Wageningen Academic Publishers [7].

Since the IENICA report was published, further concern has been expressed by investors over investment in the renewables sector in totality due to a perceived lack of coherence between different government policies and the fact that many polices have a relatively short life span, whereas investments have a significantly longer life span for repayment.

5.19.4 The Future: Extending the Envelope by Exploiting Higher Value Metabolites

While there is no one fundamental route to the identification and exploitation of higher value metabolites from biomass feedstocks, a number of options can be used to identify the most likely opportunities.

First there are several websites that give indications of occurrence of metabolites in plants. These include, for example, Dr. Duke's Phytochemical and Ethnobotanical Databases (http://www.ars-grin.gov) or http://tree-chemicals.csl.gov.uk, the latter being a database produced from the work of Turley and others as quoted above. However, it is important to recognize that these are not infallible and that previously unreported molecules can occur at significant levels in plant material, as reported by Hunt [8] in his studies on heather (*Calluna vulgaris*) and other associated *Erica* species. Similarly, in many plant species, the occurrence of metabolites has been characterized at a particular time in the physiological life of the plant, most commonly at physiological maturity, and could therefore be different at other stages of the plant's growth.

From a perspective of extraction procedures, the approach should be to develop a matrix of extraction procedures that exist in chemistry at present, including supercritical CO_2 (as a useful way of removing high-value molecules without any environmental risk) against the groups of molecules of similar structure and activity as shown in concept in **Table** 4. This shows what could be extracted in totality and by which extraction procedure.

Further elucidation of value and then market is needed. Again a matrix approach can be used, with the values of the extracted metabolites being developed within the boxes in the matrix, by calculating the product of value per unit weight against its occurrence in the plant material and then calculating the gross value by market price of the molecule (see **Table** 5).

From this gross income can be calculated the net return by deducting production and other costs to market. However, it is crucial to note that many high-value molecules have relatively small markets in terms of tonnage and estimates of market must be made to ensure reality in development.

Where more than one molecular group will be extracted by a particular extraction process, a judgment may be needed about which is the more important molecule or, if more than one is to be exploited then additional separation and purification costs may be incurred. Furthermore, decisions will need to be made as to which molecules to extract first from the energy-bound biomass, bearing in mind that the extraction procedures for one group of molecules may destroy or denature others.

On many occasions, the commercial exploitation of an extracted molecule may be limited by regulation. This is especially so with pharmaceuticals. The identification and likely activity of molecules can be predicted in many ways but full toxicity testing and assessment of long-term effects and side effects will be needed for registration of pharmaceuticals. Undoubtedly, such testing is extremely expensive and unfortunately with many pure plant products the pharmaceutical so identified may not be able to be protected by patents or other intellectual property mechanisms although extraction procedures and purification techniques may be. Hence investment may not necessarily be appropriate to develop such an opportunity.

In the case of the UK study on tree metabolites referred to above, the number of original papers identified in the study (>37 000) and the subsequent list of potential metabolites reported in them was immense. A primary schematic approach to exploitation of molecules found in this study is shown in **Figure** 5.

Table 4 Developing a matrix to identify extractives and extraction procedures from a given feedstock

Molecular groups extracted	*Extraction 1*	*Extraction 2*	*Extraction 3*	*Extraction 4*
Group A	Yes	No	Yes	Yes
Group B	Yes	No	No	Yes
Group C	No	Yes	No	Yes
Group D	No	No	Yes	No

Table 5 Developing a simple matrix to identify highest gross return from various extractions of a particular feedstock

Extraction method	*Extract 1*	*Extract 2*	*Extract 3*	*Extract 4*
Molecular group A	£X		£Q	
Molecular group B	£Y	£Z		£H
Molecular group C			£P	£J
Molecular group D	£K	£K		

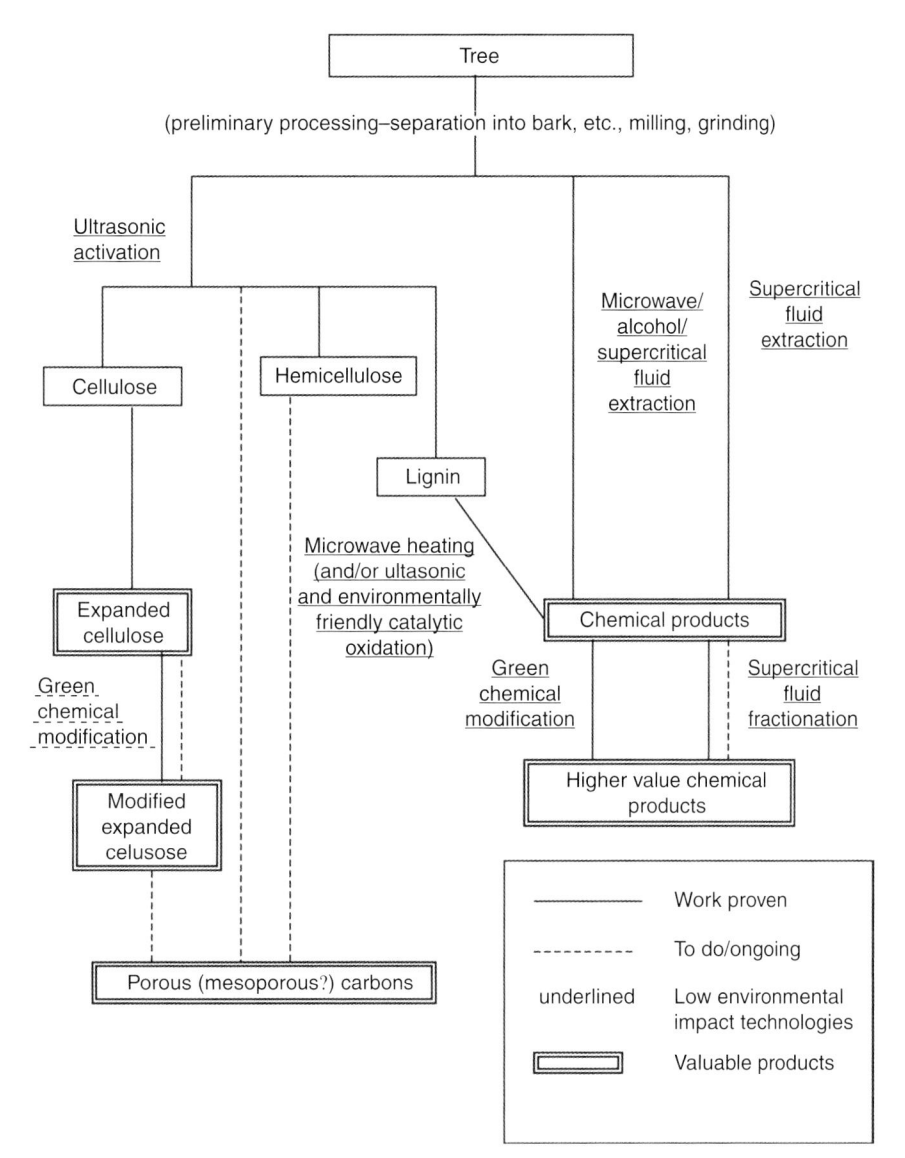

Figure 5 Roadmap for extraction of metabolites from some tree species. Reproduced from Turley DB, Chaudhry QM, Watkins RW, et al. (2006) Chemical products from temperate forest tree species – Developing strategies for exploitation. *Industrial Crops and Products* 24: 238–243 [9].

As a consequence computer-aided quantitative structure–activity relationship modeling was used to assist in identifying likely modes of activity of molecules identified in the study. Obviously this procedure creates a sound basis for selecting some high-value molecules from biomass and is already in use commercially in industry where selections are made to develop sweeteners, pharmaceuticals, catalysts, pesticides, and so on.

Some small-scale crops, for example herbs, produce a range of molecules or extracts that are well established in the marketplace. Development, especially if cost is high, of replacements from new biomass is unlikely to be easy because of the conservative nature of that market and its buyers at wholesale and retail levels. Also, the marketplace has already identified the link between the extract or essence with a particular plant and changing that perception is difficult to achieve. Furthermore, care is needed in selecting the correct chemotype, where otherwise morphologically identical plants within one variety have differing chemical constitutions (as opposed to plant species and variety being wholly genetically and phenotypically identical), and in harvesting, where time of harvesting can affect the metabolites present in the plant.

A further method for developing biomass-derived options to replace fossil oil applications has been developed by Sanders in the Netherlands (informal discussions in the BECOTEPS Workshop, Brussels, 2009 [2]). In this instance, the approach has been to apply the biomass-derived molecule to replace an existing intermediate in a chemical process and also reduce the number of steps in that process. In both instances, such an approach should lead to enhanced opportunities for sustainability.

Figure 6 High-value fashion items from cellulose obtained from the beech tree.

High-value molecules are not necessarily uncommon molecules; for example, cellulose is a very common molecule and is used as a bulk feedstock in papermaking. However, at the same time, very high-value materials can be prepared from cellulose from hardwood-based feedstocks, for example, beech (*Fagus sylvatica*) or *Eucalyptus* species, which is converted into a fine fabric for garments by an Austrian company in Vienna (see **Figure 6**).

5.19.5 Conclusion

Clearly there are a multitude of uses to which the various components of biomass can be put to. They may vary according to the composition of the plant, which in itself will be modified by physiological age, climate/$G \times E$ (genotype by environment) interaction, and other issues.

If the challenge is to add value to biomass initially intended for biofuel production, then clearly the longer term biofuels need to be identified. While there are no firm guidelines in this instance, it is fair to presume that the use of first-generation biofuels as biodiesel (a methyl ester) or as a grain-derived bioethanol is not likely to continue in the long term. Second-generation biofuels, especially using bulk lignocellulosic feedstocks, will develop further but it seems that economics and issues of sustainability will together form a basis for moving to the biorefining of biomass, a process whereby chemistry meets land-based industry and optimizes the output from a particular biomass.

In this scenario, the need is for the components of the biomass to be known and the optimal extraction procedures for their extraction and later commercialization to be developed. This approach has the advantage of being versatile in that should biomass for fuel cease to be an imperative or a policy target, the biorefining process would stand alone substantively and supply 'the other markets'. With respect to biofuel policy, it is interesting to note the change in emphasis that has occurred in the past 5 years where the focus has moved to renewable fuels as opposed to biorenewable fuels and in this instance hydrogen-fueled vehicles and electric vehicles are now coming into vogue. The likely impact of this change may be to throw the emphasis back onto developing and exploiting the most valuable molecules found in biomass but not necessarily biomass for fuel [10].

References

[1] Deswarte FEI (2006) Extraction of High Value Molecules from Wheat Straw (*Triticum aestivum*). PhD Thesis, University of York.
[2] BECOTEPS (2009) Individual comments made by experts in a non-food products workshop organised under the framework of the BECOTEPS project (The Bio-Economy ETPs EU project). To be formally published in the future, as a formal White Paper.
[3] Atterby H, Larre C, Chaudhry QM, *et al.* (2003) Isolation and characterisation of certain bioactive proteins from de-oiled rapeseed meal. In: Sorensen H (ed.) *Proceedings of the 11th International Rapeseed Congress 'Towards Enhanced Value of Cruciferous Oilseed Crops by Optimal Production and Use of the High Quality Seed Components'.* 6–10 July. Copenhagen, Denmark: The Royal Veterinary and Agricultural University.
[4] Malabat C, Atterby H, Chaudhry Q, *et al.* (2003) Genetic variability of rapeseed protein composition. In: Sorensen H (ed.) *Proceedings of the 11th International Rapeseed Congress*, pp. 205–208. 6–10 July. Copenhagen, Denmark: The Royal Veterinary and Agricultural University.
[5] Watkins RW and Turley DB (2003) A review of current knowledge on the economic potential of chemical products from main commercial tree species in U.K. *Report for UK Forestry Commission and Government Industry Forum for Industrial Crop Applications*, 256pp. http://tree-chemicals.csl.gov.uk.
[6] Riveros F (undated) *FAO Grassland Group Document.* http://www.fao.org/ag/AGP/AGPC/doc/PUBLICAT/GRASSLAND/3.pdf.
[7] Askew MF (2005) Quoting unpublished data from Turley. In: McGilloway DA (ed.) *Grassland: A Global Resource*, pp. 179–189. Wageningen, The Netherlands: Wageningen Academic Publishers.
[8] Hunt AJ (2006) The Extraction of High Value Chemicals from Heather (*Calluna vulgaris*). PhD Thesis, University of York.
[9] Turley DB, Chaudhry QM, Watkins RW, *et al.* (2006) Chemical products from temperate forest tree species – Developing strategies for exploitation. *Industrial Crops and Products* 24: 238–243.
[10] Enhance. The enhance project funded under EU funding as project QLRT-1999-01442. Enhance: Green chemicals and biopolymers from rapeseed meal with enhanced end-performances. http://www.biomatnet.org/secure/FP5/S1186.htm.

Further Reading

[1] Brown RC (undated) *The Future of Biorefining Biomass*, 13pp. USA: Iowa State University.
[2] Carvalheiro F, Duarte LC, and Girio FM (2008) Hemicellulose biorefineries: A review on biomass pretreatments. *Journal of Scientific and Industrial Research* 67: 849–864.
[3] De Jong E (undated) Task 42 biorefineries. Co-production of fuels, chemicals, power and materials from biomass. An occasional paper published by IEA Bioenergy.
[4] den Uil H, Mozzafarian H, van Ree R, *et al.* (undated) High efficiency biorefinery concepts. An occasional publication on behalf of the European Commission by the Partners of Bioenergy Network of Excellence.
[5] Domsjo Biorefinery (undated) Occasional paper produced by the Domsjo Biorefinery. Sweden.
[6] Epobio Reports from the EPOBIO project funded under Framework Programme 6 of EU funding. Project SSPE-CT-2005-022681.
[7] European Commission, Brussels (2006) *European Conference on Biorefining*. Helsinki, Finland. http://ec.europa.eu/research/energy/gp/gp_events/biorefining/article_3764_en.htm
[8] Jungmeier G, Lingitz A, and Spitzer J (undated) Biofuel production from wood. Feasibility study for a biorefinery in the Austrian province of Styria. Informal paper published on behalf of European Commission by Joanneum Research, Graz, Austria.
[9] Sanders J, Scott E, and Mooilbrock H (undated). Biorefinery, the bridge between agriculture and chemistry, 5pp. An occasional paper from the Department of Valorisation of Plant Production Chains, Wageningen University and Research Centre, Wageningen, The Netherlands.

Relevant Website

http://www.biomatnet.org – Database of projects funded under various European Commission R&D programmes.

5.20 Biomass to Chemicals

A Kazmi and J Clark, University of York, York, UK

© 2012 Elsevier Ltd. All rights reserved.

5.20.1	Introduction	395
5.20.2	Biodiesel: Conversion of Glycerine Coproduct and Other Side Streams	396
5.20.2.1	Introduction	396
5.20.2.2	Biodiesel Production without the By-Product Glycerol	396
5.20.2.3	Increasing the Value of Glycerol	396
5.20.2.3.1	Purification of crude glycerol	396
5.20.2.3.2	Current uses of glycerol	397
5.20.2.4	Chemicals from Glycerol	398
5.20.2.4.1	Recent reviews	398
5.20.2.4.2	Example 1: Citric acid	399
5.20.2.4.3	Example 2: Propylene glycol	399
5.20.3	Fuels from Fermentation Processes: Use of Biomass Raw Material, Fuel Production Intermediates, and Coproducts for Chemical Production	400
5.20.3.1	Lignocellulosic Feedstocks for Chemical Production	400
5.20.3.1.1	Converting cellulose to sugars	400
5.20.3.1.2	Sugars to chemicals	400
5.20.3.2	Lignin: Depolymerization or Direct Use?	401
5.20.3.2.1	The disassembly of lignin	401
5.20.3.2.2	Uses of lignin	404
5.20.4	Use of Bio-Alcohols as Chemicals and Chemical Intermediates	404
5.20.4.1	Ethyl Acetate	405
5.20.4.2	Single-Walled Carbon Nanotubes	405
5.20.4.3	Hydrogen	406
5.20.4.4	Ethanol Fuel Cells	406
5.20.5	Biochar (Solid Biofuel): Chemicals from Pyrolysis Oil	406
5.20.5.1	Comparison of Major Techniques	406
5.20.5.2	Polycyclic Aromatic Hydrocarbons	407
5.20.5.3	Fabricated Microwave Pyrolysis	407
5.20.6	Conclusions and Future Prospects	408
References		409

Glossary

Bioethanol Ethanol derived from biomass and used as fuel.
Biomass Any material which has been or is alive. In this field of biorefineries, biomass normally refers to agricultural materials.
Biorefinery A concept which involves using biomass as a feedback to produce chemicals, materials and energy using various processes.

Fermentation A process involving a micro-organism which converts an organic material into other chemicals.
Green chemistry Chemistry using sustainable and environmentally friendly processes and materials.
Pyrolysis The breakdown of chemical structures using an energy source in the absence of oxygen.

5.20.1 Introduction

Humans have relied on fuel since the beginning of civilization, unlike any other creature in this world. It was very fortunate that early human beings had an abundant source of fuel in the form of wood, which was used for many millennia to propagate society. As this resource dwindled, humans searched for fuel underneath the earth, and the discovery of fossil fuels not only provided a colossal amount of fuel, but also an abundant source of chemicals, which the society would use to nourish its demand for a growing population and an increasing standard of living.

However, in the process of manufacturing chemicals, industry has relied on nonrenewable resources and low-efficiency and highly wasteful methods. The broad focus of the principles of green chemistry is to avoid using such conventional methods and reduce the environmental impact for a sustainable future. A major problem the world currently faces is the disposal of waste, and the green chemistry vision primarily is that waste generation should be prevented and if not possible then valorization methods should be implemented. One method of reducing waste is to incorporate all materials used into a final usable product. In any chemical reaction or processing technology, the energy requirements should be rationalized and minimized. Energy costs have always been accounted for in financial balance sheets; however, it will not be long before CO_2 is accounted for in life cycle analysis (LCA) of processes and products. Optimizing reactions and processes to work at ambient temperature and pressure would decrease the environmental impact. In many cases, the environmental impact over the life cycle can be further improved if the feedstock is a renewable resource and the final product biodegradable.

This chapter considers chemical production from biodiesel by-products and then moves on to the production of chemicals from lignocellulosic materials derived from bioethanol supply chains and elsewhere. Additional opportunities are then explored by considering the use of bioethanol as a commodity chemical feedstock, a specialty chemical feedstock, and an electrochemical feedstock. The chapter concludes by looking at the prospects for recovering useful chemical feedstocks from the products produced when biomass is pyrolyzed.

5.20.2 Biodiesel: Conversion of Glycerine Coproduct and Other Side Streams

5.20.2.1 Introduction

The transesterification of triglycerides produces three molecules of fatty acid methyl esters (FAMEs) and a molecule of glycerol. FAME is also known as biodiesel and can be used in conventional diesel engines. Triglycerides are found in natural oils such as palm, rapeseed, or sunflower oil and in animal fat. A large industry has now developed that uses such resources to manufacture diesel and according to the 'IEA task 38' report Germany is the world's largest producer with a 29% share, which equates to 3.2 billion liters per annum worldwide [1]. The biodiesel market is highly dependent on the price of mineral diesel and therefore low crude oil prices can make mineral diesel so cheap that biodiesel is no longer economically viable. Furthermore, the production of biodiesel is not very efficient and green because the final mixture requires being separated and washed several times to meet fuel standards. Waste products such as salts add to the glycerol waste, making disposal a significant cost to the company. Therefore, it is important to utilize such materials and instead of being a cost, they could generate income for a company. Pure glycerol itself can be sold to various industries and any derivatization to produce value-added products could significantly enhance the economics. However, if novel routes to biodiesel are developed that yield no glycerol by-products, then many of the above issues would be resolved.

5.20.2.2 Biodiesel Production without the By-Product Glycerol

Notari and Rivetti [2] have shown that biofuels can be produced without glycerol by using dimethyl carbonate as a reactant. The transesterification of triglycerides with dimethyl carbonate [3–5] produces a mixture of three molecules of FAMEs and one molecule of glycerol carbonate, which is suitable for use in diesel engines. The use of enzyme technology, which can be expensive, to produce biodiesel has become popular due to its more environmentally friendly credentials and has also been used to produce biodiesel without any glycerol by-product. Using lipases, triglycerides can be converted to three molecules of esters plus one molecule of monoglyceride (MG) [6] or glycerol triacetate [7]. All of these processes are still at the research stage and no significant commercial developments have taken place. Therefore, currently and in the foreseeable future, there may continue to be a glycerol glut, which needs to be dealt with.

5.20.2.3 Increasing the Value of Glycerol

5.20.2.3.1 Purification of crude glycerol

Glycerine produced from the conventional biodiesel manufacturing process is far from pure and can contain several impurities ranging from ash to metals (Table 1).

The quality of glycerol in glycerine can be lowered when using less clean feedstocks such as food waste. Removing such impurities is expensive, so the final product, whether pure glycerol or a derivative, must have high value for the purification process to be cost-effective.

Table 1 Typical composition of the glycerol phase from biodiesel manufacturer [8]

Content	Amount	Content	Amount
Glycerol content	77–90%	Na	0.4–20 g kg^{-1}
Ash content	3.5–7%	K	0.03–40 g kg^{-1}
Moisture content	0.1–13.5%	Ca	0.1–65 mg kg^{-1}
3-Monopropylenediol	Trace	Mg	0.02–55 mg kg^{-1}
Methanol	0.01–3%	Fe	0.1–30 mg kg^{-1}
Organic, non-glycerol	1.6–7.5%	Mn	<0.5 mg kg^{-1}
Sulfate	0.01–1.04%	Acetate	0.01–6.0%
Phosphate	0.02–1.45%		

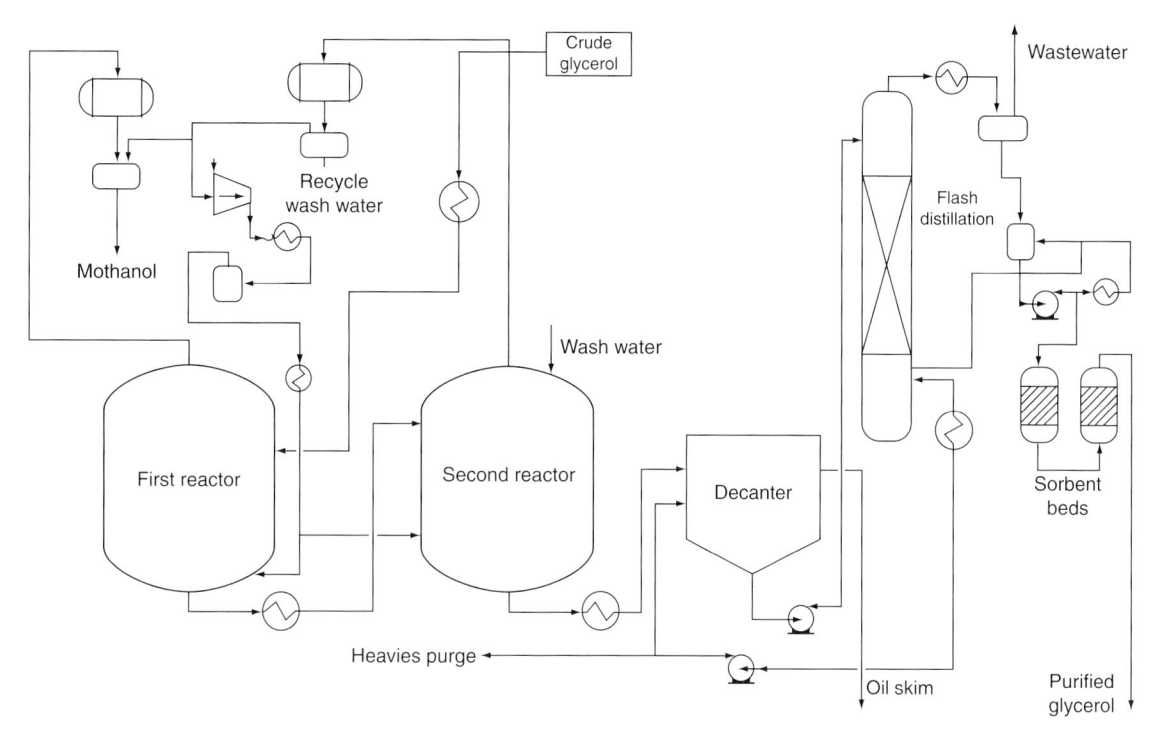

Figure 1 Novel glycerol purification process. Source: Aiken JE (2007) Purification of Glycerol. US Patent 7,126,032 B1.

In order to remove the soap and base catalyst, acid is added, which results in free fatty acids and salt. The methanol can be removed using falling film evaporators, which can purify glycerol to up to 85%. In order to increase the purity to 99.5%, other techniques such as adsorption, vacuum distillation, and ion exchange could be used [9].

In 2006, a novel process was developed to purify crude glycerol by Aiken [10] involving five steps culminating in 99.5% pure glycerol. The first step involves a heated reactor in which methyl esters are reacted with glycerol to produce glycerides and methanol. The hot liquid stream is then passed on to a second reactor, which is also heated to 120–160 °C and where any remaining methyl esters are converted to glycerides and methanol. A decanter is used to separate the oil layer and the remaining glycerol mixture is fed into a flash distillation column operating at a temperature of 185 °C and a pressure of 5–20 mmHg. The refined glycerol is then passed through adsorbents such as activated carbons, ion exchange resins, and molecular sieves to remove trace impurities and color. The schematic of the processes involved is shown in **Figure 1**.

Such purification processes increase the costs of the product; an alternative strategy is to conduct chemistry on the pure glycerine stream to produce more valuable derivatives.

5.20.2.3.2 Current uses of glycerol

Glycerol has been known since 2800 BC mainly as a by-product of soap production [11]. Currently, glycerol has numerous applications in the personal care, food, polyol, alkyd resin, tobacco, detergent, cellophane, explosives, and pharmaceutical industries [12]. Leffingwell and Lesser [13] identified 1582 applications for glycerol in 1945; however, in recent times, many glycerol production plants are closing and new plants, utilizing glycerol as a raw material, are opening [14].

Glycerol is used as a raw material for the production of flexible and rigid polyurethane foams. It is known to provide properties such as flexibility, pliability, and toughness in surface coatings and paint, regenerated cellulose films, meat casings, and special quality papers. Glycerol has the ability to absorb moisture from the atmosphere and is therefore used in many adhesives and glues to prevent early drying. In food applications, glycerol, which is nontoxic, is used as a solvent, sweetener, and preservative. Many polyols such as sorbitol, mannitol, and maltitol are used as sugar-free sweeteners; however, they are facing significant competition from glycerol. Glycerol has similar sweetness to sucrose and has the same energy as sugar. Furthermore, it does not raise blood sugar levels and does not feed plaque bacteria. Glycerol is used as an emollient, humectant, solvent, and lubricant in many products in the personal care industry such as toothpaste, mouthwashes, shaving cream, and soaps [15].

Furthermore, due to its hygroscopic properties glycerol is used in the pharmaceutical industry to prevent the drying of creams and ointments. It is also sprayed on tobacco to prevent disintegration due to dryness. As a levigating agent it reduces the particle size of drug powder and acts as a plasticizer in coatings used for tablets and beads. Although glycerol has several applications in its pure form, chemical derivatization could offer significantly more value.

5.20.2.4 Chemicals from Glycerol

The production of chemicals from glycerol is not only an economical advantage but also an environmental one as the process avoids the production of a 'waste' material, which complies with the principles of green chemistry. Furthermore, the derivatization of glycerol to high-value chemicals must be done with the principles of green chemistry in mind.

5.20.2.4.1 Recent reviews
5.20.2.4.1(i) Chemical methods

A detailed review of the glycerol transforming processes and applications is found in *The Future of Glycerol: New Usages for a Versatile Raw Material* authored by Pagliaro and Rossi [15]. The book was published in 2008 and focuses on key chemical and biochemical transformations with detailed processing conditions. In the book, relevant information on sustainability and economics of glycerol and biofuel production is also discussed. The detailed synthetic chemistry involved in the transforming processes has been reviewed by Behr *et al.* [16] in their paper titled 'Improved utilisation of renewable resources: New important derivatives of glycerol'.

A more detailed review on the chemicals that can be derived from glycerol was conducted in 2008 by Zheng *et al.* [17] in 'Commodity chemicals derived from glycerol, an important biorefinery feedstock'. Many important chemicals are identified that can be produced from glycerol-derived platform chemicals and their respective industrial applications are discussed. Furthermore, the review maps the reaction pathways of a glycerol-derived platform chemical which can form many other commodity chemicals that are not easily identifiable. Some of the important commodity chemicals identified include acrolein, dichloropropanol, epichlorohydrin, dihydroxyacetone, 1,3-propanediol, 1,2-propanediol, glycerol carbonate, diacylglycerol (DAG), MG, oxygenate fuels, glyceric acid, tartronic acid, and mesoxalic acid.

5.20.2.4.1(ii) Biochemical methods

Biochemical methods can be employed to transform glycerol into commodity chemicals and a review in 2007 by Yazdani and Gonzalez [18] titled 'Anaerobic fermentation of glycerol: a path to economic viability for the biofuels industry' discusses this research. For some transformations, a detailed description of the processes involved is shown including the overall production costs as shown in **Figure 2**.

Some of the important commodity chemicals produced using anaerobic fermentation include succinic acid, 1,3-propanediol, propionic acid, formic acid, butanol, and ethanol. A recent paper by Silva *et al.* [19] reviews glycerol as a source for industrial microbiology. The review identifies microbial reaction pathways for producing many chemicals from glycerol-derived platform chemicals and an example is shown in **Figure 3**.

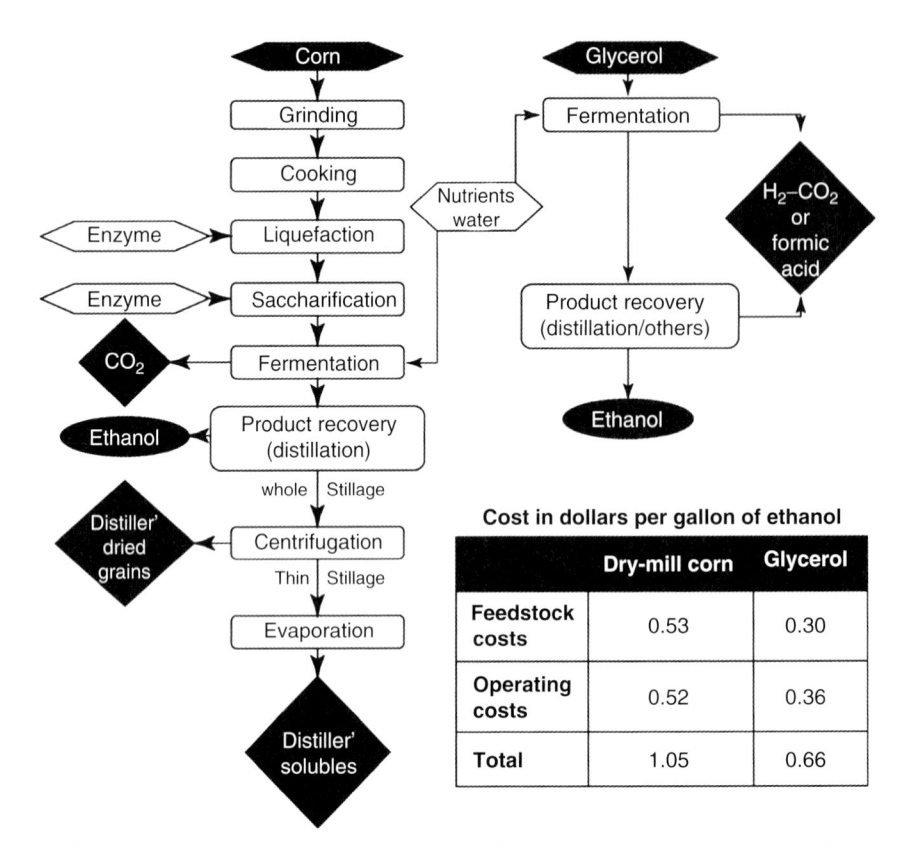

Cost in dollars per gallon of ethanol

	Dry-mill corn	Glycerol
Feedstock costs	0.53	0.30
Operating costs	0.52	0.36
Total	1.05	0.66

Figure 2 Comparison of ethanol production from corn-derived sugars (dry grind ethanol) with ethanol production from glycerol. Source: Yazdani S and Gonzalez R (2007) Anaerobic fermentation of glycerol: A path to economic viability for the biofuels industry. *Current Opinion in Biotechnology* 18: 213–219.

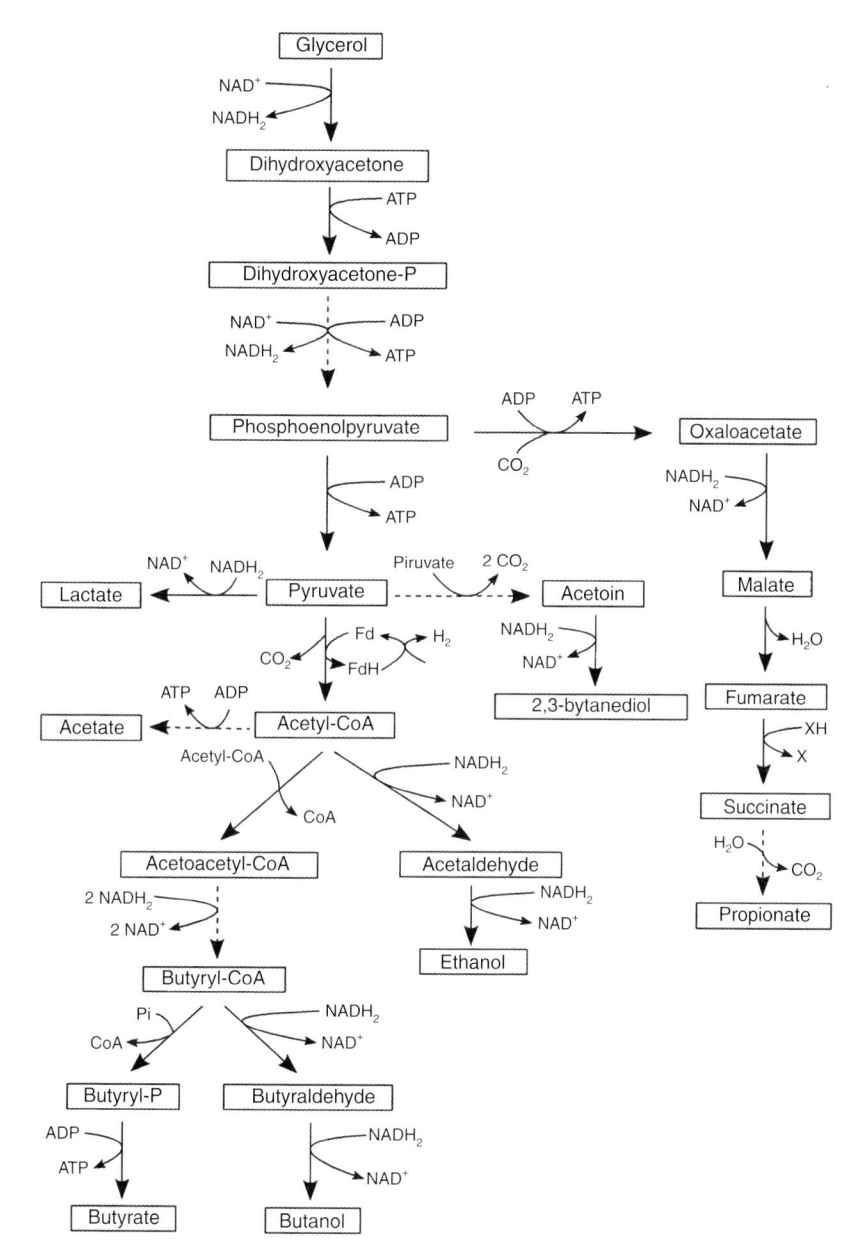

Figure 3 Overview of some possible end products for different microorganisms during glycerol degradation. Source: Silva G, Mack M, and Contiero J (2009) Glycerol: A promising and abundant carbon source for industrial microbiology. *Biotechnology Advances* 27: 30–39.

5.20.2.4.2 Example 1: Citric acid

Citric acid is industrially produced from sugars using cultures of *Aspergillus niger* and is used as a food preservative, flavorant, metabolite, environmentally benign cleaning agent, and an antioxidant. Furthermore, it is used as an additive in the pharmaceutical, cosmetic, and toiletry industries [20]. Glycerol is being considered as a cheaper alternative to sugar feedstock as Papanikolaou *et al.* [21] have shown, who produced citric acid from raw glycerol using *Yarrowia lipolytica*. When citric acid is reacted with glycerol, novel biodegradable polyesters are formed, which have potential applications in packaging and similar applications [22, 23]. Furthermore, rectangular slabs of highly crosslinked citric acid–glycerol copolymer matrix have been shown to release *in vitro* drugs such as sulfadiazine, paracetamol, diazepam, quinine hydrochloride, and doxycycline hydrochloride. Jiugao *et al.* [24] investigated the effects citric acid would have on the properties of glycerol-plasticized thermoplastic starch (GPTPS). The results showed that the addition of citric acid increased adhesion between citric acid, glycerol, water, and starch in thermoplastic starch. Rheological investigations showed that citric acid can decrease the shear viscosity and increase fluidity of thermoplastic starch.

5.20.2.4.3 Example 2: Propylene glycol

1,3-Propanediol is produced from crude oil-derived ethylene oxide using chemical catalysts developed by Shell [25]. It is also produced biologically by genetically engineered *Escherichia coli* using glucose as a feedstock. When polymerized with terephthalic acid, novel polyester fibers are formed, which are used in carpet and textile applications. Furthermore, 1,2-propanediol is a high-volume chemical (500 000 tonnes yr^{-1}) and is used to produce antifreeze. Antifreeze can be produced containing 70% propylene glycol and 30% glycerol directly from biodiesel facilities [26]. Monopropylene glycol (E1520), diacetin (E1517), and triacetin (E1518) are approved solvents in the flavoring industry (EU directive 2006/52/EC). A joint venture by Ashland Inc. and Cargill will be initially producing 65 000 tonnes yr^{-1} of high-grade propylene glycol from biodiesel glycerol. The initial capital investment is about 100 million dollars and the plant is to be constructed in a location in Europe [27]. Selective reduction can be employed to produce 1,2- and 1,3-propanediol from glycerol via hydrogenation using metallic catalysts. Propylene glycol can also be produced via dehydroxylation and biological reduction as discussed earlier.

5.20.3 Fuels from Fermentation Processes: Use of Biomass Raw Material, Fuel Production Intermediates, and Coproducts for Chemical Production

Most bioethanol is produced from the fermentation of sugar from feedstocks such as corn starch in the United States and sugarcane in Brazil. A limited amount of bioethanol is also produced from sugar beet and wheat feedstocks mainly in Europe. The main by-products are corn straw and bagasse, which are not utilized for chemical production and tend to be composted or burnt for electricity generation. These 'waste' materials are made up of lignocellulosic material, which can also be converted to sugars and subsequently bioethanol, which could have a significant impact on the overall production volumes from a plant. Other lignocellulosic materials include wheat straw, wood, and agricultural wastes, which hugely increase the volume of nonfood feedstock. However, the lignin in these materials is not converted by enzymes to any useful product and therefore novel uses for this are required. Furthermore, it causes enzyme inhibition during the fermentation process; therefore it should be removed, using the organosolv process (for example) prior to digestion.

5.20.3.1 Lignocellulosic Feedstocks for Chemical Production

5.20.3.1.1 Converting cellulose to sugars

The success of utilizing cellulosic materials for the production of fuels and chemicals depends heavily on reducing the costs of enzyme technology. The utilization of enzymes for the production of bioethanol from sugar and starch has grown significantly.

As mentioned earlier, the presence of lignin can reduce the efficiency of enzymes to convert cellulose into sugars. The lignin forms a barrier between the cellulases and the cellulose and it has also been found to bind to the enzyme [28]. The yield of sugar can be increased by using genetically engineered enzymes designed to increase specific activity by operating at high temperatures and specific pH values. Further research has been undertaken to recycle the enzymes; however, due to degradation and denaturization during the process, the method has only been proven at lab scale. The complexity of hemicelluloses requires a mixture of enzymes, which will increase the cost of production significantly. Carbon Sciences Inc. has developed a technology that encapsulates enzymes in a protective shell which increases the enzyme activity and functional life span. The enzymes convert the CO_2 into gasoline, diesel fuel, jet fuel, and other fuels [29], which makes it a promising technology for the future. Novel genetically modified corn crops have also been developed which contain all the enzymes required for cellulose breakdown. The genetic material has been copied from genes in cow stomachs and the enzymes are released from the vacuoles only when exposed to mechanical grinding after harvesting [30].

Although the cost of acid hydrolysis has prevented it from being extensively used in biomass conversion processes, HCL CleanTech Ltd., a company based in Israel, has now developed a novel process based on the Bergius method. High yields of sugars can be obtained from biomass such as wood chips using cold fuming hydrochloric acid (HCl); however, the high costs of recovery and reconcentration of the HCl made the process economically unviable. HCl CleanTech Ltd. has developed a process that allows the HCl gas to be recovered directly from the solution. Thus, there is potential to use this technology on a variety of feedstocks unlike enzymatic hydrolysis, which is substrate-specific. The lignin residues are obtained intact and they can be used in other applications or depolymerized. As the process requires small quantities of water and is energetically self-sufficient, it is estimated that the ethanol manufactured using this concept could cost as little as $1 per gallon. Furthermore, the environmentally friendly technology could be applied in other industry sectors such as the manufacture of polyvinylchloride.

5.20.3.1.2 Sugars to chemicals

Once cellulose has been converted, a wide range of chemicals can be produced from the sugars and a report in 2004 by the Department for Energy in the United States short-listed the top commodity chemicals as shown in **Table 2**. The chemicals are of high value and some of the production processes are economical and environmentally viable.

Table 2 Top 30 chemical building blocks from sugars

Carbon number	Chemicals
1	Carbon monoxide, hydrogen
2	None
3	Glycerol, 3-hydroxypropionic acid, lactic acid, malonic acid, propionic acid, serine
4	Acetoin, aspartic acid, fumaric acid, 3-hydroxybutyrolactone, malic acid, succinic acid, threonine
5	Arabinitol, furfural, glutamic acid, itaconic acid, levulinic acid, proline, xylitol, xylonic acid
6	Aconitic acid, citric acid, 2,5-furandicarboxylic acid, glucaric acid, lysine, levoglucosan, sorbitol

Source: Herseczki Z and Marton G (2009) Glycerol from biodiesel production – Existing and new glycerol purification technologies. *Work Package 3 Report, Sustoil (EU FP7)*. www.sustoil.org

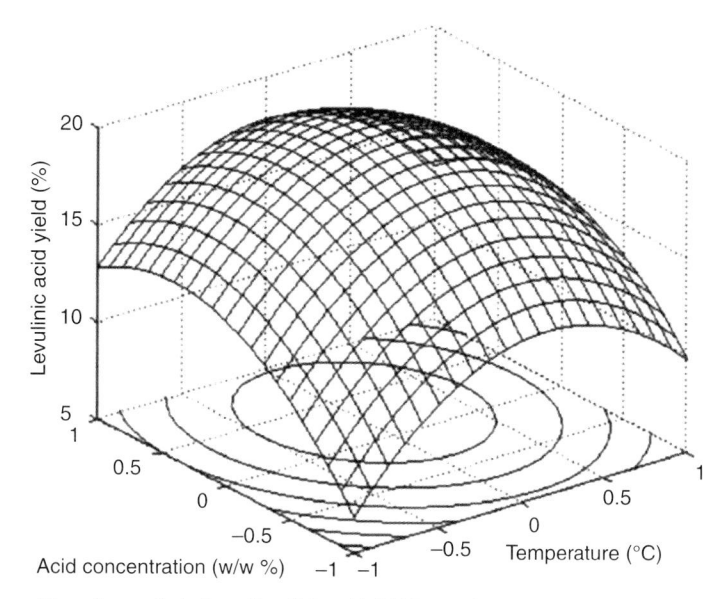

Figure 4 Three-dimensional graphic surface optimization of levulinic acid yield from wheat straw vs. temperature and acid concentration. Source: Chang C, Cen P, and Ma X (2007) Levulinic acid production from wheat straw. *Bioresource Technology* 98: 1448–1453.

5.20.3.1.2(i) Sugar to levulinic acid

The acid-catalyzed dehydration of sugar feedstocks from waste biomass produces levulinic acid (LA) in yields of around 20%. The production involves a one-step process using hydrochloric acid in water and a temperature of 200 °C for 45 min [31, 32]. The yields can be improved significantly by employing a novel two-reactor system, which uses sulfuric acid with feedstocks such as agricultural residues, paper sludges, and organic municipal waste. Although the yield is significantly higher, the net energy requirements for the two-reactor system could be higher than the conventional system, which would be an environmental and economic concern. Such concerns could be alleviated to a certain extent by generating in-house energy from burning the lignin residues (**Figure 4**).

LA can be converted to a wide variety of chemical derivatives using different chemical processing techniques. The reduction of LA leads to methyl tetrahydrofuran (MTHF), which can be used as a fuel additive and a solvent; further reduction of LA yields 1,3-propanediol, a potential alternative building block for the polyester market. Oxidation leads to acrylic molecules, which can be polymerized and blended to change the properties of numerous materials. The damaging health effects associated with bisphenol A (BPA) are a concern although BPA provides the desirable properties of hardness in polycarbonate materials. Diphenolic acid derived from LA via condensation shows similar properties to BPA and overcomes the undesired properties. The synthesis of diphenolic acid can be made more environmentally friendly by employing efficient, reusable, and water-tolerant solid acid catalysts such as mesoporous $H_3PW_{12}O_{40}$/SBA-15 [33]. The polycarbonate resin is valued at around \$4 kg^{-1} and the market is estimated at 2 billion kg yr^{-1}. Other derivatives such as delta (δ)-aminolevulinic acid are valued at \$4 kg^{-1} with a market of over 100 million kg yr^{-1} in the herbicide industry. An intermediate in the synthesis of δ-aminolevulinic acid is β-acetylacrylic acid, which can be used in the production of mass volume acrylate polymers.

5.20.3.2 Lignin: Depolymerization or Direct Use?

After using the cellulose for the production of sugars, the lignin is not utilized, which is environmentally and economically unacceptable. Lignin can be depolymerized to unlock the phenolic content or it can be directly used in various applications.

5.20.3.2.1 The disassembly of lignin

Lignin is potentially an abundant source of aromatic chemicals and its disassembly is a research challenge. Although the exact structure of lignin varies between different biomass types, in general it has a polymeric form. The structure contains hydroxyphenylpropane units such as *trans*-coumaryl alcohol, coniferyl alcohol, and sinapyl alcohol, which are connected with ether and carbon–carbon bonds in a helical structure [34, 35]. As early as 1939 Freudenberg [36] showed that it was possible to produce vanillin from lignin by using the alkali-nitrobenzene method. Supercritical water has been used to break down lignin, which requires a temperature of 647 K and a pressure of 22 MPa. When using a platinum catalyst under such conditions there is still only limited production of chemicals and Johnson *et al.* [35] could only yield a maximum of 4.4% chemical products. Increasing the pressure to 40 MPa results in the production of oil consisting of a large number of chemicals with a yield of 40% and the by-product char is at least 30%. The production of char reduces the chemical yield and is therefore undesired. Saisu *et al.* [37] have shown that in short reaction times there is limited char formation when using a water–phenol mixture at 673 K; however, at longer reaction times, the char formation increased. In a parallel study by Okuda *et al.* [38], the addition of phenol was shown to be effective in converting lignin in water to smaller molecular weight components without the production of any char. Furthermore, it has been proposed that the low-molecular-weight phenolic products should be processed via partial oxidation or gasification to produce smaller monomeric alkyl phenols and phenol, which could partially be recycled to feed the process (**Table 3**).

Table 3 Main compounds identified after pyrolysis–GC/MS of eucalypt wood and residues [39]

			Brown pulp					TCF pulp					
	Compounds	Origin	Wood	Pulp	Residue	Lignin H4	Hydrolyzate	Lignin H4	Pulp	Residue	Hydrolyzate	Lignin H4	Kraft lignin	MWL
1	3-Hydroxypropanal	PS	0.4	11.2	0.0	0.0	0.0	0.0	16.3	0.0	0.0	0.0	0.0	0.0
2	Toluene	PR	0.0	0.0	3.1	0.0	8.2	0.0	0.0	14.8	9.0	0.5	0.0	0.2
3	Unknown	PS	0.9	9.0	0.0	0.0	0.0	0.0	6.2	0.0	0.0	0.0	0.0	0.0
4	2-Furaldehyde	PS	7.7	6.1	0.6	0.0	0.2	3.7	6.9	0.5	0.0	0.0	0.0	0.2
6	2-Hydroxymethylfuran	PS	1.6	4.9	0.6	0.0	0.0	0.0	6.4	0.3	0.0	0.0	0.0	0.0
8	Styrene	PR	0.0	0.0	0.3	0.0	0.7	0.0	0.0	0.9	0.8	0.2	0.0	1.3
9	(5H) Furan-2-one	PS	0.7	4.7	0.0	0.0	0.0	0.0	5.6	0.0	0.0	0.0	0.0	0.0
11	2,3-Dihydro-5-methylfuran-2-one	PS	1.6	9.5	0.0	0.0	0.0	0.0	10.6	0.0	0.0	0.0	0.0	0.0
12	Phenol	PR	0.0	0.2	0.6	0.0	4.6	0.0	0.2	5.8	10.3	0.5	0.0	0.0
13	Unknown		0.0	0.0	2.0	0.0	2.2	0.0	0.0	9.3	6.8	0.0	0.0	0.0
14	5,6-Dihydropyran-2,5-dione	PS	1.3	2.4	0.0	0.0	0.0	0.0	2.2	0.0	0.0	0.0	0.0	0.0
15	4-Hydroxy-5,6-dihydro-(2H)-pyran-2-one	PS	5.9	2.3	0.5	2.3	0.0	2.4	2.4	0.0	0.0	0.0	0.0	0.0
17	2-Hydroxy-3-methyl-2-cyclopenten-1-one	PS	0.4	5.7	0.0	0.0	0.0	0.0	6.0	0.0	0.0	0.0	0.0	0.0
21	4-Methylphenol	PR	0.0	0.0	2.9	0.0	11.3	0.0	0.0	11.3	11.7	0.2	0.0	0.0
23	Guaiacol	LG	0.9	0.3	3.0	2.7	1.4	4.5	0.0	1.5	0.1	2.2	3.1	2.8
24	Levoglucosenone	PS	0.7	0.0	1.4	0.0	1.5	0.0	2.2	4.6	3.3	0.0	0.0	0.0
26	3,4-Dihydroxybenzaldehyde		0.6	1.0	0.0	0.0	0.0	0.0	0.9	0.0	0.0	0.0	0.0	0.0
28	4-Methylguaiacol	LG	0.9	0.0	2.5	1.0	0.5	2.4	0.0	0.3	0.0	0.6	1.1	1.2
29	Catechol	PS	0.4	6.3	0.0	0.0	0.0	0.0	6.6	0.0	0.0	0.0	0.3	1.0
30	4-Vinylphenol	PR	0.0	0.0	0.4	0.0	1.2	0.0	0.0	1.5	1.7	0.4	0.0	0.2
31	5-Hydroxymethyl-2-furaldehyde	PS	4.0	1.7	0.0	0.0	0.0	0.0	1.8	0.0	0.0	0.0	0.0	0.0
32	3-Methoxycatechol[a]	LM	0.3	0.0	2.2	0.9	1.0	2.0	0.0	0.0	0.0	1.2	4.8	1.2
33	3-Methylcatechol	PS	0.0	2.4	0.0	0.0	0.0	0.0	1.6	0.0	0.0	0.0	0.0	0.5
34	4-Ethylguaiacol	LG	0.2	0.5	0.4	1.1	0.2	1.6	0.6	0.0	0.0	0.3	0.3	0.5
35	1,4-Benzenediol	PS	0.0	1.3	0.0	0.0	0.0	0.0	1.6	0.0	0.0	0.0	0.0	0.0
36	4-Methylcatechol	PS	0.0	0.7	0.0	0.0	0.0	0.0	1.1	0.0	0.0	0.0	0.0	0.1
37	Indole	PR	0.0	0.0	4.3	0.0	24.8	0.2	0.0	21.3	29.4	1.3	0.0	0.0
38	4-Hydroxybenzaldehyde	PS	0.0	3.2	0.0	0.0	0.0	0.0	2.8	0.0	0.0	0.0	0.0	0.0
39	4-Vinylguaiacol	LG	3.0	0.4	6.0	4.8	1.9	4.4	0.0	1.8	0.1	4.3	2.2	6.9
40	2-Methyl-1,4-benzenediol	PS	0.0	1.1	0.0	0.0	0.0	0.0	1.2	0.0	0.0	0.0	0.0	0.0
41	Syringol	LS	3.0	1.6	7.9	10.5	3.5	15.7	0.3	0.9	0.1	6.9	14.7	8.1
42	Eugenol	LG	0.6	0.0	0.7	1.8	0.0	0.6	0.0	0.0	0.0	0.1	0.0	0.4
44	Pyrogallol	PS	0.3	4.0	0.0	0.0	0.0	0.0	2.8	0.0	0.0	0.0	0.0	6.5
46	1,6-Anhydrogalactopyranose	PS	1.4	0.0	0.7	0.0	0.0	0.0	0.0	4.2	0.0	0.0	0.0	0.0

47	Methylindole	PR	0.0	0.0	1.1	0.0	8.5	0.3	0.0	3.1	6.5	0.3	0.0	0.0
48	Vanillin	LG	0.9	0.1	0.4	3.6	0.0	0.8	0.0	0.0	0.0	1.1	5.1	1.4
52	4-Methylsyringol	LS	2.3	0.3	3.4	3.5	0.9	7.9	0.0	1.3	0.2	2.3	4.3	3.8
53	1,6-Anhydromannopyranose	PS	0.0	0.0	1.7	0.0	17.4	0.0	0.0	0.3	15.7	0.0	0.0	0.0
54	trans-Isoeugenol	LG	2.2	0.1	2.4	4.6	0.2	3.1	0.0	0.6	0.0	1.0	0.5	3.5
56	Acetoguaiacone	LG	0.4	0.0	0.7	0.7	0.0	0.6	0.0	0.0	0.3	0.5	1.0	0.5
57	Levoglucosane	PS	12.5	11.4	1.9	0.0	2.9	0.0	8.5	5.6	3.2	0.0	0.0	0.0
59	tert-Butylphenol	C	0.0	0.0	0.4	0.0	0.0	0.0	1.0	4.0	0.2	0.1	0.0	0.0
60	S₆	CR	0.0	0.0	0.0	0.0	0.0	0.0	0.0	0.0	0.0	0.0	1.6	0.0
62	Unknown	PS	0.0	0.7	0.0	0.0	0.0	0.0	1.0	0.0	0.0	0.0	0.0	0.0
63	4-Ethylsyringol	LS	0.8	0.3	0.3	1.2	0.2	3.7	0.1	0.0	0.0	0.6	1.1	1.5
64	Guaiacylacetone	LG	0.6	0.6	0.6	2.0	0.1	1.3	0.0	0.0	0.0	0.5	0.2	0.6
65	4-Vinylsyringol	LS	8.0	0.7	11.0	13.5	3.8	9.6	0.1	2.3	0.1	9.7	5.4	13.5
66	2,6-Dimethoxybenzoquinone	LM	0.0	0.0	0.0	0.0	0.0	0.0	0.0	0.0	0.0	0.0	13.1	0.0
69	4-Allylsyringol	LS	2.2	0.1	1.9	3.5	0.4	3.5	0.0	0.2	0.0	1.1	0.6	1.7
71	cis-4-Propenylsyringol	LS	1.3	0.0	1.0	2.6	0.2	2.3	0.0	0.2	0.0	0.5	0.2	1.6
72	Dimethoxythiophenol	LM	0.0	0.0	0.0	0.0	0.0	0.0	0.0	0.0	0.0	0.0	1.0	0.0
73	Syringaldehyde	LS	3.6	0.2	1.4	7.2	0.2	4.3	0.0	0.0	0.0	4.2	18.4	4.4
74	Homosyringaldehyde	LS	2.9	0.2	0.0	0.0	0.0	0.0	0.1	0.0	0.0	0.0	0.4	1.8
75	trans-4-Propenylsyringol	LS	8.4	0.3	9.3	19.2	2.0	12.4	0.1	2.3	0.3	4.7	1.5	9.3
76	Acetosyringone	LS	1.2	0.1	0.6	3.0	0.1	3.5	0.0	0.0	0.0	1.4	6.5	1.7
77	trans-Coniferaldehyde	LG	2.2	0.0	0.0	0.6	0.0	0.0	0.0	0.0	0.0	0.0	0.0	2.6
78	trans-Coniferyl alcohol	LG	0.4	0.0	5.5	0.1	0.0	0.3	0.0	0.0	0.0	6.3	0.0	4.8
79	Syringylacetone	LS	1.9	0.2	0.7	6.2	0.0	5.0	0.0	0.0	0.0	2.8	0.3	1.4
81	Propiosyringone	LS	0.4	0.0	0.0	2.2	0.0	2.0	0.0	0.0	0.0	0.1	0.8	0.6
82	cis-Sinapyl alcohol	LS	0.9	0.0	0.0	0.0	0.0	0.0	0.0	0.0	0.0	1.4	0.0	1.0
83	trans-Sinapaldehyde	LS	7.5	0.0	0.0	0.0	0.0	0.3	0.0	0.1	0.0	0.7	0.0	6.6
84	trans-Sinapyl alcohol	LS	0.0	0.0	5.1	0.0	0.0	0.0	0.0	0.2	0.0	41.2	0.0	4.3
85	Anthraquinone	CR	0.0	0.0	10.1	0.0	0.1	0.0	0.0	0.0	0.0	0.0	2.5	0.0
86	S₈	CR	0.0	0.0	0.0	0.0	0.0	0.0	0.0	0.0	0.0	0.0	7.0	0.0
	S/G molar ratio		3.1	2.6	1.9	3.1	2.5	3.5	1.1	1.8	1.4	2.1[b]	4.8	2.6

Source: Ibarra D, del Río JC, Gutiérrez A, et al. (2005) Chemical characterization of residual lignins from eucalypt paper pulps. *Journal of Analytical and Applied Pyrolysis* 74: 116–122.
Origin of compounds: LG, G-type lignin; LS, S-type lignin; LM, modified lignin; PS, polysaccharide; PR, protein; C, contaminant; CR, cooking reagent.
[a] Not included in S/G ratio estimation.
[b] Cinnamyl alcohols excluded (if these compounds are included, a S/G ratio of 4.5 was obtained).

A novel method of disassembling lignin without the use of energy-intensive supercritical water technique has been developed recently which uses mild oxidation with O_2 in the presence of polyoxometalates and radical scavengers [40]. The research was based on kraft lignin, which was immersed in 80% volume methanol–water with $H_3PMo_{12}O_{40}$ and after 20 min of reaction time at 170 °C, complete dissolution of the lignin was observed.

5.20.3.2.2 Uses of lignin

Although much research focuses on the depolymerization of lignin to form useful chemical monomers, lignin itself can be modified chemically and used as an additive in many useful applications [41]. The high temperatures required for breaking down lignin are not environmentally friendly and the use of metals such as molybdenum creates significant waste problems, hence deviating from the principles of green chemistry.

Ultimately, chemicals are used in industry to produce specific properties in certain products, and if the same effect can be achieved with a different, environmentally friendly option, then this approach should be used. For example, lignin contains phenol content; however, to unlock the phenols into a pure form requires energy-intensive processes. However, lignin itself could be used in certain applications to provide similar properties to phenolics.

5.20.3.2.2(i) Phenol

As lignin contains phenolics, it could be used as a substitute in phenol–formaldehyde resins. To increase reactivity, lignin can be chemically modified by reaction with methylated phenols [42]. Depending on how the lignin is extracted from the original biomass, the resulting products offer varying properties; for example, lignin derived by the organosolv process can be directly used as a substitute in formaldehyde resins with good curing properties [43].

Annual production of phenol in 2004 was around 8 million tonnes globally and is currently produced via the cumene process from benzene and propylene, which are both sourced from crude oil. With a market value of €1380 per tonne, this chemical is in high demand and considering the depletion of crude oil and in particular the effect on climate change, it is logical to replace the source of phenols with a renewable resource such as lignin. Another large market for lignin could be the epoxide resin industry, in particular the phenol–epoxy resins. Lignin has been successfully incorporated into resins for the fabrication of printed circuit boards [44]. During the production scale-up and when incorporating lignin, key properties such as resistivity, dielectric constant, loss in dielectric tangent angle, dielectric rigidity, mechanical properties, and high impact toughness should not be compromised. It has been shown that higher levels of cross-linking are observed with lignin derived from hard wood, that is, Tomlinite™ and Eucalin™.

5.20.3.2.2(ii) Urea–formaldehyde

Lignin can also be used as an adhesive for fiberboard production and although this is a high-volume, low-value product the technology could be transferred to other value applications in the future. Urea–formaldehyde (UF) resins are the most common adhesives and their low cost is a major advantage; however, the environmental problems associated with formaldehyde are a serious concern for the industry. Researchers have shown that using oxidoreductase for the cross-reaction of lignin results in fiberboards of similar strength to UF adhesives. Experiments have shown that the molecular weight of lignin increases when using oxidoreductases, which indicates that covalent-interbonding occurs [45].

5.20.3.2.2(iii) Polyolefins

The polyethylene and polypropylene markets are enormous with a global demand of 63 million and 38 million tonnes respectively. With growing demand from developing countries, it is likely that production will have to increase and lignin could play a significant role. It has been shown that epoxy-modified lignin can be successfully blended with polyolefin mixtures at concentrations of 2.5–40%. The resulting plastics exhibit good thermal and physical properties [46], and when aminated lignins are used, enhanced strength and biodegradability are observed [47, 48].

5.20.3.2.2(iv) Other applications

There are a vast number of other applications in which lignin, as a chemical, could be used, such as in concrete additives, metal sequestration, biodegradable plastics, gel formation, and others. As a treatment for acid rock damage lignin has been used for the metal sequestration. The lignin sulfonates prevent the formation of a metal coating around the lime rock [49] and enhanced metal sequestration is possible by modifying lignin with amino groups [50]. Lignin modified with acetic acid can be cross-linked with polyethylene glycol diglycidyl ether to form swellable gels [51]. The gels can swell in aqueous ethanol and alkaline solutions, which would be beneficial for certain applications. The reaction of lignin with tetraethoxysilane produces silicon carbide via the sol–gel process as shown in **Figure 5** [52].

5.20.4 Use of Bio-Alcohols as Chemicals and Chemical Intermediates

Utilization of lignin for the production of chemicals or as a chemical offers a very lucrative opportunity. The value of some chemicals is much higher than that of fuel bioethanol, so the by-product or 'waste' lignin could be of higher value than the primary product. Therefore, it would be logical to investigate high-value applications in the chemicals industry for bioethanol.

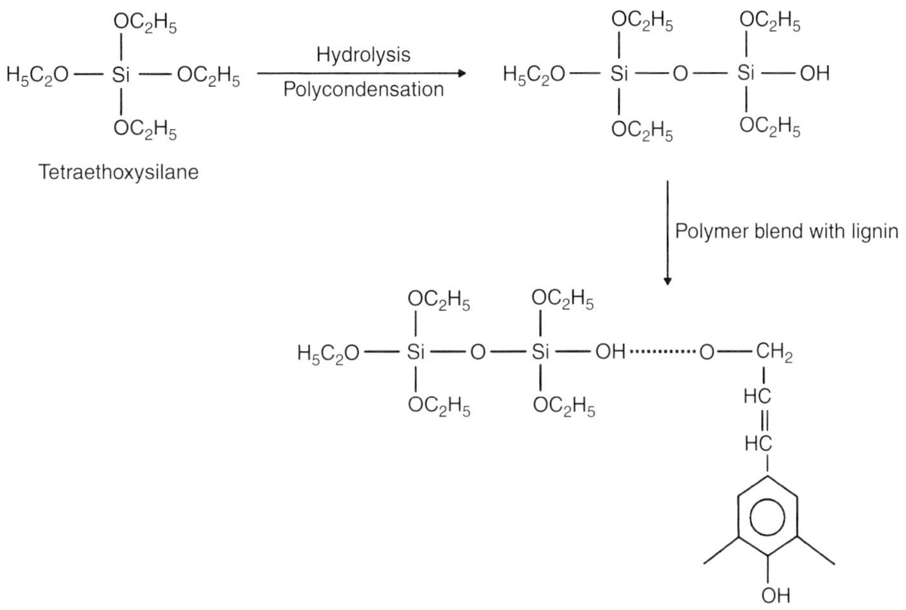

Figure 5 The reaction of tetraethoxysilane with lignin via the sol–gel process. Source: Mishra SB, Mishra AK, Krause RW, and Mamba BB (2009) Growth of silicon carbide nanorods from the hybrid of lignin and polysiloxane using sol–gel process and polymer blend technique. *Materials Letters* 63: 2449–2451.

Billions of liters of bioethanol are produced for use as an alternative fuel to power car engines throughout the world. Current production levels represent 1–2% of the global fuel market, so there is significant growth potential. Recently, a number of chemical companies have tried to use bioethanol as a feedstock for the production of chemicals. The advantages of using this feedstock are that it is a reliable source of sugars due to the well-established corn and sugarcane industries. Therefore, the chemical industry has the opportunity to use this resource to produce specialty chemicals which are much greater in value per unit than bioethanol. Ethanol can be converted to commodity chemicals such as acetaldehyde, ethylene, butadiene, and acetic acid; however, in order for the process to be economically viable, products must have a high value to cover the costs of raw materials and production processes. For example, the production of acetic acid from ethanol using a gold catalyst [53, 54] is more environmentally and economically beneficial than the conventional Monsanto process. However, there are some chemicals such as ethylene that are manufactured in such a large scale that the current bioethanol production capacity would not meet the demand. With increasing pressure from rising crude oil prices it is likely that bioethylene production will increase.

5.20.4.1 Ethyl Acetate

Commodity chemicals such as ethyl acetate are currently produced by ethanol esterification, where acetic acid is reacted with ethylene. The process, however, has a damaging effect on the environment as the substances used are corrosive. A greener method that has been developed is a one-pot synthesis, and advantages include low investment and production costs [55]. The Davy Process Technology company has commercialized the process using dehydrogenation and Cu/Cr_2O_3 as a catalyst [56, 57]. The reaction follows a pathway where ethanol is converted to acetaldehyde, which then further undergoes ethanol reaction to form hemiacetal, which is finally dehydrogenated to ethyl acetate [58]. Although this process is greener than the conventional process, the formation of butanone as a by-product is undesired and attempts to remove it make the entire process costly [59].

An alternative method for synthesizing ethyl acetate is via oxidation. This requires a number of catalysts such as Pd, Ti, and P. Other variations include Pd supported on SiO_2 with W and Zn as promoters [60]; however, the product is always a mixture of acetic acid and ethyl acetate. Other by-products include acetaldehyde and CO_2, which can be purified at a lower cost; however, a prerequisite is that very high yields of ethyl acetate are obtained.

5.20.4.2 Single-Walled Carbon Nanotubes

The chemical industry is a lucrative market for ethanol producers; however, advanced materials such as single-walled carbon nanotubes (SWNTs) could also have considerable value [61]. Huang *et al.* [61] have successfully grown SWNTs with controlled chemical vapor deposition using ethanol and bimetallic CoMo-doped mesoporous silica as a catalyst. Furthermore, the growth direction and length of the SWNTs can be controlled using this method, which allows the fabrication of parallel nanotube arrays or two-dimensional structures on flat surfaces. SWNTs are advanced materials because they exhibit electrical, mechanical, electro-optical, and electromechanical properties. In the future, these materials could form a part of nanoscale electronic devices such as field-effect transistors, single electron transistors and molecular sensors. Furthermore, the control of nanotube diameter, helicity orientation, and length will become essential if such materials are to be used in future applications.

5.20.4.3 Hydrogen

Although research has been conducted in using the carbon in ethanol for nanotube growth, the hydrogen also has huge potential for certain applications such as hydrogen fuel cells. The drive for cleaner fuels has put significant pressure on the transport industry and hydrogen is one of the key future contenders to replace fossil fuels. The industry is one of the major contributors to global carbon emissions, so there is significant governmental and environmental pressure on manufacturers to develop greener cars. Brazil and the United States produce bioethanol, which is a renewable resource, but the volumes required to fuel the world's fuel requirements would severely affect global food supplies. Therefore, an alternative technology is to use hydrogen, which can be generated from water via electrolysis and other sources. Hydrogen can be produced directly from biomass using the gasification technique; however, due to high capital costs and the lack of secure biomass sources, the technology has not been significantly commercialized. With a stable supply of bioethanol, this renewable resource could be used to produce hydrogen. If hydrogen fuel cells are deployed in the future, then this would certainly affect the biofuel markets; however, the bioethanol industry could simply divert its attention to converting the ethanol to hydrogen and supplying the new hydrogen economy. The high conversion efficiency of hydrogen energy to electricity and no emissions make this technology attractive.

Hydrogen can be produced from ethanol using the steam reforming technique, which results in CO_2 as a by-product. The reaction mechanism involves numerous steps [62] and when using noble metals in the temperature range of 500–600 °C the hydrogen yield increases. Alternatively, lower costing metals such as Ni, Cu, or Co or supported oxides for catalysis also exhibit improved activity; however, coke deposition is a major disadvantage. This can be avoided by using an oxide support such as CeO_2 with a good promoter to maximize metal–support interaction [63]. A fluorite-type oxide called ceria (Ce) is known for its redox properties, which are increased when mixed with metal oxides, that is, CeNiO [64]. Jalowiecki-Duhamel et al. [65] have used similar systems and achieved 100% conversion of ethanol at 400 °C. However, ethanol conversion and H_2 selectivity can be obtained at temperatures of only 200 °C by pretreating the solid with hydrogen.

5.20.4.4 Ethanol Fuel Cells

It may not be necessary to convert the ethanol to hydrogen in order to generate electricity for the portable electronics markets because direct ethanol fuel cells (DEFCs) have now been developed. Significant research in this area has been conducted on methanol fuel cells due to methanol having a simple form and rapid electrochemical reaction kinetics. The key disadvantage of using methanol is its toxicity, which is a health and safety concern if the resulting fuel cells are to be used in consumer products. Furthermore, methanol is currently produced from crude oil, a depleting resource, whereas bioethanol is produced on a large scale from biomass, a renewable resource.

The key step for ethanol to be used in a fuel cell is its oxidation, which takes place at the anode, the negative electrode. This is possible by using highly active catalysts that convert ethanol into CO_2 with the process releasing 12 electrons. As the process requires the cleavage of a carbon–carbon bond, which has no electron affinity or ionization energy, high temperatures are required, making it unviable for consumer products. At low temperatures, the PtSn catalysts exhibit optimal activity in acidic media due to the bifunctional mechanism and an electronic effect [66]. To avoid the use of noble metals and high catalyst loadings, research has been conducted on alkaline medium-based fuel cells. Alkaline fuel cells contain membranes that conduct hydroxide ions and offer faster reaction kinetics at the anode, where the alcohol oxidation takes place, and at the cathode, where the oxygen reduction takes place. Shen et al. [67] have shown that carbon-supported PdNi can be successfully synthesized using $NaBH_4$ as a reductant. The Pd_2Ni_3/C catalyst exhibits higher activity and stability for ethanol oxidation than a Pd/C catalyst and when used as an anode catalyst in a DEFC a maximum power density of 90 mW cm^{-2} at 60 °C can be achieved.

5.20.5 Biochar (Solid Biofuel): Chemicals from Pyrolysis Oil

As with liquid fuels, the drive for renewable alternatives is also found in the solid fuels industry. Many of the power stations in the world use coal as a feedstock to generate electricity. As coal, like other fossil fuels, is a nonrenewable resource which has a significant impact on global emissions, alternative feedstocks from renewable resources such as straws, wood chips, paper, and general agricultural waste are being investigated and used in power stations. Such feedstocks are also being used at smaller scales in combined heat and power units. However, some of the biomass can contain high concentration of water and oxygen, which decreases the combustion density and can add to transport costs. The thermochemical processing of biomass yields char, oil, and gas, or a combination of these, depending upon the type of biomass and processing conditions. The char has been used in various applications such as soil enhancement and fuel applications. It is known that the pyrolysis oil contains a cocktail of chemicals and after upgrading can be used directly in certain combustion engines as a fuel. However, as the oil and gas contain some chemicals that could add significant value to the entire process, there is a growing interest in these chemicals.

5.20.5.1 Comparison of Major Techniques

Pyrolysis of organic material in an oxygen-free atmosphere occurs upon thermal treatment where certain conditions such as temperature, heating rate, and residence time can be optimized for char, oil, or gas production [68]. The optimal conditions for producing bio-oil/biocrude/pyrolysis oil are a high heating rate, low residence time, and a temperature of around 500 °C [69] when using flash or fast pyrolysis. An alternative technique is microwave technology, which has been used on various feedstocks including

Table 4 Pollutants found in pyrolysis oil

Name of pollutant	Molecular weight	Name of pollutant	Molecular weight
Acenaphthylene	152	Benzo[b]fluoranthene	252
Acenaphthene	154	Benzo[k]fluoranthene	252
Fluorene	165	Benz[e]pyrene	252
Phenanthrene	178	Benzo[a]pyrene	252
Anthracene	178	Perylene	252
Fluoranthene	202	Indeno[1,2,3-cd]pyrene	276
Pyrene	202	Dibenz[a,h]anthracene	278
Cyclopenta[c,d]pyrene	228	Benzo[b]chrycene	278
Benz[a]anthracene	228	Benzo[ghi]perylene	276
Chrysene	228	Coronene	300

Source: Data from Vainio H and Wilbourn J (1992) Identification of carcinogens within the IARC monograph program. *Scandinavian Journal of Work, Environment & Health* 18(supplement 1): 64–73.

scrap tyres and waste straws. One of the key advantages of using this technology is that the microwaves interact directly with the molecules and atoms within the sample [70], and therefore can heat the sample much faster than conventional heating. However, atoms that are more absorbing of microwaves such as carbon need to be added to materials that are less absorbing of microwaves, and the sample heats up via conduction. Due to this interesting heating mechanism, the pyrolysis oil produced from microwaves differs from oils produced from conventional heating methods. El Harfi and others [71] have found that microwave pyrolysis of oil shales resulted in an oil that was more maltenic, less polar, and contained lower amounts of sulfur and nitrogen than oil obtained from conventional pyrolysis. Although the oil yield remains constant for both types of heating, the time required to complete pyrolysis is only 40 min (microwave power = 300 W), 25 min (450 W), and 8 min (600 W) compared to 60 min for conventional pyrolysis.

5.20.5.2 Polycyclic Aromatic Hydrocarbons

Fast pyrolysis is also a promising technique that offers a very high heating rate of 100 °C min^{-1} and rapid cooling of the pyrolysis vapors to produce biocrude products [72]. As bio-oil can contain significant oxygen content and polycyclic aromatic hydrocarbons (PAHs), the oil is not suitable directly as a fuel. Furthermore, the International Agency for Research on Cancer (IARC) has classified several PAHs such as benzanthracene, benzopyrene, and dibenzanthracene as probable human carcinogens [73]. One of the key principles of green chemistry is to avoid the production of toxic chemicals (**Table 4**).

Tsai *et al.* [74] have conducted extensive experiments on analyzing the PAH content of bio-oils obtained from flash pyrolysis of various biomass sources such as rice husk, rice straw, sugarcane bagasse, and coconut shells. The heating apparatus used in the experiment was a horizontally fixed bed reactor with a high-frequency generator set at a temperature of 500 °C with a heating rate of 400 °C min^{-1}. After a holding time of 1 min the gaseous products are cooled using a cryogenic circulating bath to result in a bio-oil, which is centrifuged and diluted before being analyzed in a gas chromatograph coupled to a mass spectrometer. The results showed that the liquid derived from coconut shells contained the most PAHs (12.7 mg l^{-1}); however, the most toxic PAHs were found in liquids derived from rice husk and sugarcane bagasse. A possible explanation for the higher PAH content could be the denser textural structure found in coconut shells compared with the loose textural structure found in straw and bagasse.

5.20.5.3 Fabricated Microwave Pyrolysis

Although the concentration of PAHs is relatively small, a real health and safety issue exists when handling the liquid, using it as a fuel or using it as a source of chemicals. If the bio-oil is to be used in such applications, the PAHs must be separated and appropriately disposed, which would incur a cost. An alternative method is to fabricate the pyrolysis process to target or avoid certain chemicals or a molecular weight range. Wan *et al.* [75] have shown that the microwave-assisted pyrolysis of corn stover and aspen wood can be fabricated using metal oxides, salts, and acids such as $K_2Cr_2O_7$, Al_2O_3, KAc, H_3BO_3, Na_2HPO_4, $MgCl_2$, $AlCl_3$, $CoCl_2$, and $ZnCl_2$. The additives have an effect not only on the final composition of the bio-oil but also on the overall product fractions of gas, oil, and char. The yield of bioliquid can be enhanced by using KAc, Al_2O_3, $MgCl_2$, H_3BO_3, and Na_2HPO_4, which may be acting as superabsorbers of microwaves or interacting with the pyrolysis vapors. With an 8% by weight loading of $MgCl_2$ within the biomass, the resulting bio-oil contains a major peak for furfural, which covers 80% of the area under the gas chromatograph spectrum. In general, chloride salts simplify the composition of bio-oils, which will make the characterization and subsequent separation of chemicals simpler.

The simplification of the bio-oil composition is a major advantage and Budarin *et al.* [76] have made further progress by using low-temperature microwave activation to achieve similar results using wheat straw as a feedstock. The experiments were based on wheat straw pellets mixed with various additives such as sulfuric acid, ammonia, and HCl. The microwave conditions were set at 1200 W and the heating rate was 17 °C min^{-1} until a maximum temperature of 180 °C was observed. The resulting bio-oils were diluted and analyzed using a GC-MS (gas chromatograph mass spectrometer). Interestingly, as the reaction was taking place under vacuum it was possible to fractionate the bio-oil as it is produced, allowing the analysis of samples as the pyrolysis proceeded. This would further aid the characterization, analysis, and use of bio-oils in various applications including chemicals (**Figure 6**).

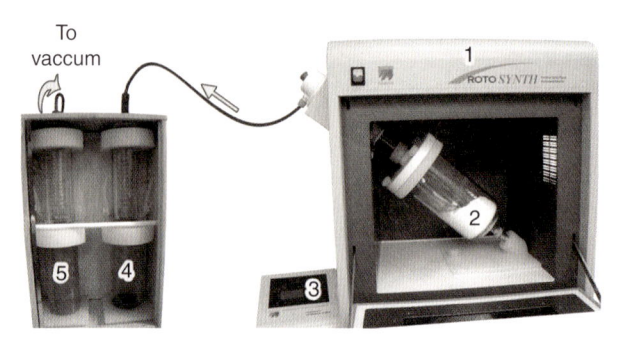

Figure 6 Schematic of microwave setup for collection of liquid fractions. (1) Microwave reactor, (2) sample vessel, (3) system control and monitoring console, (4) water-cooled condenser for collection of organic fraction, and (5) vacuum condenser for collection of aqueous fraction and low-molecular-weight components [76]. Source: Budarin VL, Clark JH, Lanigan BA, *et al.* (2009) The preparation of high-grade bio-oils through the controlled, low temperature microwave activation of wheat straw. *Bioresource Technology* 100: 6064–6068.

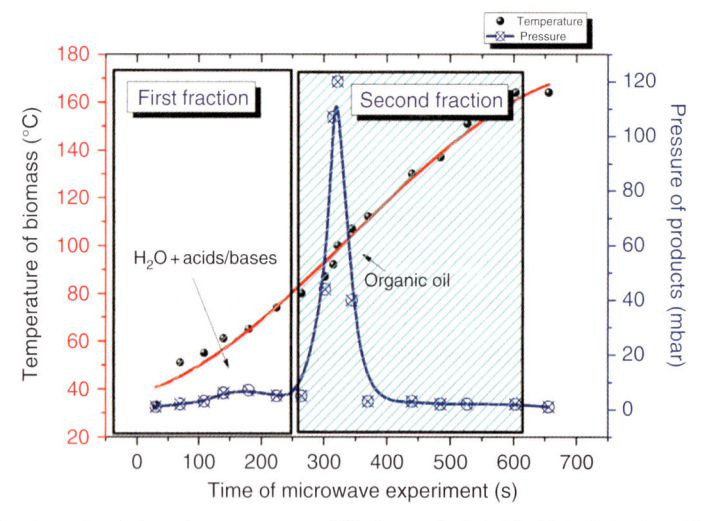

Figure 7 Stages of liquid product formation during microwave process [76]. Source: Budarin VL, Clark JH, Lanigan BA, *et al.* (2009) The preparation of high-grade bio-oils through the controlled, low temperature microwave activation of wheat straw. *Bioresource Technology* 100: 6064–6068.

It was shown that early fractions contained high concentrations of water, and after 1–2 min of reaction and at temperatures of only 120 °C, organic fractions containing less than 1% water were obtained (**Figure 7**).

5.20.6 Conclusions and Future Prospects

The new century will see a gradual transfer from petroleum-based chemistry to chemistry based on a wide diversity of feedstocks – virgin fossil- and mineral-derived resources will continue to be important for the foreseeable future, but chemicals and materials derived from nonfood biomass including food waste and agricultural and forestry by-products must gradually take over. The growth in biofuel production provides an ideal opportunity to take advantage of the logistical infrastructure these facilities provide and use both biofuel by-products and indeed biofuels themselves as raw materials for making valuable chemical products. Green chemistry can help achieve the realization of these new feedstocks as sources of valuable chemicals and materials through the proving of low environmental impact technologies and through downstream processing that utilizes the best green chemistry methodologies. Some of the major challenges for green chemistry in this context are developing low environmental impact downstream chemistry for converting biofuels and other fermentation platform molecules to higher value products, using benign extraction methods to recover chemicals from biomass both before and after bioprocessing, realizing the aromatic potential of lignin, and developing alternatives to fermentation that can also convert bulk biomass into small molecules (e.g., low-temperature pyrolysis). In this way, we will be able to achieve the essential goal for future generations of green and sustainable products.

References

[1] Warren M, John N, and Bregje VK (2009) A review of key biofuel producing countries. *IEA Bioenergy Task 39*, March.
[2] Notari M and Rivetti F (2004) Use of a Mixture of Esters of Fatty Acids as Fuel or Solvent. Patent WO2004/052874.
[3] Renga JM and Coms FD (1993) Novel methods for the preparation of glycerol carbonate esters. Patent WO9309111 to Henkel Corp.
[4] Fabbri D, Bevoni V, Notari M, and Rivetti F (2007) Properties of a potential biofuel obtained from soybean oil by transmethylation with dimethyl carbonate. *Fuel* 86: 690–697.
[5] Su EZ, Zhang MJ, Zhang JG, et al. (2007) Lipase-catalyzed irreversible transesterification of vegetable oils for fatty acid methyl esters production with dimethyl carbonate as the acyl acceptor. *Biochemical Engineering Journal* 36: 167–173.
[6] Luna D, Bautista FM, Caballero V, et al. (2007) Method for the Biodiesel Production by Using Pig Pancreatic Lipase as Enzymatic Catalyst. Patent PCT/ES 2007/000450.
[7] Kijeński J, Lipkowski A, Walisiewicz-Niedbalska W, et al. (2004) A Biofuel for Compression-Ignition Engines and a Method for Preparing the Biofuel. European Patent EP1580255.
[8] Herseczki Z and Marton G (2009) Glycerol from biodiesel production – Existing and new glycerol purification technologies. *Work Package 3 Report, Sustoil (EU FP7)*. www.sustoil.org.
[9] Knothe G, van Gerpen J, and Krahl J (2005) *The Biodiesel Handbook*. Champaign, IL: AOCS Press.
[10] Aiken JE (2007) Purification of Glycerol. US Patent 7,126,032 B1.
[11] Hunt JA (1999) A short history of soap. *The Pharmaceutical Journal* 263: 985.
[12] Pagliaro M, Ciriminna R, Kimura H, et al. (2007) From glycerol to value-added products. *Angewandte Chemie International Edition* 46: 4434–4440.
[13] Leffingwell G and Lesser M (1945) *Merck Index*, 11th edn., p. 705. Merck.
[14] McCoy M (2006) Glycerin surplus. *Chemical & Engineering News* 84: 6, 7.
[15] Pagliaro M and Rossi M (2008) *The Future of Glycerol: New Usages for a Versatile Raw Material*. RSC. England, UK.
[16] Behr A, Eilting J, Irawadi K, et al. (2008) Improved utilisation of renewable resources: New important derivatives of glycerol. *Green Chemistry* 10: 13–30.
[17] Zheng Y, Chen X, and Shen Y (2008) Commodity chemicals derived from glycerol, an important biorefinery feedstock. *Chemical Reviews* 108(12): 5253–5277.
[18] Yazdani S and Gonzalez R (2007) Anaerobic fermentation of glycerol: A path to economic viability for the biofuels industry. *Current Opinion in Biotechnology* 18: 213–219.
[19] Silva G, Mack M, and Contiero J (2009) Glycerol: A promising and abundant carbon source for industrial microbiology. *Biotechnology Advances* 27: 30–39.
[20] Soccol CR, Vandenberghe LPS, Rodrigues C, and Pandey A (2006) New perspectives for citric acid production and application. *Food Technology and Biotechnology* 44: 141–149.
[21] Papanikolaou S, Muniglia L, Chevalot I, et al. (2002) Yarrowia lipolytica as a potential producer of citric acid from raw glycerol. *Journal of Applied Microbiology* 92: 737–744.
[22] D'Aquino R (2005) Citric acid rejuvenates glycerol. *Chemical Engineering Progress* October.
[23] Pramanick D and Ray TT (1988) Synthesis and biodegradation of copolyesters from citric acid and glycerol. *Polymer Bulletin* 19: 365–370.
[24] Jiugao Y, Wang N, and Ma X (2005) The effect of citric acid on the properties of thermoplastics starch plasticized by glycerol. *Starch* 57: 494–504.
[25] Lam KT, Powell JP, and Wieder PR (1997) Preparing 1,3-Propanediol. Patent WO9716250.
[26] Boswell C (2005) Polyol partners can also hydrocrack glycerol and form propylene glycol. *Chemical Marketing Reporter* 24 January.
[27] (2007) Joint venture devoted to biobased chemicals. *Chemical & Engineering Technology Forum* 30(6): 681.
[28] Mansfield SD, Mooney C, and Saddler JN (1999) Substrate and enzyme characteristics that limit cellulose hydrolysis. *Biotechnology Progress* 15: 804–816.
[29] http://www.carbonsciences.com
[30] http://www.newscientist.com/article/dn13619-biofuel-corn-makes-cow-bug-enzyme-to-digest-itself.html
[31] Yan L, Yang N, Pang H, and Liao B (2008) Production of levulinic acid from bagasse and paddy straw by liquefaction in the presence of hydrochloride acid. *Clean* 36(2): 158–163.
[32] Chang C, Cen P, and Ma X (2007) Levulinic acid production from wheat straw. *Bioresource Technology* 98: 1448–1453.
[33] Guo Y, Li K, and Clark JH (2007) The synthesis of diphenolic acid using the periodic mesoporous H3PW12O40 – Silica composite catalysed reaction of levulinic acid. *Green Chemistry* 9: 839–841.
[34] Dorrestijn E, Laarhoven LJJ, Arends IWCE, and Mulder P (2000) The occurrence and reactivity of phenoxyl linkages in lignin and low rank coal. *Journal of Analytical and Applied Pyrolysis* 54: 153–192.
[35] Johnson DK, Chum HL, Anzick R, and Baldwin RM (1988) *Research in Thermochemical Biomass Conversion*, pp. 485–496. London: Elsevier.
[36] Freudenberg K (1939) Uber lignin. *Angewandte Chemie* 52: 362–363.
[37] Saisu M, Sato T, Watanabe M, et al. (2003) Conversion of lignin with supercritical water–phenol mixtures. *Energy Fuels* 17: 922.
[38] Okuda K, Umetsu M, Takami S, and Adschiri T (2004) Disassembly of lignin and chemical recovery – Rapid depolymerization of lignin without char formation in water–phenol mixtures. *Fuel Processing Technology* 85: 803–813.
[39] Ibarra D, del Río JC, Gutiérrez A, et al. (2005) Chemical characterization of residual lignins from eucalypt paper pulps. *Journal of Analytical and Applied Pyrolysis* 74: 116–122.
[40] von Rohr PR, Voitl T, and Nagel MV (2008) Depolymerization of lignin by aqueous polyoxometalates for the production of chemicals. *Chemie Ingenieur Technik* 80(9): 1377–1378.
[41] Stewart D (2008) Lignin as a base material for materials applications: Chemistry, application and economics. *Industrial Crops and Products* 27: 202–207.
[42] Doering GA (1993) Lignin Modified Phenol–Formaldehyde Resins. US Patent 5,202,403.
[43] Cetin NS and Ozman N (2002) Use of organosolv lignin in phenol–formaldehyde resins for particleboard production I. Organosolv lignin modified resins. *The International Journal of Adhesion and Adhesives* 22: 477–480.
[44] Kosbar LL, Gelorme J, Japp RM, and Fotorny WT (2001) Introducing biobased materials into the electronics industry. *Journal of Industrial Ecology* 4: 93–98.
[45] Felby C, Hassingboe J, and Lund M (2002) Pilot-scale production of fiberboards made by laccase oxidized wood fibers: board properties and evidence for cross-linking of lignin. Enzyme and Microbial Technology 31: 736–741.
[46] Feldman D, Lacasse MA, Wang J, and Luchian JMS (1995) Lignin and its polyblends. *Pure and Applied Chemistry* 32: 1613–1619.
[47] Wang Q, Aït-Kadfi A, and Kaliaguine S (1992) Catalytic grafting: A new technique for polymer–fiber composites. *Journal of Polymer Sciences* 44: 1107–1119.
[48] Simionescu CI, Macoveanu MM, Vasile C, et al. (1996) Polyolefins/lignosulfonates blends. *Cellulose Chemistry and Technology* 30(5–6): 411–429.
[49] Zhuang JM and Walsh T (2004) Lignor process for acidic rock drainage treatment. *Environmental Technology* 25: 1031–1040.
[50] Dizhbite T, Zakis G, Kizima A, et al. (1999) Lignin – A useful bioresource for the production of sorption-active materials. *Bioresource Technology* 67: 221–228.
[51] Nishida M, Uraki Y, and Sano Y (2003) Lignin gel with unique swelling property. *Bioresource Technology* 88: 81–83.
[52] Mishra SB, Mishra AK, Krause RW, and Mamba BB (2009) Growth of silicon carbide nanorods from the hybrid of lignin and polysiloxane using sol–gel process and polymer blend technique. *Materials Letters* 63: 2449–2451.
[53] Christensen CH, Jørgensen B, Rass-Hansen J, et al. (2006) Formation of acetic acid by aqueous-phase oxidation of ethanol with air in the presence of a heterogeneous gold catalyst. *Angewandte Chemie International Edition* 45: 4648–4651.
[54] Rass-Hansen J, Falsig H, Jørgensen B, and Christensen CH (2007) Bioethanol: Fuel or feedstock? *Journal of Chemical Technology and Biotechnology* 82: 329–333.

[55] Gaspar AB, Esteves AML, Mendes FMT, *et al.* (2009) Chemicals from ethanol – The ethyl acetate one-pot synthesis. *Applied Catalysis A: General* 363: 109–114.
[56] Colley SW, Fawcett CR, Rathmell C, and Tuck MWM (2004) Process for the preparation of ethyl acetate. US Patent 6,809,217, Davy Process Technology Limited.
[57] Colley SW, Tabatabaei J, Waugh KC, and Wood MA (2005) The detailed kinetics and mechanism of ethyl ethanoate synthesis over a Cu/Cr$_2$O$_3$ catalyst. *Journal of Catalysis* 236: 21–33.
[58] Inui K, Kurabayashi T, and Sato S (2002) Direct synthesis of ethyl acetate from ethanol over Cu-Zn-Zr-Al-O catalyst. *Applied catalysis A: General* 237: 53–61.
[59] Inui K, Kurabayashi T, Sato S, and Ichikawa N (2004) Effective formation of ethyl acetate from ethanol over Cu-Zn-Zr-Al-O catalyst. *Journal of Molecular Catalysis A: Chemical* 216: 147–156.
[60] Sano K (2002) Catalyst for production of acetic acid or acetic acid and ethyl acetate. US 2003/0092936 A1, Showa Denko K.K.
[61] Huang L, Cui X, White B, *et al.* (2004) Long and oriented single-walled carbon nanotubes grown by ethanol chemical vapor deposition. *The Journal of Physical Chemistry B* 108: 16451–16456.
[62] Ni M, Leung DYC, and Leung MKH (2007) A review on reforming bio-ethanol for hydrogen production. *International Journal of Hydrogen Energy* 32: 3238–3247.
[63] Biswas P and Kunzru D (2007) Steam reforming of ethanol for production of hydrogen over Ni/CeO$_2$–ZrO$_2$ catalyst: Effect of support and metal loading. *International Journal of Hydrogen Energy* 32: 969–980.
[64] Wrobel G, Sohier MP, D'Huysser A, *et al.* (1993) Hydrogenation catalysts based on nickel and rare earths oxides. Part II: XRD, electron microscopy and XPS studies of the cerium–nickel–oxygen–hydrogen system. *Applied Catalysis* 101: 73–93.
[65] Jalowiecki-Duhamel L, Pirez C, Capron M, *et al.* (2009) Hydrogen production from ethanol steam reforming over cerium and nickel based oxyhydrides. *International Journal of Hydrogen Energy* 35(23): 12741–12750.
[66] Song SQ, Zhou WJ, Zhou ZH, *et al.* (2005) Direct ethanol PEM fuel cells: The case of platinum based anodes. *International Journal of Hydrogen Energy* 30: 995–1001.
[67] Shen SY, Zhao TS, Xu JB, and Li YS (2010) Synthesis of PdNi catalysts for the oxidation of ethanol in alkaline direct ethanol fuel cells. *Journal of Power Sources* 195: 1001–1006.
[68] Dominguez A, Menendez JA, Fernandez Y, *et al.* (2007) Conventional and microwave induced pyrolysis of coffee hulls for the production of a hydrogen rich fuel gas. *Journal of Analytical and Applied Pyrolysis* 79: 128–135.
[69] Bridgwater AV, Meier D, and Radlein D (1999) An overview of fast pyrolysis of biomass. *Organic Geochemistry* 30: 1479.
[70] Mujundar AS (1995) *Handbook of Industrial Drying*, 2nd edn., vol. 1/2. New York: Marcel Dekker Inc.
[71] El harfi K, Mokhlisse A, Chanâa MB, and Outzourhit A (2000) Pyrolysis of the Moroccan (Tarfaya) oil shales under microwave irradiation. *Fuel* 79: 733.
[72] Czernik S and Bridgwater AV (2004) Overview of applications of biomass fast pyrolysis oil. *Energy Fuels* 18: 590–598.
[73] Vainio H and Wilbourn J (1992) Identification of carcinogens within the IARC monograph program. *Scandinavian Journal of Work, Environment & Health* 18(supplement 1): 64–73.
[74] Tsai W-T, Mi H-H, Chang Y-M, *et al.* (2007) Polycyclic aromatic hydrocarbons (PAHs) in bio-crudes from induction-heating pyrolysis of biomass wastes. *Bioresource Technology* 98: 1133–1137.
[75] Wan Y, Chen P, Zhang B, *et al.* (2009) Microwave-assisted pyrolysis of biomass: Catalysts to improve product selectivity. *Journal of Analytical and Applied Pyrolysis* 86: 161–167.
[76] Budarin VL, Clark JH, Lanigan BA, *et al.* (2009) The preparation of high-grade bio-oils through the controlled, low temperature microwave activation of wheat straw. *Bioresource Technology* 100: 6064–6068.

5.21 Bioenergy Policy Development

P Thornley, The University of Manchester, Manchester, UK

© 2012 Elsevier Ltd. All rights reserved.

5.21.1	Introduction	412
5.21.1.1	Greenhouse Gas Reductions: A Complicated Policy Driver	412
5.21.1.2	Bioenergy Potential	413
5.21.1.3	Unique Attributes of Biomass and Supply Chains	414
5.21.2	Bioenergy Policy Development	415
5.21.2.1	Achieving GHG Reductions with Biomass: A Key Policy Objective	415
5.21.2.2	Achieving Sustainable Development with Bioenergy: Key Policy Objectives	416
5.21.2.3	The Role of Energy Markets	418
5.21.2.4	Correcting Market Failures	418
5.21.2.5	Environmental Policy Options	419
5.21.2.5.1	Investment subsidies and new technology support	419
5.21.2.5.2	Command and control instruments	421
5.21.2.5.3	Incentive-based instruments	422
5.21.2.5.4	Tradable permits and green certificate schemes	422
5.21.2.5.5	Fixed prices	423
5.21.2.6	The Role of Markets in Ensuring Economic Efficiency	424
5.21.2.7	Scale of Impacts and Nonfinancial Barriers	424
5.21.3	Application of Environmental Policy Options to Bioenergy	426
5.21.3.1	Historical Bioenergy Policy Development	426
5.21.3.1.1	Bioenergy implementation in Italy, 1990–2005	426
5.21.3.1.2	Bioenergy implementation in Germany, 1990–2005	426
5.21.3.1.3	Bioenergy implementation in the United Kingdom, 1990–2005	426
5.21.3.1.4	Bioenergy implementation in Sweden, 1990–2005	427
5.21.3.2	A Multidimensional Problem	427
5.21.3.3	Attempts to Address the Problem	427
5.21.4	A Way Forward	427
5.21.4.1	The Need for a Holistic Approach	427
5.21.4.2	Land-Use Challenges	428
5.21.4.3	Biomass Action Plans	428
5.21.5	Conclusions	428
References		429
Further Reading		429

Glossary

Certification schemes A scheme under which the supply of a particular product (in this case biomass fuel) is certified by an independent verifier as having complied with a set of minimum standards (usually incorporating ecological and sometimes socioeconomic criteria).

Command and control instruments Standards (normally set by governments or local authorities) that specify the acceptable performance levels that must be met by all installations within the specified category, for example, specification of a maximum limit on specific emission levels.

Externality The impact of a private system on the external world; for example, the climate change impacts of fossil fuel-based energy systems result in environmental damage with actual social costs to society that are not generally taken into account in conventional energy system market economics.

Fixed prices or 'feed-in' tariffs A specified (normally premium) price paid to all producers of a particular form of energy for a defined period.

Green certificates An official certificate issued by a regulatory authority for every unit of qualifying output certified as produced by a supplier in accordance with a specification, for example, for renewable energy. The certificate is evidence of output toward meeting a supplier obligation or target and can be traded independently of the product, for example, electricity.

Investment subsidy A financial contribution (normally from a government or other central funding agency) that provides a specified level of financial support for the capital investment associated with a new project or installation.

Tradable permits These schemes involve the imposition of a maximum quota of a specified pollutant per country, sector, or installation. Participants who emit less than their quota may trade this with other participants, creating a market for the permits to emit, which should encourage the least-cost method of meeting the quota limitation.

5.21.1 Introduction

5.21.1.1 Greenhouse Gas Reductions: A Complicated Policy Driver

Biomass has been in use in the form of wood fuel for thousands of years, servicing mankind's basic needs for heat and fuel for cooking. More recently, it has become an option for electricity production and, more speculatively, for transport fuels. While traditional biomass development was based on the ready availability of a convenient fuel, the more recent surge in bioenergy is part of a strategic shift toward renewable and sustainable energy supply. While biomass has many potential benefits, including security of supply, employment, rural diversification, export opportunities, and so on, its ability to reduce greenhouse gas (GHG) emissions is undoubtedly the foremost in the current development impetus. The threat to mankind posed by climate change has become much more succinct in recent years. It is "the biggest challenge our civilisation has ever faced" [1] and experts view it as 'increasingly unlikely' that global agreements will allow stabilization at 450 ppmv (parts per million (volume basis)) [2]. Therefore, the importance of limiting further GHG emissions and sequestering carbon dioxide from the atmosphere becomes paramount.

Plants and trees sequester carbon dioxide from the atmosphere via photosynthesis (at very low efficiency: often around 1%), so that the plant material effectively acts as a store of solar energy and as a carbon sink. The energy stored can be released via biological or thermochemical conversion, which also returns the carbon dioxide to the atmosphere, but since this biogenic carbon was relatively recently sequestered there is no net increase in the long-term atmospheric GHG burden … in the perfect world. However, in the real world, this virtuous circle is not completely closed. First of all, there may be inputs of nonrenewable energy in order to access the biomass, for example, diesel fuel used to drive the machinery that harvests the wood, and second, the production process itself may generate GHG emissions, for example, emissions of nitrous oxide from soil on which crops are grown. The result is that the actual GHG reductions achieved by bioenergy systems are highly variable between feedstocks, technologies, and energy demand sectors. Some general trends can be identified for existing technologies (e.g., savings from forestry systems or other perennial plants are usually higher than for annual crops, savings for heat are often higher than for electricity, and both these are usually higher than for transport fuel production). However, there are many exceptions to these rules and the result is that not all bioenergy systems can be considered equal when it comes to considering the key policy objective of reducing GHG emissions.

There is also considerable discussion about the most appropriate methodology for evaluating GHG reductions. Life cycle assessment (LCA) is commonly used to evaluate the GHG savings of bioenergy systems. This involves consideration of all energy and material flows into and out of a system and then ascribing GHG emission factors or global warming potentials to each of these. It includes consideration of direct fuel use (e.g., diesel in tractors used in cultivation) and embodied energy, both for materials consumed in the process (e.g., carbon emissions associated with energy use in fertilizer production used in crop cultivation) and often for equipment and infrastructure (e.g., consideration of the GHG emissions associated with manufacture of a tractor used for ploughing, but weighting this in accordance with the fraction of its lifetime use spent on this application). This is a complex and lengthy procedure, with a requirement for a significant number of assumptions. In many cases, the relevant inputs are not well defined or are subject to natural variations due to, for example, soil types, human interfaces, and climatic conditions. This may make it very difficult to obtain an accurate figure for the actual GHG emissions of a particular bioenergy system.

It is important, from a policy perspective, to be clear about how to evaluate the GHG reductions. LCA allows an analysis of the GHG emissions associated with a particular bioenergy system, but we can only arrive at an evaluation of the savings by comparing to a reference system. Comparing electricity from a biomass-fired power plant to a coal-fired combustion power plant will result in greater savings per unit of electricity than comparison to a gas-fired combined cycle plant. Therefore, the GHG savings achieved by bioenergy systems are a function not only of the system (particularly the supply chain for the feedstock), but also what preceded it and sometimes how the bioenergy unit is integrated into the wider energy system.

The preceding system is often referred to as a reference system. The example of the power plant is fairly clear; however, in other applications, there is often a need to think carefully about the system and reference system boundaries and about how the introduction of a bioenergy system may impact on other existing energy system elements. For example, if crop cultivation is considered, it probably makes sense to consider any soil-related GHG emissions, but it could be argued that these would be incurred anyway because the soil would otherwise have hosted another crop with associated (though probably different) soil emissions. The reference system concept becomes less clear here because the land is providing two different functions in each case, one involving provision of energy and one not. LCA practitioners have developed different ways of dealing with the mechanics of carrying out such calculations. However, the important thing from a policy perspective is to be clear what we are actually trying to achieve and what we mean when we aspire to 'GHG reductions' – is this reduction for the United Kingdom? Is it compared to the previous use of land? Does it matter that the product from the land is now different? Can we allow for avoided emissions from landfilling of material that is no longer required? The answers to these questions will be different depending on the ultimate policy objective and it is important, therefore, to be clear what that objective is when developing policy instruments and supporting calculation methodologies.

The United Nations Framework Convention on Climate Change (UNFCC) has the goal of preventing dangerous human interface with the climate system. Scientific modeling and advice from the Intergovernmental Panel on Climate Change (IPCC) has allowed this to be translated into a practical policy objective of achieving global reductions in GHG emissions compared to 1990 levels, with appropriate national targets linked to the development status of participating countries. One way of reducing emissions could be through biofuel production. Existing fossil fuel diesel with a certain level of carbon emissions is considered as a primary fuel and so emissions associated with burning that fuel are allocated to the country in which it is used as part of national inventories. Suppose that instead this was replaced with biodiesel from rapeseed oil. If the growth and production of the rapeseed oil is within the same country that the biofuel is used, then that country would record sequestration of carbon dioxide during the crop growth, releases of carbon dioxide and other GHGs during crop management and processing, and releases of carbon dioxide at the point of use of the biofuel. For a well-managed fuel supply chain, the sequestration would offset the GHG releases to the extent that the net GHG emissions per unit of energy delivered are less than those for the mineral diesel equivalent. This would be seen as a net reduction in GHGs reported by that country. Consider then an alternative scenario whereby palm oil is produced in Indonesia, transported to Europe, converted to biodiesel, and ultimately used there. Assuming there has been no land-use change, Indonesia has achieved GHG sequestration via the palm growth and has also incurred some GHG emissions in processing to palm oil. The international shipping of the material is currently not included within the UNFCC. The European state incurs GHG emissions in the processing of the palm oil and then also in its utilization in a vehicle. Given that the percentage of carbon in biodiesel is very similar to that in mineral diesel, it is extremely unlikely that the European member state has incurred less GHG emissions in making this substitution. However, the emissions at the point of use are biogenic rather than fossil-derived carbon emissions and so have recently been sequestered from the atmosphere (in Indonesia) and do not, therefore, add to the net atmospheric concentration of GHGs. Globally, there has been a reduction in GHG emissions compared to the use of mineral diesel. However, this will not be recognized in the UNFCC-return of the country utilizing the biodiesel and the reduction is entirely reliant on the production procedures in a separate country that may or may not participate in the UNFCC. The potential for bioenergy to be produced and used in physically disparate locations is not only at the heart of its attractiveness as a dispatchable, storable renewable energy resource, but is also responsible for the difficulties associated with assessing the actual GHG reductions and increases the challenges associated with implementing policies to ensure that reductions are actually achieved.

5.21.1.2 Bioenergy Potential

If the key driver for bioenergy policy is reduction of GHG emissions, this suggests that a key policy objective would be maximization of low-carbon provision of bioenergy. This essentially requires two elements: that we maximize the carbon reductions achieved by a biomass energy system and that we maximize the deployment of bioenergy, which inevitably raises the question of how much bioenergy is available?

Answering this question is nontrivial. It is first necessary to focus on exactly what the question means. It would be theoretically possible to plant all of the planet's land with biomass crops and use all organic material for bioenergy. At the other extreme, we could do nothing in terms of increasing our biomass resource and just continue to process biomass at the rate we do at present, giving a certain potential. Somewhere in between these two extremes lies the bioenergy potential: how much we could have if we took positive actions to increase bioenergy. This is very difficult to quantify for two main reasons.

First, it depends upon the concept of potential. According to the Oxford English Dictionary, this is the possibility of something happening or being developed or used. In order to quantify this, we need to define what is happening, being developed or used, and variations in where the bounds are set on this can lead to wide discrepancies in the assessment of bioenergy potential.

At another extreme, we could consider the theoretical potential. This is roughly equivalent to the extreme scenario mentioned above: plant everywhere and use everything. Being more realistic, we could consider the technical potential. This equates to the bioenergy potential that is technically possible to achieve, that is, taking into account constraints on yield, physical composition, and so on. Further reductions in the resource are incurred when we consider what is practically possible, for example, the practical potential would exclude resources that are located in inaccessible areas (e.g., practical limitations to harvesting on steep slopes). However, in an open energy market, only the material that is economically available when compared to other alternatives including fossil fuels will actually become available in practice for use as a fuel. This gives rise to a further reduced economic potential. Finally, one might also consider the sustainable potential of a bioenergy system. The sustainability of a bioenergy system is discussed in more detail in Section 5.21.2, but for the purposes of considering the sustainable resource it is simply necessary to note that interactions of the system with the global ecosphere will constrain the amount of resource that can be accessed without negative impacts on the environment, economy, or society [3]. The impact of these constraints on the potential bioenergy resource pool are illustrated in **Figure 1**.

So, from **Figure 1**, the practical potential is smaller than the technical potential which is smaller than the theoretical potential. Within that practical potential, a certain quantity of bioenergy resource will be economically viable in the existing open market and that is the economic potential. Sustainability constraints are different. They take account of the need for sustainable economic development, but that does not necessarily equate to being economically viable in the current market place. Therefore, some of the practical resource will be economically viable (the economic potential) and this can be accessed in the current market for deployment purposes. Some of the practical resource will be sustainable and, as indicated there will be some overlap between the economic and sustainable potentials, marked as the central shaded area on the diagram. In reality markets will only deliver the economic potential, but society will benefit most from delivery of the sustainable potential. Therefore, a chief objective of bioenergy policy should be to increase the area of overlap in the center of the figure so that more of the sustainable potential becomes economically viable in the current market and to minimize the area of the left shaded circle, so that there is no economic incentive to

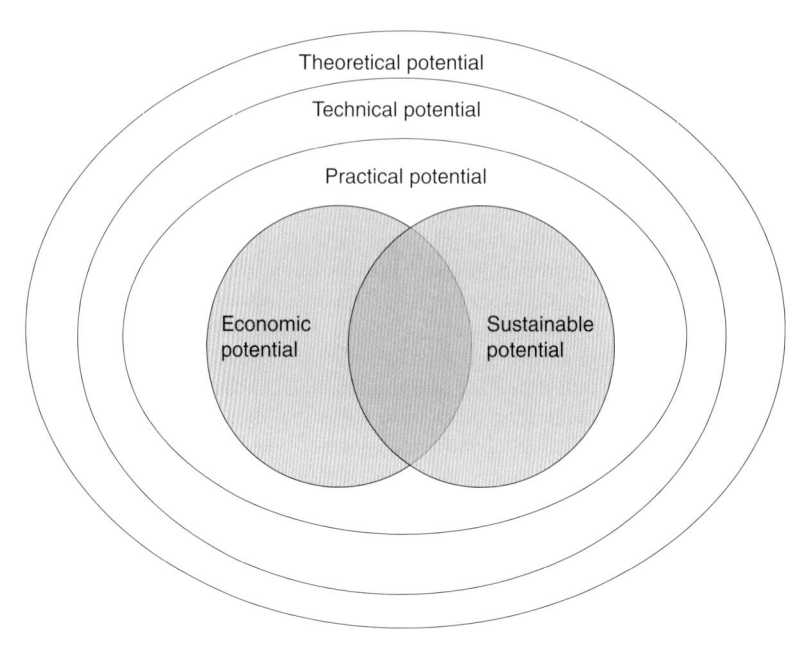

Figure 1 Constraints on biomass resource potential.

utilize unsustainable resource. In an ideal world, policy instruments would be utilized so that the two central circles were exactly coincident.

In reality, the diversity of bioenergy feedstocks and potential impacts probably renders this an impossible task. Both the economic and sustainable potential will vary depending on production methods, location, and so on, and there can never be perfect knowledge of all feedstock supply chains. Some uncertainty will always remain. Additionally, sustainability of a bioenergy system is not confined to the resource provision. It is necessary to also consider the processing, transport, and conversion of the feedstock in a holistic manner. So, while it is acknowledged that it may never be possible for the two shaded circles in **Figure 1** to be completely coincident, maximizing the overlap can still remain an objective.

5.21.1.3 Unique Attributes of Biomass and Supply Chains

Biomass is unique within the renewable energy sector in that it is the only directly storable renewable energy resource and so can be dispatched on demand, providing valuable energy security benefits. It is also uniquely flexible in terms of having potential to service the electricity, heat, and transport fuel demand sectors as well as to provide a source of renewable chemicals. It is a physical commodity that can be directly traded within or across national boundaries. These attributes provide many advantages and the trading prospects offer potential socioeconomic benefits that do not exist for other renewable energy forms. Bioenergy policy development could focus on maximizing such opportunities, but this brings with it challenges.

No other renewable energy form has such an extensive physical interface with society. Human input is required at every stage of a bioenergy fuel supply chain, and there are potential costs and benefits both for society and for the environment at practically every stage of fuel supply chains that can physically span thousands of miles and many different individuals and companies. Bioenergy systems affect many different physical entities and cross many different disciplinary/legislative areas, for example, agriculture, land use, employment, and hydrology. Additionally, the diversity of bioenergy options is huge because biomass is an umbrella term for many different types of material: forest products, energy crops, agricultural residues, wastes – all are biomass, but all with different characteristics, utilities, and impacts. Simply accumulating the information required to understand a particular supply chain can be difficult enough and to then attempt to manipulate and mange that to vary different impacts is a formidable task.

Effective supply chain management presupposes that society 'knows' what it wants to maximize and minimize. Bioenergy fuel supply chains can provide employment opportunities, GHG reductions, biodiversity, and many other benefits, but there are also costs in terms of environmental pollution, land use, and so on, and it is not possible to maximize all benefits for every supply chain. Therefore, there is a need to be aware, from a policy perspective, that nothing is perfect. Bioenergy, like every other energy system, has costs and benefits. Varying the technology, the feedstock, the geographic location, or the demand sector will alter the relative benefits and costs. The choice of options (and therefore the costs and benefits accrued by society) can be guided by the application of different policy instruments, but stakeholders must first be clear which benefits they wish to promote and which costs are to be avoided and the extent of trade-offs between these.

The challenges for bioenergy policy development are, therefore, substantial. There is a clear need to reduce global GHG emissions, and bioenergy can play a key role in that, offering additional energy security and socioeconomic and ecological benefits at the same time. However, there is also the potential for significant impacts on society and the environment. Policy objectives should be to maximize the deployment of sustainable bioenergy chains that offer real GHG reductions while minimizing other impacts. However, the diversity of bioenergy options, the complexity of supply chains, our uncertain knowledge, and variations in the priorities associated with different impacts all combine to make effective bioenergy policy development extremely challenging.

5.21.2 Bioenergy Policy Development

5.21.2.1 Achieving GHG Reductions with Biomass: A Key Policy Objective

For many years, there has been a focus on trying to increase the deployment of bioenergy systems – getting more biomass to be used to provide heat, electricity, and transport fuels. More recently, this has been tempered by a growing awareness that the GHG savings achieved by different bioenergy schemes can be very different. Increasing the deployment of bioenergy systems should, therefore, prioritize those systems that maximize the GHG savings achieved. Doing this requires some mechanism for measuring and incentivizing GHG savings. The GHG savings achievable and their measurement are discussed in more detail elsewhere in this comprehensive. This results in a policy objective for bioenergy of maximizing GHG savings. However, there are many different ways to approach the idea of 'maximization'.

The first and most obvious parameter that most people will consider is the GHG reductions obtained by replacing a unit of energy with a unit of bioenergy. We might want to choose the bioenergy system that resulted in the largest GHG savings per unit of bioenergy delivered. That will depend on a number of parameters that are actually not connected with the bioenergy system, including the energy form being displaced. An attractive way of maximizing the GHG savings might, therefore, be to ensure that bioenergy always displaces the most carbon-intensive forms of existing energy. But this does not necessarily lead to global or even national reductions in GHGs. We may simply end up with leakage from the system. Suppose that a home with a coal-fired boiler installs a biomass boiler instead. We could calculate the savings associated with the switch and assume that this actually results in a correspondingly reduced amount of GHG emissions. If this happened on a large scale across a country, we might conclude that there has been a national reduction in emissions as a result of switching from biomass to coal. However, implicit within this analysis is the assumption that everything else stays the same. For example, it could be that a switch from coal to biomass results in reduced market demand for coal for heating and possibly a slump in market price. This coal could then end up being used elsewhere, for example, it could be taken up in locations that currently use lower carbon intensity fuels such as gas. So, the direct reduction calculated at the point of use is not necessarily the same as the contribution to national emission reductions.

The key driver for most GHG reductions is the need to reduce global emissions in response to the threat of climate change. This is managed by the United Nations Environment Programme (UNEP) via the UNFCC, under which different countries commit to achieving different levels of reduction, consistent with a global target that is aimed at preventing the more extreme impacts of dangerous climate change. Therefore, most governments focus on reducing their national emission inventory. When providing national inventory returns in-line with guidance from the IPCC, countries are obliged to report the emissions associated with solid biomass as well as those associated with fossil fuels. Emission factors from the IPCC guidelines tier 1 methodology are given in Table 1.

It can be seen that the emissions from solid biomass are actually higher than those from a competing fossil fuel source (particularly when we take into account the GHG intensity of the species involved). However, the 'carbon neutrality' argument for biomass is that the carbon in this fuel has been recently sequestered from the atmosphere and, therefore, its combustion and associated release of carbon dioxide does not actually result in any net increase in atmospheric carbon dioxide emissions. From a national emissions inventory perspective, the GHG emissions from this combustion are, therefore, effectively being offset by carbon sequestration through biomass growth. This is accounted for in returns to the IPCC related to land, where national inventory compilers state the area of land planted with particular forest species, state the associated annual increment, and infer the carbon sequestered. The result is that the idea of maximizing GHG savings at a national level becomes dependent on maximizing the net terrestrial sequestration of GHGs. If the policy objective were to minimize the national emissions inventory returns, then a logical action to incentivize would be to have as much land as possible covered with fast-growing species with high annual carbon increments.

In reality, plants and trees have a growth pattern such that the carbon sequestered varies with time, as does the proportion that is sequestered in roots, soil, or standing biomass. This has implications for when trees are felled in managed forests. Optimization of forest management for maximum carbon sequestration may require different forest management practices from maximization of commercial profit for the saw log or other timber products, for example, [5]. At a very simplistic level, optimizing for carbon

Table 1 IPCC default tier 1 emission factors for biomass and coal [4]

	CO_2 emission factor (kg of greenhouse gas per TJ on a net calorific value basis)	CH_4 emission factor (kg of greenhouse gas per TJ on a net calorific value basis)	N_2O emission factor (kg of greenhouse gas per TJ on a net calorific value basis)
Primary solid biomass	100 000	30	4
Bituminous coal	94 600	1	1.5

sequestration would suggest that trees are felled once the annual rate of sequestration had decreased to the mean level of sequestration that had been experienced up to that point. At that point in time, there is no carbon benefit in maintaining the trees in the ground – it would be preferable if they were felled and replaced with a new forest. This, of course assumes that the forest would be restocked with trees of the same species with the same growth and sequestration pattern. It is obviously then of interest to ensure that the felled forest material is used in an appropriate manner. If the biomass were simply left to decompose, this would generate substantial quantities of GHGs, which would be completely counterproductive. Instead, it is more likely to be used for timber, for board or paper manufacture, or for supplying energy demand. The relative merits of these options depend on which fraction of the tree is being considered, the local markets, and what would have been used had wood not been used for these products.

This implies that preference should be given to forests and tree species with the best carbon sequestration profiles. However, it must be remembered that a forest or woodland (and indeed land generally) is a multifunctional system, servicing the demands of many different users and such decisions cannot be made on the basis of carbon efficiency alone. There is a need to consider the commercial timber specification, the visual impacts of trees, hydrology, biodiversity, climate, situation, and a whole host of other factors in determining which species should be planted in which locations.

A key issue that arises from this discussion, though, is that there is no sequestration-related inventory benefit to a particular nation in importing biomass for energy purposes that has been grown overseas, since it must report the emissions associated with the biomass combustion or other utilization on its own soil, but cannot report the sequestration benefits that are outside its own territorial limits. In many ways, the national boundaries associated with responsibility for GHG inventories are inadequate to reflect the global bioenergy trade and are certainly inadequate for assessing the GHG benefits accruing from bioenergy and identifying any potential shortcomings.

At a global level, the policy objective differs somewhat. Here the interest is in minimizing the total global emissions of all GHGs. In some ways, the 'case for bioenergy' becomes clearest at this level. When bioenergy is considered at this level, we need to look at the carbon sequestered during global production of biomass feedstocks and global utilization, not necessarily at the same location. At this scale, we are balancing the sequestration achieved on land with the displacement of more carbon-intensive forms of fossil fuel energy.

Three simultaneous policy objectives are thereby introduced:

1. To grow biomass to sequester as much carbon per unit of land as possible (which will depend on geographic location and species).
2. To ensure that the bioenergy displaces more carbon-intensive forms of fossil fuel energy.
3. To minimize the additional emissions generated in ensuring that the growth in 1 matches the demand in 2, that is, to minimize emissions associated with processing, transporting, and transforming biomass to suit end user's demands.

These objectives will be met by a very large number of different bioenergy supply chains that may cross many national boundaries. There are two basic problems with optimizing these objectives to maximize GHG reductions. First of all, there are no institutions in place that have jurisdiction at this pan-national level. Second, every supply chain is different and the extent to which the objectives are met will be variable (and in many cases, there will be insufficient information available to be able to evaluate the extent to which the objectives are being met).

5.21.2.2 Achieving Sustainable Development with Bioenergy: Key Policy Objectives

GHGs are, of course, a key element of sustainable development, but there is also a need to think far beyond the GHG issues. Sustainable development was perhaps best defined by the World Commission on Environment and Development in 1987 [6].

> **Sustainable development meets the needs of the present generation without compromising the ability of future generations to meet their needs.**

This definition of sustainable development first of all actually reiterates the case for urgently reducing GHG emissions: it is not sustainable for the present generation to continue to emit at current levels, knowing that this risks irreparable damage to the global ecosphere and/or will increase the reductions that will be required from future generations. However, it also reminds us that sustainable development is about more than just GHGs, and bioenergy systems may sometimes reduce GHG emissions at the expense of other environmental impacts, for example, increased levels of certain airborne pollutants or possibly reduced levels of biodiversity or potential contamination of watercourses. It is difficult to balance these competing factors. On the one hand, we have a parameter (GHGs) that acknowledges we need to reduce GHG emissions as much as possible – the capacity of our ecosystem to deal with continued emissions is extremely limited. On the other hand, we have a range of parameters that also have potential to cause environmental damage, but there is also some ecosystem capacity to absorb some of these impacts, and the absorption capacity depends on a huge number of different factors, for example, physical location, background levels of other activities, and timing of releases (e.g., when considering eutrophication and nitrification). It is also the case that we are dealing on the one hand with a substance (GHGs) that we are generally trying to minimize globally, but on the other hand we are often dealing with pollutants whose impact is more local and traditionally environmental protection for these would be via limits on locally or nationally issued permits. On the one hand, it could be argued that it should be sufficient for new bioenergy schemes to simply meet existing environmental protection limits, for example, with respect to airborne pollutants. On the other hand, some observers would consider it morally unacceptable for installations that cause substantial environmental impacts to be rewarded with financial premiums for being 'renewable' or 'low carbon'.

In the wider literature, sustainability is generally construed as having three main pillars:

- Ecology
- Economy
- Society

Sustainable development can, therefore, be visualized as in **Figure 2**, as a nexus that sits between these pillars, with attempts to expand within that space but constantly constrained by the tension between the pillars.

To develop sustainably, therefore, entails giving adequate consideration to not just the environmental impacts of bioenergy supply, but also to the wider impacts. These can range from impacts on market prices for food (through the interface with land) to changes in employment patterns for agricultural workers. The diversity of issues that need to be considered is huge. **Figure 3** shows some of the aspects that may be considered relevant for different bioenergy systems. Of course, not all of these will be relevant for all bioenergy systems. It depends on the feedstocks, the processing techniques, the demand form, and the geographic locations.

So, if we consider one aspect, such as conflict with local food production, there may be a whole host of bioenergy chains for which this is simply not relevant or applicable; for example, it is hard to envisage how this parameter could be directly relevant to the use of forest residues for power generation. For other bioenergy systems, the extent to which they comply with this sustainable development principle may vary. For example, most observers would agree that there is a significant difference between biomass production on land that was previously used to produce cereals, where that crop formed an integral part of the local food chain compared to where it was exported for global trade and where it was being stockpiled owing to national or international production surpluses or where its production has been displaced to nearby idle land. These various possibilities may be considered with different levels of acceptability by different observers and that will depend on the context of the activity as well as the perspective of the observer. In some cases, it may be possible to define minimum standards of acceptability, below which the supply chain would be considered unsustainable, but this is not always clear-cut. There are trade-offs involved, for example, the use of land for biomass production that was previously in private hands, but has been transferred to a national body might at first be considered to violate principles of sustainability, but this may depend on what the land was previously being used for and what the socioeconomic benefits related to the new use are, for example, how many jobs are created. Drawing lines that demarcate acceptable and unacceptable practices is morally and ethically challenging and requires some degree of knowledge of the history and context in which fuel supply chains are established.

In summary, there is an overriding incentive to develop bioenergy systems because of the carbon savings and reduced dependency on fossil fuels that can result. However, there are many other potential impacts that could result from bioenergy projects. These can be dealt with by setting minimum standards that should not be violated, but these may be difficult to apply

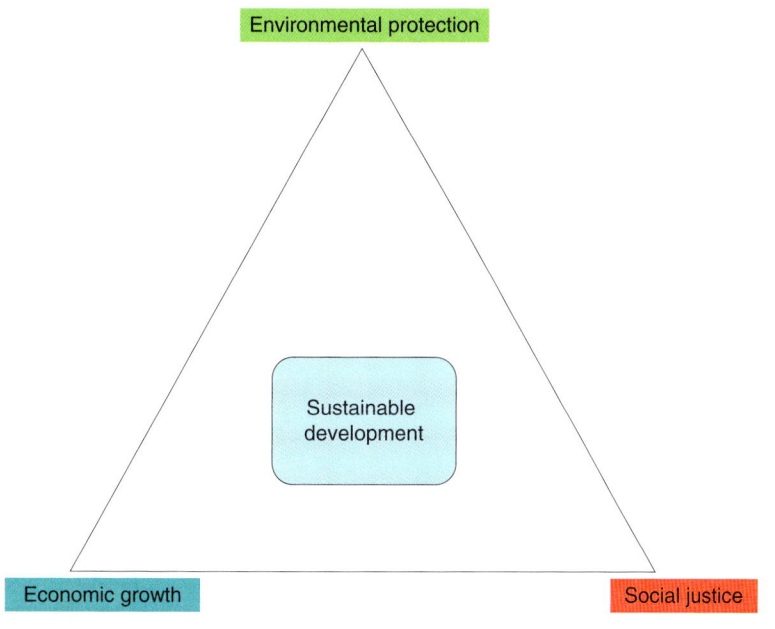

Figure 2 Sustainable development within the context of sustainability pillars.

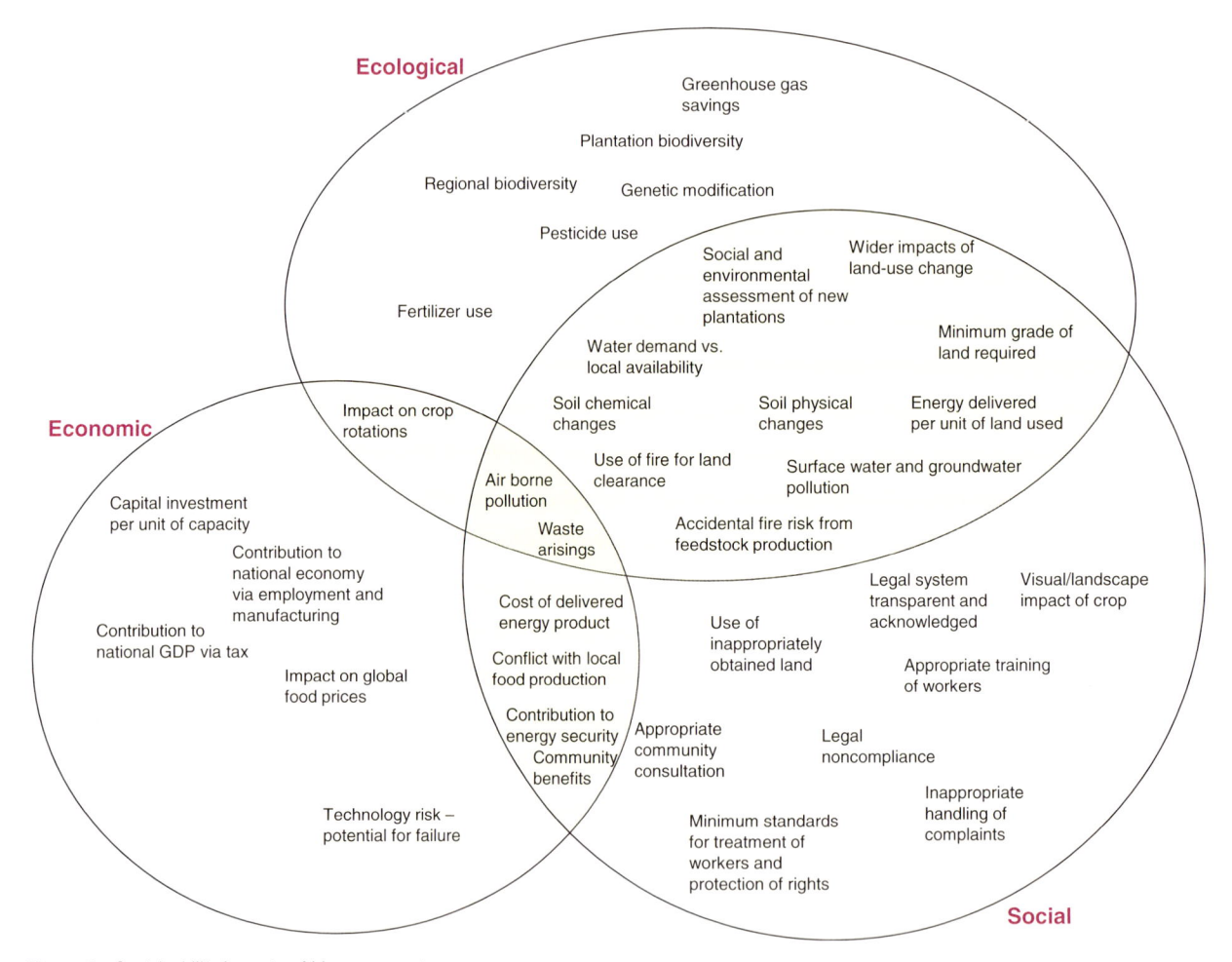

Figure 3 Sustainability impacts of bioenergy systems.

evenly across different social, cultural, and geographic contexts. Also, setting minimum standards does not actually promote the maximization on sustainability benefits or minimization of the impacts of a bioenergy system.

5.21.2.3 The Role of Energy Markets

Across Europe and many other parts of the world, there has been a huge shift from controlled, regulated national electricity and energy markets to deregulated markets in the past 20 years. The UK government was the first to make this switch in 1990 (although full market freedom was phased in over many years and there are still elements of regulation, such as the existence of a government regulator in the gas and electricity sectors (Office of Gas and Electricity Markets (OFGEM)), whose duty is to protect the interests of consumers). Since then, many others have followed suit with a program that involves introduction of wholesale and retail electricity markets and deintegration of generation and distribution activities in the electricity sector and the sale of previously state-owned assets to private shareholders. Deregulation is promoted as a means of achieving lower and more competitive prices for consumers, but it also has the advantage of providing scope for private sector investment into the energy system [7]. Availability of such investment funds is critical when we consider the huge capital costs required to transition the existing infrastructure to one consistent with a low carbon energy economy.

5.21.2.4 Correcting Market Failures

In principle, policy measures are put in place in order to address market failures in the energy system. At present, there is a need to ensure a switch from our existing energy supply system to one that results in lower levels of GHG emissions. The existing consumption pattern of predominantly fossil fuel-based energy sources in the United Kingdom results in GHG emissions. This emission has an impact on the environment and is called an externality, since it has an impact on the external world (beyond the energy provision scheme), which results in actual costs that are not taken into account by conventional economics. In this case, the costs to society of the climate change impacts associated with fossil fuel-based energy provision are not taken into account in the conventional energy system market economics. In other words, the social costs of the environmental damage caused by the private activity of providing energy are not offset by the wider social benefits of the energy provision activity.

In theory, economic markets can provide the opportunity for lowest cost provision of consumer needs. However, this 'lowest cost' is based only on the costs included within the physical system being considered. When externalities affect society as a whole (such as is the case with regard to fossil fuel-based energy provision), there are additional costs that are not taken into account by the market. Effectively the market has failed to deliver what is required because it is not taking account of the cost of external impacts. When this happens, governments may intervene and try to guide behavior in order to ensure that market failures are corrected. Thus, policy instruments are introduced by governments as an attempt to address the social costs and to reduce the externalities that the energy system brings to society.

5.21.2.5 Environmental Policy Options

In principle, there are two ways in which the externalities associated with fossil fuel-based energy systems can be addressed and previously non-monetized costs be brought into market calculations:

- provision of low or no carbon energy sources is encouraged in a way that reduces their cost or
- suppliers of fossil fuel energy sources are penalized, such that their cost is increased.

The ultimate aim is to change the energy provision practices, which equates to changing the behavior of the supply companies and/or the consumers. This can generally be achieved if either

- the change is enforced by rule or laws or
- there is a perceived economic advantage in making the change.

From a GHG perspective, the second option of penalizing fossil fuel energy supply is attractively simple. In principle, doing this should promote low carbon energy options, including bioenergy, and should provide a way to achieve an optimal lowest market cost provision.

The main problem with this approach is that it is somewhat one dimensional. It presupposes that the only parameter that needs to be considered is GHG emissions and optimizes on that basis. In reality, there are many other parameters that a government might want to take into account. These could, for example, include energy security, intermittency, and pollution impacts. For example, when we consider current energy systems, it could be argued that promoting natural gas usage at the expense of coal could be achieved by direct carbon taxation. However, this ignores the fact that for the United Kingdom at present, increased reliance on natural gas decreases energy security, increasing the vulnerability of the energy system. Similarly, when it comes to looking at the low-carbon options, bioenergy systems will generally have higher GHG emissions than, say, wind energy, but they offer a base load capability that wind does not. Therefore, there are other factors that need to be taken into account that result in the conclusion that not all forms of low carbon energy are equally sensible or desirable in specific contexts. By simply penalizing fossil fuel suppliers, a government would effectively be encouraging low-carbon alternatives, but would lose control over the portfolio of low-carbon replacements coming forward, which might not be desirable depending on how important the other factors are deemed to be in a particular set of circumstances. Moreover, the economics of different forms of energy supply can change over time, and there is a risk that the energy supply infrastructure might get developed in a way that does not make sense in the long term when the economics of future energy supply issues are taken into account. Therefore, while there is generally some utility in discouraging high carbon energy supply, as can be achieved, for example, with taxation, this is a crude instrument, which is most often supplemented (or in some cases displaced entirely) by support for more desirable low-carbon alternatives.

In most countries in the world, bioenergy is seen as having some role to play in a lower carbon energy supply system. In some countries, this is also the most economic alternative based on current economic market conditions. However, in many instances that is not the case and, therefore, there is no perceived economic advantage in making the change. Government policies, therefore, have two possible routes: they may enforce a switch to bioenergy based on rules or laws (unlikely in free market economies where one energy form should not necessarily be preferred over another) or they can put in place mechanisms or incentives that adjust the market economics to result in a perceived economic benefit in switching to a range of different renewables that include bioenergy. This option allows some tailoring of the circumstances in which the switch should be made; for example, instruments may be developed that focus only on certain demand sectors (electricity, heat, or transport) or only on a subset of existing users, for example, existing solid fuel installations. This clearly has benefits where there is a strong vision of an acceptable future energy scenario, but needs to be carefully balanced against the need to allow the markets sufficient freedom to actually find a least-cost solution.

Sections 5.21.2.5.1–5.21.2.5.5 summarize the main environmental policy instruments that may be used by a government in order to change behavior. Examples are given of how they can be used in the energy sector and their relevance and appropriateness for bioenergy are discussed.

5.21.2.5.1 *Investment subsidies and new technology support*

When we look at the established energy supply sector, it is clear that there are huge differences in cost profiles between different commercial technologies. This is part of what distinguishes one technology from another, and even within the renewable and low carbon energy technologies, there are very different economic profiles. For example, a key distinction of biomass is that it has an ongoing fuel cost, whereas most other renewable technologies have a high initial capital cost but much lower ongoing operational costs.

However, there is also an added issue in that many of the low-carbon technologies are not yet fully commercial. In general, it is assumed that new technologies will initially have high costs that will be reduced in time because production volumes and technology innovation bring down the cost of capital equipment, experience reduces maintenance costs, and replication reduces development and associated costs. For this reason, it is often the case that technologies that are in earlier stages of development will need specific support. When this is the case, governments frequently choose a variety of different schemes to support technologies through various phases of development. **Figure** 4 illustrates some of the different mechanisms that can be used to support developing technologies on their path to becoming fully commercial.

From **Figure** 4, at the early stages of technology development, funding of the science and engineering aspects of new technologies is generally achieved through support for research through academic institutes. For technologies or applications that are closer to market, support is via research or research and development funding in collaboration between industry and academia or at industrial research centers. This generally takes most technologies through demonstration of concepts. Beyond that support is needed to demonstrate the actual application and this often involves support for a pilot project followed by a demonstration plant. The technology then enters the pre-commercial stage, where multiple units begin to be installed, then the supported commercial stage, where the technology has the attributes of a commercial competitor (in terms of scale, availability, backup support, etc.) but is not yet economically competitive. Ultimately, there will be cost reduction as technology costs reduce through innovation, learning, and experience, as described above.

The transition from research project to demonstration plant is a difficult one, where new technologies are particularly likely to fail to achieve the desired or effective uptake. Capital investment grants are the most commonly used support mechanism at that phase and are shown on the diagram, but there are other options that could be considered, such as government guarantees to underwrite risk associated with demonstration/deployment. It is important to realize that capital grants will not support the ongoing costs experienced by bioenergy projects (predominantly fuel costs), and there is a risk that providing initial capital grants to support maturing technologies will facilitate construction of plants that do not have a viable long-term fuel strategy and are more prone to commercial failure in the long term [7]. Where such supported plants are particularly high profile, this can be extremely damaging to the public perceptions and long-term future of the industry.

A second common area for failure is the transition from demonstration to commercial operation (sometimes called the 'valley of death' because of the notoriety with which technologies can fail to make this transition). One of the difficulties here in a commercial market is the need, or at least perceived need, to treat different technologies equally in order for the market to operate effectively.

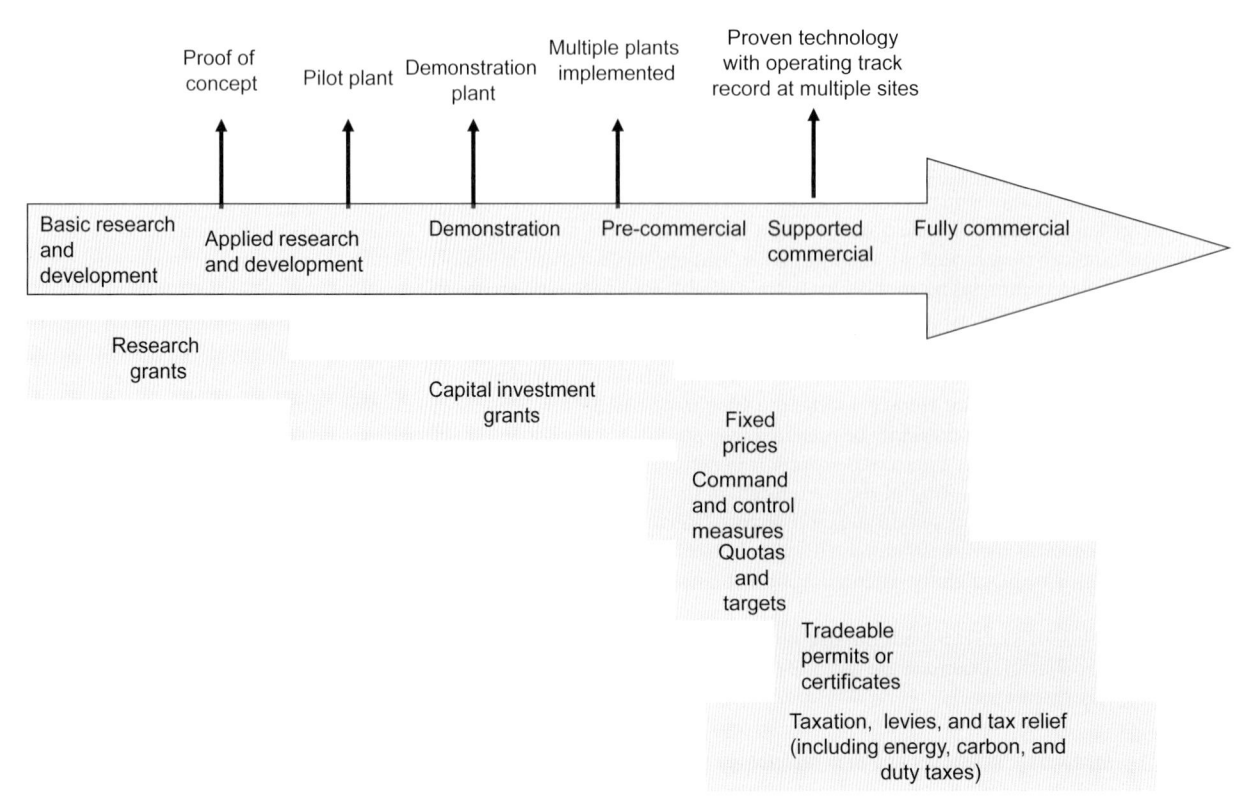

Figure 4 Chronological development of new technologies with identifiable milestones and possible support measures.

Therefore, providing extended support for a technology perceived as being at the same development stage as another technology not receiving that support is considered unreasonable.

In recent years, there have been some particularly innovative approaches to bridging these gaps. In the United Kingdom, the Carbon Trust, which is a government-backed company with private clean energy investment objectives, has supplied funding for demonstration of marine devices and for biomass systems. The Biomass Heat Acceleration Project is a particularly interesting example as the biomass heating plants that were installed were largely identical across different industrial sites, with key aims of building knowledge and capacity in a broad manner in the sector. They have also implemented a Marine Energy Accelerator Project, which focuses on supporting the particularly problematic areas for companies making the transition from demonstration to commercial operation. Focus on the medium-term operational issues has also been encouraged by strategies such as linking the financial awards in the Carbon Trust's marine energy challenge to actual generating output over a fixed period. Therefore, financial support is provided, but clearly linked to medium-term commercial performance objectives.

Once technologies have effectively proven their commercial readiness, it is still likely that they will cost significantly more than fossil fuel alternatives. This is partly because of technology immaturity and partly because the market structure does not recognize the costs associated with the environmental externalities introduced by the fossil fuel alternatives. It may therefore be necessary to continue to financially support clean technologies, including biomass, during the pre-commercial stage.

Many authors assume that experience and increased deployment of clean technologies will result in cost reductions and it is common practice to apply learning curve reduction rates when considering the economics of clean energy systems, for example, [8]. It is worth pausing to think about the applicability of this practice in relation to bioenergy. In other fields, such as solar photovoltaics (PV) or wave or tidal device development, there is potential for cost reductions due to technology or material developments, or scale-up of material or device production. However, bioenergy often relies on fairly well-established technologies, such as steam turbines or reciprocating engines. There is no real reason why the cost of these should decrease as bioenergy deployment expands. On the contrary, much of the development focus for bioenergy is in adapting these devices for particular feedstocks or local conditions. It is quite unusual for the same fuel supply to be replicated at more than one site and so the engineering challenges associated with the interfaces and integration in designing bioenergy systems tend to result in high levels of engineering costs for bioenergy systems compared to conventional ones. Scale is also important: bioenergy systems are often small-scale facilities in order to respond to the local availability of feedstock, but they can be just as complex as much larger plant and this means that the relative cost of engineering and design will generally remain higher for bioenergy facilities than for fossil fuel equivalents. This means that for many bioenergy technologies there will not necessarily be a narrowing of the gap between bioenergy costs and coal, oil, and gas equivalents in the medium term. In the absence of substantial increases in the prices of fossil fuels, it is therefore possible that if bioenergy is to play a significant role in the future energy mix, there will be a need for continued support in the long term.

5.21.2.5.2 Command and control instruments

Command and control instruments involve a government issuing a command, which sets a standard and then controlling performance by monitoring and requiring adherence to that standard. It is most commonly applied to pollution issues, where a command might be that no facility will emit more than 'x' units of pollutant per measured output unit or measure. In the case of minimizing GHG emissions and promoting renewables, including bioenergy, the pollutants of concern would obviously be GHGs. The command and control approach would therefore equate to setting a maximum limit on the amount of GHG emissions per unit of energy produced. This requires actually calculating GHG emissions for the entire energy supply chain, which is data intensive and time consuming. Different cutoff points would have to be developed for different energy demand sectors, for example, electricity is a higher grade fuel than heat with correspondingly higher levels of carbon emissions.

When command and control systems are introduced for pollution control, it is generally possible to retrofit systems to existing plants that would then allow them to comply. With the exception of carbon capture and storage technology, which is, as yet, unproven at large scale, this is generally not possible when considering GHG emissions from existing facilities. This is contrary to the deregulated 'free market' concept on which most national electricity supply systems are now based. Also in most countries, it would effectively exclude established coal-fired electricity plants, which make a valuable contribution to the stability of national electricity grid systems. While it could be argued that other options (including nuclear and indeed biomass) could provide this base load capacity, many countries do not have substantial nuclear or biomass bases and so substantial new investment would be required. Therefore, the idea of a maximum permitted level of carbon emissions in the electricity sector is not something that could be effectively implemented straightaway – a timetable plan would be needed for energy systems to adjust with minimal user disruption.

A good example of command control instruments being used effectively in the energy sector is the phased European Union ban on incandescent filament light bulbs. However, key features to note are that this applied to an object with a relatively short lifetime, so that there was not an issue with failing to make best use of existing bulbs. This is not usually the case with energy supply, where the supply infrastructure is often fuel specific (e.g., gas pipelines) and is designed to last many years. Additionally, there is, arguably, very little difference between the functionality of a filament bulb and a low energy one. Again, this is not the case when we look at the options for wider energy supply.

If a maximum GHG limit were applied, it would be fairly straightforward to determine whether fossil fuel-based plants met the standard or not because most of the GHG emissions are related to the fuel burnt, which could be easily analyzed. However, as discussed earlier for biomass, the carbon emissions that must be considered are those involved in producing, harvesting, processing, and transporting the biomass, which requires complex and lengthy calculations with significant uncertainties. The uncertainty is often due to incomplete knowledge of all of the steps in the bioenergy supply chain (e.g., not knowing what fertilizer regime was used or how far material was transported or how and when it was dried or comminuted) but also due to scientific uncertainty (e.g., the range of possible N_2O emissions that may result for fertilizer application or the gaps in understanding related to the long-term soil carbon impacts of biomass growth). The result is that it is often difficult to be able to say with a high degree of confidence what carbon emissions are actually associated with a particular unit of bioenergy. This is obviously problematic if a cutoff is introduced, where bioenergy might meet the requirements in some circumstances, but not in others, but would require a substantial body of evidence to support this, and at the time of building a plant, it is not necessarily assured that it will or will not meet certain minimum carbon thresholds – this depends on the fuel that is supplied subsequently.

In other demand sectors, the issues are slightly different. When looking at transport, it would be possible to set a maximum GHG intensity for all new (or even existing) vehicles. Some vehicles would meet that through using technologies such as use of fuel cells or batteries. Other vehicles might meet the standard with conventional petroleum products in very efficient engines. However, others might meet it by using traditional engines with low-carbon fuels, including biofuels. Licensing or approving new vehicles at the point of production would be fairly straightforward, but it is difficult to envisage a system that would facilitate continuous monitoring of the type of fuel used in vehicles throughout their lifetime. Furthermore, the efficiency of different vehicles is not the only parameter that should be taken into account. More efficient vehicles might not be suitable for different applications or users as they will have different technical performance, size, capacity, and so on. The removal of choice in this way runs counter to many of the principles and customs associated with a global consumer society.

Heat is easier to consider in many ways since the technologies are generally more directly linked to the fuel and so it is the technology–fuel combination that is characterized by a particular level of GHG emissions. Therefore, it would, in principle, be possible to implement a cutoff regulation that did not allow heat supply with high carbon intensity and there are precedents for this sort of activity; for example, the introduction of 'smokeless fuel' zones in the United Kingdom. Restricting heat supply on the basis of carbon intensity would have to be implemented on a location-specific basis taking into account other constraints. For example, it would be relatively straightforward to prohibit open coal fires (probably the most carbon-intensive form of heating), but even this could run into difficulty in regions with strong coal-mining industry links. Moving down the carbon intensity profiles, oil burning facilities would be next to come under scrutiny, but these could only realistically be banned where suitable alternatives existed in the form of biomass or natural gas. So, as the carbon threshold becomes lower, we are restricting the heating options available to consumers and this will inevitably lead to specific areas where there are no alternatives at present, so care is required.

In summary, minimum GHG emission standards for power plants could be introduced as a command and control measure to drive GHG reductions. However, these would likely increase the intermittency and unpredictability of current generation and would require phased introduction. The extent to which bioenergy would be incentivized by such a measure would depend on the level at which the threshold is set. Demonstrating the actual GHG savings for different systems is very labor and time intensive, and the results often remain highly uncertain. For transport, integration of different command and control mechanisms would be required to cover the equipment and feedstock combination. For heating the use of some command and control measures would be feasible, but specific infrastructure and geographic limitations would have to be taken into account.

However, the real issue with command and control options and establishment of minimum thresholds is that there is a need for diversity in the energy supply system in order to maximize security and resilience and minimize vulnerability. Therefore, there may be a place for some contribution from energy sources that are more carbon intensive, but this policy approach does not facilitate that.

5.21.2.5.3 Incentive-based instruments

Incentive-based instruments, in principle, incentivize the use of energy from lower carbon intensity sources compared to those with higher carbon intensities. Ideally, this should result in a financial incentive for the consumer to choose the low carbon energy supply system. However, in some cases, it may be sufficient to narrow the gap between a higher cost, low carbon energy form, and a fossil fuel equivalent.

There are a wide variety of ways in which the financial gap can be narrowed. One is to include the application of taxes or levies to the higher carbon intensity energy systems. For example, the UK government's climate change levy is payable as a percentage of the cost of delivered energy on nonrenewable generation. Swedish energy taxes are another example. Another approach is a subsidy for the lower carbon intensity system (e.g., reduction in taxes payable for renewable energy capital items, such as paying a lower rate of value added tax (VAT) on renewable energy products, such as biomass boilers, or alternative fuels, such as lower taxation rates to incentivize biofuels, practiced in many countries in Europe over the years, including the United Kingdom and Germany).

5.21.2.5.4 Tradable permits and green certificate schemes

There are two main contexts in which quotas or permits may play a role in environmental policy structures. The first is based on scenarios where we are trying to limit environmental damage caused by pollution. The largest experience based on such measures is in the fisheries industry, where concerns about overfishing have led to imposition of quotas that limit the quantities of fish removed by nations and actors in future. Translating this concept to GHGs and climate change, the aim is to limit GHG emissions and this can be achieved by imposing maximum quotas or permits to emit certain amounts of GHGs. Thus, in the European Union Emissions Trading Scheme, for example, national emissions targets are agreed at international level and nation states allocate tradable emission permits, called European Union Allowances (EUAs), to the main emitters in their country, in principle (though not necessarily in practice), at a level that obliges those emitters to either reduce their emissions or purchase those permits from other firms. Under the Kyoto Protocol, the (potentially tradable) permits are called assigned amount units. By allowing emissions permits (i.e., allowances) to be transferred from one entity to another, a market for them is created so that the least-cost method of meeting the quota requirement can theoretically be achieved. This relies on the idea that each participating entity will have knowledge of the changes it will have to make and costs it will incur in order to change its operation and reduce its GHG emission by the required amount. It therefore has two options: it can either pay this cost and reduce its emissions or it can instead purchase a permit to emit more than the quota (quantity of permits or allowances) that it has been allocated. The decision depends on the cost of purchasing the permit [9].

To date, the European Union Emissions Trading Scheme has resulted in no significant reductions in the GHG emissions of the relevant sectors. There are many reasons for this, but one reason is arguably that the initial quotas are set too high, so that industrialists actually have no incentive to abate because they can continue business as usual and the trading price of carbon is too low, so that those who do need to purchase more credits will do that in preference to abating their emissions. It is possible that, in the longer term, with tighter GHG emission limits and higher carbon prices, the scheme may be more effective, but there is little evidence of that to date. Another reason is that the system is vulnerable to economic fluctuations, notably recessions.

Given that this approach focuses on GHGs, it would suffer from many of the issues mentioned above when applied to bioenergy in that the calculations of actual carbon emission saved would be subject to a high degree of uncertainty and need to be approached with a standard methodology. It would obviously make sense if there were some harmonization of this methodology across the different national and international schemes, but that seems a long way off.

Taking the converse approach: it could be said that the secondary policy objective is actually to promote renewables (or in this case bioenergy) and a permit or quota-type system could be developed focused on mandating a minimum quantity of low carbon energy from suppliers. This is effectively the approach taken by most 'green certificate'-type schemes. Although there are variations in how these are implemented, they generally involve a mandate or target of a minimum quantity of renewable energy.

So, a typical green certificate scheme involves an obligation on electricity suppliers to supply a certain percentage of their electricity from a renewable source; for every unit of electricity they produce, they are awarded a green certificate. By law, they must ensure they have a sufficient number of certificates corresponding to the required percentage of renewables. This mechanism takes into account that some suppliers will not finance investment in alternative forms of energy, thus they are able to buy certificates from other companies who have succeeded in doing so. A market of certificates is thus created, and suppliers may trade their certificates to gain a higher price from those who have not succeeded. The detail of these schemes varies across countries; for example, there may be price controls for the certificates or a penalty may be payable for deficits, which may be recovered by central government or recycled back to certificate holders.

So far, green certificate schemes in the renewable energy sector have focused on electricity only, not heat or power. There are two main reasons for this:

- In most countries, the electricity market (although it may be open to competition) is still subject to regulation, so that suppliers must possess some form of license. This makes it easy to identify and target all those involved in energy supply.
- Existing arrangements are in place for reliable metering and tracing of the quantity of electricity traded.

To date, green certificate schemes have not been very successful in promoting bioenergy [10]. The main reason for this is that the schemes are usually 'technology blind' and so treat all renewable electricity sources as equal and pay equally for them. In reality, bioelectricity schemes often cost more than other more established forms of renewable energy and so the premium payment offered by these schemes is insufficient to make project development commercially viable [11]. There are ways to adapt the schemes to reflect this and some recent experience of this is discussed in Section 5.21.3.1.

5.21.2.5.5 Fixed prices

From Section 5.21.2.5.4, it is clear that one of the challenges of encouraging renewables by making premium payments is that different technologies have different inherent costs and this is exacerbated when new technologies are at different stages along a technology or innovation learning curve. One obvious way around this is to pay different fixed prices for different technologies. This ensures that suppliers or developers of electricity are rewarded for their renewable energy and are guaranteed a fixed price for a given number of years. Normally, this fixed price (also known as a feed-in tariff or a fixed price premium) is higher than the prices paid for conventional fossil fuel electricity. The benefits of this approach are obvious in that, provided the incentive price is set at an appropriate level, it should have the effect of bringing on stream a variety of different technologies, rather than simply the lowest cost renewables.

However, there are many issues associated with this approach. First, at an ideological level, it could be argued that governments should not necessarily be promoting all technologies equally. There is a strong argument that by the time technologies are reaching full-scale rollout, the market will and should be favoring the most cost-effective option, and this is contrary to the idea of paying different prices for different technologies. In other words, the very idea of fixed prices or feed-in tariffs runs contrary to the principles of a deregulated energy market. Second, fixed prices are only a useful tool if the price paid is pitched at the right level and this takes time, effort, and insight to address. Third, this mechanism presents no incentive for generators to actually reduce their costs, and so does not encourage long-term efficiency developments.

It is also important to remember that bioenergy (and even bioelectricity) actually comprises a range of technology, feedstock, and scale options, all with different cost profiles. Most technologists would recognize that the unit cost of electricity from a 1-MWe plant producing electricity from gasification of energy crops would be more than from a 50-MWe facility producing electricity from combusting waste. Therefore, there may be a need to distinguish on the basis of feedstock, scale, and technology. It could therefore be argued that different fixed prices could be appropriate for different types of installation. However, this presupposes that a government can or should be supporting a variety of different types of bioenergy installation and whether or not this is the case depends very much on context. It has been demonstrated [12] that the public are generally more receptive to smaller scale, local bioenergy plants, and although these generally cost more [11], the carbon savings achieved vary little [13] and the impact of other environmental pollutants is likely to be higher [14]. It is therefore a public policy decision whether or not specific support should be given to different scale and technology categories, but once that decision has been made it should be noted that fixed prices that apply differently to different bioenergy plant types provide a mechanism for targeting that support.

When considering different payment options for different feedstock types, it should be noted that a single bioenergy plant will generally be designed with a specific chemical and physical feedstock specification in mind and plant performance will generally deteriorate if this is deviated from significantly. However, some of the attributes likely to be of most interest for differential payments (such as whether a feedstock is an energy crop or was produced sustainably or has originated within a prescribed distance) are unlikely to be verifiable at the point of use other than by an audit trail, with appropriate verification and documentation. As has been stated above, such provisions generally add to the complexity and cost of the support mechanism, which could reduce uptake by developers and be less cost efficient.

5.21.2.6 The Role of Markets in Ensuring Economic Efficiency

Some of the difficulties with fixed prices can be addressed by further tweaking of the mechanism, but each time this is done, the complexity of the instrument increases and its efficiency as an instrument for delivering cost-effective carbon savings decreases, partly due to the additional effort required to administer and monitor the scheme. Ultimately, this is because we are relying on a set of artificial structures to replicate the natural dynamics of an energy market, which is inevitably imperfect.

Similarly, the green certificate schemes described above can be adapted and tweaked to provide different levels of support for different types of bioenergy plant. For example, this has been done by the UK government, which has introduced a banded version of its renewables obligation, whereby generators are not awarded one certificate for every unit of electricity produced, but multiple or fractional numbers of certificates, depending on the technology and this is discussed in Section 5.21.3.1.

However, it must be remembered that the whole point of having a competitive energy market is to allow the market to find the most cost-effective energy supply options for consumers. It was explained in Section 5.21.2.5 that this often fails to take account of the wider impacts of the energy supply and when this happens governments may intervene and try to guide behavior in order to ensure that market failures are corrected, in order to balance societal externalities originating from the energy system. The green certificate schemes are focused on effectively creating an alternative market running in parallel with the electricity one to address this, but still retaining the market capability to identify the least-cost solution for consumers. Fixed prices and other more interventionist strategies by their very nature do not have this market flexibility or capability, and so are often less acceptable in contexts where 'free market' solutions pervade and frequently will not provide the most cost-effective option.

5.21.2.7 Scale of Impacts and Nonfinancial Barriers

While there are many different impacts of bioenergy plants, there are two other key characteristics of bioenergy systems that it is particularly worth considering when thinking about renewable energy externalities. The first is the security of supply provided by biomass compared to other renewables: it is the only renewable technology that provides storable energy that can be dispatched on demand. The second is that bioenergy generally incurs significant airborne emissions and these are another form of environmental externality from the energy system. It could, therefore, be argued that bioenergy should be rewarded to a greater extent than other renewables in recognition of its 'security' attribute or to a lesser extent in recognition of the external impact of airborne emissions. But scale is a significant issue here. The environmental impact of GHG emission is global and the existing atmospheric concentration of the GHGs are at such a high level that all additional emissions can be considered 'dangerous' and so there is justification in rewarding all reductions in GHGs no matter where they occur. This is not the case with security of supply or the impact of airborne emissions. Security of supply is generally only valued in a local up to national context. Therefore, it does not make sense to link premium payments to this unless there is a local/nationally identified need and contribution.

Airborne emissions are more difficult to deal with. The main pollutants of concern for bioenergy systems are particulates, NO_x, and certain hydrocarbon compounds, but most interest has focused on particulates to date, the impact of which is largely on local rather than national or global air quality. Therefore, emission levels that are acceptable in one location may not be acceptable in another. This degree of variation makes it very difficult to incorporate consideration of these externalities into a financial reward framework. The main alternative adopted by most countries has, therefore, been to require local environmental assessment for installation of bioenergy facilities deemed to have a significant environmental impact (generally judged at a certain size threshold). However, there is increasing concern that multiple installations of very small systems may have a significant air quality impact, particularly in areas where local air quality is already poor. This could be addressed by other (command and control) policy measures, such as minimum standards and type testing of devices, to meet certain minimum emissions standards coupled with requirements that only certain grades of devices are installed in different locations. Implementation of this requires a wide-reaching legislative compass but is achievable, for example, with an accredited network of installers who will only install certain devices in certain designated areas or by linking the payment of capital grants to devices with superior emissions performance.

Also, while it is true that in a perfect market, consumers will opt for the lowest cost option, there are many barriers to be overcome to provoke consumers to exercise that choice. Policy instruments may be utilized to result in a particular technology becoming the most cost-effective way of providing an energy demand, but there is an inertia threshold below which consumers will not act, so, in a sense the policy option has to do more than make the price equivalent to the fossil alternative, it has to make it 'worth the bother' to switch. This is an example of how, even when financial or economic viability is addressed, other significant barriers to implementation will remain. One assessment of such barriers for the European bioenergy system is given in **Figure 5**. In general, nonfinancial barriers to bioenergy implementation can be categorized as follows [15].

- Structural – the characteristics and needs of bioenergy are different from fossil fuel predecessors and so its development is impeded by boundary conditions that did not impede the previous fossil fuel systems.
- Market – the new technology addresses a need or provides societal benefits that are not valued by the current market, making it difficult for the new technology to compete.
- Interaction – development is obstructed because the developing technology draws upon knowledge, skills, and products of sectors and industries that are not bound with a common goal.
- Performance – the technology falls short of delivering the end user's performance requirement.

Most of the policy options described above are aimed at addressing the market barriers by adjusting the competitive market to value the benefits provided by bioenergy. However, addressing structural barriers may require direct intervention within the industry by capital investment, reorganization, or legislation. Performance barriers require either technical development or a readjustment of market focus to circumvent a technical constraint and are more likely to be addressed by developers than the policy community. Interaction barriers are perhaps the most difficult to address, as they require greater interaction between diverse bodies or individuals with diverse interests, some of whom have commercial or technical rationales for not communicating with other parties. A forum for communication and exchange is needed but also a common alignment of objectives is required so that participants see both the benefits to themselves and the need for involvement of other parties to more effectively achieve their own/

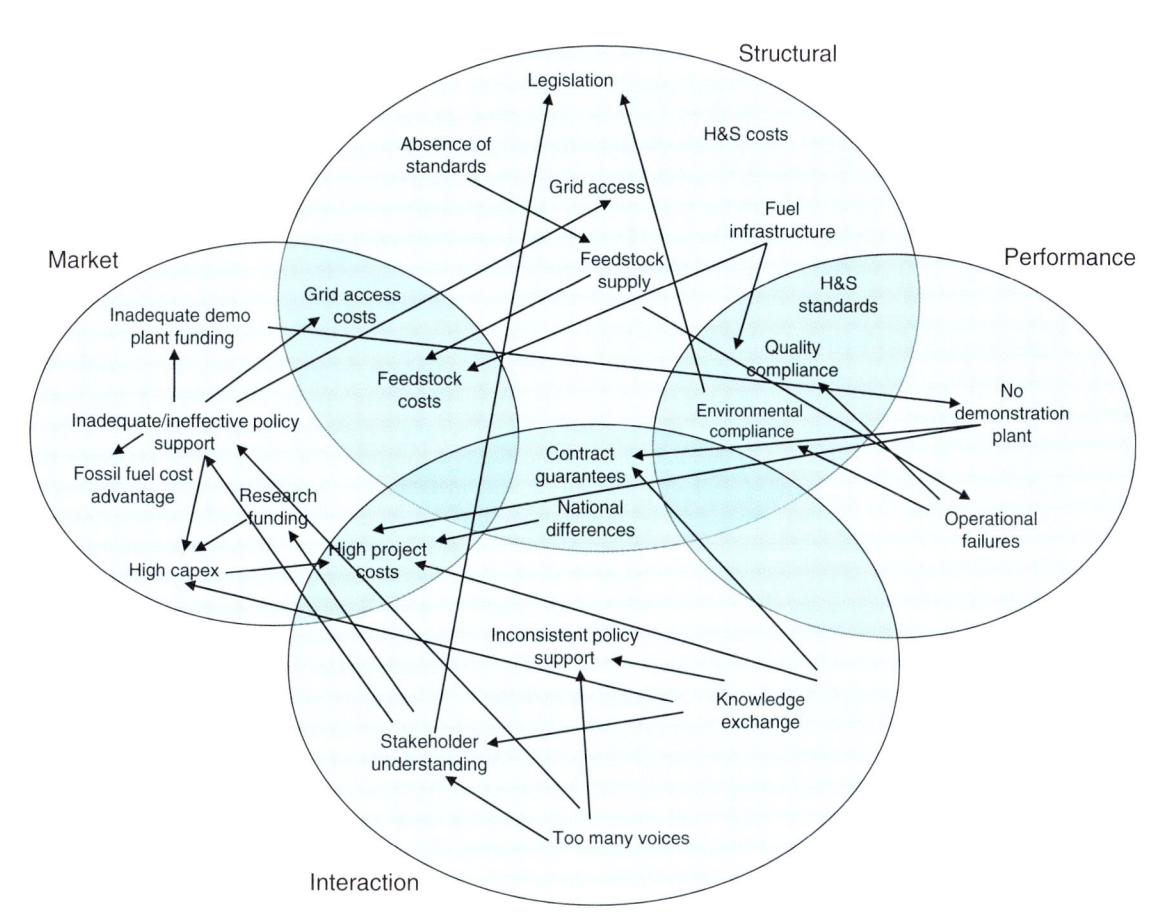

Figure 5 Barriers to development of bioenergy systems in Europe.

joint objectives. There may be some role for policy intervention to help achieve this, but it will depend on the specific market situation.

This motivational constraint is further complicated by the availability and targeting of relevant information. Work on barriers to GHG reductions in the process industries has shown that knowledge/information and its diffusion can be a key barrier [16] to implementation and this factor also applies to bioenergy.

It is therefore important that policy measures to increase bioenergy deployment actually go beyond simple financial measures to assist, where possible, in unblocking some of these other barriers. The actual measures taken will depend on the particular situation, but examples include the adaptation of German cars for biodiesel by manufacturers in 1995 followed by a prohibition on marketing of leaded petrol in 1996, which effectively liberated storage tanks for pure biodiesel in Germany, leading to a very rapid growth in biodiesel implementation between 1996 and 2003 [17]. Another example of structural changes aimed at addressing information barriers is the creation of the Biomass Energy Centre in the United Kingdom to act as a 'one-stop-shop' for bioenergy in the United Kingdom.

It is possible to recognize the benefits of particular supply chains by providing higher levels of subsidy, for example, to bioenergy systems that use energy crops from other preferred supply chains. However, another alternative is to instead target the support at another point in the bioenergy chain, for example, a more agriculturally targeted subsidy would be less likely to disrupt the existing renewable energy market [7].

5.21.3 Application of Environmental Policy Options to Bioenergy

Section 5.21.2 has considered the different policy options available to increase bioenergy deployment. This section takes a brief look at the actual experience of applying bioenergy policy instruments and the impacts achieved or expected.

5.21.3.1 Historical Bioenergy Policy Development

This section considers the actual implementation of such policy options in some example countries and analyzes the evidence related to their effectiveness. The evidence base is derived from the European ThermalNet network and, in particular, from the analysis of policy options to incentivize bioenergy carried out within that project. More detail on this can be found in the full report [17] or associated journal paper [10].

5.21.3.1.1 Bioenergy implementation in Italy, 1990–2005
A combination of investment subsidies and fixed prices were introduced in Italy in 1991 and this had a significant impact on bioenergy capacity. However, they were too expensive to maintain and the 4–5 years for which these were available were insufficient to establish the industry and so, in the absence of any new policy instrument, development subsequently stagnated. A subsequent carbon tax was effective in increasing output from lower cost waste feedstocks, but did not increase bioenergy capacity. This was only achieved after introduction of subsidies focusing on wood production in 2000 and the increase arising from this was sustained, possibly due to the parallel introduction of a green certificate scheme.

5.21.3.1.2 Bioenergy implementation in Germany, 1990–2005
Germany first implemented fixed prices for renewable energy support in 1991 and this legislation was revised or extended in 1998, 2000, 2002, and 2004. It also had investment subsidies in place for 10 years from 1992 to 2002 and implemented eco tax reforms in 1999. Initially, the fixed prices had very little impact on deployment capacity or plant operation. Investment subsidies had some effect, but this was limited. It was only when the funding for investment subsidies increased by several orders of magnitude that there was a significant impact on the installed dedicated biomass capacity in Germany. Combining this with fixed prices was successful in sustaining bioenergy development and the fixed prices were also very effective in promoting cofiring of biomass in existing coal-fired power stations. The German experience indicates the success of a two-pronged approach focusing both on overcoming the barrier to construction of new plant with investment subsidies (particularly where this is required to demonstrate the technology) and sustaining the industry with fixed prices at a sufficiently high level. It is interesting to note that the revenue for these actions has been supported by energy taxes [10].

5.21.3.1.3 Bioenergy implementation in the United Kingdom, 1990–2005
In the United Kingdom, the provision of a guaranteed, long-term power purchase agreement at an economically viable price was significant in initiating the development of the vast majority of the UK's dedicated biomass power stations [7], although the award of contracts only to the lowest priced options resulted in many of these focusing on waste feedstocks. Investment subsidies assisted in bringing forward new capacity but short-term, limited funding meant this did not translate into a long-term growth in the industry [10]. A tax on fossil fuel-based energy consumption did not have a significant impact on the energy mix, probably because of the low level at which it was set, although it provided some funding. A green certificate scheme was very successful for most of the renewable energy sector, but not for biomass, as it was technology blind, favoring lower cost renewables [10]. Recognition of this has led to modifications to the scheme, so that multiple certificates are issued for more expensive bioenergy technologies, which

now makes schemes more commercially attractive [11]. This has led to a very substantial increase in the number of planning applications during 2009–10 and it seems, therefore, that targeting bioenergy systems with appropriately priced rewards has been effective.

5.21.3.1.4 Bioenergy implementation in Sweden, 1990–2005

A long history of high levels of energy taxes in Sweden, including carbon taxes from which bioenergy was exempt, has facilitated a high level of bioenergy utilization, particularly for heating. An investment subsidy program in the electricity sector did increase capacity, but this was not sustained. A green certificate scheme in the electricity sector introduced in 2003 did seem to increase output from existing plants but did not initiate new capacity.

5.21.3.2 A Multidimensional Problem

The vast majority of policy incentives aimed at encouraging bioenergy have focused on incentivizing the servicing of energy demand. This results in a market pull for cost-effective feedstocks. In the absence of particular provisions, such as exclusion of waste, this results in an increased provision of the lowest cost feedstocks. These are often waste materials or materials with currently low market values. These can include feedstocks that have other material uses (e.g., wood products) or that can be used as food for humans or livestock. This inevitably leads to tension between the sectors, which is exacerbated by a lack of strong coordination between the agriculture, energy, and land-use planning sectors.

Bioenergy can certainly deliver GHG benefits and effectively replace fossil fuel consumption in many countries worldwide, but it has a multitude of other impacts and there is a need to find a way of effectively managing these and to promote best practice in sustainable fuel supply chains.

5.21.3.3 Attempts to Address the Problem

The challenges posed in Section 5.21.3.2 are displayed very effectively in recent European bioenergy policy developments. A 2003 European directive on biofuels mandated that 10% of liquid transport fuels should be biofuels by 2010. As several countries (notably Germany and the United Kingdom) made significant progress toward this target by biodiesel production, concerns were raised over the social and environmental impacts of the raw materials being used to achieve the biofuels target. Eventually, the 2003 directive was replaced with a Renewable Energy Directive in 2010, which covers not only biofuels, but also all forms of renewables. Alongside the targets and legal requirements, there is a substantial annex specifying certain minimum environmental criteria that must be met by liquid biofuels. These are based on seven key principles, focusing on

- preservation of biodiverse lands;
- consideration for the loss of carbon in soil;
- protection of wetlands and many forests;
- compliance with the European Commission (EC) requirements for agriculture;
- encouragement of voluntary agreements on environmental and social issues;
- monitoring of impacts on agriculture; and
- support for wastes, nonfood, and nonirrigated crops.

Consultation is now underway in the United Kingdom to transpose a similar set of provisions for solid biomass material. This illustrates the breadth of possible impacts of increased bioenergy implementation and the complexity of ensuring that even minimum standards of acceptability are met. Many observers consider that these provisions do not go far enough, particularly with respect to the socioeconomic impacts of bioenergy systems. Energy policy with respect to biomass, therefore, may start with incentivizing a demand, but quickly becomes a complex management task to ensure sustainability. Verifying and auditing these diverse impacts is likely to be extremely challenging and costly and goes way beyond the normal sphere of energy policy activity, necessitating increasingly bespoke forms of legislation.

5.21.4 A Way Forward

5.21.4.1 The Need for a Holistic Approach

Bioenergy connects national security, energy, land use, employment, economic development, and ecosystem use. In order to balance the, sometimes competing, benefits and costs in these sectors, a comprehensive overview of the minimum levels of acceptability and the areas where biomass could make the most useful contributions is needed. In theory, these strategic overviews could be prepared at a national level, taking into account specific circumstances, for example, with respect to land-use patterns, energy demands, social impacts, and competing raw material markets. Bioenergy systems can evolve in many different ways to fill perceived needs or best fits, but there is a need to first identify what these objectives are. This needs to take account not only of indigenous activities within a country but also the role of imports from which countries of what materials. The creation of a liberalized trading market for energy has, in many ways, distanced national governments from detailed energy strategy, and this has led to some difficulty in articulating a vision of 'what biomass is for'. For many other renewables, this is more straightforward: wind will produce electricity when it is windy and the network needs to be adapted to that. However, biomass can produce many different products and service many energy demand sectors in the form of many different feedstocks. If it is left entirely to the energy market to determine the shape of future bioenergy provision, it is unlikely that the sustainable development potential of biomass will be maximized. At present, this is being dealt with by using conventional policy measures, adapting them to bioenergy and adding on 'sticking plasters' to deal with different issues as they come up. It would seem much more satisfactory and straightforward to develop an actual strategy for sustainable bioenergy development and work backward from that vision to put in place specific policy measures that would facilitate that. Many of those measures might be similar to those already discussed above, but the objectives and impacts would be much clearer. A holistic approach with a coherent strategy across the different impact dimensions would have a lot to recommend it. The challenge would be to define such a strategy in a way that adequately took account of the ambitions and behavior of other trading partners.

5.21.4.2 Land-Use Challenges

Key among the challenges in defining a coherent biomass strategy is the role of land use. Its availability is a very fundamental constraint that must be recognized in policy frameworks. At present, few countries have in place any form of active land management by central government, and it is difficult to see how bioenergy can be sustainably developed on a global scale without implementation of specific policies to incentivize certain land-use and production patterns. However, this runs the risk of violating many basic principles of ownership, freedom, and justice. It is possible to discourage a landowner from producing biofuel feedstock on a certain piece of land by restricting incentives and enforcing certification or verification, but it is practically impossible to prevent production without a strictly enforced land management policy.

5.21.4.3 Biomass Action Plans

In 2005, the European Union published a biomass action plan, which aimed to increase the development of biomass energy by creating market-based incentives for use and removing barriers to market deployment. This was a first coordinating step and member states were subsequently required to develop their own biomass action plans, which have taken account of bioenergy deployment in their own country and identified specific actions that need to be taken in order to increase deployment of bioenergy in the energy mix. In many cases this has gone partway toward the idea of a defined strategy outlined in Section 5.21.4.1. It has certainly promoted a more holistic approach to bioenergy, encouraging member states to think about barriers to implementation beyond the economic factors. The UK's 2007 Biomass Strategy, for example, is supportive of an expanded role for sustainable biomass, alongside a recognition of the potential damage of unsustainable development. The document therefore includes a range of measures intended to promote particular feedstock supplies that would be generally viewed as sustainably managed and is supportive of sustainability criteria for imported material. Little detail of this is given, which is not surprising as critical examination of the possible schemes and indeed the key issues is relatively recent. However, it seems imperative that some framework is put in place alongside the economic policy measures to safeguard people and the environment. Many commentators see strong certification schemes as the answer. There are pros and cons of such an approach, which there is insufficient space to discuss here. However, it should be borne in mind that the efficacy of such schemes in ensuring sustainable feedstock supply is as yet unproven and the cost of certification is as yet uncertain. While it is obviously desirable to promote sustainability, it is undesirable to propagate a certification/auditing industry that does not provide adequate protection at a cost that could make the valuable GHG reductions unaffordable.

5.21.5 Conclusions

Bioenergy is one of the most challenging renewable energy forms to manage because we are encouraging a utilization that is physically (and often geographically) distant from the carbon sequestration benefit. Therefore, the two may not be counted the same way in the same framework, and it is difficult to actually account for and incentivize GHG savings. The existing frameworks for GHG inventories do not recognize the distinct contribution of bioenergy.

Bioenergy has more extensive and significant interactions with our ecosystems and with human behavior, livelihoods, and support services than any other renewable. This provides not only immense opportunities in terms of potential social, economic, and ecological benefits, but it also brings with it substantial risks. The risks involved are diverse and very different from one feedstock to the next. It is important to ensure that bioenergy implementation enhances benefits and minimizes risks. There are no precedents in the energy policy arena for dealing with this. A myriad of different certification frameworks and assessment systems have been developed in order to try to ensure that damage is minimized. Many of these result in a 'tick box' for meeting a set of lowest common denominators, with little encouragement of more sustainable options. In general, markets will gravitate toward a 'least-cost' option – that is, their function. With bioenergy systems, where the fuel cost is a substantial part of the overall plant economic viability that will often mean the lowest cost fuel, which may not be the one that delivers greatest sustainability benefits.

Energy policies are useful for incentivizing deployment of new conversion plant. Investment subsidies have been shown to be effective in increasing plant capacity, but facilities must be supported in the long term for this to be translated into reliable power generation with associated GHG and wider sustainability benefits. Fixed prices have been shown to be effective in the electricity sector in bringing forward new renewable generation. However, the price must be high enough to recognize the true costs of bioenergy systems and the support framework must be sufficiently long term for investors to have confidence in the sector. Green certificates have not yet been proven to be effective for bioelectricity schemes, but where adequate reward is given (e.g., by awarding multiple certificates for different types of generation), there is emerging evidence that they may have more impact.

Every bioenergy project is different and the sustainability risk profiles vary substantially. Recognition, assessment, and management of these risks are best dealt with by the project developer, who is in a position to negotiate and monitor appropriate fuel supply arrangements. Some consider that independent verification or certification is an integral part of ensuring sustainability of bioenergy systems. However, it must be recognized that such schemes have (often substantial) inherent costs. In the long term, continued reliance on onerous certification schemes may, therefore, not make sense. In an ideal world, responsible companies would assess their fuel supply chains in a transparent and robust manner without the need for costly audits and checks. A compromise may be to identify key issues for different fuel supply chains or technologies that have potential to have a significant impact on sustainability performance and to focus regulation or certification on these. That would ensure the worst impacts are prevented, while minimizing regulatory costs.

References

[1] King D (2008) *Guardian*. Science chief: greens hurting climate fight.
[2] Anderson K and Bows A (2008) *Philosophical Transactions of the Royal Society*.
[3] Thornley P, Upham P, Huang Y, *et al.* (2009) Integrated assessment of bioelectricity technology options. *Energy Policy* 37: 890–903.
[4] IPCC (2006) *IPCC Guidelines for National Greenhouse Gas Inventories. Volume 2: Energy*.
[5] Balboa-Murias MÁ, Rodríguez-Soalleiro R, Merino A, and Álvarez-González JB (2006) Temporal variations and distribution of carbon stocks in aboveground biomass of radiata pine and maritime pine pure stands under different silvicultural alternatives. *Forest Ecology and Management* 237(1–3): 29–38.
[6] Brundtland (1987) *Our Common Future: Report of the World Commission on Environment and Development*. World Commission on Environment and Development.
[7] Thornley P (2006) Increasing biomass based power generation in the UK. *Energy Policy* 34: 2087–2099.
[8] Foxon TJ, Gross R, Chase A, *et al.* (2005) UK innovation systems for new and renewable energy technologies: Drivers, barriers and systems failures. *Energy Policy* 33(16): 2123–2137.
[9] Starkey R and Anderson K (2005) *Domestic Tradable Quotas: A Policy Instrument for Reducing Greenhouse Gas Emissions from Energy Use*. Manchester: Tyndall Centre.
[10] Thornley P and Cooper D (2008) The effectiveness of policy instruments in promoting bioenergy. *Biomass and Bioenergy* 32: 903–913.
[11] Thornley P, Brammer JG, Rogers J, *et al.* (2009) Making bioelectricity economic in the UK. *17th European Biomass Conference*. Hamburg, Germany, 29 June–3 July 2009.
[12] Upham P, Shackley S, and Waterman H (2007) Public and stakeholder perceptions of 2030 bioenergy scenarios for the Yorkshire and Humber region. *Energy Policy* 35: 4403–4412.
[13] Thornley P, Upham P, and Tomei J (2009) Sustainability constraints on UK bioenergy development. *Energy Policy* 37(12): 5623–5635.
[14] Thornley P (2008) Airborne emissions from biomass based power generation systems. *Environmental Research Letters* 3(1): 014004.
[15] Thornley P and Prins W (2009) Barriers to European bioenergy expansion. *17th European Biomass Conference*. Hamburg, Germany, 29 June–3 July 2009.
[16] Thornley P and Walsh C (2010) *Addressing the Barriers to Utilisation of Low Grade Heat from the Thermal Process Industries*. Manchester: Tyndall Centre.
[17] Thornley P and Cooper D (2007) *The Effectiveness of Policy Instruments in Promoting Bioenergy*. ThermalNet: University of Manchester.
[18] UNFCC (2010) United Nations Framework Convention on Climate Change home page. http://unfccc.int/essential_background/feeling_the_heat/items/2913.php (accessed 19 October 2010).

Further Reading

[1] Boyle G (ed.) (2004) *Renewable Energy: Power for a Sustainable Future*. The Open University.
[2] Hester RE and Harrison RM (eds.) (2003) *Sustainability and Environmental Impact of Renewable Energy Resources: Issues in Environmental Science and Technology*. Royal Society of Chemistry.
[3] Perman R (ed.) (2003) *Natural Resources and Environmental Economics*. Pearson Education.
[4] Biomass Energy Centre. http://www.biomassenergycentre.org.uk.